CATALYST

**the prentice hall custom laboratory program
for chemistry**

Pearson Learning Solutions

New York   Boston   San Francisco
London   Toronto   Sydney   Tokyo   Singapore   Madrid
Mexico City   Munich   Paris   Cape Town   Hong Kong   Montreal

Senior Vice President, Editorial and Marketing: Patrick F. Boles
Executive Marketing Manager: Nathan L. Wilbur
Sponsoring Editor: Debbie Coniglio
Operations Manager: Eric M. Kenney
Development Editor: Christina Martin
Production Manager: Jennifer Berry
Art Director: Renée Sartell
Cover Designer: Kristen Kiley

Cover Art: Courtesy of Photodisc, Age Fotostock America, Inc. and Photo Researchers.

Copyright © 2010 by Pearson Learning Solutions
All rights reserved.

Permission in writing must be obtained from the publisher before any part of this work may be reproduced or transmitted in any form or by any means, electronic or mechanical, including photocopying and recording, or by any information storage or retrieval system.

Additional copyright information is included, where applicable, as a footnote at the beginning of each chapter.

Pyrex, pHydrion, Chem3D Plus, Apple, Macintosh, Chemdraw, Hypercard, graphTool, Corning, Teflon, Mel-Temp, Rotaflow, Tygon, Spec20, and LambdaII UV/Vis are registered trademarks.

Chem3D Plus is a registered trademark of the Cambridge Soft Corp.

The information, illustration, and/or software contained in this book, and regarding the above mentioned programs, are provided "as is," without warranty of any kind, express or implied, including without limitation any warranty concerning the accuracy, adequacy, or completeness of such information. Neither the publisher, the authors, nor the copyright holders shall be responsible for any claims attributable to errors, omissions, or other inaccuracies contained in this book. Nor shall they be liable for direct, indirect, special, incidental, or consequential damages arising out of the use of such information or material.

The authors and publisher believe that the lab experiments described in this publication, when conducted in conformity with the safety precautions described herein and according to the school's laboratory safety procedures, are reasonably safe for the students for whom this manual is directed. Nonetheless, many of the described experiments are accompanied by some degree of risk, including human error, the failure or misuse of laboratory or electrical equipment, mismeasurement, spills of chemicals, and exposure to sharp objects, heat, body fluids, blood or other biologics. The authors and publisher disclaim any liability arising from such risks in connections with any of the experiments contained in this manual. If students have questions or problems with materials, procedures, or instructions on any experiment, they should always ask their instructor for help before proceeding.

This special edition published in cooperation with Pearson Learning Solutions.

Printed in the United States of America.

Please visit our web site at *www.pearson custom .com.*

Attention bookstores: For permission to return any unsold stock, contact us at *pe-uscustomreturns@pearson.com.*

Pearson Learning Solutions, 501 Boylston Street, Suite 900, Boston, MA 02116
A Pearson Education Company
www.pearsoned.com

29   17

ISBN 10: 0-558-62905-9
ISBN 13: 978-0-558-62905-2

Laboratory Safety: General Guidelines

1. Notify your instructor immediately if you are pregnant, color blind, allergic to any insects or chemicals, taking immunosuppressive drugs, or have any other medical condition (such as diabetes, immunologic defect) that may require special precautionary measures in the laboratory.

2. Upon entering the laboratory, place all books, coats, purses, backpacks, etc. in designated areas, not on the bench tops.

3. Locate and, when appropriate, learn to use exits, fire extinguisher, fire blanket, chemical shower, eyewash, first aid kit, broken glass container, and cleanup materials for spills.

4. In case of fire, evacuate the room and assemble outside the building.

5. Do not eat, drink, smoke, or apply cosmetics in the laboratory.

6. Confine long hair, loose clothing, and dangling jewelry.

7. Wear shoes at all times in the laboratory.

8. Cover any cuts or scrapes with a sterile, water-proof bandage before attending lab.

9. Wear eye protection when working with chemicals.

10. Never pipet by mouth. Use mechanical pipeting devices.

11. Wash skin immediately and thoroughly if contaminated by chemicals or microorganisms.

12. Do not perform unauthorized experiments.

13. Do not use equipment without instruction.

14. Report *all* spills and accidents to your instructor immediately.

15. Never leave heat sources unattended.

16. When using hot plates, note that there is no visible sign that they are hot (such as a red glow). Always assume that hot plates are hot.

17. Use an appropriate apparatus when handling hot glassware.

18. Keep chemicals away from direct heat or sunlight.

19. Keep containers of alcohol, acetone, and other flammable liquids away from flames.

20. Do not allow any liquid to come into contact with electrical cords. Handle electrical connectors with dry hands. Do not attempt to disconnect electrical equipment that crackles, snaps, or smokes.

21. Upon completion of laboratory exercises, place all materials in the disposal areas designated by your instructor.

22. Do not pick up broken glassware with your hands. Use a broom and dustpan and discard the glass in designated glass waste containers; never discard with paper waste.

23. Wear disposable gloves when working with blood, other body fluids, or mucous membranes. Change gloves after possible contamination and wash hands immediately after gloves are removed.

24. The disposal symbol indicates that items that may have come in contact with body fluids should be placed in your lab's designated container. It also refers to liquid wastes that should not be poured down the drain into the sewage system.

25. Leave the laboratory clean and organized for the next student.

26. Wash your hands with liquid or powdered soap prior to leaving the laboratory.

27. The biohazard symbol indicates procedures that may pose health concerns.

 The caution symbol points out instruments, substances, and procedures that require special attention to safety. These symbols appear throughout this manual.

Measurement Conversions

Metric to American Standard	American Standard to Metric
Length	
1 mm = 0.039 inches	1 inch = 2.54 cm
1 cm = 0.394 inches	1 foot = 0.305 m
1 m = 3.28 feet	1 yard = 0.914 m
1 m = 1.09 yards	1 mile = 1.61 km
Volume	
1 mL = 0.0338 fluid ounces	1 fluid ounce = 29.6 mL
1 L = 4.23 cups	1 cup = 237 mL
1 L = 2.11 pints	1 pint = 0.474 L
1 L = 1.06 quarts	1 quart = 0.947 L
1 L = 0.264 gallons	1 gallon = 3.79 L
Mass	
1 mg = 0.0000353 ounces	1 ounce = 28.3 g
1 g = 0.0353 ounces	1 pound = 0.454 kg
1 kg = 2.21 pounds	

Temperature

To convert temperature:

$$°C = \frac{5}{9}(F - 32) \qquad °F = \frac{9}{5}C + 32$$

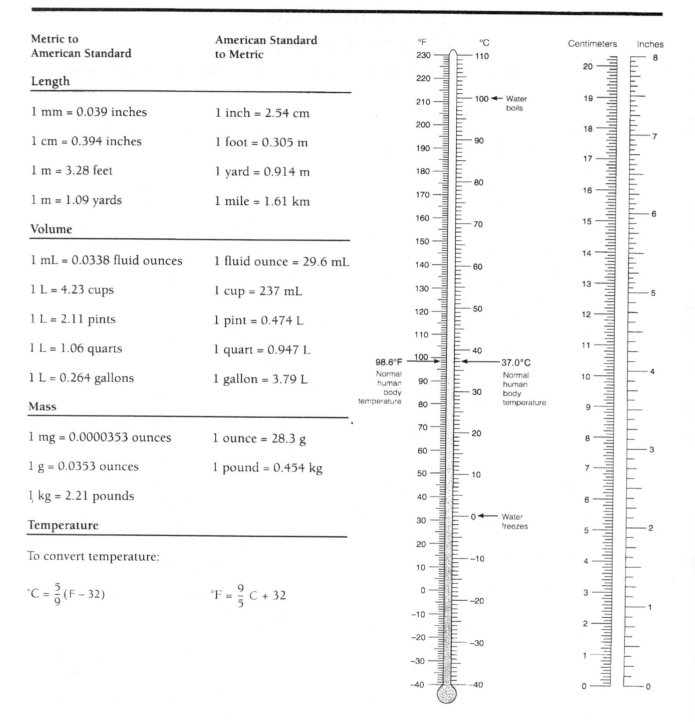

Contents

Preface

To the Instructor

During some 35 years of teaching chemistry, I've witnessed nearly everything that can go wrong in an organic chemistry lab. Having experienced more than one misadventure as a student, I have some sympathy for the hapless students who, can't seem to do anything right. To give them the benefit of my experience, I've added new "troubleshooting" sections, entitled "When Things Go Wrong," to most of the operations in this new edition of *Operational Organic Chemistry*. If a student combines the wrong layers during an extraction, obtains no product upon cooling a recrystallization solution, or records an infrared spectrum with no absorption bands, referring to the troubleshooting section should lead the student to a solution, or at least to an understanding of what went wrong.

The serious damage that can be produced by the release of hazardous chemicals into the environment and the unsustainable rate at which we consume chemical and energy resources have convinced me that chemistry students should learn how to work with chemicals in an environmentally responsible way. This edition therefore contains a new introductory section, "Chemistry and the Environment," which includes a discussion of the principles of green chemistry. Several green experiments have been added, and some experiments from the previous editions have been revised to make them greener. Information on the environmental impact of various chemicals and exercises on environmental topics have been added to nearly all of the experiments.

Some operations have been reorganized, and a new one on excluding air from reaction mixtures has been added. I have added new information about some instrumental techniques, such as the use of attenuated total reflectance devices (ATRs) and disposable cards in infrared spectrometry, and made substantive revisions of many operations, such as the one on flash chromatography.

This edition of *Operational Organic Chemistry* also differs from the third edition in the following respects:

- Sections on personal protective equipment and on finding and using chemical safety information have been added under the "Laboratory Safety" heading.
- Six new experiments have been added, replacing six experiments that were in the third edition.
- A new minilab called "Isolation of an Expectorant from Cough Capsules".
- Calculations for solution preparation have been added to "Calculations for Organic Synthesis".
- The Bibliography has been updated to include more current literature sources, necessitating a revision of "The Chemical Literature."
- Minor corrections and revisions have been made to all sections of the book.

Every experiment and minilab in this book can be performed by students using standard scale glassware, such as that available in an organic chemistry lab kit with 19/22 standard-taper joints, along with appropriate locker supplies.

In writing this and other versions of *Operational Organic Chemistry*, I have been guided by my convictions that students (1) perform better in the organic laboratory course if they master the major lab operations early and apply them throughout the course, (2) learn organic chemistry better if they keep their minds engaged by approaching each experiment as a problem-solving exercise, and (3) perform any task better if they are sufficiently motivated.

The first twelve experiments used in the catalyst database (if the "View by Lab Manual" search option is selected) are to teach the basic laboratory operations, where an *operation*, as used here, is a process that utilizes one or more basic lab techniques,

From *Operational Organic Chemistry: A Problem Solving Approach to the Laboratory*, Fourth Edition, John W. Lehman. Copyright © 2009 by Pearson Education. Published by Prentice Hall. All rights reserved.

such as heating, cooling, and vacuum filtration, to accomplish some end, such as the purification of a solid. Once students have mastered the major operations by completing the appropriate experiments selected from this set, they should be ready to apply those operations in the remaining experiments that are correlated with topics found in most organic chemistry lecture textbooks. This operational approach helps students understand that carrying out an organic synthesis, for example, is not a unique exercise that can be accomplished only by mechanically following a detailed "recipe." Rather, it is the outcome of a logical sequence of interrelated operations adapted to the requirements of the synthesis.

In addition to teaching lab skills, the experiments are designed to help students develop the observational and critical thinking skills that are essential prerequisites for a successful career in science and in virtually every other professional field. Each experiment requires the student to solve a specific scientific problem through the application of sound scientific methodology. As a motivational device and to provide a frame of reference for the problems, students are asked to regard themselves as "consulting chemists" working for an institute operated by their college or university. As described in hypothetical "Scenarios," various individuals and organizations come to the institute with their scientific problems, and the problems are relayed to the "project group" comprising each lab section, to be solved individually or (sometimes) through collaboration. Although some of the scenarios are admittedly a bit contrived, most of them describe tasks similar to those a practicing chemist might be called upon to perform.

The decision whether or how to apply this problem-solving approach is, of course, the prerogative of the instructor, but the following protocol is suggested. Each student should define the problem posed by an experiment based on information provided in the scenario. After a preliminary reading of the experiment, the student should develop a working hypothesis regarding its outcome. During the experiment, each student should gather and evaluate evidence bearing on the problem and, as necessary, reevaluate and revise the hypothesis based on experimental observations and data. Finally, each student will test his or her hypothesis by obtaining a melting point, a spectrum, a gas chromatogram, or by some other means, and arrive at a conclusion. Because of the level at which most undergraduate organic chemistry courses are taught, the problems must, of necessity, be kept relatively simple and (with a few exceptions) should not be compared to "real" research problems tackled by professional chemists. It is not the intent of this book to make every student a research chemist; most students who take an organic chemistry course have no intention of going into the field. But the critical thinking and methodological skills required to solve the problems are comparable to those applied by research scientists, and applying those skills should give the student a better understanding of the nature and practice of science.

To facilitate this problem-solving approach, each experiment includes a section, "Applying Scientific Methodology," intended to help the student understand the problem, formulate a meaningful hypothesis, and solve the problem. The Introduction and the "Effect of PH on a Food Preservative" Experiment describe in some detail how the student can apply scientific methodology to the solution of a problem, so students should read at least the "Problem Solving in the Organic Chemistry Lab" section in the Introduction and should be asked to read the Scenario and "Applying Scientific Methodology" sections, even if you choose not to assign that experiment. Because each experiment is designed as a problem for the student to solve, the outcome is not explicitly stated in the experiment itself. In a few experiments, the identity of the starting material is unknown as well. For these and other reasons, *it is essential that the instructor or laboratory coordinator obtain a copy of the Instructor's Manual,* which is provided free of charge by Prentice Hall to adopters of this book.

John W. Lehman
jlehman@lssu.edu

Problem Solving in the Organic Chemistry Laboratory

Organic chemistry is not most people's idea of a "fun" course, but that is no reason not to enjoy your organic chemistry lab experience. Many experiences can be enjoyable if they give you the opportunity to use your imagination and to test your mental and manual skills. During this lab course, you will play the role of a consultant in a Consulting Chemists Institute operated by your college or university. When D. K. Little wants to know what happens to his company's food preservative in stomach acid, when Rusty Tappet accidentally pours diesel fuel into a barrel of racing fuel, when Gilda Lilly wants to know the color of a synthetic dye, or when the Olfactory Factory needs a way to convert an oversupply of anisole to a perfume ingredient, you and the other members of your "project group" (lab section) will be called upon to solve their problems.

To solve such a problem, you must *think* before you *act*. In other words, you will need to read the experiment, understand the problem, and try to predict a likely outcome of the experiment before you actually carry out the experiment in the laboratory. Your prediction, stated clearly in writing, becomes your *working hypothesis*. In many cases, the most likely outcome will become apparent after you read the experiment, especially if you apply the concepts you have learned in the organic chemistry lecture. In other cases, there may be several reasonable outcomes, and you will have to make an educated guess about the most likely outcome. During the experiment, you will need to gather evidence that may support your hypothesis—or prove it wrong. That means making careful observations and gathering data that relate to the problem. As you evaluate the evidence, you may decide that your original hypothesis was wrong, or at least incomplete, and needs to be revised or replaced by a new one. By the time you finish the experiment, you will have tested your hypothesis and arrived at a conclusion. In this way, each experiment will help you develop your observational and critical thinking skills—as well as your lab skills—as you apply them to the solution of the problem posed in that experiment. The next section will tell you, in more detail, how to approach and solve a scientific problem.

Scientific Methodology

If you are taking an organic chemistry course, you are probably planning a career in some field of science or technology or a field that is based on scientific knowledge and principles, such as medicine. To succeed in such a field, you must learn to think and work like a scientist. Scientists follow certain basic principles that are often lumped together under the expression "the scientific method." In fact, there is no universal scientific method that all scientists follow rigorously. But most scientists take at least some of the following steps when faced with a scientific problem:

- Define the problem.
- Plan a course of action.
- Gather evidence.
- Evaluate the evidence.

From *Operational Organic Chemistry: A Problem Solving Approach to the Laboratory*, Fourth Edition, John W. Lehman. Copyright © 2009 by Pearson Education. Published by Prentice Hall. All rights reserved.

- Develop a hypothesis.
- Test the hypothesis.
- Reach a conclusion.
- Report the results.

Defining the Problem. Most people think of a "problem" in a negative sense, as in "We've got a problem here" or "What's your problem?" To a scientist, a problem is not a perceived difficulty but an *opportunity* to explore and learn more about some aspect of the physical world. A problem may be inherent in an assigned task, or it may arise from anything that the scientist is curious about, such as an unexplained phenomenon or an unexpected observation. A problem is often defined in the form of a question: What is the identity of the liquid my instructor gave me? What is the mercury concentration in Lake Michigan salmon? How do fireflies generate light? In this laboratory course, the problem associated with each experiment will be described in the Scenario that leads off the experiment.

Planning a Course of Action. A scientist must plan his or her own course of action for solving a scientific problem. This often requires that the scientist carry out a literature search to glean information and data relating to the problem, decide which experimental methods and instruments to use, and develop a detailed procedure to be followed. For many lab courses, the procedure is "in the book," and the student simply follows the procedure as if it were a recipe for baking a cake. That may be true of a few basic experiments in this textbook, but for most of them you will have to perform some calculations and develop your own experimental plan based on the information and directions given in the experiment. In a few cases, you may be required to develop a procedure on your own.

Gathering Evidence. Scientists will gather as much evidence as they feel is needed to solve a problem and convince other scientists that their solution is correct. Evidence is gathered by making careful *observations* and *measurements*.

To make valid observations you must be *objective*—reporting only what you actually saw and not what you expected to see. A wildlife biologist who expects wild chimpanzees to behave just like chimpanzees at the zoo is not likely to make any important discoveries about chimpanzees! Keep the following points in mind when you make observations.

1. Don't confuse an *observation* with an *inference*. An observation is whatever you perceive with your senses (sight, smell, touch, taste, or hearing) during an event. An inference is a guess about the *cause* of the event. Writing "The solution turned brown upon addition of 0.1 M $KMnO_4$" records an observation. Writing "The solution must have contained an alkene because it turned brown upon addition of 0.1 M $KMnO_4$" is an inference.
2. Be prepared to be surprised. If you observe something you didn't expect, don't simply disregard the observation or report what you thought you should have seen. Consider an unexpected observation an opportunity to learn something you didn't know before—something that might lead to a new discovery.
3. Write down your observations as you make them or shortly thereafter. If you wait too long, you are likely to leave out important details.

4. Record your observations clearly, completely, and systematically. For example, if you are doing repetitive measurements or carrying out the same test on a series of samples, record your observations in a table.

Making accurate measurements, such as determining the mass or melting point of the product of a chemical synthesis, requires a certain amount of skill and know-how. You can obtain such skills by, for example, watching your instructor demonstrate the operation of an instrument, and then practicing with the instrument until you obtain consistent and accurate results *before* you use it to make a measurement you intend to report. If you aren't sure how to use an instrument properly, ask the instructor to show you.

Evaluating the Evidence. Evaluating the evidence involves assessing the reliability of your experimental results and looking for clues among your results that may point to a solution to the problem. For example, searching the infrared spectrum of an unknown liquid for evidence of a specific functional group and comparing its boiling point with the boiling points of known compounds may help you solve the problem "What is the identity of the liquid my instructor gave me?" Solving such problems requires clear and logical thinking; in other situations, a more creative, intuitive approach can be valuable. In either case, all of your reasoning and intuition may be fruitless if your experimental results are unreliable. The validation of experimental results requires first asking yourself whether the results make sense physically. If you obtain a melting point that is much lower than the literature value, a product mass that is higher than the theoretical yield for a synthesis, or any other result that seems suspect, you need to find out whether the result is, in fact, erroneous. You should review everything you did that led to the result, using notes from your lab notebook to jog your memory as necessary. Perhaps you only need to repeat a melting point or dry a product longer, but in any case, you should find out what you did wrong and correct it. For some kinds of experiments (there are none in this book), validation of results may also require a statistical analysis of experimental data. If you perform such an experiment, your instructor will tell you how to do that.

Developing and Testing Hypotheses. A hypothesis can be regarded as an educated guess about the cause of some phenomenon or the outcome of an experiment. Hypotheses can help us see the significance of an object or event that would otherwise mean little. For example, the movements of the planets seemed erratic and mysterious before Copernicus developed his hypothesis that the Earth revolves around the sun. A hypothesis must be *testable* to have validity; that is, it must be formulated in such a way that experiments can be devised whose outcome might prove the hypothesis *wrong*. John Dalton's hypothesis that atoms are indivisible was proved wrong after it was shown that bombarding uranium atoms with neutrons caused them to split into smaller atoms. But Dalton's more fundamental hypothesis—that all matter is made of atoms—has been tested repeatedly over the years and has never been proven wrong, so it is generally accepted as true.

Most experiments require you to formulate and test a working hypothesis based on a problem outlined in the Scenario. A working hypothesis can be a prediction about the outcome of an experiment based on information available to the experimenter, which, for your lab course, will usually be found in the write-up for the experiment. Such a hypothesis can be proposed and revised at any time during the course of an experiment. An appropriate working hypothesis and the method of testing it may become apparent upon reading the experiment. For example, after reading "Isolation and Isomerization of Lycopene from Tomato Paste", you should be able to develop a working hypothesis such as "The red pigment in Brand X tomato paste was chemically altered when the tomatoes were processed," and then test your hypothesis by recording a spectrum of the isolated pigment in solution.

One drawback of a working hypothesis is that the scientist may become so attached to it that he or she will overlook or ignore evidence that contradicts it. For this reason, some scientists prefer to explore a problem without any preconceived ideas about the outcome—which is not always easy to do. For most of the experiments in this book, you can formulate a working hypothesis after reading the experiment, but a few require that you gather some experimental evidence first. In either case, if the experimental evidence doesn't support your initial hypothesis, you should be ready to revise or abandon it without regret.

Reaching Conclusions. If a hypothesis passes all of the tests you carry out, then you are ready to state a conclusion, such as "The liquid my instructor gave me is benzaldehyde." This doesn't necessarily mean that your conclusion is correct; you may not have carried out enough tests, or perhaps some of your test results are faulty. But if you have performed an experiment carefully and reasoned logically, you will probably arrive at a valid conclusion.

Reporting Results. You should report all results of an experiment as clearly, completely, and unambiguously as possible. Write up your results in correct English, using complete sentences and accurate spelling. Be as specific as you can, avoiding such generalities as "My yield was lower than expected due to human error." Label any tables clearly, giving names or standard abbreviations for all physical properties and the units in which they are measured.

If an experiment requires that you graph your data, use accurately ruled graph paper—never notebook paper or paper you have ruled yourself. Plot the dependent variable on the y-axis and the independent variable on the x-axis. Label both axes with the physical quantities being graphed and their units, if any. Select appropriate, uniform scale intervals so that your data points extend most of the way up and across the graph paper. If the relationship you are graphing is linear, draw the straight line that best fits the data points.

Applying Scientific Methodology

How can you apply scientific methodology in your organic chemistry lab course? Consider an experiment in which a sample of the food preservative sodium benzoate will be placed in a solution having the composition of stomach acid to find out whether a different substance will form in that environment. Based on information provided in the Scenario for the experiment, you might state the problem as, for example: "Does a new substance form when sodium benzoate is placed in a solution simulating stomach acid?" You can then formulate a working hypothesis, sometimes

The Scenarios are discussed in the following section.

6

by simply restating the problem in a form that predicts the outcome of the experiment. Such a hypothesis might be, for example: "A new substance *will* form when sodium benzoate is placed in a solution simulating stomach acid."

Once you have a working hypothesis, you will have to gather evidence that may either prove or disprove it. As you read the directions for the experiment, consider the kinds of evidence you can gather by measurement or observation. During the experiment itself, you should make careful observations of everything that might have a bearing on the problem. In the case of the sodium benzoate experiment, you would have to observe carefully what happens when you combine sodium benzoate with the simulated stomach acid to see if there is evidence for a chemical reaction that produces a different substance, such as formation of a precipitate.

After you have completed an experiment, you should evaluate the evidence, decide whether the results confirm or disprove your hypothesis, arrive at a conclusion that answers the question proposed in your problem statement, and write a report that describes your findings. Your instructor will let you know what kind of report he or she prefers.

Organization of This Book

Operations. The title page of each experiment includes a list of the operations to be used in the experiment, each preceded by an operation number, such as OP-28 for recrystallization. Operations being used for the first time are emphasized by boldface type in an experiment's list of operations; you should read their descriptions thoroughly before you come to the laboratory. After you have used an operation once or twice, you shouldn't have to reread the entire description the next time you use it, but you should at least read the Summary and review the "Directions" section (if provided) to refresh your memory. Eventually, you shouldn't need to refer to the operation description at all, unless you are applying the operation in a new situation or unexpected problems arise. If you do run into problems while carrying out an operation, read *When Things Go Wrong*, a troubleshooting guide that is included with most of the operations.

Before You Begin. Under this heading, you will find a *prelab assignment:* a list of things to do before you come to the laboratory. The prelab assignment always includes reading the experiment and reading or reviewing the operations. At times, you will also be expected to write an experimental plan for each experiment, and you will usually need to carry out some calculations. Your instructor may require that you have your experimental plan and calculations approved before you begin an experiment.

Scenario. The Scenario presents a hypothetical situation involving the scientific problem you are to solve. A typical Scenario will describe a chemistry-related problem posed by a company or an individual and tell you what role you will play in its solution.

Applying Scientific Methodology. This section is intended to help you formulate and solve the problem posed in the Scenario by following the approach described in the previous sections, "Problem Solving in the Organic Chemistry Laboratory" and "Scientific Methodology."

Background Essay.   Each background essay appears under a different descriptive heading, such as "Crime and Chemistry." The essay will often show the relation between the lab work and concepts from the lecture course. It may also relate historical sidelights or interesting facts that show the "real-world" relevance of the experiment.

Understanding the Experiment.   This section describes the main purpose of the experiment, explains the theoretical basis of the experiment (when appropriate), and helps you understand the experimental methodology. It may also provide information that will help you interpret your results or cope with unexpected complications as they arise.

Reactions and Properties.   For most experiments, this section gives balanced equations for synthetic reactions and tabulates the relevant physical properties of reactants, products, and other chemicals. The Properties table usually contains any data needed for the prelab calculations.

Directions.   This section describes the course of action you will follow to carry out the experiment. You shouldn't follow it mechanically, as you would a recipe, but try to understand the purpose of each operation you are performing. The section entitled "Understanding the Experiment" will help you do so. The Directions for most Part I experiments are more detailed than those for Part II. By the time you get to Part II, you will be expected to know how to perform most lab operations proficiently without the aid of frequent reminders.

Safety Notes.   Characteristics of some hazardous chemicals and precautions for their use are described in the Directions under this heading. See the "Laboratory Safety" section for general information about laboratory hazards.

Exercises.   Your instructor will assign exercises to be completed and turned in with your laboratory report.

Other Things You Can Do.   These suggestions may include additional experiments or minilabs that you can perform, or library research projects that you can complete. You must have your instructor's permission to start any project marked by an asterisk. Read the relevant sections of, "The Chemical Literature," and scan the Bibliography for possible sources before you begin a library research project.

Minilabs take only part of a lab period and don't require extensive reports. They are designed to add flexibility to the lab course and "fill in the gaps" when, for example, a two-week experiment can be finished in less than two full lab periods.

A Guide to Success in the Organic Chemistry Lab

What to Expect in Your Organic Chemistry Lab Course

Students are sometimes apprehensive about having to work in an organic chemistry lab. They may have heard that organic chemistry is difficult or that the lab is a dangerous place because of the hazardous nature of organic chemicals. Although some students do find the subject matter of organic chemistry difficult, most of them have little trouble completing the laboratory experiments successfully. In fact, many students enjoy the lab far more than the lecture course, and they generally receive higher grades in lab than in lecture.

It is true that some organic chemicals are quite hazardous and can cause serious injury, or even death, if not handled properly. But if the chemistry lab were a very dangerous place to work, you would expect professional chemists to have short life spans. In fact, chemists tend to live longer than professionals in most other fields; in one listing of occupational risks, chemists rank near the bottom (lowest risk), right between school administrators and ticket agents. In my 35 years of teaching organic chemistry, I've observed only a few lab accidents that caused significant injury, most of them involving broken glass. Only a handful of students were injured by contact with chemicals, and none of them suffered permanent injury. That is not to say that you can afford to be careless in the lab—the potential for a serious accident is always there. But if you follow the safety rules in the "Laboratory Safety" section and take reasonable precautions when handling chemicals, you should have little reason for concern about lab accidents.

Getting Started

By the end of the first week of your organic chemistry course, you should have read the "Laboratory Safety" section of this book and any other safety rules or data provided by your instructor. Before you begin working in the laboratory, your instructor should review the safety rules and tell you what safety supplies, such as safety goggles and protective gloves and aprons, you will need to use in the lab. During the first laboratory period, the instructor will show you where safety equipment is located and tell you how to use it. As you locate each item, check it off the following list and make a note of its location. (Your instructor may suggest additions or changes to the list.)

- Fire extinguishers
- Fire blanket
- Safety shower
- Eyewash fountain
- First aid supplies
- Spill cleanup supplies

You should also learn the locations of chemicals, consumable supplies (such as filter paper and boiling chips), waste containers, and various items of equipment such as balances and drying ovens.

Your instructor will assign you a locker and provide a list of locker supplies. You will then need to check into the laboratory. This usually involves getting a locker key or a combination lock and checking your locker for missing or damaged items. You will find illustrations of typical locker supplies in the "Laboratory Equipment" appendix, if it is included. If you find any glassware items with chips, cracks, or star fractures, you should have them replaced; they may cause cuts, break on heating, or shatter under stress. If necessary, clean up any dirty glassware in your locker (see OP-1) and organize it neatly at this time.

chip on lip of test tube

crack

star fracture

Glassware defects

Working Efficiently

Because of wide variations in individual working rates, it is usually not possible to schedule experiments so that everyone can finish in the allotted time. If all labs were geared to the slowest student, the objectives of the course could not be accomplished in the limited time available. If you fall behind in the lab, you may need to put in extra hours outside your scheduled laboratory period in order to complete the course. The following suggestions should help you work more efficiently and finish each experiment on time.

1. *Be prepared to start the experiment the moment you reach your work area.* Don't waste precious minutes at the start of a laboratory period doing calculations, reading the experiment, washing glassware, or carrying out other activities that should have been done at the end of the previous period or during the intervening time. The first half hour of any lab period is the most important—if you use it to collect the necessary materials, set up the apparatus, and get the initial operation (reflux, distillation, etc.) under way, you should have no trouble completing the experiment on time.

2. *Organize your time efficiently.* Schedule a time each week to read the experiment and operation descriptions and to complete the prelab assignment—an hour before the lab period begins is too late! Plan ahead so that you know approximately what you will be doing at each stage of the experiment. A written experimental plan is invaluable for this purpose.

3. *Organize your work area.* Before performing any operation, arrange all of the equipment and supplies you will need during the operation neatly on your benchtop, in the approximate order in which they will be used. Place small objects and any items that might be contaminated by contact with the benchtop on a paper towel, laboratory tissue, or mat. After you use each item, move it to an out-of-the-way location where it can be cleaned and returned to its proper location when time permits; for example, put dirty glassware in a washing trough in the sink. Keep your locker well organized, placing each item in the same location after use so that you can immediately find the equipment you need. This will also help you notice whether any items are missing so that you can hunt for them before you leave the lab; otherwise, the items will probably disappear before the next lab period, and you may be charged for them.

Getting Along in the Laboratory

You will get along much better in the laboratory if you can maintain peace and harmony with your coworkers—or at least keep from aggravating them—and stay on good terms with your instructor. Following these commonsense rules will help you do that.

1. *Leave all chemicals where you found them.* You will understand the reason for this rule once you experience the frustration of hunting high and low for a reagent, only to find it at another student's station in a far corner of the lab. Containers should be taken to the reagent bottles to be filled; reagent bottles should never be taken to your lab station.

2. *Take only what you need.* Whenever possible, liquids and solutions should be obtained using bottle-top dispensers, pipets, graduated cylinders, or other measuring devices so that you will take no more than you expect to use for a given operation. Solids can be weighed out directly from stock bottles.

3. *Prevent contamination of chemicals.* Don't use your own pipet or dropper to remove liquids directly from stock bottles, and don't return unused chemicals to stock bottles. Be sure to close all bottles tightly after use—particularly those that contain dying agents and other anhydrous chemicals.

4. *If you must use a burner, inform your neighbors*—unless they are already using burners. This will allow them to cover any containers of flammable solvents and take other necessary precautions. In some circumstances, you may have to use a different heat source, move your operation to a safe location (for instance, under a fume hood), or find something else to do while flammable solvents are in use.

5. *Return all community equipment to the designated locations.* This may include ring stands, lab kits, clamps, condenser tubing, and other items that aren't in your own locker. Because such items will be needed by students in other lab sections, they should always be returned to the proper storage area at the end of the period.

6. *Clean up for the next person.* Few experiences are more annoying than finding that the lab kit you just checked out is full of dirty glassware or that your lab station is cluttered with paper towels, broken glass, and spilled chemicals. The last 15 minutes or so of every laboratory period should be set aside for cleaning up your lab station and the glassware used during the experiment. Put things away so that your workstation is uncluttered. Clean off the benchtop with a towel or wet sponge; remove condenser tubing, other supplies, and debris from the sink; and thoroughly wash any dirty glassware that is to be returned to the stockroom, as well as that from your locker. Clean up any spills and broken glassware immediately. If you spill a corrosive or toxic chemical, such as sulfuric acid or aniline, inform the instructor before you attempt to clean it up.

7. *Heed Gumperson's Second Law,* which advises you to maximize the labor and minimize the oratory while in the **laboratory**. This doesn't mean that all conversation must come to a halt. Quiet conversation during a lull in the experimental activity is okay, but a constant stream of chatter directed at a student who is performing a delicate operation is distracting and can lead to an accident. For the same reason, radios, CD or MP3 players, and other audio devices should not be brought into the laboratory.

Laboratory Safety

Safety Standards

In the United States, a Federal Laboratory Safety Standard designated as OSHA 29 CFR 1910.1450 requires that any laboratory in which hazardous chemicals are handled have a written safety plan called a *chemical hygiene plan*. Your institution's chemical hygiene plan should describe safe operating procedures to be followed in carrying out various laboratory operations, and emergency response procedures to be followed in case of accident. According to the Occupational Safety and Health Administration (OSHA) standard, laboratory instructors are required to see that students know and follow established safety rules, have access to and know how to use appropriate emergency equipment, and are aware of hazards associated with specific experiments. The lab instructor alone cannot prevent laboratory accidents, however. You also have a responsibility to follow safe laboratory practices while performing experiments and to be ready to respond in case of accident.

Protecting Yourself

Just as construction workers protect themselves from accidents by wearing hard hats and steel-toed boots, people who work with chemicals should wear appropriate clothing and personal protective equipment (such as safety goggles) that reduce the likelihood of injury in case of an accident.

Eye protection is essential at all times; it is the law in many states and should be the rule in every chemistry laboratory. Safety glasses provide only limited protection because they have no side shields, so it is best to wear safety *goggles* that protect your eyes from chemical splashes and flying particles from any direction.

In any chemistry lab, you should wear clothing that is substantial enough and covers enough of your body to offer some protection against accidental chemical spills and flying glass or other particles. Long-sleeved shirts or blouses and long pants or dresses are recommended, especially when they are made of denim or other heavy materials. Some synthetic fabrics can be dissolved by chemicals such as acetone and could melt in contact with a flame or another heat source. Wear shoes that can protect you from spilled chemicals and broken glass—not open sandals or cloth-topped athletic shoes. To protect your clothing (and yourself) from chemical spills, it's a good idea to wear a lab jacket or lab apron.

Always wear appropriate gloves when handling caustic chemicals, which can burn the skin, or toxic chemicals that can be absorbed through the skin. No single type of glove protects against all chemicals, but neoprene gloves offer good to excellent protection against many commonly used chemicals, and disposable nitrile gloves are adequate for use in most undergraduate labs. Latex gloves aren't recommended, because some people are allergic to latex and because they are permeable to many hazardous chemicals.

In 1997, a Dartmouth College chemistry professor died after spilling a few drops of dimethylmercury on her latex gloves.

Preventing Laboratory Accidents

Most organic lab courses are completed without incident, apart from minor cuts or burns, and serious accidents are rare. Nevertheless, the potential for a serious accident always exists. To reduce the likelihood of an accident, *you*

From *Operational Organic Chemistry: A Problem Solving Approach to the Laboratory*, Fourth Edition, John W. Lehman. Copyright © 2009 by Pearson Education. Published by Prentice Hall. All rights reserved.

must learn the following safety rules and observe them at all times. Additional safety rules or revisions of these rules may be provided by your instructor.

1. *Wear approved eye protection in the laboratory at all times.* Even when you aren't working with hazardous materials, another student's actions could endanger your eyes, so never remove your safety goggles or safety glasses until you leave the lab. Do not wear contact lenses in the laboratory, because chemicals splashed into an eye may get underneath a contact lens and cause damage before the lens can be removed. Determine the location of the eyewash fountain nearest to you during the first laboratory session, and learn how to use it.

2. *Never smoke in the laboratory or use open flames in operations that involve low-boiling flammable solvents.* Anyone found smoking in an organic chemistry laboratory is subject to immediate expulsion. Before you light a burner or even strike a match, inform your neighbors of your intention to use a flame. If anyone nearby is using flammable solvents, either wait until he or she is finished or move to a safer location, such as a fume hood. Diethyl ether and petroleum ether are extremely flammable, but other common solvents, such as acetone and ethanol, can be dangerous as well. When ventilation is inadequate, the vapors of diethyl ether and other highly volatile liquids can travel a long way; lighting a burner at one end of a lab bench that has an open bottle of ether at its other end has been known to start an ether fire. Learn the location and operation of the fire extinguishers, fire blankets, and safety showers at the first laboratory session.

3. *Consider all chemicals to be hazardous and minimize your exposure to them.* Never taste chemicals, do not inhale the vapors of volatile chemicals or the dust of finely divided solids, and prevent contact between chemicals and your skin, eyes, and clothing. Many chemicals can cause poisoning by ingestion, inhalation, or absorption through the skin. Strong acids and bases, bromine, thionyl chloride, and other corrosive materials can produce severe burns and require special precautions, such as wearing gloves and lab aprons. Some chemicals cause severe allergic reactions, and others may be carcinogenic (tending to cause cancer) or teratogenic (tending to cause birth defects) by inhalation, ingestion (swallowing), or skin absorption. To prevent accidental *ingestion* of toxic chemicals, don't bring food or drink into the laboratory or use mouth suction for pipetting, and wash your hands thoroughly after handling any chemical. To prevent *inhalation* of toxic or carcinogenic chemicals, work under an efficient fume hood or use a gas trap (see OP-14) to keep chemical fumes out of the laboratory atmosphere. To prevent *contact* with corrosive or toxic chemicals, wear appropriate gloves and a lab apron or lab jacket. Clean up chemical spills immediately—use a neutralizing agent and plenty of water for acids and bases, and an absorbent for solvents. In case of a major spill, or if the chemical spilled is very corrosive or toxic, notify your instructor before you try to clean it up. Read the "Safety Notes" section in each experiment and use protective gloves or a fume hood when directed.

4. *Exercise great care when working with glass and when inserting or removing thermometers and glass tubing.* Among the most common injuries in a chemistry lab are cuts from broken glass and burns from touching hot glass. Protect your hands with gloves or a towel when inserting glass tubes

or thermometers into stoppers or thermometer adapters, and when removing them. Grasp the glass close to the stopper or thermometer adapter and gently twist it in or out. Remember that hot glass remains hot for some time; after you have fire-polished a glass rod or completed another glass-working operation, give the glass plenty of time to cool before you touch it. Refer to OP-3 for more information about safe glass-working procedures.

5. *Wear appropriate clothing in the laboratory.* Wear clothing that is substantial enough to offer some protection against accidental chemical spills, and shoes that can protect you from spilled chemicals and broken glass. Human hair is very flammable, so tie up your hair or wear a hair net while using a burner if you have long hair.

6. *Dispose of chemicals properly.* For reasons of safety and environmental protection, most organic chemicals shouldn't be washed down the drain. Except when your instructor or an experiment's directions indicate otherwise, place used organic chemicals and solutions in designated waste containers. Some aqueous solutions can be safely poured down the drain, but consult your instructor if there is any question about the best method for disposing of a particular chemical or solution. See the section "Disposal of Hazardous Wastes" for additional information.

7. *Never work alone in the laboratory or perform unauthorized experiments.* If you wish to work in the laboratory when no formal lab period is scheduled, you must obtain written permission from the instructor and be certain that others will be present while you are working.

Reacting to Accidents: First Aid

Notice: Only qualified personnel trained in first aid care should treat serious injuries by any of the procedures described in this section.

If you have or witness a serious accident involving poisoning or injury, report it to the instructor immediately. Serious accidents should be treated by a competent physician, but applying some basic first aid procedures before a physician arrives can help minimize any damage.

If you have an accident that requires quick action to prevent permanent injury, take the appropriate action as described here, if you can, and see that the instructor is informed of the accident. If you *witness* an accident, call the instructor immediately and leave the first aid to him or her, unless (1) no instructor or assistant is present in the laboratory area; (2) the victim requires immediate attention because of stopped breathing, heavy bleeding, or any other life-threatening condition; or (3) you have had appropriate emergency response training.

If an accident victim stops breathing or goes into shock as a result of any kind of accident, standard procedures for artificial respiration and treating shock should be applied. Descriptions of these procedures can be found in Chapter 2 of *The CRC Handbook of Laboratory Safety*, 4th ed. [Bibliography, C1].

Eye Injuries

If any chemical enters your eyes, *immediately* flush them with water from an eyewash fountain while holding your eyelids open. If you are wearing contact lenses, remove them first. Continue irrigation for at least 15 minutes (or until a nurse or physician arrives), then have your eyes examined by a physician. If foreign bodies such as glass particles are propelled into your eye, seek immediate medical attention. Removal of such particles is a job for a specialist.

Chemical Burns

If a corrosive chemical is spilled on your skin or clothing, remove any contaminated clothing and *immediately* flush the affected area with a large amount of water until the chemical is completely removed. Use a safety shower if the area of injury is extensive or if it is not feasible to wash it from a tap. Speed and thoroughness in washing are the most important factors in reducing the extent of injury. Dry the area gently with a clean, soft towel. If you (or another victim) experience pain or if the skin is red or swollen, immerse the injured area in cold water or apply cold, wet dressings. Don't use neutralizing solutions, ointments, or greases on chemical burns unless they are specifically called for in a first aid procedure. Unless the skin is only reddened over a small area, a chemical burn should be examined by a nurse or physician. First aid procedures for burns caused by specific chemicals, such as bromine, are given in the *Sigma–Aldrich Library of Regulatory and Safety Data* [Bibliography, C4] and in the *First Aid Manual for Chemical Accidents* [Bibliography, C3].

If a chemical burn is very extensive or severe, the victim should lie down with the head and chest a little lower than the rest of the body. If the victim is conscious and able to swallow, he or she should be provided with plenty of nonalcoholic liquid to drink (water, tea, coffee, etc.) until a physician or an ambulance arrives.

Thermal Burns

If you are burned by hot glass, another hot object, or a flame, try to determine the type and extent of the burn and then take the appropriate action as described next.

- *First-degree burn.* The skin is reddened but there are no blisters or broken skin. Immerse the affected area in clean, cold water or apply ice to reduce the pain and facilitate healing.
- *Second-degree burn.* Blisters are raised. Immerse the burned area in clean, cold water or apply ice, then cover the area with sterile gauze or another clean dressing. If legs or arms are burned, keep them elevated above the trunk of the body. Never puncture blisters raised by a second-degree burn.
- *Third-degree burn.* The skin is broken and underlying tissue is damaged. Place a thick sterile dressing or clean cloth over the affected area and have the burn examined by a nurse or physician as soon as possible. Don't remove burned clothing, immerse the burned area in cold water, or cover the burn with greasy ointment. If legs or arms are burned, keep them elevated above the trunk of the body.

In case of an extensive thermal burn, the burned area should be covered with the cleanest available cloth material and the victim should lie down, with the head and chest lower than the rest of the body, until a physician or an ambulance arrives. If the injured person is conscious and able to swallow, he or she should be provided with plenty of nonalcoholic liquid to drink (water, tea, coffee, etc.).

Bleeding, Cuts, and Abrasions

In case of a cut or abrasion that doesn't involve heavy bleeding, cleanse the wound and the surrounding skin with soap and lukewarm water, applying it by wiping away from the wound. Try to remove embedded glass shards, if there are any, by using tweezers if necessary. Hold a sterile gauze pad over the wound until bleeding stops. Place a fresh gauze pad over the wound and secure it loosely with a triangular or rolled bandage. Replace the pad and bandage as necessary with clean, dry ones. Avoid contact between the wound and the mouth, fingers, handkerchiefs, or other unsterile objects. If the wound is deep or extensive, it should be treated further by a nurse or physician.

In case of a major wound that involves heavy bleeding, *immediately* apply pressure directly over the wound with a cloth pad (such as a clean handkerchief or other clean cloth) or sterile dressing, pressing firmly with one or both hands to reduce the bleeding as much as possible. Then call for assistance. A compression bandage should be applied on top of the original dressing if profuse bleeding continues. (Removing the original dressing may delay clotting.) The victim should lie down, with the bleeding part higher than the heart, and the dressing should be held in place using heavy gauze or other cloth strips. A physician or an ambulance should be called as soon as possible, and the victim should be kept warm with a blanket or coat. If the injured person is conscious and able to swallow, he or she should be provided with plenty of nonalcoholic liquid to drink (water, tea, coffee, etc.) until a physician arrives.

Poisoning

If, after contact with, inhalation of, or accidental ingestion of a chemical, you experience a burning sensation in the throat, discoloration of the lips or mouth, stomach cramps, nausea and vomiting, or confusion, seek treatment *immediately* for chemical poisoning.

If a poison has been ingested, an ambulance and a poison control center should be called immediately. If a victim of poisoning is conscious, loosen tight clothing around the neck and waist. If the poison is known, a sample of it should be saved for the physician.

If a poison has been inhaled, the victim must be taken to fresh air and a physician should be called immediately. Loosen any tight clothing around the neck and waist, and use a tongue depressor or other device, if necessary, to keep the victim's airway open. Keep the victim warm and as quiet as possible until a physician arrives. If the poison is a highly toxic gas, such as hydrogen cyanide, hydrogen sulfide, or phosgene, the persons attempting to rescue the victim should wear self-contained respirators while they are in contact with the vapors.

In case of skin contact with a toxic substance, follow the same general procedure as that for chemical burns. The *Sigma–Aldrich Library of Regulatory and Safety Data* [Bibliography, C4] or another appropriate source should be consulted for specific procedures to be used for injury by certain substances.

Reacting to Accidents: Fire

Most modern organic chemical laboratories use flameless heat sources for nearly all operations. However, burners may be used for special applications, such as bending glass, and some chemicals may ignite on a hot surface, such as the top of a hot plate. Hot plates can be particularly dangerous because the absence of an open flame makes them seem safe, but heating a volatile solvent on a hot plate can easily start a fire.

In case of fire, your first response should be to *get away* as quickly as possible and let the instructor deal with the fire. However, if a fire is small and confined to a container such as a flask or beaker, you may be able to put it out by placing a watch glass or a large beaker over the mouth of the container. If no instructor is present in the laboratory, obtain a fire extinguisher of the appropriate type and attempt to put out the fire by aiming the extinguisher at the base of the fire while maintaining a safe distance. Most labs should be equipped with class BC or ABC dry-chemical extinguishers, which are effective against solvent and electrical fires. A class D fire, which involves burning metals or metal hydrides such as sodium metal and lithium aluminum hydride, can be extinguished with an appropriate class D fire extinguisher or by smothering the fire in dry sand, sodium chloride, or sodium carbonate. If a fire is too large to be put out by a fire extinguisher, sound the nearest fire alarm and evacuate the area.

If your hair or clothing catches on fire, *do not panic. Walk* (don't run) directly to the nearest fire blanket or safety shower and attempt to extinguish the fire. Don't wrap yourself in a fire blanket while you are standing, as that may direct the flames around your face; instead, *drop* to the floor and *roll* as you wrap the blanket around your body. To use a safety shower, position yourself directly under the showerhead and pull the chain. If another person's hair or clothing has caught fire, try to prevent panic as you lead him or her to a safety shower or fire blanket.

Chemical Hazards

For your own health and safety, it is essential that you *exercise caution while handling chemicals* and *minimize your exposure to them.* Most academic chemistry departments have policies and procedures for dealing with hazardous chemicals, which should be incorporated into the institution's chemical hygiene plan. Your instructor will inform you of any departmental or institutional rules that relate to the safe handling and disposal of hazardous chemicals. The experiments and some of the operations in this book describe specific chemical hazards and handling precautions under the heading "Safety Notes." The hazard descriptions are meant to inform you of the potential danger posed by certain chemicals when they aren't handled properly. If you take reasonable precautions and follow the directions in the Safety Notes, you are unlikely to suffer ill effects from working with any chemical.

There are several different kinds of chemical hazards. A chemical may be toxic and therefore capable of causing illness or death when ingested, inhaled, or allowed to contact the skin. Certain chemicals can burn when exposed to a spark, an open flame, or a high temperature. A few chemicals can explode when they are heated, subjected to shock, or mixed with certain organic materials. Some chemicals may react spontaneously or when combined with other chemicals, generating heat that could cause a fire.

The severity of any hazards associated with a chemical can be indicated by a labeling system, such as the one established by the National Fire Protection Association (NFPA), which rates the health, flammability, and reactivity hazards of chemicals on a scale ranging from 0 to 4 (where 4 is the highest hazard rating). This book uses a similar system, in which the general health hazard number is usually replaced by two numbers that indicate the hazards posed by contact with and inhalation of a chemical. Hazard information on selected chemicals used in the experiments is provided in the form of octagonal signs that contain hazard index numbers. Each hazard index is a number from 0 to 4, where 0 indicates no known hazard and 4 indicates a very great health or safety hazard. Letters such as "W" are sometimes included to warn of other hazards, such as reactivity with water. The significance of the numbers and letters is explained in Table 1.

Table 1 Meanings of numbers and letters on hazard symbols

Symbol	Health (Contact or Vapor)	Fire	Reactivity
0	No known hazard	Will not burn	Stable
1	May cause irritation if not treated	Ignites after strong preheating	Unstable only at high temperature and pressure
2	May cause injury; requires treatment	Ignites after moderate heating	Unstable, but won't detonate
3	May cause serious injury despite treatment	Ignites at normal temperatures	Detonates or explodes with difficulty
4	May cause death or major injury despite treatment	Very flammable	Readily detonates or explodes
CA	Carcinogen (cancer-causing agent)		
OX			Strong oxidant; may react violently with combustible material
P			Polymerizes readily
W			Reacts violently with water

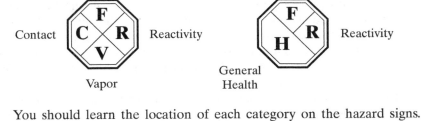

You should learn the location of each category on the hazard signs. Moving clockwise from the top, the order is Fire → Reactivity → Vapor → Contact. The *fire* index number in the upper quadrant rates the fire danger posed by the chemical. The *reactivity* index number in the right quadrant assesses the danger of a violent reaction or explosion. The *vapor* index number in the lower quadrant rates the potential health effect of inhaling the vapors of the chemical. The *contact* index number in the left quadrant rates the adverse health effects that may result from skin contact (the eye contact hazard, which isn't rated, may be even greater in some cases). For some chemicals, the vapor and contact index numbers are replaced by a single *health* index number that represents the overall health hazard of the chemical. If any quadrant is left blank, it means that no hazard index number was reported in the sources consulted; it does *not* mean that no hazard exists.

The meaning of the hazard signs is illustrated by the examples in the margin. Carbon tetrachloride is nonflammable and thermally stable, so its fire and reactivity hazard index numbers are both zero. Inhaling its vapors may be extremely harmful, and there is a moderate risk of injury from skin contact. Carbon tetrachloride has also been identified as a carcinogen in tests using laboratory animals and is suspected of causing cancer in humans. For these reasons, carbon tetrachloride is not used in the experiments in this book. The second hazard sign shows that hexane is highly flammable but very stable and its health risk is comparatively low.

Chemicals with a high fire hazard number should obviously be kept away from ignition sources, including flames, sparks, and hot surfaces. For example, diethyl ether will ignite if it is spilled on a hot plate at a temperature of 160°C or higher.

Chemicals with a high reactivity hazard number should be handled with great care, following any precautions given in the Safety Notes. Such chemicals may ignite or explode if subjected to shock or brought into contact with metal spatulas or materials that may catalyze their decomposition.

The value of a vapor or contact hazard number may suggest the appropriate response to inhalation of or contact with a chemical. If you inhale significant amounts of a chemical's vapor or the dust of a solid chemical, you should go to a window or other area where you can breathe fresh air, unless the chemical's vapor hazard number is zero. If the chemical has a high vapor hazard number, or if inhalation was prolonged, see your instructor to determine whether treatment is required. In case of skin contact with a chemical that has a contact hazard number other than zero, you should wash the area of contact with soap and water. If the chemical has a high contact hazard number, or if the exposure is extensive, see your instructor to determine whether treatment is required. If you get a chemical in your eyes, follow the procedures described under the heading "Eye Injuries" in the previous section on first aid. The higher the chemical's contact hazard number, the more likely it is that eye damage will result without prompt medical treatment.

Chemicals designated as strong oxidants (OX) must not be allowed to contact other chemicals, except for the ones specified in the experimental directions. In fact, you should never mix *any* chemicals together unless directed, because mixing incompatible chemicals may result in the generation of toxic gases, fire, or an explosion.

Chemicals that polymerize readily (P) may sometimes undergo spontaneous, rapid polymerization, which generates heat. If this reaction occurs in a capped reagent bottle, it could cause the bottle to shatter violently. Most such chemicals are stabilized by the addition of a small amount of antioxidant or other stabilizer, so they are unlikely to react unless the stabilizer has been removed.

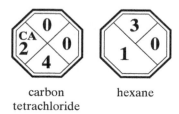

carbon
tetrachloride   hexane

Water-sensitive chemicals (W) react violently and exothermically upon contact with water, often generating toxic fumes. Some water-sensitive chemicals generate toxic fumes even when exposed to moist air. Such chemicals should be kept in tightly closed containers that are opened only for transfers and closed immediately afterward. They should be used under fume hoods at some distance from any source of water.

Carcinogens

A few chemicals used in the experiments are potential *carcinogens*—agents suspected of causing cancer. Such chemicals are identified by the symbol CA in the hazard signs. Although this label certainly should not be disregarded, it is important to recognize that these chemicals present little risk of cancer to students if used as directed. The carcinogenic activity of a compound is generally established by animal tests in which high doses of the chemical are administered by various routes for prolonged periods. For example, phenacetin taken orally has been found to cause cancer in laboratory animals, but it is highly unlikely that anyone will ingest enough phenacetin during a laboratory experiment to incur a risk of cancer. Chromium(VI) compounds have been shown to cause cancer of the lungs, nasal cavity, and sinuses in humans, but most persons at risk are industrial workers who have been continuously exposed to the dust of chromium compounds in the workplace. In this course, you will use chromic acid solutions—prepared from chromium(VI) oxide—a drop or so at a time, so there will be no possibility of inhaling chromium dust.

When handling any potential carcinogen, it is only prudent to take appropriate precautions, such as wearing protective gloves and clothing and working under a hood. Some halogenated hydrocarbons are suspected of causing cancer if inhaled, so avoid breathing the vapors of dichloromethane, chloroform, and other chlorinated solvents. Compounds such as benzene and carbon tetrachloride, which might present a significant risk of cancer under conditions likely to be encountered in an undergraduate laboratory, are not used in this book.

Teratogens

If you are pregnant or think you may be pregnant, inform your instructor before you enter the organic chemistry lab for the first time. Some organic chemicals are known or suspected *teratogens*, meaning that they may harm a developing fetus. As is the case for carcinogens, handling a chemical designated as a teratogen doesn't necessarily represent a danger to the fetus. Ethanol (ethyl alcohol) is a teratogen by ingestion, but people are far more likely to ingest ethanol in a bar, a restaurant, or at home than in a chemistry laboratory. Nevertheless, some chemicals that are routinely used in organic chemistry laboratories may represent a significant danger to a developing fetus. Therefore, it is important to contact your instructor, the laboratory coordinator, or a designated chemical hygiene officer to discuss your options if you are pregnant. The best option may be to take the laboratory course after your child is delivered. If you prefer to remain in the lab course, you should obtain the consent of your physician and then make arrangements with your instructor to minimize your exposure to potential teratogens. Such arrangements might include substituting less hazardous chemicals for teratogenic ones, performing alternative experiments that don't require the use of teratogens, or using gloves, protective clothing, and a hood when handling any teratogenic chemical.

Finding and Using Chemical Safety Information

Some basic hazard information on a number of organic compounds can be found in *The Merck Index* [Bibliography, A11]. More detailed information can be found in the *Sigma–Aldrich Library of Regulatory and Safety Data* [Bibliography, C4], which compiles safety and regulatory information for more than 20,000 chemicals. Other useful sources of chemical hazard information include *Sax's Dangerous Properties of Industrial Materials* [Bibliography, C5], *Hazards in the Chemical Laboratory* [Bibliography, C6], and *Bretherick's Handbook of Reactive Chemical Hazards* [Bibliography, C8]. You can find hazard information about some common chemicals online at the *NIOSH Pocket Guide to Chemical Hazards* Web site, http://www.cdc.gov/niosh/npg/search.html.

The labels on the containers in which chemicals are originally received must include appropriate hazard warnings, and they may provide additional hazard information along with handling precautions and emergency management procedures. To reduce waste and contamination, chemicals are ordinarily transferred to stock bottles before being used in the chemistry laboratory, but some hazard warnings may be included on the stock-bottle labels.

This lab text includes hazard information and safe-handling procedures for hazardous chemicals used in the experiments. For example, Experiment 29 contains the following Safety Note about sodium borohydride, a reducing agent used in many chemical syntheses.

> Sodium borohydride is toxic and corrosive, and it can react violently with concentrated acids, oxidizing agents, and other substances. Aqueous $NaBH_4$ solutions with pH values below 10.5 have been known to decompose violently, so be sure that your reaction mixture (if aqueous) is sufficiently alkaline. Avoid contact with $NaBH_4$, do not breathe its dust, and keep it away from other chemicals.

The most complete source of information about the hazards associated with any chemical is its *Material Safety Data Sheet (MSDS)*, which is provided by the manufacturer or vendor of the chemical and is usually available on the manufacturer's Web site. The MSDSs for chemicals used in your organic chemistry laboratory should be available from the chemistry department office, the chemical hygiene officer, or some other designated source at your institution.

The MSDS for a chemical must include the following information:

- Identity of the chemical
- Physical properties and relevant chemical characteristics
- Information on potential physical hazards such as fire, explosion, reactivity, and chemical incompatibility
- Health hazards from both short- and long-term exposure
- Toxicology data such as LD_{50} values
- Significant exposure routes such as inhalation, ingestion, or contact
- Exposure limits set by OSHA and other agencies

- Cancer-causing potential
- Precautions for safe handling and storage
- Control measures for preventing accidents, such as the use of personal protection gear
- Emergency procedures in case of accidental exposure

The MSDS for benzoic acid is shown in Figure 1.

```
                            SIGMA-ALDRICH

                    MATERIAL SAFETY DATA SHEET
                                                Date Printed: 09/08/2006
                                                Date Updated: 01/31/2006
                                                     Version  1.12


Section 1 - Product and Company Information

Product Name              BENZOIC ACID, >=99.5%, A.C.S. REAGENT
Product Number            242381
Brand                     SIAL

Company                   Sigma - Aldrich
Address                   3050 Spruce Street
                          SAINT LOUIS MO 63103 US
Technical Phone:          800-325-5832
Fax:                      800-325-5052
Emergency Phone:          314-776-6555

Section 2 - Composition/Information on Ingredient

Substance Name                  CAS #                   SARA 313
BENZOIC ACID                    65-85-0                 NO

Formula        C7H6O2
Synonyms       Acide benzoique (French) * Acido benzoico
               (Italian * Benzenecarboxylic acid *
               Benzeneformic acid * Benzenemethanoic acid *
               Benzoate * Benzoesaeure (German) * Carboxybenzene
               * Dracylic acid * E 210 * HA 1 (acid) * Kyselina
               benzoova (Czech) * Phenylcarboxylic acid *
               Phenylformic acid * Retarder BA * Retardex *
               Salvo liquid * Salvo powder * Tenn-Plas
RTECS Number:  DG0875000

Section 3 - Hazards Identification

EMERGENCY OVERVIEW
   Harmful.
   Harmful if swallowed. Irritating to eyes, respiratory system and
   skin.

HMIS RATING
   HEALTH: 2
   FLAMMABILITY: 1
   REACTIVITY: 0
```

Figure 1 Material Safety Data Sheet for benzoic acid (reprinted with permission from Aldrich Chemical Co., Inc., Milwaukee, WI).

```
NFPA RATING
   HEALTH: 2
   FLAMMABILITY: 1
   REACTIVITY: 0
```

For additional information on toxicity, please refer to Section 11.

Section 4 - First Aid Measures

ORAL EXPOSURE
   If swallowed, wash out mouth with water provided person is
   conscious. Call a physician.

INHALATION EXPOSURE
   If inhaled, remove to fresh air. If not breathing give
   artificial respiration. If breathing is difficult, give oxygen.

DERMAL EXPOSURE
   In case of skin contact, flush with copious amounts of water for
   at least 15 minutes. Remove contaminated clothing and shoes.
   Call a physician.

EYE EXPOSURE
   In case of contact with eyes, flush with copious amounts of
   water for at least 15 minutes. Assure adequate flushing by
   separating the eyelids with fingers. Call a physician.

Section 5 - Fire Fighting Measures

FLASH POINT
   250 °F   121 °C   Method: closed cup

AUTOIGNITION TEMP
   572 °C

FLAMMABILITY
   N/A

EXTINGUISHING MEDIA
   Suitable: Water spray. Carbon dioxide, dry chemical powder, or
   appropriate foam.

FIREFIGHTING
   Protective Equipment: Wear self-contained breathing apparatus
   and protective clothing to prevent contact with skin and eyes.
   Specific Hazard(s): Emits toxic fumes under fire conditions.

Section 6 - Accidental Release Measures

PROCEDURE TO BE FOLLOWED IN CASE OF LEAK OR SPILL
   Evacuate area.

PROCEDURE(S) OF PERSONAL PRECAUTION(S)
   Wear respirator, chemical safety goggles, rubber boots, and
   heavy rubber gloves.

METHODS FOR CLEANING UP
   Sweep up, place in a bag and hold for waste disposal. Avoid
   raising dust. Ventilate area and wash spill site after material
   pickup is complete.

Figure 1 (*continued*)

Section 7 - Handling and Storage

HANDLING
   User Exposure: Do not breathe dust. Avoid contact with eyes,
   skin, and clothing. Avoid prolonged or repeated exposure.

STORAGE
   Suitable: Keep tightly closed.

Section 8 - Exposure Controls / PPE

ENGINEERING CONTROLS
   Safety shower and eye bath. Mechanical exhaust required.

PERSONAL PROTECTIVE EQUIPMENT
   Respiratory: Use respirators and components tested and approved
   under appropriate government standards such as NIOSH (US) or CEN
   (EU). Where risk assessment shows air-purifying respirators are
   appropriate use a dust mask type N95 (US) or type P1 (EN 143)
   respirator.
   Hand: Compatible chemical-resistant gloves.
   Eye: Chemical safety goggles.

GENERAL HYGIENE MEASURES
   Wash thoroughly after handling.

EXPOSURE LIMITS

Country	Source	Type	Value
USA	ACGIH	TLV	10 mg/m3
Remarks: inhalable particulate			
USA	ACGIH	TLV	3 mg/m3
Remarks: respirable dust in air			
USA	OSHA.	PEL	15 mg/m3
Remarks: total dust			
USA	OSHA.	PEL	5 mg/m3
Remarks: respirable dust			

Section 9 - Physical/Chemical Properties

Appearance
                       Physical State: Solid
                       Color: White
                       Form: Fine crystals

Property	Value	At Temperature or Pressure
Molecular Weight	122.12 AMU	
pH	N/A	
BP/BP Range	248.9 °C	760 mmHg
MP/MP Range	121.0 - 125.0 °C	
Freezing Point	N/A	
Vapor Pressure	10 mmHg	132 °C
Vapor Density	4.21 g/l	
Saturated Vapor Conc.	N/A	
SG/Density	1.32 g/cm3	
Bulk Density	N/A	
Odor Threshold	N/A	
Volatile%	N/A	
VOC Content	N/A	
Water Content	N/A	

Figure 1 (*continued*)

```
Solvent Content          N/A
Evaporation Rate         N/A
Viscosity                N/A
Surface Tension          N/A
Partition Coefficient    N/A
Decomposition Temp.      N/A
Flash Point              250 °F 121 °C        Method: closed cup
Explosion Limits         N/A
Flammability             N/A
Autoignition Temp        572 °C
Refractive Index         N/A
Optical Rotation         N/A
Miscellaneous Data       N/A
Solubility               N/A
```

N/A = not available

Section 10 - Stability and Reactivity

STABILITY
   Stable: Stable.
   Materials to Avoid: Strong oxidizing agents, Strong bases, Strong
   reducing agents.

HAZARDOUS DECOMPOSITION PRODUCTS
   Hazardous Decomposition Products: Carbon monoxide, Carbon dioxide.

HAZARDOUS POLYMERIZATION
   Hazardous Polymerization: Will not occur

Section 11 - Toxicological Information

ROUTE OF EXPOSURE
   Skin Contact: May cause skin irritation.
   Skin Absorption: May be harmful if absorbed through the skin.
   Eye Contact: Causes eye irritation.
   Inhalation: Material may be irritating to mucous membranes and
   upper respiratory tract. May be harmful if inhaled.
   Ingestion: Harmful if swallowed.

SIGNS AND SYMPTOMS OF EXPOSURE
   To the best of our knowledge, the chemical, physical, and
   toxicological properties have not been thoroughly investigated.

TOXICITY DATA

   Oral
   Man
   500 mg/kg
   LDLO

   Oral
   Rat
   1700 mg/kg
   LD50

   Inhalation
   Rat

Figure 1 (*continued*)

```
> 26 mg/m3
LC50
Remarks: Sense Organs and Special Senses (Nose, Eye, Ear, and
Taste) : Eye: Lacrimation. Behavioral:Somnolence (general depressed
activity).

Intraperitoneal
Rat
1600 MG/KG
LD50

Intravenous
Rat
1700 MG/KG
LD50

Oral
Mouse
1940 mg/kg
LD50

Remarks: Behavioral:Somnolence (general depressed activity).
Lungs, Thorax, or Respiration:Respiratory depression.
Gastrointestinal:Other changes.

Intraperitoneal
Mouse
1460 MG/KG
LD50

Skin
Rabbit
> 10000 mg/kg
LD50

IRRITATION DATA
    Eyes
    Rabbit
    Remarks: Mild irritation effect

    Skin
    Human
    22 mg
    3D
    I
    Remarks: Moderate irritation effect

    Skin
    Rabbit
    500 mg
    24H
    Remarks: Mild irritation effect

    Eyes
    Rabbit
    100 mg
    Remarks: Severe irritation effect
```

Figure 1 (*continued*)

CHRONIC EXPOSURE - MUTAGEN

    Species: Human
    Dose: 5 MMOL/L
    Cell Type: lymphocyte
    Mutation test: DNA inhibition

Section 12 - Ecological Information

Section 13 - Disposal Considerations

APPROPRIATE METHOD OF DISPOSAL OF SUBSTANCE OR PREPARATION
    Contact a licensed professional waste disposal service to dispose
    of this material. Dissolve or mix the material with a combustible
    solvent and burn in a chemical incinerator equipped with an
    afterburner and scrubber. Observe all federal, state, and local
    environmental regulations.

Section 14 -Transport Information

DOT
    Proper Shipping Name: Environmentally hazardous
    substances, solid, n.o.s.
    UN#: 3077
    Class: 9
    Packing Group: Packing Group III
    Hazard Label: Class 9
    PIH: Not PIH

IATA
    Non-Hazardous for Air Transport: Non-hazardous for air
    transport.

Section 15 - Regulatory Information

EU ADDITIONAL CLASSIFICATION
    Symbol of Danger: Xn
    Indication of Danger: Harmful.
    R: 22-36
    Risk Statements: Harmful if swallowed. Irritating to eyes.
    S: 26
    Safety Statements: In case of contact with eyes, rinse
    immediately with plenty of water and seek medical advice.

US CLASSIFICATION AND LABEL TEXT
    Indication of Danger: Harmful.
    Risk Statements: Harmful if swallowed. Irritating to eyes,
    respiratory system and skin.
    Safety Statements: In case of contact with eyes, rinse
    immediately with plenty of water and seek medical advice.

UNITED STATES REGULATORY INFORMATION
    SARA LISTED: No
    TSCA INVENTORY ITEM: Yes

Figure 1 (*continued*)

```
CANADA REGULATORY INFORMATION
    WHMIS Classification: This product has been classified in
    accordance with the hazard criteria of the CPR, and the MSDS
    contains all the information required by the CPR.
    DSL: Yes
    NDSL: No
```

Section 16 - Other Information

```
DISCLAIMER
    For R&D use only. Not for drug, household or other uses.

WARRANTY
    The above information is believed to be correct but does not
    purport to be all inclusive and shall be used only as a guide. The
    information in this document is based on the present state of our
    knowledge and is applicable to the product with regard to
    appropriate safety precautions. It does not represent any
    guarantee of the properties of the product. Sigma-Aldrich Inc.,
    shall not be held liable for any damage resulting from handling or
    from contact with the above product. See reverse side of invoice
    or packing slip for additional terms and conditions of sale.
    Copyright 2006 Sigma-Aldrich Co. License granted to make unlimited
    paper copies for internal use only.
```

Figure 1 (*continued*)

Note that section 3, Hazards Identification, includes NFPA hazard ratings of the chemical. Section 8, Exposure Controls, gives Threshhold Limit Values (TLVs) and Permissible Exposure Limits (PELs) in milligrams of the chemical per cubic meter of ambient air. The TLV of a chemical reflects the level that a typical worker can experience without an unreasonable risk of disease or injury when the worker is exposed to the vapor or dust of the chemical for eight hours a day, five days a week. The PEL value is the maximum concentration of a chemical that a worker may be exposed to under OSHA regulations. Section 11, Toxicity Information, gives LD_{50} values for different methods of exposure to a chemical, in which its LD_{50} (lethal dose, 50%) is the amount of the chemical—usually expressed in milligrams per kilogram of body weight—that it takes to kill 50% of a tested group of rats, mice, or other experimental animals.

Chemical manufacturers, for reasons related to legal liability, tend to list every possible mishap that might result from the use of their chemicals, no matter how unlikely. Because MSDSs are intended primarily for chemical and industrial workers, whose exposure to chemicals may be intense and prolonged, the manufacturers often recommend protective apparatus and measures that may not be necessary when chemicals are used in small quantities for short periods of time. This makes it difficult to determine which hazards associated with the chemicals used in a given organic chemistry experiment are truly significant. Nevertheless, the MSDS for a given chemical can be very helpful if the information it provides is used appropriately.

Chemistry and the Environment

Disposal of Hazardous Wastes

Some of the chemicals and solutions generated in organic chemistry labs are regarded as hazardous wastes, which are regulated by various state and federal agencies. For example, the U.S. Environmental Protection Agency (EPA) sets Maximum Contaminant Levels (MCLs) for a variety of chemicals, where the MCL is the highest level of a chemical that is allowed in drinking water. A small number of chemicals (126 in 2007) have been designated as priority pollutants; a priority pollutant is a chemical the EPA classifies as a high priority for control or removal from waste discharges because of its toxicity or its potential to cause cancer or mutations.

Institutions that generate hazardous wastes are required to collect and dispose of the wastes in ways that pose minimum potential harm to human health and to the environment. Some hazardous wastes can be purified and reused, or converted to nonhazardous materials. Other hazardous wastes are placed in landfills, incinerated, or otherwise disposed of by commercial waste-disposal firms.

Except when prohibited by local regulations, moderate quantities of many common chemicals can be safely and acceptably disposed of down a laboratory drain if certain procedures are followed. Small quantities (less than 100 g) of most water-soluble organic compounds, including water-soluble alcohols, aldehydes, amides, amines, carboxylic acids, esters, ethers, and ketones, can be disposed of in this way. The organic compound should be mixed or flushed with at least 100 volumes of excess water. Dilute aqueous solutions of inorganic acids, bases, and salts can be disposed of down the drain if they contain cations and anions from the following list (and no other cations or anions).

Cations of these metals: Al, Ca, Cu, Fe, Li, Mg, Mo, Pd, K, Na, Sn, Zn

Anions: HSO_3^-, BO_3^{3-}, $B_4O_7^{2-}$, Br^-, CO_3^{2-}, Cl^-, OCN^-, OH^-, I^-, O^{2-}, PO_4^{3-}, SO_4^{2-}, SO_3^{2-}

Some less common cations and anions, such as Cs^+ and SCN^-, are also permissible.

Substances that should *not* be washed down the drain include the following:

- Water-soluble organic compounds that are highly flammable or boil below 50°C
- Hydrocarbons, halogenated hydrocarbons, and other water-insoluble organic compounds
- Flammable or explosive solids, liquids, or gases
- Phenols and other taste- or odor-producing substances
- Wastes containing poisons in toxic concentrations
- Corrosive wastes capable of damaging the sewer system

These and any other chemical wastes designated by your instructor should be placed in labeled waste containers, which should be provided in the laboratory.

Green Chemistry

Although chemistry has enriched our lives by providing a vast number of useful consumer products, some chemicals can create havoc when released

From *Operational Organic Chemistry: A Problem Solving Approach to the Laboratory*, Fourth Edition, John W. Lehman. Copyright © 2009 by Pearson Education. Published by Prentice Hall. All rights reserved.

into the environment. In recent years, many kinds of chemical pollutants have made the headlines, such as the chlorofluorocarbons that endanger Earth's protective ozone shield, the methyl isocyanate gas that caused 3800 deaths in India in 1984, and the polychlorinated biphenyls (PCBs) and mercury compounds that make some fish dangerous to eat. It is important for organizations and individuals that produce and use chemicals—from manufacturers such as Dow Chemical to organic chemistry students—to consider the environmental consequences of their actions.

The EPA coined the term *green chemistry* in the early 1990s to help encourage new technologies that could reduce or eliminate the use and generation of hazardous substances in chemical processes. More generally, green chemistry simply refers to doing chemistry in an environmentally responsible manner. Although Kermit the Frog famously complained, "It's not easy being green," some green chemical processes are actually simpler and less costly than the ones they replace. And being green always pays off by helping to ensure cleaner air, cleaner water, and a safer environment in general.

The 12 Principles of Green Chemistry

P. T. Anastas and J. C. Warner formulated 12 principles of green chemistry in their book *Green Chemistry: Theory and Practice* [Bibliography, L4]. Those principles are paraphrased and illustrated as follows.

1. *It is easier to prevent waste than to dispose of it afterward.*
   Waste materials must be cleaned up or treated, which costs money and creates a need for more landfills. Even after disposal, most waste material eventually causes environmental contamination.

2. *A chemical synthesis should incorporate as many reactant atoms as possible in the final product.*
   The *atom economy* of a reaction is the percentage of the total molar mass of the starting materials that would appear in a desired product if the yield were 100%.

$$\text{atom economy} = \frac{\text{molar mass of desired product}}{\text{sum of molar masses of all reactants}}$$

For example, a new process for manufacturing the pain reliever ibuprofen has an atom economy of 0.77, meaning that 77% of the mass of the reactants should end up in the ibuprofen, assuming that all of the reactant molecules are converted to product molecules. This replaces an older six-step process that had an atom economy of only 0.40, which means that 60% of the reactants' atoms were—in effect—wasted. The newer process not only reduces the amount of waste that has to be disposed of, it also decreases the cost of the process by reducing the amount of reactants needed.

The *reaction efficiency* of a chemical reaction is a good measure of its "greenness."

$$\text{reaction efficiency} = \text{atom economy} \times \text{percent yield}$$

For example, the following synthesis of ethyl acetate has an atom economy of 0.83.

$$\underset{\substack{\text{mol wt} = 60}}{CH_3\overset{\displaystyle O}{\overset{\|}{C}}OH} + \underset{\substack{\text{mol wt} = 46}}{CH_3CH_2OH} \underset{}{\overset{\text{catalyst}}{\rightleftharpoons}} \underset{\substack{\text{mol wt} = 88}}{CH_3\overset{\displaystyle O}{\overset{\|}{C}}OCH_2CH_3} + \underset{\substack{\text{mol wt} = 18}}{H_2O}$$

$$\text{atom economy} = \frac{88}{(60 + 46)} = 0.83$$

An atom economy of 83% sounds good, but if the yield is 65%, the reaction efficiency is only 0.54% (0.83 × 65%). So chemical processes need to be designed to produce high yields as well as high atom economies.

3. *A chemical synthesis should use and generate the least toxic substances possible.*

   For example, adipic acid is an important chemical used for manufacturing polyurethane, nylon, and other commercial products. It is usually made by a process that involves the oxidation of cyclohexane, which in turn is made from benzene, a toxic and carcinogenic product of petroleum refining.

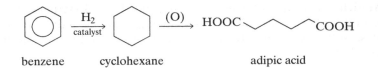

   benzene   cyclohexane   adipic acid

   A newer process, developed by Karen M. Draths and John W. Frost of Michigan State University, uses glucose, an abundant natural sugar, as the starting material.

   This process won the Presidential Green Chemistry Challenge Award in 1998.

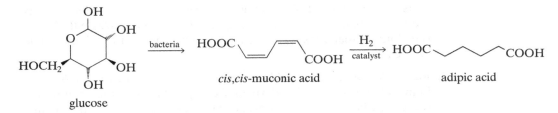

   glucose   *cis,cis*-muconic acid   adipic acid

   Glucose is nontoxic and can be derived from cellulose and other plant materials.

4. *The toxicity of chemical products should be minimized.*

   Sometimes, a relatively nontoxic product can fulfill the same function as a more toxic one. For example, methylene chloride (dichloromethane) is a toxic and possibly carcinogenic liquid that softens or dissolves many kinds of plastic and has therefore been used to weld plastic parts together. Recently, a California company cooperated with the International Reciprocal Trade Association (IRTA) to seek a safer alternative to methylene chloride. They discovered that acetone, a much less toxic solvent, worked just as well. So reducing the toxicity of chemical products requires not only actions taken by chemical manufacturers to modify their product line but also actions taken by end users that reduce the demand for the more toxic chemicals.

5. *The use of solvents, separation agents, and other auxiliary substances in a synthesis should be minimized, and any such substances used should be safe.*
Many of the solvents used in chemical processes, such as benzene and chloroform, can cause serious health and environmental problems. Whenever possible, organic solvents should be eliminated entirely or replaced by safer solvents such as water, liquid carbon dioxide, or ionic liquids. Ionic liquids are low-melting ionic organic compounds such as 1-butyl-4-methylpyridinium tetrafluoroborate.

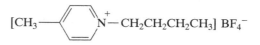

1-butyl-4-methylpyridinium tetrafluoroborate

They make excellent reaction solvents because they are nonflammable, very stable, and can dissolve a wide range of both organic and inorganic compounds. Their main liability is their high cost. For example, the Aldrich Chemical Company sells 50 g of 1-butyl-4-methylpyridinium tetrafluoroborate for about $200, so high-volume industrial use of these solvents is unlikely unless increased demand brings the prices way down.

6. *The energy requirements of chemical processes should be minimized.*
Using less energy reduces both the environmental and economic costs of manufacturing chemicals. Energy requirements can be lowered by, for example, designing reactions so that they can be carried out at ambient temperatures, thereby eliminating the energy cost of heating the reactants. The use of catalysts and microwave generators can reduce energy requirements not only by lowering reaction temperatures but also by speeding up reactions so that energy input is needed for shorter time periods.

7. *Renewable resources should be used to produce starting materials.*
Many chemicals can be derived from plants and other renewable sources rather than from nonrenewable resources such as petroleum, coal, and natural gas. For example, ethanol is a common alcohol that is used in many chemical processes. Most synthetic ethanol is made from ethylene, which is derived from petroleum, but ethanol can also be produced economically by fermentation of switchgrass and other plant products.

8. *Unnecessary derivatization should be avoided.*
Preparing derivatives of reactants during a chemical process requires additional chemicals and generates more waste.

9. *Using catalysts is better than using reagents in stoichiometric amounts.*
Catalysts are used in relatively small quantities, and they are often reusable because they accelerate reactions without being consumed. Catalysts should be as selective as possible so that they promote the formation of the desired product without also promoting the formation of by-products.

10. *Chemical products should be designed to degrade when released into the environment after use.*

    Products that are biodegradable reduce the need for landfills and are less likely to build up to hazardous levels in the environment. For example, packing "peanuts" that are made of starch—unlike Styrofoam packing materials—dissolve in water and are easily digested by organisms after they are discarded.

11. *Chemical processes should be monitored in real time to reduce or prevent the formation of hazardous substances.*

    This requires the development of analytical procedures designed to measure the composition of reactants and products throughout a synthetic process, rather than just analyzing the product after the process is completed. It also requires that there be some way to stop or slow down a process when problems arise.

12. *The substances used in a chemical process should be chosen to minimize the potential for accidents.*

    Using less hazardous materials reduces the danger to workers and helps prevent the release of hazardous chemicals into the environment in case of an accident.

Applying Green Chemistry in the Organic Chemistry Laboratory

Although green chemistry is usually thought to apply mainly to industrial processes, many of its principles can be applied in an academic laboratory setting as well. Here are some ways that you or your instructor might make your organic chemistry lab course greener.

Use Smaller Amounts of Chemicals. Carrying out experiments with small-scale glassware makes it possible to synthesize compounds using smaller amounts of starting materials, reagents, and solvents. Even experiments that use standard scale glassware can usually be scaled down, to reduce the use of chemicals.

Minimize Waste, Especially Hazardous Waste. One way to reduce waste is to use only what you need. Measure out the stoichiometric quantity of a reactant and no more. Don't measure out 10 mL of a solvent if you only need to use 8 mL—the excess shouldn't be returned to the stock bottle and will end up as waste. Just taking care to avoid unnecessary losses helps to reduce waste, and it may improve your lab grade by leading to higher product yields.

Hazardous wastes can sometimes be converted to less hazardous substances in the laboratory. For example, acidic wastes can be converted to less hazardous salts by neutralizing them with sodium carbonate. Your instructor may provide directions for treating certain hazardous wastes before they are transferred to waste containers.

Replace Toxic Reagents with Less Toxic Ones. In the past, most oxidations of secondary alcohols to ketones in academic chemistry labs were carried out using chromium(VI) oxide (CrO_3), a toxic, cancer-causing chemical that is a serious environmental contaminant. In this book, such reactions are carried out using ordinary laundry bleach—a dilute solution of sodium hypochlorite in water—as the oxidant. Although it's virtually impossible to design a lab course that uses no dangerous chemicals (even H_2O can be lethal if inhaled!), the toxicity of most chemicals used in the experiments is comparatively low.

Use Reactions with a High Atom Economy. Consider two possible laboratory syntheses of methyl *t*-butyl ether.

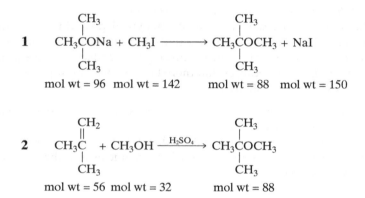

Reaction **1**, which involves the well-known Williamson synthesis of ethers, has an atom economy of only 0.37. Reaction **2**, an alkene addition reaction, has an atom economy of 1.00, or 100%!

$$\text{Reaction 1: atom economy} = \frac{88}{(96 + 142)} = 0.37$$

$$\text{Reaction 2: atom economy} = \frac{88}{(56 + 32)} = 1.00$$

All addition reactions, have atom economies of 100%, because all of the reactant atoms are incorporated into the product. Substitution reactions, such as reaction **1**, tend to have relatively low atom economies.

Reduce the Use of Organic Solvents. Water is a much less hazardous reaction solvent than common organic solvents such as dichloromethane or diethyl ether, but many organic reactants don't dissolve in it. This limitation can sometimes be overcome with the use of a special catalyst (called a phase-transfer catalyst) to facilitate the transfer of chemicals across the boundary between an aqueous solution and an organic substance, or simply by stirring vigorously to increase the surface area of a water-insoluble organic reactant that is in contact with an aqueous solution.

Organic solvents are often used to extract (see OP-18a) organic products from aqueous reaction mixtures, even when the product is relatively insoluble in water. By "salting out" (see OP-18b) such a product with sodium chloride or another salt so that it forms a distinct layer, it may be possible to separate the product directly from the aqueous layer in good yield, eliminating the need for an extraction solvent.

Reduce the Energy Requirements of Reactions.   Some reactions can be carried out in the chemistry lab at a lower temperature, or even at ambient temperature, by using a more reactive reagent or an appropriate catalyst. Other reactants can be carried out in a microwave oven rather than by direct heating. Microwave radiation is an efficient heat source because it can be tuned to heat up some substances (especially water) and not others.

Use Renewable Resources.   Some reactions can be carried out using chemicals derived from plants and other natural materials rather than chemicals synthesized from petroleum products and other nonrenewable resources. For example, aspirin is synthesized commercially from benzene, but in a chemistry lab it can be synthesized from methyl salicylate (the major ingredient in wintergreen oil). Unfortunately, most methyl salicylate is also synthesized from nonrenewable petroleum products, but wintergreen oil from natural sources such as sweet birch trees can be obtained from various suppliers.

The Effect of pH on a Food Preservative
Learning Basic Operations

EXPERIMENT

Laboratory Orientation. Acid–Base Reactions. Reaction Stoichiometry.

Operations

OP-1 Cleaning and Drying Glassware
OP-4 Weighing
OP-5 Measuring Volume
OP-6 Making Transfers
OP-16 Vacuum Filtration
OP-26 Washing and Drying Solids

Before You Begin

1. Read the Introduction and the "Laboratory Safety" section of this book.
2. Read the experiment carefully, particularly the section titled "Understanding the Experiment" and the Directions.
3. Read operations OP-l, OP-4, OP-5, OP-6, OP-16, and OP-26. Most of the descriptions are quite brief.
4. If you are required to write up your experiments in a formal laboratory notebook, prepare the notebook as directed by your instructor.

Scenario

For this and the other experiments, you will play the role of a consultant in a Consulting Chemists Institute operated by your college or university, with your instructor serving as the laboratory supervisor and the other students in your lab section as members of your project group. Most of the Scenarios describe purely hypothetical situations. Except where otherwise indicated, any similarity between a person or organization named herein and an actual person or organization is coincidental.

Fresh Foods Incorporated (FFI) is a small, family-owned chemical company that manufactures sodium benzoate and other food preservatives for sale to food processors. One of its competitors has launched an ad campaign claiming that FFI's sodium benzoate changes to a different chemical in the stomach, implying that the chemical may be harmful or ineffective. D. K. Little, FFI's marketing director, has asked your institute to find out whether the competitor's claim is valid. Your assignment is to place sodium benzoate into a medium that simulates stomach acid, which is an aqueous hydrochloric acid solution with a pH range of 1–3, to see whether or not a new substance forms in that environment. Since this is your first day on the job, your supervisor will show you around the laboratory and help you develop some basic lab skills involving measurements of mass and volume.

From *Operational Organic Chemistry: A Problem Solving Approach to the Laboratory*, Fourth Edition, John W. Lehman. Copyright © 2009 by Pearson Education. Published by Prentice Hall. All rights reserved

Applying Scientific Methodology

Read "Scientific Methodology" in the Introduction before you read this section.

The scientific *problem* to be solved is described in the Scenario. In this experiment the fundamental problem, stated as a question, is "Does a new substance form when sodium benzoate is placed into a simulated stomach acid?" After reading the experiment thoroughly, you should be ready to formulate a *working hypothesis* such as "A new substance will (or will not) form when sodium benzoate is placed into a simulated stomach acid." Your *course of action*, described in detail in the Directions, is then fairly obvious: You will have to place some sodium benzoate in an aqueous solution of hydrochloric acid that has a pH in the range of 1–3. You can do this by dissolving the sodium benzoate in water and adding enough dilute hydrochloric acid (aqueous HCl) to lower the pH to about 2. During this process, you will have to *gather evidence* about whether or not a chemical reaction has occurred. Evidence for a chemical reaction may include a color change, formation of a gas, formation of a precipitate, evolution of heat, or any combination of these. As you *evaluate the evidence* (i.e., think about what you've observed), you may decide to stay with your working hypothesis (if the evidence supports it), modify it, or discard it and formulate a new one. You then should be able to *arrive at a conclusion* based on the experimental evidence and any clues you came across while reading the experiment. You will *report your results* after referring to the "Report" section that follows the Directions.

Sodium Benzoate as a Food Preservative

A hexagon with a circle in it represents a benzene ring, whose molecular formula in these compounds is C_6H_5.

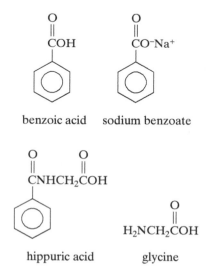

benzoic acid   sodium benzoate

hippuric acid   glycine

When resin from the Sumatran tree *Styrax benzoin* is heated to 100°C, white vapors rise and condense to form needlelike crystals of benzoic acid, which was named for the tree and its resin, gum benzoin. Benzoic acid can easily be converted to its salt, sodium benzoate, which is used widely as a food preservative, particularly in acidic foods such as fruits and fruit juices. Benzoic acid is so widely distributed in plants that the urine of all plant-eating animals (including humans) contains hippuric acid, a compound synthesized in the kidneys by the combination of benzoic acid with the amino acid glycine. Significant amounts of benzoic acid can be isolated from such diverse natural sources as anise seed, cranberries, prunes, cherry bark, cloves, and the scent glands of the beaver. In cranberries and other plant products, benzoic acid is a natural preservative that inhibits the growth of bacteria, yeasts, and molds, and thus retards spoilage.

If you read the labels on cans and bottles in a grocery store, you will find sodium benzoate (sometimes called benzoate of soda) listed on many of them. Sodium benzoate is used as a preservative in such food products as jams and jellies, soft drinks, fruit juices, pickles, condiments, margarine, and canned and frozen seafood, and even in such nonfood items as toothpaste and tobacco. Benzoic acid is also an effective food preservative, but sodium benzoate is a more popular food additive because it is much more soluble in water than is benzoic acid, making it easier to blend into water-containing food products.

Understanding the Experiment

This experiment will help you become familiar with the laboratory environment and with some fundamental laboratory operations, such as measuring mass and volume, separating solids from liquids by vacuum filtration, and drying solids.

In part **A**, you will add hydrochloric acid to a solution of sodium benzoate and, if a different substance forms, recover it and measure its mass. This is a "green" reaction because the only solvent used is water and the only by-product is nontoxic sodium chloride. Although concentrated hydrochloric acid is quite hazardous, the dilute solution of HCl used here is relatively nontoxic and safe to handle.

To understand what is happening in the reaction, you need to know something about the properties of the substances involved and remember what you have previously learned about acid–base chemistry and stoichiometry. When sodium benzoate dissolves in water, it dissociates into benzoate ions (which are weakly basic) and sodium ions, according to the reaction equation:

$$C_6H_5COONa \longrightarrow C_6H_5COO^- + Na^+$$
$$\text{benzoate ion}$$

Hydrochloric acid is a solution of hydrogen chloride (HCl) in water. The strongest acid present in this solution is the hydronium ion, formed by the transfer of a proton from an HCl molecule to a water molecule.

$$HCl + H_2O \longrightarrow Cl^- + H_3O^+$$
$$\text{hydronium ion}$$

If the hydronium ion concentration is high enough, protons will be transferred from the strong acid H_3O^+ to the basic benzoate ions. This will yield benzoic acid, which, being quite insoluble in water (sodium benzoate is about 200 times more soluble), should precipitate from solution. The reaction is

$$C_6H_5COO^- + H_3O^+ \longrightarrow C_6H_5COOH + H_2O \quad \text{(1)}$$
$$\text{benzoic acid}$$

Key Concept: In a Lowry–Brønsted acid–base reaction under standard conditions, the stronger acid transfers protons to a stronger base to yield a weaker acid and a weaker base.

The net reaction is the sum of these three reaction steps.

$$C_6H_5COONa + HCl \longrightarrow C_6H_5COOH + NaCl \quad \text{(2)}$$

The hydronium ion concentration depends on the pH of the solution; the lower the pH, the higher $[H_3O^+]$ will be. By carrying out the experiment, you will discover whether or not the pH of stomach acid is low enough to cause the conversion of sodium benzoate to benzoic acid.

Stop and Think: What is the relationship between hydronium ion concentration and pH?

In any experiment that involves the conversion of one substance to another, it is important to understand the stoichiometry of the reaction. Equation **2** shows that, if the reaction were complete at the pH used, a mole of benzoic acid would be formed for each mole of sodium benzoate in the reaction mixture. You will start with about 2.00 g of sodium benzoate, which is 13.9 mmol (0.0139 mol), so the theoretical yield of benzoic acid (if any forms) should be 13.9 mmol, which corresponds to a mass of 1.70 g. Keep in mind that you will probably not measure out *exactly* the mass of sodium benzoate specified, in which case you will need to calculate the theoretical yield (to the appropriate number of significant figures) based on your measured mass of sodium benzoate.

Whether or not your yield approaches the theoretical value will depend on a number of factors, including the following:

- You may make errors in measuring mass or volume.
- The proposed reaction may not occur or, if it does, it may not be complete.
- Some of the product may remain dissolved in the reaction mixture and may not be recovered.
- You may lose some product while transferring it from one vessel to another.

You can reduce your losses by trying to make nearly *quantitative transfers,* that is, to scrape or rinse the last traces of product from its container and from anything (such as a stirring rod or spatula) that comes in contact with the product. Get into the habit of doing the kind of careful, meticulous work that will increase your yields and save you time and effort in the long run.

The product of a chemical preparation should always be dried to *constant mass*, meaning that its mass after drying shouldn't change significantly between two successive weighings. For most preparations in this book, you can assume that a product is sufficiently dry if—following the initial drying period—its mass doesn't decrease by more than 0.5% after an additional five minutes of oven drying. If the product is being dried at room temperature in a desiccator, the interval between weighings should be longer.

In part **B**, you will determine the density of an unknown liquid by using a graphical method. The validity of your results will depend on the care you take in measuring the mass and volume of the liquid and in graphing your results.

Laboratory Safety and Orientation

Before coming to lab, you should have read the Introduction—which includes a section entitled "A Guide to Success in the Organic Chemistry Lab"—and the "Laboratory Safety" selection, if included in your manual. Before you begin to work in the laboratory, your instructor will review the safety rules and tell you what safety supplies you must have, such as safety goggles and protective gloves and aprons. During the first laboratory period, the instructor will show you where safety equipment is located and tell you how to use it. You should also learn the locations of chemicals, consumable supplies (such as filter paper and boiling chips), waste containers, and various items of equipment such as balances and drying ovens. Obtain a locker and a supply list, and check into the laboratory as directed by your instructor. If necessary, clean up (see OP-1) any dirty glassware and replace any damaged glassware in your locker at this time.

Reactions and Properties

Table 1 Physical properties

	mol wt	mp	Water solubility
benzoic acid	122.1	122	0.34
sodium benzoate	144.1	–	61.2

Note: mol wt = molecular weight; melting points (mp) are in °C; solubilities are in grams of solute per 100 mL of water at room temperature (usually 25°C).

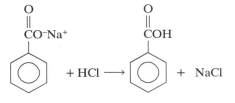

DIRECTIONS

Your instructor should demonstrate the operation of the balances and any special equipment such as automatic pipets.

A. *The Effect of pH on Sodium Benzoate*

Sodium benzoate and benzoic acid are mild irritants. Do not get them in your eyes or on your skin or clothing.

Safety Notes

Reaction. Weigh [OP-4] approximately 2.00 g of sodium benzoate to the maximum accuracy of your balance, and transfer [OP-6] it quantitatively to a 30-mL (or larger) beaker. Measure [OP-5] 10 mL of water with a graduated cylinder, pour it into the beaker, and stir with a glass rod until the sodium benzoate dissolves. Measure 5.0 mL of 3 *M* hydrochloric acid and add it slowly, while stirring, to the sodium benzoate solution until you have added about 4.0 mL. Then, while stirring, add more 3 *M* HCl drop by drop—testing the solution frequently with pH paper—until its pH is 2. To test the pH, use your stirring rod to transfer a drop of the supernatant liquid (liquid near the surface) to a strip of pH paper. Adding a little excess HCl will do no harm. Cool the solution to 10°C or below by setting the 30-mL beaker in a larger beaker containing cracked ice and a small amount of tap water.

Separation. If a new substance has formed, separate it from the reaction mixture by vacuum filtration [OP-16]. Use about 5 mL of ice-cold water to transfer any solid that adheres to the walls of the beaker and to wash the solid on the filter [OP-26a]. Let the solid air-dry on the filter for a few minutes with the vacuum turned on, then dry [OP-26b] it to constant mass. If an oven is used for drying, its temperature should be 90°C or lower, because the solid may sublime above that temperature. Weigh [OP-4] the dry product in a tared (preweighed) vial. Label the vial with the experiment number, the name of the product, its mass, your name, the current date, and any other information required by your instructor. Unless your instructor indicates otherwise, always turn in your product when you finish an experiment. If you don't, you may not get credit for the experiment.

When "water" is specified in a procedure, always use distilled or deionized water unless otherwise indicated.

Observe and Note: Can you detect any evidence for a chemical reaction? If so, describe it in your lab notebook.

Stop and Think: What is the purpose of cooling the solution?

Stop and Think: What is the substance?

Waste Disposal: Unless your instructor directs otherwise, wash the liquid from the filter flask down the drain.

B. *Measuring the Density of an Unknown Liquid*

Safety Notes

> **The unknown liquid may be harmful if inhaled or absorbed through the skin. Avoid contact with the liquid and do not breathe its vapors.**

At your instructor's request, first measure the density of room-temperature water by the procedure described here. If your measured density isn't within 2% of the expected density of water (~0.997 g/mL at room temperature), repeat the measurement.

Take Care! Avoid contact with the liquid and do not breathe its vapors.

Have ready two clean, dry, 1-dram screw-cap vials. Use a measuring pipet or a bottle-top dispenser to measure [OP-5] about 1.1 mL of the unknown liquid into one of the vials, and take both vials to a balance. Weigh [OP-4] the empty vial and its cap to the nearest milligram (0.001 g), and record the mass. (Alternatively, zero the balance with the empty capped vial and record the mass of the liquid directly.) If one is available, use an automatic pipet set to 200 μL (0.200 mL) to measure the volume [OP-5] of the liquid; otherwise, use a 1-mL measuring pipet. (Do not try to adjust the automatic pipet! If it doesn't read 200 μL, see your instructor.) Accurately measure 0.200 mL of the liquid into the empty vial, cap it immediately, and record the mass. Without delay, measure an additional 0.200-mL portion of the liquid into the vial, cap it, and again record the mass. Repeat this process until you have added a total of five 0.200-mL portions. Use the same balance for all readings.

Waste Disposal: Put the liquid in a solvent recovery container as directed by your instructor.

The cumulative volume (or mass) is the total volume (or mass) added up to a particular time; for example, after three additions the cumulative volume is 3 × 0.200 mL, or 0.600 mL.

Prepare a graph of your data, plotting cumulative volume on the *x*-axis and cumulative mass (of the liquid only) on the *y*-axis. Draw the best straight line through the data points. From the slope of the graph, calculate the density of the liquid to three decimal places. Show your graph and your calculated density to your instructor; if either is unacceptable, you may be asked to repeat your measurements or redraw your graph.

Stop and Think: What is the relationship between the slope of your graph and the density? Does your calculated density make sense physically?

Cleanup Routine. After completing this and all subsequent experiments, you should:

- Clean [OP-1] the glassware you used during the experiment.
- Clear off your work area, wipe the benchtop with a sponge or wet towel, and remove any refuse or equipment from the sink.
- Turn in any items you may have checked out of the stockroom, and return any community supplies to their proper locations.
- Turn in your labeled product to the instructor, when applicable.
- See that all the items on the locker list are safely inside your locker (you may have to pay for missing supplies), then lock it.

Report. Read the "Writing a Laboratory Report" appendix before you write your report. (Your instructor may ask you to write up your results as if you were submitting them to D. K. Little of Fresh Foods Incorporated.) Unless your instructor directs otherwise, you should do the following for this and all subsequent reports:

- State any scientific problem posed in the Scenario in your own words, and write down your working hypothesis.
- Report and interpret the relevant evidence, which may include observations, lists or tables of numerical data, and so forth.
- State your conclusion, and tell how the evidence supports it.

For a synthesis, as in part **A** of this experiment, calculate the theoretical yield of the product based on your measured mass and the percent yield of your preparation. For part **B** of this experiment, include the density of your unknown liquid, a table showing your data, and your graph. Follow your instructor's directions regarding other items to include in your report.

Exercises

1. You can confirm that a substance has been converted to a different substance by showing that the substances have different properties. Your observations should have revealed a difference in at least one property of sodium benzoate and benzoic acid. What property was that, and what observation revealed the difference?

2. Label the stronger acid, stronger base, weaker acid, and weaker base in Equation **1** for the proton transfer reaction in part **A** of the experiment.

3. (a) Based on information in the "Chemistry and the Environment" section, calculate the atom economy and reaction efficiency of the reaction you carried out in part **A**. (b) After reading "The 12 Principles of Green Chemistry" in that section, describe some green features of your benzoic acid synthesis, and any that aren't so green.

4. When you lower the pH of a solution containing aqueous sodium benzoate, a precipitate eventually forms. (a) What will happen if you then raise the pH by adding aqueous NaOH? Why will this happen? (b) Write a balanced equation for the proton-transfer reaction involved and label the stronger acid, stronger base, weaker acid, and weaker base.

5. The water solubilities of oxalic acid and sodium oxalate at room temperature are 10 g/100 mL and 3.7 g/100 mL, respectively. Could you prepare oxalic acid by adding HCl to a solution of sodium oxalate, cooling it to room temperature, and filtering the resulting mixture? Explain why or why not.

6. The equation for a straight line can be written in the form $y = mx + b$, where x and y are variables, m is the slope, and b is the intercept. Write an equation for the straight line you obtained in your graph for part **B**, and show how it yields the equation for density $d = m/v$. (Remember that m in this equation stands for mass, not the slope.)

7. (a) Calculate the ratio of dissolved benzoic acid to benzoate ion that will exist in solution at equilibrium at a pH of 2.00. The acid equilibrium constant (K_a) for benzoic acid is 6.46×10^{-5}. Note that this calculation doesn't account for the benzoic acid that has precipitated from solution, but you can assume that the higher the ratio, the more benzoic acid will precipitate. (b) Carry out the same calculation for a pH of 4.00 and explain why it was important to reduce the pH to below 4 in this experiment.

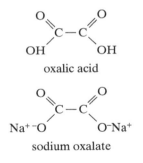

oxalic acid

sodium oxalate

Other Things You Can Do

(Starred items require your instructor's permission.)

*1. Make a flat-bottomed stirring rod and other useful laboratory items as described in the "Making Useful Laboratory Items" minilab.

*2. Try converting some other salts of organic acids, such as sodium salicylate and sodium oxalate, to the corresponding acids. You may need to look up the solubilities of the substances involved to explain your results.

3. To test the preservative effect of sodium benzoate, prepare a solution containing 0.15 g of sodium benzoate in 1 mL of water. Cut an apple into halves and use a brush to apply the solution to *one* of the cut surfaces. Leave the apple halves at room temperature and observe them over a period of several days.

4. Write a short research paper about food additives after consulting such sources as the *Kirk–Othmer Encyclopedia of Chemical Technology* [Bibliography, A8] and appropriate sources listed in section L of the Bibliography.

Separating the Components of "Panacetin"
Extraction and Evaporation

Separation Methods.

Operations

OP-7a Heat Sources
OP-15 Gravity Filtration
OP-18a Liquid-Liquid Extraction
OP-19 Evaporation
OP-4 Weighing
OP-5 Measuring Volume
OP-16 Vacuum Filtration
OP-26 Washing and Drying Solids

Before You Begin

1. Read the experiment carefully.
2. Read operations OP-7a, OP-15, OP-18a, and OP-19. Read or review the other listed operations as necessary.

Scenario

Your supervisor has been e-mailed the following message from a drug watchdog agency, the Association for Safe Pharmaceuticals (ASP).

Greetings:

Our roving agent in Southern California, Sam Surf, recently purchased some Panacetin—an analgesic drug preparation—at a drugstore in San Diego. According to the label on the bottle, the Panacetin tablets were manufactured in the United States by a legitimate pharmaceutical company, but Sam detected some discrepancies on the label and flaws in the tablets themselves that made him suspect they might be counterfeit. Such illegal knockoffs of a domestic drug can be manufactured cheaply elsewhere and smuggled into the United States, where they are sold at a big profit margin.

The label on the bottle lists the ingredients per tablet as aspirin (200 mg), acetaminophen (250 mg), and sucrose (50 mg). Aspirin and acetaminophen are presumably the active ingredients, while sucrose is an inactive ingredient used to make the tablets more palatable to children. But counterfeit drugs may contain less of an active ingredient than claimed, the wrong active ingredient, or no active ingredients at all. We have reason to believe that Panacetin does contain aspirin, sucrose, and another active component, but we're not sure what that component is or whether the amounts listed on the label are accurate. The unknown component is probably a chemical relative of acetaminophen, either acetanilide or phenacetin. Both of these kill pain as effectively as acetaminophen, so the consumer wouldn't notice their presence in an analgesic drug. But acetanilide and phenacetin are banned in the United States because of their toxicity, and we would like to keep them off the market.

We want your Consulting Chemists Institute to analyze this drug preparation to find out what percentages of aspirin, sucrose, and the unknown component it contains, and whether the unknown is acetanilide or phenacetin. You have two weeks to complete your investigation.

Les Payne, Director of Operations, ASP

Applying Scientific Methodology

The Scenario presents two problems for you to solve in this experiment and the next: (1) Is the composition of Panacetin as stated on the label accurate? (2) What is the identity of the unknown component in Panacetin? You will concentrate on the first problem in this experiment, following the course of action described in the Directions. Because of possible material losses, you must allow some margin for error in deciding whether the percentage composition derived from the label (10% sucrose, 40% aspirin, 50% unknown component) is accurate. For the purposes of this experiment, ranges of 8–12% sucrose, 35–45% aspirin, and 45–55% of the unknown component are close enough to indicate that the label is reasonably accurate. You should start with a working hypothesis, gather and interpret evidence, change your hypothesis if the evidence doesn't support it, arrive at a conclusion, and report your results.

Painkilling Drugs, from Antifebrin to Tylenol

Analgesic drugs reduce pain; *antipyretic* drugs reduce fever. Some drugs, including aspirin and acetaminophen, do both. Many of the common over-the-counter analgesic–antipyretic drug preparations contain aspirin, acetaminophen, or combinations of these substances with other ingredients. For example, acetaminophen is the active ingredient of Tylenol, and Extra Strength Excedrin contains aspirin, acetaminophen, and caffeine. From their molecular structures, you can see that acetaminophen is chemically related to both acetanilide and phenacetin, whose painkilling effects were discovered late in the nineteenth century.

In 1886, two clinical assistants named Arnold Cahn and Paul Hepp were looking for something that would rid their patients of a particularly unpleasant intestinal worm. The trick was to find a drug that would kill the worm but not the patient, and their method—not a very scientific one—was to test the chemicals in their stockroom until they found one that worked. When they came across an ancient bottle labeled NAPHTHALENE, they tried it out on a patient who had every malady in the book, including worms. It didn't faze the worms, but it reduced the patient's fever dramatically. Before Cahn and

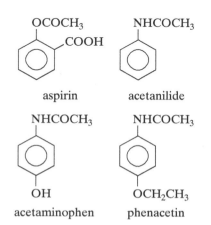

Some compounds with
analgesic–antipyretic properties

Hepp went out on a limb and endorsed naphthalene as a cure-all for fevers, someone noticed that the white substance in the bottle was nearly odorless. Since naphthalene has a strong mothball-like odor, Hepp suspected that the bottle was mislabeled and sent it to his cousin, a chemist at a nearby dye factory, for analysis. The tests showed that the new drug wasn't naphthalene at all, but acetanilide.

Acetanilide proved to have painkilling as well as fever-reducing properties and was soon being marketed under the proprietary name Antifebrin. Unfortunately, some patients who used Antifebrin developed a serious form of anemia called methemoglobinemia, in which hemoglobin molecules are altered in a way that reduces their ability to transport oxygen through the bloodstream. Even though Antifebrin is now considered too toxic for medicinal use, its discovery did much to stimulate the development of safer and more effective analgesic–antipyretic drugs.

About six months after the discovery of Antifebrin, a similar drug was developed as the result of a storage problem. Carl Duisberg, director of research for the Friedrich Bayer Company, had to get rid of 50 tons of *para*-aminophenol—a seemingly useless yellow powder that was a by-product of dye manufacturing. Rather than pay a teamster to haul the stuff away, Duisberg decided to change it into something Bayer could sell. After reading about Antifebrin, he reasoned that a compound with a similar molecular structure might have similar therapeutic uses. Duisberg knew that a hydroxyl (OH) group attached to a benzene ring is characteristic of many toxic substances (for example, phenol), so he decided to "mask" the hydroxyl group in *para*-aminophenol with an ethyl (CH$_3$CH$_2$—) group, as shown in the margin. Incorporation of an acetyl (CH$_3$CO —) group then yielded phenacetin, which proved to be a remarkably effective and inexpensive analgesic–antipyretic drug. Until recently, phenacetin was used in APC tablets (which contained aspirin, phenacetin, and caffeine) and in other analgesic–antipyretic drug preparations. It is no longer approved for medicinal use in the United States because it may cause kidney damage, hemolytic anemia, or even cancer in some patients.

Ironically, the substance Duisberg would have obtained had he not masked the hydroxyl group is acetaminophen, which has proven to be a safer drug than either acetanilide or phenacetin. In the body, acetanilide and phenacetin are both converted to acetaminophen, which is believed to be the active form of all three drugs.

Understanding the Experiment

Most natural products and many commercial preparations are mixtures that contain a number of different substances. To obtain a pure compound from such a mixture, the desired compound is separated from the other components of the mixture by taking advantage of differences in physical and chemical properties. For example, substances with very different solubilities in a given solvent may be separated by extraction or filtration, and liquids with different boiling points can be separated by distillation. Acidic or basic substances are often converted to water-soluble salts, which can then be separated from the water-insoluble components of a mixture.

In this experiment, you will separate the components of a simulated pharmaceutical preparation, Panacetin, making use of their solubilities and

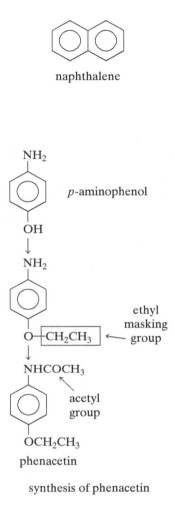

naphthalene

p-aminophenol

ethyl masking group

acetyl group

phenacetin

synthesis of phenacetin

Key Concept: *The separation of substances from one another is based on differences in their physical and chemical properties.*

acid–base properties. Panacetin contains aspirin, sucrose, and an unknown component that may be either acetanilide or phenacetin. These substances have the following characteristics:

- Sucrose is insoluble in the organic solvent dichloromethane (CH_2Cl_2, also called methylene chloride).
- Aspirin, acetanilide, and phenacetin are soluble in dichloromethane but relatively insoluble in water.
- Aspirin reacts with bases such as sodium bicarbonate to form a salt, sodium acetylsalicylate, which is insoluble in dichloromethane and soluble in water.
- Acetanilide and phenacetin are not converted to salts by sodium bicarbonate.

Mixing the Panacetin with dichloromethane should therefore dissolve the aspirin and the unknown component, leaving the sucrose behind as an insoluble solid that can be removed by gravity filtration or centrifugation. Aspirin can be removed from the dichloromethane solution by extraction with an aqueous solution of sodium bicarbonate. The base converts aspirin to its sodium salt, as shown in the margin. This salt will migrate from the dichloromethane layer, in which it is insoluble, to the aqueous layer, in which it is soluble. The unknown component will stay behind in the dichloromethane layer. After separation of the layers, aspirin can be recovered by precipitation from the aqueous layer with hydrochloric acid followed by vacuum filtration. The unknown component can then be isolated by evaporating the solvent from the dichloromethane solution.

This separation process is summarized by the following flow diagram:

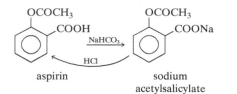

aspirin   sodium acetylsalicylate

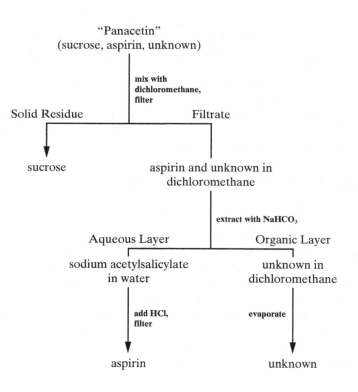

You can estimate the percentage composition of Panacetin from the masses of the dried components. Note that your calculated composition may or may not be close to the composition given in the Scenario. Careful work is required to obtain accurate results in this experiment; errors can arise from incomplete mixing with dichloromethane, incomplete extraction or precipitation of aspirin, incomplete drying of the recovered components, and losses in transferring substances from one container to another.

Dichloromethane may be harmful to the environment, especially when released into groundwater. The Environmental Protection Agency (EPA) classifies it as a priority pollutant and has established a Maximum Contaminant Level (MCL) of 5 parts per billion (ppb) for its concentration in drinking water.

*A **Greener Way:** Diethyl ether is less harmful to health and the environment than is dichloromethane, so it can be used as the extraction solvent in place of dichloromethane. Just remember that the ether layer separates on top of the water layer rather than below it. If you use dichloromethane, it is best to recover the solvent using a cold trap (see OP-15).*

DIRECTIONS

Dichloromethane may be harmful if ingested, inhaled, or absorbed through the skin. There is a possibility that prolonged inhalation of dichloromethane may cause cancer.
Minimize contact with the liquid and do not breathe its vapors.

See "Chemical Hazards" in the Laboratory Safety section for an explanation of the hazard symbols.

Separation of Sucrose. Accurately weigh [OP-4] about 3.00 g of Panacetin and transfer [OP-6] it to a clean, *dry* 125-mL Erlenmeyer flask. Add 50 mL of dichloromethane to the flask. Stir the mixture thoroughly with a glass stirring rod to dissolve as much solid as possible, and use the rod to break up any lumps or granules. Using a preweighed fluted filter paper, filter the mixture by gravity [OP-15] into a small flask, saving the filtrate (the liquid that goes through the filter paper) for the next step. Set the filter paper aside, being careful not to lose any of the sucrose, and reweigh it when it is completely dry. Record the mass of the sucrose in your laboratory notebook. If requested, submit the sucrose to your instructor in a tared (preweighed) and labeled vial.

Separation of Aspirin. Transfer the filtrate to a separatory funnel and extract [OP-18a] it with two *separate* 30-mL portions of 5% sodium bicarbonate. For each extraction, use a stirring rod to stir the liquid layers until any fizzing subsides before you stopper and shake the separatory funnel. Because the dichloromethane layer will be on the bottom, you will have to transfer each layer to a different container (label the containers) and return the dichloromethane layer to the separatory funnel before the second extraction. Combine the two aqueous extracts in the same container and save the dichloromethane layer for the following step, "Isolation of the Unknown Component."

Slowly add 7.0 mL of 6 *M* hydrochloric to the combined aqueous extracts while stirring with a glass rod. Test the pH of the solution and add more acid, if necessary, to bring the pH down to 2 or lower. Cool the mixture in an ice/water bath for at least 10 minutes, collect the aspirin by vacuum filtration [OP-16], and wash it on the filter [OP-26a] with cold water.

Safety Notes

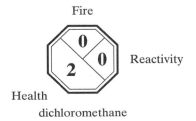

Fire

Health

Reactivity

dichloromethane

Take Care! Avoid contact with dichloromethane; do not breathe its vapors.

Stop and Think: Does all of the solid dissolve? If not, why not?

Stop and Think: What components of Panacetin are in the filtrate?

Take Care! A gas is evolved, so don't shake too vigorously.

Stop and Think: Which component of Panacetin is in the aqueous layer? In the dichloromethane layer? If you don't shake the separatory funnel long enough, how might that affect your results?

Observe and Note: Look for and record any evidence for a chemical reaction.

Waste Disposal: Unless your instructor directs otherwise, wash the filtrate down the drain.

If it is quite impure, the unknown may remain liquid after all of the solvent is removed. It should solidify upon cooling.

Waste Disposal: Put the recovered dichloromethane in a designated chlorinated solvent recovery container.

Let the aspirin dry on the filter for a few minutes with the aspirator running, then dry [OP-26b] it to constant mass. Weigh the aspirin and record its mass in your lab notebook. Submit the aspirin to your instructor in a vial.

Isolation of the Unknown Component. Use a filter flask attached to a trap and aspirator to evaporate [OP-19] the solvent from the dichloromethane solution. Heating and swirling the solution over a steam bath or in a hot-water bath [OP-7a] will increase the evaporation rate. Discontinue evaporation when only a solid residue remains in the flask or when no more solvent evaporates. Transfer the unknown component to a tared vial and let it dry [OP-26b] to constant mass. Weigh it before you begin "Identification of a Constituent of Panacetin," if included.

Calculate your percent recovery, dividing the sum of the masses of all components by the mass of Panacetin that you started with. Calculate the approximate percentage composition of Panacetin, based on the total mass of components recovered. (These percentages should add up to 100%.) In your report, be sure to include the information specified in the "Report" section of "The Effect of pH on a Food Preservative," if included, and any other information requested by your instructor.

Exercises

1. (a) Describe any evidence that a chemical reaction occurred when you added 6 *M* HCl to the solution of sodium acetylsalicylate. (b) Explain why the changes that you observed took place.
2. Describe and explain the possible effect on your results of the following experimental errors or variations. In each case, specify the component(s) whose percentage(s) would be too high or too low. (a) After adding dichloromethane to Panacetin, you didn't stir or shake the mixture long enough. (b) During the NaHCO₃ extraction, you failed to mix the aqueous and organic layers thoroughly. (c) You mistakenly extracted the dichloromethane solution with 5% HCl rather than 5% NaHCO₃. (d) Instead of using pH paper, you neutralized the NaHCO₃ solution to pH 7 using litmus paper.
3. Although acetanilide and phenacetin aren't appreciably acidic, acetaminophen (like aspirin) is a stronger acid than water. What problem would you encounter if the unknown component were acetaminophen rather than acetanilide or phenacetin, and you extracted the aspirin with 5% NaOH? Explain, giving equations for any relevant reactions.
4. Acetaminophen is a weaker acid than carbonic acid (H₂CO₃), but aspirin is a stronger acid than carbonic acid. Prepare a flow diagram like the one in this experiment, showing a procedure that can be used to separate a mixture of sucrose, aspirin, and acetaminophen.
5. Write balanced reaction equations for the reactions involved (a) when aspirin dissolves in aqueous NaHCO₃ and (b) when aspirin is precipitated from a sodium acetylsalicylate solution by HCl. Assuming that both reactions are spontaneous under standard conditions, label the stronger acid, stronger base, weaker acid, and weaker base in each equation.

Other Things You Can Do

(Starred items require your instructor's permission.)

*1. Carry out the "Extraction of Iodine by Dichloromethane" minilab to help you visualize what happens during an extraction.

2. Write a short research paper about the chemistry and physiological effects of analgesic–antipyretic drugs using such sources as the *Kirk–Othmer Encyclopedia of Chemical Technology* [Bibliography, A8] and titles from section L of the Bibliography.

Identifying a Constituent of "Panacetin"
Recrystallization and Melting-Point Measurement

Purification Methods.

Operations

OP-28a Recrystallization from a Single Solvent
OP-33 Melting Point
OP-4 Weighing
OP-7a Heat Sources
OP-16 Vacuum Filtration
OP-26 Washing and Drying Solids

Before You Begin

1. Read the experiment and operations OP-28a and OP-33. Read or review the other operations as necessary.
2. Read "Using the Bibliography" in "The Chemical Literature" appendix, and familiarize yourself with the layout of the Bibliography.
3. Calculate the minimum volume of boiling water that will be needed to dissolve all of your unknown compound if it is acetanilide *and* if it is phenacetin (see "Understanding the Experiment").

Scenario

The Scenario for this experiment is given in "Separating the Components of 'Panacetin.'"

Applying Scientific Methodology

The problem you will be trying to solve in this experiment is "What is the identity of the unknown component of Panacetin?" Your course of action is described in the Directions. During the experiment, you should gather and evaluate evidence that can help you solve the problem. No working hypothesis can be more than a guess, so you might want to wait until you carry out the *Purification* step before you formulate your initial hypothesis. You will then test your hypothesis in the *Analysis* step, which will enable you to reach a conclusion. Keep a careful record of your observations and your interpretation of the evidence so that you will be able to describe them in your report.

Using Chemical Reference Books

Knowing the physical properties of a compound—such as its melting or boiling point, refractive index, and spectral absorption bands—can help

From *Operational Organic Chemistry: A Problem Solving Approach to the Laboratory*, Fourth Edition, John W. Lehman. Copyright © 2009 by Pearson Education. Published by Prentice Hall. All rights reserved.

you identify the compound and estimate its degree of purity. Whenever a new compound is discovered or synthesized, its physical properties are measured and reported in one or more scientific journals to enable future investigators to identify that compound when they encounter it. Physical properties and other information about the more familiar compounds are reported in chemical handbooks and other reference books. For instance, from its entry in *The Merck Index*, we learn that acetaminophen is known by at least 8 chemical names and 45 proprietary drug names, including Alpiny, Bickiemol, Cetadol, Dial-a-gesic, Enelfa, Finimal, Gelocatil, Homoolan, and so on throughout the alphabet. The same source lists the compound's important physical properties and uses, provides references that describe its preparation from various starting materials, and tells where to find more information about it. For example, *The Merck Index* refers to an evaluation of acetaminophen's effect on the kidneys located on page 1238 of volume 320 (published in 1989) of the *New England Journal of Medicine*, as indicated by the following entry:

Evaluation of renal effects: D. P. Sandler *et al.*, *N. Engl. J. Med.* **320**, 1238 (1989).

In such citations, the abbreviated journal name is followed by the volume number, the page number on which the article begins, and the year of publication. Currently the preferred convention is to list the abbreviated journal name, the year of publication (in boldface type), the volume number (in italics), and the page number, as illustrated by the following citation to an article in the *Journal of Organic Chemistry*.

J. Org. Chem.	**1994**,	*59*,	2546
journal abbreviation	year	volume	page

The full names of scientific periodicals can be found in the *Chemical Abstracts Service Source Index* [Bibliography, A5].

Figure 1 reproduces the entry for acetanilide from *Lange's Handbook of Chemistry*. This handbook reports that acetanilide has a melting point of 114°C and that it is only slightly soluble in water (aq) at 25°C, dissolving to the extent of 0.56 g per 100 mL of water at that temperature. *The Merck Index* reports that a gram of acetanilide dissolves in about 185 mL of cold (near room-temperature) water or 20 mL of boiling water, and that a gram of phenacetin dissolves in 1310 mL of cold water or 82 mL of boiling water. Such entries often tell you what you need to know in order to purify a compound and identify or characterize the pure substance. These and other physical properties of acetanilide and phenacetin are summarized in Table 1 (see "Structures and Properties"), in which solubilities from *The Merck Index* are expressed in grams of solute per 100 mL of water.

No.	Name	Formula	Formula weight	Beilstein reference	Density, g/mL	Refractive index	Melting point, °C	Boiling point, °C	Flash point, °C	Solubility in 100 parts solvent
a18	Acetanilide	$CH_3CONHC_6H_5$	135.17	12, 237	1.219_4^{15}		114	304–305	173	0.56 aq^{25}; 25 acet; 29 alc; 2 bz; 27 chl; 5 eth

Figure 1 *Lange's Handbook of Chemistry* entry for acetanilide (Reprinted with permission from *Lange's Handbook of Chemistry,* 15th ed., by N. A. Lange, edited by J. A. Dean. Copyright McGraw-Hill, Inc., New York, 1999.)

Understanding the Experiment

In this experiment, you will purify and identify the unknown component of Panacetin from "Separating the components of 'Panacetin.'"

No separation is perfect; traces of impurities will always remain in a substance that has been separated from a mixture. Therefore, some kind of purification process is needed to remove them. Solids can be purified by such operations as recrystallization, chromatography, and sublimation; liquids are usually purified by distillation or chromatography. The solubility information from Table 1 indicates that both acetaminophen and phenacetin are relatively soluble in boiling water but insoluble in cold water. This suggests that the unknown component can be purified by recrystallization, in which an impure solid dissolves in a hot (usually boiling) solvent and then crystallizes from the cooled solution in a purer form.

Based on the mass of unknown that you recovered, you can estimate the volume of boiling water needed to dissolve that mass of either acetanilide or phenacetin. For example, suppose your unknown is acetanilide and you recovered 1.15 g of the crude solid. Table 1 shows that the solubility of acetanilide in boiling water is 5.0 g per 100 mL water, so the volume of boiling water you will need to dissolve it is approximately 23 mL.

$$1.15 \,\text{g acetanilide} \times \frac{100 \,\text{mL water}}{5.0 \,\text{g acetanilide}} = 23 \,\text{mL water}$$

Phenacetin, which is less soluble in boiling water, will require more water to dissolve. You should begin the recrystallization operation using the smaller volume of water (don't add it all at once; see OP-28a) and add more only if your compound doesn't dissolve in that amount of water at its boiling point.

After a compound has been purified, it should be *analyzed* to establish its identity and degree of purity. Although sophisticated instruments such as nuclear magnetic resonance (NMR) spectrometers and mass spectrometers are now used to determine the structures of most newly discovered organic compounds, an operation as simple as a melting-point measurement can help identify a compound whose properties have already been reported in the chemical literature. By itself, the melting point of a compound isn't sufficient proof of its identity, because thousands of compounds may share the same melting point. But when an unknown compound is thought to be one of a small number of possible compounds, its identity can often be determined by mixing the unknown with an authentic sample of each known compound and measuring the melting points of the mixtures. The use of a *mixture melting point* for identification is based on the fact that the melting point of a pure compound is lowered and its melting-point range broadened when it is combined with a different compound. For example, if your unknown is phenacetin, it should melt sharply near 135°C, and a mixture of the unknown with an authentic sample of phenacetin should have essentially the same melting point. But a 1:1 mixture of phenacetin with acetanilide should melt at a considerably lower temperature over a much broader range.

The melting point of a compound can also give a rough indication of its purity. If your compound melts over a narrow range (1–2°C or less) at a temperature close to the literature value, it is probably quite pure. If its melting-point range is broad and substantially lower than the literature value, it is probably contaminated by water or other impurities.

Key Concept: The solubilities of most substances decrease as the temperature is lowered.

Key Concept: Impurities lower the melting point of a pure substance.

In contrast to the environmentally harmful solvent dichloromethane, the only solvent used in this experiment is dihydrogen oxide (H_2O), also known as water. It has been established that H_2O can cause serious injury or death by inhalation (in its liquid state), thermal burns (in its gaseous state), and hypothermia (in its solid state). Nevertheless, H_2O is not officially classified as a hazardous chemical and may be released into the environment.

Structures and Properties

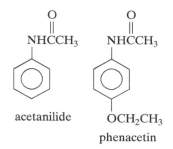

acetanilide

phenacetin

Table 1 Physical properties

	mol wt	mp	Solubility, c.w.	Solubility, b.w.
acetanilide	135.2	114	0.54	5.0
phenacetin	179.2	135	0.076	1.22

Note: Melting points are in °C; solubilities are in grams of solute per 100 mL of cold water (c.w.) or boiling water (b.w.).

DIRECTIONS

Safety Notes

Acetanilide and phenacetin can irritate the skin and eyes, so minimize contact with your unknown compound.

Purification. Recrystallize [OP-28a] the unknown drug component from "Separating the components of 'Panacetin,'" by boiling [OP-7a] it with just enough water to dissolve it completely, then letting it cool slowly to room temperature. Use an Erlenmeyer flask that will easily accommodate the largest volume of recrystallization solvent that you calculated. If necessary, induce crystallization by scratching the sides of the container with a glass stirring rod. Then cool the container further in a beaker containing ice and tap water to increase the yield of product. Collect the solid by vacuum filtration [OP-16], and wash it [OP-26a] with a small amount of ice-cold water. Dry [OP-26b] the product to constant mass and weigh [OP-4] it in a tared vial.

Analysis. Grind a small amount of the dry unknown component to a fine powder on a watch glass using a spatula or a flat-bottomed stirring rod (see OP-3). Divide the solid into four nearly equal portions. Combine portions 1 and 2. Thoroughly mix portion 3 with an approximately equal amount of finely ground acetanilide, and thoroughly mix portion 4 with an approximately equal amount of finely ground phenacetin. Measure the melting-point ranges [OP-33] for the purified unknown (portions 1 + 2), the mixture with acetanilide, and the mixture with phenacetin. In each case, record the temperature at which you see the first trace of liquid and the temperature at which the sample is completely liquid. Unless your instructor indicates

Observe and Note: How much water was needed to dissolve it? What happens as the solution cools?

Waste Disposal: Unless your instructor directs otherwise, wash the filtrate down the drain.

Stop and Think: Is your unknown reasonably pure? If not, what should you do?

otherwise, you should carry out at least two measurements with each of these. Turn in the remaining product to your instructor in a vial labeled as shown by the example in the margin (or as directed by your instructor), giving the actual name of the product as indicated by your results. Your report should include the results of your melting-point analyses and a calculation of the percent recovery of the product.

> *phenacetin*
> *1.21 g*
> *mp 112–114°C*
> *Ann A. Liszt*
> *9/23/08*

Exercises

1. (a) What is the minimum volume of boiling water needed to dissolve 1.15 g of phenacetin (see Table 1)? (b) About how much phenacetin will remain dissolved when the water is cooled to room temperature? (c) Calculate the maximum mass of solid (undissolved) phenacetin that can be recovered when the cooled solution is filtered.

2. An unknown compound **X** is one of the four compounds listed in Table 2. A mixture of **X** with benzoic acid melts at 89°C, a mixture of **X** with phenyl succinate melts at 120°C, and a mixture of **X** with *m*-aminophenol melts at 102°C. Give the identity of **X** and explain your reasoning.

Table 2 Melting points

Compound	mp, °C
o-toluic acid	102
benzoic acid	121
phenyl succinate	121
m-aminophenol	122

3. Tell how each of the following experimental errors will affect your experimental results (yield, purity, or both) and explain why. (a) You failed to dry the product completely. (b) You used enough water to recrystallize phenacetin, but your unknown was acetanilide. (c) In "Separating the Components of 'Panacetin,'" you didn't extract all of the aspirin from the dichloromethane solution.

4. Tell whether each of the experimental errors in Exercise 3 will affect the melting point of the unknown component. If it will, tell how it will affect the melting point and explain why.

5. Using one or more of the reference books listed in "The Chemical Literature" appendix, give the following information about the analgesic drug ibuprofen: chemical names, molecular weight, molecular formula, structural formula, melting point, and a suitable recrystallization solvent.

6. Locate citations for one or more journal articles that give procedures for preparing (a) aspirin and (b) propoxyphene (Darvon). Give the full name of each journal, the volume number, the page number(s), and the year.

Other Things You Can Do

(Starred items require your instructor's permission.)

*1. Purify an unknown solid by recrystallization as described in the "Purification of an Unknown Compound by Recrystallization" minilab.

*2. Carry out the purification and melting-point analysis of an acetanilide–salicylic acid mixture as described in *J. Chem. Educ.* **1989**, *66*, 1063.

3. Calibrate your thermometer by measuring the melting points of compounds listed in Table F1 of OP-33.

4. Look up the properties of a common organic compound in at least five different reference books and compare the kind of information provided by each.

Heating Under Reflux
Synthesis of Salicylic Acid from Wintergreen Oil

Preparation and Purification of Solids.

Operations

OP-2 Using Specialized Glassware
OP-7b Smooth Boiling Devices
OP-7c Heating Under Reflux
OP-4 Weighing
OP-7a Heat Sources
OP-16 Vacuum Filtration
OP-26 Washing and Drying Solids
OP-28 Recrystallization
OP-33 Melting Point

Before You Begin

1. Read the experiment and operations OP-2, OP-7b, and OP-7c. Read or review the other operations as necessary.
2. Read "Calculations for Organic Synthesis." Then calculate the mass and volume of 10.0 mmol of methyl salicylate, the theoretical yield of salicylic acid from that much methyl salicylate, and the minimum volume of water needed to recrystallize that much salicylic acid.
3. Complete the experimental plan that follows the "Reactions and Properties" section by specifying all sizes and quantities indicated by asterisks in the Chemicals and Supplies list. Note that reaction flasks (pear shaped and round bottom) come in 25-, 50-, 100-, 250-, and 500-mL sizes; Erlenmeyer flasks in 25-, 50-, 125-, and 250-mL sizes; and beakers in 30-, 50-, 150-, 250-, and 400-mL sizes.

Be sure to distinguish millimoles (mmol) from moles (mol); most prelab assignments will specify amounts of chemicals in millimoles.

Scenario

The new-age pharmaceutical company Natural Nostrums manufactures drugs from "natural" starting materials. For example, the company manufactures a painkilling drug it advertises as "organic aspirin" starting with methyl salicylate, which occurs naturally in wintergreen oil. Most commercially marketed aspirin is manufactured starting with benzene, a product of petroleum refining. An intermediate in both of these syntheses is salicylic acid.

Natural Nostrums claims that its aspirin, which is supposedly more natural than aspirin made from benzene, has fewer side effects than ordinary aspirin. Critics have accused the company of false and misleading advertising,

From *Operational Organic Chemistry: A Problem Solving Approach to the Laboratory,* Fourth Edition, John W. Lehman. Copyright © 2009 by Pearson Education. Published by Prentice Hall. All rights reserved.

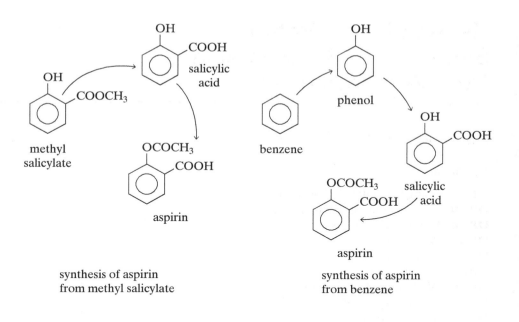

synthesis of aspirin
from methyl salicylate

synthesis of aspirin
from benzene

asserting that salicylic acid made from methyl salicylate is no different than salicylic acid made from benzene, and that the resulting aspirin is therefore no better than any other aspirin.

Les Payne, director of operations for the Association for Safe Pharmaceuticals (ASP), is investigating the company. He just shipped your supervisor a sample of salicylic acid manufactured from benzene and a bottle of methyl salicylate that one of his agents obtained from the chemical stockroom at Natural Nostrums. Your assignment is to prepare salicylic acid from this methyl salicylate and find out whether or not it differs from salicylic acid made from benzene.

Applying Scientific Methodology

You need to state the problem as a question, formulate a working hypothesis, follow the course of action described in the Directions, gather and evaluate evidence, test your hypothesis, arrive at a conclusion, and report your findings.

Wintergreen Oil

wintergreen plant

For many years, commercial methyl salicylate was obtained from wintergreen oil, an aromatic liquid distilled from the leaves of the wintergreen plant (*Gaultheria procumbens*) or from the bark of sweet birch trees (*Betula lenta*). When cheap raw materials became available from petroleum, a more economical commercial process was developed for synthesizing methyl salicylate from salicylic acid and methanol (CH_3OH, methyl alcohol).

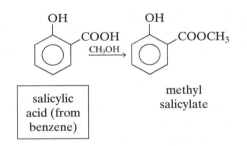

salicylic acid (from benzene)

methyl salicylate

Regardless of its source, methyl salicylate is methyl salicylate. There is no difference between its pure natural and synthetic forms, because both are composed of the same kind of molecules and must therefore have the same properties. Any differences between wintergreen oil obtained from natural sources and synthetic methyl salicylate are due mainly to impurities in the natural oil.

A natural substance is one obtained directly from plant, animal, or mineral sources. A synthetic substance is one prepared by chemically altering other substances, which may themselves be either natural or synthetic.

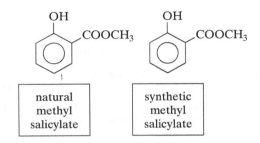

natural methyl salicylate

synthetic methyl salicylate

Methyl salicylate, both natural and synthetic, has been used for many years as a flavoring agent because of its pleasant penetrating odor and flavor. According to Euell Gibbons, author of *Stalking the Healthful Herbs* and other books about edible and medicinal wild plants, you can prepare a good wintergreen tea by pouring boiling water into a jar filled with freshly picked wintergreen leaves and letting it steep overnight or longer. The distinctive flavor of wintergreen is found in a variety of commercial products, including candy, chewing gum, root beer, and toothpaste. Medicinally, wintergreen oil has some of the painkilling properties of other *salicylates*, a group of related organic compounds that includes salicylic acid and aspirin. When absorbed through the skin, it produces an astringent but soothing sensation, and it is frequently used in preparations such as Bengay to alleviate muscular aches and arthritis.

Understanding the Experiment

In this experiment, you will be carrying out an *organic synthesis*, the preparation of salicylic acid from methyl salicylate. An organic synthesis can be described as the preparation of a desired organic compound by chemically modifying the molecules of another organic compound, which is called the *starting material*. Until 1874, all commercial salicylic acid was synthesized from natural wintergreen oil. You will reproduce this nineteenth-century synthesis of salicylic acid using methyl salicylate, the major constituent of wintergreen oil, as the starting material.

Organic reactions are slower than most inorganic reactions. For example, when aqueous solutions of silver nitrate and sodium chloride are mixed, the resulting reaction is almost instantaneous, taking place as rapidly as silver and chloride ions can come together to form silver chloride.

$$Ag^+ + Cl^- \longrightarrow \textbf{AgCl}$$

In an organic reaction, the reacting molecules may come together as frequently as the ions in a precipitation reaction, but they may not collide with enough energy or in the right orientation to react. An ion-combination reaction has such a low activation energy that ions need only "stick together" to form a product. Covalent molecules must ordinarily undergo a process of bond breaking and bond formation to be converted to product molecules, and such processes have relatively high activation energies.

Some of the bond-breaking and bond-forming steps involved in this experiment's synthesis are shown in the following *mechanism* for the conversion of methyl salicylate to salicylic acid.

Key Concept: *A mechanism is a step-by-step description of a chemical reaction, showing what bonds are broken and formed as reactant molecules are converted to product molecules.*

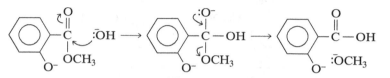

Mechanism for the reaction. Note that the —OH group of methyl salicylate is ionized at the high pH of the reaction mixture.

According to this mechanism, the formation of a bond between a hydroxide ion and a carbonyl (C=O) carbon atom is accompanied by the breaking of a pi bond in the C=O group. That pi bond is then re-formed while a bond to an —OCH₃ group is broken.

The *reaction*, then, is the crucial step in an organic synthesis—it may be over in a few minutes or require a few weeks, but enough time should be allowed to bring the reaction as close to completion as possible before proceeding to the next steps. The desired product must be *separated* from the reaction mixture, *purified* to remove residual contaminants, and *analyzed* to verify its identity and purity.

Completion *implies that as many reactant molecules as possible have been converted to product molecules under the conditions of the reaction.*

Methyl salicylate is the limiting reactant in this synthesis; sodium hydroxide is used in excess to ensure a reasonably fast, complete reaction. It is best to measure liquid limiting reactants by mass, because the mass of a liquid can be measured more accurately than its volume. To avoid waste and minimize spillage at the balance, you should dispense the estimated *volume* of liquid from the stock bottle before you take it to the balance to weigh it. This is why you were asked (in "Before You Begin") to calculate both the mass and volume of methyl salicylate required. If the mass of the methyl salicylate isn't within about 5% of your calculated value, you can add or remove liquid with a Pasteur pipet.

You will carry out the reaction by boiling a mixture of methyl salicylate and sodium hydroxide in a round-bottom flask equipped with a water-cooled condenser. A heating mantle or another flameless heat source capable of boiling water (not a steam bath) is needed for the reaction. The purpose of the condenser is to convert water and methyl salicylate vapors back to liquids and return them to the reaction flask so that they don't boil away.

The product of the initial reaction will be a salt of salicylic acid—disodium salicylate—and not salicylic acid itself. Adding 3 M sulfuric acid will then precipitate salicylic acid. When you recover the product by vacuum filtration, remember that the *solvent* in the reaction mixture is water, so use cold water (*not* 3 M sulfuric acid) to wash the product on the filter. The solubility of salicylic acid in water is about 0.18 g/100 mL at 20°C and 6.7 g/100 mL at the boiling point, so it can be purified by recrystallization from water. The melting point of your product should give you a good indication of its purity; the melting point of pure salicylic acid is reported to be 159°C. You will also carry out a mixture melting point (see OP-33) with the benzene-derived salicylic acid provided by your instructor to see whether it is identical to or different from your own.

This is a relatively green synthesis because the reactants and products (in the concentrations used) are not highly toxic, the only solvent used is water, and the overall reaction has a high atom economy. Both sodium hydroxide and sulfuric acid may be harmful to aqueous life, and sulfuric acid is classified as a hazardous air pollutant, but small-scale release of either chemical shouldn't be particularly harmful.

To help you organize your time efficiently, an experimental plan for the preparation of salicylic acid is provided. You will need to complete the plan as directed in "Before You Begin." Note that the 30-minute reaction period should be used to collect the supplies and assemble the apparatus needed for upcoming operations.

Stop and Think: Why is this the initial product? (Consider the pH of the reaction mixture.)

*A **Greener Way:** You can use natural wintergreen oil in place of synthetic methyl salicylate. The natural oil can be obtained from suppliers of essential oils, such as natural food stores, as well as certain chemical suppliers.*

Reactions and Properties

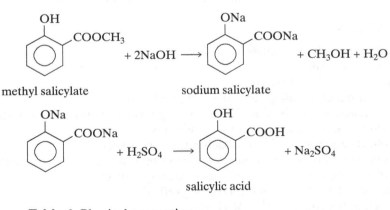

Table 1 Physical properties

	mol wt	mp	bp	d
methyl salicylate	152.1	−8	223	1.174
salicylic acid	138.1	159		

Note: Melting points and boiling points are in °C; density (d) is in g/mL.

Experimental Plan

Chemicals and Supplies Needed

* indicates a number (size or quantity) to be filled in.

> Heating under reflux [OP-7c]
> > * g (* mL) of methyl salicylate (avoid contact, inhalation)
> > * mL of 6 *M* NaOH (wear gloves, avoid contact)
> > *-mL round-bottom flask
> > *-mL graduated cylinder
> > heat source [OP-7a] (specify type), condenser, boiling chips [OP-7b], ring stand, clamps
>
> Addition of sulfuric acid
> > * mL of 3 *M* H$_2$SO$_4$
> > *-mL beaker
> > pH paper, stirring rod, Pasteur pipet
>
> Vacuum filtration [OP-16]
> > * mL of cold water for washing
> > Buchner funnel, filter flask, filter trap, filter paper, spatula, watch glass
>
> Recrystallization [OP-28]
> > * mL of water for recrystallization
> > * mL of cold water for washing [OP-26a]
> > two *-mL Erlenmeyer flasks, *-mL graduated cylinder
> > Buchner funnel, filter flask, filter trap, filter paper, spatula, watch glass
>
> Drying [OP-26b] and weighing [OP-4]
> > drying container, desiccator (or oven), tared vial
>
> Melting points [OP-33]
> > mp tubes, flat-bottomed stirring rod *or* spatula, watch glass

Lab Checklist

- Collect and clean supplies for reflux.
- Obtain heat source.
- Assemble reflux apparatus.
- Measure methyl salicylate and 6 *M* NaOH solution.
- Add reactants and boiling chips to boiling flask; turn on condenser water.
- Heat reactants under reflux for 30 minutes.
- Collect supplies for H$_2$SO$_4$ addition (during reflux).
- Collect vacuum filtration supplies and assemble apparatus (during reflux).
- Collect supplies for recrystallization (during reflux).
- Measure 3 *M* H$_2$SO$_4$ solution (during reflux).
- Precipitate product with 3 *M* H$_2$SO$_4$.
- Filter and wash product; air-dry on filter.
- Measure and boil water for recrystallization.
- Recrystallize product from boiling water.
- Filter and wash product; air-dry on filter.
- Dry product.

- Weigh product.
- Measure melting point.
- Turn in product.
- Clean up.

DIRECTIONS

> Concentrated sodium hydroxide solutions are very corrosive and can cause severe damage to skin and eyes. Wear protective gloves and goggles, and avoid contact with the 6 M NaOH. (Always wear your safety goggles in the organic chemistry lab!)
> Methyl salicylate can irritate the eyes and skin; avoid contact and inhalation.

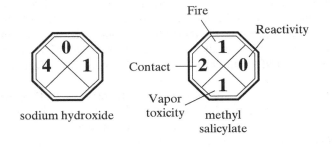

sodium hydroxide   methyl salicylate

Reaction. Obtain an appropriate heat source [OP-7a] and position it correctly. Assemble an apparatus for heating under reflux [OP-7c], using standard-taper glassware [OP-2] if available. Make sure the apparatus is clamped securely to a ring stand. Measure 10.0 mmol of methyl salicylate into the boiling flask, followed by 15 mL of 6 M sodium hydroxide and a few boiling chips [OP-7b]. Don't add both reactants through the same funnel; if you do, a solid may plug up the funnel stem. Start water flowing in the condenser jacket, then have the instructor check your apparatus *before* you begin heating. Heat the reaction mixture under reflux for 30 minutes, measuring from the time the solution starts to boil. If, after 30 minutes under reflux, the reaction mixture is cloudy or contains an oily upper layer, continue heating under reflux until the cloudiness (or oil) disappears and the reaction mixture no longer smells like wintergreen.

When the reaction is complete, remove the condenser as soon as it is cool enough to handle; otherwise, the ground joints might freeze. Remove the boiling chips and transfer the reaction mixture to a beaker large enough to contain it and the sulfuric acid to be added. Slowly add 16 mL of aqueous 3 M sulfuric acid while stirring, and test the pH of the supernatant liquid (liquid near the surface) using your stirring rod and a strip of pH paper. If the pH is above 2, add enough additional sulfuric acid drop by drop to bring it down to 2. Cool the mixture in an ice/water bath for about 10 minutes.

Separation. Collect the salicylic acid by vacuum filtration [OP-16] using a small Buchner funnel and wash it on the filter [OP-26a] with ice-cold water.

Take Care: Wear gloves; avoid contact with the NaOH.

Observe and Note: What did you observe when you combined methyl salicylate with 6 M NaOH? When you heated the reaction mixture to boiling?

Stop and Think: What do you think caused the changes you observed?

Observe and Note: What happened?

Waste Disposal: Unless your instructor directs otherwise, wash the filtrate down the drain.

Observe and Note: How much water was required?

Waste Disposal: Unless your instructor directs otherwise, wash the filtrate down the drain.

Stop and Think: Do the results support your initial hypothesis?

Purification and Analysis. Purify the salicylic acid by recrystallization [OP-28] from boiling water. There should be no need to filter the hot solution. Collect the product by vacuum filtration and wash it [OP-26a] with a little cold water. Dry [OP-26b] the product to constant mass and measure its mass [OP-4]. Measure the melting points [OP-33] of the dry product *and* of a 1:1 mixture of the product with salicylic acid synthesized from benzene. In your report, include calculations of the theoretical yield of product (based on the actual mass of your reactant) and the percent yield of your preparation, try to account for any significant material losses, and discuss the results of the mixed melting-point analysis.

Exercises

1. (a) Calculate the volume of 6 M NaOH required to react completely with the amount of methyl salicylate you used. How much of the 6 M NaOH that you used was in excess of the theoretical amount? (b) What volume of 3 M H_2SO_4 is needed to neutralize all of the disodium salicylate and the excess NaOH present after the initial reaction? How much sulfuric acid was in excess?

2. Refer to the reaction equations in the "Reactions and Properties" section as you answer the following questions. (a) Which two hydrogen atoms of salicylic acid are most likely to be acidic? Which hydrogen atom(s) of methyl salicylate would you expect to be acidic? (b) Based on your answer to (a), draw the structure of the white solid that forms immediately after NaOH and methyl salicylate are combined, and write an equation for its formation. (*Hint:* Acid–base reactions are much faster than most organic reactions.)

3. (a) Write an equation for the overall reaction in this experiment, and use it to calculate the atom economy of the synthesis and your reaction efficiency. (b) Describe some green features of your synthesis, and any that aren't so green.

4. Based on the amount of water you used during the recrystallization, estimate the amount of salicylic acid that was lost as a result of being dissolved in the filtrate. Assume that the recrystallization solution was cooled to 10°C; the solubility of salicylic acid at that temperature is 0.14 g per 100 mL of water.

5. Describe and explain the possible effect on your results of the following experimental errors or variations. (a) You added only enough 3 M H_2SO_4 to bring the pH down to 4. (b) Your reaction mixture had an oily layer on top when you added the 3 M sulfuric acid. (c) Because of a label-reading error by a lab assistant, the bottle labeled "salicylic acid from benzene" actually contained acetylsalicylic acid (aspirin).

6. From the equations in the "Reactions and Properties" section, you can see that methanol and sodium sulfate are by-products of the synthesis of salicylic acid. During which step of the synthesis would these compounds have been separated from the final product? Explain your answer, based on any relevant properties of salicylic acid and the by-products. (If necessary, you can look up the properties in a reference book.)

Other Things You Can Do

(Starred items require your instructor's permission.)

*1. Develop and test a hypothesis based on observations you make while performing the "Developing and Testing a Hypothesis" minilab. You can also test your product from this experiment with ferric chloride solution as described in this minilab.

*2. Convert your salicylic acid to aspirin by following the procedure in "Synthesis and Spectral Analysis of Aspirin." (You can omit the spectral analysis.)

3. Find some examples of organic compounds besides methyl salicylate that are available commercially in both natural and synthetic forms. You might start searching at a local drugstore or health food store. Look up the compounds in *The Merck Index* and give their chemical structures.

4. Write a research paper about salicylic acid and the salicylates using references from the Bibliography.

Preparation of Synthetic Banana Oil
Simple Distillation, Gas Chromatography

Preparation, Purification, and Analysis of Liquids. Gas Chromatography.

Operations

OP-10   Mixing (optional)
OP-24   Washing Liquids
OP-25   Drying Liquids
OP-30a Distillation of Liquids
OP-37   Gas Chromatography
OP-2   Using Specialized Glassware
OP-4   Weighing
OP-7   Heating

Before You Begin

1. Read the experiment and operations OP-10 (if you'll be using a magnetic stirrer), OP-24, OP-25, OP-30a, and OP-37. Read or review the other operations as necessary. (Reading OP-30a and OP-37 may be deferred until the second lab period for this experiment.)
2. Calculate the mass and volume of 150 mmol of isopentyl alcohol and the theoretical yield of isopentyl acetate from this amount of the alcohol.
3. Read "Planning an Experiment," and then write an experimental plan.

Scenario

Your supervisor has just received the following message from the Cavendish Distilling Company.

Greetings:

We have a problem. Cavendish Distilling Company markets the popular liqueur Banana Elixir, which is flavored with a natural banana extract from fruit grown on our Caribbean banana plantations. Last June, Hurricane Floyd blew down all of our banana trees. Our stock of banana extract is running low, and we have no alternative source of bananas at this time. As a temporary solution, we have decided to add a synthetic banana flavoring to our remaining stock of the natural extract until our plantations start producing again.

Synthetic banana flavorings are formulated mainly from isopentyl acetate, with smaller amounts of other esters. I understand that esters can be prepared economically by a process called the Fischer esterification, which involves the combination of an acid,

banana tree

From *Operational Organic Chemistry: A Problem Solving Approach to the Laboratory*, Fourth Edition, John W. Lehman. Copyright © 2009 by Pearson Education. Published by Prentice Hall. All rights reserved.

*The banana plant (*Musa cavendishii *and other species) is actually a gigantic herb and not a true tree. Each year, the foliage-bearing part withers away and is replaced by new growth from an underground stem.*

such as acetic acid, with an alcohol. According to our technical staff, one problem with this method is that Fischer esterifications don't go to completion, leaving considerable amounts of starting material in the product. We can tolerate up to 10% isopentyl alcohol in our isopentyl acetate, since the alcohol is a component of natural banana extract. But we cannot tolerate more than 2% acetic acid, because it would tend to degrade the flavor of the liqueur. Will you have your consulting chemists prepare some isopentyl acetate and analyze it to see if it falls within our tolerances?

Amy Lester, CEO

Applying Scientific Methodology

By now, you should be familiar with the steps involved in applying scientific methodology to the solution of a problem. In this experiment, the problem described in the Scenario involves the purity of the product—not its identity—so your course of action will include the use of an instrumental method, gas chromatography, to determine the composition of the product.

Esters and Artificial Flavorings

The word *flavor* is used to describe the overall sensory effect of a substance taken into the mouth. Flavor may involve tactile, temperature, and pain sensations, as well as smell and taste. Many fruits, flowers, and spices contain esters that contribute to their characteristic flavors—an *ester* is an organic compound that contains the functional group (characteristic combination of atoms) shown in the margin.

functional group
of an ester

Most volatile esters have strong, pleasant odors that can best be described as "fruity." Some esters with flavors characteristic of real and "fantasy" fruits are shown in Table 1. The ester you will prepare in this experiment, isopentyl acetate, has a strong banana odor when undiluted and an odor reminiscent of pears in dilute solution. It is used as an ingredient in artificial coffee, butterscotch, and honey flavorings, as well as in pear and banana flavorings.

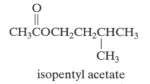

isopentyl acetate

Many different esters are included in the basic repertoire of the flavor chemist, who combines natural and synthetic ingredients to prepare artificial flavorings. These ingredients may include natural products, synthetic organic compounds identical to those found in nature, and synthetic compounds not found in nature but accepted as safe for use in food. Each flavor ingredient is characterized by one or more flavor *notes* that suggest the predominant impact the ingredient makes on the senses of taste and smell. Although the flavor note of a single ingredient may seem unrelated to the overall character of a natural flavor, the combination of carefully selected ingredients in the right proportions can often yield a good approximation of that flavor. A high-boiling *fixative*, such as glycerine or benzyl benzoate, is usually added to an artificial flavoring to retard vaporization of volatile components, and the flavor notes of the individual components are blended by dissolving them in a solvent called the *vehicle*. The most frequently used vehicle is ethanol (ethyl alcohol).

Some food products, such as cola beverages and Juicy Fruit gum, are characterized by fantasy flavors that have no counterparts in nature, but most artificial flavorings are meant to resemble natural flavors.

Table 1 Flavor notes of some esters used in artificial flavorings

Name	Structure	Flavor note
propyl acetate	$CH_3\overset{\displaystyle O}{\overset{\|}{C}}-OCH_2CH_2CH_3$	pears
octyl acetate	$CH_3\overset{\displaystyle O}{\overset{\|}{C}}-O(CH_2)_7CH_3$	oranges
benzyl acetate	$CH_3\overset{\displaystyle O}{\overset{\|}{C}}-OCH_2-$ ⬡	peaches, strawberries
isopentenyl acetate	$CH_3\overset{\displaystyle O}{\overset{\|}{C}}-OCH_2CH=\overset{\displaystyle CH_3}{\overset{\|}{C}}-CH_3$	"Juicy Fruit"
isobutyl propionate	$CH_3CH_2\overset{\displaystyle O}{\overset{\|}{C}}-OCH_2\overset{\displaystyle CH_3}{\overset{\|}{C}H}-CH_3$	rum
ethyl butyrate	$CH_3CH_2CH_2\overset{\displaystyle O}{\overset{\|}{C}}-OCH_2CH_3$	pineapples

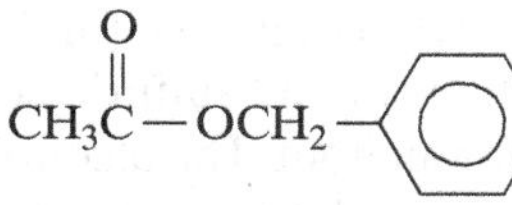

The formulation of artificial flavorings is perhaps as much an art as a science. The components of a strawberry flavoring, for example, may vary widely depending on the manufacturer and the specific application. Because natural flavors are usually very complex, a cheap artificial flavoring may be a poor imitation of its natural counterpart, but advances in flavor chemistry have made possible the production of superior flavorings that reproduce natural flavors very closely. Superior flavorings may contain natural oils or extracts that have been fortified with a few synthetic ingredients to enhance the overall effect and to replace flavor elements lost during the distillation or extraction process. Even the most experienced flavor chemist can't hope to do as well as a strawberry plant, which may combine several hundred different flavor components in its berries. But a superior strawberry flavoring with a few dozen ingredients may be hard to distinguish from the real thing—except by the most discriminating of strawberry aficionados.

Understanding the Experiment

In this experiment you will prepare synthetic banana oil, which is known by several chemical names, including isopentyl acetate, isoamyl acetate, and 3-methylbutyl ethanoate. Esters are often prepared by the Fischer esterification method, which involves heating a carboxylic acid with an alcohol in the presence of an acid catalyst, as shown by the following

Fixatives

$\overset{\displaystyle OH\ OH\ OH}{\overset{\|\ \ \ \ \|\ \ \ \ \|}{CH_2CHCH_2}}$

glycerine

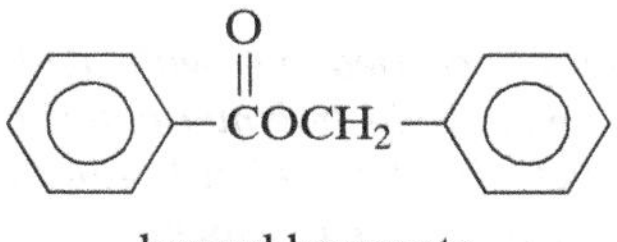

⬡ $-\overset{\displaystyle O}{\overset{\|}{C}}OCH_2-$ ⬡

benzyl benzoate

Vehicle

CH_3CH_2OH

ethyl alcohol

general equation:

$$\underset{\substack{\text{carboxylic} \\ \text{acid}}}{\text{RCOH}} + \underset{\text{alcohol}}{\text{HOR}'} \xrightarrow{\text{H}^+} \underset{\text{ester}}{\text{RCOR}'} + \text{H}_2\text{O}$$

The acid catalyst is used to increase the rate of the reaction, which would otherwise require a much longer reaction time.

You will synthesize isopentyl acetate by combining isopentyl alcohol (3-methyl-1-butanol) with acetic acid and sulfuric acid and then heating the reaction mixture under reflux for an hour. The alcohol is the limiting reactant, so it should be weighed; the acids can be measured by volume. The esterification reaction is reversible, and it has an equilibrium constant of approximately 4.2. If you were to start with equimolar amounts of acetic acid and isopentyl alcohol, only about two-thirds of each reactant would be converted to isopentyl acetate by the time equilibrium was reached. Your highest attainable yield in that case would be only 67% of the theoretical value. Thus, despite having a high atom economy, the reaction efficiency of the synthesis could be rather low. To increase the reaction efficiency, you will apply Le Châtelier's principle by using a 100% excess of acetic acid—the less expensive reactant—to shift the equilibrium toward the products. Even then, the reaction will not be complete at equilibrium, so the reaction mixture will contain some unreacted isopentyl alcohol as well as the excess acetic acid.

Key Concept: For a reaction at equilibrium, adding more of a reactant or removing a product will shift the equilibrium to favor the products.

A desired substance can be obtained from a mixture by separating it from all other components of the mixture, using procedures that take advantage of differences in solubility, boiling points, acid–base properties, and other characteristics of the components. Because isopentyl acetate is a liquid, the separation and purification operations will differ from those used previously for solid products.

At the end of the reflux period, the reaction mixture will contain (in addition to the ester) unreacted acetic acid, sulfuric acid, water, unreacted isopentyl alcohol, and some unwanted by-products (see Figure 1). Isopentyl acetate is quite insoluble in water, whereas both acetic acid and sulfuric acid are water soluble and acidic. This makes it easy to separate the two acids from the product by washing the reaction mixture with water and then with aqueous sodium bicarbonate. Water doesn't remove the acids entirely, because they are somewhat soluble in the ester as well, but it removes the bulk of them and thus helps prevent a violent reaction with sodium bicarbonate in the second washing step. The aqueous sodium bicarbonate converts the acids to their salts, sodium acetate and sodium sulfate, which are insoluble in the ester but very soluble in water; these salts migrate to the aqueous layer, where they can be removed. The rule of thumb given in OP-24 will help you estimate the quantity of aqueous sodium bicarbonate needed.

Reactions carried out with acid catalysts often yield polymeric, tarlike by-products that have high boiling points and are insoluble in water.

The water that forms during the reaction will be separated from the ester along with the wash liquids. Any traces of water that remain are then removed by a drying agent, either magnesium sulfate or sodium sulfate. The rule of thumb given in OP-25 will help you estimate the amount of drying agent needed.

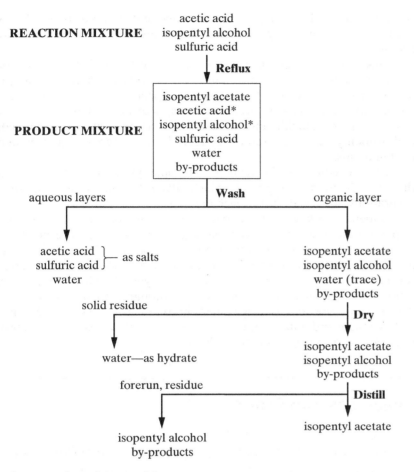

*unreacted starting materials

Figure 1 Flow diagram for the synthesis of isopentyl acetate

Because isopentyl alcohol has a lower boiling point than that of isopentyl acetate, and the by-products have higher boiling points, it should be possible — in principle — to remove the alcohol and by-products from the ester by distillation. Isopentyl alcohol should distill first, followed by the ester, and any by-products should remain behind in the pot — the vessel in which the reaction mixture is boiled. For the reasons described in OP-30a, the separation is incomplete, so you will still have some isopentyl alcohol in your isopentyl acetate after the purification step.

You will determine the composition of your distillate by injecting a very small amount into an instrument called a gas chromatograph. (Your instructor will demonstrate the operation of this instrument.) Inside the gas chromatograph, the liquid will vaporize, and the vapors of different components will travel through a packed column at different rates. As the vapors exit the column, their presence will be detected and recorded on a graph called a gas chromatogram, which should display several peaks of different sizes. The area under the peak for each component will be proportional to the amount of that component present, so by measuring the peak areas you can estimate the percentage of each component in the distillate. This will tell you how much (if any) isopentyl alcohol and acetic acid remain in your product.

This should be a green synthesis because it has a high atom economy, no organic solvents are used, and the catalyst reduces energy consumption and improves the yield. Acetic acid is expected to be slightly toxic to aquatic life, but it is a naturally occurring substance that readily breaks down to carbon dioxide and water in the environment. Isopentyl alcohol and isopentyl acetate aren't considered to be serious environmental contaminants.

The procedure for the synthesis of isopentyl acetate is summarized in the flow diagram in Figure 1, which illustrates the transformations or separations that occur during each operation.

Isopentyl acetate is known to be an *alarm pheromone* of the honeybee. A pheromone is a "molecular messenger" that produces a response, such as mating behavior or aggression toward a perceived threat, in another member of the same species. When a worker honeybee stings someone, it releases a tiny amount (about 1 μg) of isopentyl acetate in its stinger, which attracts more honeybees to the scene. Although isopentyl acetate alone doesn't cause the bees to sting (other pheromones in the stinger do that), it agitates them and puts them on guard. So it might be wise to steer clear of beehives on your way home from the lab!

Reactions and Properties

$$\underset{\text{acetic acid}}{CH_3\overset{\overset{\displaystyle O}{\|}}{C}-OH} + \underset{\text{isopentyl alcohol}}{HOCH_2CH_2\overset{\overset{\displaystyle CH_3}{|}}{C}HCH_3} \rightleftharpoons \underset{\text{isopentyl acetate}}{CH_3\overset{\overset{\displaystyle O}{\|}}{C}-OCH_2CH_2\overset{\overset{\displaystyle CH_3}{|}}{C}HCH_3} + H_2O$$

Table 2 Physical properties

	mol wt	bp	d	Solubility
acetic acid	60.1	118	1.049	miscible
isopentyl alcohol	88.1	130	0.815	2.7
isopentyl acetate	130.2	142	0.876	0.25
sulfuric acid	98.1	290	1.84	miscible

Note: Boiling points are in °C; densities are in g/mL; solubilities are in g/100 mL water.

DIRECTIONS

Safety Notes

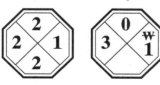

acetic acid   sulfuric acid

Acetic acid causes chemical burns that can seriously damage skin and eyes; its vapors are highly irritating to the eyes and respiratory tract. Wear gloves, dispense under a hood, avoid contact, and do not breathe its vapors.
Sulfuric acid causes chemical burns that can seriously damage skin and eyes. Wear gloves and avoid contact.
Isopentyl alcohol and isopentyl acetate can irritate the skin, eyes, and respiratory tract.

Reaction. Accurately weigh 150 mmol of isopentyl alcohol into a round-bottom flask of appropriate size and add boiling chips [OP-7b] or a magnetic stir bar [OP-10]. *Under a hood*, add 17 mL (~300 mmol) of glacial acetic acid, and then carefully mix in 1.0 mL of concentrated sulfuric acid while stirring or swirling. Connect a condenser to the reaction flask, turn on the cooling water, start the stirrer (if you are using one), and heat the reaction mixture under reflux [OP-7c] for one hour after boiling begins.

Separation. When the reaction time is up, allow the reaction mixture to cool nearly to room temperature. Turn off the cooling water and remove the reflux condenser. Transfer the reaction mixture to a separatory funnel, leaving the stir bar or boiling chips behind, and wash [OP-24] the mixture with 50 mL of water. Drain the aqueous layer and leave the organic layer in the separatory funnel. Then carefully wash the organic layer with two successive portions of 5% aqueous sodium bicarbonate, draining the aqueous layer after each washing. During the first washing, stir the layers until gas evolution subsides before you stopper the separatory funnel, and vent it frequently thereafter. Dry [OP-25] the crude isopentyl acetate with anhydrous sodium sulfate or magnesium sulfate.

Purification and Analysis. Using standard-taper glassware [OP-2], assemble an apparatus for simple distillation [OP-30a]. Be sure the thermometer bulb is positioned as shown in Figure E7, OP-30, and have your instructor check your setup before you start. Distill the crude product, collecting any liquid that distills between 136°C and 143°C. Record the actual boiling range you observe; wait until the entire thermometer bulb is moist with condensing vapors, liquid is distilling into the receiver, and the temperature is stable before you record the initial temperature reading. Stop the distillation when only a drop or so of liquid remains in the boiling flask *or* when the temperature reaches 143°C. If the distillate is cloudy or contains water droplets, dry it [OP-25]. Weigh [OP-4] the distillate in a tared, labeled vial. Using a Carbowax column or another suitable column, obtain a gas chromatogram [OP-37] of the distillate and measure the peak areas as directed by your instructor. Unless your instructor indicates otherwise, assume that the components of the distillate appear on the gas chromatogram in the order (1) isopentyl alcohol, (2) isopentyl acetate, and (3) acetic acid. From the peak areas, calculate the percentage of each component in the distillate, then calculate your percent yield of isopentyl acetate based on its percentage in the distillate.

Glacial acetic acid is a pure grade of acetic acid that freezes at about 17°C.

Take Care! Wear gloves; avoid contact with acetic acid and sulfuric acid; do not breathe their vapors.

Observe and Note: Look for and record any evidence of a chemical reaction.

Stop and Think: What is the density of isopentyl acetate? Which layer should be on top, the aqueous layer or the organic layer?

Take Care! Pressure may build up in the stoppered separatory funnel.

Waste Disposal: Unless your instructor directs otherwise, dissolve the spent drying agent in the combined wash solvents and flush the mixture down the drain.

Stop and Think: What does the boiling range of the distillate tell you about the purity of your product?

Waste Disposal: Put any forerun and any residue left in the boiling flask into a designated waste container.

Stop and Think: Can you guess which peak corresponds to which component based on the peak areas?

Exercises

1. (a) Calculate the amount of isopentyl acetate that should be present in the reaction mixture at equilibrium, based on the quantities of starting materials you used and a value of 4.2 for the equilibrium constant. (Use the quadratic equation; because volumes cancel out, moles can be used in place of molar concentrations.) (b) Estimate the mass of isopentyl acetate that was lost (1) as a result of incomplete reaction, (2) during the washings, and (3) during the distillation (see OP-30a). Assume that the ester's solubility in aqueous $NaHCO_3$ is about the same as in water.

Isopentyl acetate equilibrium

$$i\text{-PtOH} + \text{HOAc} \rightleftharpoons i\text{-PtOAc} + \text{H}_2\text{O}$$

$$K = \frac{[i\text{-PtOAc}][\text{H}_2\text{O}]}{[i\text{-PtOH}][\text{HOAc}]} = 4.2$$

Ac = acetyl, CH_3CO —
i-Pt = isopentyl, $CH_3CHCH_2CH_2$ —
|
CH_3

$$\underset{\text{isobutyl propionate}}{CH_3CH_2\overset{\displaystyle O}{\overset{\|}{C}} - OCH_2\overset{\displaystyle CH_3}{\overset{|}{C}HCH_3}}$$

Compare the sum of these estimated losses with your actual product loss and try to account for any significant differences.

2. What gas escaped during the sodium bicarbonate washing? Write balanced equations for two reactions that took place during this operation.

3. (a) Calculate the atom economy and reaction efficiency of your synthesis of isopentyl acetate. (b) Tell how the procedure for the preparation of isopentyl acetate might be modified to increase the reaction efficiency. (c) Describe some green features of your synthesis, and any that aren't so green.

4. Describe and explain how each of the following experimental errors or variations might affect your results. (a) You failed to dry the reaction flask after washing it with water. (b) You forgot to add the sulfuric acid. (c) You used twice the amount of acetic acid specified in the procedure. (d) You left out the sodium bicarbonate washing step. (e) Your thermometer bulb was 1 cm higher than it should have been.

5. (a) In the "Understanding the Experiment" section, it was stated that the reaction of an equimolar mixture of isopentyl alcohol and acetic acid will produce, at most, 67% of the theoretical amount of isopentyl acetate. Verify this with an equilibrium constant calculation, using $K = 4.2$. (b) Compare this with the corresponding percentage for the conditions used in this experiment. Are your results consistent with Le Châtelier's principle? Explain.

6. Based on the procedure that you used in this experiment and using the same molar quantities of reactants, develop a procedure that would be suitable for the preparation of isobutyl propionate. Specify the amounts of all materials required and a distillation range for the product. Obtain the necessary physical properties from one of the reference books listed in the Bibliography.

Other Things You Can Do

(Starred items require your instructor's permission.)

*1. You and your coworkers can prepare a series of esters and compare their odors as described in the "Preparation of Acetate Esters" minilab.

*2. Prepare another ester of a primary alcohol, such as butyl acetate or isobutyl propionate, by the general method described for isopentyl acetate. Work out a procedure for the synthesis (see Exercise 6) and have it approved by your instructor. In some cases, a longer reflux time may be necessary for satisfactory results.

3. Read about the isolation of isopentyl acetate (isoamyl acetate) in the alarm pheromone of the honeybee in *Nature* **1962**, *195*, 1018.

4. Read about various types of pheromones in *Chemical Communication: The Language of Pheromones* [Bibliography, L3].

Separation of Petroleum Hydrocarbons
Fractional Distillation

EXPERIMENT

Separation Methods.

Operations

OP-32 Fractional Distillation
OP-4 Weighing
OP-7 Heating
OP-37 Gas Chromatography

Before You Begin

1. Read the experiment and operation OP-32. Read or review the other operations as necessary.
2. Prepare a brief experimental plan following the directions in the "Planning an Experiment" appendix.

Scenario

The Northern Pines Chemical Company specializes in manufacturing chemicals from wood products such as turpentine. For example, they use a major component of turpentine, α-pinene, to prepare organic compounds such as isobornyl acetate and terpineol, which impart a "piney" note to perfumes. To obtain pure α-pinene, it must be separated from the other major component of turpentine, β-pinene. They have been carrying out this separation by fractional distillation using an expensive column-packing material that has to be replaced frequently. They would like to switch to a cheaper and longer-lasting packing material, but because the new packing material will be less efficient than their current type, they will need to purchase a longer column. Based on the difference between the boiling points of the pinenes (10°C), they estimate that such a column will need to have at least 20 theoretical plates (hypothetical column segments) to provide adequate separation. But the height of each theoretical plate, and thus the total length of the column, depends on the efficiency of the packing material.

Forrest Greenwood, the operations engineer at Northern Pines, has sent your supervisor some of the new packing material for testing. Your assignment is to determine its height equivalent to a theoretical plate (HETP; a measure of column efficiency) and to estimate how long their new column must be to separate α-pinene from β-pinene efficiently. To do this, you will fractionally distill a mixture of two petroleum hydrocarbons, toluene and cyclohexane, and measure the composition of the fractions by gas chromatography.

See OP-32 for information about fractional distillation and distilling columns.

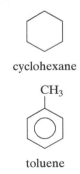

cyclohexane

toluene

Applying Scientific Methodology

No hypothesis is being tested; your job is to determine the value of a physical quantity, the HETP of the column, and to report the value as your

From *Operational Organic Chemistry: A Problem Solving Approach to the Laboratory*, Fourth Edition, John W. Lehman. Copyright © 2009 by Pearson Education. Published by Prentice Hall. All rights reserved.

conclusion. The accuracy of your results—and thus the validity of your conclusion—will depend on the care you take in performing the distillation.

Distillation in Petroleum Refining

Distillation has been used since antiquity to separate the components of mixtures—the ancient Egyptians were distilling wood to make an embalming fluid more than 3500 years ago. Today, distillation is used in the manufacture of perfumes, flavor ingredients, liquors, charcoal, coke, and a host of organic chemicals, but its most important application is in the refining of petroleum to produce fuels, lubricants, and petrochemicals.

The first step in petroleum refining is the separation of petroleum into different hydrocarbon fractions by distilling it through huge fractionating columns, called distillation towers, which may be up to 200 feet high. Since components that have different numbers of carbon atoms usually have significantly different boiling points, this process separates the petroleum into fractions containing hydrocarbons of similar carbon content. Thus, a lower-boiling fraction might contain hydrocarbons with 5 or 6 carbon atoms, and a higher-boiling fraction might contain hydrocarbons with 12 to 18 carbon atoms. Vapors from the lower-boiling hydrocarbons rise to the top of the tower, where they are condensed and collected as "top fractions." Hydrocarbons in top fractions, such as the one called straight-run gasoline, can be chemically modified and used in gasoline. The less volatile middle fractions are collected partway down the tower; these include kerosene and a gas–oil fraction used to produce diesel fuel, jet fuel, and home heating oil. The bottom fraction is usually subjected to vacuum distillation to produce vacuum gas oils, which can be used as fuel oils or converted to hydrocarbons suitable for gasoline. Such petroleum products as paraffin wax, lubricating grease, and asphalt also come from this fraction.

With an overall octane number range of 30–50, straight-run gasoline isn't a suitable motor fuel, but its octane number can be increased to nearly 100 by a process known as catalytic reforming. In this process, the straight-run gasoline is heated to about 500°C at high pressure in the presence of a suitable catalyst. Catalytic reforming converts alkanes to cycloalkanes and cycloalkanes to aromatic compounds; the result is a mixture rich in high-octane aromatics. For example, hexane may be *cyclized* to yield cyclohexane, which may then lose hydrogen atoms in a process called *dehydrogenation* to yield the aromatic compound benzene. Cyclohexane cannot easily be separated from petroleum by distillation alone, so pure cyclohexane is generally obtained by catalytic hydrogenation of benzene, the reverse of the second step shown here.

The octane number of a fuel is a measure of its antiknock properties. Most gasolines have octane numbers that range from 85 to the low 90s.

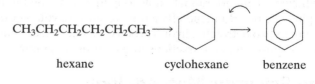

$$CH_3CH_2CH_2CH_2CH_2CH_3 \longrightarrow$$

hexane   cyclohexane   benzene

Toluene is obtained by dehydrogenation of methylcyclohexane, which can be formed by cyclization of heptane and other alkanes.

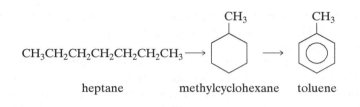

$$CH_3CH_2CH_2CH_2CH_2CH_2CH_3 \longrightarrow$$

heptane   methylcyclohexane   toluene

Understanding the Experiment

In this experiment, you will separate the components of an equimolar mixture of cyclohexane and toluene by fractional distillation and assess the efficiency of the separation by measuring the composition of the fractions. The more completely the cyclohexane and toluene are separated from each other, the more efficient the separation. The degree of separation depends not only on the column packing you use but also on such factors as the stability of the heat source, the rate of distillation, and the way the column is packed. Good separation requires a low rate of distillation to maintain a high *reflux ratio* — the ratio of liquid returned to the boiling flask to liquid that distills into the receiving vessel — so patience is required if you are to obtain good results. The efficiency of the column will be reduced if it isn't packed uniformly, so it is important to distribute the packing material as evenly as possible.

You will measure the composition of each fraction you collect by gas chromatography. Your gas chromatograms should display two peaks, the cyclohexane peak being the first to appear. The areas of the peaks can be converted to relative masses by multiplying them by the appropriate correction factors from Table 1.

Table 1 Gas chromatography correction factors for cyclohexane and toluene

	TC detector	FI detector
cyclohexane	1.11	0.942
toluene	1.05	1.02

Note: Benzene = 1.00. Your instructor will tell you what kind of detector your gas chromatograph has.

You will then determine the HETP of the column packing from the composition of the first few drops of liquid you collect, the *HETP sample*. The number of theoretical plates provided by your distillation apparatus can be calculated using the Fenske equation, expressed as follows for an equimolar mixture of two components, A and B:

$$\text{total number of theoretical plates} = \frac{\log\dfrac{n_A}{n_B}}{\log \alpha} \tag{1}$$

See OP-32 for definitions of theoretical plate and HETP and for a discussion of the Fenske equation.

In Equation **1**, n_A/n_B is the ratio of the number of moles of cyclohexane to the number of moles of toluene in the HETP sample. The volatility factor, α, for the cyclohexane–toluene mixture is 2.33. The boiling flask furnishes one theoretical plate, so you will have to subtract 1 from the total number of theoretical plates to obtain the number of plates provided by the column

*A **Greener Way:*** *The combined distillation fractions are collected in a waste container at the end of the experiment. This mixture should contain nearly equimolar amounts of cyclohexane and toluene, so the recovered "waste" from previous labs can be dried if necessary and used in subsequent ones.*

itself. From this number and the length of your column packing, you can calculate the HETP of the column packing; the lower the HETP, the more efficient the packing.

According to EPA reports, cyclohexane and toluene by themselves aren't likely to cause environmental harm at levels normally found in the environment. But toluene is quite toxic, with an MCL in drinking water of 0.5 ppb, and it can contribute to the formation of photochemical smog when it reacts with other volatile organic substances in air. Release of either hydrocarbon into the environment should be avoided.

Properties

Table 2 Physical properties of cyclohexane and toluene

	mol wt	bp	*d*
cyclohexane	84.2	81	0.774
toluene	92.2	111	0.867

Note: Boiling points are in °C; densities are in g/mL.

DIRECTIONS

Safety Notes

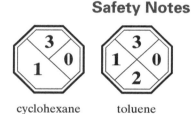

cyclohexane   toluene

Cyclohexane is very flammable and may irritate the skin, eyes, and respiratory tract.
Do not use open flames during the experiment.
Toluene is flammable, and inhalation, ingestion, or skin absorption may be harmful. Avoid contact with the liquid and do not breathe its vapors.

Take Care! Avoid contact with the liquid mixture and do not breathe its vapors.

Separation. All components of the fractional-distillation apparatus must be clean and dry. Pack a distilling column uniformly with the column packing provided and measure the height of the packing in centimeters to the nearest 0.1 cm; the column needn't be insulated. Obtain five clean, dry fraction collectors, such as a 1-dram screw-cap vial and four 4-dram screw-cap vials. Label the smaller vial "HETP" and number the other vials from 1 to 4. Then weigh vials #1–4 with their caps on. Measure 40 mL of an equimolar mixture of cyclohexane and toluene into a 100-mL round-bottom flask (keep the flask stoppered to prevent evaporation) and add some boiling chips (or a stir bar). Clamp the flask to a ring stand over an appropriate heat source [OP-7] and assemble an apparatus for fractional distillation [OP-32], using the HETP vial as the receiver.

Observe and Note: When does the thermometer begin to record the true boiling temperature? Record that temperature and describe what you observe at that point.

Heat the mixture to a gentle boil (with the stirrer turned on, if you are using one) and adjust the heating rate so that the vapors rise slowly up the column. Reduce the heating rate if the column begins to flood (fill with liquid); the packing should be moistened by condensing vapors but shouldn't contain any flowing liquid. Distillate should begin collecting not long after the rising vapors reach the still head (connecting adapter). Collect the first five drops of distillate in the HETP vial, then cap the vial tightly. Quickly replace the HETP vial with vial #1, record the distillation temperature (it should be ~81°C or higher), and adjust the heating rate as necessary so that no more than 20 drops distill per minute. You may have to gradually increase the heating rate to keep the distillation rate more or less uniform. Begin collecting in vial #2 when the temperature reaches 85°C and in vial #3 when it reaches 97°C. When the temperature reaches 107°C, remove the heat source and let all the liquid that remains in the column drain into the boiling flask. When the boiling flask has cooled, transfer its contents to vial #4. At this point, you should have four fractions covering the following approximate boiling ranges:

Stop and Think: Why does the boiling temperature rise during the distillation?

1. 81–84°C
2. 85–96°C
3. 97–106°C
4. 107–111°C

Analysis. Weigh [OP-4] fractions #1–4 (or whichever fractions your instructor specifies), and analyze them and the HETP sample by gas chromatography [OP-37]. Measure the peak areas on each gas chromatogram and use the appropriate correction factors to convert the areas to relative masses. Calculate the percentages (by mass) and the actual masses of cyclohexane and toluene in each fraction you analyzed, the number of theoretical plates provided by your fractional distillation apparatus, the HETP of your column, and the length of the column (in cm) that will provide 20 theoretical plates. At your instructor's request, plot the component masses for each fraction (on the *y*-axis) as a function of boiling temperature, using the midpoints of the appropriate boiling ranges on the *x*-axis (use different symbols, such as × and •, for different components). Draw a smooth curve connecting the data points for cyclohexane, and draw another one (overlapping the first) connecting the data points for toluene.

Waste Disposal: Combine all fractions and place them in the hydrocarbon solvent recovery container.

Exercises

1. A certain fractional-distillation apparatus contains a 24-cm Vigreux column stacked on top of a 30-cm glass tube that is half-filled with 4 × 4-mm porcelain saddles. This assembly is inserted into a boiling flask. How many theoretical plates does the entire apparatus provide if the HETP of the saddles is 5 cm, the HETP of the Vigreux column is 8 cm, and the HETP of the empty glass tube is 15 cm?
2. Describe and explain how each of the following experimental errors or variations would affect your HETP value and the efficiency of your separation. (a) You didn't collect the HETP sample until midway through the distillation. (b) All of your liquid distilled within five minutes of the time you began heating. (c) You stacked two packed columns over the boiling flask rather than using one.
3. Using the data in Table 3, construct a temperature–composition diagram like that shown in Figure E14 of OP-32. (a) From your diagram, estimate the initial composition of the distillate obtained by simple distillation of a mixture containing 20 mole percent cyclohexane and 80 mole percent toluene. (b) Estimate the initial composition if the same mixture is distilled through a three-plate column.

Table 3 Temperature–composition data for cyclohexane–toluene

	Mol % cyclohexane	
T, °C	Liquid	Vapor
110.7	0	0
108.3	4.1	10.2
105.5	9.1	21.2
103.9	11.8	26.4
101.8	16.4	34.8
99.5	21.7	42.2
97.4	27.3	49.2
95.5	32.3	54.7
93.8	37.9	59.9
91.9	45.2	66.2
89.8	53.3	72.4
88.0	59.9	77.4
86.6	67.2	81.1
84.8	76.3	86.4
83.8	81.4	89.5
82.7	87.4	92.6
81.1	96.4	97.3
80.7	100.0	100.0

4. If you were to return your 97–106°C fraction to the empty boiling flask and redistill it, you might expect it all to distill between 97°C and 106°C, as it did the first time. It actually yields some distillate in all four boiling ranges. Explain.
5. Derive Equation **1** (which is for an equimolar mixture of two components) from the Fenske equation in OP-32.
6. Suggest a chemical method that could be used to remove small amounts of toluene from cyclohexane.
7. Show how nylon 6,6 can be synthesized using cyclohexane as the starting material.

Other Things You Can Do

(Starred items require your instructor's permission.)

*1. Analyze some or all of your fractions with a refractometer [OP-35] rather than a gas chromatograph, using a graph that plots refractive index versus mole fraction. (Assume a linear relationship between these variables.) The refractive indexes at 20°C of pure cyclohexane and toluene are 1.4260 and 1.4968, respectively.
*2. Carry out a gas chromatographic analysis of commercial xylene as described in the "Gas Chromatographic Analysis of Commercial Xylene" minilab.
3. Write a research paper about distillation and its uses based on information from *Kirk–Othmer* [Bibliography, A8] and other sources listed in the Bibliography.

A Green Synthesis of Camphor
Addition and Sublimation

Preparation and Purification of Solids. Oxidation.

Operations

OP-8 Cooling
OP-9 Temperature Monitoring
OP-11 Addition of Reactants
OP-29 Sublimation
OP-4 Weighing
OP-10 Mixing
OP-16 Vacuum Filtration
OP-26 Washing and Drying Solids
OP-33 Melting Point

Before You Begin

1. Read the experiment and operations OP-8, OP-9, OP-11, and OP-29. Read or review the other operations as necessary.
2. Calculate the mass of 25.0 mmol of isoborneol and the theoretical yield of camphor from that amount of isoborneol.
3. Prepare an experimental plan for the experiment following the directions in the "Planning an Experiment" appendix.

Scenario

The Northern Pines Chemical Company was pleased with your analysis of their column packing material, so they have requested your services for another project. One of the many chemicals they manufacture from α-pinene is camphor. The last step in the preparation of camphor from α-pinene is the oxidation of isoborneol, for which Northern Pines currently uses the powerful oxidizing agent chromic acid. But the chromium-containing by-products of this reaction are classified as hazardous wastes and disposing of them properly is very costly, so Northern Pines wants your Consulting Chemists Institute to develop a more environmentally acceptable oxidation process for them to use. In searching the chemical literature, your supervisor came across an article in the *Journal of Chemical Education* that describes the use of common laundry bleach (aqueous sodium hypochlorite) to oxidize a secondary alcohol, cyclohexanol, to a ketone, cyclohexanone.

See J. Chem. Educ. **1985**, *62*, 519.

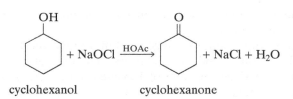

From *Operational Organic Chemistry: A Problem Solving Approach to the Laboratory*, Fourth Edition, John W. Lehman. Copyright © 2009 by Pearson Education. Published by Prentice Hall. All rights reserved.

The only significant by-products of this process are water and sodium chloride.

The oxidation of isoborneol also involves the conversion of a secondary alcohol to a ketone, so your supervisor thinks the laundry-bleach method may be just the kind of environmentally friendly process Northern Pines is looking for. The camphor that the company currently manufactures is about 95% pure; the remaining 5% is unreacted isoborneol. Your assignment is to carry out the oxidation of isoborneol with laundry bleach to find out if the reaction does in fact produce any camphor and, if so, to determine whether you can obtain camphor that has a purity of 95% or better.

Applying Scientific Methodology

You should be able to identify the problem(s) and develop one or more working hypotheses after reading the experiment. Make careful observations during the experiment to detect any evidence that a reaction is taking place. You will test your hypotheses by measuring the melting point of the product, which is very sensitive to the presence of impurities.

Camphor and the Camphoraceous Odor

The Chinese camphor tree, *Cinnamomum camphora*, is a tall, striking evergreen tree with dark, shiny leaves. When steam is forced through the chopped-up wood of a camphor tree, camphor distills with the steam and crystallizes as a translucent white solid. Just as there are left-handed and right-handed gloves, scissors, and corkscrews, there are so-called left-handed and right-handed camphor molecules that are mirror images of one another.

camphor tree

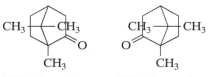

(1*R*)-(+)-camphor   (1*S*)-(−)-camphor

Isomers whose molecules differ only in their "handedness" are called *enantiomers*. (1*R*)-(+)-camphor, the enantiomer obtained from the camphor tree, is composed of the "right-handed" molecules shown here. The less common "left-handed" enantiomer, (1*S*)-(−)-camphor, has been isolated from feverfew (*Chrysanthemum parthenium*), a daisy-like plant unrelated to the camphor tree. Camphor is synthesized commercially from α-pinene (a constituent of turpentine) by the pathway outlined here.

$$\alpha\text{-pinene} \longrightarrow \text{pinene hydrochloride} \longrightarrow \text{camphene}$$
$$\longrightarrow \text{isobornyl acetate} \longrightarrow \text{isoborneol} \longrightarrow \text{camphor}$$

Most synthetic camphor contains an equal number of left-handed and right-handed molecules.

The history of camphor is longer and more involved than that of perhaps any other natural product. Scientific speculations about camphor have appeared in print since the time of Libavius (*Alchymia*, 1595). Although its molecular formula ($C_{10}H_{16}O$) was determined in 1833, its complicated

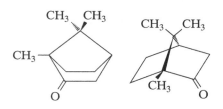

Perspective drawings that show the structure of camphor

bicyclic structure baffled nineteenth-century scientists. Over the next 60 years, they proposed more than 30 different structures for camphor, all of them wrong, before Julius Bredt finally came up with the correct structure in 1893.

The penetrating "camphoraceous" odor of camphor is shared by many compounds of similar molecular shape and size. Compounds as diverse in structure as the ones shown here all have roughly spherical molecules and similar camphoraceous odors:

The story of Bredt's quest is described in J. Chem. Educ. **1983**, *60,* 341.

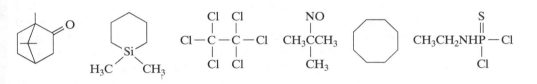

Most scientists believe that the sense of smell is based on the presence in the nasal passageways of a large number of odor receptors, each of which is programmed to detect a specific kind of odor. This idea gained support in 1996, when scientists who had induced bacteria to grow an odor receptor normally found in rats discovered that molecules of two compounds with floral odors, lilial and lyral, became strongly attached to the receptors. The similarities among molecules that have camphoraceous odors suggest that the odor of a substance may, at least in part, depend on the size and shape of its molecules. A spherical molecule, for example, might fit nicely inside a hemispherically concave odor receptor, causing it to transmit a neural message that the brain interprets as a camphorlike odor. But scientists still don't fully understand how humans and other animals can detect and recognize a multitude of different odors.

Understanding the Experiment

In this experiment, you will oxidize a secondary alcohol, isoborneol, to a ketone, camphor. Secondary alcohols can be converted to ketones by powerful oxidizing agents such as chromic acid, but many chromium compounds are highly toxic and corrosive, and some are known to cause cancer. They also present a difficult disposal problem because they cannot legally be discharged into waterways or other places where they might harm the environment. For these reasons, you will use a safer and more environmentally friendly oxidizing agent, the familiar household laundry bleach that is sold under such trade names as Clorox and Javex. Most chlorine bleaches contain either 5.25% or 6.0% sodium hypochlorite (NaOCl) in an aqueous solution. Adding a little acetic acid facilitates oxidation by converting sodium hypochlorite to hypochlorous acid (HOCl), which is probably the active oxidizing agent. Because sodium hypochlorite solutions evolve some chlorine gas, the reaction is carried out under a fume hood.

In some previous experiments, you may have heated the reaction mixture to speed up the reaction. In this experiment, you will need to slow it down instead, because the oxidation of isoborneol is exothermic and the heat evolved can lead to the formation of unwanted by-products such as camphoric acid. You will control the reaction rate by adding the sodium

This is the last step in the commercial manufacture of camphor described previously.

The bleach should be unscented and there should be no ingredient other than sodium hypochlorite listed on the label.

Key Concept: *Excessive heat can promote high-energy reaction paths that lead to the formation of unwanted by-products.*

camphoric acid

hypochlorite, a little at a time, from a separatory–addition funnel rather than combining all of the reactants at once. You will also use a cooling bath as necessary to keep down the temperature in the reaction flask, and monitor the temperature with a thermometer as described in OP-9.

When a reaction takes place under reflux, the boiling action helps mix the reactants. In this experiment, the reactants are mixed using a magnetic stirrer or by shaking and swirling the flask after each addition. To ensure a complete reaction, you must add enough sodium hypochlorite solution to keep the oxidizing agent in excess throughout the reaction. Because the NaOCl concentrations of different chlorine bleaches may differ and will decrease with age, you can't be sure that the amount of bleach that you add at first will be enough, so you will have to test the reaction mixture periodically to see whether there is still excess oxidant present. When HOCl is present in excess, a drop of the acidic reaction mixture placed on an indicator paper impregnated with starch and potassium iodide will oxidize iodide ions to iodine, which turns the starch a deep blue-black color. The color near the center of the drop may be bleached white, but some color should remain around its edges. Any excess HOCl that remains after the reaction is over can be destroyed by treatment with the reducing agent sodium bisulfite, according to the following equation:

$$HOCl + HSO_3^- \longrightarrow HCl + HSO_4^-$$

Because of its compact molecular structure, camphor changes directly from a solid to a vapor when heated, which allows it to be purified by sublimation. Isoborneol also sublimes at elevated temperatures, so the sublimed camphor will probably contain some unreacted isoborneol. Assuming that isoborneol is the only significant impurity in the product, its purity can be estimated with good accuracy from its melting point, because camphor has an unusually large freezing-point depression constant. The product can be regarded as a solid solution with camphor as the solvent and isoborneol as the solute, so you can use the following equation to calculate the molal concentration (m) of isoborneol in the product:

The melting point of a solid equals the freezing point of the corresponding liquid.

$\Delta T = K_f \times m$

ΔT = melting-point depression (reported mp – observed mp)

K_f = freezing-point depression constant for camphor = 40°C kg mol^{-1}

m = molal concentration of isoborneol (mol isoborneol/kg camphor)

Knowing m, the number of moles of isoborneol per kilogram of camphor, you can calculate the mass percent of isoborneol and camphor in the product.

This experiment has several green features in addition to the use of a more benign oxidizing agent. Isoborneol is manufactured from a component of turpentine (a renewable resource), the synthesis uses no solvents other than the water present in the laundry bleach, and the only by-products are water and sodium chloride. Because sodium hypochlorite is used widely to disinfect water, it is often present in municipal drinking water, and the EPA has concluded that such uses present no unreasonable adverse effects to the environment. It is toxic to freshwater fish and invertebrates, however, so its release into the environment should be avoided.

Reactions and Properties

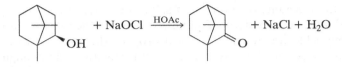

isoborneol   camphor

Table 1 Physical properties

	mol wt	mp	bp	*d*
isoborneol	154.3	212		
camphor	152.2	179	204	
sodium hypochlorite	74.4			
acetic acid	60.1	17	118	1.049

Note: mp and bp are in °C; *d* is in g/mL.

DIRECTIONS

Acetic acid causes chemical burns that can seriously damage skin and eyes; its vapors are highly irritating to the eyes and respiratory tract. Wear gloves, avoid contact with the acid, do not breathe its vapors, and dispense it under a hood.
Aqueous sodium hypochlorite can irritate the skin, eyes, and respiratory tract. Avoid contact and do not breathe its vapors.
The reaction mixture may evolve some chlorine gas, which can irritate the eyes and respiratory tract, so carry out the reaction under a fume hood.

Safety Notes

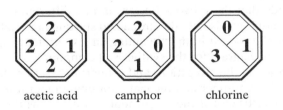

acetic acid   camphor   chlorine

Reaction. *Under the hood,* combine 25.0 mmol of isoborneol with 2.0 mL of glacial acetic acid in a 125-mL Erlenmeyer flask. Mix in 5.0 mL of 5.25% (or 4.4 mL of 6.0%) sodium hypochlorite solution (Clorox or another hypochlorite laundry bleach). Measure another 40 mL of 5.25% (or 35 mL of 6.0%) sodium hypochlorite solution into a separatory–addition funnel, stopper the funnel, and support it over the flask. Add [OP-11] the NaOCl solution to the reaction mixture in small portions, with vigorous swirling or magnetic stirring [OP-10], for a period of 10 minutes or more. Use a thermometer to monitor the temperature [OP-9] of the reaction mixture, and control the rate of addition so that the temperature remains below 50°C.

Take Care! Wear gloves, avoid contact with acetic acid and the NaOCl solution, and do not breathe their vapors.

Remember to put a strip of filter paper between the funnel and its stopper. (Why?)

Observe and Note: Look for and record any evidence of a chemical reaction.

Waste Disposal: If you have any unused sodium hypochlorite solution, place it in an appropriate waste container.

Stop and Think: What is the purpose of the sodium bisulfite addition?

Waste Disposal: Unless your instructor directs otherwise, wash the filtrate down the drain.

Your instructor may request that you purify only part of the crude camphor.

Have an ice/water bath handy to cool [OP-8] the reaction mixture if its temperature reaches 50°C.

When the addition is complete, seal the flask with Parafilm and stir [OP-10] the reactants (or swirl the flask frequently) at room temperature for 30 minutes or more. Every 5 minutes or so, test the reaction mixture for excess hypochlorite by transferring a drop of the solution to a strip of starch–iodide paper. If at any time the test is negative, add enough sodium hypochlorite solution (about 1 mL at a time) to the reaction mixture to give a *positive* test. When the reaction period is over, again test the reaction mixture with starch–iodide paper. If the test is positive, add enough saturated sodium bisulfite solution dropwise to give a *negative* test.

Separation. Cool [OP-8] the reaction mixture to 5°C or below in an ice/water bath. Collect the product by vacuum filtration [OP-16], washing it on the filter [OP-26a] with two portions of ice-cold water. Dry [OP-26b] the crude product at room temperature, *not* in an oven. At your instructor's request, weigh the crude product and save a small amount of it for a melting-point measurement.

Purification and Analysis. Purify the crude product by sublimation [OP-29], taking care not to char the solid by overheating. Weigh [OP-4] the sublimate, dry [OP-26b] it at room temperature (if necessary), and measure its melting point [OP-33]. Taking as its melting point the temperature at which the solid was completely liquefied, calculate the mass percentages of isoborneol and camphor in your purified product. Include a calculation of percent yield in your report.

Exercises

1. In this experiment, you started with a white, strong-smelling solid and ended up with a white, strong-smelling solid. What evidence leads you to conclude that these two solids are in fact different compounds and that you didn't just isolate the unreacted starting material?
2. Following the format in the "Planning an Experiment" appendix, construct a flow diagram for the synthesis of camphor.
3. The equation in the "Reactions and Properties" section shows only one isoborneol enantiomer and the camphor enantiomer it forms. Find out from your instructor if the isoborneol you used was the right-handed (*R*) enantiomer shown, the left-handed (*S*) enantiomer, or an equimolar mixture of both. Then rewrite the equation showing the correct stereochemistry of the reactants and products.
4. (a) Calculate the atom economy and reaction efficiency of this synthesis. (b) Describe some green features of your synthesis, and any that aren't so green.
5. Describe how each of the following experimental errors or variations might affect your results. (a) You omitted the 30-minute reaction period after the addition step. (b) You added the sodium hypochlorite solution all at once. (c) You mistook a negative starch–iodide test for a positive one and stopped adding sodium hypochlorite solution midway through the reaction period.

6. Write a balanced net ionic equation for the reaction of the acidified sodium hypochlorite solution with iodide ion from the starch–iodide paper, assuming that HOCl is reduced to HCl.

7. Show which carbon–carbon bond of camphor must be broken to form camphoric acid. Use molecular models if necessary.

Other Things You Can Do

(Starred items require your instructor's permission.)

*1. Isolate an expectorant from cough capsules as described in the "Isolation of an Expectorant from cough capsules" minilab.

*2. Oxidize cyclohexanol to cyclohexanone as described in *J. Chem. Educ.* **1985**, *62*, 519.

3. Write a research paper about camphor and its applications, using sources listed in the Bibliography.

Identification of a Petroleum Hydrocarbon
Boiling Point, Refractive Index

Physical Properties of Liquids. Alkanes and Cycloalkanes.

Operations

OP-34 Boiling Point
OP-35 Refractive Index
OP-4 Weighing
OP-5 Measuring Volume
OP-30 Simple Distillation

Before You Begin

1. Read the experiment and the descriptions for OP-34 and OP-35. Read or review the other operations as needed.
2. Prepare a brief experimental plan for this experiment following the directions in the "Planning an Experiment" appendix.

Scenario

An investigative organization known as The Consumer's Advocate (TCA) publishes a monthly magazine, *Caveat Emptor*, which evaluates consumer products and exposes scams. TCA is currently investigating an auto-supplies manufacturer that markets Thrust, a gasoline additive claimed to improve engine performance. TCA's preliminary tests show that the additive has no measurable effect on either power or mileage, and they suspect that the additive is nothing more than a hydrocarbon that burns along with the gasoline. To support its case against the company, TCA needs to know the identity and octane number of the hydrocarbon. If its octane number is higher than that of a typical regular no-lead gasoline (about 87), then the company's claim that the additive improves engine performance might have some validity—although the amount of improvement would be negligible when the additive is used in the quantity recommended on the can.

Because their own chemists are busy with other projects, TCA's technical director, Patsy Haven, has farmed out the job to your institute. Your assignment is to identify the hydrocarbon in Thrust and determine whether or not its octane number is greater than 87.

Applying Scientific Methodology

You should evaluate the evidence and formulate tentative hypotheses as you go along. For example, if you measure a boiling point of 79°C, your tentative hypothesis might be "The alkane in Thrust is 2,4-dimethylpentane" (see Table 2). If you then measure its density as 0.79 g/mL, you might

From *Operational Organic Chemistry: A Problem Solving Approach to the Laboratory*, Fourth Edition, John W. Lehman. Copyright © 2009 by Pearson Education. Published by Prentice Hall. All rights reserved.

have to change your hypothesis to "The alkane in Thrust is cyclohexane." Measuring a refractive index of 1.4262 would then confirm your second hypothesis and lead you to the conclusion that the alkane is indeed cyclohexane, whose octane number you can look up in Table 1.

Table 1 Octane numbers of some petroleum hydrocarbons

Hydrocarbon	Octane no.	Hydrocarbon	Octane no.
nonane	−45	2,4-dimethylpentane	82
octane	−17	methylcyclopentane	82
heptane	0	cyclopentane	83
2-methylheptane	24	2,3-dimethylpentane	89
hexane	26	2-methylbutane	89
3-methylheptane	35	butane	92
2-methylhexane	45	2,3-dimethylbutane	95
pentane	61	2,2-dimethylbutane	96
3-methylhexane	66	2,2,3-trimethylbutane	100
methylcyclohexane	71	2,2,4-trimethylpentane	100
2-methylpentane	73	2,2,3-trimethylpentane	102
3-methylpentane	75	toluene	104
cyclohexane	77	benzene	106

Gasoline—A Chemical Soup

Gasoline is a kind of "chemical soup" that contains an incredibly large number of ingredients that are carefully selected and blended to produce a fuel with the desired properties. Virtually all of the main fuel components of gasoline are derived either directly or indirectly from petroleum, which must be refined before a usable fuel is obtained. The word *refine* suggests a simple separation and purification process, but the refining of petroleum is a more complex operation that involves chemical as well as physical changes. Petroleum is first fractionated in a distillation tower, which separates its components according to their boiling-point ranges. The fraction that boils between approximately 50°C and 150°C, straight-run gasoline, isn't a good motor fuel by itself, because it contains a large proportion of straight-chain hydrocarbons such as heptane and hexane (see Figure 1). Straight-chain hydrocarbons burn very rapidly, generating a shock wave in the combustion chamber that reduces power and can damage the engine. This "knocking" doesn't occur with highly branched hydrocarbons, which burn more slowly and uniformly.

The octane number of a motor fuel is a measure of its antiknock qualities. The highly branched alkane 2,2,4-trimethylpentane (sometimes called "isooctane") is a very good motor fuel and has arbitrarily been assigned an octane number of 100. Heptane, with no branching, has been assigned an octane number of zero. The performance of a particular motor fuel is measured relative to these two alkanes; for example, a fuel that performs as well as a mixture containing 70% 2,2,4-trimethylpentane and 30% heptane is assigned an octane number of 70. Table 1 lists octane numbers of selected hydrocarbons found in gasoline.

The octane number of a hydrocarbon can vary depending on the method used to measure it.

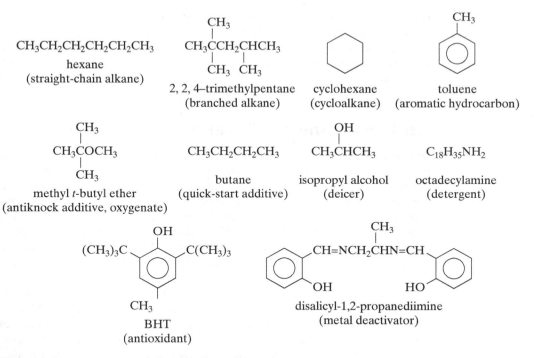

Figure 1 Some components of a typical gasoline

A major objective of petroleum refining is to convert the low-octane components of petroleum into higher-octane compounds. This can be accomplished by a variety of chemical processes, such as *isomerization*, which converts straight-chain alkanes to branched alkanes; *cracking*, which breaks down large molecules into smaller ones; *alkylation*, which combines short-chain alkane and alkene molecules to form longer, branched molecules; and *catalytic reforming*, which converts alkanes to cycloalkanes and aromatic compounds. Aromatic hydrocarbons such as toluene have particularly high octane numbers and are used to increase the octane rating of no-lead fuels.

Gasoline for use in automobile engines is prepared by combining varying amounts of straight-run gasoline, cracked gasoline, alkylated gasoline, reformate, and other hydrocarbon mixtures in the right proportions to give the desired boiling-point range and octane number. The properties of the fuel are then further adjusted with a variety of additives. Antiknock additives such as methyl *t*-butyl ether (MTBE) may be included to boost the octane rating. MTBE is also an *oxygenate* (oxygen-containing fuel) that reduces the amount of carbon monoxide produced by combustion. Quick-start additives, such as butane, facilitate cold weather starting. Antifreeze additives, such as isopropyl alcohol, reduce icing. Antioxidants, such as butylated hydroxytoluene (BHT) help improve fuel stability and reduce gum formation, particularly in fuels that contain appreciable amounts of alkenes. Certain metals, such as copper and iron,

The chemistry involved in these reactions is described in many organic chemistry textbooks.

The use of MTBE in gasoline is prohibited in some places because of its adverse environmental effects.

can catalyze gum-forming reactions, so chelating compounds such as disalicyl-1,2-propanediimine may be added to deactivate these metals. Cars with fuel injectors require detergent additives such as octadecylamine to keep their intake systems clean. Dyes are added for identification and visual appeal.

Understanding the Experiment

In this experiment, you will attempt to identify an unknown hydrocarbon that is one of the compounds listed in Table 2. Identifying an unknown organic compound is somewhat like identifying the perpetrator of a crime. The investigator compiles a list of suspects, hunts for clues that might have a bearing on the case, sifts through the evidence to eliminate most of the suspects, and then searches for additional evidence to build a case against the prime suspect. Many kinds of evidence may have a bearing on the identity of an organic compound: physical evidence, such as boiling point and density; chemical evidence, such as the appearance of a precipitate with a test reagent; and spectral evidence, such as the occurrence of an infrared band that suggests the presence of a particular functional group. Alkanes and cycloalkanes are comparatively unreactive, making it difficult to gather much chemical evidence about them, and their infrared spectra are not very revealing, so you will identify the unknown alkane by using its physical properties alone.

Before you can measure the physical properties of a liquid accurately, the liquid must be pure. In this experiment, you will purify your hydrocarbon by simple distillation. You can estimate the boiling point of the liquid as you distill it, but you will also measure its boiling point by using a semimicroscale boiling-point method, described in OP-34b. Because the boiling point of a liquid varies with the barometric pressure, you may have to apply a boiling-point correction (as described in OP-34).

The density of a liquid is usually determined by accurately weighing a measured volume of the liquid. The volume can be measured with an appropriate pipet, and the mass should be measured to at least the nearest milligram on an accurate balance.

A good refractometer can be used to determine the refractive index of a pure liquid with great accuracy. With reasonable care, you should be able to measure the refractive index of your unknown to within 0.05% or better, so this value may be the most important clue to the identity of your hydrocarbon. The refractive index of a liquid is very sensitive to temperature, however, so you will need to correct your observed value if the temperature at the refractometer is above or below 20°C.

The physical constants of the hydrocarbons listed in Table 2 are different enough that an accurate determination of all three constants should allow for the certain identification of an unknown. Your instructor may add more hydrocarbons to your list of possibilities. If so, he or she will provide you with the appropriate physical constants or ask you to look them up.

Aliphatic hydrocarbons are toxic to some forms of aquatic life, so their release into the environment should be avoided.

A Greener Way: If the unknown hydrocarbons don't require purifying and your instructor agrees, you can omit the distillation and measure your hydrocarbon's boiling point using only the semi-microscale method. This way you can reduce the amount of hydrocarbon used to a little more than 1 mL.

Properties

Table 2 List of possible hydrocarbons

Name	bp	n_D^{20}	d^{20}
cyclopentane	49	1.4065	0.746
2,2-dimethylbutane	50	1.3688	0.649
2,3-dimethylbutane	58	1.3750	0.662
3-methylpentane	63	1.3765	0.664
hexane	69	1.3749	0.659
methylcyclopentane	72	1.4097	0.749
2,4-dimethylpentane	80	1.3815	0.673
cyclohexane	81	1.4266	0.779
2,3-dimethylpentane	90	1.3919	0.695
heptane	98	1.3877	0.684
2,2,4-trimethylpentane	99	1.3915	0.692
methylcyclohexane	101	1.4231	0.769

Note: Boiling points are in °C; n_D^{20} = refractive index at 20°C using sodium D line; d^{20} = density at 20°C.

DIRECTIONS

Your instructor may suggest additional tests to carry out on your hydrocarbon.

> **Your unknown hydrocarbon is flammable; keep it away from flames and hot surfaces.**

Purification and Boiling-Point Determination. Obtain a sample of the unknown hydrocarbon from your instructor. Record its identification number and the ambient barometric pressure in your laboratory notebook. Select a suitable heat source and assemble an apparatus for small-scale simple distillation using the compact apparatus described in OP-30. Make sure that the thermometer bulb is positioned correctly in the still head (a connecting adapter). Distill the liquid slowly, setting aside a low-boiling forerun or high-boiling fraction (if any) for later disposal. Record its boiling range and the temperature when about half of it has distilled (the median boiling point) [OP-34a]. Then carry out a semi-microscale boiling-point measurement [OP-34b] on the hydrocarbon using a capillary-tube method. The resulting boiling point should be within 1–2° of the median distillation boiling point. If it is not, repeat the boiling point measurement or redistill the hydrocarbon. Apply a correction to the boiling point if the atmospheric pressure was below 750 torr.

Density Measurement. The temperature of the purified hydrocarbon should be close to 20°C. Accurately measure [OP-5] 1.00 mL of the liquid into a clean, dry, tared vial using a measuring pipet or an automatic pipet.

Safety Notes

alkanes and cycloalkanes of five to eight carbons

Take Care! Keep the hydrocarbon away from flames or hot surfaces.

If the hydrocarbon boils over a broad range, it should be redistilled and a pure fraction (collected over a range of 1–2°C) should be used for analysis.

Stop and Think: What should happen if you put 1 or 2 drops of your hydrocarbon in a test tube containing a small amount of water and shake the test tube? Do it. Was your prediction correct?

Waste Disposal: Put your recovered hydrocarbon and any liquid saved from the distillation in a designated hydrocarbon solvent recovery container.

(**Take Care!** Do not pipet by mouth.) Stopper the vial immediately and weigh [OP-4] it to the nearest milligram on an accurate balance. Calculate the density of your hydrocarbon from your results.

Refractive Index Measurement. Measure the refractive index [OP-35] of the purified hydrocarbon as directed by your instructor and record the temperature of the measurement. Apply a correction to the refractive index if the temperature of the measurement was not 20°C. In your report, give the name, structure, and octane number of your unknown hydrocarbon and discuss its suitability as a gasoline additive.

Exercises

1. The following properties were measured for an unknown hydrocarbon in a laboratory with an ambient temperature of 28°C and a barometric pressure of 28.9 inches of mercury (1 inch Hg = 25.4 torr):

   boiling point: 78.2°C
   refractive index: 1.3780
   mass of 0.200 mL: 0.133 g

   Correct the refractive index and boiling point to 20°C and 1 atmosphere, and calculate the density of the unknown. If the unknown is one of the hydrocarbons listed in Table 2, what is its probable identity?

2. Give names and structural formulas for all structural (constitutional) isomers of your unknown hydrocarbon.

3. Describe and explain the possible effect on your results of the following experimental errors or variations. In each case, tell whether the resulting physical property (bp, density, or refractive index) will be too high or too low. (a) You read the temperature when the unknown liquid began to boil and recorded that temperature as its boiling point. (b) To obtain 1.00 mL of the liquid for the density measurement, you filled a Mohr pipet to the 1-mL mark and drained it completely into the weighing vial (you can ask your instructor to show you a Mohr pipet). (c) The liquid was at a temperature of 25° when you measured its mass and volume. (d) The liquid was at a temperature of 25° when you measured its refractive index, but you forgot to correct it.

4. A large oil spill that resulted from the 1989 shipwreck of the *Exxon Valdez* caused considerable damage to Alaska's wildlife. Do you think a comparable spill of a water-insoluble liquid that has a density of 1.20 g/mL would have been as harmful to waterfowl and aquatic mammals, assuming that the toxicity of the liquid was comparable to that of petroleum? Explain your answer.

5. (a) Write a balanced equation for the complete combustion of 2,2,4-trimethylpentane in an engine's combustion chamber. (b) Show how butane can be converted to 2,2,4-trimethylpentane using petroleum-refining processes mentioned in this experiment.

6. (a) Dioxane has a boiling point of 101°C. Could you separate dioxane from methylcyclohexane by distillation? Explain why or why not, based on the liquid and vapor compositions during the distillation. (b) How might these liquids be separated?

dioxane

Other Things You Can Do

(Starred items require your instructor's permission.)

*1. Solve the missing-label puzzle described in "A Missing-Label Puzzle" minilab.

*2. With your coworkers, analyze different brands and grades of gasoline for the presence of oxygenates. Refer to *J. Chem. Educ.* **1996**, *73*, 1056 for information.

*3. Test for lead in gasoline as follows: Saturate a piece of filter paper with gasoline and expose it to strong sunlight for several hours. Moisten the paper with 3 *M* acetic acid followed by a few drops of aqueous potassium iodide solution (16.5 g/100 mL). A yellow color that appears after several minutes indicates the presence of lead.

4. Write a research paper about gasoline and petroleum refining using references cited in the Bibliography.

Isolation and Isomerization
of Lycopene from Tomato Paste
Column Chromatography,
Ultraviolet–Visible Spectrometry

Isolation of Natural Products. Ultraviolet–Visible Spectrometry. Geometric Isomers.

Operations

OP-18c Liquid–Solid Extraction
OP-21a Liquid–Solid Column Chromatography
OP-41a Ultraviolet–Visible Spectra
OP-6   Making Transfers
OP-15 Gravity Filtration
OP-19 Evaporation
OP-24 Washing Liquids
OP-25 Drying Liquids
OP-26a Washing Solids

Before You Begin

1. Read the experiment and operations OP-18c, OP-21a, and OP-41a. Read or review the other operations as necessary.
2. Prepare an experimental plan following the directions in the "Planning an Experiment" appendix.

Scenario

The Consumer's Advocate is now investigating the quality of processed foods such as tomato paste. Ideally, such processed foods would contain all of the nutrients and flavor components present in the fresh fruits or vegetables. But all too often, the processing methods used tend to degrade the color, flavor, and nutritional value of a food.

The red pigment that colors ripe tomatoes is lycopene, an antioxidant believed to fight many kinds of cancer, including cancers of the digestive tract, cervical cancer in women, and prostate cancer in men. Most of the lycopene in tomatoes and tomato products exists as the *all*-trans isomer, but heat, light, and certain chemicals may convert some of this form of lycopene to other isomers, particularly the 13-*cis* isomer. Thus, the presence of 13-*cis*-lycopene in a canned tomato product suggests that the fresh fruit may have been subjected to excessive heat or light during processing, which can degrade its flavor and possibly affect its health benefits. TCA's technical director wants your organization to assess the quality of different brands of tomato paste on the basis of their *trans*-lycopene content. Your supervisor has found a method for doing this, using ultraviolet–visible (UV–VIS) spectrometry, in the *Journal of Chemical Education*. To improve the validity of your results, you and your coworkers will work in small research teams, with each team assigned a specific brand of tomato paste.

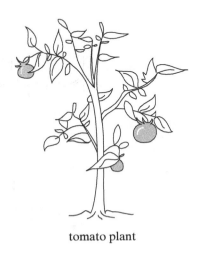

tomato plant

J. Chem. Educ. **1989**, *66*, 258.

From *Operational Organic Chemistry: A Problem Solving Approach to the Laboratory*, Fourth Edition, John W. Lehman. Copyright © 2009 by Pearson Education. Published by Prentice Hall. All rights reserved.

Applying Scientific Methodology

With your instructor's permission, you or another member of your research team may bring in a sample of a commercial tomato paste for testing. Your opinion about the quality of the tomato paste can then be the basis for a working hypothesis, which will be tested when you analyze your lycopene by ultraviolet–visible spectrometry. During the experiment, you should try to avoid conditions that promote isomerization or oxidation of lycopene, which will reduce the reliability of your results.

Carotenoids, Vitamin A, and Vision

Key Concept: The wavelength of the UV–VIS radiation absorbed by a conjugated substance increases with the length of its conjugated system.

Lycopene, a plant pigment with 13 carbon–carbon double bonds, is one of the most unsaturated compounds in nature. Because most of its double bonds are conjugated, lycopene absorbs radiation at long wavelengths in the 400–500-nm region of the visible spectrum. Its resulting deep orange-red color is responsible for the redness of ripe tomatoes, rose hips, and other fruits. Clinical studies suggest that lycopene is a micronutrient with important health benefits, because it appears to protect both men and women from a broad range of cancers. Although the lycopene in tomatoes and tomato products is about 90% all-*trans*-lycopene, human tissues contain mostly *cis*-lycopene isomers. This suggests either that the *cis*-isomers are more readily absorbed by the body or that an enzyme in the body converts all-*trans*-lycopene to the *cis*-isomers. So, although the presence of a significant amount of 13-*cis*-lycopene in tomato paste suggests that some degradation has taken place during processing, that may not necessarily be a bad thing with respect to its health benefits.

Another important plant pigment is the yellow-orange substance β-carotene, which is present not only in carrots but in all green leaves and many flowers as well. Both lycopene and β-carotene, along with most of the other natural *carotenoids*—compounds related to β-carotene—occur naturally in the all-*trans* forms shown in Figure 1.

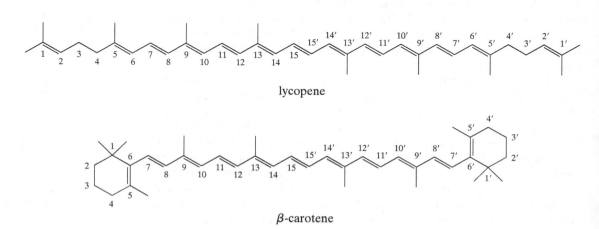

lycopene

β-carotene

Figure 1 Structures of carotenoids
Note: A single straight line branching off from a chain or ring stands for a methyl group in these and similar formulas. A carbon atom with the requisite number of hydrogen atoms is at each bend of the chain.

Although the main function of carotenoids in plants remains somewhat of a mystery, the importance of carotenes to animals is clear—β-carotene (and, to a lesser extent, α- and γ-carotene) is converted in the intestinal wall to Vitamin A, which is then stored in the liver. Generations of children have grown up hearing the mealtime refrain "Eat your carrots—they're good for your eyes!" In fact, Vitamin A from carotenes and other sources is an essential participant in the process by which light entering your eyes causes your brain to construct a visual picture of your surroundings. One step in this process involves a configurational change analogous to the isomerization of all-*trans*-lycopene, but in reverse.

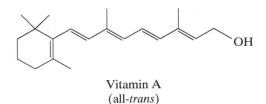

Vitamin A
(all-*trans*)

The process of vision, although extremely complex in its entirety, is based on the isomerization of an oxidized form of Vitamin A called retinal. In the rods of the retina, which are responsible for night vision, retinal occurs in combination with the complex protein opsin to form rhodopsin (visual purple). The retinal in rhodopsin assumes the shape shown in Figure 2A, with an 11-*cis* double bond and probably a *cisoid* conformation between the #12 and #13 carbon atoms as well. This allows a retinal molecule to fit comfortably into a cavity in an opsin molecule—much like a joey (a baby kangaroo) curled up in its mother's pouch. When a photon of light strikes a rhodopsin molecule, its 11-*cis*-retinal passenger suddenly straightens out and becomes all-*trans*-retinal (see Figure 2B). This process is incredibly fast—much faster than the blink of an eye—happening in only about 0.2 trillionths of a second (200 femtoseconds). The isomerized retinal molecule no longer fits into its niche in the opsin molecule, which responds much as a mother kangaroo might when her joey creates a disturbance in her pouch: It ejects its unruly passenger. This triggers the transmission of a visual message to the brain. Subsequently, the *trans*-retinal is enzymatically reduced to all-*trans*-Vitamin A, which isomerizes to 11-*cis*-Vitamin A, which is oxidized back to 11-*cis*-retinal, which promptly combines with another molecule of opsin to regenerate more rhodopsin. At this point, another photon of light can start the cycle all over again.

A similar process occurs in the cones of the retina, which are responsible for color vision.

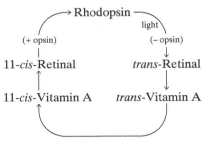

the vision cycle

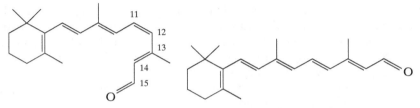

A 11-*cis*-12-*s*-*cis*-retinal   **B** all-*trans*-retinal

Figure 2 Retinal isomers

103

Understanding the Experiment

In this experiment, you will extract the carotenoid pigments (lycopene, carotenes, and xanthophylls) from canned tomato paste and separate them by column chromatography to obtain a solution that contains lycopene. Then you will record the ultraviolet–visible spectrum of this solution and analyze it for evidence of isomerization. Although lycopene can be obtained directly from ripe tomatoes, it is easier to extract it from commercial tomato paste, in which the lycopene is more concentrated—one tablespoon of tomato paste yields as much lycopene as a medium ripe tomato, about 10 mg. Lycopene will isomerize if allowed to stand in solution too long, particularly in the presence of heat, light, or acids. For this reason, it is important to avoid unnecessary delays and exposure of the pigment to heat or bright light. Acids that occur naturally in tomatoes can be removed by washing the extract with aqueous potassium carbonate. Lycopene oxidizes slowly in the presence of atmospheric oxygen, so you should try to record its UV–VIS spectrum on the same day that you isolate the lycopene solution, if possible; otherwise, oxidation products may alter the spectrum.

Petroleum ether is a general term used to describe volatile petroleum distillates that have varying compositions and boiling ranges. Don't confuse it with diethyl ether!

You will extract lycopene and other carotenoid pigments from tomato paste with a solvent mixture that contains equal volumes of acetone and petroleum ether. Acetone is very soluble in water, so washing the extracts with water removes the acetone and leaves the pigments dissolved in the petroleum ether layer. Low-boiling petroleum ether (bp ~35−60°C) is preferred for the extraction, because it can be evaporated readily at room temperature to yield a concentrated solution of the pigments. This concentrate is then transferred to the top of a chromatography column, which should be packed with neutral alumina (Brockmann grade II–III) as described in OP-21a. Be sure to read this operation carefully before you attempt to pack your column, because a poorly packed column won't provide good separation. You will elute the pigments with hexanes (a mixture of C_6H_{14} alkanes) followed by a more polar eluant containing 10% acetone in hexanes. Lycopene, with its 13 double bonds, is attracted to alumina more strongly than are β-carotene and related carotenes, which have 11 to 12 double bonds. Therefore, the yellow carotene band will move down the column faster than the orange-red lycopene band. Yellow xanthophyll pigments will trail behind the lycopene band because they contain polar hydroxyl groups that are strongly attracted to alumina.

High-boiling petroleum ether can be used in place of hexanes.

Under conditions that might be present during the processing of tomato paste, some all-*trans*-lycopene can undergo a configurational change to 13-*cis*-lycopene. You can detect such isomerization by obtaining an ultraviolet–visible spectrum of your lycopene sample; the 13-*cis* isomer absorbs at lower wavelengths than does the all-*trans* isomer, and the relative intensities of the two largest peaks in the visible region of the spectrum change significantly (see Figure 3). If you scan the ultraviolet region, you may see a characteristic *cis* peak that is associated with the bent geometry of the 13-*cis*-lycopene molecules. The *cis* peak occurs at about 360 nm, a wavelength at which all-*trans*-lycopene shows little absorption.

This method is derived from the Journal of Chemical Education *article referred to in the Scenario.*

You can estimate the percentage of all-*trans*-lycopene in your sample by the following empirical method:

- Draw a straight, horizontal line tangent to the bottom of the valley between the last (highest wavelength) two peaks on the spectrum.

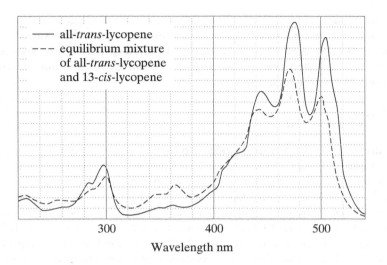

Figure 3 Ultraviolet–visible spectra of lycopene stereoisomers

- Measure the height of both peaks from that line, and call the heights *a* and *b*.
- Divide the smaller height (*b*) by the larger (*a*), subtract 0.40, multiply by 100%, and divide the product by 0.40, as shown by the following equation.

$$\frac{\left(\dfrac{b}{a} - 0.40\right) \times 100\%}{0.40}$$

If the percentage of all-*trans*-lycopene is significantly lower than 90%, the lycopene in your tomato paste may have isomerized while the tomatoes were being processed into tomato paste, during your isolation of the lycopene, or both. Before drawing any definite conclusion about the quality of your tomato paste, you should compare your results with those of the other members of your team. Such a comparison should help you select the result that was affected least by the experimental conditions.

Partial isomerization of all-*trans*-lycopene to 13-*cis*-lycopene is also catalyzed by iodine. To show the effect of isomerization, you can add a dilute solution of iodine to your lycopene solution and again obtain its spectrum (or your instructor may demonstrate the isomerization to the class).

Although this experiment requires the use of organic solvents, it features a nontoxic natural product and the majority of the solvents used can be recovered. The acetone used in the extraction ends up in the wash solvents and may not be recovered. Acetone is slightly toxic to aquatic life, but it doesn't bioaccumulate and isn't considered a serious environmental contaminant.

DIRECTIONS

Students may work together in small research teams, with each team working on a specific brand of tomato paste, agreeing on a conclusion, and comparing its results with those of other groups working with different brands.

Safety Notes

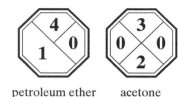

petroleum ether   acetone

Acetone and petroleum ether are very flammable, and their vapors can irritate the eyes and upper respiratory tract. Keep petroleum ether and the petroleum ether–acetone mixture away from flames and hot surfaces, and do not breathe their vapors.
The hexanes solvent is flammable, so keep it away from flames and hot surfaces.

Take Care! Keep the solvent away from flames and hot surfaces.

Preparing the Chromatography Column. Pack a column for chromatography [OP-21a] with neutral Brockmann grade II–III alumina in a 25-mL buret or other appropriate chromatography column, using hexanes as the column-packing solvent (use the method for packing with dry adsorbent described in OP-21a). See that the surface of the alumina is uniform and as horizontal as possible. Obtain a 50-mL beaker and a clean, dry 4-dram screw-cap vial to collect the eluates. Clamp the column to a ring stand over the beaker, making sure that it is as vertical as possible and that the alumina is covered with solvent. Close the column with a cork or rubber stopper.

Take Care! Keep the extraction mixture away from flames and hot surfaces.

Extraction of Pigments from Tomato Paste. Protect the pigment from undue exposure to light throughout the remainder of this experiment. Weigh about 4.0 g of tomato paste into a small beaker. Extract [OP-18c] the solid material three times with successive 10-mL portions of a 50% (by volume) mixture of acetone and low-boiling petroleum ether, each time filtering [OP-15] the extract through fluted filter paper into a small Erlenmeyer flask. After each extraction, decant the liquid extract onto the filter, pressing the residue in the beaker with a flat-bladed spatula to squeeze out as much liquid as possible. After the third extraction, transfer [OP-6] the residue to the filter and wash it [OP-26a] with 5 mL of the extraction solvent, combining the wash liquid with the extracts. Wash [OP-24] the combined extracts with 20 mL of 10% aqueous potassium carbonate followed by 20 mL of saturated sodium chloride solution. Dry [OP-25] the lycopene-containing organic layer with anhydrous sodium sulfate. Concentrate the pigment solution to a volume of about 0.5 mL by evaporating [OP-19] most of the petroleum ether *without* heating. If you inadvertently evaporate the solution to dryness, dissolve the residue in 0.5 mL of hexanes.

Stop and Think: What is the purpose of the K_2CO_3 wash?

Waste Disposal: Unless your instructor directs otherwise, flush the wash liquids down the drain.

Separation and Isolation of Lycopene. Fill the chromatography column [OP-21a] with the first eluant, hexanes, and let the liquid drain until its surface *just* disappears into the sand layer. Immediately transfer the pigment extract to the top of the column with a Pasteur pipet, using a few drops of eluant to rinse any remaining extract onto the column. When the extract surface just disappears into the sand, fill the column nearly to the top with the first eluant and continue to add eluant to keep its level more or less constant. When the yellow carotene band begins to drain out of the column, fill the column with the second eluant, 10% acetone in hexanes (or in high-boiling petroleum ether), and continue to replenish the eluant as before. When the orange-red lycopene band begins to leave the column, replace the beaker by the collection vial and elute the lycopene band, collecting a 5.0-mL sample of eluate from the center of this band. (You can save the rest of the lycopene eluate and evaporate it to obtain the pigment as described in "Other Things You Can Do.") Then replace the vial by the beaker you used before and let any remaining eluate drain into the beaker. Use the midband

Observe and Note: Describe what you see as the bands pass down the column.

Stop and Think: Why do the bands move down the column at different rates?

lycopene sample for spectral analysis as soon as possible. If you can't record its spectrum on the same day, store your sample in a tightly closed container in a refrigerator or freezer.

Spectral Analysis and Isomerization of Lycopene. Using an appropriate 1-cm sample cell and 10% acetone/hexanes in the reference cell, record a spectrum [OP-41a] of the midband lycopene sample over the 600–400 nm range (with your instructor's permission, you can scan the 400–250 nm UV range as well). If necessary, dilute the lycopene solution with 10% acetone/ hexanes to keep the strongest peak (at ~475 nm) on scale. Your instructor may demonstrate the isomerization of lycopene. To do it yourself, mix a drop of a 0.025% solution of iodine in hexanes into the lycopene solution and leave the solution in the sample beam at 475 nm, monitoring its absorbance until it remains constant (about 2 minutes). (Alternatively, leave it in bright sunlight for 15 minutes or more.) Then record another spectrum over the same wavelength range as before. Turn in your lycopene solution in a labeled vial.

Estimate the percentage of all-*trans*-lycopene in your midband sample before isomerization, as well as its percentage in your (or your instructor's) sample after isomerization. After consulting with other students who analyzed the same brand of tomato paste, decide whether the lycopene in that brand was isomerized significantly as a result of processing. (Read Exercise 1 before you do this.) Compare your team's results with those of the other research teams, and assess the relative quality of the different brands of tomato paste.

Waste Disposal: Place all eluates except the lycopene eluate in a designated solvent recovery container.

Observe and Note: Do you see any differences in the spectra? If so, describe them.

Exercises

1. To estimate the percentage of all-*trans*-lycopene present in the original tomato paste, should you average the percentages obtained by all the members of your team? If not, what should you do, and why?
2. (a) Calculate the concentration of the lycopene solution in the spectrophotometer cell before isomerization, given that the molar absorptivity of lycopene at 471 nm is 1.86×10^4. (b) Calculate the mass of lycopene in 3.0 mL of the solution that has the concentration you calculated in (a).
3. (a) Draw the structures of the 7-*cis*, 11-*cis*, and 13-*cis* isomers of lycopene. (b) Linus Pauling predicted that 13-*cis*-lycopene should be considerably more stable than the other two isomers. Explain.
4. Describe some green features of this experiment, and any that aren't so green.
5. Describe and explain the possible effect on your results of the following experimental errors or variations. (a) You used a can of tomato paste that had been left open in a refrigerator for several days. (b) You recorded the second spectrum immediately after adding the iodine solution. (c) You used acid-washed alumina for the chromatographic separation.
6. (a) Explain why some hydrocarbons (such as lycopene and β-carotene) are colored, whereas most other hydrocarbons are not. (b) The color

of a lycopene solution fades and may disappear entirely if it is treated with a larger amount of iodine than you used in this experiment. Explain this, and give an equation for a possible reaction.

7. (a) Write an equation for the reaction that occurred during the addition of iodine to all-*trans*-lycopene in this experiment. (b) Write a feasible mechanism for this reaction.

Other Things You Can Do

(Starred items require your instructor's permission.)

*1. Concentrate some lycopene-containing eluate to a small volume by evaporation [OP-19] at room temperature, and cool it in ice water to obtain crystalline lycopene. Its melting point should be about 175°C.

*2. Separate the dyes in Kool-Aid by paper chromatography as described in the "Paper Chromatography of Dyes in Commercial Drink Mixes" minilab.

*3. Make a "tomato-juice rainbow" that shows the effect of conjugation on color as described in *J. Chem. Educ.* **1986**, *63*, 1092.

4. Write a research paper about Vitamin A and vision using sources from the Bibliography.

Isolation and Identification of the Major Constituent of Clove Oil
Steam Distillation, Infrared Spectrometry

Isolation of Natural Products. Infrared Spectrometry.

Operations

OP-20 Steam Distillation
OP-39 Infrared Spectrometry
OP-4 Weighing
OP-18 Extraction
OP-19 Evaporation
OP-25 Drying Liquids

Before You Begin

1. Read the experiment and operations OP-20 and OP-39. Read or review the other operations as necessary.
2. Write an experimental plan following the directions in the "Planning an Experiment" appendix.

Scenario

Professional aromatherapist Rose Otto uses the essential oil from cloves as a treatment for toothache, muscle pain, ringworm, flatulence, warts, and general exhaustion. But the latest batch of clove oil from her current supplier is darker than usual, has a harsh odor, and appears to be less effective than the oil she received previously. She suspects that the supplier has substituted some clove leaf oil for true clove oil, which is distilled from clove buds, the dried calyxes left after the flowers of the clove tree have fallen off.

Ms. Otto has asked you to provide her with an authentic sample of freshly distilled clove oil and tell her what's in it, so that she can compare the authentic clove oil with the product she has on hand. Your assignment is to isolate clove oil from ground cloves and identify its major constituent, which is known to have the molecular formula $C_{10}H_{12}O_2$. Your supervisor believes that you can identify the constituent using infrared (IR) spectrometry.

clove bud

Applying Scientific Methodology

Reading the experiment carefully should yield a clue or two about the identity of the unknown, which is one of those illustrated in Figure 1. Then you should be able to develop a working hypothesis that will be tested when you obtain and interpret the infrared spectrum.

From *Operational Organic Chemistry: A Problem Solving Approach to the Laboratory*, Fourth Edition, John W. Lehman. Copyright © 2009 by Pearson Education. Published by Prentice Hall. All rights reserved.

Plants and Healing

As people seek alternatives to traditional medical practices, which emphasize the use of drugs and surgery to treat illness, various fields of alternative medicine are gaining adherents around the world. These include *aromatherapy*, the use of essential oils to maintain health and treat illness; *naturopathy*, a system of treating diseases using special diets, herbs, vitamins, and other natural healing methods; and *homeopathy*, which originally relied on the use of minute doses of drugs to cure illness but now utilizes carefully formulated mixtures of herbal medicines. Although some alternative medical practices may be associated with scientifically questionable theories—such as the counterintuitive idea (still accepted by some homeopathic practitioners) that the potency of a drug increases with dilution—many fields of alternative medicine utilize plant-based medicines that have a long history of healing efficacy.

At a time when most physicians prescribe commercial drugs for medical conditions, we may tend to associate herbal medicine—the use of plants to treat and prevent illness—with witch doctors, shamans, or far-out medical cults. But herbal remedies have gained popularity in recent years, as more and more people turn to echinacea, goldenseal, and even garlic to help them stay healthy and cope with illness. Europe is well ahead of the United States in conducting scientific research on herbal medicines. In fact, the popularity of six of the ten top-selling herbs in the United States has resulted mainly from European research. For example, a scientific team at the University of Dusseldorf, Germany, recently studied the active principles and biological effects of the purple coneflower, *Echinacea purpurea*, which is used to treat colds and flu by stimulating the immune system. One objective of their research was to improve the standardization of echinacea extracts, helping to ensure that each dose provides the same physiological activity.

After echinacea, the most widely used herbal remedy in America is garlic—one of the few remedies you are more likely to find in a grocery store than a drugstore. Although researchers disagree on the virtues of garlic, there is evidence that it lowers cholesterol and triglyceride levels in blood, helps prevent blood clots that could lead to heart attacks or strokes, and lowers blood pressure. The active ingredient in garlic was once believed to be a sulfur compound called allicin, which is formed by an enzymatic reaction when garlic is bruised or otherwise damaged and contributes to its distinctive and powerful aroma. But recent research has shown that allicin is highly unstable and can't be detected in the body after garlic is consumed. Other chemicals released by garlic, including *S*-allylcysteine and hydrogen sulfide (H_2S), are now believed to be responsible for garlic's medicinal properties. Cooking garlic tends to destroy its active consitituents, so most of the apparent benefits of garlic are obtained only from the raw cloves or garlic capsules. Eating lots of raw garlic could limit your social life, but that may be a small price to pay for good health!

Legend has it that Achilles, during the siege of Troy, used yarrow to treat the wounded Greeks. Its botanical name, *Achillea millefolium*, recognizes that tradition. The bruised leaves of yarrow help to stop bleeding, heal cuts, and relieve the pain of a wound, so the plant has been used in medical emergencies by backpackers and other outdoor adventurers. The ancients supposedly used St. John's wort (*Hypericum perforatum*) to drive away evil spirits; today it is touted as a natural alternative to Prozac for treating mild to moderate depression. The indigenous North American weed boneset

$$CH_2\!=\!CHCH_2\overset{\overset{\displaystyle O}{\|}}{S}\!-\!SCH_2CH\!=\!CH_2$$

allicin

$$CH_2\!=\!CHCH_2SCH_2\underset{\underset{\displaystyle NH_2}{|}}{CH}\overset{\overset{\displaystyle O}{\|}}{C}OH$$

S-allylcysteine

(*Eupatorium perfoliatum*) provides a bitter tea that was a favorite Native American remedy for fevers and other ailments. The closely related joe-pye weed (*Eupatorium purpureum*) was named after a Native American who gained fame by using it to cure typhus. It is an effective diuretic for the treatment of kidney and bladder ailments. Other popular herbal medicines include goldenseal root for treating peptic ulcers, infected gums, sore throats, and skin infections; saw palmetto berries for treating nonmalignant prostate disease; gingko leaf to improve blood flow in capillaries and arteries; aloe vera gel to heal burns, cuts, and wounds; ephedra stems to treat asthma and hay fever; and ginseng root to enhance one's general well-being and revitalize people weakened by old age or illness.

It shouldn't surprise us that natural medicines can be effective. There are, after all, far more molecules in the world's natural life forms than have been synthesized in all the world's pharmaceutical laboratories. Many natural molecules are already known to have medicinal properties, and there must be at least as many more whose properties are yet to be discovered. Most of the drugs now prescribed by physicians were either derived from natural sources or developed by modifying the molecular structures of natural substances. For example, the heart stimulant digitalis is obtained from the foxglove plant, and the molecular structure of aspirin (acetylsalicylic acid) is similar to that of natural salicylates such as salicin from willow bark, which has been used for centuries by Native Americans to treat fevers.

The six-carbon substituent in salicin is a glucose unit.

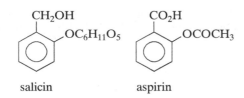

salicin   aspirin

Although herbal medicines are generally milder and have fewer side effects than traditional prescription drugs, they are not all harmless. According to the U.S. Food and Drug Administration (FDA), herbal preparations containing *Ephedra sinica* (also known as Ma huang) can cause heart attacks, strokes, seizures, and even death if used improperly. Unlike most prescription drugs, different preparations that contain the same herb may vary widely in potency and physiological effect, and because the FDA doesn't regulate them, there is no guarantee that herbal preparations will contain the ingredients claimed. But when used responsibly by well-informed individuals, herbal medicine may provide a viable alternative to the use of conventional drugs for maintaining good health and treating some medical conditions.

Understanding the Experiment

The *essential oil* of a plant is a volatile mixture of water-insoluble components that exhibits the odor and other characteristics of the plant. In this experiment, you will isolate an essential oil from cloves, which are obtained from a small evergreen tree (*Syzygium aromaticum*) that grows in places such as Indonesia, Madagascar, and Zanzibar. The essential oil of cloves is a pale yellow liquid with a sweet, spicy aroma. Clove oil is unusual among essential oils in that it has only one major component, which makes up about 85% of the oil.

Because ground cloves lose their volatile components over time, it is best to grind fresh whole cloves just before use. Essential oils are usually isolated by steam distillation, in which steam forced through the plant material vaporizes the essential oil, which is then condensed into a receiver along with water from the condensed steam. Steam distillation is preferable to ordinary distillation because the volatile components distill at temperatures below their normal boiling points, reducing or preventing decomposition due to overheating. During your steam distillation, the distillate should be cloudy or contain oily droplets at first and become clearer when most of the clove oil has distilled. You will separate clove oil from the distillate by extraction with dichloromethane. You can then separate the major component of clove oil from its minor components by extraction with aqueous sodium hydroxide, in which only the major component dissolves. The dichloromethane is removed by evaporation, leaving the strong-smelling oil behind.

The major component of clove oil is a liquid that has the molecular formula $C_{10}H_{12}O_2$. The structures of some natural compounds that have this formula are shown in Figure 1. Because these compounds have different sets of functional groups, it is possible to distinguish them using IR spectrometry. By detecting the presence or absence of IR absorption bands that correspond to specific functional groups, you should be able to arrive at the correct structure for the major component. The section "Interpretation of Infrared Spectra" in OP-39 describes the characteristic bands of organic compounds that have various functional groups.

This is a comparatively green experiment because the clove oil is obtained from a natural product by codistillation with water, and the dichloromethane

A Greener Way: You can recover the dichloromethane by evaporating the extracts under vacuum using a cold trap (see OP-15).

Key Concept: Different covalent bonds vibrate at different frequencies, producing IR absorption bands at those frequencies. Thus, a functional group that contains a particular set of bonds produces a characteristic set of IR bands, from which it can often be identified.

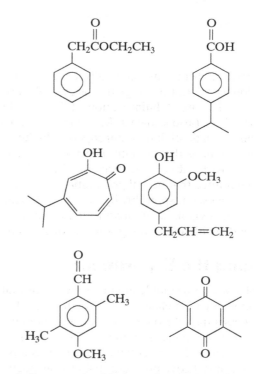

Figure 1 Compounds with the molecular formula $C_{10}H_{12}O_2$

used to extract clove oil from the aqueous distillate can be recovered by evaporation under vacuum. The EPA classifies dichloromethane as a priority pollutant and has established an MCL of 5 ppb for its concentration in drinking water.

DIRECTIONS

Live steam can cause serious thermal burns. Make sure all steam hoses are connected tightly and turn off the steam before you withdraw the steam inlet tube from the apparatus.
Dichloromethane may be harmful if ingested, inhaled, or absorbed through the skin. There is a possibility that prolonged inhalation of dichloromethane may cause cancer. Minimize contact with the liquid and do not breathe its vapors.
Clove oil irritates the skin, eyes, and respiratory tract. Avoid contact and do not breathe its vapors.

Safety Notes

dichloromethane

Isolation of Clove Oil.　If fresh whole cloves are provided, use a spice mill or a mortar and pestle to grind enough cloves to provide about 5 g of the ground spice. Weigh [OP-4] 5.0 g of ground cloves in a tared weighing dish. Assemble an apparatus for steam distillation [OP-20] using a large (250–500 mL) boiling flask and a steam trap, and have your instructor check your apparatus. Combine the ground cloves with 50 mL of water in the boiling flask, then steam distill the mixture to obtain the clove oil. Continue the distillation until a drop or two of the emerging distillate, collected on a watch glass, is odorless and water-clear, with no oily droplets. You may need to distill 150 mL of liquid or more before the distillate becomes completely clear. Be sure to vent the steam line or raise the steam inlet tube above the liquid level in the boiling flask before you turn off the steam. Extract [OP-18] the clove oil from the distillate with two 20-mL portions of dichloromethane and combine the extracts. (Which layer is the dichloromethane layer?)

Observe and Note: How does the appearance of the distillate change during the distillation?

Take Care! Turn off the steam before you remove the inlet tube from the apparatus.

Waste Disposal: Filter the clove residue through glass wool and place it in a solid-wastes container.

Separation of Minor Components.　Extract [OP-18] the active component of clove oil from the dichloromethane solution with two 15-mL portions of 1 M aqueous sodium hydroxide and combine the aqueous layers. Acidify the aqueous solution to blue litmus paper with 10 mL or more of 3 M hydrochloric acid. Extract this aqueous solution with two 15-mL portions of dichloromethane and combine the extracts.

Take Care: Avoid contact with dichloromethane and do not breathe its vapors.

Stop and Think: What does this separation procedure suggest about the nature of the major component?

Isolation and Analysis of the Major Component.　Dry [OP-25] the dichloromethane solution with anhydrous sodium sulfate or magnesium sulfate. Evaporate [OP-19] the dichloromethane under vacuum, using a cold trap, until the boiling stops and the volume of the residue remains constant. Weigh the liquid residue and leave it in an open container for a few minutes; then reweigh it. If its mass decreases significantly between weighings, continue evaporating until the mass is nearly constant. Measure the final mass [OP-4] and obtain an infrared spectrum [OP-39] of your clove oil. Calculate the percent recovery of clove oil based on the mass of cloves you started with. Identify as many bands in the IR spectrum as you can, and deduce the identity of the major component of clove oil. Turn in your IR spectrum along with the product.

If the solution is evaporated without heating, the clove oil may solidify.

Waste Disposal: Unless your instructor directs otherwise, wash the aqueous layers from all extractions down the drain. Place all of the recovered dichloromethane in a chlorinated solvent recovery container.

Exercises

1. Derive a systematic name for the active component of clove oil, and use this to find its common name in *The Merck Index* [Bibliography, A11] or another reference book.

2. (a) The active component of clove oil is separated from the minor components by the extraction process described in the procedure. What property of the active component makes this separation possible? Is this consistent with the structure you chose for it? Explain. (b) Write equations for the chemical reactions involved in the extraction and subsequent acidification of the extract.

3. (a) Clove oil contains about 10% of a minor component that can be hydrolyzed to yield the major component and acetic acid. Deduce the structure of the minor component, which has the molecular formula $C_{12}H_{14}O_3$. (b) The percentage of the major component of clove oil actually increases as the cloves are steam distilled. Explain why and give an equation for the reaction involved.

4. Describe some green features of this experiment, and any that aren't so green.

5. Describe and explain the possible effect on your results of the following experimental errors or variations. (a) You stopped the steam distillation after collecting 75 mL of distillate. (b) You forgot to wash the boiling flask, which contained a residue of sodium hydroxide left over from Experiment 4. (c) You didn't evaporate the dichloromethane long enough.

6. (a) Clove oil also contains a small amount of a substance whose systematic name is (*E*)-4,11,11-trimethyl-8-methylenebicyclo[7.2.0]undec-4-ene. Write the structure of this compound and find its common name in *The Merck Index* or another reference book.

7. Following the format in the "Planning an Experiment" appendix, construct a flow diagram for this experiment. Show how the active component is separated from the solid part of the cloves and the component mentioned in Exercise 3.

Other Things You Can Do

(Starred items require your instructor's permission.)

*1. Analyze your product by gas chromatography, and estimate the percentage of the major component. If your instructor provides a sample of the major component, compare its IR spectrum with that of your product.

*2. Obtain and analyze an essential oil from orange peel as described in the "Gas Chromatographic Analysis of an Essential Oil from Orange Peel" minilab.

*3. Steam distill the essential oils from anise seed, caraway seed, or cumin seed following the procedure in this experiment. (Omit the "Separation of Minor Components" step.) Each of these essential oils contains a single major component that can be characterized by IR spectrometry.

4. Write a research paper about herbal medicine after referring to sources cited in the Bibliography.

Identification of Unknown Ketones
Thin-Layer Chromatography, NMR Spectrometry

Qualitative Analysis. Thin-Layer Chromatography. NMR Spectrometry. Ketones.

Operations

OP-22 Thin-Layer Chromatography
OP-28b Recrystallization from Mixed Solvents
OP-40a ^{1}H NMR Spectrometry
OP-4 Weighing
OP-5 Measuring Volume
OP-16 Vacuum Filtration
OP-26 Washing and Drying Solids
OP-33 Melting Point

Before You Begin

1. Read the experiment and operations OP-22, OP-28b, and OP-40a. Read or review the other operations as necessary.
2. Prepare a brief experimental plan following the directions in the "Planning an Experiment" appendix.

Scenario

A nearby machine shop was recently destroyed by fire under conditions that strongly suggest arson. A residue recovered at the fire's point of origin was found to contain traces of methyl ethyl ketone (MEK), one of several commercial degreasing solvents that shop employees use to clean the machinery. The primary suspect is a disgruntled ex-employee who was recently fired for sleeping on the job. While searching the suspect's garage, police discovered two unlabeled cans containing flammable liquids, which the suspect claims are charcoal starters for his grill. However, most charcoal-starting fluids are mixtures of petroleum hydrocarbons, and preliminary tests indicate that the liquids found in the suspect's possession are both ketones.

Local police detective Spike Burns has asked your institute to help him solve the crime. Detective Burns provided your supervisor with samples of the two ketones. Matching one of them with the solvent recovered at the fire's point of origin will help the police discredit the suspect's claim and may result in his conviction. Your assignment is to identify the ketones and determine whether either one of them matches the solvent found at the scene of the crime. Your supervisor has requested that you use two different methods to identify your ketones.

From *Operational Organic Chemistry: A Problem Solving Approach to the Laboratory*, Fourth Edition, John W. Lehman. Copyright © 2009 by Pearson Education. Published by Prentice Hall. All rights reserved.

Applying Scientific Methodology

You will, in effect, be performing two separate experiments. Your working hypothesis for the first experiment might be, for example, "The first unknown solvent is (or is not) methyl ethyl ketone." You will then gather evidence to prove or disprove the hypothesis. In part **A**, the evidence used to test the hypothesis will be obtained by thin-layer chromatography (TLC) analysis and a melting-point determination. In part **B**, the only evidence will be provided by the nuclear magnetic resonance (NMR) spectrum of the second solvent, which should lead you to its structure. There is, of course, no guarantee that either of the two solvents will be methyl ethyl ketone.

Crime and Chemistry

Forensic chemistry is chemistry applied to the solution of crimes. It deals with the analysis of materials that were used to commit a crime or that were inadvertently left at the crime scene. Materials used to commit a crime might include the ink on a forged document, an explosive used in a terrorist bombing, a toxic substance used in a fatal poisoning, or a flammable liquid used to start a fire. Such materials can be identified and sometimes traced to a particular source. Materials found at the scene of a crime might include paint chips, pieces of fiber from clothing, and particles of dust or soil, as well as any materials that were used to commit the crime. Chips of paint or glass found at the scene of a hit-and-run accident can be analyzed both chemically and under a microscope to determine the make and model of the car involved. Clothing can be traced by the dyes contained in fibers, and dust or soil particles may link a criminal to a particular occupation or location.

Bringing a suspect to trial requires that evidence be presented to establish, first, that a crime has actually been committed, and second, that the suspect is connected with the crime. In an arson case, for example, this requires proof that the fire was deliberately set as well as evidence implicating the suspect. One way to establish that a fire was deliberately set is to prove that an *accelerant* (a flammable substance that causes a fire to intensify and spread rapidly) was used to start and spread the fire. Because fires burn upward from the point of origin, some of the accelerant may soak downward into flooring, rags, paper, or other porous materials. When an investigator traces a fire to its point of origin, he or she can often collect samples of materials containing the accelerant, which are placed in airtight containers and sent to a forensic laboratory for analysis.

In the laboratory, a forensic chemist can separate an accelerant from debris collected at the crime scene by steam distillation or extraction. Once the accelerant has been isolated, it is usually classified according to chemical type (gasoline, turpentine, etc.) by an instrumental method such as gas chromatography or spectrometry. The forensic chemist may then try to match the accelerant sample with a control material, such as a liquid in the suspect's possession or a commercial material. Some flammable liquids, such as the industrial solvent MEK—whose IUPAC name is 2-butanone—contain only one major component and can be compared to the control material using chemical or spectrometric methods. If the original accelerant was a mixture of different components, such as gasoline, its more volatile

In the popular television series C.S.I., a team of crime scene investigators uses such forensic chemistry techniques to solve crimes.

components will evaporate and burn more rapidly in a fire. For this reason, a sample of accelerant taken from the crime scene will probably not have the same composition as the original accelerant. Therefore, various control materials related to the accelerant are evaporated slowly and analyzed repeatedly by gas chromatography to determine whether the composition of a control material at any stage of evaporation matches that of the recovered material. With this procedure, it is often possible to determine the brand and grade of gasoline or other accelerant used.

Thin-layer chromatography is another important technique used by forensic chemists. TLC provides a rapid, sensitive means of analyzing many of the materials associated with various crimes. The dyes used to color gasoline can be characterized by the pattern of spots they produce on a TLC plate, making it possible in some cases to trace an arson accelerant to its source. The U.S. Treasury Department maintains a library of pen inks that are catalogued according to their TLC dye patterns, allowing an investigator to match the ink on a document with one on file. In a few cases, TLC analysis has proven that the ink used to fraudulently backdate a document didn't even exist on the date in question! Substances suspected of being illicit drugs are frequently screened by TLC; most drugs that are mixtures of several substances, such as marijuana, produce telltale patterns that are easily recognized. A thin-layer chromatogram alone may not be sufficient to establish the identity of a suspect material, but it can narrow down the list of possibilities and thus lead to positive identification of the material by other means.

Understanding the Experiment

In this experiment, you will attempt to identify one of the unknown ketones using TLC and the other using NMR spectrometry. TLC can be used in the identification of pure compounds, as well as complex mixtures such as drugs and dyes. When a TLC plate (see OP-22) spotted with structurally similar organic compounds is developed with an appropriate solvent, the R_f values obtained vary more or less regularly with chain length. This correlation is illustrated in Table 1 for a homologous series of carboxylic acids. When an unknown compound is known to be one of a limited number of compounds,

Key Concept: The R_f value of a substance depends on its relative affinities for the adsorbent on the TLC plate and the developing solvent. A substance with a higher affinity for the adsorbent spends most of its time stuck to the adsorbent and has a low R_f value. A substance with a higher affinity for the solvent spends most of its time dissolved in the solvent and has a high R_f value.

Table 1 TLC R_f values for carboxylic acids

Carboxylic acid	# Carbon atoms	R_f
methanoic (formic) acid	1	0.07
ethanoic (acetic) acid	2	0.13
propanoic acid	3	0.30
butanoic acid	4	0.40
pentanoic acid	5	0.50
hexanoic acid	6	0.57
heptanoic acid	7	0.60
octanoic acid	8	0.66

Note: Developed on silica gel using a 19:1 mixture of methyl acetate and 2.5% ammonia.

a TLC plate can be spotted with samples of the unknown and the most likely known compounds. When the plate is developed, it may be possible to match the R_f value of the unknown compound's spot with that of a known compound.

Your first unknown will be a member of a homologous series of methyl ketones represented by the formula $CH_3CO(CH_2)_nCH_3$, where n is zero or a whole number. A ketone is often converted to its 2,4-dinitrophenylhydrazone (DNPH) or another colored derivative for TLC analysis because the colored spots are easily located after the plate is developed, making a visualizing reagent unnecessary. A derivative preparation is actually a small-scale organic synthesis that may produce only a fraction of a gram of product. The 2,4-dinitrophenylhydrazone derivative of a ketone is prepared by combining the ketone with DNPH reagent, which contains 2,4-dinitrophenylhydrazine and sulfuric acid in aqueous ethanol. Traces of sulfuric acid may remain on the derivative and catalyze isomerization reactions that will lower its melting point, so the acid is removed by washing the derivative with aqueous sodium bicarbonate after vacuum filtration. The derivative is then purified by recrystallization. Some 2,4-dinitrophenylhydrazones dissolve too readily in ethanol and too sparingly in water for either of these liquids to be a good recrystallization solvent by itself, so you will use a mixture of the two, as described in OP-28b, "Recrystallization from Mixed Solvents." To obtain a solvent mixture of the right composition, you should first dissolve the derivative in the better solvent (the one in which it is most soluble), ethanol, and then add just enough of the poorer solvent, water, to saturate the hot solution.

You will also prepare derivatives of some of the known ketones listed in Table 2, spot a TLC plate with your unknown's derivative and the known derivatives, and develop the chromatogram using a solvent such as 3:1 toluene/petroleum ether. After measuring the melting point of your purified derivative and comparing its R_f value with those of the known derivatives, you should be able to identify your unknown as one of the ketones in Table 2.

Modern analytical instruments, such as IR and NMR spectrometers, can greatly reduce the time and effort required for the positive identification of an unknown. In part **B** of this experiment, you will attempt to identify an unknown saturated ketone with four to six carbon atoms from its proton NMR (^{1}H NMR) spectrum. If an NMR spectrometer is available, you can record the spectrum yourself, with help from your instructor. If not, you can generate a simulated spectrum of your assigned unknown using a computer program, such as the *NMR Simulator* described in Category M of the Bibliography, or your instructor will provide an NMR spectrum of the unknown. The section "Interpretation of ^{1}H NMR Spectra" in OP-40a contains an introduction to NMR spectral analysis that will help you deduce the structure of the second unknown.

Because 2-4-dinitrophenylhydrazine isn't a common environmental contaminant, there is little information about its effects on the environment. But similar hydrazines are very toxic, so DNPH and the derivatives should not be released into the environment. Toluene is quite toxic, with an MCL in drinking water of 0.5 ppb, so the developing solvent must be disposed of properly.

Reactions and Properties

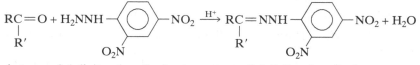

ketone   2,4-dinitrophenylhydrazine   2,4-dinitrophenylhydrazone

Table 2 Physical properties and derivative melting points for homologous methyl ketones

Ketone	mol wt	bp	d	Derivative mp
2-propanone (acetone)	58.1	56	0.791	126
2-butanone (MEK)	72.1	80	0.805	117
2-pentanone	86.1	102	0.809	143
2-hexanone	100.2	128	0.811	110
2-heptanone	114.2	151	0.811	89
2-octanone	128.2	173	0.819	58

Note: Boiling points are in °C; densities are in g/mL.

DIRECTIONS

With the instructor's permission, teams of two to three students can work together on some parts of this experiment, such as the preparation of derivatives of the known ketones.

The ketones are flammable and may be harmful if inhaled or absorbed through the skin. Avoid contact, do not breathe their vapors, and keep them away from flames.

2,4-Dinitrophenylhydrazine is harmful if absorbed through the skin and will dye your hands yellow. Wear gloves and avoid contact with the DNPH reagent.

Ethyl acetate is flammable and may be harmful if inhaled or absorbed through the skin. Avoid contact, do not breathe its vapors, and keep it away from flames.

Toluene is flammable and may be harmful if inhaled, ingested, or absorbed through the skin. Petroleum ether is extremely flammable and can be harmful if inhaled or absorbed through the skin. Avoid contact with the developing solvent, keep it away from flames and hot surfaces, and do not breathe its vapors.

Deuterochloroform is toxic and may be carcinogenic; avoid contact and inhalation.

Safety Notes

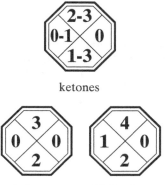

ketones

ethyl acetate   TLC solvent

A. *Identification of an Unknown Methyl Ketone Using TLC*

Preliminary Work. Obtain an unknown methyl ketone from your instructor and record its identification number in your laboratory notebook.

Pre-equilibrate the TLC developing solvent, a 3:1 mixture of toluene and petroleum ether, by filling an appropriate developing chamber containing a paper wick to a depth of about 5 mm with the solvent, covering it with a lid or plastic wrap, and sloshing the solvent up the sides of the chamber to moisten the wick (see OP-22). Then set it aside under a hood for later use.

Take Care! Avoid contact with the developing solvent, do not breathe its vapors, and keep it away from flames or hot surfaces.

Take Care! Do not pipet by mouth.

Take Care! Wear gloves and avoid contact with the reagent.

Preparation of 2,4-Dinitrophenylhydrazones. Measure [OP-5] 0.20 mL of your unknown into a test tube of appropriate size. Dissolve it in 3 mL of 95% ethanol, stir in 7.0 mL of the DNPH reagent, and set the test tube aside for 15 minutes. Collect the derivative by vacuum filtration [OP-16]. After you have removed the acidic filtrate, wash the derivative on the filter [OP-26a] with 5 mL of cold 5% sodium bicarbonate, then with cold water. Let it air-dry on the filter for at least 5 minutes. Recrystallize [OP-28b] the derivative from an ethanol/water mixed solvent. Collect it by vacuum filtration, and wash it on the filter with a cold 3:1 mixture of ethanol and water. Dry [OP-26b] the derivative, weigh it [OP-4], and measure its melting point [OP-33]. Save enough of the derivative for the TLC separation and turn in the rest in a labeled vial.

Waste Disposal: Place the initial filtrate in a designated DNPH waste container. Except when directed otherwise, wash other filtrates down the drain.

Clean and label as many small test tubes as there are known methyl ketones available (see Table 2). Measure 1 mL of the DNPH reagent into each test tube and add 1 drop of the appropriate methyl ketone. Set the test tubes aside until crystallization is complete, then collect the crystalline derivatives by vacuum filtration [OP-16].

Waste Disposal: Place the filtrates in the DNPH waste container.

TLC Separation of 2,4-Dinitrophenylhydrazones. Read OP-22 carefully before you begin. Dissolve approximately 10 mg (0.01 g) of the unknown ketone's derivative in 0.5 mL of ethyl acetate, using a spot plate or a small, labeled test tube. Do the same for each known derivative. Use the solutions to spot a silica gel TLC plate [OP-22], taking care not to touch the surface of the adsorbent layer, and label the spots with a pencil. To avoid cross-contamination, use a different micropipet (or other spotting device) for each solution. *Under the hood*, use 3:1 toluene/petroleum ether or another solvent suggested by your instructor to develop the plate in the developing chamber you prepared. Don't move or otherwise disturb the developing chamber until the plate is developed. Mark the solvent front with a pencil before the plate dries.

Waste Disposal: Put the developing solvent in a hydrocarbon solvent recovery container. Place any unused DNPH derivatives in the DNPH waste container.

Measure the distances of the spots and solvent front from the starting line and calculate all R_f values. Deduce the name and structure of the unknown ketone from your results. Turn in your TLC plate, as well as the derivative of your unknown.

B. *Identification of an Unknown Ketone by NMR Spectrometry*

If an NMR spectrometer is not available for student use, your instructor will either provide you with a copy of the proton NMR spectrum of the second unknown ketone or let you use an NMR simulation program to generate a spectrum. Otherwise, obtain a sample of the unknown ketone, record its identification number in your laboratory notebook, and prepare a solution of the ketone in deuterochloroform ($CDCl_3$) as described in OP-40a, using a tetramethylsilane (TMS) reference standard. Record and integrate the proton NMR spectrum [OP-40a] of the sample. Deduce the structure of the second unknown ketone from its spectrum and name it. Turn in your NMR spectrum with your report.

Take Care! Avoid contact with $CDCl_3$ and do not breathe its vapors.

Waste Disposal: Put the deuterochloroform solution in a designated solvent recovery container.

Exercises

1. (a) Write a balanced equation for the reaction of your unknown methyl ketone with 2,4-dinitrophenylhydrazine. (b) The DNPH reagent contains 2.9 g of 2,4-dinitrophenylhydrazine in 100 mL of solution. What was the limiting reactant for the preparation of your 2,4-dinitrophenylhydrazone? Calculate the theoretical yield and percent yield of the reaction.

2. Describe and explain any relationship between chain length and R_f value that you observed from your TLC separation.

3. (a) The purpose of the sodium bicarbonate washing was to prevent isomerization of the derivative during the melting-point determination. Write structures for two stereoisomers of the 2,4-dinitrophenylhydrazone derivative of 2-pentanone. (b) Which one would you expect to be more stable, and why?

4. Describe some green features of this experiment, and any that aren't so green.

5. Describe and explain the possible effect on your results of the following experimental errors or variations. (a) You didn't wash the derivative of your unknown with aqueous sodium bicarbonate. (b) You let the TLC plate develop too long and you can't find the solvent front. (c) You left the TMS out of your ^{1}H NMR sample.

6. Draw structures for all ketones that have the molecular formula $C_5H_{10}O$, and sketch the ^{1}H NMR spectrum you would expect to obtain from each one. Your sketches should show the relative area, multiplicity, and approximate chemical shift of each signal.

7. Account for the fact that the 2,4-dinitrophenylhydrazone derivative of 2-octanone melts at a lower temperature than the corresponding derivative of acetone, even though the molecular weight of the 2-octanone derivative is much higher.

Other Things You Can Do

(Starred items require your instructor's permission.)

*1. Use TLC to analyze some felt-tip pen inks as described in the "Identification of an Unknown Felt-Tip Pen Ink by TLC" minilab.

*2. Use NMR spectrometry to identify an alkyl chloride that has the formula $C_4H_{10}Cl$, or another compound whose molecular formula will be provided by your instructor.

3. Write a research paper about forensic chemistry, starting with sources cited in the Bibliography.

The Optical Activity of α-Pinene:
A Chemical Mystery
Vacuum Distillation, Optical Rotation

Separation of Liquids. Optical Activity. Stereoisomerism. Terpenes.

Operations

OP-31 Vacuum Distillation
OP-36 Optical Rotation
OP-4   Weighing
OP-10   Mixing
OP-34   Boiling Point

Before You Begin

1. Read the experiment and operations OP-31 and OP-36. Read or review the other operations as necessary.
2. Prepare a brief experimental plan following the directions in the "Planning an Experiment" appendix.

Scenario

Dick Hawkshaw, a private investigator, has called on you to help him solve a mystery. A wealthy American entrepreneur named Aldo Hyde was recently found murdered in his chalet in Cannes, France. Although the house was set on fire in an apparent attempt to cover up the murder, firefighters were able to extinguish the fire before the evidence was destroyed. Inside the house, a half-filled can of paint thinner was found; it had no label, but the word TURPENTINE was written on one side with a felt-tip pen. The housekeeper informed Hawkshaw that there was no turpentine in the house before the night of the fire, so the murderer must have brought it there. Gas-chromatographic analysis of a flammable residue found at the fire's point of origin revealed that liquid from this can was used to start the blaze.

The only suspects in the case are Aldo Hyde's widow, Dr. Jacqueline Hyde, a talented but unpredictable talk-show psychologist; and Guy Framboise, a hot-tempered French businessman. Aldo and Jacqueline Hyde had lived separately for more than a year, she in New York and he in Cannes. He was planning to change his will—and leave her out of it—when his untimely death intervened, so Jacqueline stands to inherit most of his fortune. Dr. Hyde arrived in Cannes from New York on the night of the murder and checked into a hotel at 10:05 p.m., approximately two hours before the murder took place, but there are no witnesses who can place her at the scene of the crime. Guy Framboise made threats against Aldo's life after a joint business operation failed, and a reliable witness saw the Frenchman's Peugeot parked near Hyde's chalet on the night of the murder.

Dick Hawkshaw just shipped your supervisor a sample of the turpentine used in the crime. Now it is up to you to discover the crucial evidence that will identify the murderer of Aldo Hyde.

From *Operational Organic Chemistry: A Problem Solving Approach to the Laboratory*, Fourth Edition, John W. Lehman. Copyright © 2009 by Pearson Education. Published by Prentice Hall. All rights reserved.

Applying Scientific Methodology

The problem is, of course, "Who murdered Aldo Hyde?" As you read the experiment, you should find some clues that will help you solve the mystery—after you have gathered the experimental evidence.

Turpentine and the Terpenes

Terpenes are among the most widely distributed natural products, occurring in nearly all plants. They are compounds that can, in principle, be broken down into two or more isopentane (2-methylbutane) units. For example, the carbon skeleton of geraniol can be separated in the middle to yield two isopentane units connected head to tail; that is, the "head" end of one unit—the end nearest the side chain—is connected to the "tail" end of the next.

Terpenes that have oxygen-containing functional groups are sometimes called terpenoids.

These isopentane units are also called isoprene units, after a diene having the same carbon skeleton.

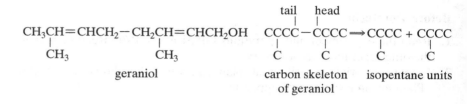

Geraniol, with its rose-blossom aroma, is an important constituent of the essential oil known as rose otto. It also plays an important role in the biosynthesis of terpenes. This process involves the enzymatic isomerization of isopentenyl pyrophosphate and a subsequent reaction with its isomer to yield geranyl pyrophosphate, from which other terpenes are produced.

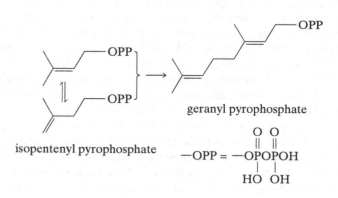

Many terpenes, especially the ones that contain oxygen, have pleasant odors and flavors and are therefore important flavoring and perfume ingredients.

An important natural source of terpenes is *turpentine*, the sticky oleoresin (pitch) obtained from conifer trees such as the southern longleaf pine, *Pinus palustris*. The "turpentine" sold as a paint thinner, more accurately called oil of turpentine, is distilled from this oleoresin. It is the world's most abundant essential oil, obtained as a by-product of paper production as well as from pine pitch. The major components of American oil of turpentine are (+)-α-pinene and (−)-β-pinene, with the former predominating.

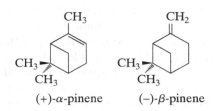

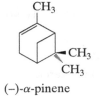

(−)-α-pinene

Constituents of American oil of turpentine

European oil of turpentine contains mostly the enantiomeric (−)-α-pinene and very little β-pinene. Both α- and β-pinene are used to synthesize other terpenes and their derivatives, which are used in perfumes, flavorings, and other commercial products. For example, α-pinene is a starting material in the synthesis of isobornyl acetate, which contributes a pine-needle note to perfumes; linalool, which has a sweet woody–floral odor; and camphor, which is used in the manufacture of cosmetics, plastics, and pharmaceuticals.

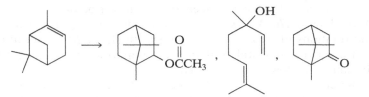

α-pinene   isobornyl acetate   linalool   camphor

Large quantities of β-pinene are converted to β-myrcene, which is then used to make perfume ingredients that have floral notes, including linalool and the aldehyde shown here.

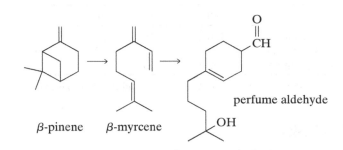

perfume aldehyde

β-pinene   β-myrcene

Understanding the Experiment

The application of chemistry to crime solving isn't just the province of the forensic chemist. Writers of mystery novels—from Arthur Conan Doyle to Dorothy L. Sayers—have made many references to forensic chemistry in their work. In Sayers's novel *The Documents in the Case*, a mushroom

Doyle's Dr. Watson claimed that Sherlock Holmes had a profound knowledge of chemistry.

collector dies after eating a stew containing mushrooms that he has picked himself. At first, the death is believed to be accidental, caused by muscarine, a toxin found in the poisonous mushroom *Amanita muscaria*. Eventually, however, a chemist discovers that the stew contains optically inactive (and therefore synthetic) muscarine, rather than the optically active muscarine that occurs in the poisonous mushroom. Sayers was actually a step ahead of the chemists of her day (the novel was published in 1930), who—based on an incorrect achiral structure for muscarine—assumed that its natural form was optically inactive. In 1957, an X-ray crystallographer proved that Sayers had guessed right: Muscarine is indeed chiral, so the premise of her novel was sound.

In this experiment, you—like the chemist in Sayers's novel—will be measuring the optical rotation of a substance to help solve a mystery. First you must obtain α-pinene in a reasonably pure form. You will purify the "turpentine" sample you are issued by distilling it, performing the distillation under vacuum to reduce the likelihood of decomposition. The α-pinene distills at about 156°C at normal atmospheric pressure, but its boiling point is reduced at lower pressure. For example, it boils at 52°C at a pressure of 20 torr, which should be attainable by a typical aspirator. Any operation carried out under vacuum involves some risk of an implosion, which can cause injury from flying glass fragments, so it is very important to inspect all parts of your apparatus carefully to be certain that they are free from cracks or other defects, and to have it checked by your instructor.

According to *The Merck Index*, (+)-α-pinene and (−)-α-pinene have specific rotations of +51° and −51°, respectively, at 20°C. Because your distilled α-pinene may still contain some impurities, its specific rotation may be somewhat lower (see Exercise 1).

Some energy must be used for the vacuum distillation, but otherwise this is a green experiment because the only chemicals used are ethanol and α-pinene, which are both natural substances with low toxicity.

Key Concept: *As a rule, chiral compounds from natural sources are optically active. Nearly all synthetic chiral compounds are racemic mixtures and therefore optically inactive.*

(+)-muscarine

Properties

Table 1 Physical properties

	mol wt	bp^{760}	bp^{20}	$[\alpha]_D$
(+)-α-pinene	136.2	156	52	+51°
(−)-α-pinene	136.2	156	52	−51°
(−)-β-pinene	136.2	163		−22°

Note: Boiling points are in °C, at 760 torr and 20 torr, respectively.

DIRECTIONS

Safety Notes

α-pinene

α-Pinene irritates the skin and eyes, and its vapors are harmful. Avoid contact and do not breathe its vapors.
A vacuum distillation apparatus may implode if any of its components are cracked or otherwise damaged. Inspect the parts for damage and have your instructor check your apparatus. Work behind a hood sash or safety shield while the apparatus is under vacuum.

Purification of α-Pinene.   If you are using an aspirator and don't have a manometer, measure the temperature of the aspirator water after the aspirator has run for a while and estimate the minimum pressure the aspirator can attain (see OP-31). Otherwise, determine the pressure as directed by your instructor. Use the nomograph in Figure E10 of OP-31 to estimate the boiling point of α-pinene at that pressure (the actual boiling temperature may be somewhat higher). After inspecting the glassware carefully, assemble an apparatus for vacuum distillation [OP-31] using a 25-mL boiling flask and vacuum grease, and have it approved by your instructor. Add 10 mL of "turpentine" and a smooth boiling device, such as a magnetic stir bar [OP-10] or a capillary bubbler. Make sure that a safety shield or hood sash is between you and the apparatus. Start the stirrer (if you are using one), turn on the vacuum, and adjust the heat until distillation begins, collecting the liquid that distills at or somewhat above the estimated boiling point. After about three-quarters of the pinene has distilled, monitor the temperature closely. When it rises or drops by 5°C or more, stop the distillation, release the vacuum, and transfer the distillate to a tared vial.

Analysis.   Measure the boiling point [OP-34] of your product by the semi-microscale method. Using a 25-mL volumetric flask, prepare a solution that contains about 2.5 g of your α-pinene, weighed [OP-4] to the maximum accuracy of your balance, in absolute ethanol. Transfer the solution to a 2-dm polarimeter cell and measure its optical rotation [OP-36]. Then measure the optical rotation of a blank that consists of pure absolute ethanol. Calculate the specific rotation of your α-pinene, and give its complete name and structure. Then decide who murdered Aldo Hyde.

Stop and Think: Why should the water temperature affect the pressure an aspirator can attain?

Take Care! Be sure that none of the components is cracked or otherwise damaged.

If the pressure changes during the distillation, the boiling temperature may vary.

Stop and Think: Was the initial boiling point different than you had estimated? If so, why?

Stop and Think: Which α-pinene enantiomer do you have? How do you know?

Waste Disposal: Place the used solution in a designated solvent recovery container. Leave the blank in its polarimeter cell.

Exercises

1. From its specific rotation, estimate the purity of your α-pinene, as the mass percent of the predominant α-pinene enantiomer: (a) if the impurity is (−)-β-pinene; (b) if the impurity is optically inactive.
2. The Aldrich Chemical Company manufactures a technical (low-purity) grade of pinene that contains 85% (+)-α-pinene and has a specific rotation of +43°. Is the 15% (by mass) impurity in this product more likely to be (−)-α-pinene, (−)-β-pinene, or some optically inactive substance? Justify your answer with calculations.
3. Describe and explain the possible effect on your results of the following experimental errors or variations: (a) Your vacuum distillation apparatus had a leaky joint. (b) The "turpentine" contained synthetic α-pinene. (c) You prepared the solution for polarimetry as directed, but you used a 1-dm tube rather than a 2-dm tube to measure the optical rotation.
4. Describe some green features of this experiment, and any that aren't so green.
5. (a) Show how α-pinene can be divided into isopentane units. (b) Do the same for linalool and camphor.
6. (a) Determine the configuration, (R) or (S), at each stereocenter of (+)-muscarine. (b) Determine the configuration at each stereocenter of (−)-β-pinene.

7. The pyrophosphate group is an excellent leaving group that can easily be lost to yield a carbocation. (a) Propose a mechanism for the synthesis of geraniol from isopentenyl pyrophosphate and its isomer (see "Turpentine and the Terpenes") in an acidic aqueous environment. (b) Propose a mechanism for the synthesis of α-pinene from geranyl pyrophosphate under similar conditions.

8. Propose a synthesis from β-myrcene of the perfume aldehyde whose structure is shown in the section "Turpentine and the Terpenes."

Other Things You Can Do

(Starred items require your instructor's permission.)

*1. Determine the percentage composition of turpentine by measuring its optical rotation as described in the "Optical Rotation of Turpentine" minilab.

*2. Purify technical grade (85–90%) α-terpineol, whose normal boiling point is 220°C, by vacuum distillation. Cool the purified product in ice, if necessary, to see if it will solidify (pure α-terpineol is said to solidify around 30°C).

3. Write a research paper about terpenes, starting with sources cited in the Bibliography.

Investigation of a Chemical Bond by Infrared Spectrometry

Resonance. Infrared Spectrometry. Molecular Mechanics. Carbonyl Compounds. Acyl Compounds.

Operation

OP-39   Infrared Spectrometry

Before You Begin

1. Read the experiment, read or review the operations as necessary, and write an experimental plan.
2. Be prepared to predict the *relative* $C{=}O$ vibrational frequencies (not their actual numerical values) of compounds your instructor will assign in the lab.

Scenario

The Olfactory Factory manufactures perfumes by mixing essential oils, resins, and other ingredients as specified by secret fragrance formulas that have been kept in the Pomander family for generations. The company's quality-control manager, Dr. Hyacinth Pomander, is responsible for measuring the relative amounts of certain key aroma chemicals in the ingredients to ensure that they remain within the tolerances specified by the formulas. Most of these chemicals are aldehydes, ketones, esters, and other compounds that contain a carbonyl ($C{=}O$) group. The Olfactory Factory recently purchased a number of infrared (IR) analyzers to quantify the key chemicals by measuring the intensity of the carbonyl band in each ingredient's infrared spectrum. Unfortunately, this method hasn't been working well because of interference by other chemicals whose molecules also possess carbonyl groups. Dr. Pomander believes that, by tuning the IR analyzers to the vibrational frequency of the carbonyl group in a key substance of each perfume ingredient, she should be able to minimize such interferences, but first she needs to know how to predict their vibrational frequencies. She has sent samples of several representative carbonyl and acyl compounds to your supervisor. Your assignment is to find a way to estimate in advance their $C{=}O$ vibrational frequencies and then to check your predictions by measuring the vibrational frequency of each compound's carbonyl band as accurately as possible.

Applying Scientific Methodology

The basic problem in this experiment is to see if there is a way to estimate the vibrational frequencies of $C{=}O$ bonds in molecules that contain such bonds. After reading the experiment, you should be able to develop

From *Operational Organic Chemistry: A Problem Solving Approach to the Laboratory*, Fourth Edition, John W. Lehman. Copyright © 2009 by Pearson Education. Published by Prentice Hall. All rights reserved.

a hypothesis, apply it to the representative compounds assigned by your instructor, and determine whether or not your predictions are verified by the experimental results.

The Art and Science of Perfumery

Throughout history, both men and women have used substances with pleasant odors to attract attention, to cover up unpleasant scents, and simply for the pleasure they provide. Elizabeth I used large quantities of lavender oil, in part to mask the stench of Elizabethan England, where streets doubled as sewers and bathing was considered unhealthful. The ancient Egyptians had no such aversion to personal hygiene; they used perfumes to scent their baths and sweeten their breath. Egyptian tomb paintings depict feasts at which revelers piled lumps of scented animal fat on their heads; as the evening progressed, the fat melted and coated their bodies with fragrant perfumes. A fat-based perfume found in an alabaster vase in the tomb of King Tutankhamen was still fragrant 3000 years later, and similar vases were found in the tombs of First Dynasty kings who reigned from about 5100 B.C. The aromatic resins frankincense and myrrh were among the gifts of the Magi in the biblical account of the birth of Jesus. The Queen of Sheba reputedly used myrrh to beguile King Solomon, and frankincense is still burned during rites of the Roman Catholic and Greek Orthodox churches.

Traditional perfume ingredients include natural resins, essential oils, concretes, and absolutes, which are obtained from plant or animal sources by such processes as distillation, solvent extraction, and expression (pressing). *Resins*, such as frankincense, are solid or semisolid materials exuded by plants. *Essential oils*, such as rose otto (also called attar of roses), are volatile liquids that are usually obtained by mixing finely divided plant materials with water and then distilling the mixture with steam. *Concretes* are waxy residues obtained by extracting plant components with a volatile solvent and then evaporating the solvent. *Absolutes* are concretes that have been processed to remove insoluble materials. Jasmine, one of the most highly prized perfume ingredients, is made by extracting jasmine flowers with hydrocarbons, then treating the resulting concrete with alcohol to produce the absolute.

Because natural materials such as jasmine are often costly and may be subject to considerable variation in composition and availability, most modern perfumes contain synthetic aroma chemicals as well as natural ingredients. Aroma chemicals include synthetic versions of natural compounds and even some compounds that have never existed in nature. Most aroma chemicals have an oxygen-containing functional group; aldehydes, ketones, alcohols, esters, and ethers are well represented in perfumes. A few hydrocarbons are also used, and smelly sulfur and nitrogen compounds may be added in very small amounts. For example, the nitrogen-containing compound indole has a repulsive fecal odor when pure, but in minute amounts it imparts a fine jasmine scent to perfumes. Some representative aroma chemicals and their odors are illustrated in Figure 1.

A perfumer creates a new perfume in much the same way that a composer creates a symphony. Inspired by perhaps a single aroma "note," such

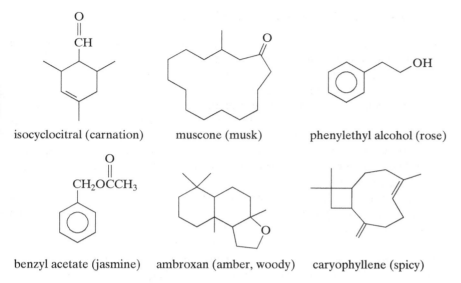

isocyclocitral (carnation)   muscone (musk)   phenylethyl alcohol (rose)

benzyl acetate (jasmine)   ambroxan (amber, woody)   caryophyllene (spicy)

Figure 1 Some aroma chemicals and their aroma notes

as a recently discovered natural product or a new synthetic aroma chemical, the perfumer creates a "theme," called an *accord*, which may consist of several related aroma chemicals. For example, Chanel No. 5 is based on an accord that consists of a blend of aliphatic aldehydes. Additional ingredients with different volatilities and aroma intensities are combined with the accord to produce a "composition" consisting of top, middle, and end notes. The top note contains the most volatile and odoriferous components, whose odors predominate immediately after a perfume is applied to the skin but fade as they evaporate. A fruity top note, for example, might consist of low molecular-weight esters and some lactones (cyclic esters). The middle note provides the basic character of a fragrance. Mixtures of floral essential oils, such as neroli oil, with flowery aroma chemicals are often used as middle notes. The end note contains less volatile materials that persist longer on the skin, such as resins and certain oils; musky aroma chemicals and woody materials such as sandalwood are among the ingredients of end notes. All perfume ingredients must be carefully selected and combined in just the right proportions to give the perfume a smooth odor profile, so that there are no abrupt changes in odor as the ingredients evaporate. For a typical perfume or cologne, the ingredients are then dissolved in ethyl alcohol or some other alcohol-containing solvent.

There is some scientific evidence that perfumes do more than just make people smell better. Pleasant odors may improve mood, bring to mind happy memories, enhance creativity, or make people feel more cooperative and less confrontational toward others. On the other hand, a perfume that smells good to one person may be objectionable to someone else, and not everyone wants to be subjected to olfactory assaults from such flagrantly fragrant consumer products as scented toilet paper and fabric softener. But an appreciation of pleasant and stimulating fragrances is rooted deeply in the human psyche, and any drawbacks of commercial scents may be outweighed by the benefits they provide.

Understanding the Experiment

In this experiment, your instructor will provide you (or your research team) with three or more compounds that contain a carbonyl group. Based on the discussion to follow, you will try to arrange the compounds in order of their $C=O$ vibrational frequencies. At your instructor's discretion, you can also use a molecular mechanics computer program to estimate specific values for the frequencies. Then you will record the IR spectra of your compounds to determine their actual vibrational frequencies and see how accurate your predictions were. Because you will be using only a drop or two of each compound and enough energy to run the instruments, this is an environmentally friendly experiment.

A chemical bond is similar in some ways to a coiled spring. Just as it takes energy to stretch a spring, energy is required to stretch a chemical bond, and a stronger bond requires more energy. A bond stretches and contracts as it vibrates, and the frequency at which the bond vibrates (ν) is proportional to the energy associated with the vibration, as given by the equation $\Delta E = h\nu$. Thus, the stronger the bond, the higher its vibrational frequency. The $C-O$ single bond in ethanol (CH_3CH_2OH) vibrates about 31 trillion (3.1×10^{13}) times a second, whereas the stronger $C=O$ double bond in ethanal ($CH_3CH=O$) vibrates about 52 trillion times a second. A bond vibrating at a certain frequency can absorb a photon of IR radiation that has exactly the same frequency. For example, a $C=O$ bond vibrating 5.2×10^{13} times a second can absorb a photon whose frequency is 5.2×10^{13} Hz, where 1 Hz $= 1$ s^{-1}.

It is convenient to express the vibrational frequency of infrared radiation in wave numbers ($\bar{\nu}$), where the wave number of a vibration expressed in cm^{-1} is the number of waves of electromagnetic radiation per centimeter. The wave number corresponding to a vibrational frequency of 5.2×10^{13} s^{-1} is about 1740 cm^{-1}, so the infrared spectrum of ethanal contains an absorption band at 1740 cm^{-1} that is generated when its carbonyl bonds absorb infrared radiation.

You can convert wave number to frequency by multiplying by the speed of light, expressed as 3.00×10^{10} cm/s.

To determine the relative vibrational frequencies for $C=O$ bonds in different compounds, you can estimate their relative strengths using resonance theory. For example, suppose the carbonyl carbon in a compound is attached to some atom or group Z, giving the compound the general formula RCOZ. Such a compound will have at least two resonance structures. We can write resonance structure **B** by moving a pair of pi electrons onto the oxygen atom.

Only those lone pairs of electrons that are involved in resonance are shown in these and subsequent resonance structures.

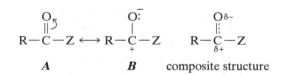

$$\begin{matrix} A & & B & & \text{composite structure} \end{matrix}$$

The actual structure of the molecule can then be depicted by the composite structure shown, which represents the superposition of **A** and **B** in a single structure. The strength of the carbon–oxygen bond depends on the relative importance of the two resonance structures. If **A** and **B** were of equal importance, the carbon–oxygen bond would be halfway between a double bond and a single bond. This "one-and-a-half bond" would be considerably weaker than a full $C=O$ double bond and would therefore vibrate at a lower frequency. As a rule, the more electronegative Z is, the less stable (and therefore less important) resonance structure **B** is, because an electronegative substituent withdraws electrons from the positively charged carbon, increasing the concentration of charge at that point. The less important structure **B** is, the smaller the contribution it will make to the structure of the compound, and the nearer the carbon–oxygen bond will be to a full double bond.

If Z is unsaturated, additional resonance structures may be drawn. For example, if Z is a vinyl (CH_2＝CH—) group, there will be three significant resonance structures, two of which have carbon–oxygen single bonds.

$$
\underset{\textbf{\textit{A}}}{\overset{\overset{\displaystyle O}{\parallel}}{R-C-CH=CH_2}} \longleftrightarrow \underset{\textbf{\textit{B}}}{\overset{\overset{\displaystyle \overset{..}{O}:^-}{\mid}}{R-\underset{+}{C}-CH=CH_2}} \longleftrightarrow \underset{\textbf{\textit{C}}}{\overset{\overset{\displaystyle \overset{..}{O}:^-}{\mid}}{R-C=CH-\overset{+}{C}H_2}}
$$

This will increase the contribution of resonance structures with C—O single bonds, giving the carbon–oxygen bond less double-bond character.

Additional resonance structures are also possible if Z contains unpaired electrons on an atom next to the carbonyl carbon, as illustrated for an amide, in which Z is an amino (NH_2) group.

$$
\underset{\textbf{\textit{A}}}{\overset{\overset{\displaystyle O}{\parallel}}{R-C-\overset{..}{N}H_2}} \longleftrightarrow \underset{\textbf{\textit{B}}}{\overset{\overset{\displaystyle \overset{..}{O}:^-}{\mid}}{R-\underset{+}{C}-\overset{..}{N}H_2}} \longleftrightarrow \underset{\textbf{\textit{C}}}{\overset{\overset{\displaystyle \overset{..}{O}:^-}{\mid}}{R-C=\overset{+}{N}H_2}}
$$

If resonance structure **C** is important, it will decrease the double-bond character of the carbon–oxygen bond. As a rule, structures like **C** are less important when the atom next to the carbonyl carbon is more electronegative than nitrogen. For the purposes of this experiment, you can disregard the effect of such resonance structures when the Z group has an oxygen atom at its point of attachment to the carbonyl carbon.

The method described will only provide relative frequencies; that is, it should help you arrange your assigned compounds in order of their C＝O vibrational frequencies, but it won't allow you to predict the actual frequencies. With a molecular mechanics program, you can use a computer to calculate vibrational frequencies from electron distributions and other features of molecules. To do so, you will first build the structure of each molecule on the computer monitor. Then you will have the program calculate the electron distribution about the C＝O bond (it may provide a pictorial representation of the electron distribution), from which it can estimate the bond's vibrational frequency, expressed in Hz or cm^{-1}.

When you record the IR spectra of your compounds, you will need to identify the carbonyl band in each spectrum and determine its wave number as accurately as possible. Generally, the C＝O band will be the only strong band within a region extending from about 1650 cm^{-1} to 1800 cm^{-1}. If you are using a Fourier transform infrared (FT–IR) spectrometer, the wave numbers of the

Key Concept: Dispersion of charge stabilizes a molecule; concentration of charge destabilizes it.

This does not mean that resonance involving such oxygen atoms is negligible, just that the method described in this experiment works better if it is disregarded.

important bands may be printed directly on the spectrum, or you may have to select the carbonyl band on a screen display of the spectrum and read its wave number from the monitor. With a dispersive IR spectrometer, it is essential that the chart paper be properly aligned, because you will have to determine the wave number of the carbonyl band from its position on the chart paper.

DIRECTIONS

Your instructor will provide several organic compounds for you to analyze and may assign you to a research team with other students.

Safety Notes

> **The compounds you are assigned may be hazardous if inhaled or absorbed through the skin. Avoid contact and inhalation.**

Estimating C=O Frequencies. If the structures of your compounds are not given, write their structures from their systematic names. Write as many significant resonance structures as you can for each compound. Based on your assessment of the relative importance of the resonance structures, predict the relative strength of the carbon–oxygen bond in each compound. Then list the compounds in order of their carbonyl vibrational frequencies, from higher to lower frequency.

At your instructor's request, and following his or her instructions, use a molecular modeling program such as *Spartan* [Bibliography, M12] to estimate the vibrational frequency of the C=O bond in each compound.

Obtaining C=O Vibrational Frequencies from Their IR Spectra.
Record the IR spectra [OP-39] of the assigned compounds. If you are working in a group, each member should record the spectrum of one compound. Accurately determine the wave number of each compound's carbonyl band from its spectrum. Calculate the vibrational frequency of each compound's carbonyl group from the wave number of its carbonyl band. In your report, compare your results with your predictions and try to account for any differences.

Waste Disposal: Place any unused liquids in a designated waste container.

Stop and Think: Were the results as you predicted? If not, why not?

Exercises

1. Predict the relative C=O vibrational frequencies of the aldehyde, ketone, and ester shown in Figure 1, listing them in order from lower to higher frequency.
2. Describe and explain the possible effect on your results of the following experimental or conceptual errors. (a) The infrared chart paper on a dispersive IR spectrometer wasn't aligned correctly when you recorded your spectrum. (b) One of your compounds was 3,7-dimethyl-2,6-octadienal. In writing its structure, you inadvertently put the #2 double bond between the #3 and #4 carbon atoms. (c) In comparing an aldehyde and a ketone, you assumed that an alkyl group is electron withdrawing relative to hydrogen, because in general chemistry you learned that carbon is more electronegative than hydrogen.

3. Calculate the wavelength in μm of the IR radiation absorbed by the carbonyl group of each compound whose wave number you recorded.
4. Write resonance structures for the following compounds and predict their relative C=O vibrational frequencies, listing them in order from lower to higher frequency.

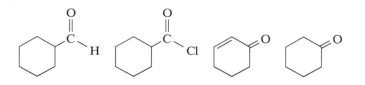

5. (a) Outline a synthesis of phenylethyl alcohol (2-phenylethanol) starting with benzene and ethylene oxide. (b) Outline a synthesis of benzyl acetate starting with toluene and ethanol.

Other Things You Can Do

(Starred items require your instructor's permission.)

1. Construct molecular models of some representative organic molecules as described in "The Structures of Organic Molecules" minilab.
2. Interpret one or more of your IR spectra by indicating what kind of bond is responsible for each significant IR band.
*3. Use a molecular mechanics program to determine the preferred geometry for one or more of your compounds or for another compound suggested by your instructor.
4. Write a research paper about perfumes, starting with sources listed in the Bibliography.

Properties of Common Functional Groups

Functional Group Chemistry. Qualitative Analysis. Infrared Spectrometry.

Operations

OP-5   Measuring Volume
OP-30 Simple Distillation
OP-34 Boiling Point
OP-39 Infrared Spectrometry

Before You Begin

1. Read the experiment, read or review the operations, and write a brief experimental plan.
2. Read or review the section "Interpretation of Infrared Spectra" in OP-39a.

Scenario

Marvelous Molecules Incorporated (MMI) manufactures fine chemicals for use by research chemists in educational institutions and industry. One of their sales representatives, Albert Keene, just flew in from Milwaukee to meet an important client. He brought along samples of some representative chemicals to demonstrate the quality of MMI's products. Federal regulations prevented him from transporting the chemicals on the airplane, so he had them sent ahead by freight carrier. On arrival, he discovered—to his dismay—that the bottles of chemicals had been exposed to high heat and humidity during transit, which caused all of their labels to fall off. The labels were salvaged, but he has no idea which label belongs to which bottle, so he placed a desperate phone call to your supervisor asking for help. Your assignment is to match each chemical with the correct label. Fortunately, Al Keene selected chemicals from different families of organic compounds, so you will only have to identify the functional group present in each compound to find out what it is.

Applying Scientific Methodology

At your instructor's discretion, you can work in teams, with each member of the team responsible for the identification of one compound. After you observe some of your compound's physical and chemical properties, you should be able to formulate a tentative hypothesis about the identity of its functional group. You will then record the infrared (IR) spectrum of your compound to test your hypothesis and arrive at a conclusion.

From *Operational Organic Chemistry: A Problem Solving Approach to the Laboratory*, Fourth Edition, John W. Lehman. Copyright © 2009 by Pearson Education. Published by Prentice Hall. All rights reserved.

Chemical Taxonomy

A botanist attempting to identify an unknown flowering plant may first examine the flowering parts to detect features that suggest the family of plants to which it belongs, and then study the whole plant systematically to determine its genus and species. For example, a botanist coming across a plant with four symmetrical flower petals and six stamens (four long and two short) might tentatively classify it as a member of the mustard family (*Cruciferae*). Further observation of white flower petals, lyre-shaped leaves, and a red, globular root might then lead the botanist to the conclusion that the plant is a specimen of *Raphanus sativus*. On the other hand, an experienced gardener might immediately recognize the same specimen as a radish plant, based only on its general appearance.

Similarly, people experienced in handling chemicals may learn how to recognize a familiar organic compound from its odor and general characteristics, but a systematic approach is needed for positive identification of a range of organic compounds. Qualitative organic analysis—the identification of organic compounds based on their physical and chemical properties— is analogous in some ways to the identification of plants according to their *taxonomy*—their structural features and presumed natural relationships. Classifying an organic compound into a given family requires first detecting a specific functional group (characteristic set of atoms) in the molecules of the compound. Table 1 lists some functional groups found frequently in organic compounds.

Because functional groups influence the physical, chemical, and spectral properties of an organic compound, a chemist can usually identify a compound's functional group by a process that may involve measuring

Table 1 Common functional groups and their families

Functional group	Functional group name	Family
$-C=C-$	carbon–carbon double bond	alkene
$-Cl$	chlorine atom	alkyl chloride
$-OH$	hydroxyl group	alcohol (also phenol)
$\overset{O}{\underset{\parallel}{-C}}-H\ (-CHO)$	carbonyl group, with H on carbonyl carbon	aldehyde
$\overset{O}{\underset{\parallel}{-C}}-\ (-CO-)$	carbonyl group, no H on carbonyl carbon	ketone
$\overset{O}{\underset{\parallel}{-C}}-OH\ (-COOH)$	carboxyl group (*carb*onyl + hydr*oxyl*)	carboxylic acid
$-NH_2$	amino group	amine (primary)

Note: Condensed representations of some of the functional groups are given in parentheses.

certain physical properties, observing its chemical behavior with different classification reagents, and studying its infrared spectrum. The chemical name and structure of the compound can then be determined by methods described in "Qualitative Organic Analysis."

Understanding the Experiment

In this experiment, you will investigate some physical, chemical, and spectral properties of a compound that belongs to one of the families listed in Table 1. Then you will share your results with your coworkers, who will be assigned the remaining compounds. All of the compounds have molecules of about the same size and mass, so differences in their properties will depend primarily on their functional groups.

Physical properties that are affected by functional groups include boiling point, density, and water solubility.

Molecular Structure and Boiling Points

Boiling of a liquid occurs when the kinetic energy of its component molecules becomes high enough to overcome the forces between them, allowing them to leave the surface of the liquid and enter the gaseous state (see Figure 1). Because the kinetic energy of molecules increases with temperature, and the energy required to separate molecules depends on the strength of the forces between them, we can expect liquids that have strong intermolecular forces to have high boiling points as well.

The important kinds of intermolecular forces occurring between organic molecules are, in order of increasing strength, (1) dispersion forces (sometimes called van der Waals forces), (2) dipole–dipole interactions, and (3) hydrogen bonding. Dispersion forces are caused by alternating transient charge separations on the surfaces of molecules. They occur among all kinds of molecules, polar or nonpolar, causing them to "stick together" on contact—somewhat like the Styrofoam peanuts used as packing material, which cling to one another by static electricity. Dipole–dipole interactions result when molecules that have permanent bond dipoles line up so that the negative end of one molecule's dipole is opposite the positive end of another's, and vice versa. Hydrogen bonding is a special kind of dipole–dipole interaction that involves the attraction of a highly polarized hydrogen atom for an electron-donating atom (such as oxygen or nitrogen) on another molecule.

Among compounds of similar molecular shape and molecular weight, those capable of forming hydrogen bonds tend to have the highest boiling points, followed by compounds with polar groups capable of dipole–dipole interactions. Hydrogen bonding makes an important contribution to the boiling point only for organic compounds that contain O—H and N—H bonds, with OH groups forming the strongest hydrogen bonds. Compounds with no polar groups, whose molecules are held together only by dispersion forces, tend to have the lowest boiling points.

You will distill your liquid to remove impurities that might affect your results. You can estimate its boiling point during the distillation if it is reasonably pure; otherwise, you may need to redistill it or carry out an alternative boiling-point determination.

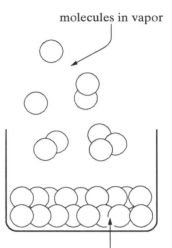

molecules in vapor

molecules in liquid

Figure 1 Boiling of a liquid

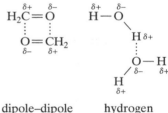

dipole–dipole interaction (formaldehyde)

hydrogen bonding (water)

Molecular Structure and Density

The density of an organic compound depends, to some extent, on the mass/volume ratio of its constituent atoms. Atoms that have a high nuclear mass confined within a small atomic volume, such as those in the top right-hand corner of the periodic table, have a high atomic density (atomic mass/atomic volume), so compounds whose molecules contain such atoms tend to have comparatively high densities. Among the atoms encountered in this experiment (other than hydrogen), oxygen has the highest atomic density, followed by chlorine, nitrogen, and carbon.

Atomic density of some "heavy" atoms, relative to carbon = 1.00

O: 1.50   Cl: 1.35   N: 1.26

The density of an organic liquid will thus depend, in part, on the number and kind of these "heavy" atoms it contains and on the fraction of its molecular weight they contribute. For example, chlorobenzene (C_6H_5Cl) has a higher density than phenol (C_6H_5OH), even though chlorine has a lower atomic density than oxygen, because the chlorine atom makes a greater contribution to the molecular weight of chlorobenzene than the oxygen atom of phenol makes to its molecular weight.

You will determine the density of your liquid by weighing a precisely measured volume of the liquid.

Molecular Structure and Solubility

Key Concept: "Like dissolves like."
Polar compounds tend to dissolve in polar solvents and nonpolar compounds in nonpolar solvents.

A compound will generally be soluble in a given solvent if the forces holding its own molecules together are similar to the forces holding the molecules of the solvent together *or* if the compound can form hydrogen bonds with the solvent. Thus, hexane dissolves readily in benzene because both compounds are hydrocarbons whose molecules are held together by dispersion forces. Ethanol dissolves in water because both compounds contain OH groups capable of forming hydrogen bonds. Formaldehyde, although it cannot form hydrogen bonds among its own molecules, can hydrogen bond to solvents that contain OH groups, so it is also soluble in water.

$CH_3CH_2CH_2CH_2CH_2CH_3$

hexane

benzene

Hydrogen bonding interactions

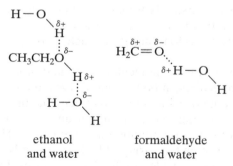

ethanol
and water

formaldehyde
and water

Keep in mind that "solubility" is a relative term; there are varying degrees of solubility. Terms commonly used to indicate the extent to which one compound dissolves in another are, in order of decreasing solubility: miscible (∞), very soluble (v), soluble (s), sparingly soluble (δ), and insoluble (i).

You will measure the solubility of your liquid by shaking it with water in a small test tube. For the purposes of this experiment, a liquid will be classified as *miscible* if it dissolves in an equal volume of water and as *soluble* if 0.20 mL of the liquid dissolves in about 6 mL of water. If the liquid dissolves, the resulting solution should be clear, like water itself. If it doesn't dissolve, you should observe a second liquid layer, cloudiness, or liquid droplets (not air bubbles) in the water. Because low-boiling liquids may evaporate rapidly, you should keep the test tube stoppered while you make your observations.

Classification Tests for Functional Groups

Chemists have developed a number of simple chemical tests that are positive only for compounds that have certain kinds of functional groups. A litmus test, for example, can be used to detect acidic and basic functional groups. When dissolved in water, carboxylic acids turn blue litmus paper red and amines turn red litmus paper blue. Compounds that are easily oxidized react with a solution of chromium (VI) oxide in sulfuric acid, commonly referred to as "chromic acid." Primary and secondary alcohols react within 2–3 seconds to form an opaque blue-green suspension. Aldehydes give the same result, but they usually take 10 seconds or more to react. Aldehydes and ketones both react with 2,4-dinitrophenylhydrazine (DNPH) reagent to yield yellow or orange precipitates. Alkenes and aldehydes react with dilute aqueous potassium permanganate ($KMnO_4$) to form a brown precipitate as the purple color of the permanganate disappears. Alkyl halides give a green flame in the Beilstein test, which involves heating a copper wire moistened with the unknown in a burner flame.

A Greener Way: In place of chromic acid, ceric ammonium nitrate can be used to test for alcohols and Schiff's reagent for aldehydes. Your instructor will provide directions for conducting such tests. Alternatively, alcohols and aldehydes can be identified from their infrared spectra alone.

The test results and their interpretations are summarized as follows.

- Blue litmus paper turns red $\Rightarrow$ carboxylic acid
- Red litmus paper turns blue $\Rightarrow$ amine
- Chromic acid forms blue-green suspension in 2–3 seconds $\Rightarrow$ 1° or 2° alcohol
- Chromic acid forms blue-green suspension in 10 seconds or more $\Rightarrow$ aldehyde
- DNPH yields orange or yellow precipitate $\Rightarrow$ aldehyde or ketone
- $KMnO_4$ yields brown precipitate $\Rightarrow$ alkene or aldehyde
- Burner flame turns green $\Rightarrow$ alkyl halide

Conflicting or ambiguous results may be produced with some tests because of impurities in the unknown or because the tests themselves may be open to misinterpretation. For example, an aldehyde often contains traces of the corresponding carboxylic acid as an impurity, leading to a false-positive litmus test; and alcohols may contain impurities that react with potassum permanganate. In such cases, it may be necessary to repeat a test or redistill the unknown. For additional information and general equations for the reactions involved, see the "Classification Tests" section of "Qualitative Organic Analysis."

Although only very small quantities of chromic acid and potassium permanganate are used for their tests, both can harm the environment and must be disposed of properly. The chromium (VI) in chromic acid is classified by the Environmental Protection Agency (EPA) as a priority pollutant; it is very toxic and can cause cancer and genetic mutation in some organisms. Potassium permanganate is harmful to aquatic life. 2-4-Dinitrophenylhydrazine isn't a common environmental contaminant, so there is little information on its

141

effects on the environment, but similar hydrazines are very toxic so DNPH and its derivatives should not be released into the environment.

Infrared Spectra

Each kind of functional group is associated with one or more characteristic IR bands that can reveal its presence. A carboxyl group (COOH), for example, contains $C=O$, $C-O$, and $O-H$ bonds, all of which give rise to strong IR absorption bands. Infrared bands that may help you classify your unknown include the two-pronged $N-H$ band characteristic of a primary amine, which is around $3400-3300$ cm^{-1}; the broad $O-H$ band centered near 3300 cm^{-1} for an alcohol and 3000 cm^{-1} for a carboxylic acid; the strong $C=O$ band near 1700 cm^{-1}; and the $C-Cl$ band between 600 and 800 cm^{-1}. Alkenes are often characterized by vinylic $C-H$ bending vibrations in the $650-1000$ cm^{-1} region and by a $C=C$ band (sometimes weak or absent) near 1650 cm^{-1}. See the "Interpretation of Infrared Spectra" section in OP-39 for more detailed information about these and other IR bands associated with common functional groups.

DIRECTIONS

Your instructor will give you the names that were on the labels described in the Scenario. The experiment can be performed in teams of as many as seven students, each team working with a full set of unknown liquids. Alternatively, students can work individually and report their data to the instructor for posting.

Safety Notes

> All of the unknown liquids are flammable, and some of them are caustic or have hazardous vapors. Avoid contact with the liquids, do not breathe their vapors, and keep them away from flames and hot surfaces. 2,4-Dinitrophenylhydrazine is harmful if absorbed through the skin and it will dye your hands yellow. Avoid contact with the DNPH reagent.
> The chromic acid reagent is corrosive, very toxic, and carcinogenic. Wear gloves and avoid contact with the reagent.

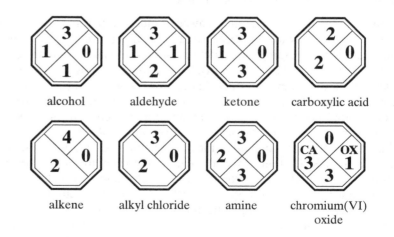

alcohol   aldehyde   ketone   carboxylic acid

alkene   alkyl chloride   amine   chromium(VI) oxide

A. *Physical Properties of the Unknowns*

Obtain a sample of an unknown organic liquid from your instructor and record its identification number in your laboratory notebook. Purify the liquid by simple distillation [OP-30] using a compact distillation apparatus. If the liquid boils over a range of 2°C or less, you can use the median distillation temperature as its boiling point [OP-34a]. Otherwise, determine the boiling point of the purified liquid by the semimicro method described in OP-34b.

Accurately measure [OP-5] 1.00 mL of the purified unknown liquid into a tared vial. Stopper the vial and weigh it to the nearest milligram on an accurate balance; then calculate the density of your unknown.

Measure 0.20 mL of the liquid into a 13 × 100-mm test tube. Add 0.20 mL of water, stopper the tube, and shake it vigorously for a few seconds. If two liquid layers separate on standing, or if the mixture is cloudy or contains undissolved droplets, add another 6 mL of water and shake it again. If the unknown dissolves, save the solution for the litmus test in part **B**.

B. *Chemical Tests*

Except for the litmus test, which is performed using an aqueous solution of the unknown, all of the following tests should be carried out with the undiluted unknown liquid. Keep a careful record of your observations in your lab notebook.

Litmus Test. If the unknown is miscible or soluble in water, test its aqueous solution (you can use the solution from the solubility test) with red and blue litmus paper.

DNPH Test. Add 1 drop of the unknown to 1 mL of the DNPH reagent in a small test tube. Stopper and shake the test tube, then let the mixture stand for 15 minutes.

Chromic Acid Test. Dissolve 1 drop of the unknown in 1 mL of reagent-grade acetone in a test tube. Add 1 drop of the chromic acid reagent, shake the mixture, and observe it for at least one minute, noting the time required for any positive test.

Potassium Permanganate Test. Dissolve 1 drop of the unknown in 2 mL of 95% ethanol, and add 10 drops of 0.1 *M* potassium permanganate while shaking.

Beilstein's Test. Make a small loop in the end of a copper wire. Heat the loop to redness in a burner flame. (Do this under a hood or in an area well away from the unknowns or other flammable liquids.) Let it cool, dip the loop into a small amount of your unknown liquid, and then hold it in the lower outside part of the flame.

C. *Infrared Spectrum*

Record an IR spectrum [OP-39] of your unknown, using the neat (undiluted) liquid, or obtain the spectrum from your instructor.

Decide which functional group is present in your compound. If your instructor assigns Exercise 1, report the chemical family, boiling point, density, and solubility of your unknown to your coworkers and obtain the same information from them. If your instructor assigns Exercise 2, make copies of

Take Care! Avoid contact with the unknown and do not breathe its vapors.

Stop and Think: Compare your boiling point with those obtained by other students in your group. What can you say about your compound's intermolecular forces?

Stop and Think: Compare your density with those obtained by other students in your group. Does your compound contain any "heavy" atoms such as O, N, or Cl?

Stop and Think: If your compound forms a separate layer, does it float or sink? Why?

Take Care! Wear gloves and avoid contact with the chromic acid reagent.

Waste Disposal: Put wastes for the DNPH, chromic acid, and potassium permanganate tests in designated waste containers.

Stop and Think: At this point, which functional group do you think your compound contains?

Waste Disposal: Place the rest of your unknown in a waste container designated by your instructor.

your IR spectrum for yourself and your coworkers, and obtain copies of their spectra in return. (Alternatively, you can examine their spectra and record the relevant spectral data.) Turn in your original spectrum to your instructor.

Exercises

1. Using the data provided by your coworkers, group together compounds with similar physical properties. You should have one set of groups arranged according to boiling point, another set according to density, and a third set according to water solubility. Then explain the differences between the groups, specifying the type of intermolecular force involved, where appropriate. For example, you can group together compounds that have boiling points within 10°C of one another, list the groups in order of boiling points (highest to lowest), and explain why the compounds in the first group have higher boiling points than those in the second group, etc.

2. Compare the IR spectra obtained by the members of your team, looking for significant similarities and differences. For each spectrum, point out any IR bands that are associated with a functional group and indicate what kind of chemical bond is responsible for each of these IR bands.

3. Describe and explain the possible effect on your results of the following experimental errors or variations. (a) You mistook a 2-mL pipet for a 1-mL pipet and used it for your density determination. (b) Most of your liquid (an aldehyde) distilled around 75°C, but some of it distilled above 100°C, and you used all of the distillate for the subsequent tests. (c) You cleaned a test tube for the DNPH test by rinsing it with acetone, but you failed to dry it completely.

4. Describe some green features of this experiment, and any that aren't so green.

5. Construct a flow diagram that could be used to efficiently classify compounds from the families in Table 1, using classification tests from this experiment. There should be two branches for each classification test: one leading to compounds that give a positive result and the other leading to compounds that give a negative result.

6. Draw structures for all possible constitutional isomers of your unknown that have the same functional group (if there are any), and give their systematic names.

7. Compound X, which has the molecular formula $C_4H_6O_2$, is believed to be one of the compounds in the margin. (a) Name the chemical family or families to which each compound belongs. (b) Draw a flow chart diagramming a procedure that could be used to determine the identity of compound X, using chemical tests described in this experiment or in "Qualitative Organic Analysis."

1. $CH_3CH_2\overset{O}{\underset{\|}{C}}-\overset{O}{\underset{\|}{CH}}$

2. $CH_3\overset{O}{\underset{\|}{C}}-\overset{O}{\underset{\|}{C}}CH_3$

3. $CH_2=CH\overset{OH}{\underset{|}{CH}}-\overset{O}{\underset{\|}{CH}}$

4. $CH_3CH=CH\overset{O}{\underset{\|}{C}}-OH$

Other Things You Can Do

(Starred items require your instructor's permission.)

*1. If the reagents are available, you can use additional or alternative classification tests, such as Tollens' test (C-23) for aldehydes, sodium iodide in acetone (C-22) for alkyl chlorides, and bromine (C-7) for alkenes.

*2. Carry out the "Who Else Has My Compound?" minilab and find out who else has the same compound that you have.

3. Write a research paper about how hydrogen bonding can be detected and studied by spectrometric methods, using sources listed in the Bibliography or elsewhere.

Thin-Layer Chromatographic Analysis of Drug Components

EXPERIMENT

Qualitative Analysis. Thin-Layer Chromatography.

Operations

OP-6   Making Transfers
OP-22   Thin-Layer Chromatography

Before You Begin

Read the experiment, read or review OP-22 carefully, and write a brief experimental plan.

Scenario

A patient who swallowed a large number of drug tablets was just wheeled into the emergency room of a local health clinic suffering from a drug overdose. The bottle that contained the drug is missing, but some unused tablets were left on a counter in the bathroom. The patient's spouse recalls seeing a bottle of an over-the-counter analgesic drug in the medicine chest but doesn't remember what was on the label. Because there was no nearby toxicology lab in operation, the clinic rushed the tablets to your supervisor for analysis. Your assignment is to determine the identity of the drug so that emergency room physicians can apply the appropriate treatment.

Applying Scientific Methodology

This experiment requires you to identify the components of an analgesic drug tablet and then identify the tablet as one of the commercial drug preparations listed in Table 1. You will probably not be able to formulate a meaningful hypothesis until after you examine your thin-layer chromatography (TLC) plate under ultraviolet light. Then you can use another visualization method to provide evidence that may either support or disprove your tentative hypothesis.

Table 1 Composition of some analgesic drug preparations (in milligrams per tablet)

Drug name	Aspirin	Acetaminophen	Ibuprofen	Salicylamide	Caffeine
Advil			200		
Anacin	400				32
Aspirin*	325				
B.C. Tablets	325			95	16
Excedrin	250	250			65
Tylenol		325			

*5-grain tablet (1 grain = 64.8 mg)

From *Operational Organic Chemistry: A Problem Solving Approach to the Laboratory*, Fourth Edition, John W. Lehman. Copyright © 2009 by Pearson Education. Published by Prentice Hall. All rights reserved.

Drugstore Chemicals

Druggists were once called *chemists*, and in Great Britain, they still are. Whenever you go to the drugstore to buy a bottle of aspirin, Advil, Tylenol, or another of the dozens of different analgesic (painkilling) drug preparations that are available, you are purchasing an organic chemical or a mixture of several chemicals. That shouldn't be surprising, since all matter—including you—is composed of chemicals, where *chemical* is just another name for a substance (element or compound). Most of the materials we encounter in daily life are complex mixtures of substances, whereas many drugs are reasonably pure substances or mixtures of only a few substances. In fact, most analgesic drug preparations contain only one or two active ingredients: aspirin, acetaminophen, ibuprofen, or some combination of these. The most popular combination is aspirin and acetaminophen, but salicylamide (a chemical relative of aspirin) is combined with aspirin in a few drug preparations. Caffeine is sometimes added to an analgesic preparation for its stimulant effect and because it interacts with some analgesics to enhance their pain-relieving effects.

Key Concept: All matter is made up of chemicals.

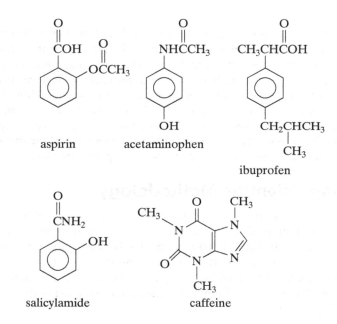

A small amount of starch is generally added as a binder to hold the tablets together. Table 1 shows the composition (not including the starch) of some representative analgesic preparations.

Most analgesic drugs do more than just kill pain. Aspirin, acetaminophen, and ibuprofen are also antipyretics, meaning that they reduce fever. Aspirin and ibuprofen are both nonsteroidal anti-inflammatory drugs (NSAIDs), meaning that they help reduce swelling and other symptoms of inflammation. Aspirin, in fact, has such a surprisingly wide range of benefits that it can be regarded as a true "wonder drug." In recent years, it has been shown to reduce the incidence of heart disease, strokes, and certain cancers. It may also help prevent cataracts, reduce the occurrence of

Certain steroids, such as cortisone, are also used as anti-inflammatory drugs.

gallstones, and improve brain function in people who have suffered small strokes.

Although aspirin (acetylsalicylic acid) is the most widely used drug in the world, nobody understood how it worked until 1971, when the British pharmacologist John Vane showed that aspirin blocks the overproduction of natural biological substances called *prostaglandins* by deactivating a key enzyme required to manufacture them, prostaglandin synthase. Although prostaglandins are essential biological regulators, an oversupply of certain prostaglandins can promote the formation of blood clots that lead to heart attacks or strokes, while others trigger pain, fever, and inflammation. Recent studies have shown that prostaglandin synthase functions like a factory assembly line; raw materials enter one end of a channel that passes through the enzyme and leave the other end as fully assembled prostaglandin molecules. Aspirin molecules sabotage this process by blocking the channel, thereby preventing raw materials from getting by. Aspirin appears to inhibit cancers of the digestive system by a different mechanism, stimulating the production of cancer-fighting substances used by the body's immune system.

If the other analgesics can't compete with aspirin in versatility, they do have certain advantages over aspirin. Aspirin tends to promote bleeding, especially in the stomach, and it has been implicated in Reye's syndrome, a rare but often fatal disease that affects children. Acetaminophen is just as effective as aspirin at reducing pain—and it has fewer side effects at normal dosages—but overdoses of acetaminophen can cause serious liver damage, especially when taken in conjunction with alcohol. Ibuprofen is a powerful analgesic with about the same painkilling effect as aspirin at one-third the dosage. It is especially effective in treating arthritis and menstrual cramps, but it can cause problems in people with asthma, ulcers, high blood pressure, and kidney, liver, or heart disease.

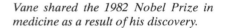

Vane shared the 1982 Nobel Prize in medicine as a result of his discovery.

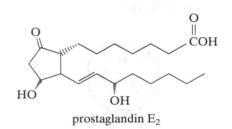

prostaglandin E_2

Understanding the Experiment

In this experiment, you will use TLC to identify the components of the analgesic drug that your instructor assigns. Your drug may contain from one to three of these substances: acetaminophen, aspirin, caffeine, ibuprofen, and salicylamide.

You will prepare a solution of the drug by dissolving part of a tablet in 1:1 ethanol/dichloromethane, then spotting a TLC plate with this solution along with standard solutions of all of the active substances the drug tablet is likely to contain. The TLC plate can be developed with a solvent mixture such as ethyl acetate/acetic acid (200:1). By using two different methods to visualize the spots and comparing the R_f values of your unknown's spot(s) with those of the standards, you should be able to match each unknown spot with the spot of a known substance. Then you can refer to Table 1 to find out which commercial drug preparation contains the components you have identified.

Caffeine is only a minor component of a drug such as Excedrin, so its spot might be too faint to see clearly in some cases. In this event, you can usually arrive at the correct commercial drug by comparing the remaining components with those in the table. For example, Excedrin is the only drug listed that contains both aspirin and acetaminophen, and B.C. is the only one that contains salicylamide.

Of the chemicals used in this experiment, ethyl acetate is considered a hazardous substance, but its toxicity is relatively low and it doesn't bioaccumulate. The EPA classifies dichloromethane as a priority pollutant and has established a maximum contaminant level (MCL) of 5 parts per billion (ppb) for its concentration in drinking water. Neither of these substances should be released into the environment and should therefore be disposed of appropriately.

DIRECTIONS

Dichloromethane may be harmful if ingested, inhaled, or absorbed through the skin. There is a possibility that prolonged inhalation of dichloromethane may cause cancer. Minimize contact with the ethanol/dichloromethane solvent mixture and the standard solutions, and do not breathe their vapors.

Ethyl acetate is flammable and may be harmful if inhaled or absorbed through the skin. Avoid contact with the developing solvent and do not breathe its vapors.

Safety Notes

dichloromethane

Take Care! Avoid contact with the developing solvent and do not breathe its vapors.

Take Care! Avoid contact with the solvent mixture and do not breathe its vapors.

You can use a scrap piece of TLC plate to practice your spotting technique.

Waste Disposal: Place the developing solvent and unused solutions in designated waste containers.

Take Care! Do not look directly at the light source.

Preparation of the Developing Chamber. Unless your instructor indicates otherwise, use ethyl acetate/acetic acid (200:1) as the developing solvent. Fill an appropriate developing chamber (see OP-22) containing a paper wick to a depth of about 5 mm with the solvent. Cover it with plastic wrap or an appropriate lid, and slosh the solvent up the sides of the chamber to moisten the wick. Then set it aside under a hood while you prepare the TLC plate.

Preparation and Development of the TLC Plate. Read or review OP-22 carefully before you begin. Obtain a quarter tablet of the unknown analgesic drug and grind it to a powder with a flat-bottomed stirring rod, or place it between weighing papers and crush it to a powder with the bottom of a beaker. (If the tablet is coated, remove as much of the coating as you can before grinding.) Transfer the powder to a test tube and add 2.5 mL of 1:1 ethanol/dichloromethane. Thoroughly mix the solid in the solvent with a stirring rod to dissolve as much of the solid as possible. Use a filter-tip pipet to transfer [OP-6] the solution to a small vial, leaving the solid behind, and cap the vial.

Spot the unknown solution and all of the standard solutions provided on a silica gel TLC plate [OP-22] that has a fluorescent indicator, and label the spots. To avoid cross-contamination, use a different micropipet (or other spotting device) for each solution. If possible, the unknown should be spotted in different concentrations (from 1–3 applications) at two or more locations along the starting line. Develop the plate *under the hood* in the developing chamber you prepared. Don't disturb the developing chamber until the plate is developed. Be sure to mark the solvent front before the plate dries.

Visualization and Analysis. When the TLC plate is dry, observe the spots under short-wavelength (254 nm) ultraviolet light, outline them with a pencil, and mark the center of greatest intensity for each spot. Then visualize the spots by using iodine vapor or another visualizing reagent selected by your instructor. Calculate the R_f value of each spot, and identify the active ingredients of your unknown by comparison with the R_f values and visualization results for the known spots. Use Table 1 to determine the commercial name of your analgesic drug preparation. (Your tablet may be a generic equivalent of one of those listed.) Turn in your TLC plate with your report.

Observe and Note: Record in your lab notebook any characteristics of the spots that might help you identify them.

Waste Disposal: Place the solution of your unknown in an appropriate waste container.

Exercises

1. Suppose you carry out a TLC separation of acetaminophen and phenacetin on silica gel using a nonpolar developing solvent. Which should have the higher R_f value, and why?

2. Assuming that the drug components whose spots you identified dissolved completely when you stirred the tablet with 1:1 ethanol/dichloromethane, what was the solid that remained behind?

3. Describe and explain the possible effect on your results of the following experimental errors. (a) You allowed your chromatogram to develop too long, and you couldn't find the solvent front. (b) The lab assistant who prepared the developing solvent mistakenly used aqueous ammonia in place of acetic acid. (c) You used an open-ended melting-point capillary rather than a Drummond Microcap to apply the spots. (d) You marked the starting line with a ballpoint pen.

4. Describe some green features of this experiment, and any that aren't so green.

5. Describe one or more simple chemical tests that would distinguish acetaminophen from ibuprofen.

6. Another analgesic drug, Aleve, contains the sodium salt of naproxen as its active ingredient. (a) Look up the systematic name and structure of naproxen. (b) The physiological effects of naproxen are very similar to those of a drug component you studied in this experiment. Which one do you think it is, and why?

Other Things You Can Do

(Starred items require your instructor's permission.)

*1. Carry out the TLC analysis of felt-tip pen inks as described in the "Identification of an Unknown Felt-Tip Pen Ink by TLC" minilab.

*2. Carry out a quantitative or qualitative analysis of an analgesic drug mixture using high-performance liquid chromatography. See OP-38 and *J. Chem. Educ.* **1983**, *60*, pages 163 and 1000.

3. Write a research paper that describes some of the methods used to test for drugs and their metabolites in body fluids, starting with sources listed in the Bibliography. For example, you might tell how the presence of proscribed drugs can be detected in professional athletes or racehorses.

Separation of an Alkane Clathrate

Reactions of Alkanes. Clathrates. Infrared Spectrometry.

Operations

OP-10   Mixing
OP-16   Vacuum Filtration
OP-18   Extraction
OP-19   Evaporation
OP-25   Drying Liquids
OP-26   Washing and Drying Solids
OP-39   Infrared Spectrometry

Before You Begin

1. Read the experiment, read or review the operations as necessary, and write a brief experimental plan.
2. Calculate the mass of 10.0 mmol of hexadecane and the mass of 200 mmol of urea.
3. Use Equation 1 to help you estimate the theoretical yield of a hexadecane–urea clathrate.

Scenario

The Petit Prix Racing Group mixes its own auto racing fuel by combining clean-burning high-octane hydrocarbons such as 2,2,4-trimethylpentane (also called "isooctane") with other racing-fuel components such as methanol and nitromethane. An inexperienced employee, Rusty Tappet, was mixing the last batch of fuel when he accidentally added a can of diesel fuel intended for his employer's Mercedes-Benz to a barrel containing 2,2,4-trimethylpentane and methanol. Diesel fuel isn't clean burning and its hydrocarbons have extremely low octane numbers, so the contents of the barrel are now worthless as racing fuel. The racing group can't afford to waste expensive fuel, so it has contacted your supervisor to see whether your institute's consulting chemists can develop a method for separating the diesel fuel components from the mixture.

Urea molecules are known to form tunnel-like channels in certain solvents by hydrogen bonding with one another. Your supervisor thinks it should be possible to trap the straight-chain hydrocarbon molecules of diesel fuel inside such channels while excluding the bulkier 2,2,4-trimethylpentane molecules. You will test this hypothesis by combining a mixture of hexadecane (a major component of diesel fuel), 2,2,4-trimethylpentane, and methanol with urea to see if the urea will remove the hexadecane from the mixture. If it does, you are to determine the ratio of urea molecules to hexadecane molecules (the host/guest ratio) in the urea–hexadecane

From *Operational Organic Chemistry: A Problem Solving Approach to the Laboratory*, Fourth Edition, John W. Lehman. Copyright © 2009 by Pearson Education. Published by Prentice Hall. All rights reserved.

complex so that the minimum amount of urea needed for the separation can be estimated.

$$CH_3CH_2CH_2CH_2CH_2CH_2CH_2CH_2CH_2CH_2CH_2CH_2CH_2CH_2CH_2CH_3$$
hexadecane

$$\begin{array}{c} CH_3 \\ | \\ CH_3CCH_2CHCH_3 \\ | \quad\quad | \\ CH_3 \quad CH_3 \end{array}$$
2,2,4-trimethylpentane

Applying Scientific Methodology

There are two problems in this experiment, so you should formulate two working hypotheses after reading it. You will test one hypothesis by recording the infrared (IR) spectrum of any hydrocarbon that you isolate, and the other by calculating the host/guest ratio from the masses of urea and hexadecane in the complex.

Clathrates and Fuel Quality

In 1976, scientists drilling into the ocean floor near Central America brought up a core sample that contained softball-sized lumps of an icelike solid that sizzled like frying bacon and emitted liquid droplets and a flammable gas, leaving nothing behind but a puddle of water. The icelike solid was a gas hydrate that consisted mostly of single methane molecules trapped inside a cage made up of water molecules. Methane hydrate (Figure 1) consists of 20 water molecules arranged to form a nearly spherical 12-sided geometric figure (a dodecahedron), with a free methane molecule floating inside its watery cage.

Recent discoveries of enormous methane hydrate deposits beneath ocean floors have attracted attention because they represent both an opportunity and a potential threat. It is estimated that about 20 quadrillion (2×10^{16}) cubic meters of methane are trapped in such hydrates; this is energetically equivalent to approximately twice the Earth's coal, oil, and gas reserves combined. If the oceans could somehow be "mined" for methane hydrates, they would represent a huge energy reserve. But methane is also an efficient greenhouse gas, and some scientists believe that global warming or geological disturbances could cause hydrate deposits to decompose, releasing huge quantities of methane into the atmosphere. This could cause a runaway global-warming effect that would drastically alter the Earth's weather patterns.

Methane hydrate is an example of a *clathrate*, a complex formed when molecules of one compound are enclosed in cavities within other molecules or crystal lattices. In 1941, a German chemist discovered that urea combines with straight-chain alkanes that have seven or more carbon atoms to form a crystalline clathrate, but it doesn't combine with most branched alkanes. This property of urea provides a means of improving fuel quality. The quality of a motor fuel is measured by its octane number, which compares its antiknock properties to those of the highly branched alkane 2,2,4-trimethylpentane (octane number = 100). Long straight-chain alkanes

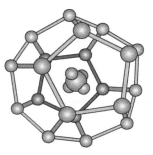

Figure 1 Structure of a methane hydrate (circles represent water molecules)

$$\begin{array}{c} O \\ \| \\ H_2NCNH_2 \end{array}$$
urea

have very low octane numbers, so treating a gasoline-grade petroleum fraction with urea to remove such alkanes increases its octane number. Jet fuels are also improved by treatment with urea, because straight-chain alkanes tend to freeze sooner than branched alkanes of the same carbon number. Unless the straight-chain alkanes are removed, wax crystals could form in jet fuel at high altitudes, where the temperature can drop to −60°C.

The quality of a diesel fuel, on the other hand, is measured by its *cetane number*, which compares its ignition properties to those of hexadecane (also called cetane). The cetane number of a fuel is established by matching the fuel's performance to that of a mixture containing hexadecane, whose cetane number is 100, and 2,2,4,4,6,8,8-heptamethylnonane (HMN), whose cetane number is 15. For example, a diesel fuel that has the same ignition properties as a mixture containing 40% hexadecane and 60% HMN is assigned a cetane number of 49, as shown by the following calculation.

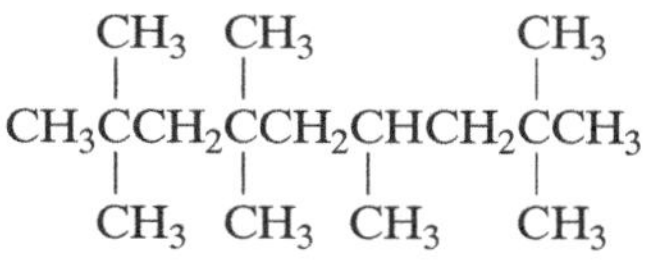

HMN

$$100(0.40) + 15(0.60) = 49$$

Most diesel fuels marketed in the United States have cetane numbers between 40 and 65.

Understanding the Experiment

In this experiment, you will combine a solution of urea in methanol with a mixture of hexadecane and 2,2,4-trimethylpentane to see if the urea will form a clathrate with one of the alkanes. Many organic compounds—not just alkanes—combine with urea in solution to form crystalline clathrates in which six or more molecules of urea, the *host* compound, form a tubular channel large enough to hold a molecule of the *guest* compound. The channel's walls are formed by interpenetrating spirals of urea molecules that are hydrogen bonded to one another. The guest molecule isn't covalently bonded to the host molecules but is held inside the channel by relatively weak intermolecular forces. Whether a compound qualifies as a guest depends mainly on the size and shape of its molecules. The diameter of the channel formed by urea molecules is about 0.52 nm, which is large enough to hold straight-chain molecules but not most branched molecules. In addition to alkanes, guest compounds can include straight-chain primary alcohols, carboxylic acids, and esters that have terminal functional groups and at least seven carbon atoms.

The longer the guest molecule, the more urea molecules are needed to surround it. The number of urea molecules per guest molecule (the host/guest ratio) can be estimated using Equation **1**, where n is the number of carbon atoms in the guest molecule.

$$\text{host/guest ratio for urea clathrates} \cong 1.5 + 0.65n \qquad \textbf{(1)}$$

For example, about eight urea molecules are sufficient to confine a molecule of decane, which has 10 carbon atoms.

$$1.5 + (0.65 \times 10) = 8.0$$

Adding water to a urea clathrate causes it to decompose, releasing the guest compound, which can then be extracted from the reaction mixture with dichloromethane.

A Greener Way: *To avoid releasing dichloromethane into the environment, evaporate the dichloromethane under vacuum and collect the solvent in a cold trap (see OP-15).*

If urea forms a clathrate with a hydrocarbon in your mixture of hexadecane and 2,2,4-trimethylpentane, you should be able to identify the guest alkane from its IR spectrum (see Figure 2). *Stretching* vibrations of C—H bonds in methyl (CH_3) groups produce IR bands around 2960 cm^{-1} and 2870 cm^{-1}. The corresponding methylene (CH_2) bands are near 2925 cm^{-1} and 2850 cm^{-1}. Often the methyl and methylene bands overlap so that only two or three peaks are observed. Methyl groups also show asymmetrical and symmetrical *bending* vibrations near 1450 cm^{-1} and 1375 cm^{-1}. If there are two or three methyl groups on the same carbon atom, the symmetrical bending band is split into two or more closely spaced peaks near 1385 cm^{-1} and 1370 cm^{-1}. Bending vibrations of methylene groups may also give rise to bands near 1465 cm^{-1}, between 1350 cm^{-1} and 1150 cm^{-1} (often weak), and around 720 cm^{-1}. The intensity of the 720 cm^{-1} band (called the methylene rocking band) increases in proportion to the number of adjacent methylene groups, so a band in this region is characteristic of unbranched long-chain alkanes. The terms used to describe certain bond vibrations—scissoring,

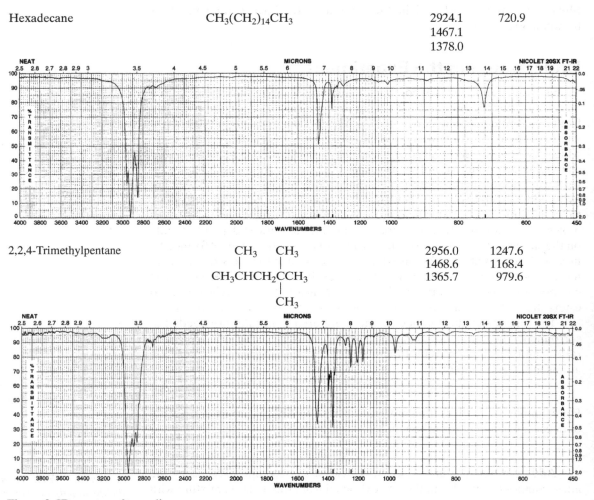

Hexadecane $CH_3(CH_2)_{14}CH_3$ 2924.1   720.9
                                                             1467.1
                                                             1378.0

2,2,4-Trimethylpentane   2956.0   1247.6
                      1468.6   1168.4
                      1365.7   979.6

Figure 2 IR spectra of two alkanes

Note: The exact wave numbers of certain absorption bands (designated by "tick" markers at the base of the spectrum) will be listed above most of the IR spectra reproduced in this book.

twisting, wagging, rocking—remind us that molecules are dynamic entities and not the static particles that molecular models might suggest (see Figure G16, OP-39). For more information about bond vibrations and IR spectra, see "Interpretation of Infrared Spectra" in OP-39.

From the masses of the clathrate and the recovered guest alkane, you can determine the host/guest ratio—the number of urea molecules that surround each alkane molecule. For this result to be valid, material losses must be kept to a minimum, and the masses of the clathrate and recovered guest alkane must be measured as accurately as possible. It is also essential that the clathrate be completely dry and the alkane entirely free of solvent.

Urea is a relatively harmless natural substance that is produced in the urine of animals and is used as an ice-melting material for roads, but it decomposes to yield ammonia, which is toxic to some aquatic life. The hydrocarbons are components of diesel fuel, which is toxic to aquatic and plant species but tends to biodegrade with time. The EPA classifies dichloromethane as a priority pollutant and has established an MCL of 5 ppb for its concentration in drinking water.

Key Concept: *Molecules are in constant translational, rotational, and vibrational motion.*

Reactions and Properties

Table 1 Physical properties

	mol wt	bp	mp	d	n_D^{20}
hexadecane	226.4	287	18	0.773	1.4345
2,2,4-trimethylpentane	114.2	99	−107	0.692	1.3915
methanol	32.0	65	−98	0.792	1.3292
urea	60.06		135	1.323	

Note: bp and mp are in °C; density is in g/mL; refractive index is for 20°C.

$$C_nH_{(2n+2)} + x\ H_2NCNH_2 \longrightarrow C_nH_{(2n+2)} \cdot [H_2NCNH_2]_x$$

alkane   urea   alkane-urea clathrate

DIRECTIONS

Hexadecane and 2,2,4-trimethylpentane are flammable; keep them away from flames and hot surfaces.
Methanol is flammable and harmful if ingested, inhaled, or absorbed through the skin. Avoid contact with the liquid and do not breathe its vapors.
Dichloromethane may be harmful if ingested, inhaled, or absorbed through the skin. There is a possibility that prolonged inhalation of dichloromethane may cause cancer. Minimize contact with the liquid and do not breathe its vapors.

Safety Notes

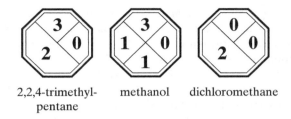

2,2,4-trimethyl-
pentane   methanol   dichloromethane

Take Care! Avoid contact with methanol and do not breathe its vapors.

Stop and Think: What do you think is in the solid?

Waste Disposal: Place the filtrate in an appropriate solvent recovery container.

Observe and Note: What happens as the clathrate dissolves?

Take Care! Avoid contact with dichloromethane and do not breathe its vapors.

Waste Disposal: Place the recovered dichloromethane in a designated solvent recovery container.

Reaction. Accurately weigh 10.0 mmol of hexadecane in a small beaker and add 5.0 mL of 2,2,4-trimethylpentane. In a 125-mL Erlenmeyer flask, combine 200 mmol of urea with 50 mL of methanol. Warm this mixture to 55–60°C, swirling or stirring magnetically [OP-10] until all of the urea has dissolved; don't heat the methanol to boiling. While the solution is still warm, add the mixture of alkanes, using a small amount of methanol for the transfer. Stir or swirl until a white solid begins to separate, set the solution aside, and let it cool slowly to 30°C or below. Then cool it in an ice/water bath for 10 minutes or more until crystallization is complete.

Separation. Collect the clathrate (the solid product) by vacuum filtration [OP-16] and wash it on the filter [OP-26a] with ice-cold methanol. Dry [OP-26b] the solid to constant mass at room temperature (heating will cause it to decompose). If the clathrate cannot be left overnight or longer to dry, it should be air-dried thoroughly on the filter and left to dry in a well-ventilated location, such as a hood. Weigh the dry product accurately.

Mix the clathrate with 25 mL of warm water in a small beaker and stir the mixture on a steam bath or in a boiling-water bath for several minutes until the crystals dissolve. Cool the mixture in an ice/water bath; the alkane may solidify on cooling. Transfer the mixture to a separatory funnel, using a small amount of dichloromethane for the transfer, and extract [OP-18] the guest alkane with two separate portions of dichloromethane. Dry [OP-25] the combined extracts over anhydrous sodium sulfate or magnesium sulfate. After removing the drying agent, evaporate [OP-18] the solvent *completely* using a cold trap. Weigh the guest alkane accurately.

Analysis. Record the infrared spectrum [OP-39] of the guest alkane and use it to identify the alkane. Calculate the percent recovery and the host/guest ratio from your experimental results. Turn in the IR spectrum and the alkane to your instructor.

Exercises

1. Estimate the host/guest ratio for hexadecane using Equation **1** and compare that value with your experimental value. Try to account for any significant differences.
2. Compare the IR spectrum of hexadecane with that of 2,2,4-trimethylpentane and point out some bands that might help you distinguish straight-chain alkanes from branched ones.
3. Describe and explain the possible effect on your results (including your host/guest ratio) of the following experimental errors. (a) The lab assistant accidentally put octane in the "isooctane" (2,2,4-trimethylpentane)

bottle. (b) The lab assistant put hexane in the hexadecane bottle. (c) You dried the clathrate in a 90°C oven. (d) The clathrate crystals weren't dry when you weighed them.

4. (a) Calculate the atom economy and estimate the reaction efficiency of your synthesis of the alkane clathrate. (b) Describe some green features of your synthesis, and any that aren't so green.

5. Rusty Tappet emptied a 5.0-gallon can of diesel fuel into a barrel containing 25 gallons of methanol and 2,2,4-trimethylpentane. Using your host/guest ratio, estimate the minimum mass of urea needed to remove the diesel fuel. You can approximate the composition of the diesel fuel by assuming that it is pure hexadecane.

6. Following the format in the "Planning an Experiment" appendix, construct a flow diagram for this experiment.

7. What is the cetane number of a fuel that has the same ignition properties as a mixture containing 20% hexadecane and 80% HMN? Would it make a good diesel fuel?

8. Thiourea (H_2NCSNH_2) forms tubular clathrates that are similar in structure to those formed by urea. Combining a mixture of hexadecane and 2,2,4-trimethylpentane with thiourea produces a crystalline solid that decomposes in water to yield 2,2,4-trimethylpentane, but no hexadecane. Propose an explanation for this result.

9. Outline a possible synthesis of 2,2,4,4,6,8,8-heptamethylnonane starting with isobutylene.

Other Things You Can Do

(Starred items require your instructor's permission.)

*1. Identify the guest alkane by measuring its refractive index [OP-35] instead of (or as well as) its IR spectrum.

*2. Recover the other alkane by adding a large amount of water to the filtrate and separating the alkane layer. After it has been dried with calcium chloride, the alkane can be characterized by obtaining its IR spectrum and refractive index.

3. Starting with sources listed in the Bibliography, write a research paper about the potential use of buckminsterfullerene to store hydrogen for fuel cells, and the feasibility of using hydrogen-based fuel cells to power vehicles.

Isomers and Isomerization Reactions

Reactions of Alkenes. Isomerization Reactions. Isomerism.

Operations

OP-10 Mixing
OP-16 Vacuum Filtration
OP-26 Washing and Drying Solids
OP-33 Melting Point

Before You Begin

1. Read the experiment, read or review the operations as necessary, and write an experimental plan.
2. Calculate the mass of 11.0 mmol of potassium cyanate and the theoretical yield of phenylurea.
3. Calculate the mass and volume of 4.00 mmol of dimethyl maleate, and the theoretical yield of dimethyl fumarate.

Scenario

A roving science historian, Dr. Perry Celsus, travels around the country delivering lectures on the history of chemistry at scientific meetings and educational institutions. Dr. Celsus would like to enliven his lectures by demonstrating some of the pivotal experiments in organic chemistry that led to major advances in the field. These experiments include:

- Friedrich Wöhler's isomerization of ammonium cyanate to urea
- The conversion of maleic acid to its geometric isomer, fumaric acid

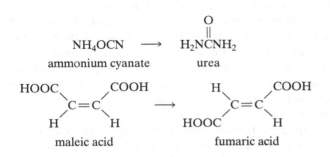

Pivotal experiments in organic chemistry

Wöhler's experiment helped demolish the vitalistic theory of organic chemistry, and the isomerization of maleic acid helped J. H. van't Hoff develop the concept of geometric (*cis–trans*) isomerism. These experiments aren't suitable for demonstrations, because of the time and conditions required, so Dr. Celsus has asked your institute for help in developing updated versions

From *Operational Organic Chemistry: A Problem Solving Approach to the Laboratory*, Fourth Edition, John W. Lehman. Copyright © 2009 by Pearson Education. Published by Prentice Hall. All rights reserved.

of the ammonium cyanate and fumaric acid experiments that still demonstrate the scientific principles involved. Your supervisor thinks it may be possible to reenact these nineteenth-century experiments in modern form by using phenylammonium cyanate in place of ammonium cyanate and dimethyl maleate in place of maleic acid. Your assignment is to find out whether these two substances do, in fact, yield constitutional and geometric isomers analogous to the ones in the original experiments.

Applying Scientific Methodology

Because you will be performing two separate experiments, you will need to develop two working hypotheses and then test them by measuring the melting points of your products.

Isomerism in the History of Chemistry

Early in the nineteenth century, most scientists believed that plants and animals possessed some "vital force" that made it possible for them to convert inorganic substances into organic compounds. Because this vital force was presumably absent in inanimate objects, it was assumed that organic compounds could not possibly be synthesized from inorganic substances in the laboratory. Vitalism received a serious blow in 1828, when Friedrich Wöhler mixed cyanic acid (HOCN) with ammonia, expecting to obtain ammonium cyanate, and came up instead with urea, a product of protein metabolism that is excreted in urine. This "lucky accident" was the first known synthesis of an organic compound from an inorganic one to take place outside a living organism. As Wöhler put it in a letter to another eminent chemist, J. J. Berzelius, "I can make urea without the aid of kidneys, either man or dog!" Wöhler's synthesis of urea suggested that there is no essential difference between inorganic and organic compounds, and it paved the way for the flowering of organic chemistry in the last half of the nineteenth century.

Ammonium cyanate and urea share the same molecular formula, CH_4N_2O, and are therefore *isomers*. At one time, scientists believed that no two compounds could be formed from the same set of atoms. There is, after all, only one kind of H_2SO_4 and one kind of NaCl. So when two independent investigators reported the same elemental composition for cyanic acid (HOCN) and fulminic acid (HONC), Berzelius thought one of them had made a mistake. After further investigation, he became convinced that a given set of atoms can indeed combine in different ways to form compounds that have different properties, and he coined the term *isomerism* to describe this phenomenon.

Isomers such as ammonium cyanate and urea, which differ in the way their atoms are attached to one another, are called *constitutional isomers* or *structural isomers*. Isomers that differ only in the way their atoms are arranged in space are called *stereoisomers*. *Geometric isomers*, also called *cis–trans* isomers, are stereoisomers that differ from one another because of restricted rotation about the bonds connecting two or more atoms. Maleic acid and fumaric acid are geometric isomers, because restricted rotation about their carbon–carbon double bonds prevents their interconversion under ordinary conditions. A geometric isomer that has certain groups other than hydrogen on the *same* side of the double bond is called a *cis* isomer, and one with those groups on *opposite* sides is a *trans* isomer. Maleic acid is thus *cis*-2-butenedioic acid and fumaric acid is *trans*-2-butenedioic acid.

Key Concept: *The properties of a substance arise from its chemical structure, not from its source.*

The term isomer *is derived from Greek words meaning "equal parts," referring to the fact that isomers have the same number and kind of atoms.*

Understanding the Experiment

Friedrich Wöhler prepared urea by several different methods. One method involved mixing ammonium chloride and silver cyanate and then evaporating the resulting ammonium cyanate solution to dryness. When heated, ammonium cyanate decomposes to ammonia and cyanic acid, which combine to form urea.

$$NH_4Cl + AgOCN \longrightarrow NH_4OCN + AgCl$$

ammonium
cyanate

$$NH_4OCN \xrightarrow{heat} NH_3 + HOC \equiv N \longrightarrow H_2N\overset{\overset{\textstyle O}{\|}}{C}NH_2$$

cyanic   urea
acid

You will attempt to isomerize the phenyl derivative of ammonium cyanate by a similar reaction. As shown in the "Reactions and Properties" section, aniline reacts with hydrochloric acid to form the organic salt phenylammonium chloride. By combining an aqueous solution of phenylammonium chloride with potassium cyanate, you can prepare a solution that contains phenylammonium cyanate. Then you will see whether heating this solution yields a different product. If it does, a melting-point determination should tell you whether you have synthesized phenylurea, a constitutional isomer of phenylammonium cyanate.

Sometimes, one of a pair of geometric isomers can be converted to the other under conditions that cause temporary cleavage of a pi bond. When maleic acid is heated with a trace of bromine in the presence of light, some of the bromine molecules break apart into bromine atoms. A bromine atom then adds to one end of the double bond of a maleic acid molecule, breaking the pi bond. This allows the molecule to rotate freely about the remaining sigma bond. If the bromine atom is ejected when the COOH groups are opposite one another, the pi bond is regenerated to yield a molecule of fumaric acid.

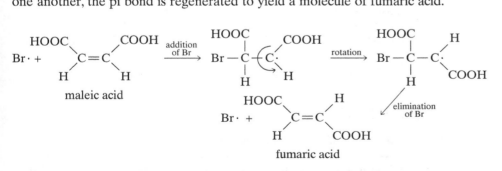

Mechanism of the isomerization of maleic acid

Maleic acid and fumaric acid are both solids, so this reaction must be run in solution, and the fumaric acid cannot be separated from the starting material by filtration. But dimethyl maleate (the methyl ester of maleic acid) is a liquid, and dimethyl fumarate is a solid, so if dimethyl maleate can be induced to isomerize to dimethyl fumarate, the liquid *cis* isomer should change to a solid *trans* isomer that can be separated by filtration. If molecular model sets are available, you can simulate the isomerization of dimethyl maleate after building a molecular model of it.

Aniline is highly toxic to aquatic life and is classified as a hazardous air pollutant, so it should not be released into the environment. Potassium cyanate is slightly toxic to fish but isn't considered a serious environmental contaminant. Bromine is toxic to marine organisms, but no water quality standards for bromine have been issued by the U.S. government.

Reactions and Properties

A PhNH$_2$ + HCl ⟶ PhNH$_3$Cl
aniline   phenylammonium
chloride

PhNH$_3$Cl + KOCN ⟶ PhNH$_3$OCN + KCl
phenylammonium
cyanate

$$\text{PhNH}_3\text{OCN} \longrightarrow \text{PhNHCNH}_2$$
phenylurea

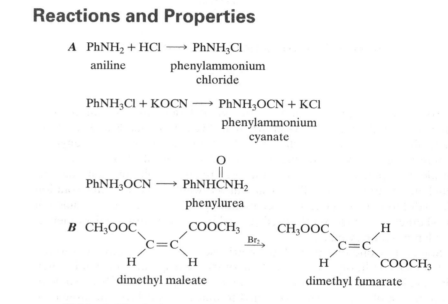

B dimethyl maleate   dimethyl fumarate

Table 1 Physical properties

	mol wt	mp	bp	*d*
aniline	93.1	−6	184	1.022
potassium cyanate	81.1	800d		
phenylurea	136.2	147	238	
dimethyl maleate	144.1	8	205	1.151
dimethyl fumarate	144.1	104	193	

Note: mp and bp are in °C; *d* is in g/mL; d = decomposes on melting.

DIRECTIONS

A. *Isomerization of Phenylammonium Cyanate*

Safety Notes

aniline

Aniline is poisonous and may be carcinogenic. It can cause serious injury or death if swallowed, inhaled, or absorbed through the skin. Wear protective gloves and dispense under a fume hood; avoid contact and do not breathe its vapors.

Under the hood, prepare a solution of phenylammonium chloride by combining 5.0 mL of 3 *M* hydrochloric acid with 5.0 mL of water in a 50-mL beaker and adding 1.0 mL (~11 mmol) of recently distilled aniline. Dissolve 11.0 mmol of potassium cyanate in 10 mL of water in another small beaker and mix this solution with the phenylammonium chloride solution to form phenylammonium cyanate. Stir [OP-10] for 2–3 minutes, then add 7.0 mL of water and heat the solution to 80°C; any solid should dissolve during this time. Let the solution cool slowly to room temperature while you proceed with part **B**, then cool it further in an ice/water bath. Collect any product by vacuum filtration [OP-16], wash it on the filter [OP-26a] with ice-cold water, and dry [OP-26b] it thoroughly. Weigh the dry product and measure its melting point [OP-33].

B. *Isomerization of Dimethyl Maleate*

Bromine is toxic and corrosive, and its vapors are very harmful. Dichloromethane may be harmful if ingested, inhaled, or absorbed through the skin. Avoid contact with the bromine/dichloromethane solution and do not breathe its vapors.

Measure 4.00 mmol of dimethyl maleate into a small test tube and mix in a drop of 1 *M* bromine in dichloromethane. Set the test tube in a small beaker that is half full of boiling water and place the beaker about 15 cm away from an unfrosted 75- or 100-watt lightbulb. Keep the water boiling for 10 minutes or more with the light switched on, then remove the test tube and cool it in ice water until crystallization is complete. Use a stirring rod to break up the product into small particles (be careful not to punch a hole through the test tube). Collect the product by vacuum filtration [OP-16], wash it on the filter [OP-26a] with a small amount of cold 95% ethanol, and dry it [OP-26b]. Measure the mass and melting point [OP-33] of the product.

If molecular-model kits are available, construct a molecular model of dimethyl maleate and show that it cannot be converted to dimethyl fumarate without breaking bonds. Using a model of Br$_2$, simulate the course of the reaction you carried out in this experiment, referring to the mechanism for the isomerization of maleic acid.

Take Care! Wear gloves, avoid contact with aniline, and do not breathe its vapors.

If the solution is dark colored, add a small amount of pelletized Norit, stir it for 2 minutes at 80°C, and filter it by gravity using a preheated funnel.

Observe and Note: What happened as the solution cooled?

Waste Disposal: Place the filtrate in a designated waste container.

Safety Notes

bromine

Take Care! Avoid contact with the bromine solution and do not breathe its vapors.

Waste Disposal: Unless your instructor directs otherwise, wash the filtrate down the drain.

Exercises

1. (a) Estimate the percentage of your dimethyl maleate that was converted to dimethyl fumarate. (b) Would it be possible to prepare dimethyl maleate in good yield from dimethyl fumarate (using bromine and light) under experimental conditions that permitted recovery of the dimethyl maleate? Why or why not?
2. Methylenemalonic acid, $CH_2 = C(COOH)_2$, is an isomer of maleic acid. (a) What kind of isomers are methylenemalonic acid and maleic acid: constitutional or geometric? (b) Would methylenemalonic acid yield a geometric isomer under the conditions of this experiment (part **B**)? If so, give the structure of the product; if not, explain why.
3. Describe and explain the possible effect on your results of the following experimental errors or variations. (a) Your instructor was out of

aniline, so *p*-toluidine (*p*-methylaniline) was substituted. (b) It was a dark and stormy day, and the lights were out in the laboratory (but the gas was on). (c) You misread the label on a bottle of dimethyl malonate and used it instead of dimethyl maleate.

4. (a) Calculate the atom economy and reaction efficiency of your synthesis of phenylurea. (b) Describe some green features of that synthesis, and any that aren't so green.

5. (a) Explain why dimethyl maleate has a higher boiling point than dimethyl fumarate. (b) Explain why dimethyl fumarate has a higher melting point than dimethyl maleate.

6. Propose a mechanism for the isomerization of phenylammonium cyanate to phenylurea.

Other Things You Can Do

(Starred items require your instructor's permission.)

*1. Investigate the structures and properties of isomers as described in the "Isomers and Molecular Structure" minilab.

*2. Make models for as many isomers that have the molecular formula C_3H_6O as you can, and identify any pairs of geometric isomers. You should also be able to construct models for pairs of molecules that, like your two hands, are nonsuperposable mirror images of each other. These are called mirror-image isomers, or enantiomers.

3. Starting with sources listed in the Bibliography, write a research paper about the manufacture of urea and its use in the production of such commercial products as urethane plastics, urea–formaldehyde resins, barbiturates, and jet fuel.

Structures and Properties
of Stereoisomers

Isomerization Reactions. Stereoisomerism. Infrared Spectrometry. Gas Chromatography.

Operations

OP-7   Heating
OP-10 Mixing
OP-18 Extraction
OP-19 Evaporation
OP-25 Drying Liquids
OP-34 Boiling Point
OP-35 Refractive Index
OP-36 Optical Rotation
OP-37 Gas Chromatography (optional)
OP-39 Infrared Spectrometry

Before You Begin

1. Read the experiment, read or review the operations as necessary, and write an experimental plan.
2. Before beginning this experiment, you should know how to draw stereochemical structural formulas, how to designate configurations at stereocenters, and how to classify stereoisomers as enantiomers and diastereomers. Review the sections of your lecture textbook on stereochemistry if you need help in any of these areas.

Scenario

The new-age herbalist Basil Wormwood explores the composition and uses of natural products from plants. For example, he isolates and analyzes essential oils from various plants using techniques he learned in his college organic chemistry course. While pursuing his studies, he observed several phenomena that puzzled him, so he has contacted the institute to see if its consulting chemists can explain them.

- While Basil was away, his assistant accidentally spilled some vinegar in a batch of peppermint oil. When he returned, he removed the vinegar by extraction, but the aroma of the oil had changed markedly.
- After isolating the major component of caraway oil (from caraway seeds) and the major component of spearmint oil (from spearmint leaves), Basil discovered that these substances, whose odors are very different, have virtually identical physical and chemical properties.
- When examined under a microscope, the tartaric acid crystals he received from a supplier looked different from the crystals of natural tartaric acid that he had used before.

caraway plant   spearmint plant

From *Operational Organic Chemistry: A Problem Solving Approach to the Laboratory*, Fourth Edition, John W. Lehman. Copyright © 2009 by Pearson Education. Published by Prentice Hall. All rights reserved.

Your assignment, then, is threefold:

- To find out what happens when menthone from peppermint oil is treated with acid
- To find out how the major components of caraway and spearmint oils differ (if they do)
- To find out whether the tartaric acid provided is natural L-(+)-tartaric acid or an "unnatural" tartaric acid stereoisomer

Applying Scientific Methodology

You should find enough information in the experiment to formulate working hypotheses for the first two problems. You will need to gather some experimental evidence before you can develop a meaningful hypothesis for the third problem.

Alice Through the Looking Glass: Dissymmetry and Life

A proposed expedition to Barnard's star was described in New Scientist **1974**, *63*, 522.

In Lewis Carroll's *Through the Looking Glass*, Alice—contemplating the world she views in her mirror—wonders aloud to her cat whether looking-glass milk would be good to drink. Such an inquiry might seem naive, even to a cat. If you hold a glass of milk in front of a mirror, the milk and its reflection look exactly alike, so why should "mirror-image milk" be any different from the milk we ordinarily drink? You may be surprised to learn that mirror-image milk wouldn't be very good to drink; it would be quite indigestible, and its taste would be bitter and unpleasant. To understand why, let's take an imaginary trip to a looking-glass world.

Imagine yourself onboard the spaceship *Icarus*, bound for the planetary system of Barnard's star. Arriving on the surface of its earthlike third planet, called *Arret* by the inhabitants, your landing party is invited to a feast by some friendly Arretians. You are served their standard banquet fare: roast *krop*, overdone *iloc'corb*, crusty *yawarac* seed rolls, and an aromatic *t'nim* tea. You had been looking forward to a change from the monotonous space diet, but you soon lose your appetite. Most of the food tastes flat or bitter, the seeds on the roll have a minty flavor, and the tea smells like caraway seeds! After politely declining a second helping of *krop*, you return to your shuttlecraft with the rest of the landing party. Before long, you and the rest of the crew are suffering from indigestion, which causes a serious breach in interplanetary relations.

Key Concept: A chiral compound is one that exhibits "handedness." Like a glove, a chiral molecule lacks a plane of symmetry and cannot be superposed on its mirror image.

Earthly organisms are composed mostly of *chiral* molecules, such as the D-monosaccharides in complex carbohydrates and the L-amino acids that make up proteins and enzymes. It is conceivable that somewhere in the universe there exists a mirror-image planet, otherwise similar to Earth, where carbohydrates are composed of L-monosaccharides and proteins of D-amino acids, and the configurations of other chiral compounds are reversed as well. On such a planet, many foods would taste different from their earthly counterparts, and we earthlings would find them indigestible. The chiral compounds on that planet would still be optically active; that is, they would rotate plane-polarized light, as ours do. But they would rotate the light in the opposite direction.

One of the great, unsolved mysteries of life concerns the origin of optically active compounds. Living systems are composed of dissymmetric (chiral) molecules, and molecular dissymmetry is necessary for life as we know it, but how did such dissymmetry come about? Was there some "molecular Adam," a single dissymmetric molecule that gave rise to all molecular dissymmetry on Earth? Or is there some kind of fundamental dissymmetry in the universe that gives rise to molecular dissymmetry? The discovery (in 1997) that some amino acids in an Australian meteorite contain an excess of the L-enantiomer appears to support the hypothesis that some natural process favors one enantiomer over another. For example, circularly polarized light from the stars might selectively alter molecules of one enantiomer in a racemic mixture, producing a small excess of the other enantiomer; under certain conditions, that small enantiomeric excess could be amplified to produce a much larger excess. But convincing proof of such a hypothesis is hard to come by, and the answer may never be fully known.

The basic molecules of life—proteins, carbohydrates, nucleic acids, and enzymes—are chiral, and they are built up of smaller units that are also chiral. A strand of deoxyribonucleic acid (DNA), for example, consists of two long chains, each having a backbone of linked D-2-deoxyribose molecules twisted into a right-handed double helix (see Figure 1). DNA and ribonucleic acid (RNA) regulate the synthesis of proteins from L-amino acids, which are combined in specific sequences inside cellular structures called ribosomes. Some of these proteins make up the enzymes that assist in the digestion of carbohydrates, yielding D-glucose to be used by the body for fuel. If life somewhere else in the universe were based on a mirror-image DNA made up of L-2-deoxyribose and twisted into a left-handed double helix, then protein synthesis could utilize only D-amino acids and the corresponding enzymes could digest only L-carbohydrates. In other words, if the configuration of one link in the chain of life (as we know it) is reversed, all the rest must be reversed as well.

If we could, by some magical contrivance, pass through the looking glass as Alice did, all of the people, plants, and other organic matter in the looking-glass world would presumably be constructed of these mirror-image molecules. We probably could not survive for long in such a world (though Alice did, in Lewis Carroll's imagination), because digestion, metabolism, reproduction, and other life processes that involve chiral molecules would be inhibited or prevented entirely.

Circularly polarized light has two perpendicular planes of polarization.

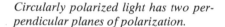

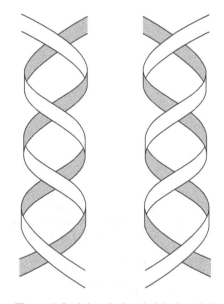

Figure 1 Left-handed and right-handed double helixes

Read the article in J. Chem. Educ. 2002, 79, 569 for a discussion of Alice's diet in a mirror-image world.

Understanding the Experiment

Peppermint oil is a mixture of several optically active components, including (−)-menthol and the corresponding ketone, (−)-menthone. When an aldehyde or ketone has a stereocenter next to its carbonyl group, the configuration at the stereocenter may change under acidic or basic conditions, as illustrated by the following mechanism for the isomerization of (R)-3-methyl-2-butanone to its enantiomer.

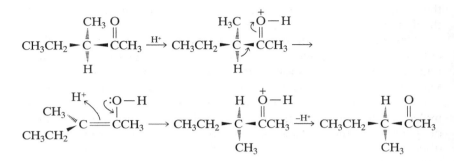

Mechanism of the acid-catalyzed isomerization of (R)-3-methyl-2-butanone to (S)-3-methyl-2-butanone

In part **A** of this experiment, you will see whether treating (−)-menthone from peppermint oil with acid can bring about a similar isomerization. Note that (−)-menthone has two stereocenters (see "Reactions and Properties"), so changing the configuration at just one of them will yield a diastereomer of (−)-menthone, not its enantiomer. If the configuration at the carbon next to the carbonyl group changes, the product will be (+)-isomenthone. You will analyze the product by polarimetry or gas chromatography to determine whether or not isomerization has taken place and, if so, what percentage of the (−)-menthone has isomerized.

Enantiomers have identical physical properties except the direction in which they rotate plane-polarized light. If one enantiomer of menthone, for example, rotates polarized light in a clockwise (+) direction, the other enantiomer will rotate polarized light by the same amount in a counter-clockwise (−) direction. Enantiomers may also differ in some chemical properties, such as the way in which they interact with chiral substrates. These differences are particularly important in biochemical systems. For example, some kinds of olfactory receptors are apparently chiral, so the (+)- and (−)-enantiomers of a compound, when they interact with such receptors, may smell different. Carvone, a ketone found in the essential oils of both caraway seeds and the spearmint plant, is an example of a chiral compound whose enantiomers have markedly different odors.

In part **B** of this experiment, you and your coworkers will compare some physical properties and the infrared (IR) spectra of the carvones from both spearmint and caraway oils, as well as their odors. You will also measure their optical rotations to find out whether the carvones are the same or different and, if they are different, which enantiomer is present in each oil.

Tartaric acid can be produced from potassium hydrogen tartrate (cream of tartar), a by-product of winemaking. This natural tartaric acid is the L-(+)-form illustrated here. Because tartaric acid has two stereocenters, several other stereoisomers are possible. In part **C** of this experiment, you will measure the optical rotation of the tartaric acid provided to determine whether it is the natural form and, if it is not, what its structure is.

If molecular models are available, you can use them in part **D** of this experiment to explore the stereochemical relationships among these compounds.

Experiments that proved the odor differences between carvone enantiomers are described in Science **1971**, *172*, 1043.

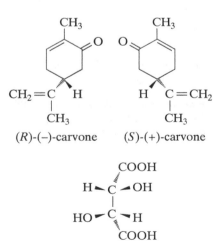

(R)-(−)-carvone   (S)-(+)-carvone

L-(+)-tartaric acid

This is a relatively green experiment, because the acetic acid and diethyl ether used in part **A** aren't considered to be serious environmental contaminants, and parts **B** through **D** require no reagents and no solvents other than water and ethanol. Acetic acid occurs naturally in living organisms and readily breaks down to carbon dioxide and water in the environment. Diethyl ether isn't considered toxic to aquatic organisms and doesn't persist for long in either air or water.

Reactions and Properties

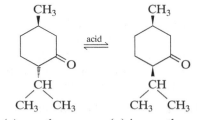

(−)-menthone   (+)-isomenthone

Table 1 Physical properties

	mol wt	d	[α]
(R)-carvone	150.2	0.96	−62°
(S)-carvone	150.2	0.96	+62°
(−)-menthone	154.2	0.895	−30°
(+)-isomenthone	154.2	0.900	+92°

Note: Densities are in g/mL.

DIRECTIONS

Acetic acid causes chemical burns that can seriously damage skin and eyes; its vapors are highly irritating to the eyes and respiratory tract. Wear gloves and dispense under a hood; avoid contact and do not breathe its vapors. Diethyl ether is extremely flammable and may be harmful if inhaled. Do not breathe its vapors; keep it away from flames and hot surfaces.

A. *Isomerization of (–)-Menthone*
Under the hood, mix 1.0 mL of (−)-menthone with 5.0 mL of glacial acetic acid and 5.0 mL of 1 *M* HCl in a small round-bottom flask. Add a stir bar and turn on the magnetic stirrer [OP-10], if you have them; otherwise, use boiling chips. Heat the mixture under reflux [OP-7] for 30 minutes, then let it cool to room temperature and transfer it to a beaker. Add enough 4 *M* NaOH to neutralize the solution to red litmus. Cool it to room temperature and extract [OP-18] it with two portions of solvent-grade diethyl ether. Dry [OP-25] the combined ether extracts with anhydrous sodium sulfate or magnesium sulfate, and evaporate [OP-19] the ether. Using 0.5–1.0 g of solute per 10 mL of solution (measure accurately), prepare a solution of the product in absolute ethanol, then measure its optical rotation [OP-34]

Safety Notes

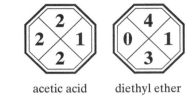

acetic acid   diethyl ether

Take Care! Wear gloves; do not breathe the vapors of acetic acid.

Take Care! Keep the ether away from flames and hot surfaces.

Waste Disposal: Place any recovered ether in a designated solvent recovery container.

Waste Disposal: Unless your instructor indicates otherwise, put the polarimetry solution in a designated waste container.

and the optical rotation of a blank. If your instructor requests, measure the optical rotation of the (−)-menthone as well. Alternatively, you can obtain gas chromatograms [OP-37] of (−)-menthone and of your product on an open tubular 10% Carbowax column or another column specified by your instructor. Calculate the percentage of (−)-menthone that isomerized to (+)-isomenthone.

B. *Properties of Carvones from Spearmint and Caraway Oils*

Work in pairs, with each student using about 1 mL of carvone from a different oil. Compare the odors of the two carvones. Measure the boiling point [OP-34] and refractive index [OP-35] of your carvone. Record its IR spectrum [OP-39] or obtain the spectrum from your instructor. Weigh the remainder of your carvone accurately and use a 10-mL volumetric flask to prepare a solution of it in 95% ethanol. Measure the optical rotation [OP-36] of this solution and of a blank in 1-dm polarimeter cells, and calculate its specific rotation. Based on your results, decide which carvone enantiomer you have. Compare the properties you measured with those of your lab partner's carvone, and compare their IR spectra as well.

Waste Disposal: Place the polarimetry solution and any unused carvone in designated waste containers.

C. *Identification of a Tartaric Acid Stereoisomer*

Using about 1.0 g of solute per 10 mL of solution (measure accurately), prepare an aqueous solution of the tartaric acid stereoisomer provided. Next, measure its optical rotation [OP-36] and the optical rotation of a blank in 1-dm polarimeter cells, and calculate its specific rotation. Using the fact that the specific rotation of L-(+)-tartaric acid is +12°, predict the specific rotations of the other stereoisomers and deduce the structure of your tartaric acid (assume that it isn't a racemic mixture).

Waste Disposal: Unless your instructor indicates otherwise, wash the tartaric acid solution down the drain.

D. *Stereochemical Exercises with Molecular Models*

Construct a molecular model of (−)-menthone in its most stable chair conformation. Show how it can be converted to a model of (+)-isomenthone by interchanging atoms or groups. Use the models to confirm that the two compounds are diastereomers, not enantiomers, and decide which one is more stable. Determine the configuration (*R* or *S*) at each stereocenter of each isomer.

Construct a molecular model of your carvone and compare it with your lab partner's molecular model to confirm that the two models represent enantiomers. Determine the configuration at the stereocenter of your model.

Construct a molecular model of your tartaric acid stereoisomer and determine the configuration at each stereocenter. Provide stereochemical drawings that represent the structures of all the models you constructed, giving the configurations at their stereocenters.

Exercises

1. Explain any similarities or differences in the properties of the carvone enantiomers and interpret your IR spectrum as completely as you can.
2. (a) Draw chair-form structures for the most stable conformations of (−)-menthone and (+)-isomenthone, and decide which diastereomer should be more stable. (b) Is the composition of your isomerization mixture consistent with this conclusion? Explain.

3. (a) Calculate the atom economy of the reaction in part **A**. (b) Describe some green features of this experiment, and any that aren't so green.

4. Describe and explain the possible effect on your results of the following experimental errors or variations. (a) In part **A**, you misread the label on a bottle of (−)-menthol and used it instead of (−)-menthone. (b) In part **B**, you mixed your carvone with an equal amount of your partner's carvone before measuring the optical rotation. (c) Your tartaric acid was the (−)-stereoisomer but in measuring its optical rotation, you read the scale when the analyzer was rotated 180° from the correct setting.

5. (a) Propose a mechanism for the isomerization of (−)-menthone to (+)-isomenthone in the presence of acid. (b) Explain why the acid-catalyzed isomerization of (−)-menthone doesn't yield its enantiomer, (+)-menthone.

6. A synthetic form of tartaric acid has a specific rotation of 0°, but its melting point is very different from that of *meso*-tartaric acid, which is also optically inactive. Explain, using stereochemical drawings.

7. The steroid cholic acid is said to have 2048 possible stereoisomers. Indicate each stereogenic carbon atom on the cholic acid molecule with an asterisk, and perform a calculation to verify this isomer number.

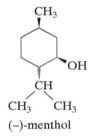

(−)-menthol

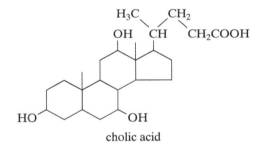

cholic acid

Other Things You Can Do

(Starred items require your instructor's permission.)

*1. You can isolate your carvone enantiomer for part **B** from spearmint or caraway oil by column chromatography. Following the procedure in OP-21 for slurry packing, pack a 25-mL buret with silica gel, using high-boiling petroleum ether. Introduce about 2 g of the essential oil onto the top of the column and elute it with the following solvents, in order: 25 mL of high-boiling petroleum ether; 50 mL of 10% dichloromethane/petroleum ether; 25 mL of 20% dichloromethane/petroleum ether; and 125 mL of 50% dichloromethane/petroleum ether. Put the first 100 mL of eluate in a designated solvent recovery container and collect the rest in 25-mL fraction collectors. Evaporate the fractions and measure the refractive indexes of the residues. Use the purest carvone fractions ($n_D \cong 1.499$ at 20°C) in part **B**.

2. Based on the article in *J. Chem. Educ.* **2002**, *79*, 569 and sources listed in the Bibliography, write a research paper about the origin and consequences of optical activity.

3. Starting with sources listed in the Bibliography, write a research paper about chiral drugs, describing differences in the physiological properties of enantiomers of the same drugs.

Bridgehead Reactivity in an S_N1 Solvolysis Reaction

Reactions of Alkyl Halides. Nucleophilic Substitution. Carbocations. Reaction Kinetics.

Operations

OP-5 Measuring Volume
OP-7 Heating
OP-10 Mixing

Before You Begin

Read the experiment, read or review the operations, and write a brief experimental plan.

Scenario

Bridgehead Meds, Inc., is a small pharmaceutical company seeking to develop new drugs, and more economical routes to existing drugs, based on the adamantane ring system. One such drug, amantadine, is an antiviral agent that is effective against rubella (German measles) and some influenza viruses.

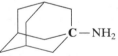

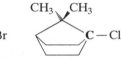

amantadine	1-bromoadamantane	apocamphyl chloride

C = bridgehead carbon

A possible route to such compounds might involve nucleophilic substitution reactions of 1-bromoadamantane, but similar cage compounds that have a halogen atom at the *bridgehead* (the point at which fused rings are joined), such as apocamphyl chloride, are quite resistant to such reactions. Bridgehead Meds has commissioned your institute to study the reactivity of 1-bromoadamantane (1) to determine whether it will undergo nucleophilic substitution reactions with hydroxylic solvents and, if so, (2) to see how its reactivity compares with that of a comparable open-chain tertiary halide, 2-bromo-2-methylpropane (*t*-butyl bromide). To compare the reactivities of these compounds quantitatively, you will need to measure the rate constants for their reactions.

From *Operational Organic Chemistry: A Problem Solving Approach to the Laboratory*, Fourth Edition, John W. Lehman. Copyright © 2009 by Pearson Education. Published by Prentice Hall. All rights reserved.

Applying Scientific Methodology

After reading the experiment, you should be able to formulate working hypotheses based on each of the problems implied in the Scenario. You will need to complete the rate measurements to obtain a quantitative result relating to the second problem, but you should be able to predict which tertiary halide should react faster before you begin.

A Gem Among Molecules

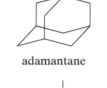

adamantane

structure of
diamond lattice

*You can read the paper by Bartlett and Knox in J. Amer. Chem. Soc. **1939**, 61, 3184.*

Adamantane, whose name is derived from a Greek word for diamond, is the simplest member of a series of hydrocarbons called *diamondoids*, whose molecules can be regarded as fragments of a tetrahedral diamond lattice. Molecular models of this elegantly symmetrical molecule reveal that it consists of four interlocking chair-form cyclohexane rings, arranged somewhat like the four planes of a tetrahedron. A space-filling model is nearly spherical, and this molecular shape results in a particularly stable crystal lattice that is responsible for adamantane's unusually high melting point of 268°C.

Like the spherical "soccer ball" structure of buckminsterfullerene (an unusual allotrope of carbon), the extraordinary structure of adamantane is intriguing to chemists because adamantyl systems have properties that make them almost ideal for the study of certain chemical phenomena. The rigid adamantane skeleton results in a system of known geometry with unstrained, tetrahedral bond angles; the cyclohexane rings that make up the adamantane molecule come together at four points, forming a bridgehead at each junction; and the cage-like structure prevents certain kinds of interactions and reaction mechanisms, thereby simplifying the analysis of reaction parameters.

In 1939, P. D. Bartlett and L. H. Knox discovered that another bridged compound, apocamphyl chloride, is surprisingly inert to reagents that usually bring about nucleophilic substitution reactions. For a nucleophile to attack from the back side of its bridgehead carbon, as required for an S_N2 reaction, the nucleophile would have to somehow get inside a cage-like molecule of apocamphyl chloride, which is highly unlikely. In an S_N1 reaction, the leaving group must leave, forming an intermediate carbocation, before the nucleophile attacks. Carbocations prefer a planar geometry, as illustrated below for the *t*-butyl carbocation—the intermediate in the S_N1 reactions of 2-bromo-2-methylpropane. But attaining a planar geometry at the bridgehead carbon is impossible in the rigid apocamphyl system.

Unlike the highly strained cage of apocamphyl chloride, a molecule of 1-bromoadamantane has normal tetrahedral bond angles with no bond-angle strain. In a 1-adamantyl carbocation, the bridgehead carbon can flatten out a bit to attain a bond angle of 113°, which is somewhere between the tetrahedral angle of the adamantane ring and the 120° angle of the *t*-butyl carbocation.

t-butyl carbocation   1-adamantyl carbocation

Key Concept: The more stable a reactive intermediate is, the faster it will form.

In an S_N1 reaction, a more stable carbocation forms faster than one that is less stable. Therefore, any factor that decreases the stability of a carbocation

176

tends to decrease the reactivity of the substrate from which the carbocation forms. You will be testing this principle as you compare the reactivities of 1-bromoadamantane and 2-bromo-2-methylpropane.

Understanding the Experiment

When Bartlett and Knox showed that bridgehead compounds such as apocamphyl chloride are quite unreactive with nucleophiles, they suggested that studies of bridgehead reactivity might yield valuable information about reaction mechanisms and the geometry of transition states. That suggestion was taken up by numerous investigators; particularly fruitful results have been obtained in the study of *solvolysis reactions* — nucleophilic substitution reactions in which the solvent acts as the nucleophile. In this experiment, you will measure the first-order rate constants for the solvolysis reactions of 1-bromoadamantane and 2-bromo-2-methylpropane with an ethanol–water mixed solvent.

The solvolysis of 2-bromo-2-methylpropane and similar halides by hydroxylic solvents, such as water and ethanol, is believed to proceed by an S_N1 mechanism involving the formation of a carbocation intermediate.

1. $t\text{-BuBr} \longrightarrow t\text{-Bu}^+ + \text{Br}^-$ (slow)

2. $t\text{-Bu}^+ + \text{SOH} \longrightarrow t\text{-Bu}\overset{\text{H}}{\underset{\oplus}{\text{OS}}}$ (fast)

(SOH = hydroxylic solvent)

3. $t\text{-Bu}\overset{\text{H}}{\underset{\oplus}{\text{OS}}} + \text{Base:} \longrightarrow t\text{-BuOS} + \text{Base:H}^+$ (fast)

t-Butyl bromide solvolysis mechanism

Dissociation of the alkyl bromide is the rate-determining step, so the reaction is first order with the rate equation:

$$\frac{-d[\text{RBr}]}{dt} = k[\text{RBr}]$$

Although the solvent doesn't appear in the rate equation, it can affect the reaction rate by assisting in the formation of the carbocation. Some solvent molecules may help push the leaving group off from the rear (except for most bridgehead compounds), whereas others pull it off from the front. Thus, the rate of an S_N1 solvolysis reaction should depend on both the polarity of the solvent and the stability of the carbocation formed in the first step; the more polar the solvent and the more stable the carbocation, the faster the reaction.

The rate constant for a first-order reaction can be calculated from the following integrated rate law, where c_0 is the initial concentration of the substrate and c is its concentration at time t:

$$\ln \frac{c}{c_0} = -kt \tag{1}$$

Role of solvent in displacement reactions

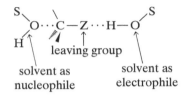

solvent as nucleophile   solvent as electrophile

A solvolysis reaction of an alkyl bromide with a hydroxylic solvent (SOH, where S = H or R) will produce hydrogen bromide according to the general equation:

$$R-Br + SOH \longrightarrow R-OS + HBr$$

Therefore, the concentration (c) in Equation **1** can be evaluated indirectly by measuring the amount of HBr that forms during the reaction. You will do this by adding measured portions of a KOH solution from a buret and recording the time it takes for the HBr evolved to neutralize the added KOH, as shown by the color change of an indicator. At any given time during the reaction, the concentration of the alkyl bromide (c) will equal its initial concentration (c_o) minus the concentration of the HBr that has formed by then (c_{HBr}). The concentration of HBr is proportional to the volume of KOH needed to neutralize it (V), and the initial concentration of the alkyl bromide is proportional to the total volume of KOH solution needed to neutralize all of the HBr produced (V_∞). So we can derive an expression for the concentration factor (c/c_o) from Equation **1** in terms of the volume of KOH solution added:

$$\frac{c}{c_o} = \frac{(c_o - c_{HBr})}{c_o} = 1 - \frac{c_{HBr}}{c_o} = 1 - \frac{V}{V_\infty}$$

The solvolysis of 1-bromoadamantane will be studied in 40% (by volume) aqueous ethanol, in which both water and ethanol act as nucleophiles. Because the reaction of 2-bromo-2-methylpropane in 40% ethanol is difficult to measure accurately, its solvolysis reaction will be conducted in 80% ethanol instead. To make a meaningful comparison between the two reactions, you will have to estimate the rate constant for 2-bromo-2-methylpropane in 40% ethanol using Equation **2** (the Winstein–Grunwald equation), which relates the rate of a solvolysis reaction to the ionizing power of the solvent.

$$\ln\frac{k}{k_o} = mY \tag{2}$$

In this equation, k_o is the rate constant for a reaction in the reference solvent, 80% ethanol, and k is the rate constant in the actual reaction solvent (40% ethanol in this experiment) at the same temperature. Y is a measure of the reaction solvent's ionizing power, and m measures the sensitivity of the substrate to changes in ionizing power. The value of m for 2-bromo-2-methylpropane is 0.94, and the value of Y for 40% ethanol is 2.20.

For each kinetic run, you will prepare the appropriate reaction solvent by combining 95% ethanol and water in such proportions that the solvent will be 40% or 80% aqueous ethanol after you have added the alkyl bromide. It is important to measure the solvents accurately, because an error in solvent composition can markedly affect the solvolysis rate. You will then add some bromthymol blue indicator and the alkyl bromide to the reaction solvent, followed by a measured portion of potassium hydroxide in the appropriate solvent. The indicator should turn blue as each portion of KOH solution is added, changing to green when enough HBr is produced by the solvolysis reaction to neutralize the added KOH. As the solution becomes more acidic, its color fades to yellow. Each portion of KOH solution will consume the HBr produced by the reaction of approximately 5%

of the alkyl halide; to obtain sufficient data for the rate calculations, you should continue the run until the reaction is at least 50% complete, which requires 10 portions or more of the KOH solution. After the last portion of KOH has been added, you will heat the reaction flask gently—to bring the reaction to completion—and then titrate the solution with more KOH to determine V_∞.

This is a relatively green experiment because the only solvents are water and ethanol, other chemicals are used in very small quantities, and none of the products should be significant environmental contaminants. Although brominated alkanes are usually somewhat toxic, no information about the environmental effects of 2-bromo-2-methylpropane or 1-bromo-adamantane is available.

Reactions and Properties

$RBr + H_2O \longrightarrow ROH + HBr$ *and*

$RBr + CH_3CH_2OH \longrightarrow ROCH_2CH_3 + HBr$

(R = 1-adamantyl or *t*-butyl)

$HBr + KOH \longrightarrow H_2O + KBr$

Table 1 Physical properties

	mol wt	mp	bp	d
1-bromoadamantane	215.1	118		
2-bromo-2-methylpropane	137.0	−16	73	1.221

Note: mp and bp are in °C; density is in g/mL.

DIRECTIONS

The alkyl halides must be protected from moisture; be sure that your glassware is clean and dry. With your instructor's permission, work in pairs, with one student recording the times and the other adding the KOH solution.

Safety Notes

2-Bromo-2-methylpropane is harmful if inhaled or absorbed through the skin, and it may be carcinogenic. Avoid contact and do not breathe its vapors.

A. Solvolysis of 1-Bromoadamantane in 40% Ethanol

Preparation of Solutions. Prepare an indicator blank by measuring 25 mL of a pH 6.9 buffer into a 50-mL Erlenmeyer flask and adding 4 drops of bromthymol blue indicator solution (the blank should be green). Set this flask aside while you prepare the reaction mixture.

Measuring [OP-5] as accurately as possible, combine 10.0 mL of 95% ethanol and 14.5 mL of distilled water in a 50-mL Erlenmeyer flask. Add

Take Care! Be sure to use the right KOH solution.

Observe and Note: Take note of the color changes throughout the kinetic runs and try to explain them.

The 1-bromoadamantane solution can be prepared by dissolving 0.11 g of 1-bromoadamantane in 5.0 mL of absolute ethanol and then shared among up to five students.

You don't have to add exactly 0.50 mL of the KOH solution each time, but you must record the exact buret reading after each addition.

The color change will be easier to see if you set the flasks on a sheet of white paper.

Observe and Note: Does the time between color changes increase, decrease, or stay the same as the reaction proceeds?

Waste Disposal: Unless your instructor directs otherwise, wash the reaction mixtures and unused KOH solutions down the drain.

Take Care! Be sure to use the right KOH solution.

4 drops of bromthymol blue solution and swirl to mix. Clamp this reaction flask to a ring stand and lower it into a water bath containing room-temperature (20–25°C) water. The water temperature should remain nearly constant throughout a kinetic run. Adjust the water level so that the bath is about two-thirds full, and measure the water temperature. Now half-fill a clean, dry 25-mL buret with 0.0050 M KOH in 40% ethanol and record the initial buret reading accurately. Obtain a timer or a watch that measures seconds, if you don't already have one.

Kinetic Run. If you have a magnetic stirrer, drop in a stir bar and begin stirring [OP-10] the reaction mixture; otherwise, swirl the flask after each addition and at intervals between additions. Add 0.50 mL of a *freshly prepared* 0.10 M solution of 1-bromoadamantane in absolute ethanol to the reaction flask and *immediately* record the time of addition to the nearest second (or start the timer). Without delay, add about 0.50 mL of the KOH/40%-ethanol solution to the reaction mixture and record the buret reading. (If the solution doesn't turn blue, add more KOH until it does, and then record the buret reading.) Place the indicator blank near the reaction mixture and record the time (to the nearest second) when the solution changes to the same shade of green as the blank. Within a minute of the color change, add another 0.50-mL portion of the KOH solution, and record the time when the solution again turns from blue to green. Repeat the addition of 0.50-mL portions of KOH, recording the buret reading and the time of the color change after each addition, until at least 10 portions have been added.

Determination of V_∞. After the last color change, seal the flask with a square of Parafilm and heat [OP-7] the reaction mixture in a 60°C water bath for 30 minutes (alternatively, let it stand overnight or longer at room temperature). Cool the solution to room temperature and then titrate it with the 0.0050 M KOH solution to the green end point. If the green color fades to yellow after standing a few minutes, heat the flask in the water bath for about 10 minutes longer. After cooling, again titrate the solution to the green end point. Subtract your initial buret reading (recorded before you started the kinetic run) from the final reading to get V_∞. For each run, compute the time (t) of each color change in seconds, measured from the time of addition of the alkyl bromide ($t = 0$). Calculate $\ln(1 - V/V_\infty)$ for each t value, where V is the total volume of KOH that has been added up to that time. Using good graph paper, plot $\ln(1 - V/V_\infty)$ versus t and determine the value of k (in s^{-1}) for the alkyl bromide from the slope of the line. (Alternatively, you may use a calculator or computer that has a linear regression program to determine the least-squares slope from your data.)

B. *Solvolysis of 2-Bromo-2-methylpropane in 80% Ethanol*

Preparation of Solutions. Accurately measure [OP-5] 21.0 mL of 95% ethanol and 4.0 mL of water into a 50-mL Erlenmeyer flask. Add 4 drops of bromthymol blue solution, swirl to mix, and support the flask in the room-temperature water bath as described in part **A**. Half-fill a clean, dry 25-mL buret with 0.10 M KOH in 80% ethanol and record the initial buret reading accurately.

Kinetic Run. If you have a magnetic stirrer, drop in a stir bar and begin stirring [OP-10] the reaction mixture; otherwise, swirl after each addition and at intervals between additions. Use an automatic pipet or a *dry* measuring pipet to measure [OP-5] 0.10 mL of 2-bromo-2-methylpropane into the reaction flask. *Immediately* record the time of addition (or start your timer). Carry out the kinetic run by the same procedure you followed in part **A**, using at least ten 0.50-mL portions of the 0.10 *M* KOH solution.

Determination of V$_\infty$. After the last color change, seal the flask with Parafilm and heat [OP-7] the reaction mixture in a water bath at 60°C for about 10 minutes. Then titrate it with the 0.10 *M* solution of KOH in 80% ethanol to the green end point, and calculate *V* $_\infty$ as in part **A**. Carry out the calculations described in part **A** to determine the rate constant for 2-bromo-2-methylpropane in 80% ethanol (k_o), and then use Equation **2** to estimate its rate constant in 40% ethanol. Calculate the relative solvolysis rate for 1-bromoadamantane by dividing its rate constant by the rate constant for 2-bromo-2-methylpropane in 40% ethanol.

Take Care! Avoid contact with the alkyl halide and do not breathe its vapors or pipet it by mouth.

Stop and Think: Why does the time between buret readings change as the reaction proceeds?

Waste Disposal: Unless your instructor directs otherwise, wash the reaction mixtures and unused KOH solutions down the drain.

Exercises

1. (a) Which tertiary carbocation is more stable, 1-adamantyl or *t*-butyl? Explain why it is more stable and tell how your experimental results support this conclusion. (b) Which solvent promotes the formation of a carbocation more effectively, 40% ethanol or 80% ethanol? Explain.

2. Write a mechanism for the solvolysis reaction of 1-bromoadamantane with ethanol.

3. Describe and explain the possible effect on your results of the following experimental errors or variations. (a) The pH of the buffer for the blank was 3.9 rather than 6.9. (b) You ran both reactions in absolute ethanol. (c) You used norbornyl bromide (1-bromobicyclo[2.2.1]heptane) in place of 1-bromoadamantane. (d) Your pipet was wet when you used it to measure the 2-bromo-2-methylpropane.

4. Describe some green features of this experiment, and any that aren't so green.

5. Hydroxide ion is a stronger nucleophile than either water or ethanol, yet the addition of KOH during the kinetic runs in this experiment has virtually no effect on the reaction rates. Explain.

6. (a) During its solvolysis reaction, some 2-bromo-2-methylpropane molecules lose HBr by an E1 reaction to form an alkene. Would you expect this to affect the measured reaction rate? Why or why not? (b) 1-Bromoadamantane does not undergo elimination during its solvolysis reaction. Explain.

7. (a) Outline a synthesis of amantadine from 1-bromoadamantane. (b) Outline a synthesis of the antiviral agent rimantadine [RCH(NH$_2$)CH$_3$, where R = 1-adamantyl] from 1-bromoadamantane using an organocuprate.

8. (a) Using your experimental rate constant, calculate the time it should take for 90% of your 1-bromoadamantane to react at room temperature. (b) How long should it take for 90% of the 2-bromo-2-methylpropane to react in 40% ethanol under the same conditions?

Other Things You Can Do

(Starred items require your instructor's permission.)

*1. Collect data for this experiment using a pH probe with a computer interface as described in *J. Chem. Educ.* **1991**, *68*, 609.

*2. Measure the relative reactivities of different alkyl halides as described in the "Reactivities of Alkyl Halides in Nucleophilic Substitution Reactions" minilab.

*3. Carry out an S_N1 reaction of trityl bromide with ethanol and isolate the product as described in "An S_N1 Reaction of Bromotriphenylmethane" minilab.

4. Write a research paper about medical uses of adamantane derivatives, starting with sources listed in the Bibliography.

Reaction of Iodoethane with Sodium Saccharin, an Ambident Nucleophile

EXPERIMENT

Nucleophilic Substitution. NMR Spectrometry. Carboxylic Acid Derivatives. Heterocyclic Compounds.

Operations

OP-38 High-Performance Liquid Chromatography (optional)
OP-16 Vacuum Filtration
OP-26 Washing and Drying Solids
OP-33 Melting Point
OP-40 Nuclear Magnetic Resonance Spectrometry

Before You Begin

1. If you will be doing the optional HPLC analysis, read OP-38. Read the experiment, read or review the other operations, and write a brief experimental plan.
2. Calculate the mass of 10.0 mmol of sodium saccharin and the theoretical yield of ethylsaccharin.

Scenario

Saccharin is a nonnutritive sweetener, meaning that it isn't metabolized by the body to produce energy. But saccharin is usually mixed with fructose or other Calorie-laden sweeteners to mask its bitter aftertaste, giving the mixture about half as many Calories as sucrose and thus making it less attractive as a sugar substitute. Dulcinea Petty IV directs a product development team at Sweet Nothings Ltd., which manufactures saccharin. She has learned that substances with N—H bonds often have bitter tastes, so she wonders if converting the N—H bond of saccharin to an N—C bond by alkylating it will mask the bitter taste and thus yield a better sweetener. Saccharin is converted to its more nucleophilic sodium salt prior to alkylation, but resonance structures of the salt reveal that it is an ambident nucleophile; that is, it has two potentially nucleophilic atoms: the nitrogen atom and an oxygen atom.

A nutritional Calorie (the C should be capitalized) is 1000 times as large as a scientific calorie.

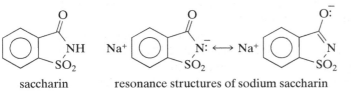

saccharin   resonance structures of sodium saccharin

Before their quest for a better sweetener can be pursued, Sweet Nothings needs to know whether or not alkylation will occur mainly on the nitrogen

From *Operational Organic Chemistry: A Problem Solving Approach to the Laboratory*, Fourth Edition, John W. Lehman. Copyright © 2009 by Pearson Education. Published by Prentice Hall. All rights reserved.

atom. Your assignment is to carry out the alkylation of sodium saccharin with iodoethane and analyze the product mixture to determine the structure of the major product.

Applying Scientific Methodology

You should be able to formulate a working hypothesis (or at least a reasonable guess) after reading the experiment and then test it by either nuclear magnetic resonance (NMR) or high-performance liquid chromatography (HPLC) analysis of your product. You will not taste the product, but you can ask your instructor about its taste after completing the experiment.

Saccharin, an Accidental Sweetener

One rule that most chemists follow scrupulously is to never, *ever* taste anything they make in the laboratory. A chemist shouldn't even eat or drink anything while working in the lab because of possible contamination by toxic chemicals. During the nineteenth century, however, chemists weren't so fastidious. It was a common practice to perform a "taste test" on any new chemical, sometimes with unfortunate results; but occasionally, an accidental or deliberate tasting paid off with a new discovery.

Ira Remsen, a Johns Hopkins University chemistry professor, studied chemistry under a protégé of the "father of organic chemistry," Friedrich Wöhler, and became the most famous American chemist of the nineteenth century. In 1878, a German student working in Remsen's research group, Constantin Fahlberg, prepared some white crystals of a previously unknown compound from *o*-toluenesulfonamide. He later ate a piece of bread and was astonished to find that it tasted intensely sweet. It didn't take Fahlberg long to trace the sweet taste to the new compound he had just handled, which he named saccharin after the Latin word for sugar, *saccharum.*

Saccharin is about 300 times sweeter than sucrose (common table sugar). Its sweetness came as a surprise, because no one was looking for a synthetic sweetener at the time—most scientists believed that only natural compounds could be sweet. Fahlberg recognized the commercial possibilities of a nonfattening sweetener, so he applied for a patent and began to manufacture saccharin. Despite its somewhat bitter aftertaste, saccharin was the most popular artificial sweetener during most of the twentieth century, outselling other synthetic sweeteners such as dulcin (from the Latin *dulcis*, meaning "sweet"), which was discovered just six years after saccharin.

Concerns about the safety of saccharin cropped up from time to time, inspiring Theodore Roosevelt to proclaim, "Anyone who says saccharin is injurious to health is an idiot!" Roosevelt, who liked to sweeten his chewing tobacco with saccharin, was no authority on the safety of commercial products, but his words must have reassured many Americans about saccharin. Then, in a Canadian study carried out in 1977, some rats developed bladder tumors when fed a diet that contained 5% saccharin. Although the rats' diet was equivalent to a human consuming about 1000 cans of diet soda per day, saccharin was promptly removed from the GRAS (generally recognized as safe) list and later banned in the United States. Reacting to protests by diabetics and overweight Americans, for whom consuming sugar was a greater health risk than the remote possibility of saccharin-induced cancer, Congress suspended the ban in 1979, but foods containing saccharin were still required to carry a warning label. Saccharin was finally removed from the U.S. government's list of suspected carcinogens in 1999 in response to evidence that the rat-bladder tumors arose from mechanisms that aren't relevant to humans.

Because of the cancer scare and competition from other synthetic sweeteners, such as aspartame and sucralose, saccharin use has declined sharply in recent years. Sucralose (in Splenda)—which, like aspartame (in NutraSweet and Equal), lacks the bitter aftertaste of saccharin—has become the world leader in the $1.5 billion artificial sweetener market. Sucralose, which is approximately 600 times sweeter than sucrose and 4 times sweeter than aspartame, is manufactured by selectively chlorinating glucose, converting three of its hydroxyl groups to chlorine atoms. Aspartame, the previous leader among artificial sweeteners, is still popular, but a French sweetener called superaspartame is 300 times sweeter than aspartame and—unlike aspartame—can be used in baking and frying. The natural sweetener thaumatin, which is extracted from the West African ketemfe plant, is reported to be nearly 100,000 times sweeter than sucrose, making it the sweetest natural substance ever discovered. It is also (like aspartame) a flavor enhancer, so it has been used to persuade farm animals to eat more—pigs gain up to 10% more weight when thaumatin is added to their feed!

Understanding the Experiment

In this experiment, you will carry out the reaction of sodium saccharin with iodoethane in the solvent N,N-dimethylformamide (DMF). This is a nucleophilic substitution reaction in which the nucleophilic atom can be either nitrogen or oxygen and the leaving group is iodide ion (I^-). The rate of a nucleophilic substitution reaction can be very sensitive to the solvent used. Polar protic solvents (solvents capable of hydrogen bonding), such as water and ethanol, form bulky solvation shells around a charged nucleophile, reducing its nucleophilic strength. Polar aprotic solvents, such as DMF, don't solvate the nucleophile strongly, leaving it free to attack the substrate. Thus, they accelerate the rates of many substitution reactions, particularly S_N2 reactions, in which the strength of the nucleophile has a large effect on the reaction rate.

As shown in the "Reactions and Properties" section, nucleophilic attack by nitrogen on iodoethane yields N-ethylsaccharin, whereas nucleophilic attack by oxygen yields O-ethylsaccharin. Thus, your product will be N-ethylsaccharin, O-ethylsaccharin, or a mixture of the two, depending on whether saccharin's nitrogen atom or oxygen atom (or both) acts as the nucleophilic atom. Predicting the most likely product isn't easy, because several competing factors may come into play. N-Ethylsaccharin is more stable than O-ethylsaccharin, so it should be the major (or only) product if the reaction reaches thermal equilibrium. But the oxygen atom of sodium saccharin has a higher partial negative charge than the nitrogen atom because oxygen is more electronegative than nitrogen, so a reaction involving oxygen as the nucleophile should occur faster than one involving nitrogen. For example, the reaction of potassium saccharin with 2-bromopropane in DMF yields mainly O-isopropylsaccharin.

You can determine the identity or composition of your product by using proton nuclear magnetic resonance (^1H NMR) spectrometry. An oxygen

DMF

Key Concept: Solvation reduces the strength of a nucleophile and therefore decreases the rates of its nucleophilic substitution reactions.

atom has a stronger deshielding effect on nearby protons than does a nitrogen atom, so the signal for the methylene protons (highlighted) of an —OCH$_2$CH$_3$ group will appear farther downfield ($\delta \approx 4.7$ ppm) than the corresponding signal for an —NCH$_2$CH$_3$ group ($\delta \approx 3.9$ ppm). Because the methylene protons have three methyl protons as neighbors, their signal in either case will be a quartet. If your product is either *N*-ethylsaccharin or *O*-ethylsaccharin, you can identify it from the chemical shift of its methylene quartet. If it is a mixture, you can measure the integrated signal areas for both quartets, calculate the percentages of *N*-ethylsaccharin and *O*-ethylsaccharin present, and decide which one is the major product. At your instructor's discretion, you can analyze your product using HPLC in addition to or instead of NMR spectrometry.

Although iodoethane is toxic, it isn't considered a highly hazardous chemical and isn't regulated by the EPA or other U.S. agencies. *N,N*-Dimethylformamide can harm aquatic organisms, but it biodegrades readily in soil and water and doesn't bioaccumulate; it is listed as a hazardous air pollutant by the EPA.

Reactions and Properties

Table 1 Physical properties

	mol wt	bp	mp	*d*
sodium saccharin	205.2			
iodoethane	156.0	72		1.950
N,N-dimethylformamide	73.1	153		0.945
N-ethylsaccharin	211.2		95	
O-ethylsaccharin	211.2		211	

Note: bp and mp are in °C; density is in g/mL.

DIRECTIONS

Safety Notes

N,N-dimethylformamide

Iodoethane severely irritates the eyes, skin, and respiratory tract. Wear gloves, avoid contact, and do not breathe its vapors.
N,N-Dimethylformamide is harmful by inhalation, ingestion, and absorption through the skin. Avoid contact and do not breathe its vapors. Deuterochloroform is harmful if inhaled, ingested, or absorbed through the skin, and it may be carcinogenic. Avoid contact and do not breathe its vapors.

Reaction. *Carry out the reaction under the hood.* Weigh 10.0 mmol of sodium saccharin and add it to 5.0 mL of *N,N*-dimethylformamide in a 125-mL Erlenmeyer flask. Heat the mixture in an 80°C water bath with swirling until the solid dissolves, and then add 0.80 mL (~10 mmol) of iodoethane using a dispenser or an automatic pipet. Cover the mouth of the flask with Parafilm and heat the mixture in the water bath with occasional swirling for 10 minutes; keep the water temperature close to 80°C during this period.

Take Care! Wear gloves; avoid contact with DMF and iodoethane, and do not breathe their vapors.

Separation. Let the reaction mixture cool to room temperature, add 40 mL of water, and shake the stoppered flask until any liquid residue that forms has solidified. Cool the flask in an ice/water bath and break up the solid with a spatula or stirring rod until it is finely divided. Collect the solid by vacuum filtration [OP-16], washing it twice with 5-mL portions of ice-cold water [OP-26a]. Dry [OP-26b] the product but do *not* taste it!

Waste Disposal: Put the filtrate in a designated solvent recovery container.

Analysis. Measure the mass and melting-point range [OP-33] of the product. Record an integrated ^{1}H NMR spectrum [OP-40] of the product in deuterochloroform or obtain one from your instructor. At your instructor's discretion, you can analyze the product mixture by HPLC [OP-38]; the instructor will demonstrate the operation of the instrument. If the product is a single compound, deduce its identity. If it is a mixture, calculate its percentage composition and decide whether *N*-ethylsaccharin or *O*-ethylsaccharin is the major product.

Stop and Think: Is the product a single compound or a mixture? How can you tell?

Take Care! Avoid contact with CDCl$_3$, and do not breathe its vapors.

Waste Disposal: Put the deuterochloroform solution in a designated solvent recovery container.

Exercises

1. (a) Assuming that the reaction was S$_N$2, which atom appears to be more nucleophilic: N or O? (b) Write a mechanism showing the transition state of the reaction that led to your major product.
2. Describe and explain the possible effect on your results of the following experimental errors or variations. (a) The reagent bottle labeled "sodium saccharin" contained saccharin instead. (b) You used water as the reaction solvent rather than DMF. (c) You heated the reaction mixture for 3 hours under reflux.
3. Following the format in the "Planning an Experiment" appendix, construct a flow diagram for this experiment.
4. (a) Calculate the atom economy and reaction efficiency of your synthesis. (b) Describe some green features of your synthesis, and any that aren't so green.
5. Most compounds that contain N—H bonds are basic, but saccharin is acidic. Explain why, using resonance structures.
6. Outline a synthesis of saccharin from *o*-toluenesulfonamide.
7. One objection raised to the use of aspartame is that it decomposes in the presence of moisture to produce phenylalanine, which must be avoided by people who have the genetic condition phenylketonuria, and methanol, which can have an effect on mental behavior. Write an equation for a hydrolysis reaction of aspartame that yields both of these products.

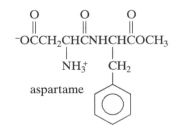

aspartame

Other Things You Can Do

(Starred items require your instructor's permission.)

*1. Add some aqueous sodium bicarbonate to a solution of saccharin (not sodium saccharin) and explain the result, writing an equation for the reaction.

*2. Carry out an S_N1 reaction of trityl bromide with ethanol as described in "An S_N1 Reaction of Bromotriphenylmethane" minilab.

3. Write a research paper about artificial sweeteners, starting with sources listed in the Bibliography.

Dehydration of Methylcyclohexanols and the Evelyn Effect

EXPERIMENT

Reactions of Alcohols. Preparation of Alkenes. Elimination Reactions. Carbocations. Regioselectivity.

Operations

OP-17 Centrifugation (optional)
OP-10 Mixing
OP-24 Washing Liquids
OP-25 Drying Liquids
OP-30 Simple Distillation
OP-37 Gas Chromatography

Before You Begin

1. Read the experiment and OP-17, read or review the other operations as necessary, and write an experimental plan.
2. Calculate the mass and volume of 150 mmol of 2- and 4-methylcyclohexanol, and the theoretical yield of methylcyclohexenes from each alcohol.

Scenario

This scenario describes a real chemical mystery, which is documented in the *Journal of Chemical Education*, **1994**, *71*, 440. Not even the names of the characters have been changed.)

For many years, the dehydration of 2-methylcyclohexanol to a mixture of alkenes has been carried out in college organic chemistry labs to demonstrate the application of Zaitzev's rule and the occurrence of the E1 mechanism in alcohol dehydration reactions. In 1994, David Todd (then a chemistry professor at Pomona College) carried out this reaction and was distilling the product alkenes from the reaction mixture when he received an invitation to lunch with the chemistry department secretary, Evelyn Jacoby. Professor Todd stopped the distillation, which was about half done, and saved the distillate in its receiver. Upon returning from lunch, he decided to collect the rest of the distillate in a new receiver, giving him two separate fractions. He then worked up both fractions and analyzed them by gas chromatography. Much to his surprise, the second fraction contained a markedly lower percentage of the expected product, 1-methylcyclohexene, than did the first. Because his decision to replace the receiver with a new one was a direct result of the secretary's invitation, Todd named this unexpected result the "Evelyn Effect."

Although several mechanistic hypotheses have been proposed to explain the Evelyn Effect, it is by no means certain that any of them are correct. Your project group's assignment is to verify the existence of the Evelyn Effect for the dehydration of 2-methylcyclohexanol and to see if a similar effect exists

From *Operational Organic Chemistry: A Problem Solving Approach to the Laboratory*, Fourth Edition, John W. Lehman. Copyright © 2009 by Pearson Education. Published by Prentice Hall. All rights reserved.

for 4-methylcyclohexanol. You may then want to speculate about some possible causes of the Evelyn Effect.

Applying Scientific Methodology

As in the previous experiments, you need to state the problem as a question, formulate a working hypothesis, follow the course of action described in the Directions, gather and evaluate evidence, test your hypothesis, arrive at a conclusion, and report your findings.

Zaitzev's Rule and the Evelyn Effect

More than a century ago at the University of Kazan, Vladimir Vasilevich Markovnikov and Alexander Zaitzev were investigating a chemical reaction both forward and backward: Markovnikov was adding hydrogen iodide to alkenes to prepare alkyl iodides, and Zaitzev was removing hydrogen iodide from alkyl iodides to prepare alkenes. Markovnikov discovered that hydrogen iodide adds to propene to form mainly 2-iodopropane.

$$CH_3CH{=}CH_2 + HI \longrightarrow CH_3\overset{\displaystyle I}{\overset{\displaystyle |}{C}}HCH_3$$

From this and other results, Markovnikov formulated his well-known rule, which can be expressed as follows for a hydrogen-containing species represented by HZ:

Markovnikov's rule: When HZ adds to the carbon–carbon double bond of an unsymmetrical alkene, hydrogen adds preferentially to the carbon atom that already has *more* hydrogens.

In the meantime, Zaitzev learned that dehydrohalogenation of 2-iodobutane by alcoholic potassium hydroxide yields mainly 2-butene.

$$CH_3CH_2\overset{\displaystyle I}{\overset{\displaystyle |}{C}}HCH_3 \xrightarrow{KOH} CH_3CH{=}CHCH_3$$

He proposed an analogous rule for elimination reactions:

Zaitzev's rule: When HZ is removed from a species to form an alkene, hydrogen is lost preferentially from the carbon atom that has *fewer* hydrogens.

Markovnikov's and Zaitzev's rules together can be paraphrased by the well-known socioeconomic maxim "The rich get richer and the poor get poorer."

These examples show that organic reactions can be *selective,* favoring some products and not others—Zaitzev's reaction might have yielded as much 1-butene as 2-butene, but it did not. When a reaction could produce two or more different structural isomers but in fact yields mainly one of them, the reaction is said to be *regioselective.* Zaitzev's rule works because, in most cases, it predicts the formation of the most stable alkene. 2-Butene was the major product of Zaitzev's reaction not because hydrogen-poor carbon atoms have some innate tendency to lose the hydrogens they have but because 2-butene is more stable than 1-butene.

Although generalizations such as Zaitzev's rule can help us predict the products of many organic reactions, organic chemistry remains an empirical science—we cannot be certain that a rule that is valid for one system under a given set of conditions will apply equally well under different circumstances. Chemists must study each system experimentally to see if it behaves in the expected manner and, if it doesn't, try to find out why.

For example, neomenthyl chloride undergoes dehydrohalogenation in the presence of a strong base such as sodium ethoxide (CH_3CH_2ONa) to yield a product mixture that consists of mostly alkene **A**, the one predicted by Zaitzev's rule. But menthyl chloride, which differs only in the geometry of the C—Cl bond, yields 100% of alkene **B** and none of the Zaitzev product. It also reacts much more slowly than neomenthyl chloride.

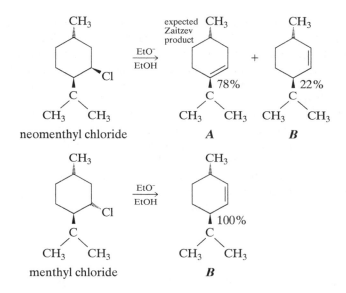

This result can be explained by assuming that the reaction occurs by an E2 mechanism, which requires that the H and Cl atoms being eliminated lie in the same plane and on opposite sides of the C—C bond separating them; this is called *anti*-periplanar geometry.

Neomenthyl chloride, in its most stable ring conformation, has the desired *anti*-periplanar geometry for formation of either **A** or **B**. Because **A** is the more stable alkene, it is the major product.

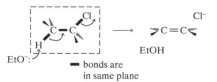

E2 mechanism for elimination of HCl

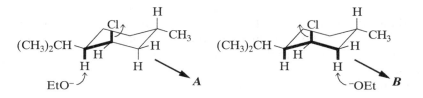

Menthyl chloride, in its more stable conformation (with all large groups equatorial), doesn't have the geometry necessary to form either product. In its less stable conformation, the *anti*-periplanar geometry needed to form product **A** cannot be attained, because the isopropyl group rather than a hydrogen atom is *anti* to the chlorine atom. This conformation is suitable for the formation of product **B**, however, so it is the only product isolated.

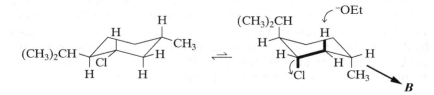

The reaction is much slower than the reaction of neomenthyl chloride because only a small percentage of the menthyl chloride molecules are in the less stable conformation at any time. This example suggests that, whenever a substrate yields the less stable alkene as a major product of an elimination reaction, there may be some stereochemical constraints inhibiting the formation of the Zaitzev product.

E2 reactions require a base strong enough to remove a proton from the carbon atom adjacent to the leaving group, but alcohols are ordinarily dehydrated in the presence of a strong acid such as sulfuric acid or phosphoric acid. Thus, the acid-catalyzed dehydration of alcohols is generally believed to occur by an E1 (elimination, unimolecular) mechanism involving protonation of the hydroxyl group, loss of water to form a carbocation intermediate, and then loss of a proton.

Key Concept: For certain kinds of reactions, stereochemical constraints may lead to unexpected results.

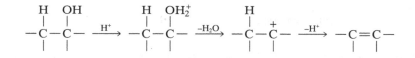

Note that there are *no* stereochemical constraints in an E1 reaction, because the leaving group leaves before the proton is lost. Thus, in the E1 dehydration of an alcohol, H and OH don't need to be *anti*-periplanar or in any other particular orientation for elimination to occur.

Unlike E2 reactions, E1 reactions may involve rearrangements in which the initial carbocation rearranges to a more stable carbocation before it loses H$^+$. A carbocation rearrangement may involve a *hydride shift*, during which a hydrogen next to the positively charged carbon moves to that carbon, taking its bonding electron pair along with it. Such rearrangements lead to alkenes whose double bond doesn't include the carbon atom that was originally bonded to the hydroxyl group. Postulating such a rearrangement can explain the formation of 2-methyl-2-butene in the dehydration of 2-methyl-1-butanol, for example.

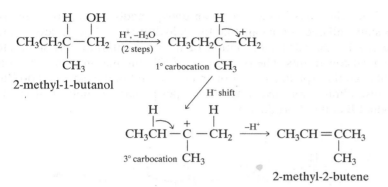

2-methyl-1-butanol

1° carbocation

H⁻ shift

3° carbocation

2-methyl-2-butene

This brings us to the Evelyn Effect. When Professor Todd carried out the dehydration of 2-methylcyclohexanol, he obtained the following mixture of alkenes.

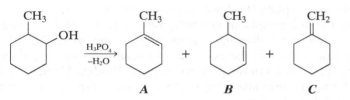

A   B   C

The reaction is performed by distilling the alkenes as they are formed, and the distillate typically contains 75–80% of product **A**, the product predicted by Zaitzev's rule. But when the distillate is collected in separate fractions and the fractions are analyzed separately, the first 10% of the distillate contains about 93% **A**, whereas the final distillate contains as little as 55% **A**. The remaining product in each case is mostly **B**, with only a trace of **C**. There is a clue to the origin of the Evelyn Effect in the catalog of the Aldrich Chemical Company, where the 2-methylcyclohexanol used by Professor Todd is described as a mixture of *cis* and *trans* isomers. In fact, it is a nearly equimolar mixture of the two isomers. Previous researchers had reported that the *cis* isomer reacts much faster than the *trans* isomer, so Todd reasoned that the initial product mixture — containing mostly **A** — formed mainly by dehydration of the *cis* isomer, whereas the final product mixture — with comparable amounts of **A** and **B** — formed mainly by dehydration of the *trans* isomer.

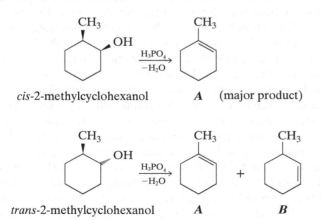

cis-2-methylcyclohexanol   **A**   (major product)

trans-2-methylcyclohexanol   **A**   **B**

Since the *trans* isomer yields an unexpectedly large percentage of the less stable alkene, it appears that the dehydration of 2-methylcyclohexanol, like the E2 dehydrohalogenation of menthyl chloride, has some stereochemical constraints. The occurrence of E2 elimination from a protonated alcohol could explain a reduction in the amount of the expected product **A**, because elimination involving an *anti*-periplanar geometry can yield only product **B** and not product **A**.

In this equation, B: represents some basic species.

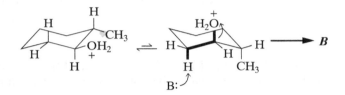

It could also explain the lower reactivity of the *trans* alcohol, which can achieve the *anti*-periplanar geometry only in its less stable *diaxial* conformation. However, it does *not* explain why the *trans* alcohol yields any **A** at all, nor does it explain the existence of a small amount of methylenecyclohexane (product **C**) in the product mixture. Product **C** might be obtained by an E1 mechanism involving a carbocation rearrangement, but not by an ordinary E2 mechanism.

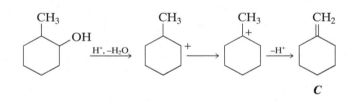

Does the reaction proceed by both E1 and E2 mechanisms? That possibility, raised by Todd, has been questioned by two other researchers, John J. Cawley and Patrick E. Lindner, who proposed an "E2-like" mechanism involving bridged ions (*J. Chem. Educ.* **1997**, *74*, 102). On the other hand, a recent senior thesis project carried out by Rachel M. Anderson under the direction of James O. Currie at Pacific University has provided evidence that either E1 or E2 elimination can occur during the phosphoric acid catalyzed dehydration of 2-methylcyclohexanol, with the mechanism depending on the stereochemistry of the alcohol's conformations. Anderson postulates that an E2 reaction can occur because the dihydrogen phosphate ion, $H_2PO_4^-$, is a strong enough base to remove a hydrogen atom adjacent to the protonated OH group. The evidence for competing mechanisms, derived from both experimental results and molecular modeling, is convincing, but does it settle the issue? A mechanism is, after all, a scientific hypothesis about processes that we can't observe directly—the things that molecules do as they redistribute their atoms and change into new molecules—and may be revised or rejected as new evidence comes to light.

The Evelyn Effect illustrates how science often works. For decades, the results of alcohol dehydration reactions were adequately explained by the E1 hypothesis; no other explanation seemed necessary. Then, a chance observation showed the inadequacy of the accepted hypothesis. A different hypothesis—that both E1 and E2 mechanisms are involved—was proposed and contested, followed by another hypothesis, and so on. The road to scientific discovery is a rocky one, and there may be many detours along the way, but every failed hypothesis yields new information, new ideas, and often new applications. Science is not simply a body of established facts and theories; the facts and theories of science are always subject to further inquiry that may disprove or modify them. Science is a dynamic *process* by which knowledge is acquired, ideas are debated, theories are proposed, and new ways of doing things are discovered.

Understanding the Experiment

In this experiment, you and your coworkers will carry out the dehydration of 2-methylcyclohexanol and 4-methylcyclohexanol by heating the alcohols in the presence of phosphoric acid. Both alcohols will be mixtures of *cis* and *trans* isomers, so either one or both may exhibit an Evelyn Effect.

Dehydration of a secondary alcohol proceeds readily with about half a mole of phosphoric acid for every mole of the alcohol. By protonating an alcohol, the acid catalyst converts the poor leaving group $-OH$ to a much better leaving group, $-OH_2^+$.

$$-\overset{\overset{\displaystyle H}{|}}{\underset{|}{C}}-\overset{\overset{\displaystyle OH}{|}}{\underset{|}{C}}- \; + \; H_3PO_4 \;\rightleftharpoons\; -\overset{\overset{\displaystyle H}{|}}{\underset{|}{C}}-\overset{\overset{\displaystyle H}{\overset{|}{\overset{\displaystyle {}^+OH}{|}}}}{\underset{|}{C}}- \; + \; H_2PO_4^-$$

Elimination of H^+ and H_2O from the protonated alcohol yields an alkene, with the unprotonated alcohol serving as the reaction solvent.

According to Le Châtelier's principle, removing a product from a chemical system at equilibrium shifts the equilibrium in the direction that favors the formation of the products. You will carry out the dehydration reaction in a distillation apparatus so that the products (water and alkene) will continuously distill from the reaction mixture as they are formed. Their removal will shift the equilibrium to the right and thus increase the yield of alkene.

$$\text{alcohol} \rightleftharpoons \text{alkene} \uparrow + \text{water} \uparrow$$

If the reaction mixture is heated to a temperature above the boiling points of the product alkenes but below that of the alcohol, most of the unreacted alcohol will remain in the reaction flask while the alkenes and water collect in the receiver.

You will follow the progress of the reaction by measuring the volume of alkene in the distillate, collecting two fractions of approximately equal volume. When the reaction is over, the residue in the reaction flask may begin to foam and emit white vapors. You should separate the apparatus from the heat source at this time because overheating the residue may form a black tar and generate toxic fumes.

The upward-pointing arrows in the equation indicate that the products are vaporized under the reaction conditions, not that they are gases at room temperature.

After washing and drying the organic layer of each fraction, you will analyze the fractions by gas chromatography. If you started with 2-methylcyclohexanol, your gas chromatograms may show peaks for both 1- and 3-methylcyclohexene (the methylenecyclohexene peak will be resolved only if you use a capillary column). If you started with 4-methylcyclohexanol, you may obtain only 4-methylcyclohexene or a mixture of products including 3-methylcyclohexene and 1-methylcyclohexene. From the relative areas of your peaks, you can estimate the percentage composition of the product mixture in each fraction. A packed GC column may not separate 3- and 4-methylcyclohexene; in that case, you should calculate their combined percentage.

This is a comparatively green experiment because the reaction has a high atom economy, no solvents other than water are used, the catalyst reduces the energy requirements of the reaction, and distilling the product increases the reaction efficiency. Little information about the environmental toxicity of phosphoric acid and the methylcyclohexanols is available, but as a rule, phosphates should not be released into the environment.

Reactions and Properties

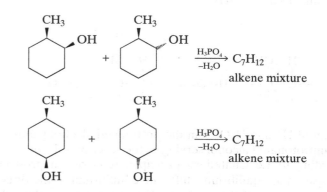

Table 1 Physical properties

	mol wt	bp	_d_
2-methylcyclohexanol*	114.2	166	0.930
4-methylcyclohexanol*	114.2	173	0.914
1-methylcyclohexene	96.2	110	0.813
3-methylcyclohexene	96.2	104	0.801
4-methylcyclohexene	96.2	102	0.799
phosphoric acid (85%)	98.0		1.70

*Mixture of _cis_ and _trans_ isomers.

Note: bp is in °C; density is in g/mL. The molecular weight given for phosphoric acid is for the pure acid; 85% phosphoric acid is about 14.7 _M_.

DIRECTIONS

You can work in pairs, with each student using one of the two methylcyclohexanols.

The methylcyclohexanols and alkenes are flammable; inhalation, ingestion, or skin absorption may be harmful. Avoid contact, do not breathe their vapors, and keep them away from flames and hot surfaces.
Phosphoric acid can cause serious burns, particularly to the eyes; avoid skin or eye contact.

Safety Notes

Reaction. Accurately weigh 150 mmol of 2-methylcyclohexanol *or* 4-methylcyclohexanol (*cis–trans* mixtures) into a 50-mL round-bottom flask. Mix in 5.0 mL of 85% phosphoric acid and drop in a stir bar or a few acid-resistant boiling chips. Clamp the flask to a ring stand over a suitable heat source and assemble an apparatus for simple distillation [OP-30]. Use a 10-mL graduated cylinder or another graduated container as the receiver. Have ready two clean, numbered 15-mL screw-cap centrifuge tubes.

Take Care! Avoid contact with the acid and alcohol; do not breathe their vapors.

Start the stirrer [OP-10], if you are using one, and then heat the reactants so that the product mixture distills at a rate of 1 drop per second or less. Record the vapor temperature after distillation begins, and observe it at intervals during the reaction. Monitor the volume of the alkene (top) layer in the distillate. When the alkene volume is about 8 mL, quickly pour the distillate into the first centrifuge tube, cap the tube, replace the graduated receiver, and continue distilling. After the alkene volume reaches about 6 mL, monitor the still-head temperature continually. Lower the heat source and turn it off when you observe a marked temperature drop at the still head, which may be accompanied by foaming and dense white fumes in the reaction flask. Pour the distillate into the second centrifuge tube and cap the tube.

The water that codistills with the alkene reduces its boiling temperature, so the still-head temperature may be lower than the expected boiling point of the product.

Waste Disposal: Place the residue from the reaction flask in a designated waste container.

Separation. For each separate fraction, wash [OP-24] the distillate by shaking it cautiously with two 5-mL portions of saturated aqueous sodium bicarbonate, and remove the aqueous (lower) layer with a Pasteur pipet. Dry [OP-25] each alkene mixture separately in the centrifuge tube with anhydrous calcium chloride or another suitable drying agent. Centrifuge it [OP-17], if necessary, and decant the liquid into a labeled, tared screw-cap vial. Measure the mass of each alkene fraction and calculate the total mass of alkenes.

Take Care: A gas may be evolved; vent as necessary.

Waste Disposal: Unless your instructor directs otherwise, wash the aqueous layers down the drain.

Analysis. Analyze both fractions by gas chromatography [OP-37] as directed by your instructor. Measure the area and retention time of each peak on your gas chromatograms. Identify the peaks by comparison with a chromatogram provided by your instructor or by spiking your product mixture with an authentic sample of 1-methylcyclohexene and obtaining a chromatogram of the resulting mixture. Assuming that the detector response factors for the alkenes are equal, calculate the percentage composition of each fraction and obtain the same data from a coworker who started with the other alcohol. Decide whether either or both alcohols exhibit an Evelyn Effect.

Stop and Think: Were the results as you expected?

If peaks for 3- and 4-methylcyclohexene are not separated on the gas chromatogram, calculate their combined percentage.

Exercises

1. (a) Which kind of mechanism can better account for the product mixture obtained from the dehydration of *cis-* and *trans-*4-methylcyclohexanol: E1, E2, or a combination of the two? (Keep in mind that the actual mechanism may be none of these.) (b) Based on your answer, write detailed mechanisms explaining the formation of all of the observed products.

2. Following the format in the "Planning an Experiment" appendix, construct a flow diagram for this experiment.
3. Describe and explain the possible effect on your results of the following experimental errors or variations. (a) You forgot to add the phosphoric acid. (b) You collected all of the distillate in one container rather than in two. (c) The 2-methylcyclohexanol you used was the pure *trans* isomer rather than a mixture of isomers.
4. In "Understanding the Experiment," 1-methylcyclohexene and 3-methylcyclohexene were mentioned as possible products of the dehydration of 2-methylcyclohexanol. Why wasn't 2-methylcyclohexene mentioned as a possible product?
5. (a) Calculate the atom economy and the reaction efficiency of your synthesis. (b) Describe some green features of your synthesis, and any that aren't so green.
6. Do you think the Evelyn Effect is more likely or less likely to occur during the dehydration of 2-methylcyclohexanol if the catalyst is sulfuric acid rather than phosphoric acid? Explain your answer.
7. (a) Predict the major alkene product that would result from dehydrating each of the following alcohols, with no carbocation rearrangements.

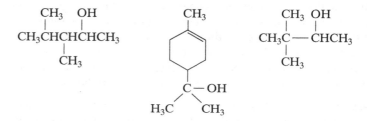

(b) In each case, predict the most stable dehydration product that could result after a single carbocation rearrangement.

Other Things You Can Do

(Starred items require your instructor's permission.)

*1. Prepare and test a gaseous alkene as described in the "Preparation and Properties of a Gaseous Alkene" minilab.
*2. Test your product mixtures with bromine or potassium permanganate solution, and interpret the results.
*3. Dehydrate another alcohol, such as cyclohexanol, 3-methylcyclohexanol, or 4-methyl-2-pentanol, by the same procedure, adjusting the distillation temperature for the alkene or alkene mixture anticipated. Analyze the product mixtures by gas chromatography and interpret the results.
4. The methylcyclohexanols used in this experiment are synthesized by catalytic hydrogenation of the corresponding cresols (methylphenols). Write a research paper about the production and uses of cresols, starting with sources listed in the Bibliography.

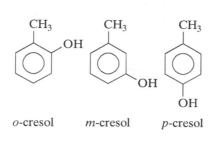

o-cresol   *m*-cresol   *p*-cresol

Testing Markovnikov's Rule

Addition to Alkenes. Preparation of Alcohols. Regioselectivity. Infrared Spectrometry.

Operations

OP-14 Trapping Gases (optional)
OP-18b Salting Out
OP-7 Heating
OP-8 Cooling
OP-10 Mixing
OP-11 Addition of Reactants
OP-18 Extraction
OP-19 Evaporation
OP-25 Drying Liquids
OP-30 Simple Distillation
OP-34 Boiling Point
OP-39 Infrared Spectrometry

Before You Begin

1. Read the experiment, read OP-14 and OP-18b, read or review the other operations as necessary, and write an experimental plan.
2. Calculate the mass and volume of 20.0 mmol of 1-hexene, the masses of 4.0 mmol of iodine and 8.0 mmol of sodium borohydride, and the theoretical yield of the product.

Scenario

At the University of Kazan in 1869, the Russian chemist Vladimir Vasilyevich Markovnikov developed a rule for addition reactions of alkenes that can be expressed as:

When HZ adds to the carbon–carbon double bond of an unsymmetrical alkene, hydrogen adds preferentially to the carbon atom that already has more hydrogens.

Here, "Z" can stand for a halide, an OH group, and so forth. During the addition of hydrogen chloride to propene, for example, the H atom of HCl adds to the carbon atom that has two hydrogens, and the Cl ends up on the carbon that has only one.

$$CH_3CH = CH_2 + HCl \longrightarrow CH_3\overset{\overset{\displaystyle Cl}{|}}{CH} - \overset{\overset{\displaystyle H}{|}}{CH_2}$$

Note that the carbon atom that has the most hydrogen atoms is also the least substituted carbon. Markovnikov's rule works well for the direct addition of water, hydrogen halides, and similar reagents to carbon–carbon double bonds.

From *Operational Organic Chemistry: A Problem Solving Approach to the Laboratory*, Fourth Edition, John W. Lehman. Copyright © 2009 by Pearson Education. Published by Prentice Hall. All rights reserved.

In 1959, a distinguished American chemist, known to his colleagues as HCB, discovered a new way of adding water indirectly to double bonds. His method involves initial addition of a compound that contains B—H bonds to an alkene's double bond, followed by oxidation and hydrolysis, as shown here for a general alkene.

$$>B-H \;+\; -C=C- \;\longrightarrow\; -\overset{|}{\underset{|}{C}}-\overset{\overset{\displaystyle |}{B}\;H}{\underset{|}{C}}- \;\xrightarrow[\text{oxidation}]{[O]}\; -\overset{|}{\underset{|}{C}}-\overset{\overset{\displaystyle |}{B}-O\;H}{\underset{|}{C}}- \;\xrightarrow[\text{hydrolysis}]{HOH}\; -\overset{|}{\underset{|}{C}}-\overset{HO\;H}{\underset{|}{C}}- \;+\; >B-OH$$

The other substituents on boron (not shown here) can be hydrogen atoms or various alkyl or aryl groups, and [O] refers to an unspecified oxidizing agent.

Markovnikov didn't anticipate such indirect addition reactions, so his rule may or may not apply in this case. Your assignment is to convert 1-hexene to an alcohol by this general method and to determine whether the reaction obeys or violates Markovnikov's rule.

Applying Scientific Methodology

You should be able to develop a working hypothesis about the structure of the product after reading the Scenario and "Understanding the Experiment." You will test your hypothesis by obtaining and interpreting an infrared spectrum of your product. Then you can arrive at a conclusion about the applicability of Markovnikov's rule in this case.

Markovnikov and His Rule

If you buy a bottle of rubbing alcohol at a drugstore, chances are it contains isopropyl alcohol (2-propanol) and not *n*-propyl alcohol (1-propanol).

$$\overset{\displaystyle OH}{\underset{\text{2-propanol}}{\underset{|}{CH_3CHCH_3}}} \qquad \overset{\displaystyle OH}{\underset{\text{1-propanol}}{\underset{|}{CH_3CH_2CH_2}}}$$

These alcohols are isomers; each contains 3 carbon atoms, 8 hydrogen atoms, and 1 oxygen atom, and their physical properties are similar. There's no obvious reason that 2-propanol should be preferred to 1-propanol as a constituent of rubbing alcohol. But if you check the prices of similar grades of the two alcohols, you'll find that 1-propanol costs about 40% more than 2-propanol. That's because the cheapest way to make an alcohol is often by acid-catalyzed hydration of an alkene. Hydration of 1-propene, which is obtained from petroleum refining, yields mainly 2-propanol and very little 1-propanol.

Isopropyl alcohol was the first organic compound made on a large scale from a petrochemical.

$$CH_3CH=CH_2 + H_2O \;\xrightarrow{H^+}\; \overset{\displaystyle OH}{\underset{\text{major product}}{\underset{|}{CH_3CHCH_3}}}$$

This result can be predicted using a simple rule (stated in the Scenario) that was first advanced by Markovnikov in 1869. Markovnikov arrived at his famous rule after noticing that, when a hydrogen halide is added to an alkene, the hydrogen atom ordinarily attaches to the carbon that already has the *most* hydrogens. Any chemical reaction that, like this example, leads primarily or exclusively to the formation of one structural isomer rather than an alternative structural isomer is said to be *regioselective*.

Like most rules, Markovnikov's has exceptions. For example, in the presence of an organic peroxide, hydrogen bromide adds to alkenes in the "wrong" direction, yielding 1-bromopropane.

$$CH_3CH{=}CH_2 + HBr \xrightarrow{peroxide} CH_3CH_2\overset{\displaystyle Br}{\overset{|}{C}}H_2$$
major product

This kind of result is known as anti-Markovnikov addition. It occurs in this case because HBr addition in the presence of peroxides involves a free-radical intermediate rather than an ionic one. This is also a regioselective reaction, because it could conceivably have yielded mainly 2-bromopropane but did not.

Key Concept: *The outcome of a regioselective reaction depends on the mechanism of the reaction.*

Markovnikov was a remarkably productive chemist whose name might not be remembered at all, were it not for his rule. Because he published only in Russian, his work was virtually unknown in the outside world for many years. Born in 1838 in Nizhny Novgorod, he studied and taught chemistry at the University of Kazan, which bills itself as "the birthplace of organic chemistry" based on research performed by Markovnikov, his mentor Aleksandr Butlerov, and others. He showed, for example, that butyric acid (butanoic acid) and isobutyric acid (2-methylpropanoic acid) are isomers. He was also the first to prove that cyclic organic compounds can contain fewer or more than six carbon atoms by synthesizing compounds that have four-membered and seven-membered rings. He was one of the first chemists who anticipated the need to know how atoms are arranged in space in order to understand the relationship between chemical reactions and structure. Shortly afterward, J. H. van't Hoff introduced his stereochemical theory, which proposed that carbon atoms can have a three-dimensional tetrahedral structure. While teaching at the University of Moscow, Markovnikov established his own school of chemists, thus insuring that his influence would extend well beyond his own lifetime.

Markovnikov also studied in Germany under Richard August Carl Emil Erlenmeyer, who is best known today for his flask.

Understanding the Experiment

In this experiment, you will be carrying out an indirect hydration of 1-hexene and identifying the product to determine whether or not the reaction follows Markovnikov's rule. Markovnikov's rule usually works, because alkyl (and aryl) groups can help stabilize a positive charge on a carbon atom. When H^+ adds to a carbon atom of an alkene, it strips away a pair of electrons from the pi bond, leaving the adjacent carbon atom with a positive

Stop and Think: What would the product be in each case?

charge. So when H^+ adds to the *less* substituted carbon atom (the one with more hydrogens), the positive charge ends up on the *more* substituted carbon, where it is stabilized by the substituents. This is shown in the following illustration, where R represents an alkyl substituent.

$$RCH = CH_2 + H^+ \longrightarrow \overset{\oplus}{R}CH - \overset{\overset{\displaystyle H}{|}}{C}H_2$$

In general, the more electropositive component of a reagent (such as the H in HCl) will tend to add to the less substituted double-bonded carbon atom of the alkene. In the following example, bromine is more electropositive (less electronegative) than chlorine, so "Br^+" adds to the less substituted carbon, leaving the positive charge on the more substituted carbon, to which Cl^- then bonds.

$$RCH = CH_2 \xrightarrow{BrCl} \overset{\oplus}{R}CH - CH_2 \xrightarrow{Cl^-} \overset{\overset{\displaystyle Cl}{|}}{R}CH - \overset{\overset{\displaystyle Br}{|}}{C}H_2$$

BH₃ is ordinarily too unstable to exist as the pure substance, but it can be generated in the reaction mixture.

HCB's original method (described in the Scenario) used chemicals that can be handled safely only by experienced chemists, but the procedure used here involves considerably less hazardous chemicals. In this experiment, the substance that adds to the double bond of 1-hexene will be a hydride of boron, BH_3, which is formed by a reaction of sodium borohydride and iodine. The resulting boron-containing intermediate, a trialkylborane represented here by $(C_6H_{13})_3B$, is oxidized by hydrogen peroxide and then hydrolyzed by aqueous NaOH. During these steps, each alkyl group of the trialkylborane acquires an —OH group at the site of its previous bond to boron (see the equations in the "Reactions and Properties" section).

You will use a separatory–addition funnel to add a solution of iodine in the solvent tetrahydrofuran to a reaction mixture containing sodium borohydride and 1-hexene in the same solvent. Each molecule of BH_3 produced in this reaction adds to the carbon–carbon double bonds of three molecules of 1-hexene. Hydrogen is evolved during the reaction, so a fume hood or a gas trap should be used to remove it. When the initial reaction is over, you will add a concentrated solution of hydrogen peroxide (30% or 35%) and 3 *M* sodium hydroxide to bring about the oxidation and hydrolysis steps. Hydrogen peroxide is a strong oxidant that can cause severe burns and bleach your skin white, so it should be handled with care, using protective gloves. The organic layer from the reaction mixture, which contains the product in tetrahydrofuran, is separated from the aqueous layer by using potassium carbonate to salt it out (see OP-18b). After the addition of some hexanes and an extraction step, the two solvents are evaporated and the alcohol is purified by simple distillation. It can then be identified from its infrared spectrum. Refer to the "Characteristic Infrared Bands" section in OP-39 to help you determine which alcohol you prepared.

A Greener Way: You can recover the solvents by evaporation under vacuum using a cold trap (see OP-15).

Iodine may be hazardous in the environment, especially to fish. Tetrahydrofuran is somewhat toxic to aquatic life but isn't expected to bioaccumulate. Little information is available about the environmental effects of hydrogen peroxide, but it is expected to be converted to water in the environment.

Reactions and Properties

$$6CH_3(CH_2)_3CH{=}CH_2 + 2NaBH_4 + I_2 \longrightarrow 2(C_6H_{13})_3B + 2NaI + H_2$$
1-hexene

$$(C_6H_{13})_3B + 3H_2O_2 + NaOH \longrightarrow 3(C_6H_{13})OH + NaB(OH)_4$$

Note: $(C_6H_{13})OH{=}CH_3CH_2CH_2CH_2CH_2CH_2OH$ or $CH_3CH_2CH_2CH_2\overset{\overset{\displaystyle OH}{|}}{C}HCH_3$

                 1-hexanol   2-hexanol

Table 1 Physical properties

	mol wt	mp	bp	d
1-hexene	84.2		64	0.678
iodine	253.8	113	184	4.93
sodium borohydride	37.8	300d		1.074
35% hydrogen peroxide	34.0	40	126	1.13*
tetrahydrofuran	72.1	−108	67	0.889
1-hexanol	102.2	−52	157.5	0.814
2-hexanol	102.2	−47	140	0.811

*The density of 30% hydrogen peroxide is 1.11 g/mL.

Note: bp and mp are in °C; density is in g/mL; d = decomposes at the melting point.

1-Hexene $CH_3CH_2CH_2CH_2CH{=}CH_2$ 2962.1   1466.1   909.2
                                                             1821.3   1379.1   739.8
                                                             1641.8   992.7   630.8

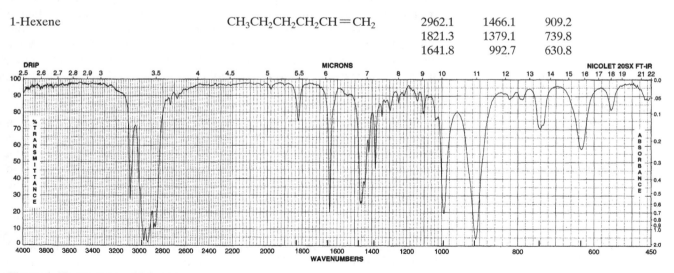

Figure 1 IR spectrum of 1-hexene

DIRECTIONS

Safety Notes

Tetrahydrofuran irritates the skin, eyes, and mucous membranes, and it is highly flammable. Avoid contact and keep it away from ignition sources. 1-Hexene irritates the skin, eyes, and mucous membranes, and it is highly flammable. Avoid contact and keep it away from ignition sources.
Sodium borohydride is toxic and corrosive, and it can react violently with concentrated acids, oxidizing agents, and other substances. Avoid contact, do not breathe dust, and keep NaBH₄ away from other chemicals.
Sodium hydroxide is toxic and corrosive, and it can cause severe damage to skin, eyes, and mucous membranes. Wear gloves and avoid contact with the NaOH solution.
Concentrated hydrogen peroxide solutions are corrosive and can cause severe burns. Hydrogen peroxide is a strong oxidant and can form explosive mixtures in the presence of certain organic compounds. Wear gloves, avoid eye and skin contact, do not breathe its vapors, and keep it away from other chemicals. In case of skin or eye contact, immediately flush thoroughly with water.

1-hexene   sodium hydroxide   sodium borohydride   tetrahydrofuran

Take Care! Avoid contact with THF.

Reaction. Prepare a solution containing 4.0 mmol of iodine in 8.0 mL of tetrahydrofuran (THF) in a small screw-cap vial and set it aside. Assemble an apparatus for addition [OP-11] under reflux [OP-7], using a 100-mL round-bottom flask. Unless you can perform the reaction under an efficient fume hood, assemble a gas trap [OP-14] that leads from the top of the condenser to a test tube containing mineral oil. Weigh 20.0 mmol of 1-hexene and transfer it to the round-bottom flask; then add 25 mL of THF and a stir bar. *Under the hood,* add 8.0 mmol of powdered sodium borohydride, reattach the flask to the apparatus, and cool [OP-8] the flask in an ice/water bath with magnetic stirring [OP-10]. Put the iodine solution in the separatory–addition funnel and add it to the reaction mixture in small portions, each about 20 drops or so. Add each new portion when the solution becomes colorless or light yellow, or after 5 minutes—whichever comes first. When the addition is complete, remove the ice/water bath and stir the reaction mixture at room temperature for at least 1 hour. During this time, rinse the separatory–addition funnel and Claisen connector with acetone to remove iodine, and let them dry; then replace them on the apparatus (attach the condenser directly to the flask while you're cleaning them).

Take Care! Avoid contact with sodium borohydride and keep it away from other chemicals.

When the reaction period is over, cool the mixture in a fresh ice/water bath for 5 to 10 minutes. Next, slowly add 10 mL of distilled water from the separatory–addition funnel, with stirring, to decompose any excess borohydride. When the reaction has subsided, remove the cold bath and

Take Care! Hydrogen gas is evolved, so keep flames away.

continue stirring until no more tiny bubbles are evolved (you'll have to stop the stirrer temporarily and look through the top layer to see them). This may take 15 minutes or more.

Heat the reaction mixture in a 30–40°C warm-water bath for 5 minutes or so, and then add 2.3 mL of 3 *M* sodium hydroxide while stirring. Transfer 4.0 mL of 30% or 35% hydrogen peroxide to the separatory–addition funnel and add it to the reaction mixture drop by drop. The reaction mixture will darken during the addition. Continue to heat the mixture at 30–40°C, with stirring, for 30 minutes.

Separation. Add about 20 g of potassium carbonate (anhydrous or sesquihydrate) to the reaction flask, then stopper and shake it vigorously for a minute or so to dissolve the K_2CO_3 (see OP-18b). Transfer the reaction mixture to a separatory funnel, using 12 mL of hexanes for the transfer, and shake to extract [OP-18] all of the product into the organic layer. Separate the organic layer, and wash [OP-24] it with 10 mL or more of 30% sodium thiosulfate solution to remove most of the color (it may be light yellow even after washing). Next, wash it with 2 portions of saturated aqueous sodium chloride. Dry the organic layer [OP-25] over anhydrous sodium sulfate or magnesium sulfate, and evaporate [OP-19] the solvent.

Purification and Analysis. Purify the product by simple distillation [OP-30], and record its boiling point [OP-34a]. Weigh the product and record its infrared spectrum [OP-39]. Give the structure and name of your product, and tell how you arrived at that structure.

Take Care! Avoid contact with sodium hydroxide. Wear gloves, and avoid contact with the hydrogen peroxide solution.

Take Care! Do not add the hydrogen peroxide too rapidly or the reaction mixture may foam up.

Stop and Think: What is the function of the potassium carbonate?

Waste Disposal: Unless your instructor directs otherwise, wash the aqueous layers down the drain. Place recovered organic solvents in a designated waste container.

Exercises

1. Show how BH_3 must have added to the C=C bond of 1-hexene, and explain why.
2. Find out who HCB was and give the name of the reaction sequence that you used in this experiment. (*Hint:* HCB won a Nobel Prize in chemistry.)
3. (a) Calculate the atom economy and reaction efficiency of your synthesis. (b) Describe some green features of your synthesis, and any that aren't so green.
4. Write a balanced equation for a reaction that would cause the solution to darken when H_2O_2 is added.
5. Following the format in the "Planning an Experiment" appendix, construct a flow diagram for this experiment.
6. Describe and explain the possible effect on your results of the following experimental errors or variations. (a) Instead of 1-hexene, you added hexanes (intended for the Separation step) to the reaction flask. (b) The lab assistant put 3% hydrogen peroxide in the reagent bottle labeled "30% H_2O_2." (c) You forgot to add potassium carbonate in the Separation step.
7. (a) In what form does BH_3 ordinarily exist? Give the name, molecular formula, and structure of this substance. (b) Write equations showing how this substance can be used to bring about the conversion of 1-hexene to the alcohol you obtained.

Other Things You Can Do

(Starred items require your instructor's permission.)

*1. Carry out the reaction of iodine with an alkene component of turpentine as described in the "Addition of Iodine to α-Pinene" minilab.

*2. Write a procedure for converting 1-hexene to the alcohol you did *not* obtain in this experiment, have it approved by your instructor, and carry it out in the lab.

3. Write a research paper about regioselectivity in addition reactions of alkenes, starting with sources listed in the Bibliography.

Stereochemistry of Bromine Addition to *trans*-Cinnamic Acid

Reactions of Alkenes. Preparation of Alkyl Halides. Electrophilic Addition. Stereoselectivity.

Operations

OP-10 Mixing
OP-11 Addition of Reactants
OP-16 Vacuum Filtration
OP-26 Washing and Drying Solids
OP-28 Recrystallization
OP-33 Melting Point

Before You Begin

1. Read the experiment, read or review the operations as necessary, and write an experimental plan.
2. Calculate the mass of 10.0 mmol of *trans*-cinnamic acid and the theoretical yield of 2,3-dibromo-3-phenylpropanoic acid.

Scenario

The Bond Triplex is a chemical specialties company that supplies alkynes to order. Many of their alkynes are prepared by adding bromine to the corresponding alkenes and dehydrohalogenating the resulting dibromides. For example, they convert *trans*-cinnamic acid to 3-phenylpropynoic acid by way of 2,3-dibromo-3-phenylpropanoic acid.

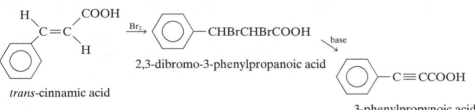

2,3-dibromo-3-phenylpropanoic acid

trans-cinnamic acid

3-phenylpropynoic acid

At a recent meeting of the three Bond partners (Sigmund, Bridget, and James) with the chemical engineers who developed their manufacturing processes, the engineers had to admit that they weren't certain of the stereochemical structures of the intermediate dibromides. They had simply assumed that the bromine addition reactions proceeded by the well-established bromonium ion mechanism (see "Understanding the Experiment"), resulting in *anti* addition of bromine, and deduced the stereochemistry of the

From *Operational Organic Chemistry: A Problem Solving Approach to the Laboratory*, Fourth Edition, John W. Lehman. Copyright © 2009 by Pearson Education. Published by Prentice Hall. All rights reserved.

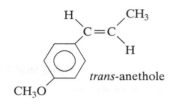

trans-anethole

Key Concept: *Changing the structure of the substrate may alter the mechanism of a reaction.*

dibromides accordingly. But some of the alkenes the Bond Triplex is using have electron-donating substituents that could affect the mechanism of the addition reaction. For example, *trans*-anethole undergoes a significant amount of *syn* addition of bromine by an alternative mechanism.

Because knowing the stereochemistry of the intermediate dibromides could help the company's chemical engineers design a more efficient process for converting them to alkynes, Sigmund Bond has contacted your institute for help in characterizing the intermediates. Your assignment is to carry out the bromination of *trans*-cinnamic acid, determine the stereochemical structure of the dibromide, and find out whether the reaction proceeds by the usual bromonium ion mechanism or by some other mechanism.

Applying Scientific Methodology

Your hypothesis should include a prediction regarding the mechanism of the reaction. You will test your hypothesis by measuring the melting point of the product. This will reveal its identity, from which you can deduce the stereochemistry of the reaction.

The Cinnamic Acid Connection

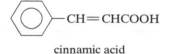

cinnamic acid

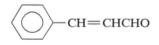

cinnamaldehyde

Cinnamic acid and its close relatives, cinnamaldehyde and cinnamyl alcohol, are naturally occurring compounds that are important as flavoring and perfume ingredients and as sources for pharmaceuticals. Cinnamaldehyde, the major component of cinnamon oil, is used to flavor many foods and beverages and to contribute a spicy "oriental" note to perfumes. Cinnamic acid itself plays an important role in secondary plant metabolism. As an intermediate in the shikimic acid pathway for plant biosynthesis, cinnamic acid is involved in the formation of an enormous number of natural substances that (to name just a few examples) contribute structural strength to wood; give flavor to cloves, nutmeg, and sassafras; and produce many of the brilliant colors of nature—the flower pigments that attract insects for pollination, the vivid and delicate shades of a butterfly's wings, and the radiant colors of leaves in autumn.

In nature, cinnamic acid is formed by the enzymatic deamination (removal of ammonia) of the amino acid phenylalanine, which in turn is biosynthesized in a series of steps from shikimic acid.

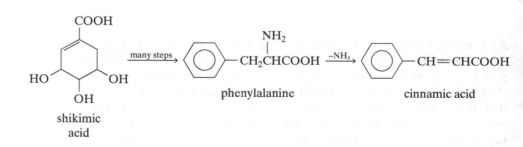

shikimic
acid

phenylalanine

cinnamic acid

It can then be converted, by various biosynthetic pathways, to coniferyl alcohol (a precursor of lignin) in sapwood, myristicin in nutmeg, safrole in sassafras bark, and flavonoids in a wide variety of plant structures.

The flavonoids are natural substances characterized by the 2-arylbenzopyran structure found in flavanone, which itself is biosynthesized from cinnamic acid by a process that involves the linkage of three acetyl residues to the carboxyl group of the acid.

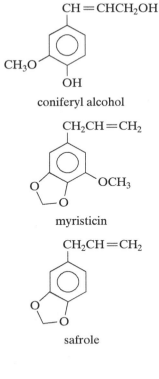
coniferyl alcohol

myristicin

safrole

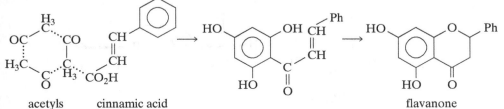

acetyls   cinnamic acid   flavanone

Flavonoids perform no single function in plants. Many are highly colored and attract insects for pollination or animals for seed dispersal; others help regulate seed germination and plant growth or protect plants from fungal and bacterial diseases. Certain flavonoids contribute the bitter taste to lemons and the bracing astringency of cocoa, tea, and beer. Some flavonoids in foods appear to act as antioxidants that may boost the immune system and help prevent cancer. Flavonoids and other derivatives of cinnamic acid provide much to delight the eye and stimulate the senses—the world would be a duller place without them!

Understanding the Experiment

In this experiment, you will carry out the addition of bromine to *trans*-cinnamic acid and identify the product from its melting point. The product, actually a mixture of enantiomers, could be either *erythro*-2,3-dibromo-3-phenylpropanoic acid [whose enantiomers have the (2R,3S) and (2S,3R) configurations], the *threo*-dibromide [(2R,3R) and (2S,3S)], or a mixture of the *erythro*- and *threo*-dibromides. The *erythro–threo* nomenclature is used to describe the configurations of compounds that have two chiral centers but no plane of symmetry. It is based on the structures of the two simple sugars erythrose and threose.

The product you obtain will depend on the stereochemical course of the reaction. A reaction is said to be regioselective if it might produce two or more structural isomers but in fact yields one of them preferentially. Similarly, a reaction is said to be *stereoselective* if it might produce two or more stereoisomers but in fact yields mainly (or entirely) one of them. For example, the electrophilic addition of bromine to cyclopentene is stereoselective because it yields *trans*-dibromocyclopentane and no *cis*-dibromocyclopentane, indicating that the components of Br$_2$ must add to opposite sides of the carbon–carbon double bond. This mode of addition is called *anti* addition, whereas addition of the components of a reagent to the same side of a double bond is called *syn* addition.

The following scenario has been proposed to explain the *anti* addition of bromine to cyclopentene. As a bromine molecule approaches perpendicular

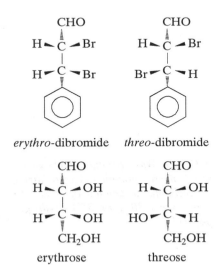

erythro-dibromide   *threo*-dibromide

erythrose   threose

to the negatively charged pi cloud of the carbon–carbon double bond, its bonding electrons are repelled away from the bromine atom nearer the double bond, leaving it with a partial positive charge. As the positively charged bromine penetrates the pi cloud, a negative bromide ion breaks away from it, leaving a cyclic *bromonium ion*, in which the positive bromine is bonded to two carbon atoms. Backside attack on the bromonium ion by a bromide ion results in the observed *trans* product.

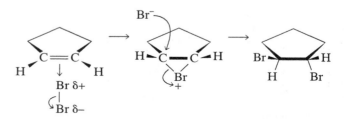

Other electrophilic addition mechanisms may lead to different stereochemical outcomes. In the addition of bromine to *trans*-anethole, conjugation with the ring stabilizes a carbocation intermediate that can be attacked on either side, leading to *syn* as well as *anti* addition.

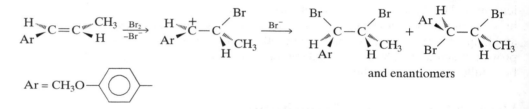

In this particular reaction, about 35% of the product results from *syn* addition and 65% from *anti* addition. It is also possible that a concerted addition to the carbon–carbon double bond could occur, leading exclusively to *syn* addition, as illustrated here.

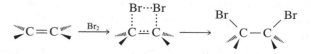

A Greener Way: Bromine can be generated in the reaction mixture by oxidizing a stoichiometric amount of 48% HBr with excess 30% or 35% hydrogen peroxide.

You will carry out the reaction by adding a solution of bromine in acetic acid to a solution of *trans*-cinnamic acid in the same solvent, and separate the resulting dibromide by vacuum filtration. Because the melting points of the *erythro-* and *threo*-dibromides differ by more than 100°C, the product can easily be identified from its melting point. A mixture of both products would melt over a broad range that shouldn't coincide with the melting point of either pure dibromide. (Note that impurities may lower the melting point of your product somewhat, so a difference of a few degrees from the expected melting point doesn't indicate that both products are present.) From the identity of your product, you should be able to deduce whether the addition of bromine to *trans*-cinnamic acid involves *syn* or *anti* addition, or a mixture of the two. Molecular models will help you relate the configurations of the *syn* and *anti* addition products to the stereochemical structures shown for the *erythro-* and *threo*-dibromides.

Acetic acid is expected to be slightly toxic to aquatic life. Bromine is toxic to aquatic organisms, but no water quality standards for bromine have been issued by the U.S. government.

Reaction and Properties

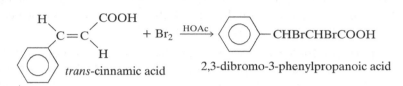

trans-cinnamic acid + Br$_2$ $\xrightarrow{\text{HOAc}}$ phenyl—CHBrCHBrCOOH

2,3-dibromo-3-phenylpropanoic acid

Table 1 Physical properties

	mol wt	mp	bp	*d*
trans-cinnamic acid	148.2	136		
bromine	159.8	−7	59	3.12
acetic acid	60.1	17	118	1.049
erythro-2,3-dibromo-3-phenylpropanoic acid	308.0	204		
threo-2,3-dibromo-3-phenylpropanoic acid	308.0	95		

Note: mp and bp are in °C; density is in g/mL.

DIRECTIONS

A. *Preparation of 2,3-Dibromo-3-phenylpropanoic Acid*

Bromine is highly toxic and corrosive, and its vapors can damage the eyes and respiratory tract. Wear gloves when handling the bromine solution and dispense it under a hood; avoid contact and do not inhale its vapors. Acetic acid causes chemical burns that can seriously damage skin and eyes; its vapors are highly irritating to the eyes and respiratory tract. Wear gloves and dispense it under a hood; avoid contact and do not breathe its vapors.

Safety Notes

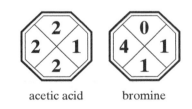

acetic acid   bromine

Reaction. *Carry out the reaction under the hood and wear gloves throughout.* In a 50-mL round-bottom flask, combine 10.0 mmol of *trans*-cinnamic acid with 6.0 mL of glacial acetic acid. Add a stir bar if you have a magnetic stirrer, or use boiling chips. Assemble an apparatus for addition [OP-11] under reflux using a separatory–addition funnel, reflux condenser, and Claisen connecting tube. Be sure the stopcock of the separatory–addition funnel is closed, then add 10 mL of a 1.0 *M* solution of bromine in acetic acid and stopper it immediately. Place the reaction mixture in a 50°C water bath and start the stirrer [OP-10] (or swirl the flask after each addition). Add the bromine/acetic acid solution in five or more portions, waiting until the color has faded to light orange before adding the next portion. The cinnamic acid should dissolve shortly after the addition of the first portion. After the last addition, heat the reaction mixture in a 50°C water bath for 15 minutes while stirring or occasionally swirling. If the mixture becomes

Take Care! Wear gloves; avoid contact with acetic acid and the bromine solution; do not breathe their vapors.

Observe and Note: Look for and record any evidence for a reaction.

Stop and Think: What is the purpose of the cyclohexene? What reaction is involved?

colorless (or nearly so) during this period, add more of the bromine/acetic acid solution dropwise until the color just persists. If the mixture has a distinct orange color at the end of the reaction period, add a drop or so of cyclohexene to turn it light yellow.

Separation. Transfer the reaction mixture to an Erlenmeyer flask and cool it in an ice/water bath for 15 minutes or more, scratching the sides of the flask to induce crystallization, if necessary. Collect the product by vacuum filtration [OP-16] and wash it on the filter [OP-26a] with portions of ice-cold water until the acetic acid odor is hardly noticeable.

Waste Disposal: Unless your instructor directs otherwise, wash the filtrate down the hood's drain.

Stop and Think: Was the result what you expected? If not, why not?

Purification and Analysis. Purify the product by recrystallization [OP-28] from 50% aqueous ethanol, washing it on the filter [OP-26a] with cold 50% ethanol. Dry [OP-26b] the 2,3-dibromo-3-phenylpropanoic acid and measure its melting point [OP-33]. Then decide whether you have prepared the *erythro* or *threo* isomer or a mixture of the two.

B. *Stereochemistry of Bromine Addition*
Construct a molecular model of *trans*-cinnamic acid (to simplify matters, use a colored ball to represent the phenyl group). Simulate the *syn* addition of bromine by removing one of the C=C connectors and inserting two orange bromine atoms, with connectors, into the vacant holes. (You may want to replace the remaining flexible connector with a rigid one.) Rotate around the carbon–carbon single bond that remains until the model corresponds to the stereochemical projection for either *threo*- or *erythro*-2,3-dibromo-3-phenylpropanoic acid. Simulate the *anti* addition of bromine by removing the upper connector of the carbon–carbon double bond and moving one end of the lower connector from the hole it occupies to the vacant hole in the same carbon atom. Be careful not to rotate either carbon atom as you do so. Insert two bromine atoms, with connectors, into the vacant holes; then rotate the model as before, until it matches one of the stereochemical projections. Decide whether your product was formed by *syn* addition or *anti* addition, or a mixture of both. Write a mechanism that explains your results.

Exercises

1. (a) Write resonance structures showing how the aryl group of *trans*-anethole stabilizes the intermediate carbocation shown in "Understanding the Experiment." (b) Based on your results, explain any differences or similarities in the stereochemistry of the bromine addition reactions of *trans*-cinnamic acid and *trans*-anethole.
2. What product or products would you expect to obtain by the addition of bromine to *cis*-cinnamic acid, assuming that it reacts by the same mechanism as the *trans* acid?
3. (a) Write mechanisms showing why bromination of *trans*-cinnamic acid yields the product you obtained as a racemic mixture of enantiomers. (b) Draw a stereochemical projection for each enantiomer and specify the configuration (*R* or *S*) at each stereocenter.

4. (a) Calculate the atom economy and reaction efficiency of your synthesis. (b) Describe some green features of your synthesis, and any that aren't so green.

5. Describe and explain the possible effect on your results of the following experimental errors or variations. (a) The cinnamic acid you used was actually a mixture of *cis* and *trans* isomers. (b) You added a total of 5 mL of the bromine solution. (c) You misread the label on a bottle of cyclohexane and used it in place of cyclohexene.

6. Following the format in the "Planning an Experiment" appendix, construct a flow diagram for the synthesis that you carried out in this experiment.

7. Draw stereochemical projections for the products of bromine addition to maleic acid and fumaric acid (*cis* and *trans* HOOCCH=CHCOOH, respectively) assuming that bromine adds to these compounds the same way it does to cinnamic acid.

8. (a) Would you expect the product from this experiment to be optically active? Could it be resolved into optically active constituents? Explain. (b) Would the product of the bromination of fumaric acid (see Exercise 7) be optically active? Could it be resolved into optically active constituents? Explain.

Other Things You Can Do

(Starred items require your instructor's permission.)

*1. Test some commercial products for unsaturation as described in the "Unsaturation in Commercial Products" minilab.

*2. Synthesize 3-phenylpropynoic acid from your product by scaling down the procedure given in *J. Am. Chem. Soc.* **1942**, *64*, 2510. Find a suitable recrystallization solvent to use in place of carbon tetrachloride.

3. Write a research paper about the industrial preparation and commercial uses of cinnamic acid and its derivatives, starting with sources listed in the Bibliography.

A Green Synthesis of Adipic Acid

Green Chemistry. Oxidative Cleavage. Reactions of Alkenes. Preparation of Carboxylic Acids. Infrared Spectrometry.

Operations

OP-6   Making Transfers
OP-7   Heating
OP-8   Cooling
OP-10 Mixing
OP-16 Vacuum Filtration
OP-26 Washing and Drying Solids
OP-28 Recrystallization
OP-33 Infrared Spectrometry

Before You Begin

1. Read the experiment, read or review the operations as necessary, and write an experimental plan.
2. Calculate the mass and volume of 25.0 mmol of cyclohexene, and the theoretical yield of the product.

Scenario

Mega Molecules, Inc. (MMI) prepares a variety of chemicals that are used to make such polymers as nylon and polystyrene. The polymers can then be used for manufacturing textiles and plastics. One of their products is adipic acid, which is used to manufacture the most common form of nylon, known as nylon 6,6.

$$\underset{\text{adipic acid}}{\overset{\overset{\displaystyle O}{\|}}{HOC}CH_2CH_2CH_2CH_2\overset{\overset{\displaystyle O}{\|}}{C}OH} \qquad \underset{\text{nylon 6,6}}{-\!\!\left[\overset{\overset{\displaystyle O}{\|}}{C}CH_2CH_2CH_2CH_2\overset{\overset{\displaystyle O}{\|}}{C}NHCH_2CH_2CH_2CH_2CH_2CH_2NH\right]_n}$$

The main commercial process for manufacturing adipic acid involves the air oxidation of cyclohexane to a mixture of cyclohexanol and cyclohexanone, followed by nitric acid oxidation of this mixture.

The nitrogen oxides produced by this process contributes significantly to global warming and depletion of the ozone layer.

From *Operational Organic Chemistry: A Problem Solving Approach to the Laboratory*, Fourth Edition, John W. Lehman. Copyright © 2009 by Pearson Education. Published by Prentice Hall. All rights reserved.

MMI would like to develop a greener method for the synthesis that produces no nitrogen oxides. One synthetic route they are considering involves the oxidation of cyclohexene using hydrogen peroxide in the presence of both a phase-transfer catalyst (PTC) and a sodium tungstate catalyst. (See "Reactions and Properties.") This synthetic route would require no organic solvents, and its only significant by-product is water. Your assignment is to test this new procedure to find out whether it does, in fact, yield adipic acid of reasonable purity.

Applying Scientific Methodology

There are two scientific problems in this experiment: (1) to determine whether the reaction of cyclohexene yields adipic acid, and (2) to determine whether or not the adipic acid is reasonably pure. The first problem can be solved by obtaining the melting point and an infrared spectrum of your product. The melting point of pure adipic acid is 152°C, so a melting point within ±2°C of that value will suggest that the product is reasonably pure.

Crossing the Boundary—The Role of the Phase-Transfer Catalyst

In this experiment, you will be mixing the organic compound cyclohexene with an aqueous solution of hydrogen peroxide and a catalyst, sodium tungstate. Tungstate ion (WO_4^{2-}) is a good oxidizing agent, so presumably it is the oxidant that actually converts cyclohexene to adipic acid. The hydrogen peroxide then converts the reduced form of the ion back to WO_4^{2-}, which therefore acts as a true catalyst by promoting the reaction without being used up. Using such a catalyst makes the reaction even greener, because the aqueous layer containing sodium tungstate can be recovered and reused in subsequent reactions.

In order for the reaction to work, tungstate ions have to come in contact with cyclohexene molecules; but, like most ionic compounds, sodium tungstate is soluble in water but not in organic phases. To get around this difficulty, we need to arrange for tungstate ions to somehow be "escorted" across the phase boundary that separates the organic cyclohexene phase from the aqueous hydrogen peroxide phase. This is where a different kind of catalyst, called a *phase-transfer catalyst*, comes in.

To understand the basic principles of PTC, consider the nucleophilic substitution reaction of an alkyl halide with sodium cyanide to form a nitrile. If a high molecular-weight halide such as 1-chlorooctane is heated with aqueous sodium cyanide, the reaction is extremely slow. Cyanide ions stay in the aqueous layer and alkyl halide molecules stay in the organic layer, so the reactants only meet infrequently at the phase boundary. If, instead of sodium cyanide, a quaternary ammonium (Q) salt such as tetrabutylammonium cyanide $[(CH_3CH_2CH_2CH_2)_4N^+CN^-]$ is used, the reaction proceeds quite readily and gives a high yield of product.

Reaction of 1-chlorooctane with sodium cyanide (R = n-C_8H_{17})

$$RCl + Na^+CN^- \longrightarrow RCN + Na^+Cl^-$$

Improved reaction with a quaternary ammonium cyanide

$$RCl + Q^+CN^- \longrightarrow RCN + Q^+Cl^-$$

$$[Q^+ = (CH_3CH_2CH_2CH_2)_4N^+]$$

There are several reasons for this enhanced reactivity of the cyanide. First, and most importantly, the 16 carbon atoms of the $(CH_3CH_2CH_2CH_2)_4N^+$ cation make it soluble in the organic phase, and where the cation goes, the anion must follow. Second, the cyanide ion is more reactive in the organic phase than it would have been in the aqueous phase, because it isn't solvated by water molecules (a solvent shell would shield it from the alkyl halide and decrease its reactivity). Finally, the bulky alkyl groups around the positive nitrogen of the cation decrease the attractive forces between cation and anion and allow the cyanide ion more freedom to attack the alkyl halide. So, substituting a quaternary ammonium ion for the sodium ion in the cyanide salt allows the desired reaction to proceed at a much higher rate. Its main drawback is that the quaternary ammonium cyanide is much more expensive than sodium cyanide.

The PTC technique gets around the high cost of quaternary ammonium salts by recycling them after each reaction step. If the quaternary ammonium cation in tetrabutylammonium chloride (represented in the previous equation by Q^+Cl^-) can be made to pick up more cyanide to react with the alkyl halide, it will function as a true catalyst, accelerating the reaction without being used up. All that is needed is a reservoir of cyanide ions and a small amount of quaternary ammonium salt to keep the reaction going. The reservoir can be provided by an aqueous layer that contains sodium cyanide.

Figure 1 diagrams the process, which occurs as follows: A catalytic amount of Q^+Cl^- combines with cyanide ion in the aqueous phase, and the Q^+CN^- that forms crosses over to the organic layer. There, it reacts with the alkyl halide to produce the nitrile (RCN) and form more Q^+Cl^-, which migrates across the interface, picks up more cyanide, shuttles it back into the organic layer to react with the alkyl halide and form more product and Q^+Cl^-, and so on, until the alkyl halide or the cyanide ion is used up.

Key Concept: A phase-transfer catalyst speeds up a reaction by bringing together reactants that would otherwise remain in separate phases.

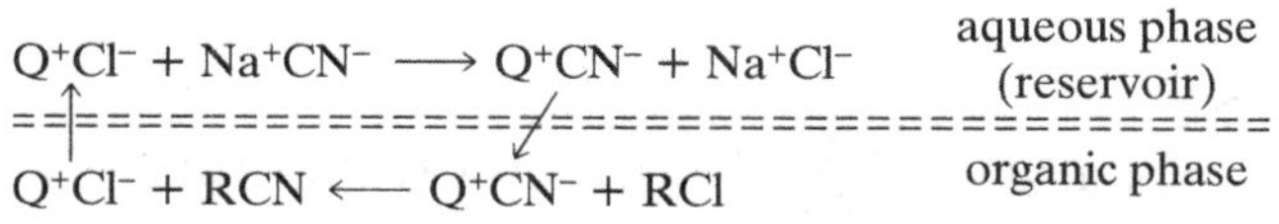

$$Q^+Cl^- + Na^+CN^- \longrightarrow Q^+CN^- + Na^+Cl^-$$
aqueous phase (reservoir)

$$Q^+Cl^- \longleftarrow RCN + Q^+CN^- + RCl$$
organic phase

Figure 1 Phase-transfer process for a nucleophilic substitution reaction

Understanding the Experiment

In this experiment, you will heat and stir cyclohexene with a mixture that contains 30% or 35% hydrogen peroxide, sodium tungstate dihydrate, a phase-transfer catalyst, and potassium bisulfate (potassium hydrogen sulfate, $KHSO_4$). A successful reaction requires a slightly acidic environment, so potassium bisulfate is used to lower the pH of the reaction mixture. The conversion of cyclohexene to adipic acid involves breaking the carbon–carbon double bond as well as oxidation of the doubly bonded carbon atoms, so it is classified as an *oxidative cleavage* reaction.

[CH$_3$(CH$_2$)$_7$]$_3$NCH$_3^+$Cl$^-$
tricaprylmethylammonium
chloride (Aliquat 336)

The phase-transfer catalyst you will use is a viscous liquid, tricaprylmethylammonium chloride, which is also known as Aliquat 336. The quaternary cation (Q$^+$) of this catalyst contains a methyl group and three alkyl chains of 8 carbons each, attached to a nitrogen atom. The initial reaction mixture will consist of an organic phase containing cyclohexene and an aqueous phase containing sodium tungstate, hydrogen peroxide, and the other substances listed previously. The PTC reacts with sodium tungstate as shown.

$$2Q^+Cl^- + Na_2WO_4 \rightarrow Q_2WO_4 + 2Na^+Cl^-$$

The resulting tricaprylmethylammonium tungstate (Q$_2$WO$_4$) is soluble in the organic phase, allowing the tungstate ions to react with cyclohexene molecules. The reduced form of tungstate then returns to the aqueous layer, where it is oxidized back to tungstate, and the process is repeated.

The product yield will depend on both the heating time and the stirring rate. The phases must be well mixed for a two-phase reaction to proceed, so the reaction mixture should be stirred as vigorously as possible throughout the reaction period. Enough product can be obtained for analysis after a minimum reaction time of one hour, but not all of the cyclohexene will have reacted by then; increasing the reaction time to two hours or more should improve the yield significantly. The solid product should crystallize out of solution upon cooling and can be collected by vacuum filtration. You can then purify it by recrystallizing it from boiling water. Once the product is dry, you will measure its melting point and obtain its infrared spectrum, which you can compare with a standard spectrum provided by your instructor or obtained from the library.

In the environment, cyclohexene should evaporate quickly; adipic acid is expected to be slightly toxic to aquatic life.

Reactions and Properties

$$\bigcirc + 4H_2O_2 \xrightarrow[\text{PTC}]{\text{NaWO}_3 \cdot 2H_2O} \underset{\text{adipic acid}}{HOCCH_2CH_2CH_2CH_2COH} + 4H_2O$$

cyclohexene

Table 1 Physical properties

	mol wt	mp	bp	d
cyclohexene	82.15	−104	83	0.809
sodium tungstate dihydrate	329.9	696		3.245
35% hydrogen peroxide	34.0	−40	126	1.13
potassium bisulfate	136.1	197		2.24
adipic acid	146.1	152	338	1.36

Note: bp and mp are in °C; density is in g/mL.

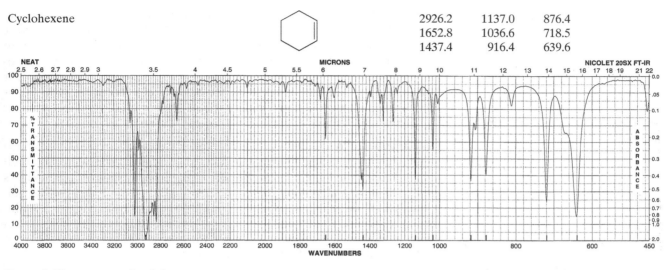

Cyclohexene

2926.2	1137.0	876.4
1652.8	1036.6	718.5
1437.4	916.4	639.6

Figure 2 IR spectrum of cyclohexene

DIRECTIONS

Cyclohexene is flammable; inhalation or skin absorption may be harmful. Avoid contact and do not breathe its vapors.

Concentrated hydrogen peroxide is very corrosive and can cause severe burns. It is a strong oxidant and can form explosive mixtures in the presence of certain organic compounds. Wear gloves, avoid eye and skin contact, do not breathe the vapors, and keep it away from other chemicals. In case of skin or eye contact, immediately flush thoroughly with water.

Sodium tungstate dihydrate is very toxic and may be harmful by inhalation. Ingestion can be fatal. Avoid contact and do not breathe its dust.

Potassium hydrogen sulfate is corrosive and can cause burns or other damage to the skin, eyes, and respiratory tract. Avoid contact and do not breathe its dust.

Adipic acid causes moderate eye irritation; it may irritate the skin and respiratory tract. Avoid contact and do not breathe its dust.

Safety Notes

cyclohexene hydrogen peroxide

Reaction.   Weigh 0.50 g of sodium tungstate dihydrate into a 50-mL round-bottom flask. Add about 0.50 g of Aliquat 336, then add 10 mL of 35% hydrogen peroxide (or 12 mL of 30% H_2O_2) followed by 0.40 g of potassium hydrogen sulfate (potassium bisulfate); swirl to mix well. Add 25.0 mmol of cyclohexene and a stir bar (preferably the largest one that will fit) and heat the mixture under reflux [OP-7c] with *vigorous* stirring [OP-10]. Make sure that the reflux ring of condensing vapors stays below the midpoint of the condenser so that cyclohexene doesn't escape.

After heating and stirring under reflux for about 30 minutes, use a Pasteur pipet to rinse down the condenser with about 3 mL of water. Then dip the tip of a long glass rod into the reaction mixture and test with

Take Care: Hydrogen peroxide can cause severe burns. Wear gloves, and avoid contact and inhalation. Avoid contact with sodium tungstate and potassium hydrogen sulfate; do not breathe their dust.

starch–iodide paper; if the paper doesn't turn blue-black within a few seconds, add hydrogen peroxide solution, about 1 mL at a time, until it does. Continue heating and stirring under reflux, testing the reaction mixture with starch–iodide paper every 15 minutes or so and adding more hydrogen peroxide if the test is negative. Carry out the reaction under reflux for a total time of at least one hour; if time permits, let it continue for another hour or so to improve your yield. By then, most or all of the oily top layer should have disappeared.

Stop and Think: What is in the top layer?

Separation. While the reaction mixture is still hot, decant it (see OP-15) carefully into a beaker, leaving behind any Aliquat that separates as an oil (the oil may form a layer on the bottom of the flask or stick to its walls). It's better to leave a little solution behind than to contaminate it with Aliquat. Cool [OP-8] the reaction mixture in an ice/water bath for at least 30 minutes after a precipitate begins to form. Scratch the sides of the flask, if necessary, to induce crystallization. Collect the precipitate by vacuum filtration [OP-16] and wash it [OP-26a] with ice water.

Waste Disposal: Unless your instructor directs otherwise, wash the filtrates down the drain.

Purification and Analysis. Recrystallize [OP-28] the product using a minimum volume of boiling water. Dry it [OP-26b] overnight or longer in a desiccator and weigh it. Measure the melting point [OP-33] of the dried product, and record its infrared spectrum [OP-39].

Exercises

1. Calculate the atom economy and reaction efficiency of your synthesis.
2. Based on the discussion of green chemistry in the "Chemistry and the Environment" section, list the principles of green chemistry that this experiment illustrates and explain how it illustrates each principle.
3. Based on the illustration in Figure 1, diagram the phase-transfer process involved in this experiment; use W_{red} to indicate the reduced form of tungstate, whose composition for this reaction isn't known. There should be four reaction steps involved, three of them in the aqueous phase.
4. Describe and explain the possible effect on your results of the following experimental errors or variations. (a) Your lab kit contained only a very small magnetic stir bar. (b) The lab assistant couldn't find any hydrogen peroxide in the stockroom, so she bought a bottle of hydrogen peroxide solution (used as an antiseptic) from the local drugstore. (c) You misread the label on a bottle of potassium bicarbonate and used it in place of potassium bisulfate. (d) When you transferred the reaction mixture to a beaker, some of the Aliquat came along with it.
5. Following the format in the "Planning an Experiment" appendix, construct a flow diagram for this experiment.
6. Using balanced equations, show how nylon 6,6 can be synthesized using adipic acid as one of the reactants.
7. Outline a synthesis of 5-oxohexanoic acid using the oxidative cleavage method described in this experiment.
8. Write a balanced equation for the reaction of hydrogen peroxide with the potassium iodide in the starch–iodide paper.

$$CH_3\overset{O}{\overset{\|}{C}}CH_2CH_2CH_2\overset{O}{\overset{\|}{C}}OH$$

5-oxohexanoic acid

Other Things You Can Do

(Starred items require your instructor's permission.)

*1. Record and interpret an ^{1}H and/or ^{13}C NMR spectrum of your product.
*2. Prepare nylon 6,10 as described in "The Nylon Rope Trick" minilab.
 3. Write a research paper about the industrial manufacture and uses of adipic acid, starting with sources cited in the Bibliography.

Preparation of Bromotriphenylmethane and the Trityl Free Radical

Reactions of Hydrocarbons. Preparation of Alkyl Halides. Free-Radical Substitution. Free Radicals.

Operations

OP-27 Cleaning and Drying Gases
OP-7 Heating
OP-10 Mixing
OP-11 Addition of Reactants
OP-14 Trapping Gases (optional)
OP-15 Gravity Filtration
OP-16 Vacuum Filtration
OP-19 Evaporation
OP-26 Washing and Drying Solids
OP-28 Recrystallization
OP-33 Melting Point

Before You Begin

1. Read the experiment and operation OP-27, read or review the operations as necessary, and write an experimental plan.
2. Calculate the mass of 4.50 mmol of triphenylmethane and the theoretical yield of bromotriphenylmethane.

Scenario

Dr. Perry Celsus wants you to re-create the experiment that led to the discovery of the first stable free radical by Moses Gomberg. In a landmark paper that was published in the 1900 *Journal of the American Chemical Society*, Gomberg described his preparation of the triphenylmethyl (trityl) free radical by the reaction of bromotriphenylmethane with various metals. Dr. Celsus has requested that you prepare some bromotriphenylmethane and find out whether it can, in fact, be converted by metallic zinc to the free radical that Gomberg described.

J. Am. Chem. Soc. **1900**, *22*, 757.

Applying Scientific Methodology

Your working hypothesis should deal with the likelihood that the free radical will be produced and detected by the procedure described in part **B** of the Directions. You will test the hypothesis by observing and interpreting

From *Operational Organic Chemistry: A Problem Solving Approach to the Laboratory*, Fourth Edition, John W. Lehman. Copyright © 2009 by Pearson Education. Published by Prentice Hall. All rights reserved.

the behavior of the reaction mixture obtained by treating bromotriphenyl-methane with zinc.

The Case of the Disappearing Dimer

In the mid-nineteenth century, many chemists were convinced that carbon could exist in a trivalent state as a free *radical*, where a radical is a group of atoms such as methyl (CH_3—) that generally exists only in combination with other atoms or groups, as in methyl bromide (CH_3Br). For example, it seemed reasonable to believe that, if magnesium chloride could react with sodium metal to yield magnesium, methyl halides should react with sodium to form methyl. But when Charles Wurtz added sodium to methyl iodide, he obtained not methyl but ethane in a reaction known today as the Wurtz reaction.

Reaction of methyl iodide and sodium

$$CH_3I + Na \longrightarrow CH_3 + NaI \qquad \text{(expected reaction)}$$

$$2CH_3I + Na \longrightarrow CH_3CH_3 + 2NaI \qquad \text{(actual reaction)}$$

After many similar attempts to make free radicals ended in failure, chemists began to doubt that they could exist at all. Then, in 1900, Moses Gomberg, a young chemistry instructor at the University of Michigan, published a remarkable paper describing his discovery of the world's first stable free radical, triphenylmethyl.

Gomberg never meant to make a free radical. He was trying to synthesize hexaphenylethane to prove a point that, had he been successful, would be remembered today by only a handful of scientists. His initial attempts to prepare this compound using the Wurtz reaction weren't successful, so he tried different metals, such as silver and zinc.

Gomberg's attempted synthesis of hexaphenylethane (Ph = phenyl,C_6H_5—)

$$2Ph_3CBr + Zn \longrightarrow Ph_3C—CPh_3 + ZnBr_2 \qquad \text{(expected reaction)}$$

Each time, he obtained a snow-white solid that melted at 185°C and had the wrong molecular formula for hexaphenylethane. After repeated attempts to prepare this compound, it finally occurred to him that the product might be reacting with oxygen in the air and forming triphenylmethyl peroxide, $Ph_3COOCPh_3$. When Gomberg next ran the reaction, he was careful to exclude air from the reaction mixture, and he obtained a white solid that melted at 147°C and had the molecular formula expected for hexaphenylethane. But this compound behaved very strangely for a hydrocarbon. It reacted in solution with air to form triphenylmethyl peroxide, and it rapidly decolorized dilute halogen solutions—something no ordinary hydrocarbon would do. Gomberg eventually concluded that he had synthesized the world's first stable free radical, triphenylmethyl.

$$2Ph_3CBr + Zn \longrightarrow 2Ph_3C\cdot + ZnBr_2$$

He had, in a way, reversed Wurtz's experiment; Wurtz tried to make a radical and obtained its dimer, while Gomberg tried to make the dimer of a radical and ended up with the radical itself. Although he didn't know it at the time, the dimer he finally made wasn't even the one he expected.

Gomberg believed that the colored triphenylmethyl (trityl) radical was in equilibrium with hexaphenylethane in solution.

Gomberg's proposed equilibrium

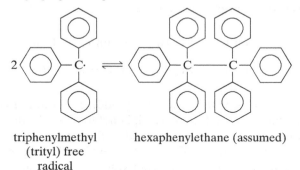

triphenylmethyl   hexaphenylethane (assumed)
(trityl) free
radical

But, in 1968, a team of chemists from the Netherlands reported that they had prepared a similar free radical that wouldn't dimerize. This new radical, tris(4-*t*-butylphenyl)methyl, had bulky *t*-butyl groups at each *para* position. Because the Dutch chemists couldn't explain why *para* substituents would prevent the formation of a hexaphenylethane-type dimer, they decided to prepare Gomberg's dimer and find out whether it had the structure he proposed. It didn't—NMR analysis showed that it actually has the following structure:

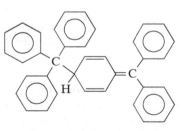

dimer of triphenylmethyl

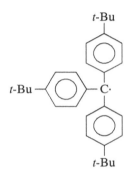

tris(4-*t*-butylphenyl)methyl

So Gomberg's dimer wasn't hexaphenylethane after all—that elusive hydrocarbon has probably never existed!

Understanding the Experiment

In this experiment, you will brominate triphenylmethane with elemental bromine using light to initiate the reaction. The bromination reaction proceeds by a chain mechanism similar to that for the chlorination of methane and other hydrocarbons. A source of atomic bromine is needed to initiate the chain reaction. In a typical alkane bromination, bromine atoms are produced by irradiating molecular bromine in solution.

$$Br_2 \xrightarrow{h\nu} 2Br\cdot$$

The symbol hv over a reaction arrow means that some kind of electromagnetic radiation, such as ultraviolet or visible light, is used to catalyze the reaction.

In the chain-propagating stage of the reaction, triphenylmethane should react with bromine atoms to produce trityl radicals. Thus, you could actually be making this radical twice during the experiment: once as an intermediate in the synthesis of bromotriphenylmethane, and later as a result of its reaction with zinc. Each trityl radical then reacts with a molecule of bromine, yielding a molecule of the product and another bromine atom that starts another cycle of chain-propagating steps.

Key Concept: A chain reaction involves the initial formation of a reactive species that is regenerated after each cycle of product-forming steps and initiates the next cycle.

$$Ph_3C-H + Br\cdot \longrightarrow Ph_3C\cdot + HBr$$

$$Ph_3C\cdot + Br_2 \longrightarrow Ph_3C-Br + Br\cdot$$

You will carry out the reaction by adding a solution of bromine in dichloromethane to a solution of triphenylmethane in the same solvent while heating the reaction mixture under reflux and irradiating it with light to generate bromine atoms. The reaction evolves hydrogen bromide, and bromine vapors may also escape from your apparatus, so you must either work under a fume hood or use a gas trap. When the reaction is complete, some excess bromine may remain that will color the reaction mixture. It can be removed by adding a little cyclohexene.

Removal of excess bromine

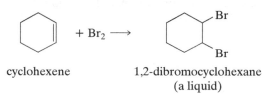

cyclohexene   1,2-dibromocyclohexane
(a liquid)

A Greener Way: Dichloromethane can be recovered by evaporating it under vacuum using a cold trap (see OP-15).

After evaporating the solvent, you will purify the product by recrystallization from hexanes (a mixture of six-carbon alkanes). As always, you will want to minimize material losses by making nearly quantitative transfers, avoiding unnecessary transfers, and using minimal amounts of recrystallization and washing solvents. You can reduce the number of transfers by evaporating the solvent directly from the reaction flask and recrystallizing the product in the same flask.

You will attempt to prepare the triphenylmethyl radical by treating bromotriphenylmethane with metallic zinc in toluene. Exposing the solution to air may provide evidence for the existence of a dynamic equilibrium between the radical and its dimer.

The EPA classifies dichloromethane as a priority pollutant and has established an MCL of 5 ppb for its concentration in drinking water. Bromine is toxic to marine organisms, but no water quality standards for bromine have been issued by the U.S. government. Hexane and related hydrocarbons break down in air, water, and soil, and apparently don't persist for long in the environment. Toluene is a serious environmental contaminant that shouldn't be released into the environment.

Reactions and Properties

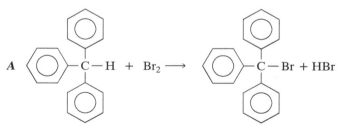

triphenylmethane   triphenylmethyl bromide

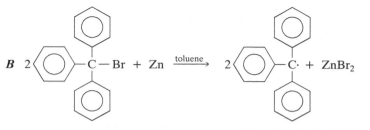

triphenylmethyl radical
(dimerizes in solution)

Table 1 Physical properties

	mol wt	mp	bp	d
triphenylmethane	244.3	94	359	
bromine	159.8	−7	59	3.12
dichloromethane	84.9	−97	40.5	1.326
bromotriphenylmethane	323.2	154		

Note: mp and bp are in °C; density is in g/mL.

DIRECTIONS

A. *Preparation of Bromotriphenylmethane*

Safety Notes

Bromine is highly toxic and corrosive; its vapors can damage the eyes and respiratory tract. Wear gloves when handling the bromine solution and dispense it under a hood; avoid contact and do not inhale its vapors.
Dichloromethane may be harmful if ingested, inhaled, or absorbed through the skin. There is a possibility that prolonged inhalation of dichloromethane may cause cancer. Avoid contact with the liquid and do not breathe its vapors.
Bromotriphenylmethane is harmful if inhaled or absorbed through the skin. Avoid contact with the product.
Hexanes and petroleum ether are highly flammable, so keep them away from flames and hot surfaces.

bromine   dichloromethane   petroleum ether

Stop and Think: What will happen if your glassware is wet?

Take Care! Wear gloves, avoid contact with dichloromethane and the bromine solution, and do not breathe their vapors.

Waste Disposal: Unless your instructor directs otherwise, wash the rinse liquid down the drain.

Waste Disposal: Place any recovered dichloromethane in a chlorinated-solvent recovery container.

Take Care! Keep hexanes and petroleum ether away from flames and hot surfaces.

Waste Disposal: Place the filtrate in a hydrocarbon-solvent recovery container.

Reaction. *All glassware that will be in contact with the reaction mixture or the product must be dry.* Assemble an apparatus for addition [OP-14] under reflux, using a 50-mL round-bottom flask. Assemble a gas trap [OP-14] containing dilute NaOH and use a length of rubber tubing to attach it to the top of the reflux condenser. (The gas trap can be omitted if the reaction is carried out under a hood.) Clamp an unfrosted 100–200-watt lightbulb within a few inches of the reaction flask; several students can use the same light. Weigh 4.50 mmol of triphenylmethane and dissolve it in 10 ml of dichloromethane in the reaction flask. Add a stir bar if you have a magnetic stirrer [OP-10]; otherwise, add some boiling chips.

Carefully measure 5.0 mL of *freshly prepared* 1.0 M bromine in dichloromethane and put it in the separatory–addition funnel, then stopper the funnel immediately. Turn on the light and magnetic stirrer (if used), and heat the mixture to a gentle reflux using a hot-water bath or steam bath [OP-7]. Add the bromine solution in five or more portions, waiting until the color of the solution has faded to light yellow-orange before adding the next portion. (If you don't have a stirrer, shake the apparatus carefully after each bromine addition to mix the reactants.) Continue heating for 30 minutes after the last addition, or until the solution becomes light yellow, and then let the reaction mixture cool to room temperature and disassemble the apparatus. If the reaction mixture has a distinct orange or red-brown color, add cyclohexene drop by drop until the color fades to yellow. Under the hood, use 10% sodium thiosulfate solution (which reduces bromine to bromide ions) to rinse out everything that contacted the bromine solution except the reaction flask.

Separation. Evaporate [OP-19] the dichloromethane under vacuum. You can evaporate it directly from the reaction flask using the setup illustrated in Figure C11c of OP-19.

Purification and Analysis. Recrystallize [OP-28] the crude bromotriphenylmethane using 15–20 mL of hexanes. The recrystallization mixture can be heated in the reaction flask with magnetic stirring, using a condenser to prevent solvent loss. If the solution is quite dark, use a small amount of pelletized Norit to decolorize it. If undissolved solid remains, filter [OP-15] the hot solution by gravity. Allow the product to crystallize, then collect it by vacuum filtration [OP-16] and wash it on the filter [OP-26a] with a small amount of cold, low-boiling petroleum ether. Dry [OP-26b] the bromotriphenylmethane; measure its mass and melting point [OP-33]. Save enough product for part **B** and turn in the rest to your instructor.

B. *Preparation and Reactions of the Trityl Free Radical*
At your instructor's discretion, this part can be carried out in small groups using either commercial trityl bromide or the purest product from each group. The quantities can be scaled up, if desired.

> **Toluene is flammable; inhalation, ingestion, or skin absorption may be harmful. Avoid contact with the liquid and do not breathe its vapors.**

Dissolve about 40 mg of *pure* bromotriphenylmethane in 1 mL of toluene in a 13 × 100-mm test tube. If the solution is significantly colored, add enough pelletized Norit to decolorize it. Add 0.10 g of 40-mesh zinc, stopper the tube immediately, and shake it for 10 minutes. Filter [OP-15] the mixture through a thin layer of glass wool (or a Pasteur pipet containing a loose cotton plug) into another 13 × 100-mm test tube and observe the color. Without delay, bubble dry air [OP-27] through the solution until any color fades, stopper and shake the test tube, and let it stand for 3–4 minutes. Repeat this process until the solution remains colorless for at least a minute after stoppering. Describe any evidence you observed for the existence of the trityl radical and for a dynamic equilibrium involving its dimer. Give names and structures of all species and equations for all reactions for which you saw evidence.

Safety Notes

toluene

Take Care! Avoid contact with toluene and do not inhale its vapors.

Observe and Note: During this procedure, take careful notes and describe your observations in detail.

Waste Disposal: Place the solution in a designated waste container.

Exercises

1. (a) Show how Gomberg's dimer, whose true structure was given previously, can form by the combination of two trityl radicals. (b) Explain why tris(4-*t*-butylphenyl)methyl doesn't form an analogous dimer.
2. Describe and explain the possible effect on your results of the following experimental errors or variations. (a) You forgot to turn on the light. (b) The reaction flask for part **A** was wet. (c) In part **B**, you bubbled nitrogen, rather than air, into the reaction mixture.
3. Following the format in the "Planning an Experiment" appendix, construct a flow diagram for the synthesis of bromotriphenylmethane.
4. (a) Calculate the atom economy and reaction efficiency of your synthesis of bromotriphenylmethane. (b) Describe some green features of this synthesis, and any that aren't so green.
5. Assuming a free-radical mechanism for the bromination of the following compounds, arrange them in order of their expected reactivity, starting with the most reactive.

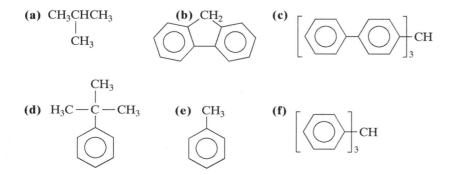

229

6. Gomberg's dimer will decolorize a solution of iodine in dichloromethane. Explain why, and write equations for all relevant reactions.

7. Write equations for three chain-terminating steps that can occur during the synthesis of bromotriphenylmethane.

Other Things You Can Do

(Starred items require your instructor's permission.)

*1. Convert your bromotriphenylmethane to an ether as described in "An S_N1 Reaction of Bromotriphenylmethane" minilab.

*2. Measure the bromination rates of some aromatic hydrocarbons as described in the "Free-Radical Stability" minilab.

*3. Collect the precipitate that formed in part **B** of this experiment by vacuum filtration and wash it with petroleum ether. Measure the melting point of the dry solid and give its structure.

4. Read the selections from Gomberg's work in *A Sourcebook in Chemistry, 1400–1900*, edited by H. M. Leicester and H. S. Klickstein (Boston: Harvard University Press, 1952). Describe the reasoning that led Gomberg to the conclusion that he had prepared the trityl free radical, and tell why he tried to prepare hexaphenylethane in the first place.

Chain-Growth Polymerization of Styrene and Methyl Methacrylate

Reactions of Alkenes. Preparation of Vinyl Polymers. Addition Polymerization. Free Radicals.

Operations

OP-7   Heating
OP-10 Mixing
OP-16 Vacuum Filtration
OP-26 Washing and Drying Solids
OP-30 Simple Distillation
OP-39 Infrared Spectrometry

Before You Begin

1. Read the experiment, read or review the operations as necessary, and write an experimental plan.
2. Calculate the mass of 20.0 mmol of styrene and the theoretical yield of polystyrene from part **A**.

Scenario

The Consulting Chemists Institute has two clients this week, both seeking information about polymers and polymerization reactions. Polly von Ilek, an artisan who specializes in nature crafts, plans to embed natural objects such as leaves, insects, and flowers in a matrix of clear, recycled plastic. She wants you to develop a procedure for depolymerizing granulated poly(methyl methacrylate) and then repolymerizing the monomer under conditions that would allow objects to be embedded in the matrix before it hardens.

Mega Molecules, Inc., which manufactures Styrofoam packing "peanuts" and other polymer-based products, has been manufacturing polystyrene by a process that involves benzene as an organic solvent. Because benzene is a known carcinogen, the company wants to phase it out and switch to the less toxic solvent toluene.

Your assignments are as follows:

- To see whether granulated poly(methyl methacrylate) can be depolymerized and then repolymerized to a clear plastic in which objects can be embedded.
- To find out whether the solution polymerization of styrene can be performed successfully in toluene.

From *Operational Organic Chemistry: A Problem Solving Approach to the Laboratory*, Fourth Edition, John W. Lehman. Copyright © 2009 by Pearson Education. Published by Prentice Hall. All rights reserved.

Applying Scientific Methodology

In each part of this experiment, the scientific problem is, in effect, to try something and find out whether it works. If you can convert each starting material to a solid that has the properties of a plastic, that provides evidence that a polymerization reaction has occurred. At your instructor's discretion, you may be able to confirm the structure of your polystyrene by obtaining its infrared (IR) spectrum.

Chain-Growth Polymers

The giant molecules we call *polymers* are immensely important to humankind—the meat, fruit, and vegetables we eat, the clothing we wear, and the wood we use for housing and furniture all consist partly or entirely of organic polymers. In fact, we are *made* of polymers, such as the proteins in muscles, organs, blood cells, enzymes, and protoplasm, and the nucleic acids in the chromosomes that control our heredity. Compared to these natural polymers, synthetic polymers are newcomers on the scene. Polystyrene was first synthesized in 1839 (the year that Charles Goodyear learned how to vulcanize another polymer, natural rubber), but its properties weren't appreciated at the time. The first commercially useful synthetic polymer didn't appear until 1907, when Leo Baekeland synthesized Bakelite from phenol and formaldehyde. Bakelite is a good electrical insulator that is still used to make electrical plugs and switches. The synthesis of nylon 6,6 and polyethylene in 1939, and the development of synthetic rubbers by German chemists during World War II, when Germany's supply of natural rubber was cut off, gave added impetus to the search for useful synthetic polymers. Today, it is possible to design "tailor-made" polymers that have almost any desired combination of properties by using special catalysts (called Ziegler–Natta catalysts) to regulate the stereochemistry of a polymer, and by programming the sequence of monomers in copolymers, in which two or more different monomers are combined in various ways.

Synthetic polymers are often classified as addition or condensation polymers. *Addition polymerization* involves the combination of monomer units without eliminating any by-product molecules. The repeating unit of the polymer, therefore, has the same chemical constitution as the monomer, as illustrated in the margin for polyethylene. *Condensation polymerization* involves the combination of monomer units containing two or more reactive functional groups that lose a small molecule, such as a water or HCl molecule, as they combine. Thus, the repeating unit of a condensation polymer doesn't have the same formula as the monomer (or monomers), as illustrated for nylon 6 synthesized from 6-aminohexanoic acid. Note that nylon 6 can also be formed by a ring-opening polymerization reaction from ω-caprolactam, so it is somewhat arbitrary to classify polymers according to the method used to prepare them.

The terms *chain-growth* and *step-growth* polymerization are used to describe two basic polymerization processes. Chain-growth polymerization is a process in which some monomer molecules are first activated by a polymerization initiator. Each polymer chain then grows very rapidly from the activated monomer by adding more monomer molecules to its reactive end—somewhat like adding beads to a string. Step-growth polymerization

In a sense, polystyrene is a natural polymer, because it is found in styrax from the sweet gum tree.

Formation of polyethylene by addition polymerization

$$n\text{CH}_2\!=\!\text{CH}_2 \longrightarrow \overset{\text{repeating unit}}{-(\text{CH}_2\text{CH}_2)_n-}$$

ethylene   polyethylene

(*n* is a large but indeterminate number.)

Formation of nylon 6 by condensation polymerization

$$n\text{H}_2\text{N(CH}_2)_5\overset{\text{O}}{\overset{\|}{\text{C}}}\text{OH} \longrightarrow$$

6-aminohexanoic acid

$$-[\text{NH(CH}_2)_5\overset{\text{O}}{\overset{\|}{\text{C}}}]_n- + \text{H}_2\text{O}$$

nylon 6

Formation of nylon 6 by ring-opening polymerization

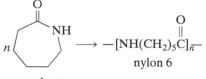

ω-caprolactam $\longrightarrow -[\text{NH(CH}_2)_5\overset{\text{O}}{\overset{\|}{\text{C}}}]_n-$

nylon 6

refers to a process in which each polymer chain grows from both ends of a monomer molecule through a series of individual reaction steps.

The polymerization of styrene with a free-radical initiator is a typical example of chain-growth polymerization. The initiator (usually an organic peroxide) decomposes under the influence of heat or light to form free radicals, which add to styrene molecules according to Markovnikov's rule. Each activated styrene molecule then adds in similar fashion to another styrene molecule, leaving an unpaired electron at the end of the chain after each step. This process continues indefinitely until a reaction, such as radical coupling or disproportionation, occurs between chain ends (or with impurities) and deactivates the chain ends by forming stable products.

Key Concept: Free-radical addition reactions obey Markovnikov's rule because radicals add in the direction that yields the most stable free-radical intermediate.

Initiating step:

1. Initiator $\xrightarrow{\text{heat or light}}$ Rad· (free radical)

Propagating steps:

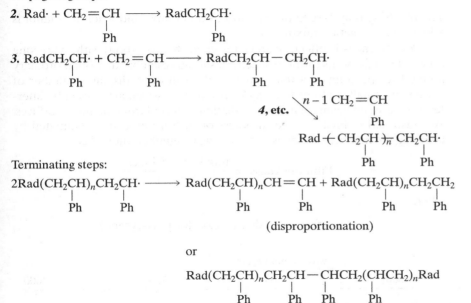

2. Rad· + CH₂=CH ⟶ RadCH₂CH·
             | |
             Ph   Ph

3. RadCH₂CH· + CH₂=CH ⟶ RadCH₂CH — CH₂CH·
              | | | |
              Ph   Ph   Ph   Ph

                        n – 1 CH₂=CH
4, etc. |
                                   Ph

              Rad—(CH₂CH)ₙ— CH₂CH·
                        | |
                        Ph   Ph

Terminating steps:

2Rad(CH₂CH)ₙCH₂CH· ⟶ Rad(CH₂CH)ₙCH=CH + Rad(CH₂CH)ₙCH₂CH₂
        | | | | | |
        Ph   Ph   Ph   Ph   Ph   Ph

(disproportionation)

or

Rad(CH₂CH)ₙCH₂CH — CHCH₂(CHCH₂)ₙRad
        | | | |
        Ph   Ph   Ph   Ph

(radical coupling)

Mechanism of chain-growth polymerization of polystyrene

Throughout a chain-growth polymerization, the bulk of the reaction mixture will consist of finished polymer molecules and unreacted monomers waiting to meet up with a reactive chain end. Because chain growth is so rapid once activation occurs, only one among many millions of molecules may be involved in the growth process at any given instant.

A number of different experimental methods are used to conduct chain-growth polymerization reactions. *Bulk polymerization* is the simplest; it is carried out by adding a suitable initiator to the pure monomer and using heat or light to promote the reaction. Bulk polymerization can be used to preserve a botanical or zoological specimen (such as a desiccated flower or beetle) by suspending the specimen in a liquid monomer, which is then allowed to polymerize around it. Poly(methyl methacrylate), known by the trade names

Lucite and Plexiglas, is often used for that purpose. A *solution polymerization* reaction is carried out in an organic solvent. Because it may be difficult to remove the solvent entirely, solution polymerization is often used to make polymers that are commonly used in solution, such as acrylic finishes.

Understanding the Experiment

In the first part of this experiment, you will attempt to carry out the solution polymerization of styrene in toluene using benzoyl peroxide as the polymerization initiator. Benzoyl peroxide decomposes on heating to yield phenyl radicals, which add to the double bonds of styrene molecules to start the polymerization process.

Heating benzoyl peroxide also forms benzoyloxy radicals ($PhCO_2\cdot$), which may participate in the initiation process.

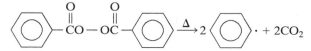

The resulting polystyrene precipitates as a gummy solid when methanol is added to the reaction mixture.

Polystyrene is, in effect, an arene (aromatic hydrocarbon) with a very long alkyl side chain, so its infrared spectrum should resemble that of an ordinary arene. The spectrum of a thin polymer film will often display a number of extraneous small peaks called *interference fringes*, which are caused by interference between beams of infrared radiation reflected from the film's surfaces. As illustrated in Figure 1, the thickness of such a film can be estimated by counting the number of fringes in a given wave number interval $\Delta\bar{v}$.

$$\text{Film thickness} = \frac{\text{number of fringes}}{2n(\Delta\bar{v})}$$

where

$$n = \text{refractive index } (\sim1.60 \text{ for polystyrene})$$

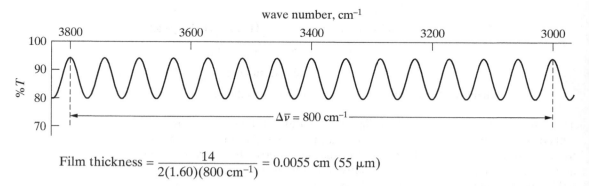

$$\text{Film thickness} = \frac{14}{2(1.60)(800 \text{ cm}^{-1})} = 0.0055 \text{ cm } (55 \text{ }\mu\text{m})$$

Figure 1 Determination of film thickness by counting interference fringes

In part **B**, you will heat some poly(methyl methacrylate) in a distillation apparatus to break it down into the monomer, methyl methacrylate. This monomer will be free of the polymerization inhibitors (usually aromatic phenols) that are added to commercial monomers to keep them from polymerizing in storage. You will add a small amount of a polymerization initiator, *t*-butyl peroxybenzoate, to the monomer and (if you like) suspend a small object of your choice in it. During the next lab period, you can see whether or not it has polymerized. With your instructor's permission, you can break the glass to recover the clear polymer (be sure to get permission, or you may be charged for the breakage!).

Styrene is toxic to fish, but it decomposes rapidly in the environment. Toluene is a hazardous chemical and a serious environmental contaminant that shouldn't be released into the environment. Methyl methacrylate has low toxicity to aquatic life and isn't likely to cause environmental harm at levels normally found in the environment.

A Greener Way: You can attempt to recycle a ground-up Lucite product rather than using poly(methyl methacrylate) from a chemical supply company. Note that high molecular-weight Lucite products may not depolymerize readily.

Reactions and Properties

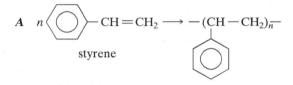

A n styrene $\longrightarrow$ polystyrene

B $nCH_2=CCOOCH_3$ $\longrightarrow$ poly(methyl methacrylate)

methyl methacrylate

Table 1 Physical properties

	mol wt	mp	bp	d
styrene	104.2	−31	146	0.909
benzoyl peroxide	242.2	106		
methyl methacrylate	100.1	−48	100	0.944

Note: mp and bp are in °C; density is in g/mL.

Styrene — CH=CH$_2$

3026.8	1494.3	908.6
1630.0	1082.9	775.8
1575.6	991.1	697.1

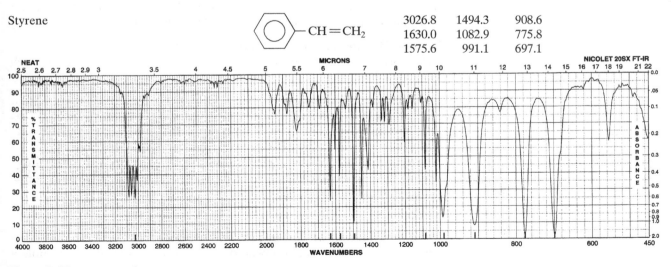

Figure 2 IR spectrum of styrene

DIRECTIONS

A. *Solution Polymerization of Styrene*

Styrene has irritating vapors; inhalation, ingestion, or skin absorption may be harmful. Avoid contact with the liquid, do not breathe its vapors, and keep it away from flames.

Toluene is flammable; inhalation, ingestion, or skin absorption may be harmful. Avoid contact with the liquid and do not breathe its vapors.

Benzoyl peroxide can explode due to shock or friction, and its decomposition can be catalyzed by metals. Do not allow it to contact any metal object and keep it away from other chemicals.

Safety Notes

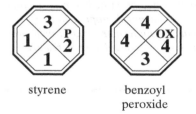

styrene   benzoyl
                 peroxide

Take Care! Avoid contact with styrene and toluene, and do not breathe their vapors.

Take Care! Do not allow benzoyl peroxide to come in contact with a metal or another chemical. Clean up any spills as directed by your instructor.

Waste Disposal: Place all wash solvents and the filtrate in a designated waste container.

Reaction. Weigh 20.0 mmol of styrene and transfer it to a 25-mL round-bottom flask, then add 10 mL of toluene. Use a *plastic* microscoop (see OP-6) to transfer approximately 0.10 g of benzoyl peroxide to the reaction mixture. Drop in a stir bar [OP-10], add a condenser, and heat the mixture in a boiling-water bath or over a steam bath for *at least* one hour while stirring. (A longer reaction time will result in a higher yield.) Work on part **B** during the reaction period.

Separation and Purification. Pour the reaction mixture into a beaker, using 25 mL of methanol for the transfer. Use a flat-bladed spatula to stir the polystyrene in the methanol for 3–5 minutes, pressing the gummy solid against the sides of the beaker to squeeze out absorbed toluene. Remove the toluene–methanol mixture by decanting, add 10 mL of fresh methanol, and repeat the stirring until the solid has hardened and is no longer sticky. Use additional 10-mL portions of methanol, if necessary, removing most of the methanol after each treatment. Collect the polymer by vacuum filtration [OP-16], wash it on the filter [OP-26a] with methanol, and let it air-dry for a few minutes. Dry [OP-26b] the product and weigh it.

Analysis. Record the infrared spectrum [OP-39] of a polystyrene film provided by your instructor. Interpret the spectrum as completely as you can and calculate the thickness of the film. (Alternatively, try to prepare a thin film from your product as described in "Other Things You Can Do.")

B. *Bulk Polymerization of Methyl Methacrylate*
Your instructor may opt to omit the depolymerization procedure, in which case you can start at the polymerization step.

Methyl methacrylate is flammable and lachrymatory (tear inducing); it can irritate the skin and eyes. Avoid contact, do not breathe its vapors, and keep it away from flames. Use protective gloves and a fume hood.

t-Butyl peroxybenzoate may react violently with strong oxidizing or reducing agents, or explode when strongly heated. Keep it away from combustible materials, heat, and flames.

Safety Notes

methyl   *t*-butyl
methacrylate   peroxybenzoate

Depolymerization of Poly(methyl methacrylate). Position your heating mantle so that it can be lowered quickly if necessary, then assemble a

236

compact apparatus for simple distillation [OP-30] using a 25-mL round-bottom flask. Weigh a clean, dry 13 × 100-mm test tube or soft-glass shell vial to use as the receiver. Place approximately 10.0 g of granulated low molecular-weight poly(methyl methacrylate) and a boiling chip or two in the reaction flask; heat [OP-7] it at a medium-high power setting until the solid softens and starts to liquefy. Then reduce the heating rate so that the liquid distills slowly and collect the methyl methacrylate in the test tube. Stop the distillation when the residue in the flask begins to darken and become viscous. Clean all parts of the distillation apparatus *thoroughly* with acetone as soon as it has cooled. If any residue solidifies in the reaction flask, cover it with ethyl acetate and let it stand until the residue dissolves (this may take several hours or days).

Polymerization of Methyl Methacrylate. Add 5 drops of *t*-butyl peroxybenzoate to the distillate; shake gently to dissolve it and mix the solution. Heat the mixture in a boiling-water bath for 20 minutes or more. If you like, suspend a small object in the liquid by inserting the straight end of a hook (made from a piece of copper wire or part of a paperclip) into a cork of the appropriate size and hanging the object from a thread. Metal objects should first be coated with clear enamel or nail polish. Stopper the test tube or vial loosely with the cork (or seal it with Parafilm) and set it in direct sunlight until the next laboratory period or until the clear polymer has hardened. With your instructor's permission, wrap the glass container in a towel and *carefully* break it inside a cardboard box, using a pestle or other hard object; then remove the polymer and place the glass in a sharps collector.

Waste Disposal: Place the residue and the acetone wash liquid in a designated waste container.

Take Care! Keep *t*-butyl peroxybenzoate away from combustibles and heat sources.

Exercises

1. Propose a mechanism for the polymerization of methyl methacrylate in the presence of *t*-butyl peroxybenzoate, which decomposes as shown here.

$$\underset{\substack{\| \\ \text{PhCO}}}{\overset{O}{}} - \underset{\substack{| \\ \text{CH}_3}}{\overset{\text{CH}_3}{\text{OCCH}_3}} \longrightarrow \text{Ph}\cdot + \underset{\substack{| \\ \text{CH}_3}}{\overset{\text{CH}_3}{\text{CH}_3\text{CO}\cdot}} + \text{CO}_2$$

2. Compare your polystyrene spectrum with the infrared spectrum of styrene in Figure 2, and try to account for any significant similarities and differences.

3. Describe and explain the possible effect on your results of the following experimental errors or variations. (a) In part **A**, you forgot to add the benzoyl peroxide. (b) So that it would dry faster, you washed the polystyrene with petroleum ether rather than methanol. (c) For the polymerization step of part **B**, you used commercial methyl methacrylate containing 50 ppm of 4-methoxyphenol.

4. (a) Calculate the atom economy and reaction efficiency of each polymerization reaction. (b) Describe some green features of each synthesis, and any that aren't so green.

5. Draw the structures of the monomers needed to prepare polymers that have the following repeating units.

a. $-(CHClCHCl)-$ **b.** $-(CF_2CFCl)-$
c. $-(CH_2CH_2NH)-$ **d.** $-(CH_2C=CHCH_2)-$
$\overset{|}{CH_3}$
e. $-(CH_2CH)-$ **f.** $-(CH_2CH-CH_2CH)-$
$\overset{|}{CH_2CH_3}$ $\overset{|}{CN}$

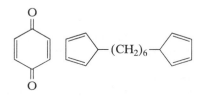

$-(CH_2CH_2O)-$

poly(ethylene glycol) repeating unit

OH OH   O
| | / \
CH_2CH_2 CH_2CH_2
ethylene   ethylene
glycol   oxide

6. Show how the two monomers illustrated in the margin could combine to form a Diels–Alder addition polymer, and give the structure of the polymeric repeating unit.

7. Poly(ethylene glycol) can be prepared from either ethylene glycol or ethylene oxide. Write a balanced equation for each reaction, and classify each as addition or condensation polymerization.

8. Methyl methacrylate can be prepared commercially from acetone, hydrogen cyanide, and methanol. Propose a synthesis of methyl methacrylate from these starting materials, using any necessary inorganic reagents or solvents.

Other Things You Can Do

(Starred items require your instructor's permission.)

Take Care! Keep 2-butanone away from flames, avoid contact, and do not breathe its vapors.

Take Care! Don't cut yourself.

*1. You can attempt to prepare a polystyrene film from your product using the following method. Dissolve about 50 mg of the product in 0.5 mL of 2-butanone. This solution can be shared among several students. Use a Pasteur pipet to transfer about 10 drops of the solution to a *very clean* microscope slide and tilt the slide to coat it evenly. Let the solvent evaporate completely under the hood. Carefully strip off the polymer film with a very sharp double-edged razor blade and mount it between salt plates in an infrared cell holder.

*2. Three students can work together on part **B**—one using the standard procedure, the second using no *t*-butyl peroxybenzoate, and the third using 0.1 g of hydroquinone in place of the *t*-butyl peroxybenzoate. Compare and explain the results.

*3. Prepare nylon 6,10 as described in "The Nylon Rope Trick" minilab.

*4. Beginning with sources from the Bibliography, write a research paper on the use of Ziegler–Natta catalysts to synthesize stereoregular polymers; describe some properties and uses of these polymers.

Synthesis of Ethanol
by Fermentation

Reactions of Carbohydrates. Preparation of Alcohols. Biosynthesis of Organic Compounds.

Operations

OP-16   Vacuum Filtration
OP-32   Fractional Distillation
OP-34   Boiling Point

Before You Begin

1. Read the experiment, read or review the operations as necessary, and write an experimental plan.
2. Calculate the mass of 100 mmol of sucrose and the theoretical mass and volume of ethanol that can be produced from that much sucrose.

Scenario

The Great Plains Farm Cooperative helps farmers market their crops to help ensure that they receive a fair price. Recently, a bumper crop of sugar beets resulted in a surplus of beet sugar and drastically lowered the price of the product. The co-op has advised farmers to store their beets until the price rises; in the meantime, it is exploring alternative uses for the surplus beets. One alternative would be to convert the beet sugar to ethanol for use as an energy source in gasahol and other commercial fuels.

The co-op has sent your institute a quantity of beet sugar to see whether an ethanol conversion process would be feasible. To price the beet-sugar ethanol low enough to make it competitive with ethanol from corn and other sources, they require a product that is at least 180 proof. Your assignment is to ferment the sugar, distill it to concentrate the ethanol, and find out whether your product meets their specifications.

Applying Scientific Methodology

Whether or not you solve the problem in this experiment—that is, prepare ethanol that is 180 proof or higher—depends on your skill in performing the experiment.

The Chemistry of Brewing and Winemaking

The single-celled fungi called *yeasts* obtain the chemical energy they need to grow and reproduce by breaking down molecules of monosaccharides (simple sugars), such as glucose and fructose, and disaccharides (two-unit

From *Operational Organic Chemistry: A Problem Solving Approach to the Laboratory*, Fourth Edition, John W. Lehman. Copyright © 2009 by Pearson Education. Published by Prentice Hall. All rights reserved.

sugars), such as sucrose and maltose. To the yeast cells, ethyl alcohol is a useless by-product of this energy-generating process, but humans have developed a liking for that by-product as it exists in alcoholic beverages.

The fermentation of plant carbohydrates to produce alcohol is as old as civilization and probably began in prehistoric times. The first alcoholic beverage may have been a kind of mead (honey wine), which was probably discovered when some honey-sweetened water was forgotten and allowed to ferment. Early civilizations discovered that starchy grains such as barley, wheat, and millet could be treated to make them fermentable, leading to the brewing of beer and similar grain-based beverages. A poem dedicated to the Sumerian goddess of brewing contains a recipe for beer that dates back to about 2800 B.C. Because grains contain starch but no sugars that yeast cells can ferment, they are first allowed to germinate for several days in a process called *malting*. The dried, malted grain (usually barley) is soaked in warm water, allowing enzymes formed during the malting process to break down the starch into simple sugars. The liquid that contains the sugars and flavor components, known as *wort*, is then separated from the solid residue. Additional cereals (rice, corn, or wheat) may be added to boost the wort's carbohydrate content; hops are included as a preservative and for their bitter, aromatic flavor; and the wort is boiled to sterilize and concentrate it. Brewer's yeast is then added and the wort is allowed to ferment, during which the yeast cells transform the sugars into alcohol.

Grapevines grew wild in Central Asia and Western Europe long before humans appeared on Earth. By the sixth millennium B.C., grapes had been domesticated in Asia Minor, and the cultivation and use of grapes for food and wine spread from there to Egypt and Mesopotamia. Legend has it that Dionysus, the Greek god of wine, introduced wine drinking in Crete; by Homer's time (ca. 700 B.C.), the ancient Greeks were making strong, sweet, thick wine that was always watered down before drinking. In Roman times, the Gauls, who occupied much of present-day France, produced the best wine in Europe. Their wines were popular in Rome until the emperor Domitian, to protect Italian winemakers from Gallic competition, demanded that half of the grapevines in Gaul be uprooted. Wine may have contributed to the decline and fall of Rome, because a syrup used to preserve wines was boiled in lead-lined pots, and one of the symptoms of lead poisoning is mental confusion. After Rome fell to the barbarians, the art of winemaking was kept alive by monks in European monasteries, who cultivated grapes to supply their sacramental wine. A Benedictine monk, Dom Pérignon, is usually credited with the invention of champagne, and many of the best wines of France are still grown around former monasteries.

Even today, winemaking may be as much an art as a science. The first step is crushing ripe grapes into juice, called the *must*, which contains glucose and fructose along with smaller quantities of fruit acids (such as tartaric acid), tannins, and other components. To make white wine, the grape skins are removed before fermentation, so the wine contains little pigmentation or tannic material. Red wine musts are fermented in contact with red grape skins for most of the fermentation period. The longer the must is in contact with the skins, the deeper is its color and the more astringent

In 1989, an American brewer reproduced this honey-sweetened beer following the ancient Sumerian recipe.

or "tannic" its taste. Sulfur dioxide is added to prevent oxidation of flavor components and to inhibit the growth of bacteria and wild yeasts that could convert the must to vinegar. To balance their sweet and sour components, sugar is added to overly acidic musts, and tartaric acid is added to musts that have insufficient acid.

Some grape skins are covered with a natural dusting of yeasts of the type needed for fermentation (saccharomycetes); with other grapes, a yeast culture must be added. The yeast not only converts grape sugars to alcohol, it also biosynthesizes flavor components—mainly esters and long-chain alcohols—that don't exist in the grapes themselves. A long, slow fermentation process at low temperature produces the most flavor components, giving the wine a more pronounced "nose" (aroma). Fermentation stops when nearly all of the sugar has been transformed. The yeast is then allowed to settle and the new wine is drawn off; this *racking* process is repeated several times as the wine ages. The wine may also be *fined*—that is, treated with a substance that coagulates suspended fine particles and carries them to the bottom. New wine has a harsh, raw flavor and a simple aroma, so it is aged in wooden casks to soften the flavor and enrich the aroma. A large number of chemical reactions take place during this stage, forming more flavor components and removing some components that have disagreeable characteristics. Many of these are oxidation reactions, made possible by pores in the wooden casks that allow air to enter the wine. The cask itself may contribute flavor, as vanillin and other substances from the wood leach into the wine. If oxidation proceeds too long, it begins to degrade the wine, so after 6–24 months of aging, the wine is bottled to protect it from excessive oxidation. The chemical composition of a bottled wine continues to change, and a good wine may improve in flavor when aged in the bottle for several years, or even several decades.

Distilled beverages, such as whiskey, brandy, and vodka, are made by distilling beer, wine, or another fermented beverage to increase the alcohol content and concentrate the volatile flavor components. Thus, brandy is distilled from wine, scotch from a special distiller's beer, rum from fermented molasses or sugarcane juice, and vodka from fermented potatoes or grain. The distillate is usually aged to make the flavor richer and mellower.

Drinking alcoholic beverages of any kind can be both beneficial and harmful. Wine may enhance our enjoyment of a good meal, and a drink or two can help us relax and stimulate social interactions. In moderation, wine and other alcoholic beverages confer certain health benefits. Beer, wine, and liquor all raise the concentration of "good cholesterol" (HDL) in the blood, which may reduce the risk of heart attacks. Chemicals in wine may also boost the immune system, inhibit cancer, and reduce the risk of Alzheimer's disease.

Balanced against these beneficial effects of moderate drinking are the unquestionably harmful effects of excessive drinking, which include drunkenness, hangovers, alcoholism, cirrhosis of the liver, cancer, birth abnormalities, antisocial behavior, broken homes, wasted lives, and death. Alcohol is a drug—often a highly addictive one—that depresses the central nervous system. Its apparent stimulating influence, which is associated with a loss of inhibitions, is actually a result of alcohol's depressant effect on the brain centers that normally keep our social behavior in check. Because the destructive potential of beverage alcohol is so much greater than its apparent health benefit, most medical professionals agree that nondrinkers shouldn't begin drinking alcohol for their health, and drinkers should limit their alcohol intake to one or two drinks a day.

Understanding the Experiment

In this experiment, you will ferment an aqueous solution of beet sugar (sucrose) with commercial dry yeast (*Saccharomyces cerevisiae*) to obtain a dilute ethanol solution, which you will concentrate by fractional distillation. The fermentation mixture will contain Pasteur's salts, a mixture of nutrients that supports the growth and reproduction of yeast. The fermentation takes time, so you should be prepared to get it started a week or so in advance. Carbon dioxide produced during the fermentation excludes air, which would otherwise oxidize the ethanol to acetic acid or other unwanted by-products. In this experiment, the carbon dioxide will bubble through limewater (aqueous calcium hydroxide) beneath a layer of mineral oil; formation of a precipitate of calcium carbonate indicates that the fermentation is proceeding, and the mineral oil keeps air out of the limewater.

Sucrose is a disaccharide having molecules that contain units of the two simple sugars glucose and fructose. The yeast you will use contains many *enzymes* that are necessary for the conversion of sucrose to ethanol. Invertase catalyzes the hydrolysis of sucrose to glucose and fructose. Then zymase, which is actually a group of at least 22 separate enzymes, catalyzes a series of steps in the very complex conversion of these simple sugars to ethanol and carbon dioxide.

The nutrient solution called Pasteur's salts contains 2.0 g potassium dihydrogen phosphate, 0.20 g calcium dihydrogen phosphate, 0.20 g magnesium sulfate, and 10 g ammonium tartrate per liter of water.

Key Concept: *Enzymes are very efficient biochemical catalysts, produced by living cells, that facilitate the chemical processes necessary for life. Unlike most chemical catalysts, an enzyme is very specific about the kind of substrate it acts upon and the kind of reaction it catalyzes.*

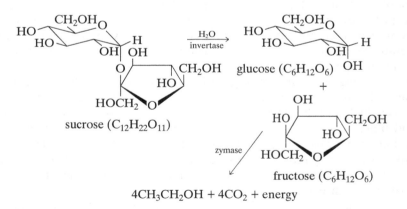

$$4CH_3CH_2OH + 4CO_2 + energy$$

From a yeast cell's viewpoint, the important product of this process is energy. Ethanol is a waste product that is actually harmful to the yeast cells, which are deactivated after the alcohol concentration reaches 15% (v/v) or so.

Fermentation produces a number of by-products by various pathways. These include ethanal, glycerol, and fusel oil. Ethanal (acetaldehyde) is produced along the biosynthetic pathway that leads to ethanol, and some of it remains at the end of the fermentation. Glycerol improves a wine's "legs"—its ability to coat the inside of a wine glass—by increasing its surface tension. Fusel oil is a mixture of alcohols (including 1-propanol, 2-methyl-1-propanol, 2-methyl-2-butanol, and 3-methyl-1-butanol) that is responsible for the headaches that cheap wines often cause.

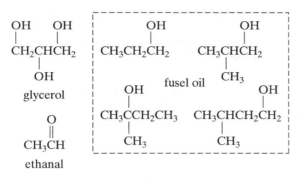

Some by-products of fermentation

To prepare alcohol for non-beverage purposes, all of these by-products must be removed from the fermentation mixture, along with excess water and spent yeast cells. You will remove the yeast cells, which collect as a sediment at the bottom of the fermentation flask, by decanting and filtration. The remaining components, including most of the water, will be removed by fractional distillation. Acetaldehyde boils at 21°C, ethanol at 78°C, water at 100°C, the fusel oil alcohols at temperatures ranging from 97°C to 132°C and higher, and glycerol at 290°C. Thus, any acetaldehyde present should escape as vapor, while most of the water and the other components should remain in the boiling flask after the ethanol has distilled. Water and ethanol form an *azeotrope*—a constant-boiling mixture—with a composition of 95.6% ethanol and 4.4% water (by mass), so it is impossible to obtain ethanol purer than 95.6 mass percent by distillation alone. Your percentage may be substantially lower because of such factors as the column-packing efficiency and the rate of distillation.

See OP-32 for a discussion of azeotropes.

The *proof* of a commercial alcohol or alcoholic beverage is calculated by doubling its volume percent; that is, 1 degree of proof is equivalent to 0.5 volume percent. Thus, an 80-proof bourbon contains 40% ethanol by volume. You can determine the volume and mass percent of ethanol in your product, and from that its proof and your percent yield, by measuring its density and using the data in Table 2.

This is a green experiment because sucrose and yeast are benign natural products and no solvents other than water are used. The only by-product, carbon dioxide, is a greenhouse gas, but the amount of CO_2 your reaction will produce is considerably less than the amount you will exhale during the experiment! (See Exercise 4.)

Reactions and Properties

$$C_{12}H_{22}O_{11} + H_2O \longrightarrow 4CH_3CH_2OH + 4CO_2$$

sucrose   ethanol

Table 1 Physical properties

	mol wt	mp	bp
sucrose	342.3	186d	
ethanol	46.1	−115	78.3

Note: mp and bp are in °C; d = decomposes at melting point.

Table 2 Density and composition of ethanol–water solutions at 20°C

Density at 20°C	Mass % ethanol	Volume % ethanol
0.914	50.0	57.8
0.903	55.0	62.8
0.891	60.0	67.7
0.879	65.0	72.4
0.868	70.0	76.9
0.856	75.0	81.3
0.844	80.0	85.5
0.831	85.0	89.5
0.818	90.0	93.3
0.804	95.0	96.8
0.789	100.0	100.0

DIRECTIONS

Ordinary bread-baking yeast will work, but you can also use brewer's yeast or wine yeast.

Stop and Think: What is the purpose of the limewater? The mineral oil?

Fermentation. In a 500-mL Erlenmeyer flask, dissolve 0.100 mol of sucrose in 250 mL of distilled water that has been warmed to about 30°C. Then add 30 mL of Pasteur's salts and 3.5 g (about one-half packet) of dry baker's yeast. Mix the contents by shaking the flask vigorously. Insert a one-hole rubber stopper fitted with a bent glass tube, connect a length of rubber tubing and a 6-inch length of straight glass tubing, and insert the straight tube into a bottle or beaker containing limewater (saturated aqueous calcium hydroxide) with a thin layer of mineral oil on top (see Figure 1). Label the flask with your name and let the mixture stand at room temperature (preferably 25°C or higher) for a week or more, until no more gas is evolved.

Separation. At the end of the fermentation period, remove the stopper from the Erlenmeyer flask. Trying not to disturb the sediment, which contains tiny yeast cells, decant (pour off) the fermentation mixture into a large beaker. Stop decanting—leaving some liquid behind—when the sediment begins to rise and is about to pass into the beaker. If the liquid in the beaker isn't clear, filter it by the following procedure. Assemble an apparatus for vacuum filtration [OP-16], using the largest available filter flask and including a trap if you are using a water aspirator. Turn on the vacuum, then measure about 10 g of Celite filtering aid into a large Erlenmeyer

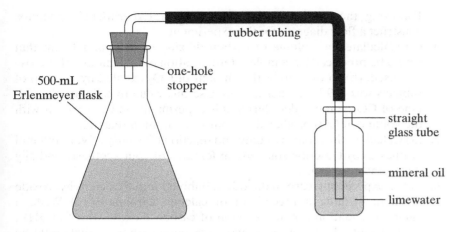

Figure 1 Fermentation apparatus

flask, and shake the Celite with 200 mL of water until it is well dispersed. Swirling to keep the Celite suspended, pour this mixture onto the filter paper to form a thin layer of Celite on top of it. Discard the water in the filter flask, then filter the decanted liquid. You may also be able to filter some of the liquid that remains with the sediment and combine it with the decanted liquid, but stop filtering if the filtrate becomes cloudy or the filtration rate becomes very slow.

Purification. Assemble an apparatus for fractional distillation [OP-32] using a 500-mL round-bottom flask and an appropriate column packing. See that the thermometer is positioned correctly in the still head (see Figure E7, OP-30). Distill the ethanol–water mixture and collect all of the distillate that boils between 77°C and 82°C. Stop the distillation when the temperature reaches 82°C.

Analysis. Measure the mass and boiling point [OP-34] of the distillate. With the temperature of this liquid as close to 20°C as possible, use an automatic pipet, volumetric pipet, or another appropriate measuring device to accurately measure 1.00 mL of distillate into a tared screw-cap vial. Then weigh it and calculate its density. From the data in Table 2, prepare a graph of mass percent and volume percent ethanol (both on the *y*-axis) versus density. Use the graph to determine the percentage composition and proof of your distillate. Calculate the mass of ethanol contained in the distillate (remember that it's not pure ethanol) and use it to calculate your percent yield.

Waste Disposal: Unless your instructor directs otherwise, wash the sediment and supernatant liquid down the drain.

Waste Disposal: Unless your instructor directs otherwise, wash the contents of the boiling flask down the drain after the distillation is complete.

Exercises

1. A strong vodka has a density of 0.909 g/mL. What is its proof? (Vodka is essentially a solution of ethanol and water.)
2. Describe and explain the possible effect on your results of the following experimental errors or variations. (a) You forgot to add the Pasteur's salts. (b) During the fractional distillation, you continued to collect distillate until the temperature reached 98°C. (c) Unknown to you, someone reset the automatic pipet for the density determination to 0.950 mL.

3. Following the format in the "Planning an Experiment" appendix, construct a flow diagram for the experiment.

4. (a) Calculate the volume of carbon dioxide at 25°C and 1 atm that would be produced by complete fermentation of the amount of sucrose you used. (b) In one study, the amount of CO_2 exhaled by a group of subjects was 469 L/day per person. Use this value to estimate the volume of CO_2 you exhaled during this experiment, and compare it with the volume of CO_2 produced by your fermentation reaction.

5. (a) Calculate the atom economy and reaction efficiency of your ethanol synthesis. (b) Describe some green features of your synthesis, and any that aren't so green.

6. In the experiment, carbon dioxide is bubbled into a calcium hydroxide solution, forming a precipitate of calcium carbonate. (a) Write a balanced equation for the reaction of carbon dioxide with $Ca(OH)_2$. (b) Calculate the theoretical mass of calcium carbonate that could be produced by the CO_2 generated from the amount of sucrose you used (see Exercise 4).

7. A by-product of this fermentation is diethylacetal, $CH_3CH(OCH_2CH_3)_2$. Write a balanced equation for its formation from components of the fermentation mixture.

Other Things You Can Do

(Starred items require your instructor's permission.)

*1. Estimate the ethanol concentration of a commercial vodka by the method used in this experiment.

2. Find out how absolute (100%) ethanol is manufactured and how ethanol is denatured to make it undrinkable.

3. Write a research paper about the chemistry and technology of wine-making, starting with sources listed in the Bibliography.

Reaction of Butanols with Hydrobromic Acid

Reactions of Alcohols. Preparation of Alkyl Halides. Nucleophilic Aliphatic Substitution. Infrared Spectrometry.

Operations

OP-7   Heating
OP-10 Mixing
OP-14 Trapping Gases (optional)
OP-20 Steam Distillation
OP-24 Washing Liquids
OP-25 Drying Liquids
OP-30 Simple Distillation
OP-34 Boiling Point
OP-39 Infrared Spectrometry

Before You Begin

1. Read the experiment, read or review the operations as necessary, and write an experimental plan.
2. Calculate the mass and volume of 72.0 mmol of 1-butanol, and the theoretical yield of 1-bromobutane (both mass and volume). Repeat these calculations for 2-butanol and 2-bromobutane.

Scenario

The Bond Triplex manufactures not only alkynes but a variety of chemicals that can be prepared from ethyne (acetylene) and other alkynes. For example, the company manufactures 1-butanol from ethyne by the following process:

$$HC \equiv CH \xrightarrow[H^+, Hg^{2+}]{H_2O} CH_3\overset{O}{\overset{\|}{C}H} \xrightarrow{NaOH} CH_3\overset{OH}{\overset{|}{C}H}CH_2\overset{O}{\overset{\|}{C}H}$$

$$\xrightarrow{H^+} CH_3CH = CH\overset{O}{\overset{\|}{C}H} \xrightarrow[\Delta, \text{ pressure}]{H_2, \text{ Ni-Cr}} CH_3CH_2CH_2\overset{OH}{\overset{|}{C}H_2}$$

Now they want to manufacture 1-bromobutane and 2-bromobutane by treating the corresponding butanols with hydrogen bromide in the presence of a sulfuric acid catalyst. Economic considerations require that they use the amount of catalyst that will produce each alkyl bromide at the lowest cost per kilogram. They want your research team to carry out the syntheses of 1- and 2-bromobutane using different catalyst/substrate ratios, and then do a cost analysis to find out which ratio produces each product most economically.

From *Operational Organic Chemistry: A Problem Solving Approach to the Laboratory*, Fourth Edition, John W. Lehman. Copyright © 2009 by Pearson Education. Published by Prentice Hall. All rights reserved.

Applying Scientific Methodology

Your working hypothesis should include a prediction of the effect on *each* reaction of changing the catalyst/substrate ratio.

The Controversial Halides

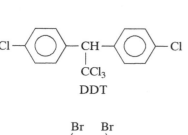

DDT

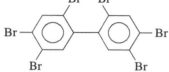

2,2',4,4',5,5'-hexabromobiphenyl

The familiar expression "You can't get along with them and you can't get along without them" applies to many organic halides (organohalogen compounds). Organohalogens tend to be very stable. However, the stability that makes a particular organohalogen a useful commercial chemical can be a liability if the compound is released into the environment, where it may remain unchanged for decades—or even centuries. Most people first became aware that chlorinated organics might be a problem with the publication of Rachel Carson's book *Silent Spring*, in which she documented the effect of DDT on wildlife and the environment.

The polybrominated and polychlorinated biphenyls (PBBs and PCBs) have also caused serious environmental problems, because they are toxic and believed to be carcinogenic and because they persist in the environment. PBBs are mixtures of various bromine derivatives of biphenyl, such as 2,2',4,4',5,5'-hexabromobiphenyl, a major component of fire-retardant mixtures such as Firemaster BP-6. In 1973, Firemaster BP-6 was accidentally added to cattle feed in Michigan, resulting in the illness of some dairy farmers and the death of many farm animals; it has since been withdrawn from the market. In past years, polychlorinated biphenyls were used in a number of commercial products, ranging from coolants for electrical transformers to plastic liners for baby bottles. In the United States, the manufacture, processing, and distribution of PCBs has been prohibited since 1979. Nevertheless, PCBs have persisted in the environment and may now be the most widespread pollutants on Earth. They occur in dangerously high concentrations in some fish from the Great Lakes, and they have been detected in the tissues of many other organisms—even polar bears from the high Arctic.

Because of these and other instances of pollution, some environmental groups have called for a total ban on the manufacture of chlorine and chlorinated compounds, and the International Joint Commission, a U.S.–Canadian government-appointed group whose function is to preserve water quality in the Great Lakes, supports a gradual phasing out of these chemicals. People on opposite sides of this issue could hardly be farther apart. According to a spokesman for Dow Chemical Company, one of the largest producers and users of chlorine, "It is the single most important ingredient in [industrial] chemistry." Chlorine is used to manufacture an enormous number of consumer products, including plastics, pharmaceuticals, perfume bases, cosmetics, paper, medical devices, household adhesives, anesthetics, nonstick cookware, dry-cleaning solvents, refrigerants, photographic film, magnetic recording tape, floor coverings, wallpaper, food wraps, PVC pipe and fittings, electrical insulation, seat covers, baby strollers, compact discs, shoes, paints, solvents, brake fluid, food additives, and crop-protection chemicals. Reliable estimates are hard to come by, but chlorine probably accounts for tens of billions of dollars worth of commerce and one million or so jobs. Yet a Greenpeace research analyst has stated, "There are no uses of chlorine that we regard as safe."

Media reports on the issue tend to give the impression that all organohalogens are synthetic compounds that have never occurred naturally. In fact, there are a number of natural organohalogens. Tyrian purple is a bromine-containing dye derived from spiny carnivorous snails of the murex family. Because of its rarity—about 9000 snails are needed to produce one gram of the dye—Tyrian purple was a costly status symbol in the ancient world. Recently, a vial of 85-year-old whale oil collected during the last voyage of an old whaling ship was found to contain 11 halogenated organic compounds, including derivatives of polybrominated biphenyls and polybrominated diphenyl ethers. Because the whale oil was collected well before the production of similar synthetic halogen compounds, these compounds must have been produced naturally in the ocean. Some seaweeds produce trichloromethane (chloroform, $CHCl_3$) and tetrachloromethane (carbon tetrachloride, CCl_4), compounds that are also produced as by-products of water chlorination. Bromomethane (methyl bromide, CH_3Br), an important insect fumigant, is formed in large quantities by ocean algae. These and other organohalogens are, in part, responsible for the sharp smell of seawater. As various forest fungi break down dead trees and other plant materials, they produce about 200 times as much natural chloromethane (methyl chloride, CH_3Cl) as humans produce synthetically. Volcanoes also produce chloromethane, along with dichloromethane (methylene chloride) and chlorofluorocarbons such as dichlorodifluoromethane (Freon 12). Our own bodies utilize organic iodides in the form of thyroid hormones, and our white blood cells oxidize chloride ions in the blood to molecular chlorine, which kills invading bacteria and other microorganisms.

Polychlorodibenzodioxins (PCDDs) and polychlorodibenzofurans (PCDFs) are considered to be among the most hazardous organohalogens.

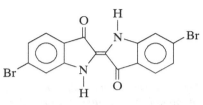

Tyrian purple (dibromoindigo)

2,3,6,7-tetrachlorodibenzodioxin
(a PCDD)

2,3,6,7-tetrachlorodibenzofuran
(a PCDF)

2,3,6,7-Tetrachlorodibenzodioxin, called "dioxin" by the news media, occurs as a by-product when the herbicide 2,4,5-trichlorophenoxyacetic acid (2,4,5-T) is manufactured from 2,4,5-trichlorophenol.

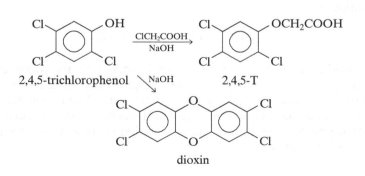

2,4,5-trichlorophenol

2,4,5-T

dioxin

2,4,5-T was the main constituent of Agent Orange, the defoliant believed to have caused health problems for many Vietnam War veterans.

Key Concept: *A naturally occurring compound is not safe because it is natural, nor is a synthetic compound harmful because it is synthetic. The physiological effect of any substance, natural or synthetic, depends on its molecular structure, not on its source.*

Thus, 2,4,5-T is almost invariably contaminated with this chemical. Dioxin is regarded as one of the most toxic substances known, and some PCDFs may be even more toxic. Yet, both PCDDs and PCDFs are produced by burning wood, which contains natural chlorides, and some researchers believe that forest fires and brush fires are the major source of dioxins in the environment. Dioxins have been identified in ancient marine sediments from as early as 6000 B.C., and they are even produced in garden compost piles.

This is not to say that synthetic organohalogens aren't harmful because many of them also occur naturally. Many naturally occurring substances are hazardous to our health, and the levels of certain organohalogens in humans, including PCDDs and PCDFs, are considerably higher now than they were in preindustrial times, when the only sources of these substances were natural. Environmental groups and health organizations are concerned that they may already be causing reproductive problems, such as declining sperm counts, and other health problems in humans.

Most scientists agree that we should weigh the hazards and benefits of each organohalogen individually, rather than banning a whole family of compounds simply because it contains some bad actors. But those who support a chlorine ban believe we face a potential crisis that can't wait for a chemical-by-chemical study of all 15,000 or so chlorine-containing products that are now on the market. Meanwhile, measures are being taken to reduce the production of the most hazardous organohalogens. For example, the Environmental Protection Agency is developing new regulations that should force pulp and paper mills—a major source of dioxin—to curtail their use of chlorine for bleaching. Nevertheless, the demand for many organohalogens has continued to grow, and there is little evidence to date of a slowdown in the production of industrial chlorine and its compounds.

Understanding the Experiment

In this experiment, you will convert either 1-butanol or 2-butanol to the corresponding alkyl bromide with HBr, using sulfuric acid as a catalyst. A *catalyst* is a substance that accelerates chemical reactions without being consumed in the process. For example, an alcohol cannot be converted to an alkyl bromide by sodium bromide, because hydroxide ion (OH^-) is too poor a leaving group to be displaced by bromide ion. A strong acid is needed to convert this poor leaving group to a better one, H_2O, by protonating it.

$$R - OH + H^+ \longrightarrow R - OH_2^+$$

See your lecture course textbook for a more detailed discussion of nucleophilic substitution reactions.

Sulfuric acid catalyzes the overall reaction by increasing the concentration of the protonated alcohol, which can then react with bromide ion by either an S_N1 or S_N2 mechanism to form an alkyl bromide. Primary alcohols tend to react by the direct substitution (S_N2) mechanism; secondary and tertiary alcohols are more likely to form an intermediate carbocation, which then combines with halide ion.

S_N2 reaction of 1-butanol

1. $\underset{\underset{|}{CH_3CH_2CH_2CH_2}}{\overset{OH}{}} + H^+ \longrightarrow \underset{\underset{|}{CH_3CH_2CH_2CH_2}}{\overset{OH_2^+}{}}$

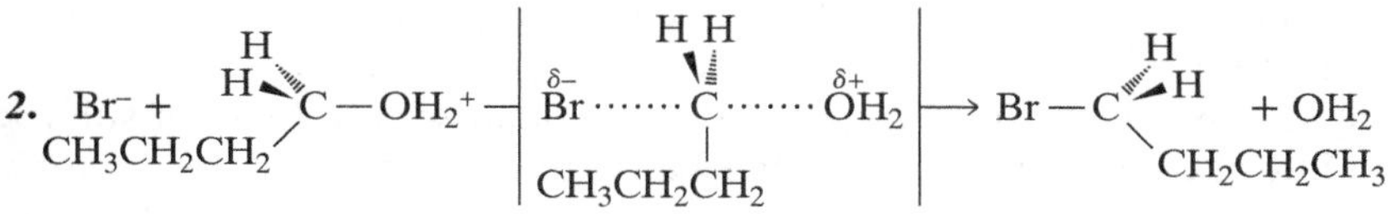

2. $Br^- + \underset{CH_3CH_2CH_2}{\overset{H}{H}}C-OH_2^+ \rightarrow \left[\overset{\delta-}{Br}\cdots\cdots\overset{H\ H}{\underset{CH_3CH_2CH_2}{C}}\cdots\cdots\overset{\delta+}{OH_2} \right] \rightarrow Br-\overset{H}{\underset{CH_2CH_2CH_3}{C}}H + OH_2$

S_N1 reaction of 2-butanol

$\underset{\underset{|}{CH_3CH_2CHCH_3}}{\overset{OH}{}} \xrightarrow{H^+} \underset{\underset{|}{CH_3CH_2CHCH_3}}{\overset{OH_2^+}{}} \xrightarrow{-H_2O} CH_3CH_2\overset{+}{C}HCH_3 \xrightarrow{Br^-} \underset{\underset{|}{CH_3CH_2CHCH_3}}{\overset{Br}{}}$

Because the reaction rate for both mechanisms depends on the concentration of the protonated alcohol, increasing the catalyst concentration should increase the rate. We might expect this to, in turn, increase the amount of alkyl bromide produced in a given reaction time, but it could increase the rates of side reactions as well. Accelerating such side reactions as E1 elimination, polymerization, and ether formation could actually reduce the product yield by converting the substrate into unwanted by-products.

By varying the volume of sulfuric acid added, your research team will be varying the ratio of catalyst to substrate from 0.25 to 1.00 for each of the two alcohols (see Table 1). Using the yields of the resulting alkyl bromides, you will carry out a cost analysis to determine which catalyst/substrate ratio will produce each product at the lowest cost per kilogram. Because variable product losses during the purification step may invalidate the results, the masses of the crude products will be used for the cost analyses.

You will carry out the reaction by heating the alcohol under reflux with a small excess of 48% hydrobromic acid and the assigned volume of sulfuric acid. Because sulfur dioxide and HBr fumes are evolved during the reaction, a hood or gas trap must be used to keep them from escaping into the laboratory. The alkyl bromide will be separated from the reaction mixture by internal steam distillation using the water present in the reaction flask. The product ordinarily separates below the aqueous layer in a mixture with water, but with a low catalyst/substrate ratio there may be enough unreacted alcohol in the organic layer to make it separate above the aqueous layer. The organic layer will contain varying amounts of HBr, sulfuric acid, unreacted alcohol, and by-products; these impurities will be removed by washing with sulfuric acid, water, and aqueous sodium bicarbonate, followed by distillation. The alkyl bromides are less dense than sulfuric acid but denser than water, so the alkyl bromide layer will be on top after the first washing, but on the bottom in the next two.

The results will be more reliable if average yields from several research groups are compared.

251

You can confirm the conversion of reactant to product using infrared (IR) spectrometry. The IR spectra of alkyl bromides are characterized by a strong C—Br stretching band at low frequency, from 690 to 515 cm^{-1}. Because the range of some IR spectrometers doesn't extend below 600 cm^{-1}, the entire C—Br band isn't observed in all cases.

1-Butanol and 2-butanol should degrade rapidly in the environment and aren't expected to be toxic to aquatic life. The EPA has classified sulfuric acid as a hazardous air pollutant, but small-scale release of sulfuric acid into the environment shouldn't be particularly harmful. Little information is available about the environmental fate and toxicity of hydrobromic acid.

Reactions and Properties

$$CH_3CH_2CH_2CH_2OH + HBr \xrightarrow{H_2SO_4} CH_3CH_2CH_2CH_2Br + H_2O$$

$$or \quad \underset{\displaystyle CH_3CH_2CHCH_3}{\overset{\displaystyle OH}{|}} + HBr \xrightarrow{H_2SO_4} \underset{\displaystyle CH_3CH_2CHCH_3}{\overset{\displaystyle Br}{|}} + H_2O$$

Table 1 Ratio of catalyst to alcohol in the eight runs

Run	Alcohol	ml	Catalyst/substrate mole ratio
1	1-butanol	1.0	0.25
2	1-butanol	2.0	0.50
3	1-butanol	3.0	0.75
4	1-butanol	4.0	1.00
5	2-butanol	1.0	0.25
6	2-butanol	2.0	0.50
7	2-butanol	3.0	0.75
8	2-butanol	4.0	1.00

Note: 1 mL of concentrated (~96%) sulfuric acid contains about 18 mmol of the acid.

Table 2 Physical properties

	mol wt	bp	*d*
1-butanol	74.1	117	0.810
2-butanol	74.1	99.5	0.808
hydrobromic acid (48%)	80.9		1.49
sulfuric acid (~96%)	98.1		1.84
1-bromobutane	137.0	102	1.276
2-bromobutane	137.0	91	1.259

Note: bp is in °C; density is in g/mL.

252

1-Butanol

$CH_3CH_2CH_2CH_2OH$

3335.4	1378.6	952.2
2959.7	1072.6	846.7
1466.0	1010.6	737.5

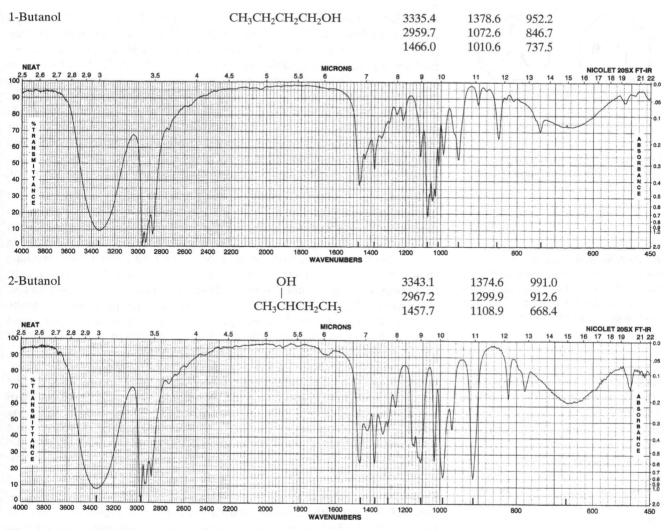

2-Butanol

OH
|
$CH_3CHCH_2CH_3$

3343.1	1374.6	991.0
2967.2	1299.9	912.6
1457.7	1108.9	668.4

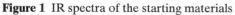

Figure 1 IR spectra of the starting materials

DIRECTIONS

You will be assigned one of the two alcohols and either 1.0, 2.0, 3.0, or 4.0 mL of sulfuric acid. Measure the quantities of all chemicals carefully for the cost analysis.

Safety Notes

Hydrobromic acid is toxic and very corrosive; it can cause very serious damage to the skin, eyes, and respiratory tract. Wear gloves and dispense under a hood. Avoid contact with the acid and do not inhale its vapors. Sulfuric acid causes chemical burns that can seriously damage the skin and eyes. Wear gloves and avoid contact.

1-Butanol and 2-butanol are flammable and may cause eye or skin irritation. Avoid contact.

1-Bromobutane and 2-bromobutane are flammable and may be harmful if inhaled or absorbed through the skin. 2-Bromobutane is a suspected carcinogen. Avoid contact with the products and do not breathe their vapors.

sulfuric acid

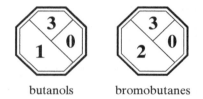

butanols   bromobutanes

Take Care! Wear gloves, avoid contact with the acids, and do not breathe their vapors.

Waste Disposal: The residue is corrosive and produces very irritating fumes. Let it cool to room temperature, then place it in an acid wastes container under the hood.

Take Care! Possible violent reaction! Wear gloves and avoid contact with the acid.

Stop and Think: What does the NaHCO$_3$ wash remove?

Waste Disposal: Place the sulfuric acid in the acid wastes container. Unless your instructor directs otherwise, wash all aqueous layers down the drain.

Reaction. Assemble an apparatus for heating under reflux [OP-7] using a 50-mL round-bottom flask, a water-cooled reflux condenser, and a gas trap [OP-14] containing 1 *M* NaOH. The gas trap can be omitted if you are performing the reaction under an efficient fume hood. Add 72.0 mmol of your assigned alcohol (1-butanol or 2-butanol), accurately weighed, to the round-bottom flask and add some acid-resistant boiling chips or a stir bar [OP-10]. *Under the hood,* cool the flask in ice water and cautiously add 10.0 mL (88 mmol) of 48% aqueous hydrobromic acid while swirling or stirring. Using a measuring pipet, add your assigned volume of concentrated sulfuric acid to the reaction mixture while swirling or stirring. Heat the mixture under reflux for one hour from the time the solution starts to boil.

Separation. Codistill [OP-20] the alkyl bromide with the water present in the reaction mixture, using a simple distillation apparatus (no addition funnel) with a graduated cylinder as the receiver. Stop the distillation when the distillate is no longer cloudy and the organic layer no longer increases in volume over a period of 5–10 minutes. Add 10 mL of water to the distillate, shake the mixture in a separatory funnel, and separate the layers cleanly. Ordinarily, the alkyl bromide is on the bottom and the aqueous layer on top, but occasionally the aqueous layer may be dense enough to end up on the bottom—in this case, the bottom layer will be the larger one. If you aren't sure which layer to save, test each one by adding a drop of water to a drop of the layer. If the drops do *not* mix, the layer contains the alkyl bromide.

Wash [OP-24] the organic layer cautiously with 5 mL of cold, concentrated sulfuric acid, shaking gently with occasional venting. Remove the bottom (H$_2$SO$_4$) layer, and then wash the alkyl bromide layer with 10 mL of water followed by 10 mL of saturated aqueous sodium bicarbonate, saving the organic (bottom) layer each time. Dry [OP-25] the alkyl bromide with a small amount of anhydrous sodium sulfate or calcium chloride. Transfer the crude product to a tared vial, weigh it, and report the yield to your instructor or coworkers.

Purification and Analysis. Purify the alkyl bromide by simple distillation [OP-30], using the compact distillation apparatus shown in Figure E8. Collect the product over a 3–4°C range centered around the expected boiling point. Measure the mass and boiling point [OP-34] of the purified product. At your instructor's discretion, obtain its IR spectrum [OP-39]. Using prices provided by your instructor, calculate the total cost of all the chemicals (except water) that you used in the experiment. Because sulfuric acid can be recycled (at some cost), divide its cost by 3. Divide the total cost in dollars by the mass of your crude product in kilograms and obtain the cost/mass values reported by other members of your team. Then determine the optimum catalyst/substrate ratio for each reaction.

Exercises

1. Based on their structures, attempt to explain any differences in the optimum catalyst/substrate ratios for the two alcohols.
2. (a) Write structures for at least three by-products that might have formed during the reaction of 2-butanol. (b) Propose a mechanism for the formation of each by-product.

3. If you recorded the IR spectrum of your product, interpret the spectrum as completely as you can, and use the appropriate starting material spectrum in Figure 1 to show that the expected functional group conversion has taken place.

4. (a) Calculate the atom economy and reaction efficiency of your synthesis. (b) Describe some green features of your synthesis, and any that aren't so green.

5. Following the format in the "Planning an Experiment" appendix, construct a flow diagram for this experiment.

6. Describe and explain the possible effect on your results of the following experimental errors or variations. (a) After adding water to the distillate during the "Separation" step, you kept the bottom layer and discarded the smaller top layer. (b) You omitted the sulfuric acid wash. (c) You used a boiling-water bath to heat a reaction mixture containing 1-butanol.

7. Write balanced equations showing how HBr and SO_2 are consumed in a gas trap that contains NaOH.

8. Write a mechanism showing how 2,4,5-trichlorophenol is converted to 2,4,5-T.

Other Things You Can Do

(Starred items require your instructor's permission.)

*1. Obtain a nuclear magnetic resonance (NMR) spectrum of your product in deuterochloroform, and interpret it as completely as you can.

*2. Compare the nucleophilic substitution rates of some alcohols as described in the "Identification of an Unknown Arene by NMR Spectrometry" minilab.

3. Starting with sources from the Bibliography, write a research paper describing the manufacture, uses, and environmental effects of some chlorinated pesticides.

Borohydride Reduction of Vanillin to Vanillyl Alcohol

EXPERIMENT

Preparation of Alcohols. Reactions of Carbonyl Compounds. Reduction Reactions. Nucleophilic Addition.

Operations

The operations you use will depend on the procedure you develop.

Before You Begin

After reading the experiment, develop a procedure and an experimental plan for the sodium borohydride reduction of 25.0 mmol of vanillin to vanillyl alcohol. Calculate or estimate the quantities of reactants and other chemicals you will need, and calculate the theoretical yield of vanillyl alcohol. Describe the reaction conditions, and tell how you intend to separate and purify the product. Your procedure should be clear and detailed enough so that anyone with sufficient background could carry it out successfully. (Alternatively, a group of students can work out a set of procedures in which some experimental parameters are varied to see how such variations alter the yield and purity of the product.)

Scenario

Pulpchem Inc., a subsidiary of a large paper company, produces useful chemicals from lignin and other by-products of paper production. Chemical treatment of lignin yields large quantities of vanillin, a white solid that is also responsible for the characteristic aroma of vanilla beans. Woody Aspin, Pulpchem's product development manager, has asked your institute to develop a method for reducing vanillin to vanillyl alcohol, which shows promise as a starting material for the synthesis of synthetic drugs and flavoring ingredients. A procedure for the preparation of vanillyl alcohol appeared in an obscure Swedish journal, *Acta Universitatis Lundensis*, which ceased publication in the 1960s. Unless you understand Swedish and can get your hands on a copy of the journal article, you will have to develop your own procedure for the synthesis.

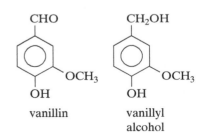

vanillin   vanillyl alcohol

Applying Scientific Methodology

The problem—whether vanillin can be converted to vanillyl alcohol by a procedure that you have developed yourself—will be solved when (and if) you obtain and characterize the product. You will test your working hypothesis by measuring the product's melting point, and you can record its infrared (IR) spectrum for confirmation.

From *Operational Organic Chemistry: A Problem Solving Approach to the Laboratory*, Fourth Edition, John W. Lehman. Copyright © 2009 by Pearson Education. Published by Prentice Hall. All rights reserved.

Fragrant and Fiery Aromatics

Chemists recognized at an early date that certain compounds obtained from natural sources showed a higher ratio of carbon to hydrogen than did typical aliphatic compounds. These compounds also had distinctive chemical properties. Because many of them came from such pleasant-smelling sources as the essential oils of cloves, sassafras, cinnamon, anise, bitter almonds, and vanilla, they were called *aromatic* compounds. The name stuck, although it is no longer associated with the odors of such compounds but with their structures and properties. Many aromatic compounds do live up to the original meaning of the term, however. Among the most interesting and important of these are vanillin and the *vanilloids*, structurally related compounds that exhibit vanillin's characteristic ring-substitution pattern.

In 1520, the Spanish conquistador Hernando Cortez was served an exotic drink by Montezuma II, emperor of the Aztecs, at his capital of Tenochtitlán on the site of modern Mexico City. Cortez enjoyed this *xocolatl*, a chocolate-based beverage flavored with honey and vanilla, and it soon found its way back to Europe. The vanilla plant (*Vanilla planifolia*), a climbing orchid, was also shipped back to the Old World in the hope that it could be cultivated there. The transported plants grew well but, mysteriously, would not fruit. This mystery remained unsolved for more than 300 years, until someone discovered that the plant was pollinated by a native Mexican bee with an exceptionally long proboscis. A method of hand pollination was soon developed, allowing the cultivation of vanilla outside of Mexico.

vanilla plant

Vanilla flavoring comes from the fruit of the vanilla plant—a long, narrow pod that, after curing, looks somewhat like a dark brown string bean. The principal component of vanilla flavoring, vanillin (3-methoxy-4-hydroxybenzaldehyde), doesn't exist as such in the fresh vanilla bean, but is formed by the enzymatic breakdown of a glucoside during the curing process. Although the finest vanilla flavoring is still obtained from natural vanilla, synthetic vanillin is far less costly. It is used as a component of flavorings and perfumes and as a starting material for the synthesis of such drugs as L-dopa, which is used to treat Parkinson's disease.

At one time, synthetic vanillin was made mostly from isoeugenol, a naturally occurring phenol used widely as a perfume ingredient.

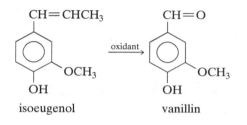

isoeugenol   vanillin

Most vanillin is now synthesized using lignin derived from wood pulp. Lignin is a complex polymer that gives rigidity to trees and other woody plants; after cellulose, it is the second most abundant organic material on

Earth. Many of the basic structural units of lignin are guiacylpropane units, and such units can be broken down chemically to yield vanillin.

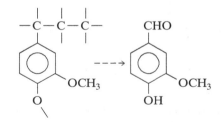

guiacylpropane unit

Safrole, a fragrant liquid derived from the roots and bark of the sassafras tree (*Sassafras albidum*), is structurally related to vanillin. Once widely used as a flavoring in root beer, toothpaste, and chewing gum, safrole can no longer be added to such products because of its toxic, irritant qualities and because it produces liver tumors in rats and mice. But black pepper, anise, nutmeg, and other spices contain minute amounts of safrole, so you probably consume a little of it every day. Safrole has also been used by illicit-drug manufacturers to synthesize the dangerous designer drug "Ecstasy" (methylenedioxymethamphetamine), which can cause mental confusion, kidney failure, and death. For this reason, the sale of safrole is now strictly controlled.

Black pepper gets its "bite" from piperine, which contains the methylenedioxy ($- OCH_2O -$) unit also found in safrole.

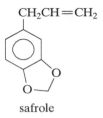

safrole

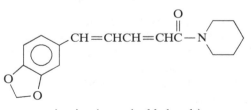

piperine (*trans* double bonds)

Another hot compound with the vanillin structural unit is zingerone, the pungent principle of ginger.

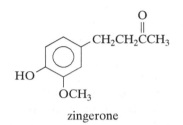

zingerone

Capsaicin, zingerone's much hotter cousin, is a fiery component of many *capsicums*, pungent peppers such as cayennes, jalapeños, and the ultrahot habaneros.

259

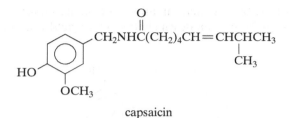

capsaicin

Capsicum peppers are used to make Tabasco sauce, Jamaica Hell Fire, and other hot sauces, as well as most commercial salsas. Recent research has shown that the human tongue, in addition to containing receptors that detect sweet, sour, salty, bitter, and umami (MSG-like) tastes, also has vanilloid receptors that produce a sensation of heat when triggered by capsaicin and related vanilloids. So, the structural units that we associate with the pleasant flavor of vanillin contribute to a far different taste sensation in these fiery aromatics!

Understanding the Experiment

When organic chemists attempt to synthesize a new compound, they have no set procedure to follow. Instead, their options are to

- Adapt and modify an existing procedure for a similar synthesis
- Devise a procedure based on their knowledge of the substrate, reagent, product, and reaction involved
- Invent a new way of synthesizing the compound they wish to make

In this experiment, you will follow the second option. You will develop your own procedure for reducing vanillin to vanillyl alcohol based on information that you will find in this section about the reducing agent, sodium borohydride, and the reaction, reduction of a carbonyl compound to an alcohol, as well as information in the "Reactions and Properties" section about the substrate and the product.

Neither vanillin nor sodium borohydride is likely to be a significant environmental pollutant.

Key Concept: Developing a successful procedure for an organic synthesis requires a comprehensive knowledge of the characteristics of the reactants and a good understanding of the reaction.

Reduction Reactions. In organic chemistry, *reduction* usually refers to a reaction that is accompanied by a gain of hydrogen atoms or a loss of oxygen atoms, or both. For example, a carbonyl compound is reduced to an alcohol when its carbonyl group gains two hydrogen atoms. The hydrogen is provided by an appropriate reducing agent.

Reducing Agents. When lithium aluminum hydride ($LiAlH_4$) was introduced as a reducing agent in the late 1940s, it brought about a revolution in the preparation of alcohols by reduction. At that time, the two most popular reducing agents for carbonyl compounds were hydrogen and sodium metal. The greater simplicity and convenience of hydride reduction soon made it the preferred method for a broad spectrum of chemical reductions. Lithium aluminum hydride is a powerful reducing agent whose high reactivity is a disadvantage in some applications. Because it reacts violently with water and other hydroxylic solvents to release hydrogen gas, it can only be

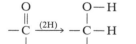

Reduction of a carbonyl group

used in aprotic solvents, such as diethyl ether, under strictly anhydrous conditions. It is also expensive and somewhat hazardous to use—even grinding it in a mortar may cause a fire. By contrast, sodium borohydride ($NaBH_4$) is a much milder reducing agent that is comparatively safe to handle in its solid form. Unlike lithium aluminum hydride, it can even be used in aqueous or alcoholic solutions. $NaBH_4$ does decompose slowly in moist air, so its container should be tightly capped when it is not in use.

Sodium borohydride reductions involve nucleophilic addition of hydride ion ($H:^-$) to the carbonyl carbon, but apparently no free hydride ions are generated. Kinetic evidence suggests that one solvent molecule bonds to the boron atom while it is transferring hydride to the carbonyl compound, and another solvent molecule provides a proton to the carbonyl oxygen.

$$R-\overset{\frown}{O}-H + O=C\overset{\nearrow}{\underset{\nwarrow}{}} + H\overset{\ominus}{-}B\overset{H}{\underset{}{\overset{|}{\nwarrow}}} + O-R \longrightarrow R-\overset{\ominus}{O} + H-O-\overset{|}{\underset{|}{C}}-H + \overset{}{\underset{}{B}}\overset{\ominus}{-}OR + H^+$$

(R = alkyl or H)

This process can continue until all of the hydride ions from BH_4^- have been used up.

Reaction Stoichiometry.   The overall stoichiometry of the borohydride reduction of a carbonyl compound is given by the following general equation (R, R′ = alkyl, aryl, or H):

$$4R\overset{O}{\overset{\|}{C}}R' + NaBH_4 + 4H_2O \longrightarrow 4R\overset{OH}{\overset{|}{C}}HR' + H_3BO_3 + NaOH$$

In practice, it is best to use a 50–100% excess of sodium borohydride to compensate for any that reacts with the solvent or decomposes from other causes. Because the reaction is first order with respect to sodium borohydride (as well as the carbonyl compound), using an excess will also increase the reaction rate.

Reaction Solvents.   Sodium borohydride reductions are usually carried out in a dilute (~1 M) aqueous NaOH solution or in an alcohol, such as methanol, ethanol, or 2-propanol. The reagent isn't stable at low pH, and even in a neutral aqueous solution it decomposes to the extent of about 4.5% per hour at 25°C. Acidic functional groups, such as COOH and the OH group of a phenol, may cause rapid decomposition of sodium borohydride. When a carbonyl compound having such a functional group is being reduced, enough 1 M NaOH should be used to neutralize the functional group *and* maintain a pH of 10 or higher. Sodium borohydride reacts slowly with alcohols, but ethanol and methanol are usually suitable solvents when there are no acidic functional groups and the reaction time is no more than 30 minutes at 25°C. For longer reaction times or reactions at higher temperatures, isopropyl alcohol is a better solvent, but it is more difficult to remove after the reaction is over.

Reaction Conditions. In most reactions with sodium borohydride, the aldehyde or ketone is dissolved in the reaction solvent and a solution of sodium borohydride is added, with external cooling if necessary, at a rate slow enough to keep the reaction temperature below 25°C. Higher temperatures may decompose the hydride, and adding the carbonyl compound *to* the alkaline sodium borohydride solution may cause side reactions of base-sensitive substrates. The amount of solvent isn't crucial, but enough should be used to completely dissolve the reactants and facilitate the workup of the reaction mixture. The solubility of sodium borohydride per 100 g of solvent is reported to be 55 g in water at 25°C, 16.4 g in methanol at 20°C, and 4.0 g in ethanol at 20°C.

The time required to complete the reaction depends on the reaction temperature and the reactivity of the substrate. Kinetic studies of borohydride reduction in isopropyl alcohol have shown that aldehydes are considerably more reactive than ketones and that aliphatic carbonyl compounds are more reactive than aromatic ones. Most reactions of aldehydes and aliphatic ketones are complete in 30 minutes at room temperature, but those of aromatic ketones or particularly hindered ketones may require more time or higher reaction temperatures. For example, the comparatively reactive ketone 4-*t*-butylcyclohexanone is completely reduced at room temperature in 20 minutes, but benzophenone is reduced by boiling it in isopropyl alcohol for 30 minutes.

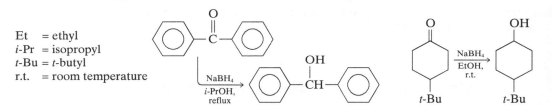

Et   = ethyl
i-Pr = isopropyl
t-Bu = *t*-butyl
r.t.   = room temperature

Reaction conditions in borohydride reductions

Workup of the Reaction Mixture. After the reaction is complete, the excess sodium borohydride is decomposed by acidifying the reaction mixture to pH 6 or lower (slowly, while stirring) using dilute (~3 M) hydrochloric acid. Hydrogen gas is evolved as the excess sodium borohydride decomposes, so there must be no flames in the vicinity. Working under a hood is advisable. Addition of acid may also generate some diborane (B_2H_6), which can cause side reactions if other reducible groups, such as COOH, COOR, and C=C, are present.

Depending on the properties of the product and the reaction solvent used, the product can be separated from the reaction mixture by filtration, extraction, or partial evaporation of the solvent followed by extraction. If the product is a solid that crystallizes from the reaction mixture, it can be collected by vacuum filtration. The yield of the solid product can usually be increased by extracting the filtrate with diethyl ether or another suitable solvent, and then drying and evaporating the ether. Liquids or water-soluble products are generally separated from an aqueous reaction mixture by extraction with diethyl ether and recovered by evaporating the dried ether. If the reaction solvent is an alcohol, the reaction mixture is usually concentrated by evaporating most of the alcohol. Water is then added and the product is extracted with a suitable solvent.

Purification. The product can be purified by any appropriate method, based on its physical state and properties. Vanillyl alcohol is reported to be soluble in hot and cold ethanol, hot and cold ether, and hot water. It is relatively insoluble in cold water, and it tends to form supersaturated solutions in water.

Reactions and Properties

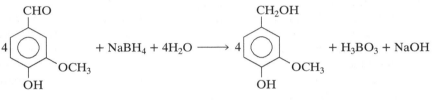

Table 1 Physical properties

	mol wt	mp	bp
vanillin	152.2	79	285
sodium borohydride	37.83	37	400d
vanillyl alcohol	154.2	115	d

Note: mp and bp are in °C; density is in g/mL; d = decomposes.

Vanillin

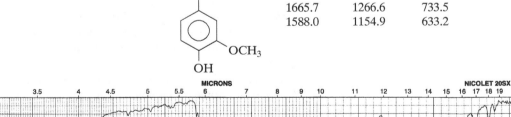

3171.4	1509.6	859.6
1665.7	1266.6	733.5
1588.0	1154.9	633.2

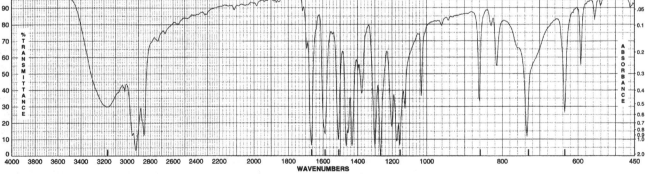

Figure 1 IR spectrum of vanillin

DIRECTIONS

Safety Notes

sodium borohydride

Sodium borohydride is toxic and corrosive; it can react violently with concentrated acids, oxidizing agents, and other substances. Aqueous NaBH$_4$ solutions with pH values below 10.5 have been known to decompose violently, so be sure that your reaction mixture (if aqueous) is sufficiently alkaline. Avoid contact with NaBH$_4$, do not breathe its dust, and keep it away from other chemicals.

Hydrogen is generated when the reaction mixture is acidified, so be sure that there are no flames nearby during this step.

Develop your own procedure for this experiment and submit it to your instructor for approval. Carry out the synthesis in the laboratory, measure the yield and melting point of the purified product, and turn it in. At your instructor's discretion, you can obtain the IR spectrum of your product and compare it with the spectrum of the starting material to confirm that the expected functional-group conversion has occurred. Dispose of any wastes as directed by your instructor. Calculate your percent yield and compare your results with those of other students in your laboratory section.

Exercises

1. Write a mechanism for the reduction of vanillin by sodium borohydride under the reaction conditions you used.
2. Write a balanced equation for the decomposition of sodium borohydride in water to which HCl has been added.
3. Describe and explain the possible effect on your results of the following experimental errors or variations during the synthesis of vanillyl alcohol. (a) You used pure water as the reaction solvent. (b) You used 5 mL of 1 M NaOH for the NaBH$_4$ solution and 10 mL of 1 M NaOH for the vanillin solution. (c) Because you started with 25 mmol of vanillin, you assumed that a 100% excess of NaBH$_4$ was 50 mmol and used that amount.
4. (a) Calculate the atom economy and reaction efficiency of your synthesis. (b) Describe some green features of your synthesis, and any that aren't so green.
5. Following the format in the "Planning an Experiment" appendix, construct a flow diagram for the experiment.
6. Sodium borohydride is a strong base as well as a reducing agent. Explain why it is better to add the NaBH$_4$ solution *to* a base-sensitive substrate than to add the substrate to the NaBH$_4$ solution.
7. (a) Draw the structure of the product you would have isolated if you had used NaBD$_4$ in D$_2$O in this experiment, and write a mechanism explaining the result. (b) Give the product structure for the same reaction using NaBD$_4$ in H$_2$O. Assume that there is no hydrogen exchange between NaBD$_4$ and the solvent.
8. A careless student, Will Bobble, misread the label on a bottle of 10 M sodium hydroxide and used it (rather than 1 M NaOH) to dissolve his

vanillin. Then he stored the solution and left the lab early to catch a ride home. During the next lab period, he added $NaBH_4$ and finished the experiment. Although his product was a white solid, it melted over a broad temperature range that was much lower than the melting point of vanillyl alcohol. His instructor suggested washing the product with dilute sodium bicarbonate; when he did so, about half of the product dissolved and the remainder melted at 115°C. Explain what happened and write an equation for the reaction.

Other Things You Can Do

(Starred items require your instructor's permission.)

*1. Carry out the following tests from Part IV on vanillin and on your product: 2,4-dinitrophenylhydrazine (Test C-11), ferric chloride (Test C-13), and Tollens' test (Test C-23). Interpret the results and comment on the purity of your product.

*2. Compare the oxidation rates of some alcohols in the "Oxidation of Alcohols by Potassium Permanganate" minilab.

*3. Reduce another carbonyl compound (such as benzaldehyde or camphor) with sodium borohydride after developing a detailed procedure, and turn in a pure sample of the resulting alcohol. Your instructor must approve the procedure before you start.

 4. Starting with sources listed in the Bibliography, write a research paper on the sources, nature, and uses of lignin, including a description of a commercial process for producing vanillin from the by-products of papermaking.

Synthesis of Triphenylmethanol and the Trityl Carbocation

Reactions of Carbonyl Compounds. Reactions of Organic Halides.
Preparation of Alcohols. Nucleophilic Addition. Organometallic
Compounds. Carbocations. Infrared Spectrometry.

Operations

OP-12a Using Drying Tubes
OP-7 Heating
OP-10 Mixing
OP-11 Addition of Reactants
OP-15 Gravity Filtration
OP-16 Vacuum Filtration
OP-19 Evaporation
OP-24 Washing Liquids
OP-25 Drying Liquids
OP-26 Washing and Drying Solids
OP-28 Recrystallization
OP-33 Melting Point
OP-39 Infrared Spectrometry (optional)

Before You Begin

1. Read the experiment and operation OP-12a, read or review the other operations as necessary, and write an experimental plan.
2. Calculate the mass of 22.0 mmol of magnesium, the mass of 20.0 mmol of benzophenone, the mass and volume of 22.0 mmol of bromobenzene, and the theoretical yield of triphenylmethanol. Calculate the theoretical yield of trityl fluoborate from 1.00 g of triphenylmethanol.

Scenario

The Complementary Colors Company manufactures synthetic dyes, including a number of triphenylmethane dyes. Gilda Lillie, product development director for the company, would like to develop some new colors to improve its market share in the dye industry. She has learned, for example, that having two *para*-dimethylamino groups on two of the three benzene rings in the parent structure yields a green dye (Malachite Green), while having three of them yields a violet dye (Crystal Violet).

From *Operational Organic Chemistry: A Problem Solving Approach to the Laboratory*, Fourth Edition, John W. Lehman. Copyright © 2009 by Pearson Education. Published by Prentice Hall. All rights reserved.

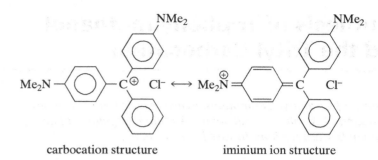

carbocation structure   iminium ion structure

Two resonance structures for Malachite Green, a triphenylmethane dye

triphenylmethyl (trityl)
fluoborate

The company's technicians need to know how the kinds and positions of substituents on the parent triphenylmethyl ring structure affect the color of triphenylmethane dyes. For that, they need a sample of the unsubstituted parent compound of these dyes, the triphenylmethyl (trityl) carbocation. Your assignment is to prepare triphenylmethanol and convert it to trityl fluoborate, a salt that contains the trityl carbocation.

Applying Scientific Methodology

The main scientific problem—determining the color of trityl fluoborate—will be solved when you prepare this substance.

The Colorful Career of the Triphenylmethanes

During his Easter vacation from London's Royal College of Chemistry, 18-year-old William Perkin was trying to synthesize quinine when he came up with an unpromising black solid that had none of the properties of quinine. Undeterred, Perkin used similar methods to synthesize mauve, a light purple dye whose commercial success launched the synthetic dye industry. The first triphenylmethane dye, fuchsin, was synthesized a few years later, and it was followed soon after by Malachite Green, Crystal Violet, and other triphenylmethane dyes. The race to develop commercially marketable dyes also stimulated research into the molecular basis of color. Why, for example, is Malachite Green green and its reduced form colorless?

The *chromophore* of a compound is the part of its molecule over which electrons can be delocalized and which is responsible for its absorption of ultraviolet or visible light. Triphenylmethane dyes come in all colors of the rainbow, from the red of rosaniline through Malachite Green and Victoria Blue to Crystal Violet. The chromophores responsible for these colors appear to be nitrogen-substituted triphenylmethyl (trityl) cations, but they aren't true carbocations, because most of their positive charge is distributed to the nitrogen atoms, as in the iminium ion form of Malachite Green shown previously. According to resonance theory, the iminium ion and carbocation forms are contributing structures of a resonance hybrid that has some characteristics of each. The electron delocalization suggested by such

The synthesis of quinine wasn't accomplished until 1944—88 years after Perkin had attempted it.

Reduced form of Malachite Green

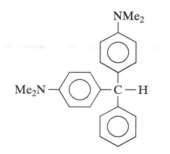

Key Concept: *When a substance cannot be represented satisfactorily by a single structural formula, its actual structure is regarded to be a composite of two or more contributing structures.*

structures is responsible for their colors. As a rule, compounds with extensive chromophores that allow electron delocalization over many atoms tend to be colored; the longer the chromophore, the higher the wavelength of light it absorbs. The reduced form of Malachite Green isn't colored, because the saturated carbon that connects the rings prevents electron delocalization over the three-ring system.

Although it is nearly a trillion times less stable than Crystal Violet, the triphenylmethyl cation is unusually stable for a true carbocation. When protected from atmospheric moisture, trityl salts will keep almost indefinitely. The cation owes this unusual stability to delocalization of the positive charge about its three benzene rings. The cation is shaped somewhat like a propeller with the "blades" (benzene rings) pitched at a 32° angle, because steric interference between the *ortho* hydrogen atoms makes a planar configuration impossible.

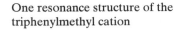

One resonance structure of the triphenylmethyl cation

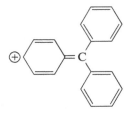

Shape of triphenylmethyl cation

Understanding the Experiment

The year 1900 featured two milestones in organic chemistry: Moses Gomberg announced his discovery of the trityl free radical, and Victor Grignard reported his development of Grignard reagents. Just a year later, trityl carbocations were being prepared from triphenylmethanol, which is most easily synthesized using a Grignard reagent.

Grignard's original procedure for preparing a Grignard reagent was as follows: Approximately 1 mole of magnesium metal was placed in a dry, two-necked round-bottom flask fitted with a reflux condenser and addition funnel. A mole of the organic halide was dissolved in diethyl ether, and 50 mL of this solution was added to the magnesium. When a white turbidity appeared at the metal surface and effervescence began, more ether was added in portions, with cooling, followed by drop-by-drop addition of the remainder of the halide/ether solution. The reaction was brought to completion by heating under reflux in a hot-water bath.

Although extensive studies of the reaction have led to some modifications of the reaction conditions, essentially the same method is used today to make most Grignard reagents. It is important that the reagents and apparatus be very dry, because water not only reacts with Grignard reagents but also inhibits their formation. In a study using butyl bromide, it was found that the *induction period* (the time between the combination of reactants and the start of a noticeable reaction) for forming the Grignard reagent was $7\frac{1}{2}$ minutes using sodium-dried diethyl ether, 20 minutes using commercial absolute diethyl ether, and 2 hours using diethyl ether half saturated with water. It is apparent that careful drying of the reaction apparatus and reagents saves time in the long run; it should increase the yield of the desired product as well. An especially effective drying technique is to add the magnesium to the reaction flask and heat it (well away from any container of diethyl ether!) in a soft, blue Bunsen burner flame for 2–3 minutes, then set it on a cork ring or in a beaker to cool. If the bromobenzene/ether solution is then added and the magnesium pieces are rubbed with a stirring rod for about 10 seconds, the reaction should start almost immediately.

The type and quantity of reagents and solvents used are also important. When magnesium metal is exposed to air, it forms a thin film of magnesium oxide on its surface, so you will crush dry magnesium turnings with a glass rod to remove some of the oxide film and provide a fresh surface for reaction. Commercial anhydrous diethyl ether is suitable for most routine preparations, but the optimum quantity of ether depends on the kind of Grignard reagent being prepared. One study showed that the highest yields of phenylmagnesium bromide were obtained with 5 moles of diethyl ether per mole of bromobenzene.

In this experiment, you will prepare phenylmagnesium bromide by adding a solution of bromobenzene in anhydrous diethyl ether to magnesium metal. The reaction can usually be started by cupping the reaction flask in the palm of the hand to warm the ether while crushing the magnesium with a stirring rod. The onset of the reaction is signaled by the formation of small bubbles on the surface of the magnesium accompanied by the appearance of a cloudy precipitate. You can sometimes jump-start a balky Grignard reaction by adding a small amount of previously prepared Grignard reagent to the reaction mixture; consult your instructor for help.

Using a high concentration of bromobenzene helps to get the reaction started, but it can promote the formation of an undesirable by-product, biphenyl, through a side reaction on the metal's surface. For this reason, the bromobenzene solution is diluted by adding diethyl ether as soon as the reaction gets under way. Phenylmagnesium bromide reacts rapidly with water to form benzene and more slowly with oxygen to form a magnesium salt of phenol, so the reaction apparatus must be protected from moisture and the Grignard reagent should be used shortly after it is prepared.

When benzophenone is added to the Grignard reagent, a magnesium salt of triphenylmethanol precipitates from the reaction mixture, which usually turns pink during the addition. This salt is converted to triphenylmethanol by water, and dilute hydrochloric acid is added to dissolve the basic magnesium salts that form along with the product. The ether solution containing triphenylmethanol is washed to remove impurities, and the solvent is evaporated. The crude product is then *triturated* with hexanes or petroleum ether to remove biphenyl and is purified by recrystallization.

Carbocations can be prepared by mixing alcohols with a strong acid such as fluoboric acid (tetrafluoroboric acid); the fluoborate anion is a very weak nucleophile that doesn't react with the resulting carbocation. You will prepare trityl fluoborate by the reaction of triphenylmethanol with 48% fluoboric acid. The water in the aqueous fluoboric acid solution, as well as that produced during the carbocation-forming reaction, could prevent or

Trituration of a solid involves rubbing and grinding it, usually in the presence of a solvent.

Preparation of carbocations using fluoboric acid

$$ROH + HBF_4 \rightleftharpoons ROH_2^+ + BF_4^-$$
$$\longrightarrow R^+BF_4^- + H_2O$$

reverse the reaction. Acetic anhydride is added to consume the water by the following reaction:

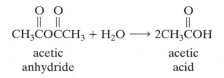

$$\underset{\substack{\text{acetic} \\ \text{anhydride}}}{CH_3\overset{\overset{\displaystyle O}{\|}}{C}O\overset{\overset{\displaystyle O}{\|}}{C}CH_3} + H_2O \longrightarrow \underset{\substack{\text{acetic} \\ \text{acid}}}{2CH_3\overset{\overset{\displaystyle O}{\|}}{C}OH}$$

Of the chemicals used in part **A**, diethyl ether isn't considered toxic to aquatic organisms and doesn't persist for long in either air or water; bromobenzene is toxic to aquatic organisms and shouldn't be released into the environment; and benzophenone is harmful to aquatic organisms. In water, acetic anhydride hydrolyzes to acetic acid, which readily breaks down to form carbon dioxide and water. Little information is available about the environmental effects of fluoboric acid, but it is likely to be toxic to aqueous organisms.

Reactions and Properties

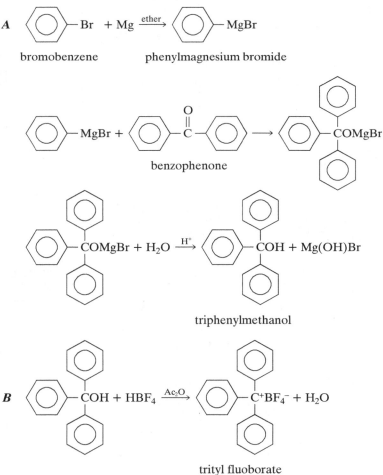

Table 1 Physical properties

	mol wt	mp	bp	*d*
bromobenzene	157.0	−31	156	1.495
magnesium	24.3			
diethyl ether	74.1	−116	34.5	0.714
benzophenone	182.2	48	306	
triphenylmethanol	260.3	164	380	
fluoboric acid (48%)	87.8			1.41
acetic anhydride	102.1	−73	140	1.082
trityl fluoborate	330.1			

Note: mp and bp are in °C; density is in g/mL.

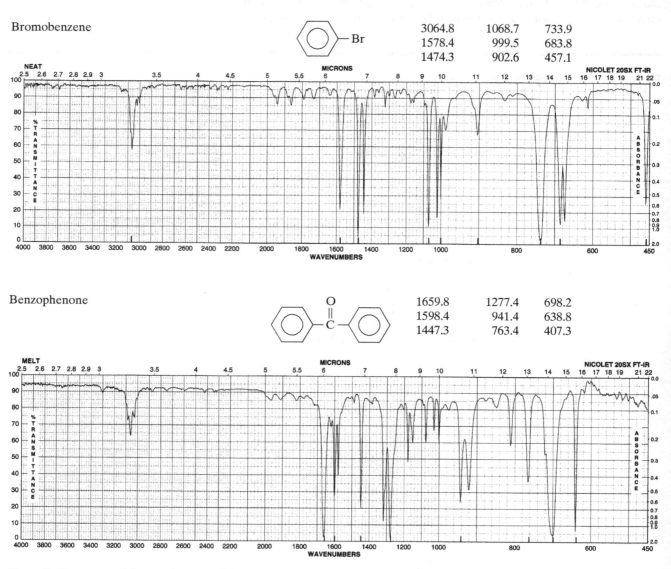

Bromobenzene

3064.8	1068.7	733.9
1578.4	999.5	683.8
1474.3	902.6	457.1

Benzophenone

1659.8	1277.4	698.2
1598.4	941.4	638.8
1447.3	763.4	407.3

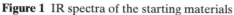

Figure 1 IR spectra of the starting materials

DIRECTIONS

A. *Preparation of Triphenylmethanol*

If possible, clean and pre-dry the glassware needed for the reaction before the lab period to reduce the drying time.

> Bromobenzene causes eye and skin irritation; inhalation, ingestion, or skin absorption may be harmful. Avoid contact with the liquid and do not breathe its vapors.
>
> Diethyl ether is extremely flammable and may be harmful if inhaled. Do not breathe its vapors; keep it away from flames and hot surfaces.
>
> Magnesium can cause dangerous fires if ignited; keep it away from flames and hot surfaces.
>
> Petroleum ether is extremely flammable and may be harmful if inhaled or absorbed through the skin. Avoid inhalation and prolonged contact; keep it away from flames and hot surfaces.

Safety Notes

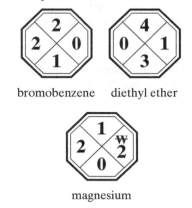

bromobenzene   diethyl ether

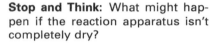

magnesium

Reaction of Bromobenzene with Magnesium. *It is essential that all apparatus used during this reaction step be clean and scrupulously dried.* Clean the following items and dry them in a 110°C oven for at least 30 minutes: 100-mL round-bottom flask, Claisen adapter, West condenser, separatory–addition funnel, glass stopper, thermometer adapter (remove the rubber connector), drying tube filled with calcium chloride (see OP-12a), flat-bottomed stirring rod, and 50-mL Erlenmeyer flask. Meanwhile, weigh 22.0 mmol of clean, dry magnesium turnings and leave them in the round-bottom flask for the last 5 minutes of drying. As soon as the glassware is cool enough to handle, assemble an apparatus for addition under reflux [OP-11], inserting the drying tube [OP-12a] in the top of the reflux condenser. Weigh 22.0 mmol of dry bromobenzene into the dried Erlenmeyer flask and dissolve it in 5.0 mL of *anhydrous* diethyl ether. Then transfer this solution to the separatory–addition funnel and stopper it, placing a strip of filter paper between the stopper and the neck of the funnel. Add the bromobenzene solution all at once to the reaction flask, and replace it in the addition funnel by 6.5 mL of anhydrous diethyl ether. Detach the flask momentarily, cup it in the palm of your hand to warm the ether, and *carefully* (don't punch a hole in the flask!) crush and rub the magnesium turnings with the flat end of your stirring rod for at least 30 seconds; then reattach the funnel to the reaction apparatus.

Observe the reaction mixture closely for evidence of a reaction, such as cloudiness and the evolution of bubbles from the magnesium surface. If the reaction doesn't begin within 5 minutes or so, detach the flask and rub the magnesium turnings with your stirring rod as before; if the reaction still doesn't start, consult your instructor. When the reaction mixture begins to boil quite vigorously without external heating, add the ether, drop by drop, at a rate just sufficient to keep the reaction mixture boiling. When all of the ether has been added, let the reaction continue until the boiling has nearly stopped, and then use a heating mantle or a warm-water bath to heat the reaction mixture under gentle reflux [OP-7] for another 10–15 minutes. The reflux ring of condensing ether should be in

Stop and Think: What might happen if the reaction apparatus isn't completely dry?

Alternatively, heat the flask containing the magnesium pieces as described in "Understanding the Experiment."

Take Care! Keep diethyl ether away from flames and hot surfaces.

Stop and Think: What is the purpose of the filter paper?

If the reaction starts but then stops, add some more ether as described next.

the lower third of the condenser. If a significant amount of ether evaporates, reducing its volume in the reaction flask, replace it with fresh anhydrous ether. Don't stop at this point, because the phenylmagnesium bromide solution won't keep for long.

Reaction of Phenylmagnesium Bromide with Benzophenone. Dissolve 20.0 mmol of benzophenone in 10 ml of anhydrous diethyl ether in a dry Erlenmeyer flask and place it in the separatory–addition funnel. When the reaction mixture has cooled so that the ether is no longer boiling, add this solution, drop by drop, to the reaction mixture with shaking or magnetic stirring [OP-10]. The solution should be added fast enough to keep the ether boiling gently without external heating. When the addition is complete, use a heating mantle or a warm-water bath to heat the reaction mixture under gentle reflux for another 15 minutes. (If you stop after the addition and allow the reaction mixture to stand overnight or longer, this heating period can be omitted.)

After the reaction mixture has cooled to room temperature, add 5.0 mL of water, drop by drop, through the separatory–addition funnel while shaking or stirring, and then add 15 mL of 5% (1.4 *M*) hydrochloric acid. Wait for the reaction to subside and continue stirring or shaking until most or all of the white solid has dissolved (some magnesium may remain undissolved). If any undissolved white solid remains, detach the reaction flask from the apparatus and use a spatula to break up the solid, then shake the flask, adding enough solvent-grade (not anhydrous) diethyl ether or 5% HCl (or both) as needed to dissolve all of the solid. There should be at least 20 mL of ether in the reaction mixture at this time; if necessary, add solvent-grade diethyl ether to replace any ether that evaporated.

Separation. If there is undissolved magnesium present, remove it by gravity filtration [OP-15] through glass wool, washing the magnesium and glass wool with a small amount of solvent-grade diethyl ether. Transfer the reaction mixture to a separatory funnel, shake gently to mix the layers thoroughly, then drain and discard the aqueous layer. Carefully wash [OP-24] the ether layer with 15 mL of aqueous 5% sodium bicarbonate. Then wash it with 15 mL of saturated aqueous sodium chloride. Dry [OP-25] the ether solution over anhydrous sodium sulfate or magnesium sulfate. Evaporate [OP-19] the ether under vacuum, using a cold trap, to leave a solid residue. Add 10 mL of hexanes (or high-boiling petroleum ether) to the solid residue, and then use a spatula or flat-bottomed stirring rod to triturate (see OP-26a) the solid in this solvent for 2–3 minutes. Collect the product by vacuum filtration [OP-16], wash it [OP-26a] with fresh solvent, and let it air-dry on the filter.

Purification and Analysis. Recrystallize [OP-28] the crude triphenylmethanol from a 2:1 mixture of hexanes (or high-boiling petroleum ether) with absolute ethanol. Triphenylmethanol crystals form slowly, so allow 30 minutes or more for crystallization. Dry [OP-26b] the purified triphenylmethanol, weigh it, and measure its melting point [OP-33]. If requested, obtain an infrared spectrum [OP-39] of the product.

Stop and Think: What is the limiting reactant in this synthesis?

Observe and Note: What happens during the addition?

Take Care! A gas may be evolved; vent as necessary.

Waste Disposal: Unless your instructor directs otherwise, wash the aqueous layers down the drain. Place recovered diethyl ether and the filtrate in designated solvent recovery containers.

Waste Disposal: Place the filtrate in a designated solvent recovery container.

B. *Preparation of Trityl Fluoborate*

Acetic anhydride can cause severe damage to skin and eyes. Its vapors are very harmful if inhaled, and it reacts violently with water. Use gloves and a hood, avoid contact with the liquid, do not breathe its vapors, and keep it away from water.

Fluoboric acid is poisonous and corrosive, its solutions can cause severe damage to skin and eyes, and its vapors irritate the respiratory system. Use gloves and a hood. Avoid contact with the acid solution and do not breathe its vapors.

Safety Notes

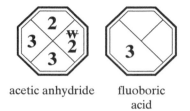

acetic anhydride   fluoboric acid

Under the hood, mix about 1.00 g of triphenylmethanol with 7.0 mL of acetic anhydride in a small, dry Erlenmeyer flask. Carefully add 1.0 mL of 48% fluoboric acid and swirl to dissolve the solid. Stopper the flask and let the mixture stand for about 15 minutes; then cool it in ice until crystallization is complete. Collect the product by vacuum filtration [OP-16] on a Hirsch funnel, wash it [OP-26a] with cold anhydrous diethyl ether, and let it air-dry on the filter. Weigh the dry trityl fluoborate in a *dry* tared vial.

Take Care! Wear gloves, avoid contact with acetic anhydride and fluoboric acid, and do not breathe their vapors.

Observe and Note: What color is the product?

Waste Disposal: Place the filtrate in a designated waste container.

Exercises

1. (a) Write a balanced equation for the coupling reaction of bromobenzene on the metal surface to form biphenyl. (b) Write balanced equations for the reactions of phenylmagnesium bromide and trityl fluoborate with water.

2. If you obtained an IR spectrum of triphenylmethanol, compare it with the spectra in Figure 1 and describe the evidence indicating that the expected reaction has taken place. Interpret your spectrum as completely as you can.

3. Describe and explain the possible effect on your results of the following experimental errors or variations. (a) You used solvent-grade (not anhydrous) diethyl ether for the reaction in part **A**. (b) After adding the bromobenzene solution in part **A**, you forgot to add anhydrous diethyl ether to the reaction mixture. (c) You used diethyl ether, rather than petroleum ether, to remove biphenyl from the crude triphenylmethanol.

4. (a) Calculate the atom economy and reaction efficiency of your synthesis. (b) Describe some green features of your synthesis, and any that aren't so green.

5. Following the format in the "Planning an Experiment" appendix, construct a flow diagram for the synthesis of triphenylmethanol (part **A**).

6. The reaction of phenylmagnesium bromide with benzophenone to form the salt of triphenylmethanol is an example of nucleophilic addition; its reaction with ethyl benzoate to yield the same product involves nucleophilic substitution followed by a nucleophilic addition step. Write reasonable mechanisms for both reactions.

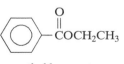

ethyl benzoate

7. Outline a synthetic pathway for preparing each of the following compounds, using the Grignard reaction and starting with benzene or toluene: (a) 1,1-diphenylethanol; (b) 1,2-diphenylethanol; (c) 2,2-diphenylethanol; (d) 2,3-diphenyl-2-butanol.

8. Excluding alternative Kekulé structures for the benzene rings, (a) draw all possible resonance structures for the trityl cation; (b) draw all possible resonance structures for Malachite Green.

9. One possible by-product from the triphenylmethanol synthesis is ethoxy-triphenylmethane. Tell how and when it might form, and give an equation and a mechanism for the reaction.

Other Things You Can Do

(Starred items require your instructor's permission.)

*1. Record the ultraviolet–visible spectrum (200–600 nm) of trityl fluoborate in dry acetone.

*2. Dissolve a small amount of trityl fluoborate in dry methanol, and record your observations. Dissolve about 0.1 g of trityl fluoborate in 1 mL of dry acetone; then add a solution of sodium iodide in dry acetone (0.1 g NaI in 1 mL acetone), drop by drop, until no more changes are observed. Write balanced equations to explain your observations.

*3. Prepare the fluorescent dye fluorescein as described in the "Preparation of a Fluorescent Dye" minilab.

4. Write a research paper about the structures, properties, and applications of Grignard reagents, starting with sources listed in the Bibliography.

An Unexpected Reaction of 2,3-Dimethyl-2,3-butanediol

EXPERIMENT

Reactions of Hydroxyl Compounds. Carbocations. Reaction Mechanisms. Structure Determination. Infrared Spectrometry. NMR Spectrometry.

Operations

OP-10 Mixing
OP-24 Washing Liquids
OP-25 Drying Liquids
OP-30 Simple Distillation
OP-34 Boiling Point
OP-39 Infrared Spectrometry
OP-40 Nuclear Magnetic Resonance Spectrometry

Before You Begin

1. Read the experiment, read or review the operations as necessary, and write an experimental plan.
2. Calculate the mass of 60.0 mmol of 2,3-dimethyl-2,3-butanediol and the theoretical yield of the product, $C_6H_{12}O$.

Scenario

Willy Hackett, a graduate student at Miskatonic University, has a reputation for carrying out apparently straightforward reactions and coming up with unexpected results. Now his research mentor has asked Willy to develop a simple synthesis of 2,3-dimethyl-1,3-butadiene, which he should then be able to convert to a rubber-like polymer. Willy is familiar with the acid-catalyzed dehydration of alcohols to alkenes in the presence of a sulfuric acid catalyst, so he thinks it should be possible to convert a suitable diol to the target diene by the same method. The most readily available diol that has the same carbon skeleton as the diene is 2,3-dimethyl-2,3-butanediol, so he heated this reactant with some sulfuric acid, expecting to get the following reaction.

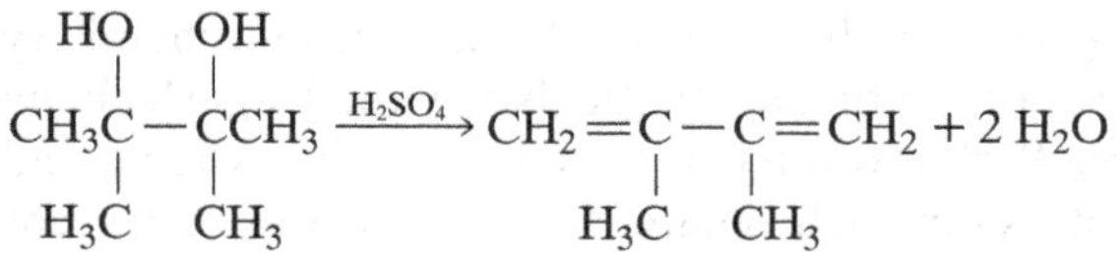

2,3-dimethyl-2,3-butanediol — 2,3-dimethyl-1,3-butadiene

But the product he obtained has the chemical formula $C_6H_{12}O$, rather than the expected formula, C_6H_{10}, so it is obviously not the diene he was trying to make. Your assignment, and that of your coworkers, is to carry out the reaction of 2,3-dimethyl-2,3-butanediol with sulfuric acid and deduce the structure of Willy Hackett's unexpected product, with the help of its infrared (IR)

From *Operational Organic Chemistry: A Problem Solving Approach to the Laboratory*, Fourth Edition, John W. Lehman. Copyright © 2009 by Pearson Education. Published by Prentice Hall. All rights reserved.

and nuclear magnetic resonance (NMR) spectra. You can also attempt to show how the product was formed by writing a reasonable mechanism for the reaction.

Applying Scientific Methodology

To develop a working hypothesis about the structure of the product, you can draw the structures of some compounds with the molecular formula $C_6H_{12}O$ and decide which one is the most likely. If you have some knowledge of reaction mechanisms involving carbocations, you may even be able to predict the structure of the product before you make and analyze it.

Unexpected Outcomes in Chemistry

Chemistry, like other sciences, often advances as a result of fortuitous accidents, as when a chemist tries to synthesize a certain substance and ends up with something completely different. Perhaps the first person known to have discovered a chemical substance while looking for something else was Hennig Brandt, a seventeenth-century alchemist. Brandt was trying to find the so-called philosopher's stone, an illusory substance that was believed to have the ability to turn base metals such as lead into gold, but he was looking in an unlikely place for this magical material—human urine! One of his "recipes" called for no fewer than 50 pailfuls, which he evaporated from a large kettle until the urine was reduced to a paste. After further processing, he recovered a shining liquid that emitted glowing fumes and burst into flames. When cooled, it became a green-glowing solid that we know as white phosphorus. Unfortunately for Brandt, who spent much of his wife's fortune experimenting with white phosphorus, it failed to turn anything to gold.

A famous example of lucky accidents in chemistry is the synthesis of urea by Friedrich Wöhler, who was trying to prepare ammonium cyanate by a reaction of potassium cyanate and ammonium sulfate, and synthesized urea instead.

$$2KOCN + (NH_4)_2SO_4 \longrightarrow 2NH_2CONH_2 + K_2SO_4$$
$$\text{urea}$$

This was the first synthesis of an organic compound from inorganic starting materials, and it helped to demolish vitalism, the theory that organic substances contain some "vital force" that precludes their synthesis in the laboratory.

Another discovery that helped advance organic chemistry was the accidental synthesis of the first synthetic dye by the English chemist William H. Perkin in 1856. Perkin was trying to make quinine when he mixed allyltoluidine with potassium dichromate. Instead, he isolated a colored product that led him to experiment further with other aromatic amines, such as aniline. Treating the crude aniline available at that time with potassium dichromate yielded a purplish substance that he was soon selling to dyers as Aniline Purple (called *mauve* by the French). The subsequent establishment of a profitable synthetic dye industry led to a great surge of interest in organic chemistry in the later nineteenth century.

In 1965, a chemist working for G. D. Searle & Company, James M. Schlatter, was trying to synthesize a tetrapeptide that he'd planned to use as a standard in the production of a potential anti-ulcer drug. In the course of making the tetrapeptide (a substance that contains four amino acid units), he had prepared L-aspartyl-L-phenylalanine methyl ester, an ester of a dipeptide, as an intermediate. When he unthinkingly licked his unwashed finger, he noticed an intensely sweet taste that he associated with the dipeptide ester. This was a surprise, because neither of its component amino acids is sweet; L-aspartic acid has an umami taste like that of MSG, and L-phenylalanine is bitter. The dipeptide ester, whose common name is aspartame, is now marketed as an artificial sweetener under such trade names as NutraSweet and Equal.

A practical synthesis for a naturally occurring dye resulted from a rather hazardous laboratory mishap. A chemist working for the German corporation Badische Anilin und Soda Fabrik (BASF) was trying to sulfonate naphthalene by heating it with fuming sulfuric acid when he accidentally broke the mercury thermometer he was using to monitor the reaction temperature. Its mercury dropped into the reaction mixture, forming mercury(II) sulfate, which catalyzed a different reaction that yielded phthalic anhydride. Since naphthalene is readily available from coal tar, and indigo can be manufactured from phthalic anhydride, this accident led to the first commercially useful indigo synthesis in 1897.

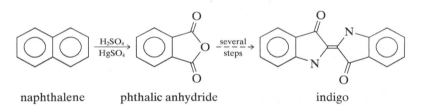

naphthalene   phthalic anhydride   indigo

Today, nearly all of the world's blue jeans are dyed with synthetic indigo. So even the Willy Hacketts of the world sometimes blunder their way to important scientific discoveries!

Understanding the Experiment

The reaction is catalyzed by acids, so the reactant (a low-melting solid) will be heated with dilute sulfuric acid, with rapid stirring to mix the layers. You will carry out the reaction in a distillation apparatus so that the product, whose boiling point is close to that of water, distills from the reaction mixture along with some water (remember that H_2SO_4 solutions contain water). You will separate the organic product from the distillate, wash it with saturated aqueous sodium chloride, and dry it. Then you can purify it by simple distillation and record its boiling point.

You should be able to arrive at the structure of the unknown product from its molecular formula and its IR and ^{1}H NMR spectra. Note that the product has an oxygen atom, so it must have some oxygen-containing functional group. Its infrared spectrum should help you identify that functional group and the chemical family to which the compound belongs. Its NMR spectrum will then help you work out the rest of its structure. But keep an open mind; the structure may be one you wouldn't otherwise expect!

aspartame

To write a mechanism for the reaction, you'll need to know something about the reactions of hydroxyl groups and carbocations. What happens to an —OH group in the presence of a strong acid? How can this lead to the formation of a carbocation? What kinds of reactions can carbocations undergo? If you can answer these questions and use a little imagination, you should be able to figure out just how the unexpected product was formed.

This is a relatively green experiment because it requires no solvents but water, and use of a catalyst improves the reaction efficiency and reduces energy consumption. Sulfuric acid is harmful to aquatic organisms and is classified as a hazardous air pollutant, so it should not be released into the environment.

Key Concept: A carbocation is electron deficient, so it undergoes reactions in which it can obtain an electron pair from another atom to form a covalent bond.

Reactions and Properties

$$\underset{\substack{\text{2,3-dimethyl-}\\\text{2,3-butanediol}}}{\overset{\displaystyle\overset{\text{HO}\quad\text{OH}}{\underset{\text{H}_3\text{C}\quad\text{CH}_3}{\text{CH}_3\text{C}-\text{CCH}_3}}}{}}\xrightarrow{\text{H}_2\text{SO}_4}\text{C}_6\text{H}_{12}\text{O} + \text{H}_2\text{O}$$

Table 1 Physical properties

	mol wt	mp	bp	d
2,3-dimethyl-2,3-butanediol	118.2	40–43	172^{739}	
sulfuric acid	98.1		290	1.84

Note: mp and bp are in °C; density is in g/mL; superscripts indicate pressure in torr.

2,3-Dimethyl-2,3-butanediol

$$\underset{\substack{\text{CH}_3\quad\text{CH}_3}}{\overset{\text{OH}\quad\text{OH}}{\text{CH}_3\text{C}-\text{CCH}_3}}$$

3439.0	1369.4	884.0
2982.4	1156.5	828.7
1467.6	950.4	495.5

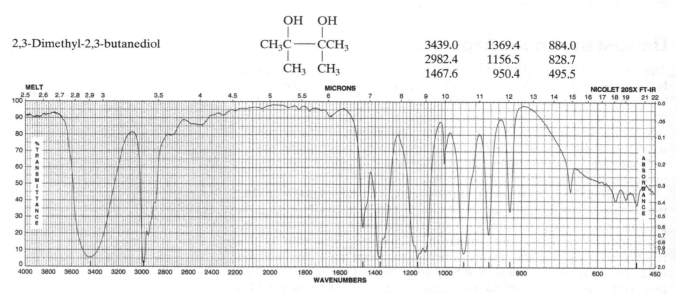

Figure 1 IR spectrum of 2,3-dimethyl-2,3-butanediol

DIRECTIONS

> **Sulfuric acid, even when dilute, can irritate skin and eyes. Avoid contact with the 3 *M* sulfuric acid.**

Safety Notes

sulfuric acid

Reaction. Assemble a compact apparatus for simple distillation [OP-30] using a 50-mL round-bottom flask as the boiling flask and a 25-mL round-bottom flask, cooled in an ice/water bath, as the receiving flask. Weigh 60.0 mmol of 2,3-dimethyl-2,3-butanediol into the boiling flask, then add 20 mL of 3 *M* sulfuric acid and some boiling chips or a stir bar. Start the stirrer [OP-10], if you are using one, and heat the reaction mixture so that liquid distills slowly into the receiver, until the receiver is nearly half full. The temperature should be around 100°C at this time and there should be 10–12 mL of distillate.

Take Care! Avoid contact with the acid.

Separation. Transfer the distillate to a separatory funnel, using a little distilled water for the transfer. Separate the organic layer and wash [OP-24] it twice with 5-mL portions of saturated aqueous sodium chloride. Transfer the organic layer to a clean, dry Erlenmeyer flask and dry it [OP-25] with anhydrous sodium sulfate or magnesium sulfate.

Waste Disposal: Place the residue in a designated waste container.

Purification and Analysis. Purify the product by simple distillation [OP-30] and record its boiling point [OP-34]. Weigh the product. Record its IR spectrum [OP-39] and ^{1}H NMR spectrum [OP-40] (or obtain them from your instructor), and then deduce the structure of the product.

Waste Disposal: Unless your instructor directs otherwise, wash the aqueous layers down the drain.

Exercises

1. Draw the structure of your product and explain in detail how you arrived at that structure from the spectral information.
2. Using references from the Bibliography, find the common name of your starting material and the name of the reaction you carried out.
3. Write a mechanism that shows how 2,3-dimethyl-2,3-butanediol is converted to the unknown product.
4. (a) Calculate the atom economy and reaction efficiency of your synthesis. (b) Describe some green features of your synthesis, and any that aren't so green.
5. Following the directions in the "Planning an Experiment" appendix, construct a flow diagram for the synthesis of your product.
6. Give the structure of the product that the BASF chemist (see "Unexpected Outcomes in Chemistry") should have obtained from the reaction of naphthalene with an equivalent amount of sulfuric acid if he hadn't broken his mercury thermometer.
7. (a) Outline a synthesis of 2-3-dimethyl-1,3-butadiene (the product Willy Hackett was trying to make) from 2,3-dimethyl-2-butene. (b) Outline the synthesis of a rubber-like polymer that can be made from this diene.

Other Things You Can Do

(Starred items require your instructor's permission.)

*1. As an alternative to the structure determination method described in this experiment, identify the functional group in the product using one or more chemical tests and determine its identity by preparing one or more derivatives, as described in "Qualitative Organic Analysis."

*2. Prepare a vicinal diol by the photoreduction of benzophenone as described in the "Photoreduction of Benzophenone" minilab.

3. Starting with sources listed in the Bibliography, write a research paper about reactions related to the one you carried out in this experiment.

Identification of a Conjugated Diene from Eucalyptus Oil

EXPERIMENT

Reactions of Dienes. Preparation of Bicyclic Compounds. Cycloaddition.
Infrared Spectrometry. Qualitative Analysis.

Operations

OP-7   Heating
OP-16   Vacuum Filtration
OP-26   Washing and Drying Solids
OP-28   Recrystallization
OP-33   Melting Point
OP-37   Gas Chromatography
OP-39   Infrared Spectrometry

Before You Begin

1. Read the experiment, read or review the operations as necessary, and write an experimental plan.
2. Be prepared to carry out the calculations described in part **A** of the Directions.
3. If time permits, record the gas chromatogram of the "eucalyptus oil" during a previous experiment.

Scenario

In 1927, Otto Diels and Kurt Alder treated a constituent of one kind of eucalyptus oil with maleic anhydride and obtained a new compound that they described as forming *"grosse glasglänzende Krystalle von ungewöhnlicher Schönheit"* (large, lustrous crystals of unusual beauty). The reaction Diels and Alder used for this preparation was eventually named for them, and the lustrous crystals belonged to the Diels–Alder adduct of a natural diene. Gondwana Natural Products, Ltd. (GNP), which obtains and markets useful products from Australian flora, is investigating the commercial possibilities of an essential oil from *Eucalyptus dives* that has been used to treat colds, as well as malaria and other fevers. The ultraviolet–visible spectrum of the eucalyptus oil suggests that it contains the same diene that Diels and Alder studied—one of the natural dienes described next. GNP wants your institute to identify the diene from a sample of the eucalyptus oil they have provided. Because only conjugated dienes undergo the Diels–Alder reaction, this reaction can be used to separate the diene from the eucalyptus oil, as well as to identify it.

maleic anhydride

From *Operational Organic Chemistry: A Problem Solving Approach to the Laboratory*, Fourth Edition, John W. Lehman. Copyright © 2009 by Pearson Education. Published by Prentice Hall. All rights reserved.

Applying Scientific Methodology

Because the problem involves the identity of an unknown diene, your working hypothesis can only be a guess, but you should be able to eliminate some of the possibilities from those mentioned in the next section before you begin. Your hypothesis will be tested when you obtain the melting point of the adduct. Note that a triene that has two conjugated double bonds can also qualify as the "diene" for a Diels–Alder reaction.

Dienes and Trienes in Nature

Dienes and trienes occur in the essential oils of a number of plants and contribute to the flavors and aromas of such plants. For example, limonene has a pleasant lemony odor that enhances the flavor of lemons, oranges, and other citrus fruits, whereas β-myrcene is responsible for much of the fragrance and flavor of bay leaves (*Myrcia acris*). β-Myrcene is also present in hops, verbena, and lemongrass oil. β-Ocimene was first isolated from the Javanese oil of basil (*Ocimium basilicum*) and is usually found in combination with *allo*-ocimene, which can be synthesized from α-pinene, the most abundant component of oil of turpentine. Both of the phellandrenes derive their name from the water fennel, *Phellandrium aquaticum*, but α-phellandrene apparently doesn't even occur in that plant; it was mistaken for its isomer, β-phellandrene, which does. α-Phellandrene *is* found in the oils of bitter fennel, ginger grass, cinnamon, and star anise; β-phellandrene also occurs in lemon oil and Japanese peppermint oil. Another cyclic diene, α-terpinene, is obtained from the essential oils of cardamom, marjoram, and coriander.

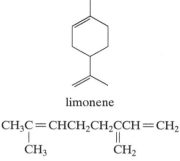

limonene

$$CH_3C = CHCH_2CH_2CCH = CH_2$$
$$\;\;\; | \qquad\qquad\qquad ||$$
$$\;\; CH_3 \qquad\qquad\quad CH_2$$

β-myrcene

$$CH_3C = CHCH_2CH = CCH = CH_2$$
$$\;\;\; | \qquad\qquad\qquad\; |$$
$$\;\; CH_3 \qquad\qquad\quad CH_3$$

β-ocimene

$$CH_3C = CHCH = CHC = CHCH_3$$
$$\;\;\; | \qquad\qquad\qquad |$$
$$\;\; CH_3 \qquad\qquad\quad CH_3$$

allo-ocimene

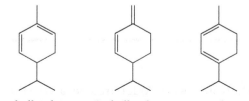

α-phellandrene β-phellandrene α-terpinene

Understanding the Experiment

Most conjugated dienes can form Diels–Alder adducts with maleic anhydride. Trienes such as β-myrcene may also form such adducts if at least two of their double bonds are conjugated. The adducts are usually crystalline solids that can be separated from the other components of an essential oil and used to identify the diene.

The Diels–Alder reaction is classified as a $[4 + 2]$ cycloaddition reaction, because one reactant (the *diene*) contributes four carbon atoms and the other reactant (the *dienophile*) contributes two carbon atoms to the six-membered ring of the resulting cyclic compound (the *adduct*). As illustrated for the following reaction of 1,3-butadiene and ethene, the diene must be able to exist in an *s-cis* conformation, in which the carbon atoms that will bond to the dienophile are on the same side of the C—C single bond.

A 4 + 2 cycloaddition reaction

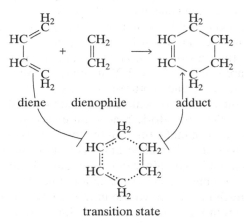

The dienophile must have either a double or a triple bond, often connected to one or more carbonyl groups or other electron-withdrawing groups.

The Diels–Alder reaction is stereoselective, usually yielding only one of several possible stereoisomers. For example, maleic acid could react with cyclopentadiene to yield either of two adducts, designated *exo* and *endo*. In fact, it yields entirely the *endo* adduct, in which the bulkier parts of the dienophile are closer to the developing carbon–carbon double bond. This orientation results from the fact that overlap between the pi electrons of the diene and those of the dienophile stabilizes the transition state leading to the *endo* adduct. Such overlap is possible only when the carbon–carbon double bonds of the diene are in close proximity to the carbonyl groups of the dienophile.

Key Concept: *During a concerted (one-step) cycloaddition reaction, the new sigma bonds form simultaneously as electrons flow from the highest occupied pi molecular orbital of one reactant to the lowest unoccupied pi molecular orbital of the other.*

exo adduct

endo adduct

Diels–Alder reaction of cyclopentadiene with maleic anhydride.

Sometimes, more than one *endo* adduct is possible; in that event, the dienophile will tend to approach the diene from its less hindered side to give the more stable adduct.

For many years, it has been assumed that the Diels–Alder reaction proceeds only by this kind of concerted mechanism, but recent research using ultrafast laser techniques suggests that it may also follow an alternative path involving a diradical intermediate.

In this experiment, you will prepare the Diels–Alder adduct of the unknown conjugated diene in "eucalyptus oil," separate the adduct, and identify the diene from the melting point of its adduct. The unknown (whose molecular formula is $C_{10}H_{16}$) will be one of four conjugated dienes that were discussed in the previous section. Their names and the melting points of their adducts are listed in Table 2. You will determine the approximate percentage of diene in the eucalyptus oil from its gas chromatogram so that you can estimate the amount of maleic anhydride needed to react with the diene. Powdered maleic anhydride reacts quite rapidly with atmospheric moisture, so it is usually manufactured in the form of briquettes, which must be pulverized before use. If maleic anhydride is provided in powdered form, you should open its container only momentarily and replace the cap immediately after you have removed the amount needed. It is important to avoid using too much maleic anhydride in the reaction, because the excess can be difficult to remove from the product. Since both maleic anhydride and the adduct can be hydrolyzed by water, it is important to use dry glassware and to keep out moisture during the reaction and workup.

You will carry out the reaction by heating the reactants under reflux in diethyl ether. The adduct should precipitate from the reaction mixture as beautiful rectangular crystals; slow cooling may yield crystals several centimeters long. The adduct is then separated by vacuum filtration and purified by recrystallization from methanol. Because the adduct may react with methanol to form a solvolysis product, you should avoid prolonged boiling during recrystallization. For the same reason, it is not a good idea to leave the crystallized adduct in methanol for more than a few hours.

Once you have identified the adduct, you should be able to deduce its structure with the help of molecular models. You can also characterize the adduct by recording its infrared (IR) spectrum. The IR spectra of anhydrides show two carbonyl stretching bands that arise from symmetric and asymmetric stretching modes; maleic anhydride itself has $C{=}O$ bands near 1780 and 1850 cm^{-1}, as shown in Figure 1. The $C-CO-O-CO-C$ grouping can vibrate as a unit, causing additional bands that occur near 900 cm^{-1} and 1250 cm^{-1} for cyclic anhydrides.

Like all addition reactions, the Diels–Alder reaction has an atom economy of 100%. Of the chemicals used, maleic anhydride hydrolyzes readily to maleic acid, which is toxic to aquatic organisms; diethyl ether isn't considered toxic to aquatic organisms and doesn't persist for long in either air or water; and methanol is slightly toxic to aquatic organisms but biodegrades readily in water and soil.

Hydrolysis of maleic anhydride

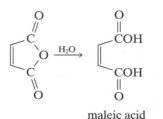

maleic acid

Reaction and Properties

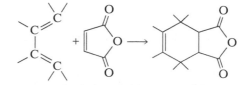

The actual structure of the adduct depends on the structure of the unknown diene.

286

Table 1 Physical properties

	mol wt	mp	bp	d
maleic anhydride	98.1	53	202	
diethyl ether	74.1	−116	34.5	0.714

Note: mp and bp are in °C; density is in g/mL.

Table 2 Melting points of maleic anhydride adducts of the possible dienes

Diene	mp of adduct (°C)
β-myrcene	34
allo-ocimene	84
α-phellandrene	127
α-terpinene	61

Maleic anhydride

3118.7	1240.1	840.6
1851.1	1058.1	695.9
1778.5	890.8	561.7

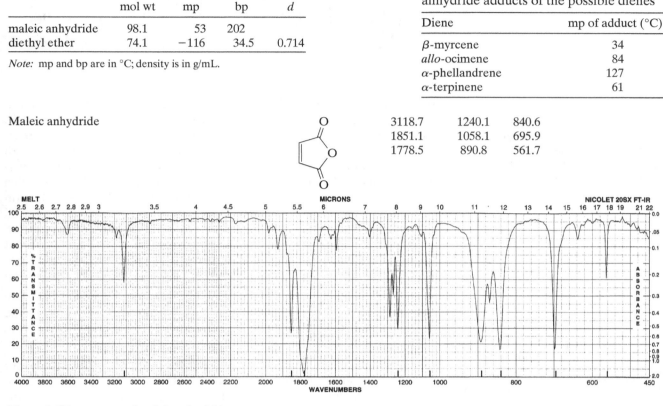

Figure 1 IR spectrum of maleic anhydride

DIRECTIONS

A. *Preliminary Analysis and Calculations*

Obtain a gas chromatogram [OP-37] of the eucalyptus oil provided, using the column and conditions recommended by your instructor. Assuming that the unknown diene is responsible for the largest peak on the chromatogram and that peak areas are proportional to component masses, estimate the mass of the unknown diene (molecular formula $C_{10}H_{16}$) in 5.00 g of the oil. Then calculate the mass of maleic anhydride needed to react with that much diene, and the theoretical yield of the reaction.

B. *Preparation of the Adduct*

Safety Notes

Maleic anhydride is corrosive; it can cause severe damage to the eyes, skin, and upper respiratory tract. Avoid contact with skin, eyes, or clothing; do not breathe the dust. If you must pulverize maleic anhydride briquettes, wear gloves and work under the hood.

Diethyl ether and petroleum ether are extremely flammable and may be harmful if inhaled. Do not breathe their vapors and keep them away from ignition sources.

Methanol is harmful if inhaled or absorbed through the skin. Avoid contact and do not breathe its vapors.

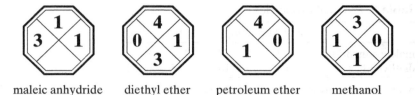

maleic anhydride   diethyl ether   petroleum ether   methanol

Take Care! Keep diethyl ether away from flames and hot surfaces. Avoid contact with maleic anhydride and do not breathe its dust.

Reaction. *All glassware must be dry.* In a clean, dry round-bottom flask, dissolve 5.00 g of the eucalyptus oil in 10 mL of anhydrous diethyl ether. Add the calculated amount of powdered maleic anhydride. Heat the reaction mixture under gentle reflux [OP-7] on a steam bath or hot-water bath for 45 minutes or more. At the end of the reaction period, transfer the mixture to a small Erlenmeyer flask while it is still warm. Cover the flask with a watch glass and let it cool slowly to room temperature. If no crystals form by the time it reaches room temperature, dip the tip of a glass stirring rod into the reaction mixture, remove it long enough for the ether to evaporate, and then reinsert it in the reaction mixture to induce crystallization. If that doesn't work, rub the rod tip against the inside walls of the vial. When crystallization seems nearly complete, cool the flask in an ice/water bath for a few minutes.

Take Care! Keep petroleum ether away from flames and hot surfaces.

Waste Disposal: Place all filtrates in designated solvent recovery containers.

Separation. Collect the adduct by vacuum filtration [OP-16], washing the crystals on the filter [OP-26a] with 10 mL of cold, low-boiling petroleum ether.

Purification and Analysis. Recrystallize [OP-28] the adduct from dry methanol, avoiding prolonged boiling. Dry [OP-26b] the adduct; measure its mass and melting point [OP-33]. Deduce the identity of the eucalyptus oil diene from the melting point of its adduct. Record the IR spectrum [OP-39] of the adduct or obtain a spectrum from your instructor.

C. *Stereochemistry of the Adduct*
Construct molecular models for maleic anhydride and the diene. By moving their bonds around, find a way to connect them to make a model representing one form of the adduct. Disconnect and reconnect the diene and dienophile units until you have made models representing all possible structures for the adduct, and sketch stereochemical drawings of them for your report. Based on the description of the Diels–Alder reaction in "Understanding the Experiment," decide which is the most likely structure.

Exercises

1. If you obtained an IR spectrum of the adduct, interpret it as completely as you can. Compare the adduct's spectrum with that of maleic anhydride; point out and explain any significant similarities or differences.
2. Write a balanced equation for the reaction. Show the stereochemistry of the adduct and explain why it has that stereochemistry.
3. Which two dienes whose structures are shown in this experiment will not form Diels–Alder adducts with maleic anhydride? Explain why in each case.

4. (a) Calculate the atom economy and reaction efficiency of your synthesis. (b) Describe some green features of your synthesis, and any that aren't so green.

5. Describe and explain the possible effect on your results of the following experimental errors or variations. (a) You calculated the mass of maleic anhydride needed based on the total mass of the eucalyptus oil. (b) Your reaction flask or vial was wet. (c) You dissolved the adduct in hot methanol and then stored the recrystallization solution until the next lab period.

6. Write the structure of the compound that would result if the adduct were heated too long in the recrystallization solvent. Write a balanced equation for its formation.

7. Following the format in the "Planning an Experiment" appendix, construct a flow diagram for this experiment.

8. The side reaction most often encountered in Diels–Alder syntheses is dimerization, in which the diene also acts as a dienophile. For example, butadiene can react with itself to yield 4-vinylcyclohexene as shown. Draw the structures of four possible Diels–Alder dimers of your diene.

Dimerization of 1,3-butadiene

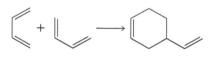

Other Things You Can Do

(Starred items require your instructor's permission.)

*1. Prepare the Diels–Alder adduct of an aromatic "diene" as described in the "Diels–Alder Reaction of Maleic Anhydride and Furan" minilab.

2. A number of polychlorinated insecticides, such as dieldrin, aldrin, and chlordane, are synthesized using one or more Diels–Alder reactions. Starting with sources listed in the Bibliography, write a research paper about such insecticides. Give equations for their manufacture from cyclopentadiene, and report on their uses and environmental effects.

Spectral Identification of Monoterpenes

Infrared Spectrometry. Ultraviolet–Visible Spectrometry. Qualitative Analysis.

Operations

OP-39 Infrared Spectrometry
OP-40 Nuclear Magnetic Resonance Spectrometry (optional)
OP-41 Ultraviolet–Visible Spectrometry

Before You Begin

Read the experiment, read or review the operations as necessary, and write an experimental plan.

Scenario

Uncommon Scents, Inc., extracts essential oils from various plants and ships them to buyers around the world. Some of their buyers are aromatherapists from countries that classify aromatherapy oils as drugs and strictly regulate their contents. These countries require that the suppliers of essential oils report their major ingredients and list them on the label. Uncommon Scents has air-freighted your institute samples of the major components of one of their products, the essential oil of the motley marigold, *Calendula salmagundi.* Your project group's assignment is to identify the components using appropriate spectral methods and thereby determine what names should appear on the label.

Applying Scientific Methodology

This experiment can be performed as a group project in which each individual obtains the spectra for one of the components, and then the group members — working together — arrive at the identities of all of the components. You should be able to formulate a working hypothesis regarding the identity of your component after you record its spectra, but be prepared to have your hypothesis tested and either accepted or rejected by the other members of your group.

Monoterpenes from Plants

Terpenes are substances whose molecules can, in principle, be broken down into two or more isopentane units (also called isoprene units). Monoterpenes are composed of two such units, sesquiterpenes of three, diterpenes of four, and so forth.

Terpenes that contain oxygen or other atoms in addition to carbon and hydrogen are often called terpenoids.

From *Operational Organic Chemistry: A Problem Solving Approach to the Laboratory*, Fourth Edition, John W. Lehman. Copyright © 2009 by Pearson Education. Published by Prentice Hall. All rights reserved.

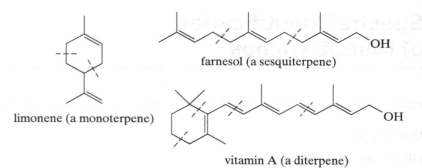

farnesol (a sesquiterpene)

limonene (a monoterpene)

vitamin A (a diterpene)

Isopentane units in terpenes

Many terpenes are found in the essential oils of plants. Essential oils are usually obtained by steam distilling the roots, bark, leaves, flowers, or other parts of plants. Their components are volatile, water-insoluble substances that often have pronounced aromas.

Structures of some monoterpenes obtained from essential oils are shown in Figure 1. Many of these compounds occur in a wide variety of plants. For example, limonene occurs in the oils of bergamot, black pepper, cardamom, caraway, coriander, cypress, dill, eucalyptus, grapefruit, lemon, lime, neroli, and orange, among others. Carvone, which is obtained from caraway, coriander, dill, and peppermint oils, is used to flavor liqueurs and perfume soaps. Citronellal, the active ingredient of insect-repelling citronella candles, occurs in lemon and lemongrass oils, as well as oil of citronella. Citronellol is also a constituent of citronella oil, but it is found in rose and geranium oils as well. The aromatic hydrocarbon *p*-cymene is a component of marjoram and oregano oils. Geranial and its geometric isomer neral often occur together in essential oils. The isomer mixture, called citral, is the major component of lemongrass oil and is also found in oils of lemon, orange, and verbena. Geraniol occurs in the oils of citronella,

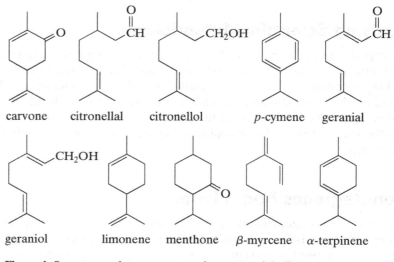

carvone   citronellal   citronellol   *p*-cymene   geranial

geraniol   limonene   menthone   β-myrcene   α-terpinene

Figure 1 Structures of monoterpenes from essential oils

292

lemongrass, and roses, and is used widely in perfumery. Menthone, like the corresponding alcohol, menthol, is a constituent of peppermint oil, and it also occurs in the oils of pennyroyal and geranium. β-Myrcene is found in the oils of bay, juniper, and hops, and it is an important intermediate in the manufacture of perfumes. α-Terpinene is a constituent of the oils from cardamom and marjoram.

You might think that the aromas of plant constituents should resemble the aromas of the plants in which they occur. In a few cases, this is so. For example, cinnamaldehyde—the major component of cinnamon bark—has an odor much like that of the spice. But most plants contain many different volatile components, and the odor of a single component may bear little or no resemblance to the overall odor of the plant or its essential oil. That aroma is due to the combined effect on your olfactory receptors of many different kinds of molecules. The aroma of a given compound may also depend on its stereochemistry. Thus, one carvone enantiomer has an odor of spearmint, whereas the other smells like caraway seeds.

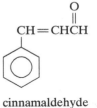

cinnamaldehyde

Understanding the Experiment

In this experiment, you will use infrared (IR) and ultraviolet–visible (UV–VIS) spectrometry to identify the unknown compounds, which will be chosen either from those in Figure 1 or from a list provided by your instructor. With your instructor's permission, you may use ^{1}H NMR spectrometry as well.

The spectral interpretation section of OP-39 will help you interpret the IR spectra of the compounds assigned. The four functional groups found in the compounds of Figure 1, as well as the aromatic ring of p-cymene, are relatively easy to identify. Both aldehydes and ketones give rise to a strong carbonyl (C=O) band near 1700 cm^{-1}, and aliphatic aldehydes also show medium-intensity C—H stretching bands near 2720 and 2840 cm^{-1}. Primary alcohols are characterized mainly by their O—H and C—O stretching bands around 3300 and 1050 cm^{-1}. The carbon–carbon double bonds of alkenes usually give rise to =C—H stretching bands just above 3000 cm^{-1}, moderate to weak C=C stretching bands in the 1670−1640 cm^{-1} region (sometimes these are quite weak), and =C—H bending bands that are sensitive to substitution patterns in the 1000−650 cm^{-1} region. Aromatic rings are characterized by Ar—H stretching bands just above 3000 cm^{-1} and Ar—H bending bands in the 900−690 cm^{-1} region. The Ar—H bending patterns vary with the number and location of substituents on the benzene ring. Other structural features may affect the positions of certain IR absorption bands. For example, carbonyl groups that are conjugated with carbon–carbon double bonds or aromatic rings appear at lower wave numbers than usual. Thus, while most saturated ketones have C=O bands near 1715 cm^{-1}, α,β-unsaturated ketones have C=O bands closer to 1670 cm^{-1}. Conjugation with a carbonyl group also affects both the position and intensity of the C=C stretching band; its intensity increases while its wave number is lowered by about 30 cm^{-1}. Unsymmetrical conjugated dienes may have two C=C stretching bands near 1650 cm^{-1} and 1600 cm^{-1}.

UV–VIS spectra of organic compounds usually contain only a few relatively broad absorption bands. Compounds that appear colored to the human eye absorb radiation in the visible range ($\sim$400−800 nm) and sometimes in the ultraviolet range (~200−400 nm) as well. Such compounds have extensive chromophores, usually with many conjugated double bonds or aromatic rings. Colorless compounds with less extensive conjugated systems absorb ultraviolet radiation above 200 nm. Compounds with unconjugated double bonds and no nonbonded electrons don't show significant absorption above 200 nm.

When a compound absorbs radiation in the UV–VIS region of the electromagnetic spectrum, its electrons undergo transitions from lower to higher energy levels. In a $\pi-\pi*$ transition, pi (π) electrons in their ground-state energy levels (π molecular orbitals) jump to unoccupied higher energy levels ($\pi*$ molecular orbitals). The energy of the transition, and thus the wavelength of the resulting absorption band, depends on a number of factors, including the length of the conjugated system and the presence of certain substituents and structural features. Often, it is possible to estimate the λ_{max} value (wavelength of maximum absorption) of a conjugated compound's $\pi-\pi*$ absorption band using a set of rules developed by chemistry Nobel laureate Robert B. Woodward and modified by Louis Fieser. Woodward–Fieser rules for conjugated dienes are given in Table 1.

Key Concept: The wavelength of the UV–VIS radiation absorbed by a conjugated substance increases with the length of its conjugated system and the presence of substituents on the conjugated system.

Table 1 Woodward–Fieser rules for C=C—C=C systems

Structural feature	Wavelength or increment
base value for conjugated diene	214 nm
homoannular diene	+39 nm
double bond extending conjugation	+30 nm
alkyl substituent	+5 nm
exocyclic double bond	+5 nm

Note: Wavelengths are for ethanol solutions.

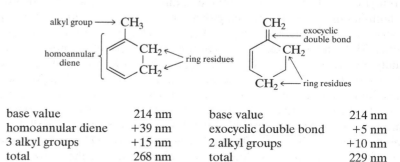

base value	214 nm	base value	214 nm
homoannular diene	+39 nm	exocyclic double bond	+5 nm
3 alkyl groups	+15 nm	2 alkyl groups	+10 nm
total	268 nm	total	229 nm

Examples illustrating Woodward–Fieser rules for dienes

An alkyl substituent can be either an open-chain group, such as methyl, or a ring residue—a carbon-containing group that is part of a ring. To be counted, the alkyl group must be attached directly to one of the carbons of the conjugated system. A homoannular diene is one in which both double bonds of the diene are in the same ring. An exocyclic double bond is one attached to a ring carbon from outside the ring. To apply the rules, start with the base value for the conjugated system and add wavelength increments for each of the designated structural features, as shown by the examples following Table 1.

Rules for α,β-unsaturated carbonyl compounds are given in Table 2, which is followed by examples. An α-alkyl group is on the carbon atom adjacent to the carbonyl group, and a β-alkyl group is on the second carbon from the carbonyl group.

Table 2 Woodward–Fieser rules for $C{=}C{-}C{=}O$ systems

Structural feature	Wavelength or increment
base value for conjugated ketone	215 nm
base value for conjugated aldehyde	210 nm
homoannular double bond extending conjugation	+69 nm
α-alkyl group	+10 nm
β-alkyl group	+12 nm
exocyclic double bond	+5 nm

Note: Wavelengths are for ethanol solutions.

base value, aldehyde	210 nm
α-alkyl group	+10 nm
2 β-alkyl groups	+24 nm
total	244 nm

base value, ketone	215 nm
exocyclic double bond	+5 nm
α-alkyl group	+10 nm
β-alkyl group	+12 nm
total	242 nm

Examples illustrating Woodward–Fieser rules for α,β-unsaturated carbonyl compounds

Similar rules can be used to estimate the λ_{max} value for the strongest band of an aromatic compound. The benzene ring has a base value of 204 nm. Adding a methyl substituent increases its λ_{max} by about 3 nm. An additional alkyl group increases λ_{max} by about 3 nm if it is *ortho* or *meta* to an existing substituent and by 10 nm if it is *para* to an existing substituent.

Your instructor may allow you to record ^{1}H NMR spectra of the monoterpenes to help you confirm their structures. If so, you should refer to "Interpretation of ^{1}H NMR Spectra" in OP-40 and the appropriate chapter of your lecture textbook for help. Note that deuterochloroform, like protic chloroform, is expected to be toxic to aquatic organisms and shouldn't be released into the environment.

DIRECTIONS

Unless your instructor indicates otherwise, you should work in groups. Each group can be provided with a selection of unknowns to be apportioned among its members, or the instructor can assign individual unknowns. Record the identification number of your unknown in your lab notebook as soon as you receive it. If necessary, the instructor will show you how to operate the instruments.

Citral, a mixture of geranial and its (Z)-isomer neral, may be substituted for geranial.

Safety Notes

> The monoterpenes may irritate the eyes and skin, and some are quite flammable. Minimize contact and keep them away from ignition sources. Deuterochloroform is harmful if inhaled or absorbed through the skin; it is a suspected human carcinogen. Avoid contact with the liquid and do not breathe its vapors.

Infrared Spectrum. Obtain an infrared (preferably FT–IR) spectrum [OP-39] of your unknown monoterpene as the neat liquid. Record accurate wave numbers for all significant absorption bands in the spectrum.

Ultraviolet Spectrum. Using a microliter syringe, measure 1 µL of the unknown monoterpene and dissolve it in 25 mL of 95% ethanol in an Erlenmeyer flask. Using a 1-cm quartz or silica sample cell, 95% ethanol as the reference solvent, and a scanning UV–VIS spectrophotometer [OP-41], scan the ultraviolet spectrum of the solution over the 200–400 nm range. By adjusting the instrument's absorbance range or by diluting the sample with more 95% ethanol, obtain a spectrum in which the top of the highest absorption band is between the midpoint and top of the absorbance scale. Record the λ_{max} value for the strongest band and for any other significant bands.

Waste Disposal: Turn in your unknown when you are finished with it.

Take Care! Avoid contact with $CDCl_3$ and do not breathe its vapors.

Waste Disposal: After use, place the deuterochloroform solution in a designated waste container.

¹H NMR Spectrum (optional). Obtain a proton NMR spectrum [OP-40] of your unknown compound in deuterochloroform.

Identification of the Unknowns. From its IR spectrum, decide what functional groups are present in your compound and deduce any other structural information you can, such as the existence of conjugation in a carbonyl compound. Based on this information, decide which of the compounds in Figure 1 have structures that are consistent with your IR spectrum. From its UV spectrum, use the Woodward–Fieser rules to help you decide which structure is most consistent with both spectra. Use your ¹H NMR spectrum, if you obtained one, to confirm the structure. Share your spectrum with the other members of your group and examine their spectra until you come to a group consensus regarding the identities of all of the monoterpenes. Interpret your spectra as completely as you can and turn them in with your report.

Weak UV bands near 200 nm may arise from transitions of nonbonded electrons rather than conjugated systems.

Exercises

1. Describe and explain the possible effect on your results of the following experimental errors or variations. (a) You used a solution cell with a 0.1-mm spacer for the infrared spectrum. (b) You dissolved your unknown in petroleum ether for the UV analysis. (c) There was no deuterochloroform available for the NMR sample, so you used ordinary chloroform instead.

2. Tell how infrared spectrometry can be used to differentiate the following compounds. In each case, indicate the significant IR bands that will be observed and their approximate wave numbers. (a) 1-butanol,

2-butanol, and 2-methyl-2-butanol; (b) *ortho*-xylene, *meta*-xylene, and *para*-xylene (the xylenes are dimethylbenzenes); (c) butanal, 1-butanol, 2-butanone, butanoic acid, and butyl acetate.

3. Tell how UV–VIS spectrometry can be used to differentiate the compounds in each of the following groups. Calculate approximate λ_{max} values for the compounds when you can. (a) 1,4-hexadiene, 2,4-hexadiene, and 1,3-cyclohexadiene; (b) cyclohexanone, 2-cyclohexenone, and 2,4-cyclohexadienone; (c) the following compounds.

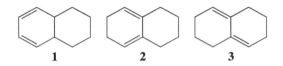

1   **2**   **3**

4. Would you consider this a green experiment? Why or why not?
5. Classify each of the following (as a monoterpene, sesquiterpene, etc.) and show how each can be divided into isopentane units.

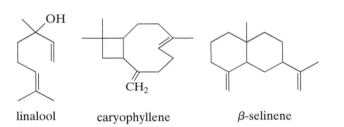

linalool   caryophyllene   β-selinene

6. Tell how you could use a spectrometric method to distinguish geranial from neral.

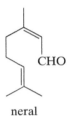

neral

Other Things You Can Do

(Starred items require your instructor's permission.)

*1. Identify an unknown arene by NMR spectrometry as described in the "Identification of an Unknown Arene by NMR Spectroscopy" minilab.
*2. Obtain and interpret the mass spectrum of a compound as described in the "Interpetation of a Mass Spectrum" minilab.
3. Starting with sources listed in the Bibliography, write a research paper about cholesterol and its biological functions, including a discussion of the biosynthesis of cholesterol from the triterpene squalene.

Synthesis and Spectral Analysis of Aspirin

Reactions of Phenols. Preparation of Esters. Nucleophilic Acyl Substitution.
Infrared Spectrometry. NMR Spectrometry.

Operations

OP-7   Heating
OP-10 Mixing
OP-16 Vacuum Filtration
OP-26 Washing and Drying Solids
OP-28 Recrystallization
OP-39 Infrared Spectrometry
OP-40 Nuclear Magnetic Resonance Spectrometry

Before You Begin

1. Read the experiment, read or review the operations as necessary, and write an experimental plan.
2. Calculate the mass of 15.0 mmol of salicylic acid and the theoretical yield of aspirin.

Scenario

The Spectrum Publishing Co., a subsidiary of the Fulcourt Press, wants to produce a DVD illustrating the principles of spectral interpretation for use with their new instrumental analysis textbook. The DVD would, for example, use animated molecular models of aspirin to simulate bond vibrations and their relationship to infrared (IR) spectral bands, and various graphics to illustrate nuclear magnetic transitions and how they give rise to ^{1}H and ^{13}C nuclear magnetic resonance (NMR) signals. To make the DVD as accurate as possible, they have asked your institute to perform an in-depth analysis of the IR and NMR spectra of aspirin. You can't use aspirin tablets because they contain impurities such as starch, which is used as a binder. Your assignment, therefore, is to prepare some pure aspirin, record its IR and NMR spectra, and propose assignments for its significant NMR signals and IR bands.

Applying Scientific Methodology

The initial scientific problem in this experiment is whether or not pure aspirin (free from unreacted starting material) can be prepared as described in the Directions. You will use a simple chemical method to test your initial hypothesis. As you study the spectra, you can develop hypotheses about the origins of various IR bands and NMR signals, and then test your hypotheses by consulting sources of spectral data and studying the spectra of related compounds.

From *Operational Organic Chemistry: A Problem Solving Approach to the Laboratory*, Fourth Edition, John W. Lehman. Copyright © 2009 by Pearson Education. Published by Prentice Hall. All rights reserved.

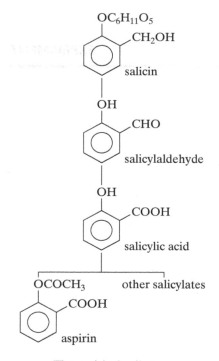

The aspirin family tree

Kolbe achieved scientific infamy with a vitriolic attack on J. H. van't Hoff, who helped develop the stereochemical theory of organic chemistry.

phenol

The Aspirin Saga

The more we learn about aspirin, the more it appears to be a true wonder drug. The family doctor who advises you to "take two aspirin and call me in the morning" knows that aspirin lowers fever, reduces inflammation, and relieves pain. In recent years, aspirin has been shown to reduce the incidence of heart disease, strokes, and certain cancers as well. It may also improve brain function in people who have suffered small strokes, help prevent cataracts, and reduce the occurrence of gallstones. But when it was first prepared about a century and a half ago, aspirin was considered so unremarkable that it was set aside and temporarily forgotten.

The aspirin saga begins with some relatives on its "family tree," a group of related compounds known as salicylates. An Egyptian papyrus from about 1500 B.C. described some medicinal uses of willow bark, and Native American tribes have used the bark to relieve pain and fight fever. The bark of the white willow and related *Salix* species contains salicin, a natural salicylate chemically related to aspirin. Salicin can be broken down in the presence of water and an oxidant to form molecules of glucose (a simple sugar) and a sweet-smelling liquid named salicylaldehyde. German chemists discovered that salicylaldehyde obtained from a different source, the meadowsweet plant (*Spiraea* species), reacts with strong alkali to yield a white solid on neutralization. The new compound was named *spirsäure* (from Spiraea + säure, the German word for "acid") by its discoverers but was called salicylic acid by the English, who traced its lineage back to the willow tree.

Salicylic acid can also be synthesized from phenol and carbon dioxide using a method developed by the brilliant but irascible German chemist Hermann Kolbe. Phenol, also known as carbolic acid, has long been used as a surgical antiseptic. It is much too caustic to be taken internally, causing painful burns in the mouth and upper digestive tract. But Kolbe had an idea—what if the formation of salicylic acid from phenol and CO_2 were reversed inside the human body? Then a patient could swallow salicylic acid, which would break down inside the body to yield phenol, which would then (Kolbe hoped) kill the germs responsible for the patient's illness. He carried out tests that "proved" to his satisfaction that salicylic acid was indeed an effective germ killer, and soon recommended its use on patients suffering from a variety of bacterial diseases and infections. The first reports seemed promising—patients were still dying after salicylic acid treatments, but they felt much better while doing so! Before long, doctors began to suspect that the salicylic acid "cured" only those patients who would have survived without any medication.

Kolbe's idea was wrong; salicylic acid does not produce phenol in the body, and his tests were later found to be invalid. But, like many scientific hypotheses that fail, this one led to important new discoveries. Although salicylic acid doesn't cure bacterial illnesses, it reduces fever and is a better pain reliever than salicin, so it was soon being prescribed for rheumatism, sciatica, headaches, and other painful conditions. But salicylic acid has a serious side effect—it strongly irritates mucous membranes that line the mouth, esophagus, and stomach. Arthur Eichengrün, head of the pharmaceutical group at Friedrich Bayer & Company, saw the need for a derivative of salicylic acid that lacked its irritant qualities. He assigned the task of finding one to a young chemist, Felix Hoffman, who would have known that phenolic compounds are corrosive because of the presence of a free hydroxyl (OH) group on the benzene ring. He must have reasoned that "masking" the OH with some easily removed substituent would provide the benefits of salicylic acid without the irritation. Studying the chemical literature would have led him to a paper by Charles Gerhardt that described the first known synthesis of acetylsalicylic acid 44 years earlier. In 1897, Hoffman replicated Gerhardt's experiment by treating salicylic acid with acetic anhydride, which replaced the hydrogen of its OH group with an acetyl (CH_3CO-) group. This yielded needlelike crystals of acetylsalicylic acid, which Eichengrün sent out for testing. The tests showed that acetylsalicylic acid was superior to all known painkillers, in both its effectiveness against pain and fever and its freedom from serious side effects. Bayer soon marketed acetylsalicylic acid under the trade name "aspirin" (derived from its German name, *acetylspirsäure*), and it has become the world's most popular drug.

According to an anecdote originating with the Bayer company, Hoffman was inspired to find a substitute for salicylic acid because his father, who took it for rheumatism, was suffering from its side effects. This story was probably invented after the fact.

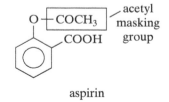

aspirin

Understanding the Experiment

In this experiment, you will use acetic anhydride to convert salicylic acid to aspirin, and also to serve as a solvent for the reaction. Because acetic anhydride is very reactive, it won't be necessary to heat the reactants under reflux; warming them in a water bath is sufficient. When the reaction is complete, water is added to destroy the excess acetic anhydride, converting it to water-soluble acetic acid. Aspirin can be purified by recrystallization from an ethanol–water mixture. One possible impurity in the aspirin is salicylic acid itself. You will test both your crude and purified aspirin for the presence of salicylic acid with ferric chloride, which forms highly colored complexes with phenolic compounds. From the results, you may be able to tell whether the impurity (if there is any) resulted from incomplete reaction of the starting materials or was formed by hydrolysis of aspirin during the workup of the product.

Aspirin is both an ester and a carboxylic acid, so its IR spectrum shows characteristics of both kinds of compounds. The O—H stretching vibration of a free carboxylic acid molecule leads to a sharp band near $3520\ cm^{-1}$, but in the liquid and solid states the molecules are held together by strong hydrogen bonding, causing the O—H band to shift to a lower frequency and spread out over much of the region between $3300\ cm^{-1}$ and $2500\ cm^{-1}$. The IR spectrum of a typical carboxylic acid also features a C=O stretching band around $1725\ cm^{-1}$, an acyl C—O stretching band in the $1315-1280\ cm^{-1}$ region, and an out-of-plane O—H bending band near $920\ cm^{-1}$. (The "C—O" bond vibrations for carboxylic acids and esters are actually coupled vibrations involving some adjacent atoms.) Conjugation with a benzene ring or a C=C bond moves a carbonyl band to a lower frequency. For example, the C=O band of benzoic acid occurs at $1688\ cm^{-1}$. The carbonyl stretching band of an ester usually occurs at a higher frequency than that of a carboxylic acid, and the acyl C—O stretching band of an ester ranges from about $1240\ cm^{-1}$ to $1140\ cm^{-1}$. The aromatic ring of an aryl ester increases the C=O frequency and decreases the acyl C—O frequency of the ester function. For example, these bands occur at $1765\ cm^{-1}$ and $1193\ cm^{-1}$, respectively, for phenyl acetate, compared to $1742\ cm^{-1}$ and $1241\ cm^{-1}$ for ethyl acetate.

CH_3C—O—CCH_3
acetic anhydride

Aspirin decomposes at high temperatures, so its melting point is not a reliable indicator of its purity.

Stretching vibrations of carboxylic acids and esters

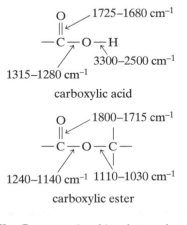

Key Concept: *Anything that weakens a C=O bond, such as conjugation, decreases its vibrational frequency. Anything that strengthens the bond, such as an electron-withdrawing group, increases its vibrational frequency.*

The ^{1}H NMR spectrum of aspirin shows a complex pattern of aromatic proton signals characteristic of *ortho* substitution by groups of differing electronegativity. The —COOH substituent withdraws electrons from the ring, deshielding nearby ring protons, and the —OCOCH$_3$ substituent donates electrons by resonance, shielding the ring protons. This effect is particularly noticeable for proton H$_a$ in Figure 1, whose signal occurs well downfield of the rest because of its proximity to the —COOH group. Although H$_a$ has only one nearest-neighbor proton, its ^{1}H NMR signal has four peaks, because the delocalized pi cloud of the ring allows long-range coupling between nonadjacent protons. Thus, the signal due to H$_a$ is split into a doublet by proton H$_b$, and each peak of that doublet is split into another—more closely spaced—doublet by proton H$_c$, as illustrated in Figure 1. The long-range coupling constant for protons *meta* to one another is only about 1–3 Hz, compared to typical coupling constants for *ortho* protons of 6–10 Hz.

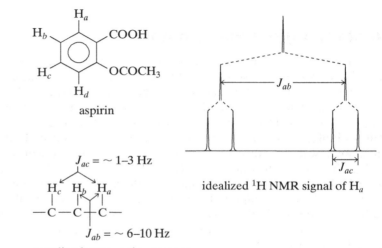

Figure 1 The effect of long-range coupling on an aromatic proton signal

If you obtain a ^{13}C NMR spectrum of your aspirin, refer to OP-40b and your lecture textbook or another source to help you interpret it.

In water, acetic anhydride is converted to acetic acid, which readily breaks down to carbon dioxide and water in the environment. Salicylic acid is expected to biodegrade in water and soil, and to persist for only a short time in the atmosphere. Sulfuric acid is harmful to aquatic organisms and is classified as a hazardous air pollutant. Deuterochloroform is toxic to aquatic organisms and shouldn't be released into the environment.

Reactions and Properties

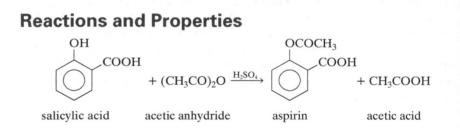

Table 1 Physical properties

	mol wt	mp	bp	*d*
salicylic acid	138.1	159		
acetic anhydride	102.1	−73	140	1.082
aspirin	180.2	135d		

Note: mp and bp are in °C; density is in g/mL; d = decomposes while melting.

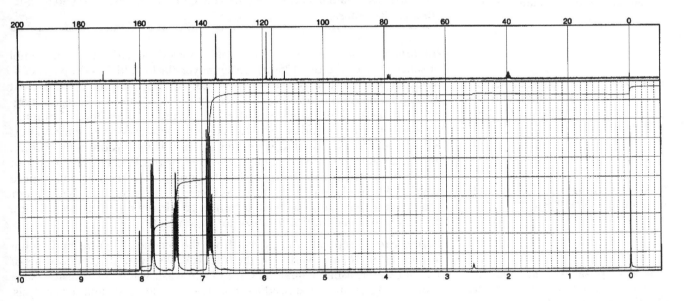

Salicylic acid

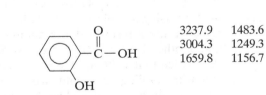

3237.9	1483.6	759.9
3004.3	1249.3	698.6
1659.8	1156.7	660.5

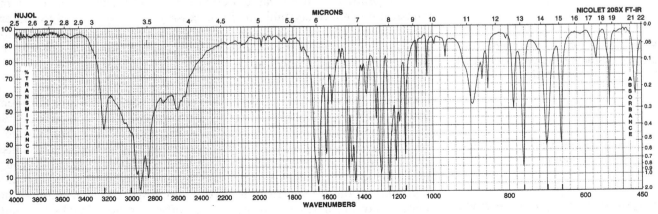

Figure 2 NMR and IR spectra of salicylic acid

DIRECTIONS

Safety Notes

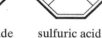

acetic anhydride   sulfuric acid

Acetic anhydride can cause severe damage to skin and eyes, its vapors are very harmful if inhaled, and it reacts violently with water. Use gloves and a hood; avoid contact with the liquid, do not breathe its vapors, and keep it away from water.

Sulfuric acid causes chemical burns that can seriously damage skin and eyes. Wear gloves and avoid contact.

Deuterochloroform is harmful if inhaled or absorbed through the skin; it is a suspected human carcinogen. Avoid contact with the liquid and do not breathe its vapors.

Take Care! Wear gloves, avoid contact with acetic anhydride and sulfuric acid, and do not breathe their vapors.

Reaction. *Under the hood*, add 5.0 mL of acetic anhydride to 15.0 mmol of salicylic acid in a dry 125-mL Erlenmeyer flask. Add 3–4 drops of concentrated sulfuric acid and stir or swirl [OP-10] the resulting mixture. Heat [OP-7] the mixture in a 45–50°C water bath with frequent swirling or magnetic stirring until the salicylic acid dissolves, and then for about 5 minutes more. Let the flask stand at room temperature until crystallization begins. If no product has precipitated when the solution is near room temperature, induce crystallization by scratching the wall of the flask at the surface of the solution with a glass stirring rod, or by adding a few seed crystals of pure aspirin. When a heavy precipitate has formed, stir in 30 mL of cold water and break up any lumps with a flat-bottomed stirring rod. Cool the mixture in an ice/water bath until crystallization is complete.

Stop and Think: Why might this help induce crystallization?

Separation. Separate the aspirin from the reaction mixture by vacuum filtration [OP-16] and wash it on the filter [OP-26a] with several portions of ice-cold water, using a small amount of the wash water for transfer. Save about 20 mg of the crude product in a clean, labeled test tube for analysis, and transfer the rest to a beaker.

Waste Disposal: Unless your instructor directs otherwise, wash the filtrate down the drain.

Purification. Recrystallize [OP-28] the aspirin from an ethanol/water mixture, using the following procedure to reduce the likelihood of hydrolysis. Dissolve the aspirin in the minimum volume of boiling 95% ethanol and add another 1 mL of ethanol, measuring the total volume of ethanol used. Add twice that volume of warm (~60°C) water to the solution while it is still at the boiling point, and swirl to mix. If any precipitate forms, heat the solution gently until it is clear, but don't boil it. Let it cool slowly to room temperature, induce crystallization if necessary, and cool it in an ice/water bath until crystallization is complete. Collect the aspirin by vacuum filtration [OP-16] and wash it on the filter [OP-26a] with ice-cold water. Save another small sample of the aspirin in a clean, labeled test tube for analysis. Dry [OP-26b] and weigh the remaining aspirin.

Stop and Think: What products would result from hydrolysis?

Waste Disposal: Unless your instructor directs otherwise, wash all filtrates down the drain.

Stop and Think: Which aspirin is the purest, and why?

Analysis. Place about 20 mg of salicylic acid in a clean, labeled test tube, then dissolve each reserved aspirin sample and the salicylic acid in 1 mL of 95% ethanol. The aspirin samples need not be completely dry. Add a drop of aqueous 2.5% ferric chloride to each test tube; record and explain your observations.

Record the IR spectrum [OP-39] of your aspirin as directed by your instructor. Identify as many IR bands as you can, indicating the kind of bond vibration responsible for each. Record its ^{1}H NMR spectrum [OP-40] in deuterochloroform. If you can, use a sweep offset for the COOH signal and a scale expansion for the aromatic proton signals when you record the

Take Care! Avoid contact with CDCl$_3$ and do not breathe its vapors.

NMR spectrum. Locate the ^{1}H NMR signal for the proton designated H$_a$ in Figure 1, determine the values of J_{ab} and J_{ac}, and assign as many other signals as you can. At your instructor's discretion, you can obtain and interpret a ^{13}C NMR spectrum of aspirin.

Waste Disposal: Place the deutero-chloroform solution in a designated waste container.

Exercises

1. Compare your IR and ^{1}H NMR spectra of aspirin with those of salicylic acid in Figure 2, and explain any significant similarities and differences.

2. (a) Write an equation for a reaction that might form salicylic acid during the workup of the product. (b) Tell how you could reduce or prevent the contamination of your product due to this reaction.

3. Describe and explain the possible effect on your results of the following experimental errors or variations. (a) The reagent bottle labeled "acetic anhydride" actually contained acetic acid. (b) The test tube used for analysis of the purified aspirin was rinsed with water and not completely dried, and you stored the aspirin sample for a week before testing it. (c) You boiled the recrystallization mixture after adding water.

4. (a) Calculate the atom economy and reaction efficiency of your synthesis. (b) Describe some green features of your synthesis, and any that aren't so green.

5. Following the format in the "Planning an Experiment" appendix, construct a flow diagram for the synthesis of aspirin.

6. Write a detailed mechanism for the reaction of salicylic acid with acetic anhydride, showing clearly the function of the catalyst, sulfuric acid.

7. A small bottle of 5-grain aspirin tablets holds 100 tablets, each containing 0.325 g of aspirin. Calculate the cost of the acetic anhydride and salicylic acid required to prepare the aspirin in such a bottle, assuming equimolar quantities of the reactants (the sulfuric acid, being a catalyst, can be recovered). You can look up their current prices in the *Chemical Marketing Reporter*, or in another source recommended by your instructor.

8. Which would you expect to be the stronger acid, aspirin or salicylic acid? Explain your answer.

Other Things You Can Do

(Starred items require your instructor's permission.)

*1. Interpret the mass spectrum of a compound as described in the "Interpretation of a Mass Spectrum" minilab.

*2. Test commercial aspirin tablets for salicylic acid by the ferric chloride test described in the Directions. Try the test on freshly purchased aspirin and on aspirin that has been in use for some time. (Try to find some old aspirin that has a "vinegar" odor.) Test them for starch (often used as a binder) by boiling 2 mg of a ground-up tablet in 2 mL of water and adding a drop of a solution of iodine in potassium iodide. Starch forms a blue-violet complex with iodine.

3. Starting with sources listed in the Bibliography, write a research paper on some commercial uses for acetic anhydride other than in aspirin production.

Directive Effects in the Bromination of Vanillin

Reactions of Aromatic Compounds. Preparation of Aryl Bromides.
Electrophilic Aromatic Substitution. Directive Effects.

Operations

OP-10 Mixing
OP-16 Vacuum Filtration
OP-26 Washing and Drying Solids
OP-28 Recrystallization
OP-33 Melting Point

Before You Begin

1. Read the experiment, read or review the operations as necessary, and write an experimental plan.
2. Calculate the mass of 10.0 mmol of vanillin and the theoretical yield of bromovanillin from this amount of vanillin.

Scenario

Pulpchem Inc., a subsidiary of a large paper company, produces useful chemicals from lignin and other by-products of paper production. Chemical treatment of lignin can yield vanillin, a white solid that is responsible for the characteristic aroma of vanilla extract. The product development manager of Pulpchem, Woody Aspin, wants to develop new products from vanillin that might be marketed commercially. He has heard of a new way to brominate aromatic compounds on the benzene ring using hydrobromic acid and potassium bromate rather than hazardous liquid bromine, but he doesn't know what products to expect from the reaction. If the *ortho-para* directing methoxyl group of vanillin controls product formation, the product could be 2-bromovanillin, 6-bromovanillin, or a mixture of the two. But, if the hydroxyl group and the *meta*-directing aldehyde group win out, the product should be 5-bromovanillin.

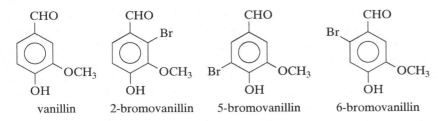

vanillin   2-bromovanillin   5-bromovanillin   6-bromovanillin

Your assignment, and that of your coworkers, is to carry out the bromination of vanillin and identify the product.

From *Operational Organic Chemistry: A Problem Solving Approach to the Laboratory*, Fourth Edition, John W. Lehman. Copyright © 2009 by Pearson Education. Published by Prentice Hall. All rights reserved.

Applying Scientific Methodology

Your working hypothesis should involve a prediction of the product (or products) you think the bromination of vanillin should yield. You will test your hypothesis by measuring the melting point of the product.

The Flavor of Vanilla

Most good cooks have a bottle labeled "pure vanilla extract" in the cupboard. It contains a brown liquid with the delightful scent and flavor that we associate with vanilla ice cream, vanilla pudding, cream soda, and many baked goods. Although cheaper forms of vanilla may consist mainly of vanillin synthesized from guaiacol or wood pulp, the real thing comes from the seedpod of a tropical orchid. One of these pods—often called a vanilla bean—looks much like a long (12–15 cm) green bean and has virtually no odor. The characteristic vanilla odor develops during a curing process in which sugar derivatives called glycosides are broken down into vanillin and other flavorful substances. Cured vanilla beans typically contain more than 400 such components. Vanilla extract is made by shredding the beans into small pieces, typically in a machine that works like a giant blender, and soaking the pieces in successive quantities of hot 65–70% ethanol.

Vanilla orchids were probably first discovered and used in southeastern Mexico more than 1000 years ago. By the time Spanish conquistadors discovered Mexico's Aztec Empire in the 1500s, Aztecs were flavoring a cocoa-containing beverage called *xocolatl* (*chocolatl* in Spanish) with honey and vanilla. Vanilla has long had a reputation as an aphrodisiac; the Aztec emperor Montezuma drank xocolatl from a golden goblet before visiting his wives, and in Europe newly married men were once advised to drink beverages flavored with vanilla. There is some scientific support for such practices; recent tests at the Institute for Smell and Taste in Chicago showed that the aroma of vanilla is a powerful stimulant to men.

Today, about half of the world's vanilla is grown in the tropical forests of Madagascar, with smaller amounts from Indonesia, Mexico, Tahiti, and the Comoro Islands. Bourbon vanilla, which is usually considered to be the world's finest, is grown in Madagascar, the Comoros, and the nearby island of Réunion, which was once ruled by the Bourbon kings of France. In addition to vanillin, Bourbon vanilla contains the flavor ingredient bourbonal, an ethyl homolog of vanillin.

Although vanillin is vanilla's dominant flavor ingredient, its other components contribute to the rich, complex flavor of a natural vanilla extract. Many so-called vanilla extracts are actually blends of natural vanilla extract and synthetic vanillin. Because natural vanilla extract costs more than $500 a kilogram, the cheaper products are mostly synthetic vanillin, and the blend labeled "imitation vanilla" is made entirely from synthetic substances. Carbon-13 nuclear magnetic resonance (see OP-40b) can be used to determine the origin of vanillin by measuring the intensities of the ^{13}C signals for each of its eight carbon atoms and calculating their ^{13}C/^{12}C ratios. This method can reveal any attempt to fraudulently substitute cheap synthetic vanillin for the natural substance.

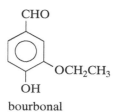

bourbonal

Understanding the Experiment

Aromatic compounds can be brominated on the ring by elemental bromine (Br_2) in the presence of a Lewis acid catalyst such as iron(III) bromide, $FeBr_3$. But liquid bromine, with its toxic red fumes, is dangerous to inhale and can cause severe burns. Paul F. Schatz of the University of Wisconsin–Madison discovered that a mixture of potassium bromate and hydrobromic acid in acetic acid is an efficient reagent for aromatic bromination. This combination generates bromine in the reaction mixture rather than requiring its direct addition.

$$5HBr + KBrO_3 + CH_3COOH \rightarrow 3Br_2 + CH_3COOK + 3H_2O$$

The bromine generated could cause bromination at either the 2, 5, or 6 position of vanillin's benzene ring. Both the methoxyl ($-OCH_3$) and hydroxyl ($-OH$) substituents are *ortho-para* directing, whereas the aldehyde functional group ($-CHO$) is *meta* directing. Thus, the $-OCH_3$ group can direct electrophiles to both the #2 position, which is *ortho* to it, and the #6 position, which is *para* to it, but electrophiles tend to attack less crowded ring sites, so one of these positions is more likely to be attacked than the other. (**Stop and Think:** Which position is it?) The OH group would tend to direct incoming electrophiles to the #5 position, which is the only open position that is *ortho* or *para* to it. The *meta*-directing $-CHO$ also directs to the #5 position, but *meta*-directors are more weakly directing than *ortho-para* directors, so having two substituents directing to the same position doesn't necessarily mean the electrophile will end up in that position—a strong *ortho-para* director could overpower both.

The procedure isn't difficult and involves only operations that you should have performed before. Because your conclusion will depend on the melting point of your product, it is important to be sure that the product is dry and to measure its melting point accurately.

This is a relatively green experiment because it requires no organic solvents but acetic acid, which occurs naturally in living organisms and readily breaks down to carbon dioxide and water in the environment. Little information is available about the environmental fate and toxicity of hydrobromic acid and potassium bromate.

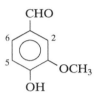

Key Concept: *Electron-donating substituents like* $-OCH_3$ *tend to make the* ortho *and* para *positions of a benzene ring more inviting to incoming electrophiles than the* meta *position. Electron-withdrawing substituents like* $-CHO$ *tend to make the* ortho *and* para *positions less inviting than the* meta *position.*

Reactions and Properties

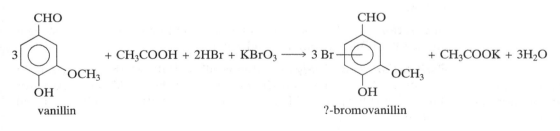

vanillin   ?-bromovanillin

Table 1 Physical properties

	mol wt	mp	d
vanillin	152.15	81–83	
2-bromovanillin	231.0	155	
5-bromovanillin	231.0	166	
6-bromovanillin	231.5	178	
acetic acid	60.05		1.049
potassium bromate	167.0	~350	3.27
48% hydrobromic acid	80.9		1.490

Note: mp is in °C; density is in g/mL.

DIRECTIONS

Safety Notes

> **Acetic acid causes chemical burns that can seriously damage skin and eyes; its vapors are highly irritating to the eyes and respiratory tract. Wear gloves, dispense under a hood, avoid contact, and do not breathe its vapors.**
>
> **Hydrobromic acid is toxic and very corrosive; it can cause very serious damage to the skin, eyes, and respiratory tract. Wear gloves and dispense under a hood. Avoid contact with the acid and do not inhale its vapors. Potassium bromate is toxic; avoid ingestion.**

acetic acid   hydrobromic acid   potassium bromate

Take Care! Wear gloves, avoid contact with hydrobromic acid, and do not breathe its vapors.

Reaction. *Under the hood*, dissolve 10.0 mmol of vanillin in 20 mL of acetic acid in a 50-mL Erlenmeyer flask. Add 0.75 g of potassium bromate, followed by 2.0 mL of 48% hydrobromic acid. Stir [OP-10] the reaction mixture at room temperature for 45 minutes. Pour the mixture into an Erlenmeyer flask containing 150 mL of ice-cold water and continue to stir for 15–20 minutes. If the liquid is an orange color, add 10% sodium thiosulfate solution, drop by drop with stirring, until it turns yellow.

Separation. Collect the product by vacuum filtration [OP-16], washing it on the filter [OP-26a] with ice-cold water.

Purification and Analysis. Recrystallize [OP-28] the product from 50% ethanol/water. Dry [OP-26b] the product thoroughly in a desiccator until the next lab period. Measure its mass and melting point [OP-33], and name it.

Waste Disposal: Unless your instructor directs otherwise, wash all filtrates down the drain.

Exercises

1. Explain why the major product was the one you obtained, rather than either of the other two possible products.
2. What did you observe immediately after you added hydrobromic acid to the reaction mixture? Write a chemical equation that explains this result.
3. Describe and explain the possible effect on your results of the following experimental errors or variations. (a) The lab assistant set out a bottle of potassium bromide rather than potassium bromate. (b) You used anisaldehyde (4-methoxybenzaldehyde) in place of vanillin.
4. (a) Calculate the atom economy and reaction efficiency of your synthesis. (b) Describe some green features of your synthesis, and any that aren't so green.
5. Following the format in the "Planning an Experiment" appendix, construct a flow diagram for the experiment.
6. Write a complete mechanism for the reaction you carried out.
7. Show how vanillin is synthesized commercially from guaiacol.

guaiacol

Other Things You Can Do

(Starred items require your instructor's permission.)

*1. Use a different kind of bromination reaction to determine the relative stabilities of free radicals in the "Free-Radical Stability" minilab.
2. Record a ^{13}C NMR spectrum of vanillin and identify as many of the signals as you can.
3. Starting with sources listed in the Bibliography, write a research paper about artificial flavorings and their constituents.

Mechanism of the Nitration of Arenes by Nitronium Fluoborate

EXPERIMENT

Reactions of Arenes. Preparation of Nitro Compounds. Electrophilic Aromatic Substitution. Reaction Rates. Reaction Mechanisms.

Operations

OP-18 Extraction
OP-19 Evaporation
OP-24 Washing Liquids
OP-25 Drying Liquids
OP-37 Gas Chromatography

Before You Begin

Read the experiment, read or review the operations as necessary, and write an experimental plan.

Scenario

(*Note:* Professor Olah is a real chemist whose research group carried out the work described here.)

The research group of George A. Olah, recipient of the 1994 Nobel Prize in chemistry, developed a highly reactive nitrating reagent, nitronium fluoborate (NO_2BF_4), and used it in a study of the mechanisms of aromatic nitration reactions. During its investigation, the group found evidence suggesting that the initial intermediate formed in some reactions of nitronium fluoborate is different from the one formed in most other aromatic nitration reactions, which use a mixture of nitric and sulfuric acids. According to Olah, such an intermediate could be a sigma complex, a symmetrical pi complex, or an oriented pi complex. Your supervisor has devised two experiments that may reveal the nature of the initial intermediate involved in some reactions of NO_2BF_4: (1) nitration of a mixture of toluene and mesitylene and measurement of their relative reaction rates; and (2) nitration of *t*-butylbenzene and measurement of the product mixture's *ortho/para* ratio. Your assignment is to carry out these nitration reactions and, based on Olah's hypothesis and your experimental results, propose a reasonable structure for the intermediate in question.

Applying Scientific Methodology

After reading the experiment, you can formulate a working hypothesis about the nature of the intermediate, which you and your coworkers will test by analyzing the product mixtures from the reactions described in the Scenario. Keep in mind that, as a rule, experiments cannot prove that a hypothesis is

From *Operational Organic Chemistry: A Problem Solving Approach to the Laboratory*, Fourth Edition, John W. Lehman. Copyright © 2009 by Pearson Education. Published by Prentice Hall. All rights reserved.

true but can only support or refute the hypothesis, so your conclusion may be incorrect or incomplete regardless of your experimental results.

Intermediates in Nitration Reactions

The electrophile in aromatic nitration is the nitronium ion (NO_2^+), which is usually generated by mixing nitric acid with sulfuric acid.

$$HNO_3 + 2H_2SO_4 \rightleftharpoons NO_2^+ + H_3O^+ + 2HSO_4^-$$

With this "mixed acid" reagent, the equilibrium concentration of NO_2^+ is so low that elevated temperatures and long reaction times are generally required for successful nitration. Nitronium fluoborate (NO_2BF_4) is a salt that ionizes to yield NO_2^+ at a much higher concentration, allowing rapid nitration of most aromatic compounds at room temperature or below.

The nitronium ion is an electron-hungry species—an *electrophile*—that can steal a pair of pi electrons from a benzene ring's aromatic sextet. In a general mechanism proposed for electrophilic aromatic substitution, such an electrophile attacks the aromatic ring to form a *sigma complex*, in which the electrophile (symbolized here by E^+) is connected to a ring carbon by a sigma bond.

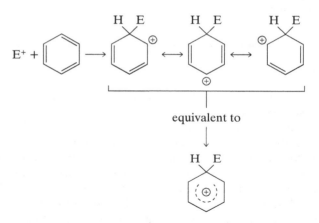

equivalent to

The sigma complex (also called an *arenium ion*) then loses a proton to a basic species in the reaction mixture to yield the corresponding substituted benzene, as shown in the margin. The ring atoms *ortho* and *para* to the incoming electrophile bear most of the positive charge in the sigma complex. Thus, electron-donating groups located on those atoms stabilize the complex, favoring the formation of *ortho*- and *para*-substituted products. For example, only 4% of the product obtained from the nitration of toluene in mixed acid is *meta*-nitrotoluene; the other 96% is a mixture of *ortho*- and *para*-nitrotoluene.

In some aromatic substitution reactions, the initial intermediate may be a pi complex, in which the electrophile is loosely bonded to the pi electrons of an aromatic ring. Such an intermediate would presumably rearrange to a sigma complex before giving rise to the product. A pi complex that involves a nitronium ion and benzene might be pictured as shown, with the electrophile sitting atop a "doughnut" of pi electrons, equidistant from all of the ring atoms. The pi cloud of an alkyl-substituted benzene is "lumpier" than that of benzene, with bulges at the positions *ortho* and *para* to the alkyl group. An electrophile that spends more time near these regions of higher

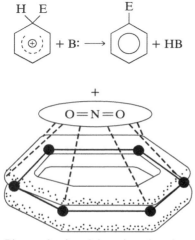

Pi complex involving nitronium ion and benzene

314

electron density will form an *oriented* pi complex rather than a symmetrical benzene-type complex. Both possibilities are illustrated in the margin.

Although alkyl groups alter the electron distribution in a pi cloud, they have only a small effect on its total electron density. Thus, increasing the number of methyl groups on a benzene ring shouldn't increase the stability of its pi complexes very much. On the other hand, the stabilities of sigma complexes are very sensitive to the electronic effects of substituents. Mesitylene, with three methyl groups, forms a sigma complex with HBF_4 that is nearly 300,000 times more stable than the corresponding sigma complex involving toluene; but the pi complex that mesitylene forms with HCl is only about twice as stable as the complex that toluene forms. As a rule, the more stable an intermediate is, the faster it will form. If the initial intermediate in nitration by nitronium fluoborate is a pi complex, the nitration rates for mesitylene and toluene should be within a factor of 10 or so of one another. But, if the initial intermediate is a sigma complex, the nitration rate for mesitylene should be thousands of times greater than that for toluene.

When a substituent influences the outcome of a reaction as a result of its bulkiness (as opposed to its electronic effects), we say that a *steric effect* is operating. Steric effects in aromatic substitution reactions can be detected by measuring the ratios of *ortho* products to *para* products for the same reaction with different substituents. There are twice as many *ortho* as *para* hydrogens in a monosubstituted arene, suggesting that the ratio of *ortho*- to *para*-substituted products should be about 2:1 in the absence of steric effects. As shown in Table 1, *ortho/para* ratios for the nitration of arenes in mixed acid are considerably lower than 2:1, especially for very bulky substituents such as *t*-butyl. Apparently, a bulky alkyl group hinders substitution at the *ortho* position by crowding the attacking electrophile in the transition state that leads to the sigma complex.

The steric requirements of pi complexes haven't been as thoroughly studied as those of sigma complexes. If an incoming electrophile approaches the ring from the top to form a symmetrical pi complex, there should be little if any steric effect, even with a bulky substituent such as the *t*-butyl group. On the other hand, the formation of an oriented pi complex should be markedly influenced by steric factors, giving product ratios comparable to those observed for mixed-acid nitrations.

Understanding the Experiment

Nitronium fluoborate is prepared by treating nitric acid with hydrofluoric acid and boron trifluoride:

$$HNO_3 + HF + 2BF_3 \longrightarrow NO_2BF_4 + BF_3 \cdot H_2O$$

The stable crystalline salt ionizes in polar solvents to provide "ready-made" nitronium ions:

$$NO_2BF_4 \longrightarrow NO_2^+ + BF_4^-$$

In this experiment, you will nitrate a mixture of mesitylene and toluene with nitronium fluoborate and analyze the product mixture by gas chromatography to determine the relative reaction rates of the two arenes. You will also nitrate *t*-butylbenzene and measure the *ortho/para* ratio of the product. From the results, you should be able to decide whether the initial intermediate is more likely to be a sigma complex, a symmetrical pi complex, or an oriented pi complex.

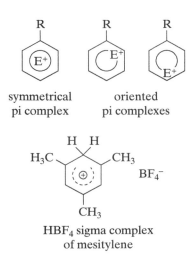

symmetrical pi complex

oriented pi complexes

HBF_4 sigma complex of mesitylene

Key Concept: *Anything that stabilizes a reactive intermediate will also stabilize the transition state leading to that intermediate, lowering the activation energy and speeding up the reaction.*

An arene is an aromatic hydrocarbon, such as toluene.

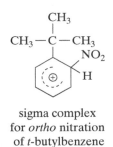

sigma complex for *ortho* nitration of *t*-butylbenzene

Table 1 *Ortho/para* ratios for the nitration of arenes in mixed acid

Arene	*o/p* ratio
toluene	1.57
ethylbenzene	0.93
isopropylbenzene	0.48
t-butylbenzene	0.22

You will measure the relative rates of nitration for mesitylene and toluene by carrying out a competitive nitration reaction in which equimolar quantities of the two arenes compete for a limited amount of nitronium fluoborate. The arene that competes most successfully will form the most product, so the relative rates for the two arenes should be proportional to the relative amounts of nitroarene they produce:

$$\frac{\text{reaction rate for mesitylene}}{\text{reaction rate for toluene}} = \frac{\text{moles of nitromesitylene}}{\text{moles of nitrotoluenes}}$$

For a meaningful rate comparison, you must determine the relative rates per reaction site; otherwise toluene, with five ring hydrogens, will have a statistical advantage over mesitylene, with only three. The rate per reaction site is proportional to the number of moles of product divided by the number of reaction sites, so the relative reactivity of a mesitylene site is given by this equation:

$$\frac{\text{reactivity of mesitylene site}}{\text{reactivity of toluene site}} = \frac{\text{moles of nitromesitylene}/3}{\text{moles of nitrotoluenes}/5}$$

Because the area of a peak on a gas chromatogram is proportional to the mass of the component that produces it, you can estimate the relative number of moles of each product by dividing its peak area by its molecular weight. (The relative masses of different components may not be in the exact ratio of their peak areas, but they will be close enough for the purposes of this experiment.) The peak areas for the three nitrotoluenes should be combined for this calculation.

The nitration reactions will be carried out at room temperature by adding nitronium fluoborate in sulfolane to an excess of each arene in the same solvent. The excess reactant prevents the formation of di- and trinitrated products, which would skew the results. Sulfolane is an excellent solvent for the reaction, because it dissolves both the nitronium salt and the arene, thus providing a homogeneous reaction mixture. It is also miscible with water, making it easy to separate the products from the reaction mixture. When water and diethyl ether are added to the reaction mixture, sulfolane and fluoboric acid (a by-product of the reaction) end up in the water layer, and the aromatic compounds are extracted into the ether layer. Evaporation of the ether leaves a mixture of unreacted arenes and nitrated products.

The reaction mixtures will be analyzed by gas chromatography on a column that separates aromatic compounds in order of their boiling points. Unreacted arenes should elute from the column first, followed by *ortho-*, *meta-*, and *para-*nitroarenes, in that order. The nitromesitylene peak should appear later than all of the nitrotoluene peaks. If you failed to evaporate the diethyl ether completely, you will see an initial ether peak, and there may be additional peaks due to impurities in the commercial arenes used as starting materials. Compare your chromatograms with chromatograms of those arenes if such peaks make interpretation difficult.

Toluene is a hazardous chemical and a serious environmental contaminant that shouldn't be released into the environment. The other aromatic compounds used in this experiment, mesitylene and *t*-butylbenzene, are expected to have similar environmental effects. Diethyl ether isn't considered toxic to aquatic organisms and does not persist for long in either air or water. Little information is available about the environmental effects of sulfolane and nitronium fluoborate.

sulfolane

*A **Greener Way:** The ether can be recovered by evaporating it under vacuum using a cold trap (see OP-15).*

Reactions and Properties

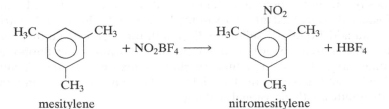

R = methyl or *t*-butyl

(NO₂ is predominantly *ortho* and *para*)

mesitylene + NO₂BF₄ ⟶ nitromesitylene + HBF₄

Table 2 Physical properties

	mol wt	mp	bp	*d*
toluene	92.1	−95	111	0.867
t-butylbenzene	134.2	−58	169	0.867
mesitylene	120.2	−45	165	0.862
nitronium fluoborate	132.8			
sulfolane	120.2	28	285	1.260
o-nitrotoluene	137.1	10	222	1.163
m-nitrotoluene	137.1	16	233	1.157
p-nitrotoluene	137.1	55	238	1.104
nitromesitylene	165.2	44	255	

Note: mp and bp are in °C; density is in g/mL.

DIRECTIONS

At the instructor's discretion, students can work in pairs, with each student being responsible for one nitration reaction.

Safety Notes

The nitronium fluoborate solution is toxic and corrosive. Wear gloves and avoid contact.

The aromatic hydrocarbons are flammable, and inhalation or skin absorption may be harmful. Avoid contact and inhalation, and keep them away from flames.

Diethyl ether is extremely flammable and may be harmful if inhaled. Do not breathe its vapors, and keep it away from flames and hot surfaces.

Aromatic nitro compounds are toxic and may cause serious harm if inhaled or absorbed through the skin. The reaction mixtures will also contain fluoboric acid and hydrofluoric acid, which cause very serious burns and have harmful vapors. Avoid contact with the reaction mixtures and products, and do not breathe their vapors.

toluene   diethyl ether   *p*-nitrotoluene

Take Care! Do not breathe the vapors of the arenes or their solutions, and keep them away from flames. Wear gloves and avoid contact with nitronium fluoborate.

Take Care! Keep diethyl ether away from ignition sources and do not breathe its vapors. Wear gloves when shaking the tube and vent it often.

Waste Disposal: Place the aqueous layer, which contains hydrofluoric acid and fluoboric acid, in a designated waste container. Place recovered ether in a designated solvent recovery container.

Stop and Think: Is there any evidence of incomplete evaporation? What gives rise to the largest peak(s) on each chromatogram?

Reactions. *Carry out the reactions under a hood and wear protective gloves. All glassware must be clean and dry.* Clean, dry, and label two 15-mL centrifuge tubes with screw caps. Measure 0.60 mL of an equimolar mixture of mesitylene and toluene into the first centrifuge tube, and add 1.0 mL of sulfolane. Measure 0.50 mL of dry *t*-butylbenzene into the second centrifuge tube and add 1.0 mL of sulfolane. Cap both tubes and shake them gently to mix the contents. Slowly add 1.0 mL of 0.5 *M* nitronium fluoborate in sulfolane to each centrifuge tube, swirling to mix the reactants. Again cap both tubes and shake gently. Then let the tubes stand at room temperature for 10 minutes, with occasional shaking.

Separation. Carry out the following procedure with each reaction mixture. Add 2 mL of solvent-grade diethyl ether and 3 mL of water to the centrifuge tube, then cap it and shake to extract [OP-18] the products and unreacted arene into the ether layer. Carefully remove the aqueous layer with a Pasteur pipet. Wash [OP-24] the ether layer with 2 mL of water. Then remove the water layer, dry [OP-25] the ether solution with anhydrous calcium chloride or sodium sulfate, and decant it into another container for evaporation. Under the hood, carefully evaporate [OP-19] the diethyl ether.

Analysis. Obtain a gas chromatogram [OP-37] of each product mixture as directed by your instructor. Identify the peaks on the gas chromatograms and measure the peak areas for all of the nitrated products. Calculate the *ortho/para* ratio for the nitration of *t*-butylbenzene and the reactivity per reaction site of mesitylene relative to toluene. Decide whether the initial intermediate in these nitrations by nitronium fluoborate is more likely to be a sigma complex, a symmetrical pi complex, or an oriented pi complex. Turn in the gas chromatograms with your report.

Exercises

For another interpretation of Olah's results, see J. H. Ridd, Accounts of Chemical Research, **1971,** *4,* 248.

1. Based on your experimental results, explain your conclusion regarding the nature of the initial intermediate in nitration by nitronium fluoborate.
2. Based on your results, propose a detailed mechanism for the reaction of *t*-butylbenzene with nitronium fluoborate to yield *p*-nitro-*t*-butylbenzene.
3. (a) It has been estimated that the *meta* product arising from direct nitration of *t*-butylbenzene by NO_2BF_4 makes up about 2.0% of the product mixture, the remaining *meta* product arising from isomerization of the *ortho* product. Use this estimate to calculate a more accurate value of your *ortho/para* nitration ratio for *t*-butylbenzene. (b) Propose a mechanism for the isomerization reaction, which is apparently promoted by the HBF_4 formed during the reaction.

4. Describe and explain the possible effect on your results of the following experimental errors or variations. (a) You rinsed your reaction tubes with water and didn't dry them completely. (b) You added toluene rather than *t*-butylbenzene to the second centrifuge tube. (c) When analyzing the gas chromatogram from the *t*-butylbenzene nitration, you misidentified the *t*-butylbenzene peak as the peak for the *ortho* product and assumed that the next two peaks were for the *meta* and *para* products.

5. (a) Calculate the atom economy of the nitration of mesitylene. (b) Describe some green features of the experiment, and any that aren't so green.

6. Following the format in the "Planning an Experiment" appendix, construct a flow diagram for the nitration of *t*-butylbenzene.

7. In a solution of bromine in acetic acid, mesitylene is brominated nearly 300 million times faster than benzene. Do you think a sigma complex or a pi complex is formed in the rate-determining step of this reaction? Explain.

8. Predict the major product or products of the mononitration of (a) ethyl benzoate, (b) phenyl acetate, (c) phenyl benzoate, (d) *m*-nitrotoluene, and (e) *p*-methoxybenzaldehyde.

Other Things You Can Do

(Starred items require your instructor's permission.)

*1. Carry out the mixed-acid nitration of naphthalene by the procedure in the "Nitration of Napthalene" minilab.

2. Read the paper by George A. Olah and his coworkers that describes the nitration of arenes with nitronium fluoborate (*J. Am. Chem. Soc.* **1961**, *83*, 4571), and compare their results and conclusions with your own.

Friedel–Crafts
Acylation of Anisole

Reactions of Aromatic Ethers. Preparation of Carbonyl Compounds.
Electrophilic Aromatic Substitution. Infrared Spectrometry.

Operations

OP-7   Heating
OP-10   Mixing
OP-11   Addition of Reactants
OP-12   Excluding Water from Reaction Mixtures
OP-14   Trapping Gases (optional)
OP-16   Vacuum Filtration
OP-24   Washing Liquids
OP-25   Drying Liquids
OP-26   Washing and Drying Solids
OP-30   Simple Distillation
OP-33   Melting Point
OP-39   Infrared Spectrometry

Before You Begin

1. Read the experiment, read or review the operations as necessary, and write an experimental plan.
2. Calculate the mass and volume of 10.0 mmol of anisole, and the theoretical yield of methoxyacetophenone.

Scenario

The Canadian purchasing agent for the Olfactory Factory—being used to working with metric units—ordered 500 kilograms of anisole rather than 500 pounds, so the company needs to find some way to use up the excess anisole by converting it to perfume ingredients. One possibility is to prepare 4′-methoxyacetophenone, also known as crataegon, which occurs naturally in hawthorn blossoms (*Crataegus* spp.). The company's chemical technicians think it should be possible to synthesize 4′-methoxyacetophenone from anisole by a Friedel–Crafts reaction, but they are concerned that the reaction may yield the wrong isomer or a mixture of isomers that will be difficult to separate. According to their business manager, the Olfactory Factory cannot sell the product at a competitive price if they have to invest in expensive separation equipment. Your assignment is to see whether or not the Friedel–Crafts acetylation of anisole yields mainly 4′-methoxyacetophenone, another isomer, or a mixture of isomers.

Applying Scientific Methodology

After reading the experiment, you should be able to develop a working hypothesis related to the problem, which you will test by obtaining the melting point and infrared (IR) spectrum of the product.

hawthorn blossom

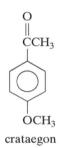

crataegon

From *Operational Organic Chemistry: A Problem Solving Approach to the Laboratory,* Fourth Edition, John W. Lehman. Copyright © 2009 by Pearson Education. Published by Prentice Hall. All rights reserved.

acetophenone

benzophenone

Friedel, Crafts, and Phenones

Aromatic ketones that have the carbonyl group adjacent to the benzene ring are called *phenones*. The simplest member of this group is acetophenone, a pleasant-smelling liquid that has been used to impart an odor of orange blossoms to perfumes, and has also been used as a sleep-producing drug under the generic name hypnone. Charles Friedel first prepared acetophenone in 1857 by distilling a mixture of calcium benzoate and calcium acetate. Another fragrant phenone, benzophenone, is a white solid with a geranium-like odor that has been used as a fixative for perfumes and as a starting material for the manufacture of drugs and insecticides.

The natural and synthetic musks are powerfully odoriferous substances that supply the long-lasting, musky "end note" characteristic of some perfumes, deodorants, and aftershave lotions. The large-ring ketone called muscone (3-methylcyclopentadecanone) is the major constituent of natural musk, which is a secretion from the musk pod of the male musk deer. Muscone is very costly and its use threatens the existence of the deer, so it has been almost entirely replaced by synthetic musks. Among these are the phenones known as musk ketone and Celestolide.

Natural and synthetic musks

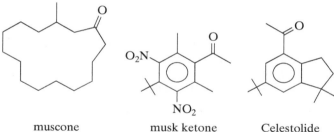

muscone   musk ketone   Celestolide

Musk ketone is prepared from *m*-xylene by two Friedel–Crafts reactions—alkylation with *t*-butyl chloride and acylation with acetyl chloride—followed by nitration of the aromatic ring.

A Friedel–Crafts reaction involves the catalytic alkylation or acylation of an aromatic ring.

Synthesis of musk ketone

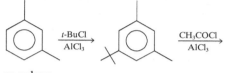

m-xylene

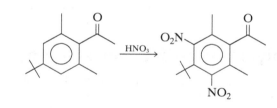

Like the synthetic musks, most phenones can be prepared by Friedel–Crafts reactions of aromatic compounds with appropriate acylating agents. Theodor Zincke first prepared benzophenone by heating benzoyl chloride with a metal in benzene. This was essentially a Friedel–Crafts reaction, but Zincke didn't know it because that reaction hadn't been discovered yet! In fact, the Friedel–Crafts reaction might well have been named the Zincke reaction if Zincke had understood the significance of an experiment that failed. In 1869, Zincke tried to synthesize 3-phenylpropanoic acid by combining benzyl chloride and chloroacetic acid in the presence of metallic silver—a variation of the Wurtz reaction. While carrying out the reaction with benzene as the solvent, Zincke observed, to his surprise, that a great deal of hydrogen chloride was evolved and that the major product was diphenylmethane instead of the expected carboxylic acid.

Zincke's attempted synthesis

$$PhCH_2Cl + ClCH_2COOH \xrightarrow[\text{benzene}]{Ag} PhCH_2CH_2COOH$$

The "Zincke reaction"

$$PhCH_2Cl + PhH \text{ (benzene)} \xrightarrow{Ag} PhCH_2Ph + HCl$$

About four years later, a Frenchman named Charles Friedel was watching a student in Wurtz's laboratory perform a Zincke reaction using (appropriately) powdered zinc as the catalyst. When the reaction suddenly became violent, Friedel helped the student separate the solution from the zinc powder, thinking that removing the catalyst would moderate the reaction. To the astonishment of both, the reaction was just as violent in the absence of zinc. Although there is no record of his thought processes after this event, Friedel must have recognized its significance. In 1877, Friedel and his collaborator, an American named Charles Mason Crafts, published a paper that marked the inception of the Friedel–Crafts reaction as one of the most important synthetic procedures in the history of organic chemistry. Friedel and Crafts' major discovery was a simple one: It is a chloride of the metal, and not the metal itself, that catalyzes the reaction of organic halides with aromatic compounds. For example, during Zincke's attempted synthesis of 3-phenylpropanoic acid, a small amount of silver had been converted to silver chloride. Friedel and Crafts eventually determined that anhydrous aluminum chloride was the most effective catalyst available at the time. It is still the catalyst of choice for most Friedel–Crafts reactions.

Understanding the Experiment

The Friedel–Crafts reaction isn't a single reaction type, although the term has most often been applied to alkylations and acylations of aromatic compounds that use aluminum chloride (or another Lewis acid catalyst) and a suitable alkylating or acylating agent. A typical Friedel–Crafts acylation reaction uses a carboxylic acid chloride as the acylating agent and anhydrous aluminum chloride as the catalyst. As illustrated in Figure 1 for the reaction of benzene with an acyl chloride, aluminum chloride removes a leaving group from the acylating agent, forming an acylium ion. The acylium ion then attacks the benzene ring to form an arenium ion, which loses a proton to yield the product and regenerate the catalyst.

Key Concept: During an electrophilic aromatic substitution reaction, the aromatic sextet of the benzene ring acts as an electron source, contributing a pair of pi electrons to the electrophile to form the arenium ion intermediate.

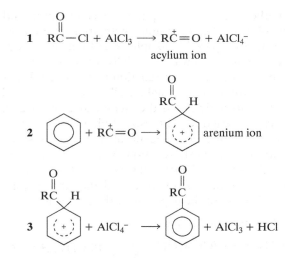

Figure 1 Mechanism of the Friedel–Crafts acylation of benzene

Aluminum chloride complex with acyl compound

When the acyl group is acetyl (CH_3CO), acetic anhydride is often used as the acylating agent rather than acetyl chloride. The anhydride is safer to work with, and it usually provides better yields and a simpler workup. More catalyst is needed with acetic anhydride, however, because some of the aluminum chloride forms complexes with the acetic acid produced during the reaction, making it ineffective as a catalyst. As a rule, 2–3 moles of $AlCl_3$ are used per mole of acetic anhydride.

In this experiment, you will use acetic anhydride as the acylating agent and dichloromethane as the reaction solvent. The reaction is highly exothermic, so it will be carried out by adding acetic anhydride slowly to the other reactants, and then heating under reflux to complete the reaction. Pouring the product into ice water will decompose the aluminum chloride complex of the product and transfer inorganic salts to the aqueous phase. The dichloromethane is removed by distillation, and the product is then purified by distillation from the same apparatus. The infrared spectrum of the product can be obtained by one of the methods described in OP-39.

In principle, acylation of a monosubstituted benzene can yield any or all of three different disubstituted products. From the melting point and IR spectrum of your product, you should be able to determine whether it is predominantly a single compound or a mixture of isomers and, if it is a single compound, to establish its identity. Disubstituted benzenes can be distinguished by the location of their out-of-plane C — H bending bands, which occur at frequencies (expressed in wave numbers) below 850 cm^{-1}. The frequency of such a band decreases with the number of adjacent hydrogens on the ring, as shown in Table 1. Thus, a *para*-disubstituted benzene, with its two sets of two adjacent hydrogens, should have an absorption band in the 840−810 cm^{-1} region; *meta* compounds, with three adjacent ring hydrogens, absorb in the 810−750 cm^{-1} region; and *ortho* compounds, with four adjacent ring hydrogens, absorb in the 770−735 cm^{-1} region. Absorption by the isolated hydrogen of a *meta* compound is usually very weak, and its frequency may vary. Monosubstituted and *meta*-disubstituted

Table 1 Frequencies of C — H out-of-plane bending bands in aromatic hydrocarbons

No. of adjacent hydrogens	Frequency range, cm^{-1}
1	900–860 (weak)
2	840–810
3	810–750
4	770–735
5	770–730

benzenes have an additional band in the $710-680$ cm^{-1} region, which arises from a vibration that involves the entire benzene ring.

Possible products from the Friedel–Crafts acylation of anisole

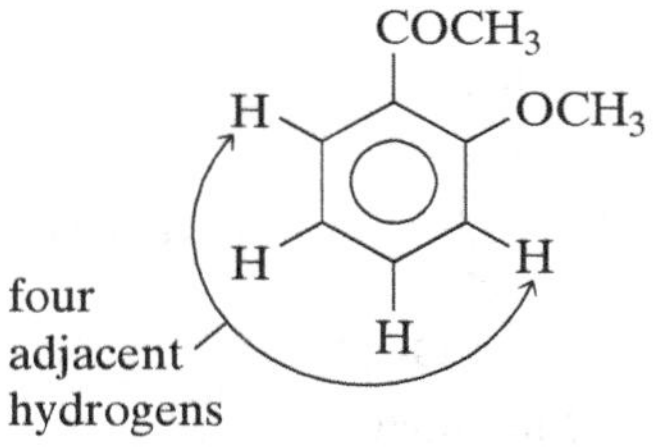

four
adjacent
hydrogens

2′-methoxyacetophenone

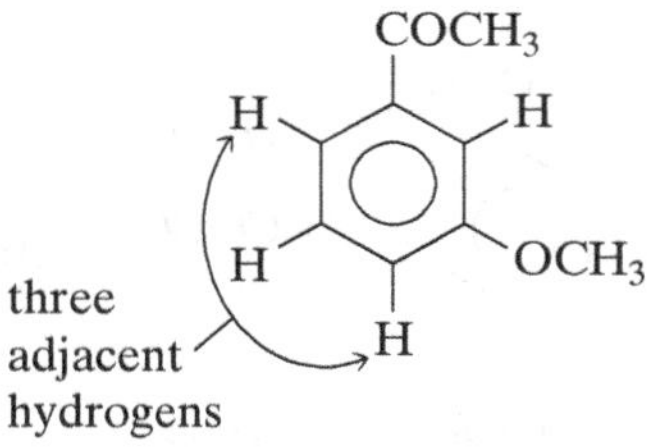

three
adjacent
hydrogens

3′-methoxyacetophenone

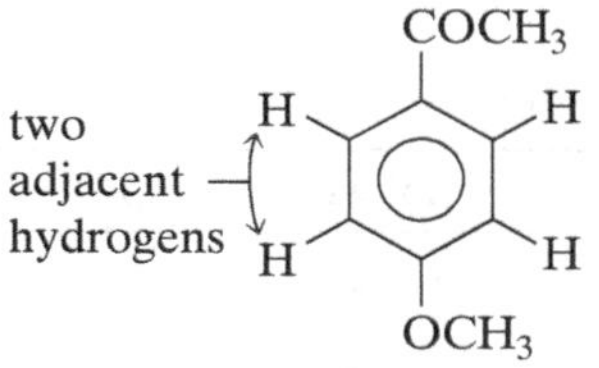

two
adjacent
hydrogens

4′-methoxyacetophenone

Your product will be an ether as well as a ketone, so its IR spectrum will contain bands characteristic of both functional groups. The carbonyl band of a phenone usually appears in the $1685-1665$ cm^{-1} region, and a weak carbonyl overtone band may be observed at twice the frequency of the fundamental band. Aryl alkyl ethers display an asymmetrical C—O—C stretching band at $1275-1200$ cm^{-1} and a symmetrical C—O—C band near $1075-1020$ cm^{-1}. These ether bands can be seen in the spectrum of anisole in Figure 2.

Most Friedel–Crafts syntheses aren't very green, because they require organic solvents and comparatively hazardous reagents and catalysts. Although this synthesis uses acetic anhydride rather than the more environmentally unfriendly acetyl chloride, the trade-off is the need for more catalyst. Because most Lewis acid catalysts are water sensitive, they aren't usually recovered and instead end up as a source of waste. Lanthanide trifluoromethanesulfonates are effective Lewis acid catalysts that aren't water sensitive and can therefore be recycled, but they are much more expensive than aluminum chloride and similar Lewis acids. More benign catalysts—such as phosphoric acid—have been used, but most of them give poor yields except with highly reactive aromatic compounds such as ferrocene. So the path to truly green syntheses is often a rocky one, and it may involve trade-offs that limit their applicability.

In water, acetic anhydride is converted to acetic acid, which readily breaks down into carbon dioxide and water in the environment. Aluminum chloride is toxic to aquatic life; it hydrolyzes to aluminum hydroxide and

For example, pure ytterbium(III) trifluoromethanesulfonate cost about $5 a gram in 2008.

hydrochloric acid in water. The EPA classifies dichloromethane as a priority pollutant and has established an MCL of 5 ppb for its concentration in drinking water.

Reactions and Properties

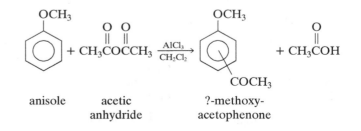

anisole   acetic   ?-methoxy-
        anhydride   acetophenone

Table 2 Physical properties

	mol wt	mp	bp	d
anisole	108.2	−38	155	0.996
acetic anhydride	102.1	−73	140	1.082
aluminum chloride	133.3	193	subl	
dichloromethane	84.9	−95	40	1.327
2′-methoxyacetophenone	150.2		245	1.090
3′-methoxyacetophenone	150.2		240	1.034
4′-methoxyacetophenone	150.2	39	258	1.082^{41}

Note: mp and bp are in °C; density is in g/mL; subl = sublimes.

Anisole

1600.9	1247.3	784.1
1497.9	1172.6	754.4
1303.0	1040.5	692.0

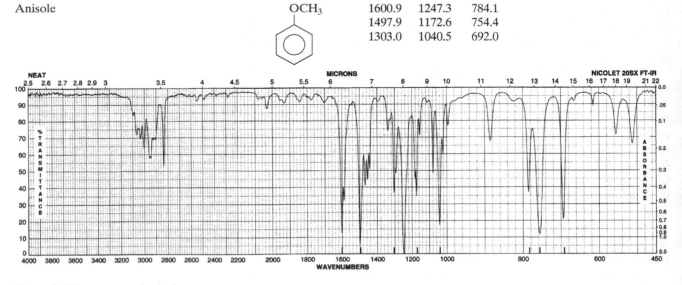

Figure 2 IR spectrum of anisole

DIRECTIONS

> **Aluminum chloride reacts with atmospheric moisture and violently with water, generating HCl vapors. It can cause painful burns on moist skin and eyes, and inhaling the dust or vapors can damage the respiratory tract. Weigh it under a hood, wear gloves and safety goggles, avoid contact, do not inhale dust or vapors, and keep it away from water.**
>
> **Acetic anhydride can cause severe damage to skin and eyes, its vapors are very harmful if inhaled, and it reacts violently with water. Use gloves and a hood; avoid contact with the liquid, do not breathe its vapors, and keep it away from water.**
>
> **Dichloromethane may be harmful if ingested, inhaled, or absorbed through the skin. There is a possibility that prolonged inhalation of dichloromethane may cause cancer. Minimize contact with the liquid and do not breathe its vapors.**

Safety Notes

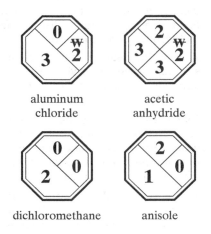

aluminum chloride

acetic anhydride

dichloromethane

anisole

Reaction. *Wear gloves and eye protection! Work under a hood, if possible.* Anhydrous aluminum chloride is deactivated by water, so protect it from atmospheric moisture and be sure that your glassware is thoroughly dried (oven drying is recommended). Assemble an apparatus for addition [OP-11] under reflux using a 25-mL round-bottom flask, and attach a drying tube [OP-12a] containing calcium chloride to the top of the reflux condenser. If you cannot carry out the reaction under a hood, attach a gas trap [OP-14] containing dilute sodium hydroxide to react with any HCl evolved. Clamp the apparatus securely to a ring stand, raising it high enough so that you can remove the boiling flask to add the reactants without disturbing the rest of the apparatus. *Under the hood,* carefully weigh 2.9 g (~22 mmol) of finely powdered anhydrous aluminum chloride into a large, *dry* screw-cap vial (don't let it tip over). Immediately cap the vial and the aluminum chloride container. Weigh 10.0 mmol of anisole and add it, with 10 mL of dichloromethane and a stir bar or boiling chips, to the reaction flask. Have a beaker of cold water ready to cool the mixture if it begins to boil. Cautiously add the aluminum chloride in small portions through a dry powder funnel, stirring or shaking [OP-10] the flask after each addition. If necessary, use a Pasteur pipet to wash any adherent aluminum chloride into the flask with a little dichloromethane. Reassemble the apparatus. *Under the hood,* measure 1.0 mL (~11 mmol) of acetic anhydride into the separatory–addition funnel. Stopper the funnel immediately and put it in place on the reaction apparatus. Add the acetic anhydride slowly (about a drop every 3 seconds), so that the reaction mixture boils gently, while stirring or shaking to mix the reactants. Have a beaker of cold water handy to moderate the reaction if necessary. When the addition is complete, use a hot-water bath or steam bath to heat the reaction mixture under gentle reflux [OP-7], while stirring or occasionally shaking, for 30 minutes.

Separation and Purification. *Wear gloves and eye protection! Under the hood,* pour the warm reaction mixture *slowly,* with vigorous stirring, onto about 10 g of cracked ice in a large beaker. Use a small amount of ice water

Stop and Think: How can HCl be formed during the reaction?

Take Care! Wear gloves and goggles, avoid contact with AlCl$_3$ and dichloromethane, and do not breathe their vapors.

Take Care! Wear gloves, avoid contact with acetic anhydride, do not breathe its vapors, and keep it away from water.

Take Care! Splattering may occur.

Stop and Think: Which is the dichloromethane layer? What does NaOH remove from the dichloromethane solution?

Waste Disposal: Unless your instructor directs otherwise, wash all aqueous layers down the drain.

Take Care! If distillate begins to solidify in the vaccum adapter drip tube, stop the distillation and melt it with a heat gun or other heating device before you proceed.

Waste Disposal: Place the dichloromethane and petroleum ether in designated solvent recovery containers.

to rinse any residue out of the flask and into the beaker. Remove the aqueous layer in a separatory funnel; wash [OP-24] the dichloromethane layer with 5 mL of 3 *M* sodium hydroxide followed by 5 mL of saturated aqueous sodium chloride. Dry [OP-25] the dichloromethane layer with anhydrous sodium sulfate or magnesium sulfate.

Assemble a compact apparatus for simple distillation [OP-30], cooling the receiving flask in an ice/water bath. Transfer the dry dichloromethane solution to the flask and, heating gently with a hot-water bath or steam bath, remove the dichloromethane by distillation (it should distill around 40°C). Then remove the cooling bath and use a heating mantle or other heat source to distill the product, collecting everything that distills above a temperature of 240°C. If the distillate solidifies in the receiver, melt it with a beaker of hot water. While it is still liquid, transfer the distillate to a watch glass or evaporating dish, and set it aside to crystallize. Wash the product [OP-26a] (preferably on a Hirsch funnel [OP-16]) with a small amount of cold, low-boiling petroleum ether and dry it [OP-26b].

Analysis. Weigh the dry product and measure its melting point [OP-33]. Record its IR spectrum [OP-39] or obtain a spectrum from your instructor. Interpret the spectrum as completely as you can and turn it in with your report.

Exercises

1. If your product was a single compound, explain why it was that compound rather than another isomer.
2. Write a mechanism for the Friedel–Crafts reaction of anisole with acetic anhydride.
3. Describe and explain the possible effect on your results of the following experimental errors or variations. (a) You used only 10 mmol of aluminum chloride for the reaction. (b) You used acetic acid as the acylating agent. (c) You used acetophenone as the substrate.
4. (a) Calculate the atom economy and reaction efficiency of your synthesis. (b) Describe some green features of your synthesis, and any that aren't so green.
5. (a) Write an equation for the reaction of aluminum chloride with a large excess of water. (b) Write equations for one or more reactions that would account for the production of HCl during the acylation reaction.
6. Following the format in the "Planning an Experiment" appendix, construct a flow diagram for this experiment.
7. Explain why Friedel–Crafts reactions are usually carried out by adding the alkylating or acylating agent *to* the aromatic compound rather than vice versa.
8. 2,5-Dichloro-2,5-dimethylhexane is an important starting material for the aroma chemicals called tetralin musks. Outline a synthesis of the tetralin musk versalide from this starting material and benzene, using any necessary inorganic or organic reagents.

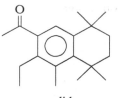

versalide

Other Things You Can Do

(Starred items require your instructor's permission.)

*1. Record the ^{1}H NMR spectrum of the product in deuterochloroform. Interpret it as completely as you can, assigning the signals from protons on the ring as well as those from protons on the side chains.

*2. Carry out some Friedel–Crafts reactions that yield colored products as described in the "Preparation of Carbocations by the Friedel–Crafts Reaction" minilab.

 3. Starting with sources listed in the Bibliography, write a research paper about the Friedel–Crafts reaction, including specific examples and industrial applications.

Determination of the Structure of a Natural Product in Anise Oil

Reactions of Alkenylbenzenes. Preparation of Carboxylic Acids. Side-Chain Oxidation. Structure Determination. Infrared Spectrometry.

Operations

OP-7   Heating
OP-10 Mixing
OP-16 Vacuum Filtration
OP-26 Washing and Drying Solids
OP-28 Recrystallization
OP-33 Melting Point
OP-39 Infrared Spectrometry

Before You Begin

Read the experiment, read or review the operations as necessary, and write an experimental plan.

Scenario

Basil Wormwood, the new-age herbalist with a chemistry degree, has a puzzle for you. He obtained some Chinese star anise from an oriental-foods wholesaler, steam distilled its essential oil, and isolated the major component of the oil. Not knowing its identity, he tentatively named this compound "anisene." He sent it off to a chemical analyst for elemental analysis, and from the results found its molecular formula to be $C_{10}H_{12}O$. He also carried out some experiments (described next) showing that the compound contains a methoxyl group and a three-carbon side chain on a benzene ring, but he doesn't know the identity of the side chain or where it is located with respect to the methoxyl group. He has just shipped a sample of the compound to your supervisor, hoping that your institute's consulting chemists can solve this structure puzzle. Your supervisor thinks that the position of the side chain can be determined by oxidizing it to a COOH group, and that its structure can be determined by infrared (IR) analysis. Your assignment is to determine the complete structure of anisene.

Applying Scientific Methodology

You will have to carry out some experimental work before you can propose a hypothesis about the structure of anisene.

From *Operational Organic Chemistry: A Problem Solving Approach to the Laboratory*, Fourth Edition, John W. Lehman. Copyright © 2009 by Pearson Education. Published by Prentice Hall. All rights reserved.

The Structure Puzzle—Taking Molecules Apart and Putting Them Back Together

Star anise seed clusters

Key Concept: *Chemists determine the structures of organic molecules by breaking them down into smaller fragments and identifying the fragments, probing them with different kinds of electromagnetic radiation and interpreting the resulting signals, or both.*

Chinese star anise (*Illicium verum*) is a small evergreen tree of the magnolia family. When its dried, star-shaped seed clusters are ground up and steam distilled, they yield an oily liquid with a strong odor of licorice. Anise oil (from star anise and other spices) or its synthetic equivalent is widely used as a flavoring for licorice, cough drops, chewing gum, and liqueurs such as ouzo and anisette. In this experiment, you will use both classical and modern methods of structural analysis to determine the complete structure of its major component, which we will call "anisene" (not its real name).

Today, when a chemist can run an NMR spectrum or a mass spectrum of an organic compound and often determine its structure in a matter of minutes, it is hard to imagine how much time and effort were once required to determine the structures of even the simpler natural products. In a classical structure determination, the molecular formula of a compound is first obtained by elemental analysis and molecular-weight measurement. Then the compound is degraded (broken down) into smaller structural units that are isolated and, if possible, identified. Finding how the smaller units fit together to form the original molecule is an intellectual challenge that might be compared to putting together a jigsaw puzzle with some pieces missing, others that don't belong, and still others that have been chewed up by the family dog and are no longer recognizable. Finally, when enough information has been gathered to suggest a possible structure, that structure must usually be proven by an independent synthesis in which the compound is built up again, from known compounds, by reactions whose outcomes can be reliably predicted.

In many cases, classical structure determinations involved the efforts of dozens or even hundreds of chemists over many decades, and included the generation of much irrelevant or misleading information and many synthetic dead ends. The advent of modern spectrometric methods has simplified the process enormously by providing detailed structural information that wasn't readily available to the chemists of earlier times.

Understanding the Experiment

In this experiment, you will attempt to determine the structure of the major component of star anise oil, which has the molecular formula $C_{10}H_{12}O$. Most open-chain saturated organic compounds (except those containing nitrogen, phosphorus, or halogen atoms) have $2n + 2$ hydrogen atoms for every n carbon atoms. If anisene were such a compound, it would have $2(10) + 2 = 22$ hydrogen atoms, but since it has only 12, it is said to be "deficient" by 10 hydrogens. Every ring or pi bond in a molecule represents a deficit of two hydrogens. That is, an open-chain compound must lose two hydrogen atoms to form a ring, and a saturated compound must lose two hydrogens to form a pi bond (or a pi-bond equivalent in the Kekulé structure of an aromatic ring). Thus, its deficiency of 10 hydrogens indicates that there must be a total of five rings and pi bonds (or pi-bond equivalents) in an anisene molecule; this is called its *index of hydrogen deficiency* (IHD).

The IHD of a compound that has n carbon atoms and x hydrogen atoms can be calculated using the following formula:

$$\text{IHD} = \frac{(2n + 2) - x}{2}$$

Catalytic hydrogenation of anisene under high pressure yields a saturated compound with the formula $C_{10}H_{20}O$. The gain of eight hydrogens indicates that anisene has four pi bonds, so it must contain only one ring. A high carbon/hydrogen ratio often indicates an aromatic structure, and we can account for the ring and three pi bonds by assuming that anisene contains a benzene ring.

Heating anisene with hydriodic acid yields a phenol with the molecular formula C_9H_9OH and a volatile compound identified as methyl iodide. This reaction is used to test for certain ether functions. Methyl ethers yield methyl iodide, and the formation of a phenol indicates that anisene is an aryl methyl ether, whose formula we write as $C_9H_9OCH_3$ in the following equation for the reaction:

$$C_9H_9OCH_3 + HI \longrightarrow C_9H_9OH + CH_3I$$

At this point, we know that anisene contains a methoxyl ($-OCH_3$) group and a benzene ring, which accounts for seven carbon atoms and three pi bonds. That leaves three more carbons and one pi bond to be accounted for. This remaining fragment could be a three-carbon unsaturated side chain, whose formula can be determined by subtracting the fragments already identified from the molecular formula of anisene:

molecular formula	$C_{10}H_{12}O$
disubstituted benzene ring	$-C_6H_4$
methoxyl group	$-CH_3O$
side chain	C_3H_5

Now we can write a partial structure for anisene, shown in the margin. All that remains is to determine the structure of the unsaturated side chain and its location on the benzene ring.

Potassium permanganate is capable of oxidizing most aliphatic side chains all the way down to the benzylic carbon atom, leaving a COOH group where the side chain was originally located. Oxidizing anisene should yield one of three possible methoxybenzoic acids, whose melting points are given in Table 3. By identifying the oxidation product as one of these three, you will establish the position of anisene's side chain.

Although aqueous potassium permanganate is a powerful oxidizing agent, it reacts slowly with water-insoluble organic compounds because $KMnO_4$ is essentially insoluble in the organic phase. In 1974, Herriot and Picker added a quaternary ammonium salt to a stirred heterogeneous mixture of aqueous $KMnO_4$ and benzene, which caused permanganate ions to dissolve in the organic layer and form "purple benzene." The quaternary salt acted as a phase-transfer catalyst, escorting the permanganate ions across the phase boundary into the organic phase. When an oxidizable organic compound is dissolved in purple benzene, it reacts much more rapidly and under milder conditions than it would with aqueous $KMnO_4$.

Benzene is toxic and can cause leukemia in humans, so you will use a simplified procedure in which anisene and a phase-transfer catalyst

Another possibility, that anisene has two side chains, is explored in Exercise 3.

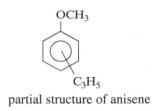
partial structure of anisene

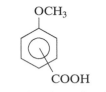
a methoxybenzoic acid

(tricaprylmethylammonium chloride) are combined directly with aqueous potassium permanganate. Thus, anisene itself will be the organic phase of the two-phase system, and no organic solvent is needed. Because you require only enough product for a melting point, you will start with only a few drops of anisene. An excess of potassium permanganate is used because some of it may decompose during the reaction. As the reaction proceeds, permanganate ion is reduced to manganese dioxide, which forms a fine brown precipitate that is difficult to filter and wash. Fortunately, this precipitate can be dissolved during the workup by acidifying the solution and adding sodium bisulfite, which reduces manganese dioxide (and any unreacted permanganate ion) to soluble manganese(II) sulfate.

Removal of manganese dioxide

$$MnO_2 + NaHSO_3 + H^+ \longrightarrow MnSO_4 + H_2O + Na^+$$

The methoxybenzoic acid can then be separated by vacuum filtration and purified by recrystallization from water.

Carbon–carbon double bonds give rise to characteristic $=C-H$ out-of-plane bending bands in the $1000-650$ cm^{-1} region of an IR spectrum. The wave numbers of these bands can reveal the number and location of substituents on the carbon–carbon double bond, as shown in Table 1. There are four possible structures for an unsaturated C_3H_5 side chain, corresponding to the four structure types in the table. From the wave number(s) of anisene's $=C-H$ bending band(s), you should be able to deduce the structure of the side chain. But first you must locate the right absorption bands, which is more easily said than done, because aromatic $C-H$ bonds give rise to strong bands in the same region (as shown in Table 2).

The carbon atom of a vinylic $C-H$ bond is doubly bonded to an adjacent carbon.

Table 1 Out-of-plane bending vibrations of vinylic $C-H$ bonds

Structure type	Frequency range, cm^{-1}
RCH=CH$_2$	995–985 and 915–905
RCH=CHR (*cis*)	730–665
RCH=CHR (*trans*)	980–960
R$_2$C=CH$_2$	895–885

Note: R = alkyl or aryl.

Table 2 Out-of-plane bending vibrations of aromatic $C-H$ bonds

Ring substitution	Frequency range, cm^{-1}
ortho	770–735
meta	810–750 and 710–690
para	840–810

Once you learn the position of the side chain on anisene's benzene ring, you should be able to locate any bands due to aromatic $C-H$ bonds in its infrared spectrum, which will help you pick out one or more vinylic $C-H$ bands from the remaining strong bands in the $1000-650$ cm^{-1} region.

This is a relatively green experiment in that no organic solvents are used for the synthesis. Potassium permanganate and manganese dioxide are harmful to aquatic life, but the by-product MnO_2 and any excess $KMnO_4$ are converted to manganese(II) sulfate, which isn't known to be a serious environmental contaminant.

Reactions and Properties

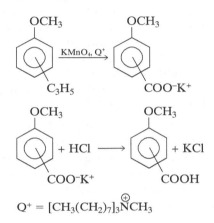

$$Q^+ = [CH_3(CH_2)_7]_3\overset{\oplus}{N}CH_3$$

Table 3 Physical properties

	mol wt	mp	bp	d
potassium permanganate	158.0			
2-methoxybenzoic acid	152.2	101		
3-methoxybenzoic acid	152.2	110		
4-methoxybenzoic acid	152.2	185		
toluene	92.2	−95	111	0.867

Note: mp and bp are in °C; density is in g/mL.

DIRECTIONS

Potassium permanganate can react violently with oxidizable materials; keep it away from other chemicals and combustibles.
Sodium bisulfite produces harmful vapors when it reacts with acids; do not inhale the vapors.

Safety Notes

potassium
permanganate

Take Care! Keep $KMnO_4$ away from oxidizable materials.

Reaction. Obtain some anisene (or anise oil) from your instructor, or isolate anise oil from anise seeds as described in "Other Things You Can Do." Add 0.50 g of crystalline potassium permanganate and 2 drops of tricaprylmethylammonium chloride (Aliquat 336) to 10 mL of water in a 25-mL Erlenmeyer flask, and then drop in a stir bar. Heat [OP-7] the mixture in a boiling-water bath, while stirring [OP-10], for 5 minutes or more to dissolve most of the $KMnO_4$. Add 5 drops of anisene or anise oil using a medicine dropper (not a Pasteur pipet), place a watch glass (convex side down) over the mouth of the flask to prevent evaporation, and heat the mixture in a boiling-water bath—with vigorous magnetic stirring—for 15 minutes or more. (Alternatively, the flask can be swirled and shaken vigorously over a steam bath for 15 minutes.)

Separation. Cool the reaction mixture to room temperature and transfer it to a small beaker. *Under the hood,* add 1 mL of 6 *M* hydrochloric acid and test the solution with blue litmus paper; if it isn't acidic, add more HCl until it is. Add just enough solid sodium bisulfite, in small portions, while stirring or swirling, to reduce any excess permanganate and remove the brown manganese dioxide (0.5–1.0 g of $NaHSO_3$ should be sufficient). Test the solution with pH paper after each bisulfite addition; add 6 *M* HCl as needed to keep it acidic. When all of the brown precipitate has disappeared and only a white precipitate remains, again test the solution with pH paper. If the pH is higher than 2, add enough 6 *M* HCl to reduce it to 2. Collect the product from the reaction mixture by vacuum filtration [OP-16] and wash it on the filter [OP-26a] with ice-cold water.

Purification and Analysis. Recrystallize [OP-28] the product from boiling water and dry [OP-26b] it to constant mass. Measure the melting point [OP-33] of the methoxybenzoic acid. Record the IR spectrum [OP-39] of anisene (*not* of the methoxybenzoic acid) or obtain its spectrum from your instructor. Deduce the location and structure of the side chain, and draw the structure of anisene. Turn in the IR spectrum with your report.

Take Care! Do not breathe the vapors that may be produced.

Stop and Think: What vapors may form, and how are they produced? What are the brown and white precipitates?

Waste Disposal: Place the filtrate in a designated waste container.

Exercises

1. Derive a systematic name for anisene and find its common name in *The Merck Index* or another reference book.

2. (a) Write a balanced equation for the reaction of anisene with potassium permanganate, assuming that the products include manganese dioxide and the potassium salt of acetic acid. (*Note:* The reaction mixture is alkaline.) (b) Assuming that 5 drops of anisene is about 1.0 mmol, calculate the mass of potassium permanganate required to oxidize that much anisene and the percentage in excess that was actually used.

3. (a) The three carbon atoms of anisene's side chain might have formed two separate side chains rather than one. Give the structures of these side chains. (b) Give the structures of all of the dicarboxylic acids that could have resulted from complete side-chain oxidation of anisene had it contained these two side chains.

4. (a) Using a balanced equation for the oxidation reaction (see Exercise 2a), calculate the atom economy and reaction efficiency of your synthesis. (b) Describe some green features of your synthesis, and any that aren't so green.

5. Describe and explain the possible effect on your results of the following experimental errors or variations. (a) You forgot to add the tricapryl-methylammonium chloride. (b) The pH of the reaction mixture was 7 when you filtered it, and you obtained a brown solid. (c) You recorded the IR spectrum of the oxidation product rather than that of anisene itself.

6. Describe the probable role of the phase-transfer catalyst in this reaction, giving equations for the relevant reactions.

7. Following the format in the "Planning an Experiment" appendix, construct a flow diagram for the synthesis of your methoxybenzoic acid.

8. (a) Draw the structure of the compound $C_{10}H_{20}O$ that is obtained by the catalytic hydrogenation of anisene. (b) Draw the structure of the compound C_9H_9OH that is obtained when anisene is treated with hydriodic acid.

9. You could confirm the structure of anisene by synthesizing it from known starting materials. Outline a synthesis of anisene from benzene and alcohols that have four carbon atoms or fewer.

10. The structure in the margin has been proposed for coniferyl alcohol, which can be obtained by the hydrolysis of coniferin, a natural product found in the sap of conifer trees. Assuming that the structure of coniferyl alcohol hadn't been reported in the literature, describe how you would go about proving its structure. Indicate what chemical tests and degradations might be carried out, and describe the expected results and conclusions. Summarize the information that could be derived from infrared analysis. Then show how the alcohol could be synthesized from readily available starting materials.

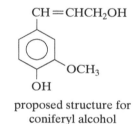

proposed structure for coniferyl alcohol

Other Things You Can Do

(Starred items require your instructor's permission.)

*1. Isolate anise oil from anise seeds (or star anise) as follows. Weigh out 10 g of fresh anise seeds and grind them finely, using a spice grinder or a mortar and pestle. Isolate the anise oil by steam distillation and extraction of the distillate with dichloromethane, following the procedure for clove oil given in the "Isolation and Identification of the Major Constituent of Clove Oil" experiment (but omitting the extraction of the dichloromethane layer with NaOH). Dry the dichloromethane solution and evaporate the solvent completely. You can obtain a gas chromatogram of the oil and estimate the percentage of anisene it contains.

*2. Use air as an oxidizing agent to convert fluorene to fluorenone as described in the "Air Oxidation of Fluorene to 9-Fluorenone" minilab.

3. Starting with sources listed in the Bibliography, write a research paper on the use of chemical methods for structure determination of natural products. Illustrate it with examples of actual structure determinations.

Identification of an Oxygen-Containing Organic Compound

EXPERIMENT

Reactions of Aldehydes and Ketones. Reactions of Alcohols. Infrared Spectrometry. Qualitative Analysis.

Operations

OP-26 Washing and Drying Solids
OP-28 Recrystallization
OP-30 Simple Distillation
OP-33 Melting Point
OP-34 Boiling Point
OP-39 Infrared Spectrometry
OP-40 Nuclear Magnetic Resonance Spectrometry (optional)

Before You Begin

1. Read the experiment, read or review the operations as necessary, and write an experimental plan.
2. Read, "Qualitative Organic Analysis," except for the "Directions" sections.

Scenario

Dr. Keziah Armitage, professor of medieval metaphysics at Miskatonic University in Arkham, Massachusetts, was exploring an abandoned and nearly forgotten room in the basement of the metaphysics building when she came across a grime-encrusted bottle containing an unknown liquid. Its label had long since decomposed to dust, but the liquid in the bottle was clear and colorless. Curious about its origin, she sent the bottle and its contents to your institute for analysis. She thinks it might be a potion used in unmentionable rites practiced by her ancestor, Keziah Mason, a witch whose trial scandalized Arkham in 1692. Your supervisor thinks it is more likely to be an alcohol or carbonyl compound misplaced by an absent-minded alchemy professor and then forgotten. Your assignment is to find out what family the mysterious liquid belongs to and then identify it.

You can find a description of Arkham in the Dictionary of Imaginary Places *(Harcourt, 2000).*

Applying Scientific Methodology

As you carry out the experiment, you should propose provisional hypotheses about the nature and identity of your unknown. You will test—and perhaps reject or revise—your hypotheses as you gather additional experimental evidence. Your conclusion should, if possible, be consistent with all of the experimental evidence you obtain. If any evidence is not consistent with your conclusion, you should attempt to explain why.

From *Operational Organic Chemistry: A Problem Solving Approach to the Laboratory*, Fourth Edition, John W. Lehman. Copyright © 2009 by Pearson Education. Published by Prentice Hall. All rights reserved.

The Chemist as Detective

Qualitative organic analysis, the process of identifying unknown organic compounds, can be compared to the approach used by a detective in identifying the perpetrator of a crime. The detective first looks for clues that help to characterize the criminal and indicate the most productive areas of investigation. Once a list of possible suspects has been assembled, the detective can evaluate the evidence already acquired and gather additional evidence to help narrow the list of suspects, focusing the investigation on the most likely suspects. Finally, the detective must evaluate all of the evidence, come to a conclusion regarding the identity of the perpetrator, and organize the facts of the case in such a way as to convince a jury that the accused is, in fact, guilty of the crime.

In carrying out the identification of an organic compound, you, like the detective, should be constantly on the lookout for clues to its identity. Chemical and spectral data should allow you to confine your search to a particular chemical family. Additional physical and chemical evidence will help you narrow down the list of "suspects" and focus your attention on a few of the most probable compounds. Finally, the preparation of one or more derivatives should lead you to a definite conclusion. In your report, you should present your evidence in such a way as to convince the "jury" (your instructor) that it justifies your conclusion.

As with any other problem, you must first ask yourself the right questions before you can arrive at the correct solution. Some important questions to be answered regarding an unknown compound are as follows: (1) What are its physical properties? (2) What functional group(s) does it contain? (3) What other significant structural features does it have? Each bit of evidence you obtain should, if interpreted correctly, help reveal the answer to one or more of these questions. All of them combined should provide you with an answer to the ultimate question, "What is it?"

A detective trying to solve a case will almost invariably come upon clues that lead nowhere or, even worse, to false conclusions. The same is true in chemical problem solving, so it is important to keep an open mind throughout your investigation and to avoid jumping to conclusions before all the evidence is in. You may formulate tentative assumptions based on your initial observations (for example, "It turns chromic acid reagent green, so it may be an alcohol"), but you should be ready to revise or discard such assumptions if they aren't supported by subsequent observations (for example, "Its IR spectrum has a $C=O$ stretching band but no $O-H$ band, so it may be an aldehyde instead").

Chemical and physical evidence can be misleading for a variety of reasons:

- Some compounds of a given family may undergo an atypical reaction with a given reagent and yield either a false positive or a false negative result.
- Some reagents give positive tests with more than one functional group.
- Impurities may complicate or invalidate a test.
- Spectral bands may occur outside the expected frequency ranges or may be incorrectly assigned.

Because of these and other possible sources of error, it is best not to rely on a single piece of evidence in formulating a conclusion. For example, the classification of an unknown as a secondary alcohol can be convincingly

Key Concept: Identifying an unknown organic compound involves matching the physical and chemical properties of the unknown with those of some known compound.

340

established by a positive chromic acid test, a slow reaction with Lucas' reagent, *and* an infrared (IR) band in the 1100 cm^{-1} region, but not by any one of these alone.

Understanding the Experiment

This section provides a general discussion of most of the procedures you will follow to identify your unknown. See the appropriate sections of "Qualitative Organic Analysis" for more detailed information about the interpretation of test results. For information about the interpretation of spectra, see the corresponding operations.

Throughout this experiment, you should have your lab notebook handy to record the data you collect and all of your observations as you make them. Keeping meticulous records can often mean the difference between the successful identification of a compound and a failure that could prove very costly, insofar as it affects your lab grade.

Because an unknown liquid may be impure, it should be purified by distillation before any chemical tests or spectra are run. The median distillation temperature should also give you a good estimate of its boiling point. Solids can be purified by recrystallization, but unless your instructor indicates otherwise, you can assume that an unknown solid is pure enough to use without purification. It is very important to measure the boiling point or melting point of your unknown as accurately as you can, because your list of possibilities will be based on the value you obtain. If your measured boiling point or melting point is inaccurate, your list of possibilities may not even contain the name of your unknown compound, and identifying it correctly may then be impossible.

A preliminary examination of your unknown may provide some clues that will help you identify it. For example, observing that a compound is a liquid at room temperature eliminates most compounds with reported melting points of 30°C or higher. The ignition behavior of a substance can provide clues about its structure; many oxygen-containing compounds burn with a blue flame, but those with a high molecular weight may exhibit a clean yellow flame, and those with aromatic rings a sooty yellow flame. The solubility behavior of your unknown compound in water can also tell you something about its structure. Most alcohols and carbonyl compounds containing up to four carbon atoms are soluble, and most with six carbons or more are relatively insoluble.

To find out what family your compound belongs to, you will carry out several classification tests and record its IR spectrum. To find procedures for the classification tests and directions for their interpretation, see "Classification Tests" in "Qualitative Organic Analysis". The tests you will include the following:

- The 2,4-dinitrophenylhydrazine (DNPH) test, which is positive for both aldehydes and ketones
- The chromic acid test, which is positive for 1° and 2° alcohols and for aldehydes, but which gives a faster reaction with alcohols
- Tollens' test, which is positive only for aldehydes

IR bands that you should look for include a strong, broad O—H stretching band near 3300 cm^{-1}, a strong carbonyl (C=O) stretching band near 1700 cm^{-1}, and one or two weak-to-moderate bands in the 2700–2850 cm^{-1} region, which arise from C—H stretching vibrations involving the carbonyl carbon of an aldehyde.

*A **Greener Way**: In place of chromic acid, ceric ammonium nitrate can be used to test for alcohols and Schiff's reagent to test for aldehydes. Your instructor may provide directions for conducting such tests.*

Additional structural information can be obtained both from chemical tests and from your infrared spectrum. The iodoform test is positive for methyl carbinols (alcohols having a CH_3 group on the carbon that holds the OH) and methyl ketones. The bromine test can show whether your compound contains any carbon–carbon double or triple bonds. And Lucas' test can tell you whether an alcohol is primary, secondary, or tertiary, *if* the alcohol's boiling point is below 150°C (the test is invalid for most alcohols with higher boiling points). The IR spectrum of an alcohol may also help you decide what kind of alcohol it is. The C—O bands of most open-chain primary, secondary, and tertiary alcohols occur near 1050 cm^{-1}, 1110 cm^{-1}, and 1175 cm^{-1}, respectively. The wave number of the C—O band is about 25–50 cm^{-1} lower (to the right) for cyclic alcohols and alcohols that have aromatic rings or C=C groups on the carbinol carbon. Other structural features that can be detected from IR spectra include aromatic rings and carbon–carbon double or triple bonds. (See OP-39 for more detailed information on the interpretation of IR spectra.)

NMR spectra can provide a great deal of information about the structure of a molecule. If your instructor allows you to obtain an ^{1}H or ^{13}C NMR spectrum of your unknown, see OP-40 or your textbook for information about NMR spectral interpretation.

After you carry out the classification tests and interpret your spectra, you should be ready to prepare a short list of possible compounds. Keep in mind, however, that classification tests and spectral interpretations are subject to error, so later you may want to reconsider some of the compounds you eliminated to arrive at your list. To decide which of the compounds on your list is the correct one, you will need to prepare a derivative. A derivative preparation is a small-scale chemical synthesis in which the unknown compound is converted to a different compound, a solid whose melting point may indicate the identity of the unknown. As for any synthesis, the formation of by-products, incomplete purification, and insufficient drying can lower the melting point of the product. This makes it important to follow the directions carefully and to be certain that the product is completely dry before you measure its melting point. It is also important to select the right derivative. Depending on the reagents available, you can prepare a *p*-nitrobenzoate, 3,5-dinitrobenzoate, α-naphthylurethane, or phenylurethane if you have an alcohol; and a 2,4-dinitrophenylhydrazone, semicarbazone, or oxime if you have an aldehyde or ketone. But a derivative may be unsuitable because its melting point is too low or is not listed for some of the compounds on your list. Derivatives with melting points of 60° or below are often hard to purify, because they tend to melt to an oil in the hot recrystallization solvent. You should also avoid derivatives whose melting points (for the compounds on your list) are too close together. For example, the semicarbazones of 3-methyl-2-butanone and 2-pentanone melt at 113°C and 112°C, whereas their 2,4-dinitrophenylhydrazones melt at 124°C and 143°C, making the second derivative a better choice for distinguishing between these ketones. If you have difficulty preparing a certain derivative, or if the derivative you prepare doesn't eliminate all of the possibilities but one, you should prepare a second derivative.

When you think you have gathered enough evidence to identify your unknown with some certainty, you are free to write down your conclusion. Keep in mind that your evidence should be sufficient to convince your instructor—and yourself—that it justifies your conclusion. Thus, you should go back over the evidence and make sure that it all points to the same conclusion. If some evidence isn't consistent with that conclusion—for example, if a chemical test doesn't give the result expected for a compound with the proposed structure—be prepared to either reevaluate your conclusion or explain the inconsistency.

The chromium(VI) in chromic acid reagent is classified as a priority pollutant and is very toxic to aquatic life. Hydrazines (such as 2,4-dinitrophenylhydrazine) and silver nitrate (from Tollens' reagent) are also toxic to aquatic organisms. Some of the unknowns may also be harmful to the environment, so take care to prevent the release of your unknown, the test reagents, or the derivative preparation reagents into the environment.

Reactions and Properties

General equations for classification test reactions are given in the "Classification Tests" section of "Qualitative Organic Analysis." General equations for derivative preparations are given in the "Preparation of Derivatives" section of "Qualitative Organic Analysis." The properties of the different classes of compounds and their derivatives are given in the "Properties of Organic Compounds" appendix.

DIRECTIONS

You should consider your unknown compound to be flammable and harmful by inhalation, ingestion, and skin absorption. Minimize your contact with the unknown and do not breathe its vapors.
Safety information for chemicals used in classification tests and derivative preparations is included with the corresponding procedures in Part IV.

Safety Notes

Preliminary Work. Obtain a numbered vial containing your unknown compound from your instructor and record its identification number in your laboratory notebook. If the unknown is a liquid, purify it by simple distillation [OP-30]; record its distillation boiling range and median boiling temperature. Then measure the boiling point [OP-34] of the pure liquid using a capillary-tube method. If it is a solid, measure its melting point [OP-33]. Describe the physical state, general appearance, and any other notable characteristics of the purified compound in your lab notebook. Carry out an ignition test (see "Ignition Test" in "Qualitative Organic Analysis"), and test the solubility of the unknown in water (see "Solubility Tests" in "Qualitative Organic Analysis").

Take Care! Minimize contact with the unknown and do not breathe its vapors.

Functional-Class Determination. Test the unknown with 2,4-dinitrophenylhydrazine reagent (DNPH, classification test C-11), chromic acid reagent (C-9), and Tollens' reagent (C-23), or carry out other classification tests suggested by your instructor. Record the IR spectrum [OP-39] of your unknown. Use it and the results of the classification tests to decide whether your unknown is an alcohol, aldehyde, or ketone.

Waste Disposal: Dispose of all wastes as directed by your instructor.

Detection of Structural Features. In your lab notebook, list all compounds from the appropriate table in the "Properties of Organic Compounds" appendix that have melting or boiling points within ±10°C of your observed value; record their melting or boiling points and the melting points of their derivatives. At your instructor's discretion, show him or her your list; the instructor may approve the list if it includes your unknown or suggest additional work if it doesn't. Write the structure of every compound on your list and consider whether additional classification tests, such as the bromine test (C-7), iodoform test (C-16), or Lucas' test (C-17), will help you eliminate any compounds from the list. Also look for evidence from your observations and your IR spectrum that suggests specific structural features, such as aromatic rings, conjugation with double bonds, or the structural class (1°, 2°, or 3°) of an alcohol. With your instructor's permission, you can obtain and interpret an ^{1}H or ^{13}C NMR spectrum [OP-40] of your unknown as well. At this point, prepare a short list of compounds by eliminating the least likely possibilities.

Waste Disposal: Dispose of all wastes as directed by your instructor. Return any unused unknown to your instructor in its original vial.

Preparation of a Derivative. Using procedure D-1, D-2, D-3, or D-4, (see "Preparation of Derivatives" in "Qualitative Organic Analysis"), prepare a suitable derivative of your unknown. Purify the derivative by recrystallization [OP-28] as described in the appropriate procedure, dry [OP-26b] it thoroughly, and obtain its melting point [OP-33]. Deduce the identity of your unknown from the derivative melting point and all other relevant evidence.

Exercises

1. Interpret the spectrum or spectra you obtained as completely as you can.
2. (a) Write balanced equations for the reactions involved in all of the classification tests for which you obtained a positive result. (b) Write balanced equations for the reaction(s) involved in your derivative preparation(s).
3. Describe and explain the possible effect on your results of the following experimental errors or variations. (a) The test tube you used to carry out a DNPH test had just been rinsed with acetone. (b) The watch glass you used for the ignition test had previously been used to weigh sodium sulfate. (c) You performed Lucas' test on a compound that had a boiling point of 175°C. (d) Your derivative formed an oil when you heated it in the recrystallization solvent, but the oil solidified on cooling, so you used it to obtain a melting point.
4. Calculate the atom economy of your derivative preparation(s).
5. Construct a flow diagram showing the process you followed to identify your unknown.
6. The unknown assigned to a student was an aldehyde, but about half of the sample distilled around 65°C and the rest of it distilled near 155°. (a) What is the name of the aldehyde? (b) What else was in the sample, and why? Write a balanced equation for its formation.
7. An unknown liquid is water soluble and reacts with chromic acid within 2 seconds. It dissolves in Lucas' reagent, but the solution remains clear for 30 minutes. The iodoform test yields a yellow precipitate. Give the name and structure of the unknown.
8. An unknown liquid with a boiling range of 179–181°C is insoluble in water, gives a blue-green suspension with chromic acid, and immediately forms a separate layer when shaken with Lucas' reagent. Its IR spectrum contains bands at 3060 cm^{-1}, 2805 cm^{-1}, 2730 cm^{-1}, 1705 cm^{-1}, 745 cm^{-1}, and 690 cm^{-1}. Give the name and structure of the unknown.

9. Write mechanisms for the following reactions, which are used in chemical tests and derivative preparations: (a) the reaction of butanal with 2,4-dinitrophenylhydrazine reagent; (b) the preparation of the 3,5-dinitrobenzoate of 1-butanol; (c) the iodoform reaction of 2-butanone; (d) the reaction of 2-methyl-2-butanol with Lucas' reagent.

Other Things You Can Do

(Starred items require your instructor's permission.)

*1. Observe the effect of aqueous potassium permanganate on different classes of alcohols as described in the "Oxidation of Alcohols by Potassium Permanganate" minilab.

*2. Use ^{1}H NMR to identify an unknown arene as described in the "Identification of an unknown Arene by NMR Spectrometry" minilab.

3. Starting with sources listed in the Bibliography, write a research paper about the use of gas chromatography–mass spectrometry (GC–MS) to identify illicit drug samples and trace them back to their sources.

Oxidation of the Insect Repellent "6-12"

Reactions of Diols. Preparation of Carbonyl Compounds. Selective Oxidation. Infrared Spectrometry.

Operations

OP-10   Mixing
OP-11   Addition of Reactants
OP-18   Extraction
OP-19   Evaporation
OP-25   Drying Liquids
OP-30   Simple Distillation
OP-39   Infrared Spectrometry

Before You Begin

1. Read the experiment, read or review the operations as necessary, and write an experimental plan.
2. Calculate the mass and volume of 20.0 mmol of 2-ethyl-1,3-hexanediol, and the theoretical yields of each of the possible products.

Scenario

2-Ethyl-1,3-hexanediol, sold under the name "6-12," was used widely as an insect repellent until it was superseded by the more effective repellent *N,N*-diethyl-*m*-toluamide (deet). That left Skeeters 'n Such, a manufacturer of pest-control chemicals, with a large backlog of unsold 2-ethyl-1,3-hexanediol. They would like to convert this substance to a more useful product, perhaps even a better insect repellent. A simple method of transforming a hydroxyl compound to a potentially useful carbonyl compound is oxidation, which can be carried out using the environmentally friendly oxidizing agent aqueous sodium hypochlorite (NaOCl). But there are three possible products of the oxidation of 2-ethyl-1,3-hexanediol, and because Skeeters 'n Such recently downsized by laying off most of its organic chemists, none of the remaining employees knows which product to expect.

Your assignment, and that of your coworkers, is to carry out the oxidation of 2-ethyl-1,3-hexanediol and record its infrared spectrum so that you can identify it as one of the three possible products shown.

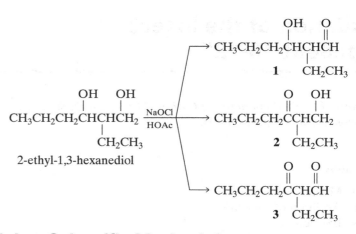

Applying Scientific Methodology

Unless you have a good knowledge of oxidation reactions, your working hypothesis may be only a guess. To find out whether your hypothesis is correct, you will need to consider how compounds **1**, **2**, and **3** can be distinguished by infrared spectrometry.

Ethylene Glycol and Other Diols

Beginning in October 1937, 107 people—most of them children—died after taking a newly developed version of the "wonder drug" of that era, sulfanilamide. At that time, new drugs were not required to be tested for safety or approved by the U.S. federal government. Because children had a hard time swallowing sulfanilamide pills, the drug's manufacturer used ethylene glycol to dissolve the sulfanilamide and marketed the resulting liquid as an easy-to-swallow form of the drug—without testing it first. The glycol was later shown to be responsible for the deaths. This tragedy led to passage of the 1938 Food, Drug, and Cosmetic Act, which required that drugs be cleared for safety before going on the market.

Ethylene glycol, $HOCH_2CH_2OH$, is the simplest common diol, where a *diol* is an alcohol that contains two hydroxyl ($-OH$) groups. It is the most widely used antifreeze for motor vehicles, and it is used to de-ice aircraft and airport runways as well. Methanol is a better antifreeze for some purposes (for example, in windshield washer fluids), because it lowers water's freezing point nearly twice as much as an equal mass of ethylene glycol does, but it tends to boil away much faster. Like methanol, ethylene glycol is quite toxic. Unfortunately, its sweet taste makes it attractive to children, as well as to dogs and other pets, who may die after lapping up spilled antifreeze.

Another important use of ethylene glycol is in the manufacture of plastics and fibers. One of the most widely used plastics, polyethylene terephthalate (PET), is manufactured by combining ethylene glycol with terephthalic acid.

Key Concept: Impurities lower the freezing point of any liquid. The magnitude of the freezing-point depression is proportional to the number of molecules of the impurity present, so low molecular-weight compounds cause a larger freezing-point depression than those with higher molecular weights.

$$n HOCH_2CH_2OH + n HOC\!-\!\bigcirc\!-\!COH \longrightarrow -[OCH_2CH_2OC\!-\!\bigcirc\!-\!C]_n\!- + n H_2O$$

ethylene glycol   terephthalic acid   polyethylene terephthalate

Polyethylene terephthalate is used to manufacture plastic bottles, packaging materials, and films.

Ethylene glycol can be converted to di- and triethylene glycols, as well as higher homologs, by reactions with ethylene oxide.

$$HOCH_2CH_2OH \xrightarrow{\triangle} HOCH_2CH_2OCH_2CH_2OH \xrightarrow{\triangle} HOCH_2CH_2OCH_2CH_2OCH_2CH_2OH$$

ethylene glycol   diethylene glycol   triethylene glycol

A mixture of these three substances has been used in some kinds of hydraulic brake fluids. Triethylene glycol is very *hygroscopic*, meaning that it absorbs water vapor from the atmosphere, so it is used as a drying agent to prevent condensation in natural gas pipelines.

2-Ethyl-1,3-hexanediol, formerly used in the insect repellent 6-12, is manufactured by an aldol condensation reaction of butanal (butyraldehyde) followed by reduction.

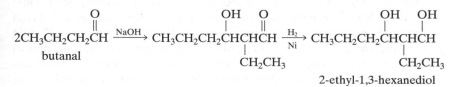

butanal   2-ethyl-1,3-hexanediol

In 1991, Union Carbide, the sole manufacturer of the insect repellant, filed a report with the Environmental Protection Agency (EPA) on possible adverse developmental effects of 2-ethyl-1,3-hexanediol on laboratory animals. The EPA subsequently asked retailers to remove from their shelves all products that contained it and advised women of childbearing age not to use such products. At this time, the only really effective insect repellents on the market are those that contain *N,N*-diethyl-*m*-toluamide (deet). Repellents that contain citronella and other ingredients appear to be much less effective than those that contain deet.

Some diols are found in nature, such as 1,18-octadecanediol, $HOCH_2(CH_2)_{16}CH_2OH$, which has been isolated from the plant Spanish broom (*Spartium junceum*). A natural diol with the intriguing common name sirenin (after the sirens of Greek mythology) is a sperm attractant for a water mold, *Allomyces javanicus*.

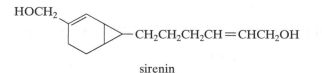

sirenin

Understanding the Experiment

You will use a commercial chlorine bleach such as Clorox or Javex to oxidize 2-ethyl-1,3-hexanediol. At one time, most chlorine bleaches were 5.25% aqueous NaOCl, but many newer products contain 6.0% NaOCl; either form can be used, but a smaller volume of the 6.0% bleach is needed.

The bleach should be unscented and there should be no ingredient other than sodium hypochlorite listed on the label.

349

Because the actual NaOCl concentration of the bleach tends to decrease with age, it may be necessary to use more than the amount given in the directions. Acetic acid is added to the reaction mixture to convert some of the NaOCl to hypochlorous acid, HOCl, which is probably the actual oxidant.

You can find out whether hypochlorite is present in the reaction mixture by periodically testing it with starch–iodide test paper, which turns a blue-black color in the presence of excess OCl⁻. If the test is negative at any time, you will need to add more bleach. Because the reaction mixture is heterogeneous—having separate organic and aqueous layers—it is important to stir the reactants vigorously to keep the layers well mixed. Inadequate stirring will result in a low yield. At the end of the reaction, any unreacted NaOCl can be converted to common table salt, NaCl, by adding a little sodium bisulfite ($NaHSO_3$).

$$NaOCl + NaHSO_3 \longrightarrow NaCl + NaHSO_4$$

A Greener Way: You can recover the diethyl ether by evaporating it under vacuum using a cold trap (see OP-15).

You will extract the product from the reaction mixture with diethyl ether, evaporate the ether, and purify the product by simple distillation.

Infrared spectrometry is a good method for identifying functional groups, and it may provide additional structural information as well. From an infrared spectrum, it is relatively easy to distinguish an alcohol's OH group from the carbonyl ($C{=}O$) group of an aldehyde or ketone, and to distinguish an aldehyde from a ketone. It may also be possible to distinguish a primary from a secondary alcohol. Read "Interpretation of Infrared Spectra" in OP-39 to find out how.

The use of acetic acid as a catalyst, the use of hypochlorite bleach as the oxidant (rather than environmentally harmful reagents such as chromic acid), and the harmless nature of the by-products make this a relatively green synthesis. Sodium hypochlorite is often used to disinfect drinking water, and the EPA has concluded that such uses present no unreasonable adverse effects to the environment. Acetic acid occurs naturally in living organisms and readily breaks down to carbon dioxide and water in the environment. Sodium hydroxide may be harmful in the environment, especially to aqueous organisms, but it is used to neutralize excess acetic acid and is itself neutralized in this experiment.

Reactions and Properties

$$\underset{\substack{\\ \text{CH}_2\text{CH}_3}}{\text{CH}_3\text{CH}_2\text{CH}_2\overset{\text{OH}}{\underset{|}{\text{CH}}}\overset{\text{OH}}{\underset{|}{\text{CH}}}\text{CHCH}_2} + \text{NaOCl} \xrightarrow{\text{CH}_3\text{COOH}} \mathbf{1} \text{ or } \mathbf{2} + \text{NaCl} + \text{H}_2\text{O}$$

or

$$\underset{\substack{\\ \text{CH}_2\text{CH}_3}}{\text{CH}_3\text{CH}_2\text{CH}_2\overset{\text{OH}}{\underset{|}{\text{CH}}}\overset{\text{OH}}{\underset{|}{\text{CH}}}\text{CHCH}_2} + 2\text{NaOCl} \xrightarrow{\text{CH}_3\text{COOH}} \mathbf{3} + 2\text{NaCl} + 2\text{H}_2\text{O}$$

2-ethyl-1,3-hexanediol

Table 1 Physical properties

	mol wt	mp	bp	*d*
2-ethyl-1,3-hexanediol	146.2	−40	244	0.942
acetic acid	60.05	16	118	1.049
sodium hypochlorite	74.4			

Note: mp and bp are in °C; density is in g/mL.

2-Ethyl-1,3-hexanediol

$$\underset{\underset{\displaystyle CH_2CH_3}{|}}{CH_3CH_2CH_2\overset{\overset{\displaystyle OH}{|}}{CH}CH\overset{\overset{\displaystyle OH}{|}}{CH}CH_2}$$

3357.7	1379.6	1115.7
2960.1	1321.8	1036.6
1464.5	1225.3	974.2

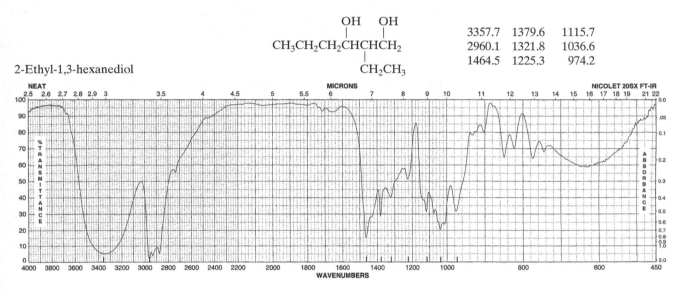

Figure 1 IR spectrum of 2-ethyl-1,3-hexanediol

DIRECTIONS

Safety Notes

Acetic acid causes chemical burns that can seriously damage skin and eyes; its vapors are highly irritating to the eyes and respiratory tract. Wear gloves and dispense under a hood; avoid contact and do not breathe its vapors.

2-Ethyl-1,3-hexanediol is moderately irritating to the eyes and mucous membranes but not to the skin.

Aqueous sodium hypochlorite can irritate the skin, eyes, and respiratory tract. Avoid contact and do not breathe its vapors.

Sodium hydroxide is toxic and corrosive, causing severe damage to skin, eyes, and mucous membranes. Wear gloves and avoid contact with the NaOH solution.

acetic acid

ˡsodium hypochlorite

sodium hydroxide

Take Care! Wear gloves, avoid contact with acetic acid and aqueous sodium hypochlorite, and do not breathe their vapors.

Reaction. Weigh 20.0 mmol of 2-ethyl-1,3-hexanediol into a 125-mL Erlenmeyer flask. Add 3.0 mL of glacial acetic acid and a stir bar; cool the reaction mixture in an ice/water bath. While stirring [OP-10], use a separatory–addition funnel to add [OP-11] 30 mL of 6.0% (or 34 mL of 5.25%) aqueous sodium hypochlorite (NaOCl), drop by drop, during a period of 4–5 minutes. Remove the flask from the cold bath and stir the reaction mixture vigorously for 1 hour at room temperature. Test it every 10 minutes or so with starch–iodide paper; if the paper doesn't turn blue-black in few seconds, add more NaOCl solution, about 1 mL at a time, until you get a positive test. At the end of the reaction period, add just enough saturated sodium bisulfite to give a negative starch–iodide test, unless the solution already tests negative.

Take Care! Wear gloves and avoid contact with 3 *M* NaOH.

Stop and Think: What is the purpose of adding NaCl?

Waste Disposal: Place any recovered diethyl ether in an appropriate waste container.

Separation. Add 3 *M* sodium hydroxide to the stirred reaction mixture, about 1 mL at a time, until it tests basic to red litmus paper. Transfer the reaction mixture to a separatory funnel, add 6 g of sodium chloride, and stopper and shake to dissolve the NaCl. Extract [OP-18] the product from this solution using two 20-mL portions of diethyl ether. Dry [OP-25] the combined ether layers with anhydrous sodium sulfate or magnesium sulfate. Evaporate [OP-19] the ether from the solution.

Purification and Analysis. At your instructor's request, purify the product by simple distillation [OP-30] using a compact distillation apparatus. Collect the liquid that distills between 200°C and 210°C. Weigh the product and record its infrared spectrum [OP-39]. Draw the structure of the product and give its IUPAC name.

Exercises

1. Tell how you arrived at the structure of your product from its infrared spectrum.
2. What was the purpose of adding sodium chloride during the separation step?
3. Describe how each of the following experimental errors or variations might affect your results. (a) The lab assistant didn't know what glacial acetic acid is, so she put out 1 *M* acetic acid instead. (b) You mixed up the vials of test paper and used red litmus paper when you should have used starch–iodide paper. (c) You used Clorox that was purchased several years ago.
4. (a) Calculate the atom economy and reaction efficiency of your synthesis. (b) Describe some green features of your synthesis, and any that aren't so green.
5. Following the directions in the "Planning an Experiment" appendix, construct a flow diagram for the synthesis of your product.
6. The diol 1,4-cyclohexanedimethanol reacts with terephthalic acid to form the polyester known as PCT. Draw the structure of a repeating unit of this polyester.
7. Outline a synthesis of dioxane starting with ethylene glycol.

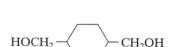

1,4-cyclohexanedimethanol

dioxane

Other Things You Can Do

(Starred items require your instructor's permission.)

*1. Prepare 2.0 mL of a 1% solution of borax (sodium tetraborate) and add enough phenolphthalein indicator solution to yield a definite pink color. Add 2 drops of each of the following to 0.5 mL of the solution: (a) 2-ethyl-1,3-hexanediol; (b) 2-butanol; (c) ethylene glycol. Decide what structural feature is necessary to yield a positive test.

*2. Obtain a sample of a suitable alcohol from your instructor, develop a procedure for oxidizing it to a carbonyl compound using sodium hypochlorite and acetic acid, and have your procedure approved by your instructor. Then carry out the oxidation reaction and turn in your product, along with its infrared spectrum and a lab report.

3. Starting with sources listed in the Bibliography, write a research paper about commercial processes for manufacturing ethylene glycol and some of its commercial uses.

Isomerization of a Cyclic Ketone

Isomerization. Reactions of Alkenes. Reactions of Carbonyl Compounds. Infrared Spectrometry.

Operations

OP-7   Heating
OP-8   Cooling
OP-10 Mixing
OP-18 Extraction
OP-19 Evaporation
OP-24 Washing Liquids
OP-25 Drying Liquids
OP-39 Infrared Spectrometry
OP-40 Nuclear Magnetic Resonance Spectrometry (optional)

Before You Begin

1. Read the experiment, read or review the operations as necessary, and write an experimental plan.
2. Calculate the mass and volume of 10.0 mmol of carvone and the theoretical yield of the product.

Scenario

New-age herbalist Basil Wormwood often steam distills chopped-up spearmint leaves to isolate their essential oil, whose main component is (*R*)-carvone. This time he decided to *digest* the leaves in aqueous sulfuric acid before distillation to reduce their volume and make it possible to process a larger batch each time. He was surprised to find that the resulting oil smelled more like thyme than spearmint. Curious about this outcome, he carried out the same procedure with ground caraway seeds, which he knew to contain (*S*)-carvone (the enantiomer of spearmint's carvone), and obtained the same thyme-scented product. Despite its odor, the unexpected product isn't thymol—but, like thymol, it is mildly acidic.

In chemistry, to digest *something is to soften or disintegrate it by means of moisture, heat, or a chemical reaction.*

Thymol is an isomer of carvone and the main component of thyme's essential oil.

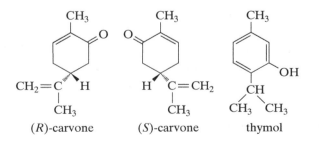

(*R*)-carvone   (*S*)-carvone   thymol

From *Operational Organic Chemistry: A Problem Solving Approach to the Laboratory*, Fourth Edition, John W. Lehman. Copyright © 2009 by Pearson Education. Published by Prentice Hall. All rights reserved.

Your assignment is to carry out the reaction of either (R)- or (S)-carvone with sulfuric acid and identify the product. Your supervisor has already had the product analyzed and found its molecular formula to be $C_{10}H_{14}O$, the same as that of carvone, so Basil must have carried out an acid catalyzed *isomerization* reaction—one in which a compound is converted to one of its possible isomers.

Applying Scientific Methodology

There should be enough clues in the Scenario and elsewhere to help you formulate a reasonable working hypothesis about the structure of the product, based on the structure of the reactant and your knowledge of the chemistry of C=C and C=O double bonds. You will test your hypothesis using spectral analysis.

Chemicals from Herbs and Spices

The carvones that are found in spearmint leaves and caraway seeds also occur in other herbs and spices, such as dill seed, which contains (S)-carvone. An *herb* is a flowering plant that has a non-woody stem, or parts of such a plant, such as thyme leaves. A *spice* is a pungent or aromatic plant product used as a seasoning, often a dried fruit or seed or even the bark of a tree, such as cloves and cinnamon. Spices are at their best when bought whole and ground just before use, because powdered spices lose their volatile flavor components rapidly. A good cook will have dozens of herbs and spices in the cupboard to add flavor to foods and to make teas and other beverages.

Many of the flavorful chemicals found in herbs and spices, including carvone, are terpenes. For example, coriander seeds contain linalool, camphor, α-pinene, and a host of other terpenes.

Terpenes that contain atoms other than carbon and hydrogen are also called terpenoids.

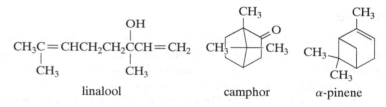

linalool camphor α-pinene

Aromatic compounds—some of which are also terpenes—are major flavor constituents of many herbs and spices. These include aromatic aldehydes, ketones, and ethers, such as cuminaldehyde from cumin seed, cinnamaldehyde from cinnamon, zingerone from ginger, eugenol from cloves, and anethole from fennel seeds.

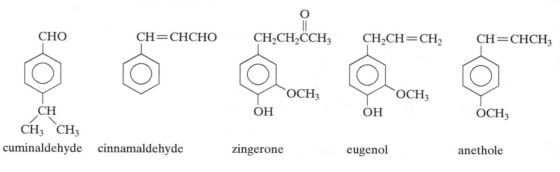

cuminaldehyde cinnamaldehyde zingerone eugenol anethole

Turmeric, a major ingredient of curry powder, is used widely in East Indian and other Asian cooking, and has also been used as a food coloring for mustard and other food products. Its main constituent is a yellow pigment, curcumin, which appears to be effective for treating digestive disorders, osteoarthritis, and cancer, and for preventing the buildup of plaque in arteries. Curcumin is easily oxidized to vanillin, the main flavor ingredient of vanilla. In fact, curcumin—along with zingerone and eugenol—contains the same 4-hydroxy-3-methoxy combination found in vanillin. These substances are therefore classified as *vanilloids*.

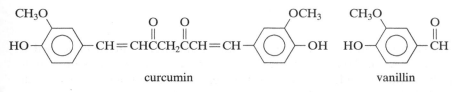

curcumin   vanillin

Several of the previous compounds are *phenols*—compounds having one or more OH groups on an aromatic ring. Phenols are abundant in the plant kingdom. They include simple phenols such as thymol, the main flavor ingredient of thyme, and carvacrol, which occurs in both winter savory and summer savory. Apigenin, which occurs in parsley, is one member of a chemical family called the *flavones*. Flavones and similar multi-ring phenolics, which are lumped under the term *flavonoids*, are widely distributed in the plant world. Flavonoids are potent antioxidants that contribute to the health benefits of plant-based foods. The Mediterranean diet is particularly high in flavonoids. For example, Greeks consume unusually large quantities of apigenin from parsley, which is an essential ingredient of the grain salad tabouli.

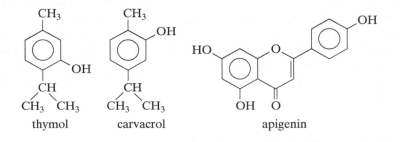

thymol   carvacrol   apigenin

Pungent herbs and spices such as garlic, horseradish, and mustard usually contain sulfur compounds. A sulfoxide called alliin is an important constituent of garlic. When garlic cloves are crushed or otherwise damaged, the cell membranes are ruptured so that alliin comes into contact with an enzyme, alliinase, which catalyzes a reaction that forms allicin. Allicin is actually a chemical defense agent for the garlic plant, protecting it from insects and fungi. It is also partly responsible for the characteristic "garlicky" odor that many people enjoy but others find offensive. Allicin is quite unstable and rapidly decomposes into other substances such as diallyl disulfide, so the flavor of garlic changes with cooking or standing.

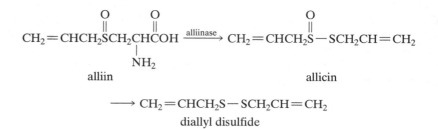

Horseradish roots contain sinigrin and the enzyme myrosinase, which combine when the root is grated, forming some very pungent sulfur compounds that include allyl isothiocyanate. Most store-bought horseradish isn't very potent, but when the root is fresh it generates enough of this volatile substance to cause a nose-clearing burst of stinging vapors that can bring tears to your eyes.

$$CH_2=CHCH_2\overset{\displaystyle S-C_6H_{11}O_5}{\underset{\displaystyle C=NOSO_3K}{|}} \xrightarrow{\text{myrosinase}} CH_2=CHCH_2N=C=S$$

sinigrin   allyl isothiocyanate

Sinigrin is also a constituent of the black mustard plant; white mustard contains a related compound, sinalbin, which yields a different isothiocyanate after an enzyme-catalyzed reaction analogous to that of sinigrin. Such isothiocyanates produce the "heat" of prepared mustards, which usually contain both black and white mustard seeds. The Japanese use a relative of horseradish called wasabi to flavor sashimi (raw fish), sushi, and noodles. Like horseradish and mustard, wasabi produces pungent isothiocyanates by an enzyme-catalyzed reaction. True wasabi is very expensive and, when fresh, loses its flavor within 15 minutes, so most of the "wasabi" that makes its way to North America is a paste or dry powder that consists mainly of artificially colored European horseradish and may contain less than 0.1% of the true wasabi.

Understanding the Experiment

Key Concept: The first step in an acid-catalyzed reaction of an unsaturated compound is usually addition of a proton to one or more double bonds.

A Greener Way: You can recover the petroleum ether by evaporating it under vacuum using a cold trap (see OP-15).

The isomerization of carvone is catalyzed by aqueous mineral acids, so you will heat your carvone under reflux with 6 M sulfuric acid. The reaction mixture has a tendency to boil up rather violently, so it is important to use vigorous magnetic stirring or enough boiling chips to prevent bumping. You will separate the unknown product from the reaction mixture by extraction with low-boiling petroleum ether, which isn't a true ether but a mixture of low-boiling hydrocarbons. Because of its low boiling range (usually ~35–60°C), this solvent can be removed easily by evaporation. The product is somewhat corrosive, so you should clean your glassware thoroughly after use. It also darkens over time, so it is best to record its infrared (IR) spectrum on the same day that you prepare it.

From the infrared spectrum of your product, you should be able to identify its functional group(s) and determine what family or families of organic compounds it belongs to. That will help you check (and perhaps modify) your working hypothesis and come up with a reasonable structure for the product, which you may be able to verify by comparing your IR spectrum to standard spectra in *The Aldrich Library of FT-IR Spectra* or some other collection of IR spectra listed in the Bibliography. At your instructor's discretion, you can also obtain the ^{1}H NMR spectrum of the product and use it to confirm your structure or figure out a better one.

This is a relatively green experiment; it has a high atom economy, and the organic solvent used for extraction can be recovered and recycled. Sulfuric acid is harmful to aquatic organisms, so it shouldn't be released into the environment.

Reactions and Properties

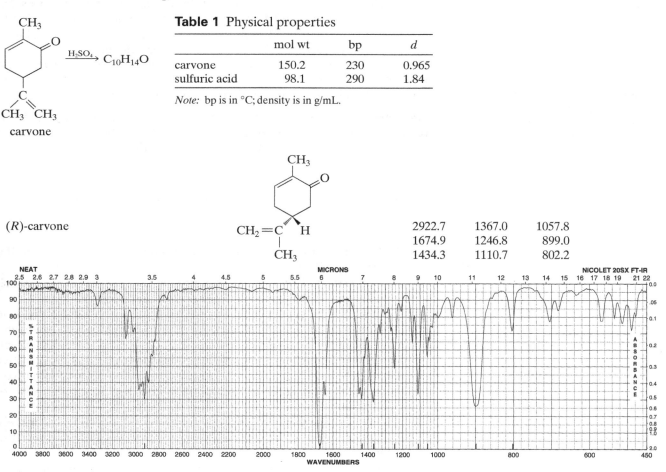

carvone

Table 1 Physical properties

	mol wt	bp	d
carvone	150.2	230	0.965
sulfuric acid	98.1	290	1.84

Note: bp is in °C; density is in g/mL.

(*R*)-carvone

2922.7	1367.0	1057.8
1674.9	1246.8	899.0
1434.3	1110.7	802.2

Figure 1 IR spectrum of (*R*)-carvone

DIRECTIONS

At the instructor's discretion, students can use different enantiomers of carvone and compare their results.

Safety Notes

sulfuric acid

Take Care! Wear gloves and avoid contact with sulfuric acid.

If severe bumping occurs, cool the reaction mixture and add more boiling chips (if you are using them), then raise the flask just enough so that it doesn't contact the heating manual and resume heating.

Waste Disposal: Place the aqueous layer, wash acetone, and any recovered petroleum ether in appropriate waste containers.

> **Sulfuric acid causes chemical burns that can seriously damage skin and eyes. Wear gloves and avoid contact.**
> **The product can cause chemical burns to skin and eyes. Wear gloves and avoid contact.**

Reaction. Combine 10.0 mmol of (*R*)- or (*S*)-carvone with 15 mL of 6 *M* sulfuric acid in a 50-mL round-bottom flask. Add some boiling chips (preferably microporous chips) or a stir bar and attach a condenser. Start the stirrer [OP-10] (if you are using one) and heat the reaction mixture under gentle reflux [OP-7] for 35 minutes. Cool [OP-8] the reaction mixture in an ice/water bath and then disassemble the apparatus. Use acetone to rinse, into a waste container, any glassware that comes in contact with the product.

Separation. *Under a fume hood,* transfer the reaction mixture to a separatory funnel and use two 10-mL portions of low-boiling petroleum ether to extract [OP-18] the product from the reaction mixture (wear gloves during the extraction). Wash [OP-24] the combined petroleum ether layers with 5% aqueous sodium bicarbonate; this process releases CO_2 gas, so stir and shake gently at first. Dry [OP-25] the organic layer over anhydrous sodium sulfate or magnesium sulfate and then evaporate [OP-19] the solvent.

Analysis. Weigh the product and record its infrared spectrum [OP-39]. If requested, record its ^1H NMR spectrum [OP-40] or obtain one from your instructor. Then deduce the structure of your product.

Exercises

1. Write a reasonable mechanism for the isomerization of carvone in the presence of sulfuric acid.
2. (a) Derive the IUPAC name of your product and give its common name. (b) List some herbs that contain the product as a major component.
3. Describe and explain the possible effect on your results of the following experimental errors or variations. (a) You used high-boiling petroleum ether for the extraction. (b) You used 5% sodium bisulfate rather than 5% sodium bicarbonate to wash the petroleum ether solution. (c) After adding 5% sodium bicarbonate to the petroleum ether solution, you immediately stoppered the separatory funnel and shook the mixture vigorously.
4. (a) Calculate the atom economy and reaction efficiency of your synthesis. (b) Describe some green features of your synthesis, and any that aren't so green.
5. Following the directions in the "Planning an Experiment" appendix, construct a flow diagram for the synthesis of your product.

6. Tell which compounds whose structures are shown in "Chemicals from Herbs and Spices" are terpenes. Don't include the three terpenes identified as such.
7. Outline a synthesis of vanillin from curcumin.

Other Things You Can Do

(Starred items require your instructor's permission.)

*1. Following the procedure for solubility tests in "Qualitative Organic Analysis", test your product for solubility in 5% NaOH and 5% NaHCO$_3$; explain your results.
*2. Carry out the isomerization reaction of dimethyl maleate described in the "Isomers and Isomerization Reactions" experiment and use a spectrometric method to show that the expected isomerization has taken place.
3. Starting with sources listed in the Bibliography, write a research paper about the components and therapeutic applications of some culinary herbs.

A Wittig Reaction
of *trans*-Cinnamaldehyde

Reactions of Carbonyl Compounds. Preparation of Dienes. Nucleophilic Addition. Wittig Reaction. Ylides.

Operations

OP-7   Heating
OP-10   Mixing
OP-16   Vacuum Filtration
OP-18   Extraction
OP-19   Evaporation
OP-25   Drying Liquids
OP-26   Washing and Drying Solids
OP-28   Recrystallization
OP-33   Melting Point

Before You Begin

1. Read the experiment, read or review the operations as necessary, and write an experimental plan.
2. Calculate the mass and volume of 10.0 mmol of *trans*-cinnamaldehyde, and the theoretical yield of 1,4-diphenyl-1,3-butadiene.

Scenario

Marvelous Molecules Incorporated (MMI) has experienced a lower than expected demand for its product line of aldehydes, so it has a large inventory of cinnamaldehyde that it would like to reduce. Penny Wise, MMI's peripatetic marketing executive, has learned that there is some demand for novel dienes such as 1,4-diphenyl-1,3-butadiene, which can be converted to interesting products such as *p*-terphenyl by means of Diels–Alder reactions.

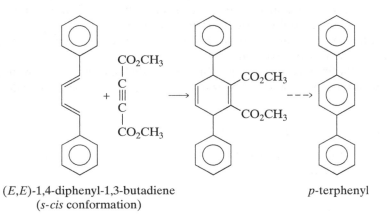

(*E,E*)-1,4-diphenyl-1,3-butadiene
(*s-cis* conformation)   *p*-terphenyl

From *Operational Organic Chemistry: A Problem Solving Approach to the Laboratory*, Fourth Edition, John W. Lehman. Copyright © 2009 by Pearson Education. Published by Prentice Hall. All rights reserved.

A staff chemist has informed her that it should be possible to prepare 1,4-diphenyl-1,3-butadiene from cinnamaldehyde by a procedure known as the Wittig synthesis, but its value as a Diels–Alder diene will depend on its stereochemistry. The (*E,E*) diene can easily attain the *s-cis* conformation needed to form a Diels–Alder adduct, but the (*E,Z*) diene is less likely to do so. Your assignment is to find out whether or not you can prepare 1,4-diphenyl-1,3-butadiene from *trans*-cinnamaldehyde and whether or not the major product has the desired (*E,E*) stereochemistry.

Applying Scientific Methodology

The scientific problems in this experiment are implicit in the Scenario. After reading the experiment, you should be able to develop a working hypothesis for the second problem, which you will test by obtaining the melting point of the major product.

Bark Spices and Cinnamaldehyde

cinnamon stick

Despite claims by wild foods advocate Euell Gibbons that the inner bark of the slippery elm and other trees is edible and nutritious, tree bark is not, as a rule, a popular source of food products. The most notable exceptions to the rule are certain trees of the genus *Cinnamomum,* which provide the spices cinnamon and cassia. True cinnamon is obtained from *Cinnamomum zeylanicum,* a tree that grows in Sri Lanka (formerly Ceylon) and southern India. Cinnamon is obtained by peeling the bark from the cut branches of the cinnamon tree and then scraping off any wood and the outer layers of bark. The thin strips of inner bark are dried in the sun, forming rolled-up "quills" that extend up to a meter in length. The quills are generally cut into shorter lengths to produce cinnamon sticks, or ground up to make powdered cinnamon. Cinnamon bark from Sri Lanka contains 1–2% of an aldehyde-rich essential oil, of which about 70% is cinnamaldehyde (3-phenyl-2-propenal). Other components of cinnamon oil include benzaldehyde, *p*-isopropylbenzaldehyde, 3-phenylpropanal, nonanal, and 2-furaldehyde, along with such nonaldehyde ingredients as 2-heptanone, caryophyllene, and various other flavor components. Cinnamon leaves, surprisingly, contain no cinnamaldehyde but are rich in eugenol, the main flavor component of cloves.

Nearly all of the "cinnamon" consumed in the United States is actually cassia, which is obtained from the Chinese cassia tree, *Cinnamomum cassia,* and several related species grown in southeast Asia. Chinese cassia oil is 80–95% cinnamaldehyde, but its strong, spicy-sweet flavor is quite different from that of true cinnamon oil, which is less sweet but more complex and fragrant, with citrus overtones.

Synthetic cinnamaldehyde, which is mainly the *trans* isomer, is prepared by an aldol condensation of benzaldehyde and ethanal (acetaldehyde).

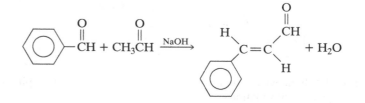

Cinnamaldehyde, as well as natural cinnamon and cassia oils, is used to flavor candies, chewing gum, and baked goods, and as an ingredient in perfumes.

Understanding the Experiment

The German chemist Georg Wittig developed the Wittig reaction in 1954, but 25 years passed before he received full recognition for originating one of the most synthetically useful reactions in organic chemistry. In 1979, Wittig shared the Nobel Prize in chemistry with another well-known synthetic organic chemist, Herbert C. Brown of the United States.

Like the aldol condensation, the Wittig reaction is used to construct larger molecules from smaller ones, by connecting the components of the smaller molecules with carbon–carbon double bonds. Both reactions involve the attack of a nucleophilic carbon atom, stabilized by a neighboring electron-withdrawing group, on the carbonyl carbon atom of an aldehyde or ketone, as shown by the following examples.

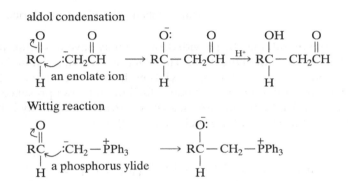

In the aldol condensation, the nucleophile is an enolate ion, which is stabilized by resonance involving the carbonyl group. In the Wittig reaction, the nucleophile is a phosphorus ylide (pronounced ILL-ide), which is stabilized by resonance involving a triphenylphosphonium group. In both reactions, the carbon–carbon double bond then forms by elimination (in several steps) of a molecular species; H_2O in the case of the aldol condensation, and $Ph_3P=O$ in the case of the Wittig reaction.

Key Concept: Carbon is ordinarily not nucleophilic, because it has no unshared electron pairs, but a nucleophilic carbon atom can be formed by transfer of a proton from a C—H bond to a strong base. This transfer is facilitated by the presence of some group that can stabilize the resulting species.

aldol condensation

$$RC\overset{HO}{\underset{H}{\overset{|}{\underset{|}{C}}}}\overset{H}{\overset{|}{\underset{}{C}}}H\overset{O}{\overset{||}{\underset{}{C}}}H \xrightarrow{-H_2O} RCH=CHCH$$

Wittig reaction

$$RC\overset{\overset{-}{O}:}{\underset{H}{\overset{|}{\underset{|}{C}}}}\overset{\overset{+}{PPh_3}}{\overset{|}{\underset{}{C}H_2}} \xrightarrow{-Ph_3P=O} RCH=CH_2$$

During a Wittig reaction, the Ph_3P group needed to stabilize the nucleophilic carbon atom is lost along with the carbonyl oxygen. Thus, the Wittig reaction, unlike the aldol condensation, can be used for the synthesis of unsaturated hydrocarbons that have no additional functional groups.

See your lecture textbook for a more complete description and mechanism of the Wittig reaction

The key intermediate in a Wittig synthesis is the resonance-stabilized phosphorus ylide, which is typically prepared by the reaction of triphenylphosphine with an alkyl halide to yield a phosphonium salt, followed by treatment with a strong base such as butyllithium.

$$Ph_3P + CH_3I \longrightarrow [Ph_3\overset{+}{P}-CH_3]I^- \xrightarrow{C_4H_9Li} [Ph_3\overset{+}{P}-\overset{-}{C}H_2 \longleftrightarrow Ph_3P=CH_2]$$

In this experiment, the phosphonium salt will be benzyltriphenylphosphonium chloride, which is prepared by the reaction of triphenylphosphine with benzyl chloride. This is an S_N2 reaction in which triphenylphosphine (the nucleophile) displaces chloride ion (the leaving group) from benzyl chloride (the substrate).

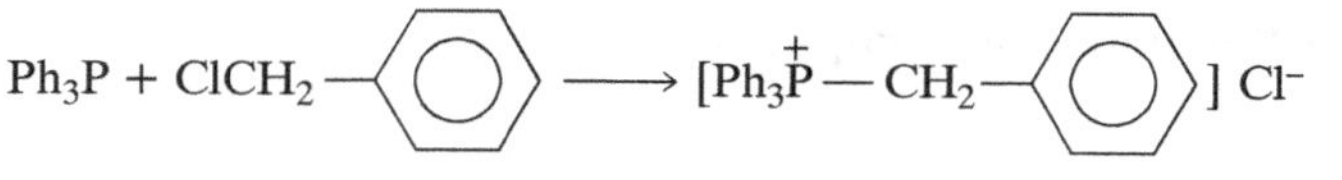

benzyltriphenylphosphonium chloride

The phosphonium salt may be provided, or you may have to synthesize it as described in part **A** of the Directions. The reaction is carried out in the high-boiling solvent *p*-cymene (1-isopropyl-4-methylbenzene) over a 2-hour reaction period. Formation of the ylide is facilitated by the presence of the phenyl group, which helps stabilize it, so concentrated sodium hydroxide is used rather than a stronger base such as butyllithium.

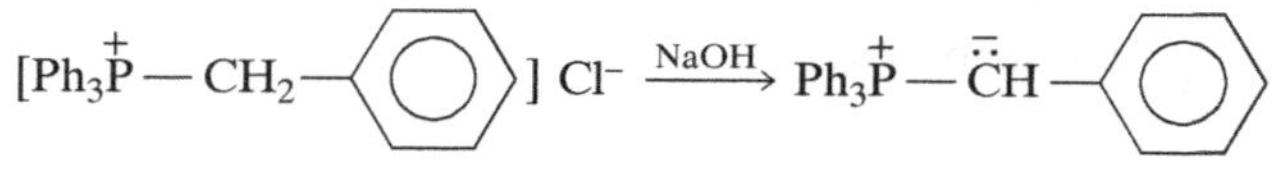

You will carry out the ylide-forming reaction in the presence of cinnamaldehyde, which reacts with the ylide to form the product, 1,4-diphenyl-1,3-butadiene.

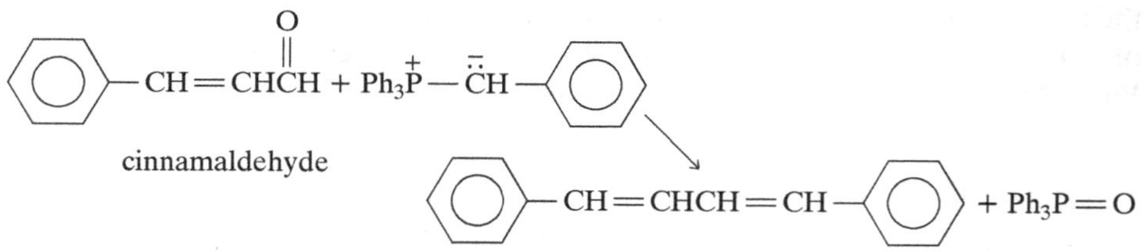

cinnamaldehyde

1,4-diphenyl-1,3-butadiene

This reaction takes place at room temperature in a two-phase mixture, with dichloromethane as the organic phase. Benzyltriphenylphosphonium chloride itself acts as a phase-transfer catalyst, apparently escorting the polar ylide from the aqueous to the organic layer, where it can encounter and react with cinnamaldehyde. Most of the major product will remain in the organic phase; the rest is extracted from the aqueous phase with additional dichloromethane, which is removed by evaporation. The crude product is triturated (see OP-26a) with aqueous 60% ethanol to remove triphenyl-phosphine oxide (Ph₃PO) and a by-product of the reaction (which can be isolated as described in "Other Things You Can Do"), and then purified further by recrystallization from 95% ethanol. The flat crystals tend to stick to glass surfaces and are hard to scrape off, so you should avoid any unnecessary transfers.

You will be using the *trans* isomer of cinnamaldehyde, so the geometry of one double bond of the major product will also be *trans*. The geometry of the second double bond—the one formed in the reaction—could be either *cis* or *trans*, allowing for the formation of two possible products, (*E,E*)- and (*E,Z*)-1,4-diphenyl-1,3-butadiene.

*A **Greener Way:** The dichloromethane can be recovered by evaporating it under vacuum using a cold trap (see OP-15).*

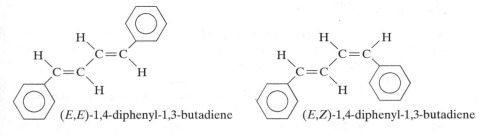

(*E,E*)-1,4-diphenyl-1,3-butadiene   (*E,Z*)-1,4-diphenyl-1,3-butadiene

A melting-point measurement should tell you whether or not you obtained the desired (*E,E*) isomer. Ultraviolet spectrometry can also be used to distinguish geometric isomers, as described in "Other Things You Can Do."

The Wittig reaction has a low atom economy because it produces triphenylphosphine oxide as a by-product. Although the oxide can be recycled to triphenylphosphine, the process is expensive and produces some waste by-products. Benzyl chloride and triphenylphosphine are somewhat toxic to aquatic organisms. The EPA classifies dichloromethane as a priority pollutant and has established an MCL of 5 ppb for its concentration in drinking water.

Reactions and Properties

A $Ph_3P + PhCH_2Cl \longrightarrow [Ph_3\overset{+}{P}-CH_2Ph]\ Cl^-$

   benzyl chloride   benzyltriphenylphosphonium chloride

B $[Ph_3\overset{+}{P}-CH_2Ph]\ Cl^- + NaOH \longrightarrow Ph_3\overset{+}{P}-\overset{\bar{\bar{}}}{C}HPh + H_2O + NaCl$

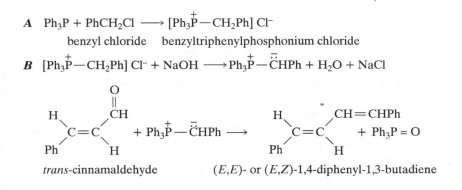

trans-cinnamaldehyde   (*E,E*)- or (*E,Z*)-1,4-diphenyl-1,3-butadiene

Table 1 Physical properties

	mol wt	mp	bp	d
benzyl chloride	126.6	−43	179	1.100
triphenylphosphine	262.3	80.5	377	
benzyltriphenylphosphonium chloride	388.9			
p-cymene	134.2	−68	177	0.857
trans-cinnamaldehyde	132.2	−7.5	246	1.050
dichloromethane	84.9	−97	40.5	1.326
(*E,E*)-1,4-diphenyl-1,3-butadiene	206.3	153		
(*E,Z*)-1,4-diphenyl-1,3-butadiene	206.3	88		

Note: mp and bp are in °C; density is in g/mL.

DIRECTIONS

A. *Preparation of Benzyltriphenylphosphonium Chloride*
This step can be omitted if commercial or previously prepared benzyltriphenylphosphonium chloride is available.

Safety Notes

benzyl chloride   *p*-cymene

> Benzyl chloride is toxic when inhaled and highly irritating to the skin and eyes. It is a suspected carcinogen and an experimental teratogen (a substance that may harm a developing fetus). It may react violently with oxidants. Wear gloves and use a hood; avoid contact, do not breathe its vapors, and keep it away from other chemicals.
> Triphenylphosphine is toxic when ingested and may be harmful if inhaled; do not breathe its vapors.
> *p*-Cymene is flammable and irritates the skin. Avoid contact and keep it away from flames.

Take Care! Wear gloves, avoid contact with the reactants and solvent, and do not breathe their vapors.

Stop and Think: Why does the product precipitate from this reaction mixture?

Waste Disposal: Place the *p*-cymene in a designated solvent recovery container.

Reaction. *Under the hood*, combine 2.0 mL of benzyl chloride with 6.0 g of triphenylphosphine and 30 mL of *p*-cymene in a 100-mL round-bottom flask. Add a stir bar [OP-10], attach a condenser, and heat the reaction mixture under reflux [OP-7] for 2 hours or more, stirring to prevent bumping as the solid product forms. Let the mixture cool to room temperature, and then cool it in an ice/water bath for 15 minutes. Collect the product by vacuum filtration [OP-16], and wash it on the filter [OP-26a] with 10 mL of cold, low-boiling petroleum ether to remove *p*-cymene. Dry [OP-26b] the benzyltriphenylphosphonium chloride and measure its mass.

B. *Preparation of 1,4-Diphenyl-1,3-butadiene*
If you obtained less than 3.9 g of benzyltriphenylphosphonium chloride from part **A**, scale down all quantities of reactants and solvents proportionately.

Safety Notes

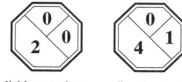

dichloromethane   sodium hydroxide

> *trans*-Cinnamaldehyde is a skin irritant; avoid contact.
> Dichloromethane may be harmful if ingested, inhaled, or absorbed through the skin. There is a possibility that prolonged inhalation of dichloromethane may cause cancer. Minimize contact with the liquid and do not breathe its vapors.
> Sodium hydroxide is toxic and corrosive, causing severe damage to skin, eyes, and mucous membranes. Wear gloves and avoid contact with the NaOH solution.

Reaction. In a clean, dry 50-mL Erlenmeyer flask, combine 10.0 mmol of pure *trans*-cinnamaldehyde, 10 mL of dichloromethane, and 3.9 g of benzyltriphenylphosphonium chloride. Drop in a magnetic stir bar; then add 5.0 mL of 50% (~19 *M*) aqueous sodium hydroxide and stir [OP-10] the mixture vigorously at room temperature for 30 minutes.

Take Care! Avoid contact with dichloromethane and do not breathe its vapors. Wear gloves and avoid contact with the NaOH solution.

Stop and Think: What is the purpose of the sodium hydroxide?

Separation. Transfer the reaction mixture to a separatory funnel using 20 mL of dichloromethane followed by 15 mL of water for the transfer. Shake gently but thoroughly to extract [OP-18] the product into the dichloromethane, and drain the dichloromethane layer into a clean, dry Erlenmeyer flask. Dry [OP-25] the dichloromethane solution over anhydrous sodium sulfate or magnesium sulfate. Evaporate [OP-19] the dichloromethane until only an oily or solid residue remains. If the residue is an oil, it should solidify as it cools; if necessary, cool it in an ice/water bath.

Waste Disposal: Unless your instructor directs otherwise, flush the aqueous layer down the drain with plenty of water. Place any recovered dichloromethane in a chlorinated solvents recovery container.

Purification and Analysis. Add 35 mL of aqueous 60% (by volume) ethanol to the solidified residue and triturate [OP-26a] the solid thoroughly with a spatula or flat-bottomed stirring rod. This procedure removes triphenylphosphine oxide and other impurities. Collect the solid by vacuum filtration [OP-16], and wash it on the filter [OP-26a] with several small portions of ice-cold 60% ethanol. Recrystallize [OP-28] the crude 1,4-diphenyl-1,3-butadiene from 95% ethanol. Then dry it [OP-26b], and measure its mass and melting point [OP-33]. Decide whether your product is the (*E*,*E*) or the (*E*,*Z*) isomer.

Waste Disposal: At your instructor's discretion, save the initial filtrate for further work. Otherwise, dispose of it and the recrystallization filtrate as directed by your instructor.

Exercises

1. Why do you think the product you obtained, rather than another isomer, is the major product of the Wittig reaction?
2. (a) Of the three 1,4-diphenyl-1,3-butadiene isomers, (*E*,*E*), (*E*,*Z*), and (*Z*,*Z*), which would be most suitable as a diene in the Diels–Alder reaction? Which would be least suitable? Explain. (b) Why is (*Z*,*Z*)-1,4-diphenyl-1,3-butadiene not a likely product of the reaction you carried out?
3. Describe and explain the possible effect on your results of the following experimental errors or variations. (a) The lab assistant, thinking that chlorobenzene and benzyl chloride are different names for the same compound, put chlorobenzene in the benzyl chloride bottle. (b) There was no *p*-cymene available, so you used toluene instead. (c) You didn't have a magnetic stirrer, so in part **B** you shook the reaction mixture for a few seconds every minute or so.
4. (a) Calculate the atom economy and reaction efficiency of your synthesis. (b) Describe some green features of your synthesis, and any that aren't so green.
5. Following the format in the "Planning an Experiment" appendix, construct a flow diagram for the synthesis of 1,4-diphenyl-1,3-butadiene in part **B**.

6. Outline a Wittig synthesis of each of the following compounds from an appropriate alkyl halide and carbonyl compound.

(a) CH₃CH

(b) CH₃O

(c)

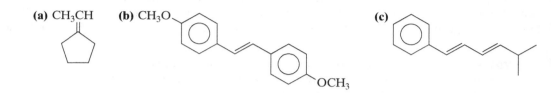

Other Things You Can Do

(Starred items require your instructor's permission.)

*1. Isolate and characterize another isomer of 1,4-diphenyl-1,3-butadiene from the filtrate saved from the first vacuum filtration in part **B**. First, transfer the filtrate to a centrifuge tube (or conical vial) and withdraw any insoluble oil using a Pasteur pipet. Dissolve the oil in 10 mL of dichloromethane (or more, if necessary), dry the dichloromethane solution, and evaporate the solvent. Protect this substance from light, which can convert it to yet another isomer. Dissolve a small crystal of the substance in 10 mL of hexanes and obtain its UV spectrum [OP-41] between 200 and 400 nm, diluting the solution with more hexanes as necessary to keep the peaks on scale. Add a small crystal of iodine and illuminate the solution with a 100-watt lightbulb for 10 minutes or more; then obtain its UV spectrum in the same region. Compare both spectra with the UV spectrum of your original isomer from part **B**, recorded in the same way, and explain your results.

*2. Carry out a synthesis that involves C=N bond-forming reactions as described in the "A Nucleophilic Addition–Elimination Reaction of Benzil" Minilab.

3. Starting with sources listed in the Bibliography, write a research paper about the mechanism, stereochemistry, and applications of the Wittig reaction.

Effect of Reaction Conditions on the Condensation of Furfural with Cyclopentanone

Reactions of Carbonyl Compounds. Preparation of α,β-Unsaturated Carbonyl Compounds. Nucleophilic Addition. Condensation Reactions. Carbanions. NMR Spectrometry.

Operations

OP-8   Cooling
OP-10 Mixing
OP-16 Vacuum Filtration
OP-18 Extraction
OP-19 Evaporation
OP-24 Washing Liquids
OP-25 Drying Liquids
OP-26 Washing and Drying Solids
OP-28 Recrystallization
OP-31 Vacuum Distillation
OP-33 Melting Point
OP-40 Nuclear Magnetic Resonance Spectrometry

Before You Begin

1. Read the experiment, read or review the operations as necessary, and write an experimental plan. Read OP-31 carefully if you haven't performed a vacuum distillation before.
2. For part **A**, calculate the mass and volume of 50.0 mmol of cyclopentanone and of 50.0 mmol of furfural.
3. For part **B**, calculate the mass and volume of 10.0 mmol of cyclopentanone.

Scenario

Grits 'n Groats, a breakfast-cereal manufacturer, produces huge quantities of oat hulls and corncobs while processing cereal grains. In the past, the company has simply disposed of such by-products, but the rising cost of waste disposal has convinced the board of directors that Grits 'n Groats should find a way to profit from them rather than paying to get rid of them. Oat hulls, corncobs, and other agricultural by-products can be processed to yield furfural, an aldehyde with an aromatic furan ring. While searching the chemical literature for references to furfural, project leader Farina Millet came across a paper in the *Journal of Organic Chemistry* that described a Claisen–Schmidt reaction (a type of aldol condensation) between cyclopentanone and furfural. Under one set of conditions, the reaction yields a low-melting yellow solid, but, under a different set of conditions, it produces a

Key Concept: *Different products can sometimes be produced from the same set of reactants by varying the reaction conditions.*

high-melting golden-orange solid. Dr. Millet needs some samples of these compounds and their structures so that she can explore their potential for commercial development. Your assignment is to synthesize both compounds and identify them using your chemical intuition, with some help from NMR spectrometry.

Applying Scientific Methodology

After reading the experiment and comparing the reaction conditions, you should be able to formulate a tentative hypothesis about the structures of the products and predict the kind of ^1H NMR spectrum each product should have. You will test your hypothesis when you obtain the actual NMR spectra of the products.

From Oats to Furfural

Furfural, also known as 2-furaldehyde, is the most important member of the furan series of aromatic compounds. The furan ring is aromatic because it has six pi electrons (two from the oxygen atom) distributed about a five-membered ring (see Figure 1). The aromatic sextet of a furan ring is less stable than that of a benzene ring, so furans undergo such reactions as electrophilic addition, cycloaddition, and cleavage more readily than the corresponding benzene compounds.

Furfural can be prepared in large quantities by treating such agricultural by-products as bran, oat hulls, corncobs, and peanut shells with dilute acids. These materials contain polysaccharides known as pentosans that are hydrolyzed to pentoses (simple five-carbon sugars) under acidic conditions. The pentoses are then converted to furfural by acid-catalyzed dehydration.

furfural

Conversion of a pentose to furfural. (This equation represents the overall process, not the reaction mechanism.)

a pentose   furfural

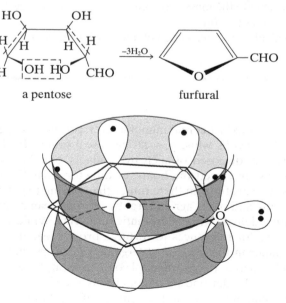

Figure 1 Aromatic furan ring

372

The first commercial process for the manufacture of furfural was developed in 1922 by the Quaker Oats Company, which was trying to convert oat hulls into a better cattle feed at the time. Instead, it came up with a valuable commercial product that can be made cheaply on a large scale. Furfural is used in the purification of lubricating oils, the extractive distillation of 1,3-butadiene (used in the manufacture of rubber), the synthesis of phenolic resins, and the manufacture of a large number of chemical intermediates.

Furfural behaves like a typical aromatic aldehyde in many of its reactions. It can be oxidized to the corresponding carboxylic acid and reduced to the corresponding alcohol, and, like benzaldehyde, it undergoes the Cannizzaro reaction and the benzoin condensation. It also reacts with compounds that have active α-hydrogen atoms, such as aldehydes and ketones, to yield condensation products. For example, the reaction of furfural with acetone yields furfurylideneacetone by a Claisen–Schmidt reaction, and its condensation with acetic anhydride and sodium acetate forms furylacrylic acid by a Perkin reaction.

furylacrylic acid

Claisen–Schmidt reaction of furfural and acetone

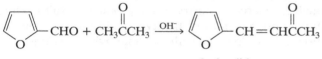

furfurylideneacetone

Understanding the Experiment

The Claisen–Schmidt reaction is a kind of crossed aldol condensation between an aromatic aldehyde and an aliphatic aldehyde or ketone that yields an α,β-unsaturated aldehyde or ketone. As illustrated in the margin for the reaction of benzaldehyde and acetone, the aliphatic carbonyl compound loses a proton to form an enolate ion, which attacks the carbonyl carbon of the aromatic aldehyde to yield (after protonation) a β-hydroxy carbonyl compound. This intermediate is generally not isolated but undergoes base-catalyzed dehydration by an E1cb mechanism; the base removes a proton from the α-carbon to form another enolate ion, which loses an OH⁻ ion to yield the unsaturated product.

In one of the procedures referred to in the Scenario, equimolar amounts of cyclopentanone and furfural are dissolved in diethyl ether and stirred with an aqueous solution of dilute sodium hydroxide. Furfural tends to oxidize and turn dark brown in storage, so furfural from a previously opened bottle should be distilled before use. Because the organic reactants aren't very soluble in water, they tend to stay in the ether phase, necessitating vigorous stirring to mix the layers. Extraction of the reaction mixture with diethyl ether followed by evaporation of the ether yields an impure yellow liquid, which is distilled under vacuum to produce a liquid product that should crystallize to a low-melting yellow solid, product **A**. Although the product usually doesn't solidify until the distillate is cooled, the vacuum distillation should be monitored closely to make sure that a solid doesn't form in the vacuum adapter and plug it up. Product **A** can be purified further by mixed-solvent recrystallization from methanol and water.

Mechanism of a Claisen–Schmidt condensation

$$CH_3CCH_3 \xrightarrow{OH^-} \overset{\ominus}{CH_2}CCH_3 \xrightarrow{PhCHO}$$

$$PhCH - CH_2CCH_3 \xrightarrow{H_2O}$$

$$PhCHCH_2CCH_3 \xrightarrow{OH^-}$$

$$PhCHCHCCH_3 \xrightarrow{-OH^-}$$

$$PhCH = CHCCH_3$$

*A **Greener Way:** You can recover the diethyl ether by evaporating it under vacuum using a cold trap (see OP-15).*

When cyclopentanone in diethyl ether is stirred with excess furfural in the presence of an effective phase-transfer catalyst such as tricaprylmethylammonium chloride (Aliquat 336), golden-orange crystals of product **B** begin to crystallize from the reaction mixture almost immediately. The exothermic reaction generates enough heat to vaporize the ether, making it necessary to cool the reactants in an ice/water bath before and during the reaction period. Product **B** is separated by filtration and purified by recrystallization from 2-butanone. The role played by the phase-transfer catalyst in aldol-type condensations is not entirely clear, but the catalyst may carry hydroxide ions into the organic phase where they can generate enolate ions, which then react with furfural molecules.

From the structures of the reactants and your knowledge of aldol-type condensation reactions, you should be able to propose likely structures for the two products. The ^{1}H NMR spectra will show clearly which product you have actually prepared in each case. In interpreting the spectra, you should pay particular attention to the number and multiplicity of signals produced by the methylene protons of the cyclopentanone ring. Comparing your spectra with the ^{1}H NMR spectra of the reactants in Figure 2 should help you assign the signals in your spectra to specific proton sets.

Although the stereochemistry of the products hasn't been reported in the literature, most reactions of this type yield the (*E*) isomers, as in the condensation of benzaldehyde with 4,4-dimethyl-1-tetralone.

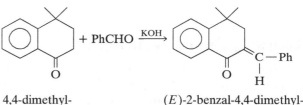

4,4-dimethyl-   (*E*)-2-benzal-4,4-dimethyl-
1-tetralone   1-tetralone

The nearby carbonyl group has a deshielding effect on the vinylic proton of the (*E*) isomer, raising its chemical shift to 7.7 ppm, compared to a value of 6.6 ppm for the (*Z*) isomer.

Furfural may be harmful to the environment, especially with regard to aquatic organisms. Diethyl ether isn't considered toxic to aquatic life and doesn't persist for long in either air or water. Deuterochloroform is toxic to aquatic organisms and shouldn't be released into the environment. 2-Butanone isn't expected to be toxic to aquatic organisms or to bioaccumulate significantly.

Reactions and Properties

cyclopentanone   furfural   (equation not balanced)

Table 1 Physical properties

	mol wt	mp	bp	d
furfural	96.1	−39	162	1.159
cyclopentanone	84.1	−51	131	0.949
2-butanone	72.1	−86	80	0.805
tricaprylmethylammonium chloride	404.2			0.884
product **A**	162.2	60.5	154[15]	
product **B**	240.3	162		

Note: mp and bp are in °C; superscripts indicate pressure in torr; density is in g/mL.

Cyclopentanone

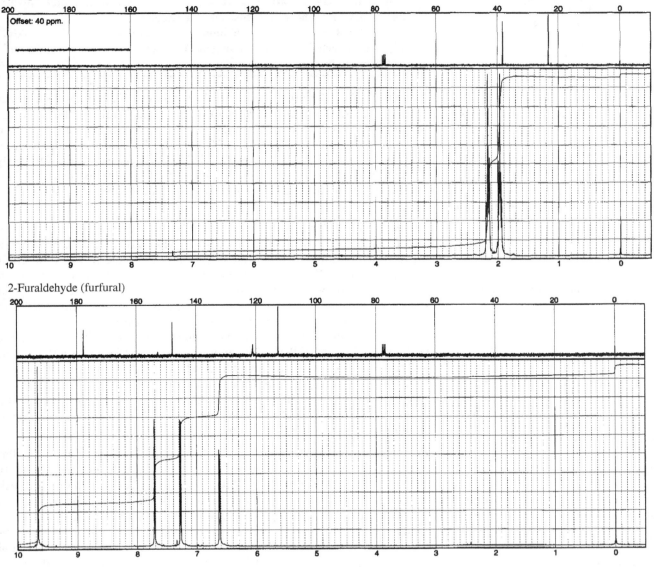

2-Furaldehyde (furfural)

Figure 2 NMR spectra of the starting materials

DIRECTIONS

A. *Claisen–Schmidt Reaction of Cyclopentanone and Furfural*

Safety Notes

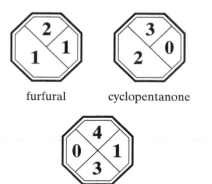

furfural   cyclopentanone

diethyl ether

Cyclopentanone is a skin irritant and a severe eye irritant; avoid contact. Diethyl ether is extremely flammable and may be harmful if inhaled. Do not breathe its vapors, and keep it away from flames and hot surfaces. Furfural irritates the skin, eyes, and respiratory tract, and it may cause allergic skin or respiratory reactions. Wear gloves while handling furfural and the reaction mixture (which will stain your hands yellow), and do not breathe their vapors.

A vacuum-distillation apparatus may implode if any of its components are cracked or otherwise damaged. Inspect the parts for damage and have your instructor check your apparatus. Protect yourself with a safety shield or hood sash while the apparatus is under vacuum.

Deuterochloroform is harmful if inhaled or absorbed through the skin, and it is a suspected human carcinogen. Avoid contact with the liquid and do not breathe its vapors.

Take Care! Keep diethyl ether away from ignition sources and do not breathe its vapors. Wear gloves, avoid contact with furfural, and do not breathe its vapors.

Observe and Note: What happens during the reaction period?

Stop and Think: What could this solid be?

Waste Disposal: Place any recovered ether in a solvent recovery container. Unless your instructor directs otherwise, wash all aqueous layers down the drain.

Take Care! A vacuum-distillation apparatus may implode if any of its components are cracked or otherwise damaged. Follow the precautions described in OP-31 and the Safety Notes.

Stop and Think: At about what temperature should the product distill?

Reaction. In a 125-mL Erlenmeyer flask, dissolve 50.0 mmol of cyclopentanone in 25 mL of solvent-grade diethyl ether. Add 45 mL of 0.10 M sodium hydroxide and a magnetic stir bar. Cool [OP-8] the mixture to 5°C in an ice/water bath and add 50.0 mmol of freshly distilled furfural while stirring. Seal the flask with Parafilm and stir [OP-10] the reaction mixture vigorously in a cold-water bath (10–15°C) for 45 minutes. (Parafilm dissolves in ether, so don't let it contact the reaction mixture.) Replace any ether that evaporates during the reaction.

Separation. Using a clean filter flask, filter the reaction mixture by vacuum filtration [OP-16] and save the filtrate, which contains product **A**. Turn off the vacuum immediately after filtration is complete to keep the ether from evaporating. Wash any solid on the filter with 10 mL of diethyl ether, and combine the wash liquid with the filtrate. If your instructor assigned Exercise 2, save this solid and weigh it when it is dry. If any solid remains in the filtrate, it will be removed during subsequent operations.

Place the filtrate in a separatory funnel and separate the layers, saving both layers. Extract [OP-18] the aqueous layer with 15 mL of diethyl ether, and combine the ether extract with the initial ether layer. Wash [OP-24] this solution with two separate portions of saturated aqueous sodium chloride. Dry [OP-25] it over anhydrous sodium sulfate or magnesium sulfate. Evaporate [OP-19] the ether under vacuum until the volume of the liquid residue remains essentially constant.

Purification and Analysis. Assemble an apparatus for vacuum distillation [OP-31], using the compact apparatus shown in Figure E8 of OP-30; have your instructor approve it. Make sure that a safety shield or hood sash is between you and the apparatus, and then purify the residue by vacuum distillation using *no* cooling bath. Monitor the distillation carefully; if any solid begins to form in the outlet tube, melt it with a heat gun or another appropriate heating device. Any unreacted starting materials and residual ether should distill below 100°C and should be removed before the main fraction begins to distill. While the distillate is still liquid (warm it gently, if necessary), transfer it to a container suitable for recrystallization. Cool it in ice water, if necessary, until it completely solidifies. Purify the solid further by mixed-solvent recrystallization [OP-28b] from methanol and water, taking measures to prevent oiling. Dry [OP-26b] the solid at room temperature. Measure the mass and melting point [OP-33] of product **A**. Record its ^{1}H NMR spectrum [OP-40] in deuterochloroform or obtain a spectrum from your instructor. Interpret the NMR spectrum as completely as you can, deduce the structure of product **A**, and name it.

B. *Claisen–Schmidt Reaction Using a Phase-Transfer Catalyst*

2-Butanone is flammable, and ingestion, inhalation, or skin absorption may be harmful. Avoid contact, do not breathe its vapors, and keep it away from flames and hot surfaces.
See part A for safety notes about cyclopentanone, diethyl ether, furfural, and deuterochloroform.

Reaction. Weigh 10.0 mmol of cyclopentanone into a 125-mL Erlenmeyer flask and dissolve it in 10 mL of diethyl ether. Add 12 mL of aqueous 0.10 *M* sodium hydroxide, 6 drops of tricaprylmethylammonium chloride (or 0.2 g of a suitable solid phase-transfer catalyst), and a stir bar. Cool [OP-8] the mixture to 5°C in an ice/water bath and add 2.0 mL of freshly distilled furfural, with stirring [OP-10]. Seal the flask with Parafilm and stir it vigorously at room temperature for 15 minutes, occasionally swirling it in the ice/water bath to reduce pressure buildup from vaporizing ether. (Parafilm dissolves in ether, so don't let it contact the reaction mixture.) Then let the reaction mixture stand at room temperature, with stirring or occasional shaking, for 10 minutes.

Separation. Collect the product by vacuum filtration [OP-16], wash it on the filter [OP-26a] with two portions of diethyl ether, and air-dry it on the filter.

Purification and Analysis. Recrystallize [OP-28] product **B** from 2-butanone, using about 12 mL of the solvent per gram of crude product. Wash the product on the filter [OP-26a] with diethyl ether, dry it [OP-26b], and weigh it. Measure the melting point [OP-33] of product **B**. Record its ^{1}H NMR spectrum [OP-40] in deuterochloroform, or obtain a spectrum from your instructor. Interpret the NMR spectrum as completely as you can, deduce the structure of product **B**, and name it.

Waste Disposal: Place any low-boiling forerun in an appropriate waste container.

Take Care! Avoid contact with $CDCl_3$ and do not breathe its vapors.

Safety Notes

2-butanone

Take Care! Keep diethyl ether away from ignition sources and do not breathe its vapors. Wear gloves, avoid contact with furfural, and do not breathe its vapors.

Observe and Note: Compare your observations during this reaction with your observations during the first reaction.

Waste Disposal: Unless your instructor directs otherwise, place all filtrates in designated solvent recovery containers.

Take Care! Do not breathe the vapors of 2-butanone and keep it away from ignition sources.

Take Care! Avoid contact with $CDCl_3$ and do not breathe its vapors.

Exercises

1. Discuss the effect of reaction conditions on the outcome of the Claisen–Schmidt reaction, telling what reaction conditions promote the formation of each product, and why.
2. (a) What is the probable identity of the solid that was filtered from the reaction mixture in part **A**? How could you have confirmed its identity? (b) What percentage of the cyclopentanone that you started with in part **A** was converted to condensation products? (This is *not* the same as the percentage yield of **A**.)

3. Write balanced equations and detailed mechanisms for the formation of both products, **A** and **B**.

4. (a) Using balanced equations (see Exercise 3) for the reactions you carried out, calculate the atom economy and reaction efficiency of each synthesis. (b) Describe some green features of your syntheses, and any that aren't so green.

5. Describe and explain the possible effect on your results of the following experimental errors or variations. (a) You used 10 *M* NaOH rather than 0.10 *M* NaOH in part **A**. (b) In part **A**, you rinsed the reaction flask with acetone and didn't dry it completely. (c) You left out the tricaprylmethylammonium chloride in part **B**. (d) You used 50 mmol of cyclopentanone in part **B** as well as in part **A**.

6. Diagram a possible phase-transfer process for the formation of product **B**, using the format illustrated in the "A Green Synthesis of Adipic Acid" experiment.

7. (a) Following the format in the "Planning an Experiment" appendix, construct a flow diagram for the synthesis in part **A**. (b) Construct a flow diagram for the synthesis in part **B**.

8. From your ^{1}H NMR spectra, is it more likely that your products are (*Z*) or (*E*) stereoisomers? Explain your answer.

9. An error-prone student, Mel A. Droyt, forgot to add the furfural in part **A**, but he recovered a small amount of liquid that distilled at 139–142°C at 20 torr and didn't solidify on cooling. The ^{1}H NMR spectrum of the liquid showed no signals from vinylic or hydroxylic protons. Propose a structure for this product and write a mechanism for its formation.

Other Things You Can Do

(Starred items require your instructor's permission.)

*1. As a group project, carry out part **B** using different phase-transfer catalysts and compare the crude yields to find out which catalysts are most effective. Suggested catalysts are tetrabutylammonium bromide, tetrabutylphosphonium bromide, cetyltrimethylammonium bromide, and 1-hexadecylpyridinium chloride.

*2. Prepare some other aldol condensation products as described in the "Preparation of Aldol Condensation Products" minilab.

3. Starting with sources listed in the Bibliography, write a research paper about the production and uses of furan, furfural, and some derivatives of these compounds.

Electronic Effect of a *para*-Iodo Substituent

Reactions of Aromatic Amines. Preparation of Aryl Halides. Aromatic Nucleophilic Substitution. Carboxylic Acids. Diazonium Salts. Linear Free-Energy Relationships.

Operations

OP-7   Heating
OP-8   Cooling
OP-10 Mixing
OP-16 Vacuum Filtration
OP-26 Washing and Drying Solids
OP-28 Recrystallization

Before You Begin

1. Read the experiment, read or review the operations as necessary, and write an experimental plan.
2. Calculate the masses of 10.0 mmol of *p*-aminobenzoic acid, 10.0 mmol of sodium nitrite, and 15 mmol of potassium iodide. Calculate the theoretical yield of *p*-iodobenzoic acid.
3. For each acid listed in Table 1, calculate the mass of 0.80 mmol of the acid.

Scenario

Si Starr, an energetic professor of metaphysical chemistry at Miskatonic University, is using molecular orbital theory to predict the electronic effects of various substituents on such reactions as the ionization of aromatic carboxylic acids. Substituent effects can be expressed quantitatively by empirical parameters called sigma values. To test the validity of his results, Professor Starr wants to compare his calculated sigma values with experimentally measured sigma values. Sigma values have been determined for most of the common substituents, but Starr has been unable to locate reliable sigma values for the iodo substituent ($-I$) on a benzene ring. Your assignment is to prepare *p*-iodobenzoic acid, measure its pK_a value, and use that to determine the sigma value for a *para*-iodo substituent.

Applying Scientific Methodology

After reading the experiment, you can propose a hypothesis about the electronic effect of a *p*-iodo substituent. The sigma value you obtain will show whether or not your hypothesis is correct.

From *Operational Organic Chemistry: A Problem Solving Approach to the Laboratory*, Fourth Edition, John W. Lehman. Copyright © 2009 by Pearson Education. Published by Prentice Hall. All rights reserved.

Linear Free-Energy Relationships

In general chemistry, you learned that electrons in a covalent bond tend to migrate toward the more electronegative atom, building up its electron density at the expense of the less electronegative atom. The situation isn't always so simple in conjugated organic compounds, where the electrons of unshared pairs or in pi bonds sometimes migrate *away* from a more electronegative atom into the "electron sink" of a delocalized pi-electron system. For example, lone-pair electrons from an oxygen-containing substituent such as methoxyl (—OCH₃) tend to migrate toward and overlap with the pi-electron cloud of a benzene ring, as illustrated for anisole (methoxybenzene). The net electronic effect of a substituent is indicated by an empirical (experimentally measured) parameter called its *sigma value.* Electron-withdrawing groups have positive sigma values, and electron-donating groups have negative ones. For example, the measured sigma value of —OCH₃ is −0.27, indicating that it has a net electron-donating effect at the *para* position of a benzene ring, even though oxygen is considerably more electronegative than carbon.

Consider a general substituent Z at the *para* position of a substituted benzoic acid. If Z is more electronegative than carbon, it will tend to withdraw electrons through the sigma-bond framework of the benzene ring by an *inductive effect,* and this should increase the strength of the acid by stabilizing its conjugate base. Conversely, a substituent that is more electropositive than carbon can donate electrons inductively and weaken an acid. But inductive effects decrease rapidly with distance, and because a *para* substituent is remote from the reaction site (the COOH group), its inductive effect may be quite small.

Substituents that have unpaired electrons and are adjacent to a conjugated system tend to donate electrons by a *resonance effect.* Electron donation by resonance can cause a buildup of electron density at locations within the ring and on conjugated substituents, as illustrated by the following resonance structures for the conjugate base of a substituted benzoic acid:

Overlap of lone-pair electrons with pi system in anisole

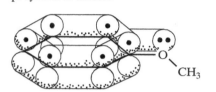

Conjugate base is stabilized by inductive electron withdrawal.

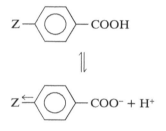

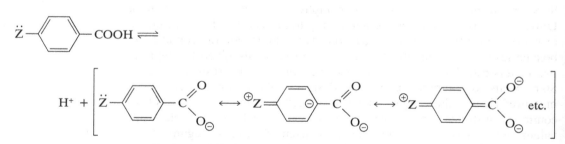

Conjugate base is destabilized by electron donation
transmitted through the pi-electron system.

In this example, the conjugate base is destabilized by a concentration of negative charge near the reaction site. Destabilization of the conjugate base shifts the ionization equilibrium to the left and reduces the strength of the acid. Resonance effects are transmitted freely throughout a conjugated system and don't decrease significantly with distance. They are most important when the substituent is *ortho* or *para* to the ring carbon nearest the reaction

Key Concept: *Stabilization of the conjugate base of an acid strengthens the acid; destabilization of its conjugate base weakens the acid.*

site. Substituents such as the methoxyl group can donate electrons by resonance but withdraw them inductively, and thus may either weaken or strengthen an acid, depending on the relative importance of the two effects. Thus, a *meta*-methoxyl substituent (for which the resonance effect is weak) increases the acidity of a substituted benzoic acid by an inductive effect, whereas a *para*-methoxyl substituent decreases the acidity of such an acid by resonance.

The pK_a of an acid is defined as the negative logarithm of its ionization constant:

$$pK_a = -\log K_a$$

For example, the pK_a of *m*-cresol, which has a K_a value of 1.0×10^{-10}, is 10.00. At a given temperature, the pK value for any equilibrium reaction is directly proportional to its standard free-energy change, $\Delta G°$. This can be shown by using the definition of pK to rewrite the thermodynamic equation that relates $\Delta G°$ to the equilibrium constant:

$$\Delta G° = -(2.303 \cdot RT) \log K = (2.303 \cdot RT) \, pK$$

The value of $\Delta G°$ for a reaction is a measure of its tendency to go to completion, so pK must measure the same tendency. Negative pK_a and $\Delta G°$ values are observed for strong acids that dissociate completely, or nearly so. Most organic acids have positive pK_a values because they are only partly dissociated in ionizing solvents; a high positive pK_a value indicates a weak acid, and a low one indicates a stronger acid.

Suppose we compare the pK_a values for a pair of acids that differ in only one respect—one acid has a substituent at a site where the other has only a hydrogen atom. Because each acid's pK_a is a measure of its acid strength, the difference between their pK_a values must measure the substituent's effect on acid strength. For example, in water at 25°C, benzoic acid has a pK_a value of 4.19 and *p*-nitrobenzoic acid has a pK_a value of 3.41. The difference between these pK_a values, $4.19 - 3.41 = 0.78$, is a quantitative measure of the *para*-nitro substituent's acid-strengthening effect. Similarly, *p*-toluic acid (p-$CH_3C_6H_4COOH$) has a pK_a value of 4.36; subtracting this value from the pK_a for benzoic acid gives a difference of -0.17, indicating that the methyl substituent has a small acid-weakening effect. The difference between the pK_a value for the unsubstituted acid and that for the substituted acid, which we shall call ΔpK, is a measure of the substituent's ability to donate or withdraw electrons.

$$\Delta pK = pK_a \text{ of unsubstituted acid} - pK_a \text{ of substituted acid} \quad \textbf{(1)}$$

Because substituents that give negative ΔpK values weaken acids, they must be electron donors, whereas those that give positive ΔpK values are electron acceptors. The numerical value of ΔpK in either case measures the magnitude of the substituent's effect.

The ionization of benzoic acid in water at 25°C has been selected as the reference reaction for measuring substituent effects. *Substituent constants—* symbolized by the Greek letter sigma (σ)—are, in effect, adjusted ΔpK values for substituted benzoic acids.

$$\sigma = \Delta pK \text{ (benzoic acids)} = pK_a \text{ (bz)} - pK_a \text{ (Zbz)} \quad \textbf{(2)}$$

(bz = benzoic acid; Zbz = substituted benzoic acid)

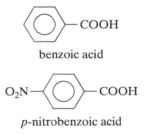

benzoic acid

p-nitrobenzoic acid

Don't confuse a negative ΔpK value, which is associated with an acid-weakening substituent, with a negative pK_a value, which indicates a strong acid.

CH$_2$COOH

phenylacetic acid

O$_2$N—CH$_2$COOH

p-nitrophenylacetic acid

Table 1 in the "Reactions and Properties" section lists the reported sigma values for some common *para* substituents.

The effect of a substituent will usually change if the substrate or the reaction type is changed, or even if the reaction conditions are varied. For example, the pK_a values for phenylacetic acid and *p*-nitrophenylacetic acid in water are 4.28 and 3.85, respectively; thus, ΔpK for the *para*-nitro group on this substrate is 0.43, which is considerably less than its ΔpK of 0.78 in the benzoic acid system. We can use the ratio of these ΔpK values to estimate the relative effect of a substituent on the ionization of the substituted phenylacetic acid (keeping in mind that $\sigma \approx \Delta$pK for the benzoic acid system):

$$\frac{\Delta\text{p}K(\text{phenylacetic acids})}{\sigma} = \frac{0.43}{0.78} = 0.55$$

So the nitro group has only about half the acid-strengthening effect on phenylacetic acid that it does on benzoic acid. This is to be expected, because the substituent is farther from the reaction site in phenylacetic acid. Comparing the effects of a large number of substituents on the same reaction yields an averaged ΔpK/σ value of 0.49 for the ionization of phenylacetic acid. This value, called the *reaction constant,* is symbolized by the Greek letter rho (ρ). Rearranging the equality $\rho = \Delta$pK/σ leads to the *Hammett equation,*

$$\Delta\text{p}K = \rho\sigma \qquad (3)$$

which, for organic acids, can also be written as

$$\log\frac{K_a(\text{substituted acid})}{K_a(\text{unsubstituted acid})} = \rho\sigma$$

According to the Hammett equation, the effect that any substituent (Z) will have on the pK of a particular reaction can be estimated by multiplying the sigma value for Z (the parameter that measures the electronic effect of Z on a reference reaction) by the rho value for the reaction in question (the parameter that measures the sensitivity of the reaction to the electronic effects of substituents). Because of the proportionality between pK and $\Delta G°$ mentioned previously, the Hammett equation is called a *linear free-energy relationship.*

By definition, the reaction constant (rho value) for the ionization of benzoic acids in water is 1; reactions that are more sensitive to substituent effects than the reference reaction have rho values greater than 1, and reactions that are less sensitive have rho values between 0 and 1. Negative rho values are observed for reactions in which electron donors increase the extent of reaction and electron acceptors decrease it, rather than the other way around. The rho value for a particular reaction may change if the solvent or other reaction conditions are changed. Just as a car's power is needed more on a steep hill than on the level, substituents have the greatest effect when a reaction is most difficult and the least effect when it is easiest.

Understanding the Experiment

In this experiment, you will prepare *p*-iodobenzoic acid from *p*-aminobenzoic acid (PABA). Determining the pK_a value of your product and other acids (from Table 1) in 95% ethanol will then allow you to determine the

σ value for p-iodobenzoic acid and the ρ value for the reaction. An aryl iodide can be prepared by treating the corresponding aromatic amine with nitrous acid in the presence of a mineral acid such as HCl, and then heating the resulting diazonium salt with aqueous potassium iodide.

$$ArNH_2 + HONO + HCl \longrightarrow ArN_2^+Cl^- + 2H_2O$$

$$ArN_2^+Cl^- + KI \longrightarrow ArI + N_2 + KCl$$

Although some displacement reactions of diazonium salts may involve free-radical intermediates, others appear to be S_N1 reactions in which the diazonium salt loses nitrogen (as N_2) to form an intermediate aryl carbocation (Ar^+). A nucleophilic species then combines with the carbocation to form either the product or another intermediate that yields the product after a proton exchange.

You will prepare the diazonium salt of p-aminobenzoic acid by dissolving or suspending the amine in dilute HCl, cooling the solution to 5°C or below, and adding aqueous sodium nitrite. Sodium nitrite reacts with some of the acid to generate nitrous acid according to the equation:

$$NaNO_2 + HCl \longrightarrow HONO + NaCl$$

The diazonium salt solution must be kept cold, because diazonium salts can react with the solvent at elevated temperatures. When you mix this solution with a solution of potassium iodide and heat the mixture, p-iodobenzoic acid should separate as a fine precipitate that may take some time to filter.

To determine the pK_a of p-iodobenzoic acid or another acid in 95% ethanol, you will first dissolve some of the acid in 95% ethanol to obtain an approximately 0.1 M solution. You will measure two equal portions of this solution and add just enough dilute NaOH to one of the portions to convert all of the acid it contains to the conjugate base, according to the following reaction equation:

*Although the product should be a light tan color, some preparations yield a reddish solid. The lighter-colored products should be used to determine the pK_a value for p-iodobenzoic acid in part **B**.*

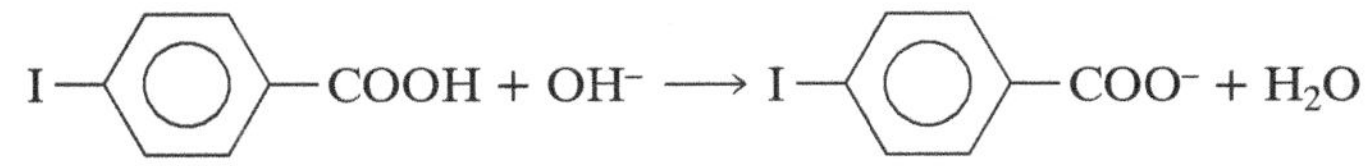

You will then combine this neutralized portion with the second portion containing the unneutralized acid, which results in a solution that contains equimolar amounts of the acid and its conjugate base. After preparing solutions of p-iodobenzoic acid and most or all of the acids listed in Table 1, you and your coworkers will measure the pH of each solution with a pH meter. Equation **4**, where n_{HA} = moles of acid and n_{A^-} = moles of conjugate base, relates the pH of a solution to the pK_a of the acid.

$$pK_a = pH + \log\frac{n_{HA}}{n_{A^-}} \qquad (4)$$

When n_{HA} and n_{A^-} are equal, the logarithmic term equals zero, so pK_a = pH. Thus, you can determine the pK_a and ΔpK values of the acids from the measured pH values of their solutions. Graphing the ΔpK values for the acids against the sigma values for the substituents yields a *Hammett plot* of Equation **3**, from which you should be able to determine the sigma value for the *para*-iodo substituent and the rho value for the ionization of benzoic acids in 95% ethanol.

Sodium nitrite is very toxic to aquatic organisms, but the other chemicals used in this experiment—at the concentrations stated—don't appear to be particularly harmful to the environment.

Reactions and Properties

Table 1 Molecular weights and sigma values for *para*-substituted benzoic acids

Acid	mol wt	Substituent (Z)	σ
p-aminobenzoic acid	137.1	—NH$_2$	−0.66
p-hydroxybenzoic acid	138.1	—OH	−0.37
p-anisic acid	152.2	—OCH$_3$	−0.27
p-toluic acid	136.2	—CH$_3$	−0.17
benzoic acid	122.1	none	0.00
p-chlorobenzoic acid	156.6	—Cl	0.23
terephthalic acid	166.1	—COOH	0.45
p-nitrobenzoic acid	167.1	—NO$_2$	0.78

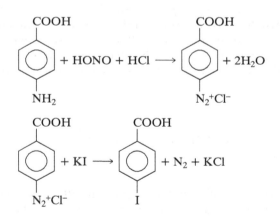

Table 2 Physical properties

	mol wt	mp
p-aminobenzoic acid	137.1	189
p-iodobenzoic acid	248.0	270
potassium iodide	166.0	681
sodium nitrite	69.0	271

Note: mp is in °C.

DIRECTIONS

A. *Preparation of* p-*Iodobenzoic Acid*

> Sodium nitrite may cause a fire if mixed with combustible materials. Keep it away from such materials.
> Benzoic acid and the substituted benzoic acids in Table 1 may be harmful if inhaled, ingested, or absorbed through the skin. Minimize contact with the acids and do not breathe their dust.

Safety Notes

benzoic acid

Reaction. Weigh 10.0 mmol of *p*-aminobenzoic acid (PABA) into a 50-mL Erlenmeyer flask. Add 10 mL of 3 *M* hydrochloric acid, and warm the solution gently—with swirling or stirring—until the PABA dissolves. Dissolve 10.0 mmol of sodium nitrite in 10 mL of water in another small flask or beaker. Cool [OP-8] both solutions in an ice/water or ice–salt bath until their temperatures are 5°C or below. To form the diazonium salt, add the sodium nitrite solution, with swirling or magnetic stirring [OP-10], to the flask containing the PABA; add it slowly enough so that the temperature remains below 10°C (leave the solution in the cold bath during the addition). Test the solution with starch–iodide paper; if the test is positive, add just enough urea to give a negative test (no immediate blue-black color).

Dissolve 15 mmol of potassium iodide in 100 mL of water in a 400-mL beaker. Pour the diazonium salt solution into the potassium iodide solution, with stirring (rinse the reaction flask's contents into the beaker with a little water). Heat [OP-7] the reaction mixture on a steam bath or in a boiling-water bath for 10–15 minutes, stirring occasionally. If the resulting foam threatens to overflow, poke it with a stirring rod to make it subside. Cool the reaction mixture in an ice/water bath for 5–10 minutes.

Separation and Purification. Collect the crude *p*-iodobenzoic acid by vacuum filtration [OP-16], and wash it on the filter [OP-26a] with cold water. Some product may be in the foam, so transfer it to the funnel along with the liquid. Purify the product by recrystallization [OP-28] from 80% aqueous ethanol. If desired, use pelletized Norit to partly decolorize the dark solution. Dry [OP-26b] the product to constant mass and measure its mass.

B. *Determination of* pK_a *Values*

This part can be performed by teams of three to four students. Each team should carry out pH measurements with *p*-iodobenzoic acid (preferably using the product with the lightest color) and all of the acids listed in Table 1 that are provided. For each acid, prepare an approximately 0.10 *M* solution in 95% ethanol by dissolving 0.80 mmol of the acid in 8.0 mL of 95% ethanol, with gentle heating if necessary. Prepare half-neutralized solutions of all of the acids by the following procedure. For each acid, transfer two accurately measured 2.00-mL portions of its solution to two labeled test tubes. Add a drop of phenolphthalein indicator to *one* of the portions; neutralize *that* portion to a light pink end point by adding ~0.1 *M* NaOH

Stop and Think: Why is it important to keep the temperature low?

Observe and Note: Describe what happens as the reaction proceeds.

Take Care! A vigorous reaction with considerable foaming will occur.

Stop and Think: What gas is responsible for the foaming?

Waste Disposal: Unless your instructor directs otherwise, wash the filtrates down the drain.

in 95% ethanol, drop by drop, from a disposable narrow-tipped transfer pipet. Use a glass stirring rod to keep the solution well mixed during the titration. (If you go past the end point, discard the mixture and titrate a fresh portion of the same solution.) Combine the neutralized and unneutralized solutions in a labeled container that will accommodate the pH meter's probe, and mix them thoroughly with a stirring rod. Measure the pH values of all of the solutions you have prepared.

Report your pH values to your coworkers and obtain the pH values for the remaining acids from them. Tabulate the pK_a and ΔpK values for all of the acids and construct a Hammett plot. From your plot, determine the sigma value for the *para*-iodo substituent and the rho value for the ionization of benzoic acids in 95% ethanol. Decide whether an inductive or resonance effect of the *para*-iodo substituent can best account for your results.

Waste Disposal: Dispose of the solutions as directed by your instructor.

Stop and Think: How is the pK_a of each acid related to the pH of its solution?

Exercises

1. Is the ionization of benzoic acids in 95% ethanol more sensitive or less sensitive to substituent effects than its ionization in water? Explain why.
2. Derive Equation **4** (see "Understanding the Experiment") from the equilibrium constant expression for the ionization of an acid, HA.
3. Describe and explain the possible effect on your results of the following experimental errors or variations. (a) You misread the label on a bottle of sodium nitrate and used it in place of the sodium nitrite. (b) When titrating the *p*-iodobenzoic acid solution, you added enough dilute NaOH to turn it dark red. (c) You misread the directions and neutralized both portions of the *p*-iodobenzoic acid solution before combining them for the pH measurement.
4. (a) Calculate the atom economy and reaction efficiency of your synthesis of *p*-iodobenzoic acid. (b) Describe some green features of the synthesis, and any that aren't so green.
5. Following the format in the "Planning an Experiment" appendix, construct a flow diagram for the synthesis of *p*-iodobenzoic acid.
6. (a) Bea Wilder heated the diazonium salt solution *before* adding potassium iodide and isolated a white solid with a melting point of 215°C. What did she make instead of *p*-iodobenzoic acid? (b) Propose a mechanism for the reaction.
7. Using resonance structures, explain why *p*-methoxybenzoic acid is less acidic than benzoic acid, but *m*-methoxybenzoic acid is more acidic than benzoic acid.
8. Predict the acid ionization constant (K_a) of *p*-trifluoromethylbenzoic acid in water and in 95% ethanol, given that a *para*-trifluoromethyl substituent ($-CF_3$) has a sigma value of 0.54.
9. (a) Would you expect the rho value for the ionization of *para*-substituted phenols ($p\text{-}ZC_6H_4OH$) in water to be greater than or less than 1? Explain. (b) Give examples of reactions that you would expect to have negative rho values.

Other Things You Can Do

(Starred items require your instructor's permission.)

*1. As an alternative to the method described in part **B**, you can measure the pK_a of *p*-iodobenzoic acid (or the other acids) by carrying out a pH titration. Dissolve approximately 1 mmol of the acid in 20 mL of 95% ethanol. Titrate this solution with ~0.05 *M* KOH in 95% ethanol, adding about 1 mL at a time and measuring the pH after each addition. When the pH begins to rise rapidly, add the KOH in 0.5-mL increments and continue to titrate until the pH begins to level off. Plot pH versus volume of base, mark the inflection point of the curve (where it changes direction), and determine the volume of KOH solution added at that point. The pH reading at exactly half that volume equals the pK_a of the acid.

*2. Determine the relative strengths of some common organic acids and bases by carrying out the "Acid–Base Strengths of Organic Compounds" minilab.

3. Starting with sources listed in the Bibliography, write a research paper about the natural sources, physiological functions, and commercial uses of *p*-aminobenzoic acid (PABA).

Synthesis and Identification of an Unknown Carboxylic Acid

EXPERIMENT

Reactions of Acid Anhydrides. Reactions of Carbon–Carbon Double Bonds. Preparation of Carboxylic Acids. Qualitative Analysis.

Operations

OP-10   Mixing
OP-15   Gravity Filtration
OP-16   Vacuum Filtration
OP-26   Washing and Drying Solids
OP-33   Melting Point

Before You Begin

1. Read the experiment, read or review the operations as necessary, and write an experimental plan.
2. Calculate the mass of 25.0 mmol of maleic anhydride and of 28 mmol of zinc.

Scenario

Tetrahydrofuran (THF), a versatile organic solvent, is ordinarily manufactured by the catalytic hydrogenation of maleic anhydride.

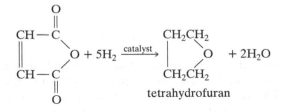

Reduction of maleic anhydride to tetrahydrofuran

Willy Hackett, an inexperienced graduate student at Miskatonic University, was attempting to develop an improved method for preparing this useful solvent as part of his thesis research project. He reasoned that if zinc and hydrochloric acid were combined in the presence of maleic anhydride, they would react to form hydrogen, which would then reduce the maleic anhydride to tetrahydrofuran.

$$Zn + 2HCl \longrightarrow H_2 + ZnCl_2$$

He thought this procedure would avoid most of the hazards associated with the use of hydrogen gas, as well as the need for expensive apparatus and catalysts. So he dissolved maleic acid in boiling water, stirred in some zinc followed by concentrated HCl, and was pleased when the reaction mixture started fizzing vigorously, as expected. But when the reaction mixture cooled

From *Operational Organic Chemistry: A Problem Solving Approach to the Laboratory*, Fourth Edition, John W. Lehman. Copyright © 2009 by Pearson Education. Published by Prentice Hall. All rights reserved.

down, a white solid crystallized from solution. Since tetrahydrofuran is a low-boiling liquid, Willy realized that something had gone wrong.

Not wishing to admit to his research mentor that the experiment had failed, Willy has decided to study the reaction as part of his research project. But first, he must find out what the white solid is, and whether his results can be reproduced by other chemists. Your supervisor learned of his predicament and has agreed to have the Consulting Chemists Institute work on the problem. Preliminary tests suggest that the white solid is a carboxylic acid. Your assignment is to see whether you can prepare the unknown acid by Hackett's method and, if so, to identify it.

Applying Scientific Methodology

After reading the experiment, you should be able to formulate a hypothesis about the structure of the unknown carboxylic acid by considering the structure of the starting material and the composition of the reaction mixture. You will test your hypothesis by determining the melting point and equivalent weight of the acid, which you will use to identify it.

Maleic Anhydride and Reid's Reaction

Maleic anhydride is manufactured by air oxidation of benzene in the presence of a vanadium oxide catalyst.

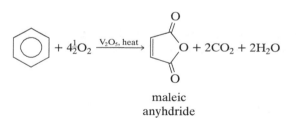

maleic
anyhdride

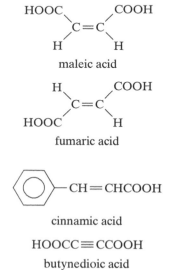

maleic acid

fumaric acid

cinnamic acid

HOOCC≡CCOOH

butynedioic acid

The reaction with cinnamic acid requires a zinc–mercury amalgam rather than pure zinc.

Because both air and benzene are cheap and abundant, maleic anhydride is an attractive starting material for the preparation of many other marketable chemicals. Besides being used in the production of tetrahydrofuran, maleic anhydride is used to manufacture agricultural chemicals, polyester resins, surface coatings, dye intermediates, pharmaceuticals, lubricant additives, and other commercially useful products. It is also an excellent dienophile that forms Diels–Alder adducts with most conjugated dienes.

The chemical transformation described in the Scenario is an example of a little-known reaction that (unknown to Willy Hackett) was first reported by Dr. E. Emmett Reid. When Reid added maleic anhydride to a mixture of granular zinc and boiling water, he noticed an immediate reaction and the separation of a white precipitate. After acidifying the reaction mixture with hydrochloric acid, he recovered the product and identified it as a carboxylic acid. This result wasn't published until 1972, when it was mentioned—almost as an afterthought—in a "chemical autobiography" describing Reid's 76 years of research. Reid's reaction works only with maleic anhydride and certain other unsaturated carboxylic acids and anhydrides—such as maleic acid, fumaric acid, cinnamic acid, and butynedioic acid, whose structures are shown in the margin.

Understanding the Experiment

You will synthesize the unknown acid by adding granular zinc to a hot aqueous solution of maleic anhydride. Because powdered maleic anhydride reacts quite rapidly with atmospheric moisture, it is usually manufactured in the form of briquettes, which must be pulverized before use. If maleic anhydride is provided in powdered form, you should open its container only momentarily and replace the cap immediately after you've removed the amount needed. Once the initial reaction is complete, concentrated hydrochloric acid is added to liberate the final product and dissolve any excess zinc. Because the product is somewhat soluble even in cold water, the solution should be concentrated to increase the yield. The product should require no further purification after it crystallizes from the cold solution.

The *equivalent weight* of an acid, sometimes called its neutralization equivalent, can be defined as the mass of the acid that provides a mole of protons (H^+) in a neutralization reaction. For example, 1 mole of acetic acid (CH_3COOH, M.W. = 60) and $\frac{1}{2}$ mole of oxalic acid ($HOOCCOOH$, M.W. = 90) both contain 1 mole of acidic hydrogens that can be removed as H^+ ions by a strong base. Thus, the equivalent weight of acetic acid is 60, but the equivalent weight of oxalic acid is 45 — half its molecular weight. If the structure of an acid is known, its equivalent weight can be calculated by dividing its molecular weight by the number of acidic hydrogens per molecule.

The equivalent weight of an unknown acid can be measured by titrating an accurately weighed sample of the acid with a standardized solution of sodium hydroxide. The volume of the base required for the titration and its molar concentration are used to calculate the number of moles of base neutralized by the acid, which is equal to the number of moles of protons that the acid provided. For example, suppose 0.222 g of an unknown carboxylic acid with a melting point of 210°C was titrated with 23.2 mL of 0.115 M NaOH. Multiplying the molarity of the base by the volume used (in liters) gives the number of moles of base and protons. Dividing the mass of the acid by the number of moles of protons it contains then yields the equivalent weight of the acid, which is about 83.

Key Concept: An equivalent of a substance is the amount of that substance that has a mass equal to its equivalent weight, in grams. One equivalent of an acid or base is the amount that will produce or react with one mole of protons, so x equivalents of any acid should neutralize x equivalents of any base.

$$\text{moles of } H^+ = \text{moles of NaOH} = \frac{0.115 \text{ mol}}{1 \text{ L}} \times 0.0232 \text{ L}$$

$$= 2.67 \times 10^{-3} \text{ mol}$$

$$\text{equivalent weight} = \frac{\text{mass of acid}}{\text{moles of } H^+} = \frac{0.222}{2.67 \times 10^{-3}} = 83.2$$

Note that equivalent weight, like molecular weight, is dimensionless.

The melting point of this unknown compound is too high for a carboxylic acid having a molecular weight near 83, so the unknown acid must have two or more carboxyl groups and a molecular weight that is some multiple of 83. From the data in Table 7 of the "Properties of Organic Compounds" appendix, we can deduce that the unknown is phthalic acid, whose molecular weight is 166.

The unknown acid you will synthesize in this experiment is also listed in Table 7, so you should be able to identify it after you have measured its equivalent weight and melting point. With your instructor's permission, you can obtain the IR or ^1H NMR spectrum of the acid to help confirm its identity.

In the environment, maleic anhydride hydrolyzes to maleic acid, which is toxic to aquatic organisms. Hydrochloric acid is expected to be toxic to aquatic life.

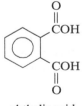

phthalic acid

Properties

Table 1 Physical properties

	mol wt	mp	bp
maleic anhydride	98.1	53	202
zinc	65.4	419	907d

Note: mp and bp are in °C; density is in g/mL; d = decomposes.

DIRECTIONS

Safety Notes

maleic anhydride   hydrochloric acid

> **Maleic anhydride is corrosive and toxic; it can cause severe damage to the eyes, skin, and upper respiratory tract. Wear gloves, avoid contact, and do not breathe its dust. If you must powder maleic anhydride briquettes, do it under the hood, and wear safety goggles and protective clothing.**
>
> **Concentrated hydrochloric acid is poisonous and corrosive. Contact or inhalation can cause severe damage to the eyes, skin, and respiratory tract. Wear gloves and dispense under a hood; avoid contact and do not breathe its vapors.**
>
> **The reaction of zinc with hydrochloric acid produces hydrogen gas, which is highly flammable. Keep the reaction mixture away from flames.**
>
> **The product may irritate the eyes, skin, or respiratory tract. Avoid contact and do not breathe its dust.**

Take Care! Avoid contact with maleic anhydride and do not breathe its dust.

Observe and Note: Look for and record any evidence that a reaction is occurring.

Take Care! Wear gloves, avoid contact with concentrated HCl, and do not breathe its vapors.

Reaction. Dissolve 25.0 mmol of maleic anhydride in 15 mL of water in a 50-mL Erlenmeyer flask by heating the water just to boiling. Remove the flask from the heat source and immediately add 28 mmol of 40-mesh zinc in three or four portions, stirring or swirling [OP-10] after each addition. Let the flask stand for 15 minutes, with magnetic stirring or occasional swirling. *Under the hood*, slowly add 5.0 mL of concentrated HCl, with stirring or swirling.

Separation. When the zinc (or most of it) has dissolved, heat the mixture to boiling under the hood. Any white solid that formed during the reaction should dissolve. Filter [OP-15] the hot solution through fluted filter paper. Boil the filtrate under the hood until the solution becomes *just* cloudy at the boiling point. Cover the beaker with a watch glass and set it aside to cool to room temperature. Then cool the beaker in an ice/water bath until crystallization is complete. Collect the product by vacuum filtration [OP-16], and wash it on the filter [OP-26a] with cold acetone. Air-dry the product on the filter for a few minutes; then dry [OP-26b] it to constant mass.

Waste Disposal: Unless your instructor directs otherwise, wash the filtrate down the drain.

Analysis. Measure the mass and melting point [OP-33] of the thoroughly dried product. Weigh about 0.20 g of the product to the nearest milligram and dissolve it in 25 mL of water in a 125-mL Erlenmeyer flask. Add 2 drops of phenolphthalein indicator and titrate with a standardized ~0.2 M NaOH solution to the light pink end point. Calculate the equivalent weight of your unknown acid and identify it by referring to Table 7 of the "Properties of Organic Compounds" appendix. Write the structure of the product and a balanced equation for its formation, and give its systematic and common names.

Observe and Note: Record the exact concentration of the NaOH solution in your lab notebook.

Exercises

1. Estimate the amount of product that was lost in the filtrate, assuming that the volume of the reaction mixture was 5.0 mL when you collected the product by vacuum filtration. Compare this with the amount of product you would have lost if you hadn't boiled off most of the water. The solubility of the product is 6.8 g/100 mL at 20°C.

2. (a) What was wrong with Willy Hackett's idea (see the Scenario) that the reaction of maleic acid with zinc and aqueous HCl would yield tetrahydrofuran? (b) The actual synthesis that you carried out involves two separate reaction steps. Write a balanced equation for each step.

3. Describe and explain the possible effect on your results of the following experimental errors or variations. (a) You used phthalic anhydride (1,2-benzenedioic anhydride) instead of maleic anhydride. (b) After filtering the hot solution in the separation step, you forgot to boil down the filtrate. (c) You didn't record the concentration of the NaOH solution (which was 0.255 M) but assumed a concentration of exactly 0.2 M.

4. (a) Calculate the atom economy and reaction efficiency of your synthesis. (b) Describe some green features of your synthesis, and any that aren't so green.

5. Following the format in the "Planning an Experiment" appendix, construct a flow diagram for the synthesis you carried out in this experiment.

6. Propose structures for the products you would obtain by treating fumaric acid, cinnamic acid, and butynedioic acid with zinc and HCl. Write balanced equations for the reactions.

7. Suppose that 0.196 g of an unknown carboxylic acid is titrated using 19.3 mL of 0.196 M aqueous NaOH. What is the probable identity of the unknown if its melting point is 132±5°C? (Use Table 7 in the "Properties of Organic Compounds" appendix.)

8. Sketch the ^{1}H NMR spectrum you would expect from the product of this experiment, giving peak areas, multiplicities, and approximate chemical shifts for all signals.

9. Write balanced equations for the reactions of maleic anhydride with water, cyclohexanol, aniline, and isoprene (2-methyl-1,3-butadiene).

Other Things You Can Do

(Starred items require your instructor's permission.)

*1. Record the infrared spectrum of the product and compare it with the spectrum of the starting material in Figure 1 (from the "Identification of a Conjugated Diene from Eucalyptus Oil" experiment). Interpret both spectra as completely as you can.

*2. After you predict the ^{1}H NMR spectrum you would expect from the product (see Exercise 8), record its spectrum in DMSO-d_6 or another suitable solvent and see how accurate your prediction was.

*3. Observe the relative hydrolysis rates of some esters in the "Hydrolysis Rates of Esters" minilab.

4. Starting with sources listed in the Bibliography, write a research paper about the manufacture and uses of maleic anhydride, maleic acid, and fumaric acid.

Preparation of the Insect Repellent
N,N-Diethyl-*meta*-toluamide

Reactions of Carboxylic Acids. Preparation of Amides. Nucleophilic Acyl Substitution. Acid Chlorides. Infrared Spectrometry.

Operations

OP-7   Heating
OP-8   Cooling
OP-10 Mixing
OP-11 Addition of Reactants
OP-14 Trapping Gases (optional)
OP-18 Extraction
OP-19 Evaporation
OP-21 Column Chromatography
OP-24 Washing Liquids
OP-25 Drying Liquids
OP-37 Gas Chromatography
OP-39 Infrared Spectrometry
OP-40 Nuclear Magnetic Resonance Spectrometry (optional)

Before You Begin

1. Read the experiment, read or review the operations as necessary, and write an experimental plan.
2. Calculate the mass of 30 mmol of *m*-toluic acid, the mass of 25.0 mmol of diethylamine hydrochloride, and the theoretical yield of *N,N*-diethyl-*m*-toluamide.

Scenario

Skeeters 'n Such manufactures insect repellents such as *Skeedaddle*, whose main active ingredient is *N,N*-diethyl-*m*-toluamide, better known as deet. Its current process for the manufacture of deet requires the use of diethyl ether as a solvent and a 2:1 molar ratio of nucleophile (diethylamine) to substrate. To reduce production costs, Skeeters 'n Such wants your institute to develop a synthetic method that uses a cheaper and more environmentally friendly solvent, such as water, and a 1:1 or lower nucleophile:substrate ratio. Your supervisor thinks a procedural variation called the Schotten–Baumann reaction may accomplish both of these objectives but isn't sure whether the product will be pure enough to meet specifications. Your assignment is to determine whether or not deet can be synthesized in at least 95% purity using the Schotten–Baumann procedure.

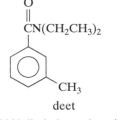

deet
(*N,N*-diethyl-*m*-toluamide)

From *Operational Organic Chemistry: A Problem Solving Approach to the Laboratory*, Fourth Edition, John W. Lehman. Copyright © 2009 by Pearson Education. Published by Prentice Hall. All rights reserved.

Applying Scientific Methodology

You should develop a working hypothesis, based on the Scenario, which will be tested when you analyze the product by gas chromatography and infrared (IR) spectrometry.

Chemical Mosquito Evasion

a hungry mosquito

Is there anyone on Earth who hasn't cringed upon hearing the high-pitched whine of a hungry mosquito? Besides their capacity to torment us, these bloodthirsty insects have a well-earned reputation for spreading diseases, including malaria, yellow fever, West Nile disease, and viral encephalitis. Numerous methods of controlling mosquitoes have been developed, but the hardy creatures can withstand a variety of adverse conditions. Mosquitoes have been known to breed in the hot alkaline volcanic pools of Uganda, and even in a tank of hydrochloric acid in India! Because we aren't likely to eradicate mosquitoes from the Earth anytime soon, we must resign ourselves to living with them. This fate is made more tolerable by the availability of effective insect repellents. Among the best of these is deet, which is the major ingredient of most commercial mosquito repellents manufactured in North America.

Mosquito "repellents" don't really repel mosquitoes in the same way that a disagreeable odor might repel a human from its source. Instead, they appear to jam the insect's sensors so that it can't find its victim. Warm objects generate convection currents in the air around them; warm living objects also emit carbon dioxide, which alerts a mosquito to the presence of a blood source and starts it on its flight. This flight is initially random, but when the insect encounters a warm, moist stream of air, it moves toward the source, which is generally a living object. Unless the object takes rapid evasive action, the mosquito follows the convection current until it makes contact — unless it gets squashed first.

When you (the intended victim) are protected by an effective insect repellent, the mosquito still knows you're around but is unable to find you. This is because the repellent prevents the insect's moisture sensors from responding normally to the high humidity of your convection current. Ordinarily, when a mosquito passes from warm, moist air into drier air, its moisture sensors send fewer signals to its central nervous system, causing it to turn back into the air stream. By blocking these sensors, the repellent reduces the signal frequency and convinces the mosquito that it is heading into drier rather than moister air, so it turns away before landing. Individual variations in diet, skin chemistry, or other factors — such as the color of one's clothing (dark colors attract mosquitoes) — may help explain why some unlucky individuals are eaten alive by mosquitoes and others escape unscathed. For example, thiamine (Vitamin B_1) taken orally is excreted through the skin, where it acts as an insect repellent. On the other hand, lactic acid and many other chemicals that emanate from human skin attract mosquitoes.

Scientists from the U.S. Department of Agriculture's research station have identified more than 340 different skin chemicals.

The molecular features that make a compound a good insect repellent are not well understood at this time. Repellents occur in nearly every chemical family and exhibit a large variety of molecular shapes, as shown in Figure 1. A number of *N,N*-disubstituted amides similar to deet are represented, including the diethylamide of thujic acid, a constituent of the western red cedar that may be partly responsible for that tree's resistance to insect attack. Other effective repellents include esters such

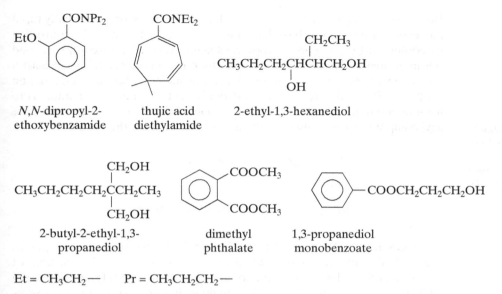

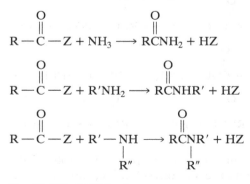

N,N-dipropyl-2-ethoxybenzamide   thujic acid diethylamide   2-ethyl-1,3-hexanediol

2-butyl-2-ethyl-1,3-propanediol   dimethyl phthalate   1,3-propanediol monobenzoate

Et = CH₃CH₂—   Pr = CH₃CH₂CH₂—

Figure 1 Some typical insect repellents

as dimethyl phthalate and diols such as 2-ethyl-1,3-hexanediol (also known as 6-12).

Recent lab tests with catnip oil, which contains two nepetalactone stereoisomers, have shown it to be 10 times more effective than deet as a mosquito repellent. Further tests are needed (perhaps with both mosquitoes and cats) to see whether the oil can be used safely and effectively by humans. When more is learned about the structural features that make a substance act as an insect repellent, it should be possible to develop even more effective and convenient repellents for long-term protection against insect bites.

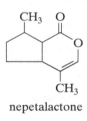

nepetalactone

Understanding the Experiment

Amides are usually prepared by treating a carboxylic acid derivative with ammonia or with a primary or secondary amine. This is a nucleophilic acyl substitution reaction, in which ammonia or the amine acts as the nucleophile. Acid anhydrides and esters are sometimes used as the acid derivative, but acyl chlorides are the most useful for preparing the widest variety of amides.

General reactions for preparing amides

$$R-\overset{\overset{\displaystyle O}{\|}}{C}-Z + NH_3 \longrightarrow R\overset{\overset{\displaystyle O}{\|}}{C}NH_2 + HZ$$

$$R-\overset{\overset{\displaystyle O}{\|}}{C}-Z + R'NH_2 \longrightarrow R\overset{\overset{\displaystyle O}{\|}}{C}NHR' + HZ$$

$$R-\overset{\overset{\displaystyle O}{\|}}{C}-Z + R'-\underset{\underset{\displaystyle R''}{|}}{N}H \longrightarrow R\overset{\overset{\displaystyle O}{\|}}{C}\underset{\underset{\displaystyle R''}{|}}{N}R' + HZ$$

Z = Cl, OR, OCOR, etc.

Because of the high reactivity of acyl chlorides, the reactions are usually rapid and exothermic—so much so that, in many cases, the rate must be controlled by cooling or by using an appropriate solvent. When the reaction is carried out in an inert solvent such as diethyl ether, it is necessary to use at least a 2:1 mole ratio of amine (or ammonia) to the substrate because the reaction produces HCl, which reacts with one equivalent of amine (or ammonia) to form an ammonium salt. The salt isn't nucleophilic, so it can't react with the acyl compound; it may also be difficult to separate from the product.

Key Concept: *A nucleophile is usually basic enough to accept a proton from an acid. A protonated nucleophile, having donated a lone pair, is either a much weaker nucleophile or is not nucleophilic at all.*

Example of reaction in inert solvent

$$\underset{O}{\overset{\parallel}{R}CCl} + 2R'NH_2 \longrightarrow \underset{O}{\overset{\parallel}{R}CNHR'} + R'NH_3^+Cl^-$$

The Schotten–Baumann reaction is a synthetic method that uses aqueous sodium hydroxide (or potassium hydroxide) as a solvent for the reactions of certain acyl chlorides. Some of the sodium hydroxide (NaOH) neutralizes the HCl produced during the reaction, making it unnecessary to add excess amine for that purpose. Some acyl chlorides, particularly low molecular-weight aliphatic ones, hydrolyze rapidly in water to form carboxylic acids and thus are unsuitable candidates for the Schotten–Baumann reaction. However, aromatic and long-chain aliphatic acyl chlorides are nearly insoluble in water and therefore hydrolyze much more slowly. The small amount of acyl chloride lost by hydrolysis can be compensated for by using an excess of this reactant. The presence of aqueous NaOH in the reaction mixture also makes it possible to use an amine hydrochloride in place of the free amine, since the amine hydrochloride reacts with base to liberate the amine *in situ*. Because many amines are volatile, corrosive, and quite unpleasant to handle, the use of the comparatively well-behaved amine salt is a definite advantage.

Schotten-Baumann method for preparing amides

$$\underset{O}{\overset{\parallel}{R}CCl} + R'NH_2 + NaOH \longrightarrow$$

$$\underset{O}{\overset{\parallel}{R}CNHR'} + NaCl + H_2O$$

Reaction of an amine hydrochloride with a base

$$RNH_3^+Cl^- + NaOH \longrightarrow$$

$$RNH_2 + NaCl + H_2O$$

The acyl chlorides used for preparing amides are usually made from the corresponding carboxylic acids. Several reagents can be used for this transformation, each with its advantages and disadvantages. Thionyl chloride (SOCl$_2$) is often the reagent of choice, because its inorganic reaction products (HCl and SO$_2$) are gases that can easily be removed from the acyl chloride, which can thus be used for further reactions without purification.

Methods for preparing acyl chlorides

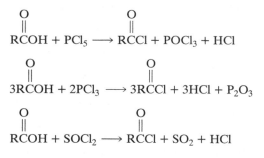

In this experiment, you will prepare *m*-toluoyl chloride by heating *m*-toluic acid with excess thionyl chloride, and then treat the acid chloride with diethylamine (from the hydrochloride) in aqueous NaOH to obtain *N,N*-diethyl-*m*-toluamide. The excess thionyl chloride from the first step is destroyed by sodium hydroxide in the second. Because corrosive gases are released, you will need to carry out the reaction under a fume hood or with a gas trap to keep them out of the atmosphere. Since the acid chloride is relatively insoluble in the aqueous reaction mixture, efficient mixing is necessary to provide adequate contact between the phases. The detergent sodium lauryl sulfate helps disperse the acyl chloride into smaller droplets, increasing the area of contact between phases and thus increasing the reaction rate.

After the product has been isolated by extraction with diethyl ether and evaporation of the ether, it will be purified by column chromatography and then analyzed by gas chromatography to assess its purity. By comparing the infrared spectrum of your product with those of the starting materials in Figure 2, you should find evidence indicating whether or not the expected reaction has taken place.

*A **Greener Way**: You can recover the diethyl ether by evaporating it under vacuum using a cold trap (see OP-15).*

When released into moist soil or water, thionyl chloride hydrolyzes to yield hydrochloric acid and sulfur dioxide, which are expected to be toxic to aquatic life. Diethylamine is not expected to be toxic to aquatic life. Diethyl ether isn't considered toxic to aquatic organisms and doesn't persist for long in either air or water. Deet is slightly toxic to birds, fish, and aquatic invertebrates, but it has very low toxicity potential in mammals.

Reactions and Properties

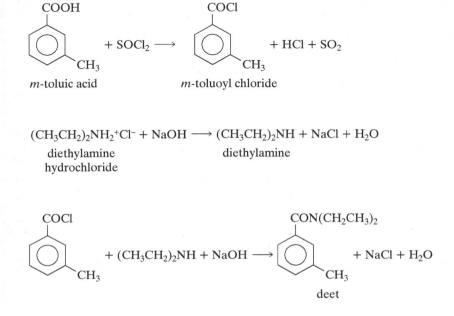

m-toluic acid $+ SOCl_2 \longrightarrow$ m-toluoyl chloride $+ HCl + SO_2$

$(CH_3CH_2)_2NH_2^+Cl^- + NaOH \longrightarrow (CH_3CH_2)_2NH + NaCl + H_2O$
diethylamine hydrochloride $\qquad$ diethylamine

m-toluoyl chloride $+ (CH_3CH_2)_2NH + NaOH \longrightarrow$ deet $+ NaCl + H_2O$

Table 1 Physical properties

	mol wt	mp	bp	d
m-toluic acid	136.2	113		
thionyl chloride	119.0		79^{746}	1.65
m-toluoyl chloride	154.6		86^{5}	1.173
diethylamine hydrochloride	109.6	227–230		
hexanes	86.2		~68−70	~0.67
N,N-diethyl-*m*-toluamide	191.3		160^{19}	0.996

Note: mp and bp are in °C; density is in g/mL; superscripts indicate pressure in torr.

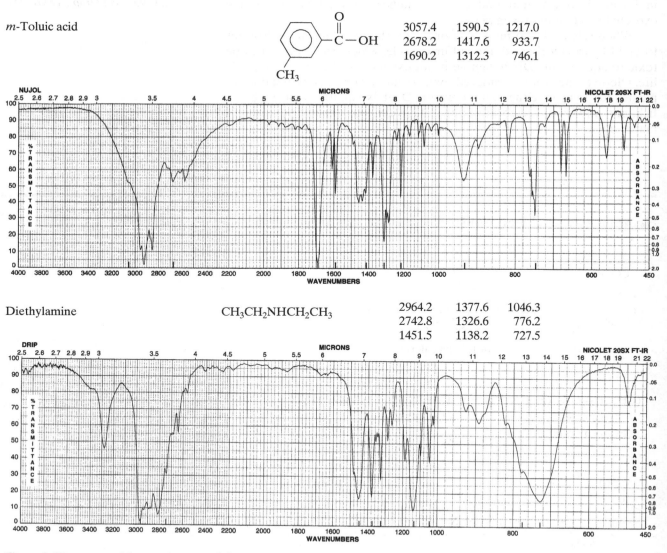

m-Toluic acid

3057.4	1590.5	1217.0
2678.2	1417.6	933.7
1690.2	1312.3	746.1

Diethylamine   CH₃CH₂NHCH₂CH₃

2964.2	1377.6	1046.3
2742.8	1326.6	776.2
1451.5	1138.2	727.5

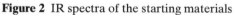

Figure 2 IR spectra of the starting materials

m-Toluic acid

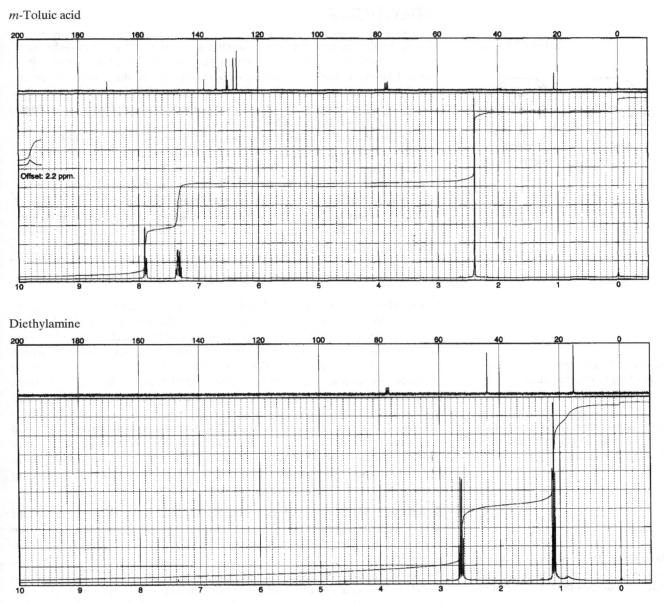

Diethylamine

Figure 3 NMR spectra of the starting materials

DIRECTIONS

Safety Notes

diethylamine   diethyl ether

Thionyl chloride and *m*-toluoyl chloride are both corrosive and lachrymatory (tear inducing); they can damage the eyes, skin, and respiratory system. Thionyl chloride decomposes violently on contact with water to produce corrosive gases. Wear gloves, work under a hood, avoid contact with thionyl chloride and the reaction mixture, keep them away from water, and do not breathe their vapors.
Diethylamine hydrochloride irritates the skin, eyes, and respiratory tract; avoid contact and inhalation. In the reaction mixture, it forms diethylamine, which is corrosive and has toxic vapors.
Diethyl ether is extremely flammable and may be harmful if inhaled. Avoid breathing its vapors; keep it away from flames and hot surfaces.
Hexanes (a mixture of isomeric 6-carbon alkanes) is very flammable, and it may irritate the eyes and respiratory tract. Avoid breathing its vapors; keep it away from flames and hot surfaces.

Stop and Think: What reactions will take place in the gas trap?

Take Care! Wear gloves, avoid contact with thionyl chloride, and do not breathe its vapors.

Take Care! Wear gloves, avoid contact with diethylamine hydrochloride, and do not breathe its vapors.

Stop and Think: What is the purpose of the sodium lauryl sulfate?

Take Care! Keep diethyl ether away from ignition sources.

Preparation of m-Toluoyl Chloride. All glassware must be thoroughly dried for this step. Assemble an apparatus for addition under reflux [OP-11] using a clean, *dry* 100-mL round-bottom flask. The reaction should be carried out under a hood, if possible; if not, equip the reflux condenser with a gas trap [OP-14] containing dilute NaOH. Be sure that the apparatus is securely clamped so that you can remove and reattach the reaction flask safely. Detach the reaction flask and measure 30 mmol of *m*-toluic acid into it, then drop in a magnetic stir bar. *Under the hood,* add 2.6 mL (~36 mmol) of thionyl chloride, then reattach the flask to the reaction apparatus. If you must take the reaction flask out of the hood, stopper it first. Start the stirrer [OP-10] and heat the reaction mixture gently under reflux [OP-7] for at least 20 minutes. Cool the reaction mixture in an ice/water bath while you prepare the diethylamine solution in the next step.

Reaction. Measure 35 mL of 3.0 *M* NaOH into an Erlenmeyer flask and cool [OP-8] the flask in an ice/water bath for 5 minutes or more. *Under the hood,* add 25.0 mmol of diethylamine hydrochloride to the NaOH solution in small portions, with manual stirring or swirling. The amine salt will be converted to diethylamine as it is added. Then mix in about 0.10 g of sodium lauryl sulfate. Transfer this solution to the separatory–addition funnel on the reaction apparatus, using a few milliliters of water for the transfer. Leaving the reaction flask containing *m*-toluoyl chloride in its ice/water bath with the condenser water and stirrer running, add the diethylamine solution to the reaction flask, drop by drop (or in small portions), for a period of about 5 minutes. Test the pH of the solution with pH paper; if it isn't strongly basic, add more 3.0 *M* NaOH until it is. Then heat the reaction mixture using a steam bath or boiling-water bath, with vigorous stirring, for 15 minutes or more. At this point, the acid chloride odor should be gone and the reaction mixture should still be basic.

Separation. Allow the reaction mixture to cool to room temperature. Transfer it to a separatory funnel, and extract [OP-18] it with three separate 20-mL portions of solvent-grade diethyl ether. Wash [OP-24] the combined ether extracts with 30 mL of 1 *M* HCl, and then with 30 mL of saturated aqueous sodium chloride. Dry [OP-25] the ether solution over anhydrous sodium sulfate or magnesium sulfate. Evaporate [OP-19] the ether to obtain crude deet as an oily residue.

Purification. (*Note:* The product can also be purified by vacuum distillation [OP-31] using a compact apparatus.) Obtain about 50 mL of hexanes; a *dry,* tared 125-mL filter flask; and a 50-mL graduated beaker. Using hexanes as the column-packing solvent and placing the beaker at the outlet, pack a chromatography column [OP-21] with about 20 g of Brockmann grade III activated alumina. Add a $\frac{1}{2}$-cm layer of clean sand at the top. Let the solvent drain until the liquid surface just reaches the top of the sand layer; add the impure deet immediately, using a little hexanes for the transfer. When the liquid surface just disappears beneath the sand surface, fill the column nearly to the top with hexanes. Continue to add hexanes during elution to keep the eluant level reasonably constant. Collect about 10 mL of eluate in the 50-mL beaker, collect the next 30–40 mL of eluate in the filter flask, and then replace it by the beaker until the column has drained dry. Evaporate [OP-19] the solvent from the solution in the filter flask under vacuum.

Analysis. Measure the mass of the product. Analyze it by gas chromatography [OP-37] and estimate its purity as mass percent deet. Record the IR spectrum [OP-39] of the neat liquid or obtain a spectrum from your instructor. Compare it with the IR spectra of the reactants in Figure 2 and describe the evidence indicating that the expected reaction has taken place. At your instructor's request, record its ^{1}H NMR spectrum [OP-40] as well.

Waste Disposal: Unless your instructor directs otherwise, wash all aqueous layers down the drain. Place recovered ether in the appropriate solvent recovery container.

Take Care! Keep hexanes away from ignition sources.

Waste Disposal: Place the recovered hexanes in the appropriate solvent recovery container.

Exercises

1. If you recorded the product's ^{1}H NMR spectrum, compare it with the spectra of the reactants in Figure 3 and try to account for any similarities or differences. Interpret your spectrum as completely as you can.

2. (a) Write balanced equations for the reactions of HCl and SO$_2$ with the NaOH in a gas trap. (b) Write balanced equations for the reactions of aqueous NaOH with excess *m*-toluoyl chloride and with excess thionyl chloride.

3. Describe and explain the possible effect on your results of the following experimental errors or variations. (a) The reaction flask you used for the preparation of *m*-toluoyl chloride was wet. (b) Instead of 3.0 *M* NaOH, you used the same volume of 1.0 *M* NaOH for the reaction step. (c) You didn't stir the reaction mixture during the reaction of diethylamine with the acid chloride.

4. Following the format in the "Planning an Experiment" appendix, construct a flow diagram for the synthesis of deet.

5. (a) Calculate the atom economy and reaction efficiency of your synthesis. (b) Describe some green features of your synthesis, and any that aren't so green.

6. Write reasonable mechanisms for (a) the reaction of *m*-toluic acid with thionyl chloride, and (b) the reaction of *m*-toluoyl chloride with diethylamine.

7. (a) Calculate the total volume of 3.0 *M* NaOH required for the preparation, including the amount used up in combining with excess reactants (see Exercise 2). (b) Calculate the percentage excess of NaOH that was actually used.

8. A student misread the label on a reagent bottle and used a 50% NaOH solution in this experiment instead of the 3.0 *M* (11%) solution. Very little deet was obtained from the ether layer after extraction, but acidification of the aqueous layer yielded a white solid that melted at 112°C. Identify the solid and write balanced equations showing how it formed.

9. Hair is made up of the protein keratin, which is a polyamide that contains many *α*-amino acid residues. Hair is often responsible for clogged drains, which can be unclogged by drain cleaners that contain lye (sodium hydroxide). Explain how such drain cleaners remove hair.

Other Things You Can Do

(Starred items require your instructor's permission.)

*1. Test the effectiveness of your product as a mosquito repellent. Deet is a mild irritant, and your product might contain harmful impurities, so do *not* apply it directly to your skin. Instead, prepare a 15% solution of the deet in isopropyl alcohol and use it to saturate a piece of absorbent cheesecloth. Saturate an identical piece of cheesecloth with pure isopropyl alcohol to use as a control. When the treated cloths are dry, take them to a mosquito-infested area, drape one over each arm, and see which arm is targeted by more mosquitoes.

*2. Prepare another amide, benzamide, as described in the "Preparation of Benzamide" minilab.

3. Deet repels insects, but certain other chemicals attract them. Starting with sources listed in the Bibliography, write a research paper about some of the pheromones that function as insect attractants and tell how they can be used for insect control.

Synthesis of Dimedone and Measurement of Its Tautomeric Equilibrium Constant

Reactions of α,β-Unsaturated Carbonyl Compounds. Preparation of Dicarbonyl Compounds. Nucleophilic Addition to Carbon–Carbon Double Bonds. Condensation Reactions. Decarboxylation. Reaction Equilibria. NMR Spectrometry.

Operations

OP-7   Heating
OP-10 Mixing
OP-13 Excluding Air from Reaction Mixtures
OP-16 Vacuum Filtration
OP-19 Evaporation
OP-26 Washing and Drying Solids
OP-28 Recrystallization
OP-33 Melting Point
OP-40 Nuclear Magnetic Resonance Spectrometry

Before You Begin

1. Read the experiment, read or review the operations as necessary, and write an experimental plan.
2. Calculate the mass and volume of 25.0 mmol of dimethyl malonate, and the theoretical yield of dimedone.

Scenario

Harry Lingo, a punctilious chemistry editor for the Fulcourt Press, is faced with the dilemma of how to deal with compounds that exist in two tautomeric forms. In a soon-to-be-published encyclopedia of organic compounds, he wants to list such a compound under the name corresponding to the major species present. For example, acetylacetone, which goes by the IUPAC name 2,4-pentanedione, contains four times more enol than keto tautomer, so he plans to list this compound under the name 4-hydroxy-3-penten-2-one.

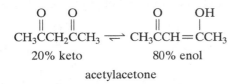

20% keto   80% enol

acetylacetone

The organic compound known by the common name dimedone is represented as a β-diketone in most textbooks of organic chemistry. But many β-diketones contain a substantial amount of enolic tautomer, so Mr. Lingo has asked your institute for help in determining the most appropriate

From *Operational Organic Chemistry: A Problem Solving Approach to the Laboratory*, Fourth Edition, John W. Lehman. Copyright © 2009 by Pearson Education. Published by Prentice Hall. All rights reserved.

Keto–enol equilibrium for dimedone

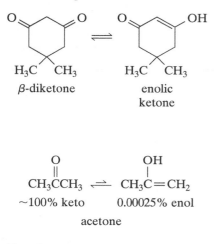

β-diketone   enolic
                              ketone

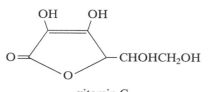

~100% keto   0.00025% enol

acetone

Key Concept: *The enolic form of a β-dicarbonyl compound is stabilized by conjugation of its* C=C *bond with a carbonyl group and by hydrogen bonding between the enolic OH and the carbonyl oxygen.*

vitamin C
(ascorbic acid)

structure and name for dimedone. Your assignment is to prepare dimedone, measure its tautomeric equilibrium constant to determine whether the predominant species present is the β-diketone or the enolic ketone, and give this species an appropriate IUPAC name.

Applying Scientific Methodology

Your working hypothesis should include an "educated guess" about the structure of dimedone. You will test your hypothesis by analyzing its ^{1}H NMR spectrum.

Tautomers and Life

Enols have long been known as unstable intermediates in reactions involving carbonyl compounds, such as the bromination of acetone. Although acetone exists overwhelmingly in the keto form, it is the minute amount of the enolic form present that actually reacts with bromine under acidic conditions. Other enols are considerably more stable than that of acetone. For example, ethyl 3-oxobutanoate (ethyl acetoacetate) contains about 7.5% enol at equilibrium, and 2,4-pentanedione (acetylacetone) contains about 80% enol. Certain natural compounds—such as vitamin C, an enediol—exist almost entirely in the enolic form.

The Kekulé structures of phenols are enol-like, suggesting that some phenols may exist in keto forms as well. For example, phlorglucinol (1,3,5-trihydroxybenzene) forms carbonyl-type derivatives with hydroxylamine and similar derivatizing agents, which indicates that its phenolic form may exist in equilibrium with a triketone.

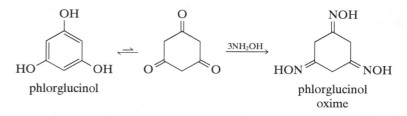

phlorglucinol   phlorglucinol
                                 oxime

A molecule's preference for one of several possible tautomeric structures might appear to be a matter of interest only to a few chemists, but in fact it plays a crucial role in living systems. Ordinarily, the keto form of a phenolic compound is the less stable tautomer by far, because its formation is accompanied by a loss of resonance energy. In the early 1950s, however, chemists discovered that certain biological amines (bases) such as guanine and thymine exist mainly in the keto forms at the pH of physiological systems.

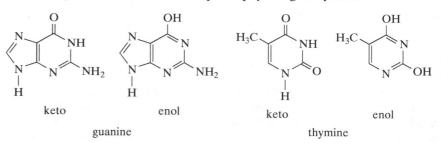

keto   enol   keto   enol

guanine   thymine

406

This discovery provided Francis Crick and James D. Watson with the key to the structure of DNA, and thus to the genetic code. The four bases that are attached to the polyester backbone of a nucleic acid molecule—guanine, thymine, adenine, and cytosine—are responsible for both the transmission of genetic traits (by DNA) and the synthesis of proteins (by RNA) in living beings. Only the keto forms of guanine and thymine allow for the formation of adenine–thymine and guanine–cytosine base pairs, and such base pairing is essential for nucleic acid molecules to function. If these two bases existed only in enolic forms rather than keto forms, life as we know it might be impossible!

Watson's book The Double Helix *provides a fascinating account of the discovery of the DNA structure.*

Understanding the Experiment

In this experiment, you will synthesize dimedone starting with the α,β-unsaturated ketone 4-methyl-3-penten-2-one, commonly known as mesityl oxide. This synthesis involves four distinct reactions that take place in sequence (see "Reactions and Properties"). The first reaction is a *Michael addition* of dimethyl malonate to mesityl oxide. Combining sodium methoxide with dimethyl malonate generates an enolate ion that undergoes nucleophilic addition to the carbon–carbon double bond of mesityl oxide, yielding a keto diester (**1**). In the presence of sodium methoxide, the methyl group next to the keto carbonyl group loses a proton, forming another enolate ion that attacks the carbonyl carbon of one of the ester functions and displaces its methoxyl group. The result of this Claisen-type *cyclization* reaction is a diketo ester (**2**) with a six-membered ring. Both of these reactions occur spontaneously in the same reaction mixture. Subsequent *hydrolysis* of the ester yields a carboxylic acid that, when heated, undergoes *decarboxylation* to form dimedone.

A literature procedure in *Organic Syntheses* [Bibliography, B20] for the synthesis of dimedone requires the *in situ* preparation of sodium ethoxide by adding sodium metal to absolute ethanol. Because any operation that involves elemental sodium can be hazardous, commercial sodium methoxide in methanol will be used instead. The enolate ion of dimethyl malonate, $[CH(COOCH_3)_2]^-$, forms immediately when sodium methoxide is added to dimethyl malonate. This species reacts rapidly and exothermically with mesityl oxide, which should therefore be added slowly to prevent side reactions. The Michael addition and the subsequent cyclization reaction should go virtually to completion during a 1-hour reflux period. After this reaction, you will evaporate most of the methanol, hydrolyze the cyclic ester with 3 M NaOH, and acidify the solution to form the carboxylic acid, which loses carbon dioxide on heating. You will then isolate the resulting dimedone by vacuum filtration and recrystallize it from aqueous acetone.

A **Greener Way:** *You can recover the methanol by evaporating it under vacuum using a cold trap (see OP-15).*

One of the best ways to detect and analyze enol content is by ^{1}H NMR spectrometry. The enolic OH protons of β-diketones absorb far downfield, with chemical shift values in the $10-16$ δ range. Enols also show vinylic proton (H—C=C) absorption in the usual range for these signals, about $4.5-6.0$ δ. The keto form of a β-diketone can usually be recognized by the signal of the protons alpha to both carbonyl groups [H—C(C=O)$_2$]; these protons absorb near 3.5 δ. Because there are two such protons for every enolic vinyl proton in the enol form of dimedone, the equilibrium constant for dimedone's keto–enol equilibrium can be determined from the integrated areas of these two signals using the following formula:

$$K = \frac{[\text{enol}]}{[\text{keto}]} = \frac{2 \times \text{area of the H}-\text{C}=\text{C signal}}{\text{area of the H}-\text{C(C}=\text{O})_2 \text{ signal}}$$

Enols are stabilized by hydrogen-bonding interactions with other polar species, so the equilibrium constant might vary depending on the solvent used. The "Other Things You Can Do" section describes some additional studies you can carry out with your product.

Methanol is slightly toxic to aquatic organisms but biodegrades readily in water and soil. Mesityl oxide isn't expected to be toxic to aquatic life. Deuterochloroform, like chloroform, is toxic to aquatic organisms and shouldn't be released into the environment. Although acetone is slightly toxic to aquatic life, it doesn't bioaccumulate and isn't considered a serious environmental contaminant.

Reactions and Properties

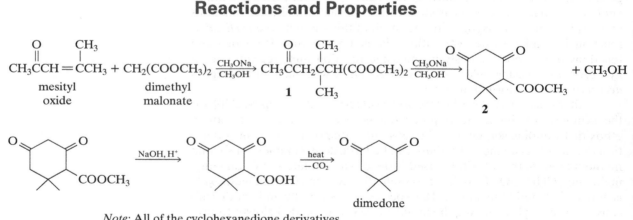

Note: All of the cyclohexanedione derivatives shown can also be represented by enolic forms.

Table 1 Physical properties

	mol wt	mp	bp	d
mesityl oxide	98.2	−52	129	0.858
dimethyl malonate	132.1	−62	181	1.154
sodium methoxide	54.0			
methanol	32.0	−94	65	0.791
dimedone	140.2	151		

Note: mp and bp are in °C; density is in g/mL. A 25% solution of sodium methoxide in methanol has a density of 0.945 g/mL.

Mesityl oxide (4-methyl-3-penten-2-one)

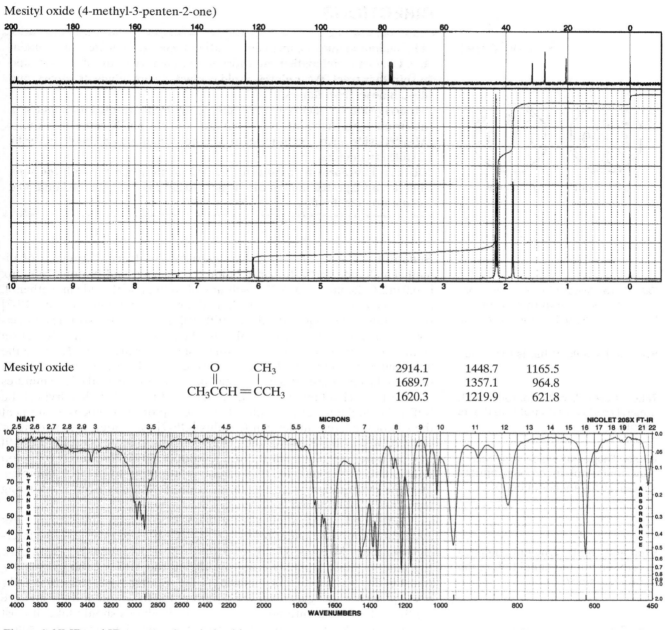

Mesityl oxide

$$CH_3\overset{O}{\overset{\|}{C}}CH=\overset{CH_3}{\overset{|}{C}}CH_3$$

2914.1	1448.7	1165.5
1689.7	1357.1	964.8
1620.3	1219.9	621.8

Figure 1 NMR and IR spectra of mesityl oxide

DIRECTIONS

Safety Notes

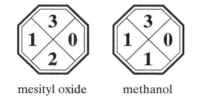

mesityl oxide   methanol

The sodium methoxide/methanol solution is corrosive, toxic, and flammable. Contact or inhalation can cause severe damage to the skin, eyes, and respiratory tract. Wear gloves, avoid contact, do not inhale its vapors, and keep it away from flames.

Mesityl oxide is a lachrymator and a strong irritant; inhalation and skin absorption are harmful. Avoid contact and do not breathe its vapors. Mesityl oxide forms explosive peroxides on standing, so it should never be distilled to dryness.

Deuterochloroform is harmful if inhaled or absorbed through the skin, and it is a suspected human carcinogen. Avoid contact with the liquid and do not breathe its vapors.

Take Care! Wear gloves, avoid contact with the sodium methoxide solution, and do not breathe its vapors.

Stop and Think: What is the solid?

Take Care! Avoid contact with mesityl oxide and do not breathe its vapors.

Waste Disposal: Place any recovered methanol in an appropriate solvent recovery container.

Stop and Think: Why did you have to remove the methanol before the hydrolysis step?

Take Care! Foaming may occur.

Stop and Think: What gas is evolved?

Waste Disposal: Unless your instructor directs otherwise, wash the filtrates down the drain.

Reaction. *The reaction apparatus must be dry.* Place 25.0 mmol of dimethyl malonate and a stir bar or boiling chips in a round-bottom flask; mix in 6.0 mL (~26 mmol) of a 25% solution of sodium methoxide in methanol. Attach a condenser and use a steam bath or hot-water bath to heat [OP-7] the solution to boiling, with stirring [OP-10] (if you have a stirrer) or shaking. Any solid in the reaction mixture should dissolve (or nearly so) on heating; the stir bar may not spin until most of it has dissolved. Remove the heat source and add 3.0 mL (~26 mmol) of recently distilled mesityl oxide through the condenser, in several small portions, for a period of 2–3 minutes (swirl after each addition, if you don't have a stirrer). Attach a drying tube [OP-13] containing calcium chloride to the top of the condenser and heat the reaction mixture under gentle reflux [OP-7] for 1 hour, with stirring or occasional shaking. Remove the reflux condenser and evaporate [OP-19] the methanol directly from the round-bottom flask. The stirrer will stop functioning as the mixture thickens, so heat gently to prevent bumping. Stop the evaporation when the solid residue is still moist but all standing liquid has been removed.

Add 20 mL of 3.0 *M* aqueous sodium hydroxide to the reaction flask and heat the mixture under reflux [OP-7] for 1 hour to hydrolyze the intermediate ester. Measure 15 mL of 6.0 *M* hydrochloric acid into a 125-mL Erlenmeyer flask; while swirling or stirring the HCl solution manually, transfer the warm reaction mixture to the Erlenmeyer flask. *Under the hood*, place a watch glass over the mouth of the flask and boil the mixture gently, with stirring, until no more gas is evolved; this should take at least 10 minutes. Add water, if necessary, to replace any that evaporates. Allow the reaction mixture to cool to room temperature. Scratch the inside of the flask to induce crystallization, if necessary, and then cool the flask in an ice/water bath until crystallization is complete.

Separation. Collect the product by vacuum filtration [OP-16] and let it air-dry on the filter.

Purification and Analysis. Purify the air-dried dimedone by recrystallization [OP-28] from aqueous 50% acetone. Dry [OP-26b] and weigh the dimedone; measure its melting point [OP-33]. Record the ^{1}H NMR spectrum [OP-40] of dimedone in deuterochloroform or obtain a spectrum from your instructor. On your NMR spectrum, identify the enol H—C=C and keto H—C(C=O)$_2$ signals. Calculate the keto–enol equilibrium constant, decide which species (if either) predominates in the solution, and give it an IUPAC name.

Take Care! Avoid contact with CDCl$_3$ and do not breathe its vapors.

Exercises

1. (a) Compare the ^{1}H NMR spectrum of your product to that of mesityl oxide shown in Figure 1, and interpret both spectra as completely as you can. (b) Interpret the infrared (IR) spectrum of mesityl oxide as completely as you can. Account for the wave number of the carbonyl band, comparing it with the usual value of ~1715 cm^{-1} for an aliphatic ketone.

2. (a) Write a mechanism for the Michael addition of dimethyl malonate to mesityl oxide in the presence of sodium methoxide/methanol. (b) Write a mechanism for the cyclization step in the synthesis of dimedone. (c) Write a mechanism for the decarboxylation step of this synthesis, showing the structure of the transition state.

3. Describe and explain the possible effect on your results of the following experimental errors or variations. (a) You didn't evaporate the methanol from the reaction mixture. (b) The mesityl oxide bottle was contaminated with water. (c) The bottle labeled "dimethyl malonate" actually contained dimethyl maleate.

4. (a) Calculate the atom economy and reaction efficiency of your synthesis. (b) Describe some green features of your synthesis, and any that aren't so green.

5. Following the format in the "Planning an Experiment" appendix, construct a flow diagram for this experiment.

6. What inexpensive starting material do you think is used to prepare mesityl oxide commercially? Outline the synthesis of mesityl oxide from this starting material.

7. A rather confused student, Ina Fogg, hydrolyzed the intermediate ester with 6 M HCl rather than 3 M NaOH and then boiled the reaction mixture with 50% NaOH instead of 6 M HCl. Filtration of the cooled solution yielded only a little dimedone. Finally realizing her mistake, she acidified the filtrate and a white solid precipitated, but its melting point was different from that of dimedone. What was this solid, and how did it form?

8. Draw structures of some by-products that might be present in your product if you neglected to use a drying tube during the first step of the synthesis of dimedone. Write reaction pathways for their formation.

9. When heated with sodium ethoxide in ethanol, the diethyl esters of butanedioic acid and heptanedioic acid both yield products that have six-membered rings. Write structures for both products and mechanisms for their formation.

10. Write a mechanism for the following reaction of dimedone with 3-buten-2-one.

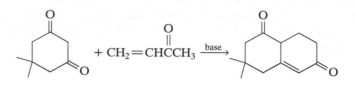

Other Things You Can Do

(Starred items require your instructor's permission.)

*1. Record ^{1}H NMR spectra [OP-40] of dimedone in solvents other than deuterochloroform, such as DMSO-d_6, and compare the keto–enol equilibrium constants for the different solvents. Try to explain any differences.

*2. Record the infrared spectrum [OP-39] of dimedone using a KBr disc or Nujol mull and then using a chloroform solution. Look for absorption bands arising from the enolic form and the diketo form in both spectra, and compare the relative amounts of enol. Try to explain any differences.

*3. Use your product to prepare dimedone derivatives of benzaldehyde as described in the "Synthesis of Dimedone Derivatives of Benzaldehyde" minilab.

4. Like the synthesis of dimedone from mesityl oxide, a Robinson annulation sequence involves a Michael addition followed by a ring-forming condensation reaction. Starting with sources listed in the Bibliography, write a research paper about the Robinson annulation, describing some of its applications in the synthesis of terpenoids and steroids.

Preparation of Para Red and Related Azo Dyes

Reactions of Amines. Reactions of Diazonium Salts. Preparation of Azo Compounds. Electrophilic Aromatic Substitution.

Operations

OP-8   Cooling
OP-10 Mixing
OP-16 Vacuum Filtration
OP-26 Washing and Drying Solids

Before You Begin

1. Read the experiment, read or review the operations as necessary, and write an experimental plan.
2. Calculate the mass of 10.0 mmol of *p*-nitroaniline, the mass of 10.0 mmol of 2-naphthol, and the theoretical yield of Para Red. Be prepared to calculate the mass of 10.0 mmol of any other coupling component or diazo component, and the theoretical yield of any other azo dye.

Scenario

The despotic king of the somewhat backward kingdom of Erewhon has just been overthrown in a coup led by Sergeant Obmar, a soldier of fortune from California. In the sergeant's honor, the provisional government has authorized a new flag, consisting of a navel orange on a field of blue. But the first flags they ordered were sent back because the orange was the wrong color—it looked more like a pink grapefruit. Acting president Gib Retsim has asked your institute to come up with a dye that will produce just the right shade of orange. Your supervisor knows how to make "American Flag Red," an orange-red dye the color of the stripes in the U.S. flag, and thinks that by tinkering with its molecular structure, your project team should be able to come up with a suitable orange dye for the new flag.

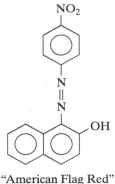

"American Flag Red"
(Para Red)

Applying Scientific Methodology

Based on the information in the experiment, you should develop a hypothesis regarding a pair of reactants from Table 1 that you think might produce a dye the color of a navel orange. Alternatively, members of your project group can get together and select a different reactant pair for each member to work on.

Dyes and Serendipity

In the Persian fairy tale *The Three Princes of Serendip*, the title characters were forever discovering things they weren't looking for at the time. Thus,

From *Operational Organic Chemistry: A Problem Solving Approach to the Laboratory*, Fourth Edition, John W. Lehman. Copyright © 2009 by Pearson Education. Published by Prentice Hall. All rights reserved.

serendipity is the aptitude for making happy discoveries by accident. The preparation of the first commercially important synthetic dye by William Henry Perkin in 1856 is a good example of a serendipitous discovery in science. During the nineteenth century, quinine was the only drug known to be effective against malaria, and it could be obtained only from the bark of the cinchona tree, which grew in South America. French chemists had isolated pure quinine from cinchona bark in 1820, but the inaccessibility of the tree made natural quinine very expensive. Perkin, then an 18-year-old graduate student working for the eminent German chemist August Wilhelm von Hofmann, realized that anyone who could make synthetic quinine might well become rich and famous. Perkin knew nothing about the molecular structure of quinine—structural organic chemistry was in its infancy in the mid-1800s—but he knew its molecular formula, $C_{20}H_{24}N_2O_2$. So he oxidized some allyltoluidine ($C_{10}H_{13}N$), apparently thinking that two molecules of allyltoluidine plus three oxygen atoms minus a molecule of water would magically yield $C_{20}H_{24}N_2O_2$—quinine!

Perkin's idea

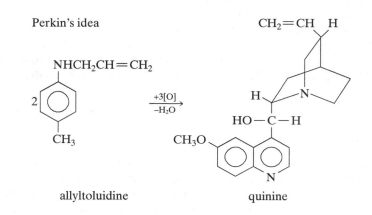

allyltoluidine   quinine

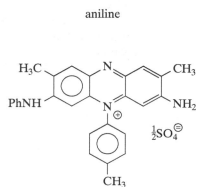

aniline

mauve

Of course, Perkin had attempted the impossible—the molecular structure of allyltoluidine bears no resemblance to that of quinine, which wasn't synthesized until 1940. When he oxidized allyltoluidine with potassium dichromate, he came up with a reddish-brown precipitate that he quickly realized was not quinine. Most chemists would have thrown out the stuff and started over, but it had properties that interested Perkin, so he decided to try the same reaction with a simpler base, aniline. This time he obtained a black precipitate that, when extracted by ethanol, formed a beautiful purple solution that impressed some of the local dyers. Perkin knew a good thing when he saw it, so he gave up his study of chemistry and went into the business of manufacturing "aniline purple," or mauve, as the dye soon came to be known. Ironically, Perkin became rich and famous by *failing* to synthesize quinine. His dyestuffs plant was so successful that he was able to retire at the age of 36 and devote the rest of his life to pure research.

While Perkin was getting the synthetic-dye industry under way, other chemists were experimenting with aniline and many other compounds that can be extracted from coal tar. One of these was a brewery chemist named Peter Griess, who took time off from the brewing of Allsopp's Pale Ale to discover the azo dyes. Undiscouraged by the fact that many of the diazo

compounds he prepared had a tendency to explode, Griess did some fundamental research into the diazotization of aromatic amines and went on to
discover the coupling reaction by which virtually all azo dyes are now
synthesized. Aniline Yellow and Bismarck Brown were synthesized in the
1860s, and the production and use of azo dyes grew rapidly thereafter.

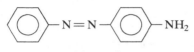

Aniline Yellow

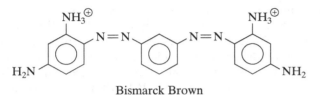

Bismarck Brown

The advancement of organic chemistry as a science is due, in large part, to
the discovery that chemists could prepare synthetic colors that were in
many ways superior to the natural ones.

Understanding the Experiment

In this experiment, you will prepare the azo dye Para Red and at least one
other azo dye, and use your products to dye cloth. Para Red, which is
made from *para*-nitroaniline and 2-naphthol, was once called "American
Flag Red" because it was used to dye the cloth used for the stripes in the
American flag.

Most azo dyes can be prepared by combining a diazonium salt (the *diazo
component*) with an activated aromatic compound (the *coupling component*).
The preparation of the dye involves two stages, known as *diazotization* and
coupling. In the diazotization stage, a primary aromatic amine reacts with
nitrous acid (HONO) to form the diazonium salt. Nitrous acid is generated
in situ from sodium nitrite and a mineral acid. The reaction is carried out at a
low temperature because diazonium salts react with water to form phenols
and other by-products at higher temperatures. In the coupling stage, the
diazonium salt is added to a solution of the coupling component, which is
usually a phenol or an aromatic amine. Phenols couple most readily in mildly
alkaline solutions, whereas amines react best in acidic solutions. However, too
low a pH will prevent an amine from reacting by causing protonation of the
amino group, whereas too high a pH will cause the diazonium salt to change
to a diazotate ion, which is incapable of coupling.

Diazotization

$$ArNH_2 \xrightarrow{\text{HONO}} Ar-N_2^+$$
$$\text{diazonium salt}$$

Coupling

$$Ar-N_2^+ + H-Ar' \xrightarrow{-H^+}$$
$$\text{coupling}$$
$$\text{component}$$
$$Ar-N=N-Ar'$$
$$\text{azo compound}$$

(Ar' must contain an activating group
such as $-OH$ or $-NR_2$.)

Low pH: $ArNR_2 \underset{}{\overset{H^+}{\rightleftharpoons}} ArNHR_2^+$

High pH: $ArN_2^+ \underset{}{\overset{OH^-}{\rightleftharpoons}} ArN=N-O^-$
$$\text{diazotate ion}$$

Formation of unreactive species at low and high pH

The coupling reaction is an electrophilic aromatic substitution reaction, with the diazonium salt acting as the electrophile. Because the diazo group, $-N_2^+$, is only weakly electrophilic, the coupling component must contain one or more strongly activating groups, such as OH or NR_2, for coupling to occur.

To prepare the diazonium salt, a primary aromatic amine is dissolved in about 2.5 equivalents of dilute hydrochloric acid (or another suitable acid), and the solution is cooled to 5°C or below. Aqueous sodium nitrite is then added, and the solution is tested for excess nitrous acid using starch–iodide paper. If the amine is insoluble, the diazotization reaction is carried out in suspension, with stirring.

The coupling reaction is carried out by adding the diazo compound, with cooling and stirring, to a solution of a coupling component in dilute acid or base. If the coupling component is a phenol, it is dissolved in about 2 equivalents of 1 *M* NaOH and cooled before adding the diazonium salt solution. If necessary, the pH can be adjusted after the addition to obtain a better yield of azo dye. If the coupling component is an amine, it is dissolved or suspended in 1 equivalent of 1 *M* HCl. After the diazo component is added and coupling is complete, the solution is neutralized to litmus paper by adding 3 *M* aqueous sodium carbonate. The dye is then cooled in an ice bath before filtering. The azo dye should be dried at room temperature, because it may decompose on heating.

Cloth can be dyed by several different processes. In the *direct process*, the dye is dissolved in water, the solution is heated, and the cloth is immersed in the hot solution. The dye molecules attach themselves to the cloth fibers by direct chemical interactions. In the *disperse process*, a water-insoluble dye is suspended in water, and a small amount of a carrier substance is added. The carrier dissolves the dye and carries it into the fibers. In the *ingrain process*, a dye is synthesized on the cloth itself, usually by the combination of a diazonium salt with a coupling component. The cloth is immersed in a solution of one of the components, allowed to dry, and then immersed in a solution of the other component to develop the color. The comparatively small molecules of the separate components can diffuse into the spaces between the fibers; after they combine to form the dye, the larger dye molecules are trapped there. You will be using the ingrain method of dyeing in this experiment, but you can experiment with the other dyeing methods as described in "Other Things You Can Do."

The color of a dye depends on the wavelengths of visible light it absorbs. If a dye absorbs light at certain wavelengths, the color perceived by the human eye arises from the wavelengths that aren't absorbed and are therefore reflected to the eye. The color of each dye you prepare in this experiment should be some shade of yellow, orange, or red; a yellow color is associated with absorption of light of relatively short wavelengths, and a deep red color with absorption of light of longer wavelengths. The light-absorbing portion of a dye molecule, called a *chromophore*, is a conjugated system of delocalized pi electrons. The chromophoric system of Para Red, for example, includes the benzene and naphthalene rings, the two doubly bonded nitrogen atoms that connect them, and the unsaturated nitro group. In general, the more extended the chromophore, the longer the wavelength of the light it absorbs. Thus, Para Red, with 21 atoms in its chromophore, absorbs light of considerably longer wavelengths than does Aniline Yellow, with only 14 atoms in its chromophore.

Key Concept: Increasing the length of a conjugated system decreases the energy separation between its pi molecular orbitals and therefore the ΔE of its $\pi - \pi^*$ electronic transitions. The wavelength of light absorbed during a transition is inversely proportional to the energy of the transition, so decreasing ΔE increases λ.

Certain saturated substituents called *auxochromes* can, in effect, extend a conjugated system by resonance. Auxochromes such as the OH, OCH_3, and NR_2 groups have one or more pairs of nonbonded electrons that they can share with a chromophore, thereby increasing the wavelength of the light it absorbs. Such groups exert the greatest effect if they are *ortho* or *para* to the $-N=N-$ group so that they can participate in resonance with the rest of the chromophore.

p-Nitroaniline is only slightly toxic to aquatic life, but aniline is very toxic to terrestrial and aquatic organisms (some of the other aromatic amines may be also). Phenol and some of the substituted phenols are expected to be toxic to aquatic life. Sodium nitrite is very toxic to aquatic organisms.

Reactions and Properties

Equations are given for the preparation of Para Red only.

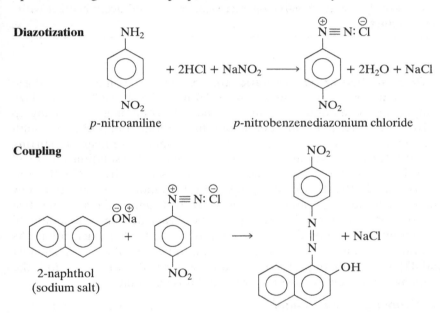

Diazotization

p-nitroaniline   *p*-nitrobenzenediazonium chloride

Coupling

2-naphthol (sodium salt)

Para Red

Table 1 Suggested diazo and coupling components

Diazo component	mol wt	Coupling component	mol wt
aniline	93.1	aniline	93.1
m-anisidine	123.2	*N*-methylaniline	107.2
m-nitroaniline	138.1	*N,N*-dimethylaniline	121.2
m-toluidine	107.2	*m*-phenylenediamine	108.1
p-anisidine	123.2	phenol	94.1
p-nitroaniline	138.1	1-naphthol	144.2
p-toluidine	107.2	2-naphthol	144.2
		resorcinol	110.1

Note: Select one diazo component and one coupling component for each dye you prepare.

417

DIRECTIONS

Each student should prepare Para Red and at least one other dye. With the instructor's permission, students can work in small groups, with each person preparing a different dye. Any diazo component from Table 1 can be used in combination with any coupling component from that table.

A. *Preparation of an Azo Dye*

> Aromatic amines are very harmful if inhaled, ingested, or absorbed through the skin. Some aromatic amines are suspected carcinogens. Wear gloves and dispense under a hood. Avoid contact and do not inhale their vapors.
>
> Most phenols are harmful if inhaled, ingested, or absorbed through the skin; some are very corrosive, causing severe irritation or damage to skin and eyes. Some phenols are suspected carcinogens. Wear gloves, avoid contact, and do not inhale their dust or vapors.
>
> Some azo dyes may be carcinogenic; wear gloves and avoid contact with the products.

1. *Diazotization of an Aromatic Amine.* Mix 10.0 mmol of the diazo component (an aromatic amine) with 8.0 mL of 3 *M* HCl. If the diazo component doesn't dissolve completely, heat the solution gently, adding up to 10 mL of water to get most or all of it in solution. Cool [OP-8] this solution to 5°C in an ice/water or ice–salt bath, with manual or magnetic stirring [OP-10]. The amine salt may precipitate as you cool the solution, but it will diazotize satisfactorily if the reaction mixture is well stirred. Continue to stir as you add 10 mL of freshly prepared 1 *M* sodium nitrite at a rate slow enough that the temperature remains below 10°C during the addition. Test the solution with starch–iodide paper; if necessary, add enough additional sodium nitrite, drop by drop, to give a positive test (blue-black color). As accurately as you can, divide the solution into two equal parts (labeled **d1** and **d2**), keeping both parts cold in an ice/water bath. Go to step *2a* if the coupling component is a phenol or to *2b* if it is an amine.

2a. *Coupling with a Phenol.* Dissolve or suspend 10.0 mmol of the phenol in 20 mL of 1 *M* NaOH (use 40 mL of 1 *M* NaOH for resorcinol), and cool the solution in an ice/water bath. As accurately as you can, divide the solution into two equal parts (labeled **c1** and **c2**). Slowly add diazonium salt solution **d1** to coupling component solution **c1**, with manual stirring, and leave the mixture in the cold bath for 15 minutes or more. (Keep solution **d2** cold; save it and **c2** for part **B.**) If little or no colored solid appears, adjust the pH with dilute HCl or NaOH to induce coupling. Collect the azo dye by vacuum filtration [OP-16], washing it on the filter [OP-26a] with water. Dry [OP-26b] your azo dye at room temperature and weigh it.

2b. *Coupling with an Amine.* Dissolve or suspend 10.0 mmol of the aromatic amine in 10 mL of 1 *M* HCl (use 20 mL of 1 *M* HCl for *m*-phenylenediamine), and cool the solution in an ice/water bath. As accurately as you can, divide the solution into two equal parts (labeled **c1** and **c2**). Slowly add diazonium salt solution **d1** to coupling component solution **c1**, with manual

---

Waste Disposal: Dispose of all wastes as directed by your instructor.

Safety Notes

aromatic amines   phenols

Take Care! Wear gloves, avoid contact with the amine, and do not breathe its vapors.

Take Care! Wear gloves, avoid contact with the phenol, and do not breathe its dust or vapors.

Observe and Note: Look for and record any evidence for a reaction.

Stop and Think: Why may adjusting the pH help induce coupling?

Take Care! Wear gloves and avoid contact with the azo dye.

Take Care! Wear gloves, avoid contact with the amine, and do not breathe its vapors.

stirring. (Keep solution **d2** cold; save it and **c2** for part **B**.) Neutralize the solution to litmus with 3 *M* aqueous sodium carbonate (add it slowly to minimize foaming), and leave the mixture in the cold bath for 15 minutes or more. Collect the azo dye by vacuum filtration [OP-16], washing it on the filter [OP-26a] with water. Dry [OP-26b] your azo dye at room temperature and weigh it.

B. *Dyeing a Cloth by the Ingrain Process*
Mix 40 mL of water into coupling component solution **c2** and soak a piece of clean white cloth in it for 2–3 minutes. Remove the cloth with forceps or a pair of stirring rods, blot it between paper towels to remove most of the water, and hang it up to dry. Mix 40 mL of ice-cold water with diazonium salt solution **d2**, insert the dry cloth, and agitate the solution with a stirring rod for long enough to dye the cloth uniformly.

If your coupling component was an aromatic amine, dip the cloth briefly into a small amount of 3 *M* sodium carbonate solution. Remove the cloth and dry it as before. If there is a navel orange handy, compare its color to that of your dyed cloth. Prepare a table describing the colors of the cloths dyed by the azo dyes prepared by your group or lab section.

Observe and Note: Look for and record any evidence for a reaction.

Stop and Think: What is the purpose of the neutralization step? How should it affect the color of the dye?

Take Care! Wear gloves and avoid contact with the azo dye.

Stop and Think: What is happening on the cloth to account for your observations?

Exercises

1. Discuss the effects of structural features (such as substituents and chromophore size) on the colors of the dyes prepared by your group.
2. Write a mechanism for the coupling reaction of *p*-nitrobenzenediazonium chloride with 2-naphthol.
3. Describe and explain the possible effect on your results of the following experimental errors or variations. (a) You forgot to cool the solution of your diazo component before adding aqueous sodium nitrite. (b) Your coupling component was a phenol, but you followed the procedure in *2b* to couple it. (c) You tried to dye a cloth by dipping it into a solution of 2-naphthol in 1 *M* NaOH, drying it, and then dipping it into a solution of aniline in 1 *M* HCl.
4. (a) Calculate the atom economy and reaction efficiency of your synthesis of Para Red. (b) Describe some green features of this synthesis, and any that aren't so green.
5. Following the format in the "Planning an Experiment" appendix, construct a flow diagram for your synthesis of Para Red in part **A**.
6. Mel A. Droyt was trying to prepare *p*-dimethylaminoazobenzene (Butter Yellow) by coupling 2.0 mmol of *N,N*-dimethylaniline with an equimolar amount of aniline. He first added 4.0 mL of 1 *M* sodium nitrite to the diazo component. Mixing this solution with the coupling component yielded some Butter Yellow, along with a pale yellow oil. (a) What did he do wrong, and what was the yellow oil? (b) Write a balanced equation for its formation.
7. Bea Wilder was attempting to prepare chrysoidine by coupling 2.0 mmol of *m*-phenylenediamine with 2.0 mmol of aniline. To her surprise, she had to add 4.0 mL of 1 *M* sodium nitrite in the diazotization step before the solution turned starch–iodide paper blue. After pouring the diazonium salt solution into the solution of the other component, she recovered a

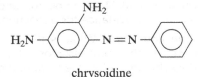

chrysoidine

dark-colored precipitate that wasn't chrysoidine. The following day, the filtrate contained another precipitate that she identified as resorcinol. (a) What did she do wrong, and what was the structure of the azo dye she synthesized? (b) Write balanced equations for its synthesis and for the reaction that formed resorcinol.

8. Why is it important to keep the temperature low during diazotization and coupling? Give the structure of the product that might form if the reaction mixture is heated during the diazotization of *p*-nitroaniline, and write an equation for its formation.

9. Explain why coupling of *p*-nitrobenzenediazonium chloride occurs mainly *para* to the $-N(CH_3)_2$ group of *N,N*-dimethylaniline but *ortho* to the $-OH$ group of 2-naphthol.

Other Things You Can Do

(Starred items require your instructor's permission.)

Take Care! Wear gloves and avoid contact with H_2SO_4.

*1. Use your dye for direct dyeing by suspending 0.5 g of the dye in 100 mL of hot water and acidifying the mixture with a few drops of concentrated sulfuric acid. Immerse pieces of wool or cotton cloth in the mixture for 5 minutes or more. Remove the cloth, rinse it with water, and let it dry. Adjusting the pH of the dyeing mixture with dilute HCl or NaOH may give better results in some cases.

*2. Use your dye for disperse dyeing by suspending 0.5 g of the dye in 100 mL of hot water and stirring in 0.1 g of biphenyl (the carrier) and 2–3 drops of liquid detergent. Then immerse a piece of cloth made of Dacron or another polyester in the mixture, and heat the solution in a boiling-water bath, with stirring, for 15–20 minutes. Remove the cloth and let it dry.

*3. Dissolve 3–5 mg of an azo dye in 10 mL of 95% ethanol. If any solid remains undissolved, filter the solution. Record the ultraviolet–visible spectrum [OP-41] of the dye over the tungsten lamp range ($\sim800-350$ nm), diluting the solution with more ethanol if necessary. Compare the λ_{max} values of different dyes and try to explain some of the differences you observe. Note that such comparisons are meaningful only if the bands you are comparing arise from the same kind of electronic transition; such bands should be similar in appearance and intensity.

*4. In "A Diazonium Salt Reaction of 2-Aminobenzoic Acid" minilab, see what happens when you diazotize anthranilic acid and heat the resulting solution.

5. Starting with sources listed in the Bibliography, write a research paper about the chemistry and uses of food colorings. Outline syntheses for some azo dyes that have been used as food colorings and discuss the controversy surrounding such dyes as FD&C Red No. 2.

Reaction of Phthalimide with Sodium Hypochlorite

Reactions of Amides and Imides. Nucleophilic Acyl Substitution. Functional Derivatives of Carboxylic Acids. Molecular Rearrangements.

Operations

OP-7   Heating
OP-8   Cooling
OP-9   Temperature Monitoring
OP-10 Mixing
OP-16 Vacuum Filtration
OP-26 Washing and Drying Solids
OP-28 Recrystallization
OP-33 Melting Point

Before You Begin

1. Read the experiment, read or review the operations as necessary, and write an experimental plan.
2. Calculate the mass of 34.0 mmol of phthalic anhydride, 17.0 mmol of urea, and 20.0 mmol of phthalimide. Calculate the theoretical yield of $C_7H_7NO_2$.

Scenario

Otto Fökus, a nearsighted chemistry professor from Miskatonic University, was attempting to hydrolyze some phthalimide to phthalic acid when he mistook a bottle of chlorine bleach for a similar bottle containing aqueous sodium hydroxide (NaOH). By the time he took a close look at the label and realized his error, he had already added some bleach to the reaction mixture. Thinking he might still salvage the experiment, he then added the designated amount of sodium hydroxide and heated the reaction mixture, but the crystalline solid he obtained had the wrong melting point for phthalic acid. Curious about this unexpected result, Professor Fökus sent a sample of the product to a commercial laboratory for analysis. The analytical report showed that the product contained nitrogen but no chlorine.

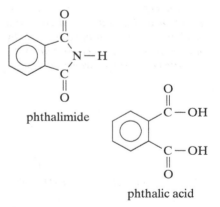

phthalimide

phthalic acid

Analysis of sample	
Carbon	61.30%
Hydrogen	5.15%
Nitrogen	10.23%
Chlorine	0.00%

Based on the product's elemental composition and an estimate of its molecular weight, the professor determined that its molecular formula is $C_7H_7NO_2$. But when he consulted his edition of the *CRC Handbook of*

From *Operational Organic Chemistry: A Problem Solving Approach to the Laboratory*, Fourth Edition, John W. Lehman. Copyright © 2009 by Pearson Education. Published by Prentice Hall. All rights reserved.

Chemistry and Physics, he found 18 compounds with that formula listed. Because of an inadequate science equipment budget, Professor Fökus doesn't have access to the instruments needed to determine the structure of this compound, so he has asked your institute for help. Your supervisor suspects that the reaction of phthalimide with chlorine bleach (which contains sodium hypochlorite, NaOCl) may involve some kind of molecular rearrangement. Your assignment is to carry out the reaction of phthalimide with sodium hypochlorite and sodium hydroxide, and to identify the product from its melting point and by using your chemical intuition. If there is no phthalimide in the institute's chemical stockroom, you may have to prepare it from a less expensive starting material, phthalic anhydride.

Applying Scientific Methodology

The following sections on the Curtius rearrangement and the reactions of imides contain some clues that should lead you to a reasonable hypothesis regarding the structure of $C_7H_7NO_2$, which is one of the 18 compounds listed in Table 1. You will test your hypothesis by measuring the melting point of the product.

The Curtius Rearrangement

Acyl azides are compounds that contain the azide ($—N_3$) functional group on a carbonyl carbon. They can be prepared by treating acid chlorides with sodium azide (NaN_3). When an acyl azide is heated, it evolves gaseous nitrogen to yield an isocyanate by a reaction called the Curtius rearrangement. At one time, it was thought that the rearrangement involved an electron-deficient intermediate called a *nitrene,* as illustrated in the margin for the Curtius rearrangement of benzoyl azide. This reaction resembles a carbocation rearrangement, except that the migrating group moves to an electron-deficient nitrogen atom instead of to a carbon atom. In this example, migration of a phenyl group to the nitrogen atom would restore its missing pair of electrons and yield a stable product.

More recent studies of such rearrangements suggest that free nitrenes are probably not involved. The rearrangement step is thought to proceed by a concerted mechanism, as shown in the following general example, where Z is a good leaving group (such as $—N_3$) and R is an alkyl or aryl group:

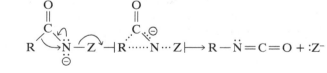

Thus, the migration to a *potentially* electron-deficient nitrogen occurs as the leaving group is being ejected, not after it has already left to form a nitrene.

Depending on the reaction conditions, the resulting isocyanate may be isolated as such, or it may react further with the solvent. If the Curtius rearrangement is run in an alcoholic solution, for example, the alcohol adds to the C=N bond of the isocyanate to form a urethane. In water, a carbamic acid is formed at first, but it loses carbon dioxide spontaneously to yield an amine as the final product. The carbon dioxide is converted to carbonate ion under the alkaline reaction conditions used in some rearrangements of this type.

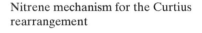

Nitrene mechanism for the Curtius rearrangement

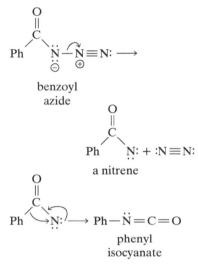

benzoyl azide

a nitrene

phenyl isocyanate

Key Concept: A hydrogen atom, alkyl group, or aryl group may migrate to a neighboring electron-deficient site by moving its bonded electron pair to the new site via a bridged transition state.

$$RN{=}C{=}O + R'OH \longrightarrow RNHCOR'$$

a urethane

$$RN{=}C{=}O + HOH \longrightarrow RNHCOH$$

a carbamic acid

$$\longrightarrow RNH_2 + CO_2$$

Reactions of isocyanates with hydroxylic solvents

Imides and Their Reactions

Imides are nitrogen analogs of carboxylic anhydrides, compounds that contain a —CONRCO— functional group, where R is H, alkyl, or aryl. The chemistry of imides resembles that of amides and other acyl compounds. For example, imides can undergo nucleophilic acyl substitution reactions with good nucleophiles.

Nucleophilic acyl substitution with an imide (H^+ may be obtained from water or another solvent)

$$
\underset{\substack{\|\ \ \ \|\\ RCNHCR'}}{O\ \ \ O} \xrightarrow{Nu:}\ \xrightarrow{H^+}\ \underset{\substack{\|\\ RCNu}}{O} + \underset{\substack{\|\\ R'CNH_2}}{O}
$$

The amide formed in such a reaction may react further under appropriate conditions. Thus, phthalimide is hydrolyzed easily by dilute aqueous sodium hydroxide to give the sodium salt of phthalamic acid, which yields phthalamic acid upon acidification. Heating phthalamic acid (or phthalimide itself) for 30 minutes or more with concentrated NaOH and acidifying the reaction mixture then yields phthalic acid.

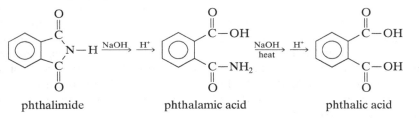

phthalimide   phthalamic acid   phthalic acid

Because of the two carbonyl groups adjacent to nitrogen, the N—H hydrogen of an imide is acidic enough to be removed by moderately strong bases. For example, phthalimide reacts with potassium hydroxide or potassium carbonate to form potassium phthalimide.

Reaction of phthalimide with potassium carbonate

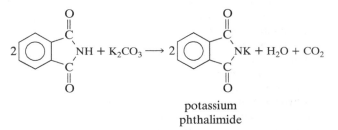

potassium
phthalimide

Imides and most other compounds that have N—H bonds can be chlorinated by sodium hypochlorite. For example, NaOCl converts indole to *N*-chloroindole by the following reaction:

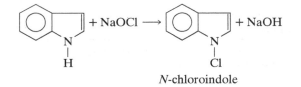

N-chloroindole

Understanding the Experiment

In this experiment, you will prepare phthalimide by heating phthalic anhydride with urea, unless the phthalimide is provided. Then you will treat phthalimide with sodium hypochlorite and sodium hydroxide, and attempt to identify the product.

The reaction of phthalic anhydride with urea is a green reaction, because the two solids react without the use of a solvent and the atom economy is quite favorable. During the reaction, the solid mass expands to about three times its initial volume because of the rapid evolution of carbon dioxide.

You will carry out the reaction of phthalimide by heating it with a chlorine laundry bleach (such as Clorox or Javex) and aqueous sodium hydroxide. Most chlorine bleaches of this type now contain about 6.0% sodium hypochlorite (NaOCl) by mass, in water. When the reaction is complete, the resulting alkaline solution should contain the sodium salt of the product, which is precipitated with acetic acid after most of the sodium hydroxide has been neutralized with hydrochloric acid. Considerable foaming may occur during the acidification step, but it can be reduced by keeping the reactants cool and adding the acid slowly. The solid product is separated from the reaction mixture by vacuum filtration and purified by recrystallization from water.

Until recently, most chlorine laundry bleaches contained 5.25% NaOCl.

The product will be one of the compounds listed in Table 1, some of whose structures are shown in Figure 1. (Structures of the remaining compounds can easily be deduced from the ones given.) After reading the experiment, you should be able to propose one or more reasonable structures for the product and a mechanism for its formation. The melting point of the product should then lead you to the correct structure. With your instructor's permission, you can also use the infrared (IR) spectrum of the product to help verify its structure.

Table 1 Compounds with the molecular formula $C_7H_7NO_2$

Compound	mp
2-hydroxybenzaldoxime*	63
3-hydroxybenzaldoxime	90
benzohydroxamic acid*	132
2-aminobenzoic acid*	147
3-aminobenzoic acid	174
4-aminobenzoic acid	189
2-hydroxybenzamide*	142
3-hydroxybenzamide	170.5
4-hydroxybenzamide	162
methyl 3-pyridinecarboxylate*	43
methyl 4-pyridinecarboxylate	8.5
1-methyl-3-pyridinecarboxylic acid*	218
2-hydroxy-5-nitrosotoluene	135
5-hydroxy-2-nitrosotoluene*	165
α-nitrotoluene	(bp 227)
2-nitrotoluene*	−10
3-nitrotoluene	16
4-nitrotoluene	54.5

Note: The structures of the compounds designated by asterisks are illustrated in Figure 1.

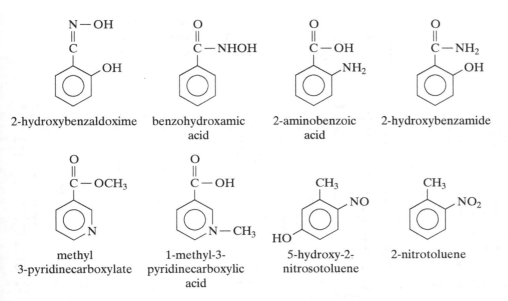

2-hydroxybenzaldoxime   benzohydroxamic acid   2-aminobenzoic acid   2-hydroxybenzamide

methyl 3-pyridinecarboxylate   1-methyl-3-pyridinecarboxylic acid   5-hydroxy-2-nitrosotoluene   2-nitrotoluene

Figure 1 Structures of some representative compounds from Table 1

Sodium hypochlorite is toxic to freshwater fish and invertebrates, so its release into the environment should be avoided. Acetic acid occurs naturally in living organisms and readily breaks down to yield carbon dioxide and water in the environment. Sodium hydroxide and hydrochloric acid are expected to be toxic to aqueous life. Phthalic anhydride hydrolyzes to phthalic acid in water and moist soil, but little is known about the effects of either chemical in the environment.

Reactions and Properties

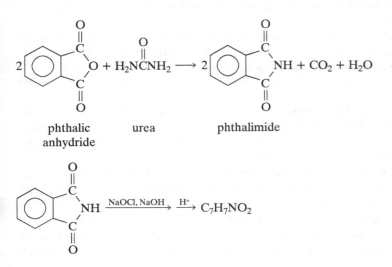

phthalic anhydride   urea   phthalimide

Table 2 Physical properties

	mol wt	mp
phthalic anhydride	148.1	132
urea	60.1	135
phthalimide	147.1	238
sodium hydroxide	40.0	322
sodium hypochlorite	74.5	

Note: mp is in °C; density is in g/mL.

Phthalimide

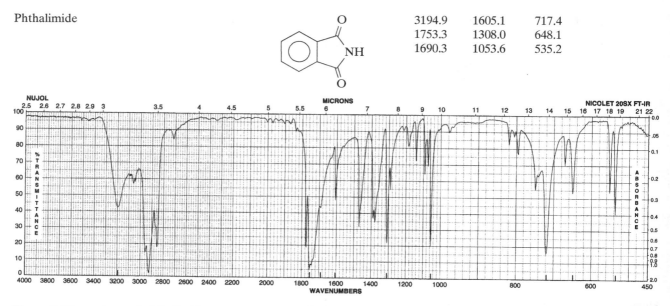

3194.9	1605.1	717.4
1753.3	1308.0	648.1
1690.3	1053.6	535.2

Figure 2 IR spectrum of phthalimide

DIRECTIONS

Safety Notes

phthalic anhydride   sodium hydroxide

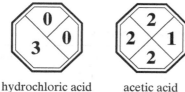

hydrochloric acid   acetic acid

Phthalic anhydride irritates the skin and eyes, and its dust can irritate the respiratory system. Avoid contact and do not breathe its dust.

Hot oil causes serious burns and may ignite above its flash point. Support the oil bath securely, keep it away from flames, and monitor its temperature closely.

Sodium hydroxide is toxic and corrosive, causing severe damage to skin, eyes, and mucous membranes. Wear gloves and avoid contact with the NaOH solution.

Concentrated hydrochloric acid is poisonous and corrosive; contact or inhalation can cause severe damage to the eyes, skin, and respiratory tract. Wear gloves and dispense under a hood. Avoid contact and do not breathe its vapors.

Acetic acid causes chemical burns that can seriously damage skin and eyes; its vapors are highly irritating to the eyes and respiratory tract. Wear gloves and dispense under a hood. Avoid contact and do not breathe its vapors.

Take Care! Avoid contact with phthalic anhydride and do not inhale its dust. Do not heat oil above its flash point; keep flames away.

Stop and Think: What causes the frothing?

Preparation of Phthalimide. This part can be omitted if commercial phthalimide is provided. Intimately mix 34.0 mmol of pure phthalic anhydride with 17.0 mmol of urea in a 100-mL round-bottom flask; attach a wide-bore condenser (a distilling column works well) but do *not* connect it to a water line. Heat [OP-7] the reaction flask in an oil bath that has been pre-heated to 130–135°C. Within about 20 minutes, the mixture should suddenly froth up and become nearly solid. At this point, stop heating the oil bath but leave the reaction flask in the oil while it cools. Add about 5 mL of cold water and break up the solid. Collect the product by vacuum filtration [OP-16], washing it on the filter [OP-26a] with a small amount of cold water.

Dry [OP-26b] the phthalimide, and measure its mass and melting point [OP-33]. Grind it to a powder in a mortar or put it between glazed weighing papers and pulverize it with the bottom of a beaker.

Reaction of Phthalimide with Laundry Bleach. (If you obtain less than 20 mmol of phthalimide, scale down the quantities of other reactants and solvents proportionately.) Measure 26 mL of 6.0% aqueous sodium hypochlorite (or 30 mL of 5.25% aqueous NaOCl) into a 250-mL Erlenmeyer flask, and then add 10 mL of 8 *M* (25%) NaOH. Cool [OP-8] the solution below 5°C in an ice/water or ice–salt bath. Add 20.0 mmol of finely powdered phthalimide and stir or swirl vigorously to mix [OP-10] the reactants. Add another 6.0 mL of the 8 *M* NaOH solution, stir or swirl to mix, and monitor the temperature [OP-9] of the reaction mixture. After the temperature drops about 5°C below its highest point, heat the reaction mixture to 80°C, with stirring or occasional swirling. Keep it at that temperature for 10 minutes, then let it stand for about 10 minutes at room temperature.

Under the hood, cool the reaction mixture in an ice/water bath, and then carefully stir in 9.5 mL of concentrated hydrochloric acid. Test the solution with pH paper and slowly add *just* enough additional concentrated HCl to bring its pH down to 10 (if the pH is already below 10, add enough 8 *M* NaOH dropwise to raise it to 10). Don't add too much HCl or the product will dissolve. Still under the hood, add 3.3 mL of glacial acetic acid *slowly*, with continuous stirring or swirling. (Don't let the reactants foam out the top of the flask.) Let the reaction mixture stand in the ice/water bath until precipitation is complete.

Separation. Collect the precipitate by vacuum filtration [OP-16], wash it on the filter with ice water until the odor of acetic acid is gone, and let it air-dry on the filter.

Purification and Analysis. Purify the product by recrystallization [OP-28] from boiling water, using decolorizing carbon as necessary to remove colored impurities. Dry [OP-26b] the product at room temperature, and measure its mass and melting point [OP-33]. Deduce the structure of the product, name it, and write a detailed mechanism that shows how phthalimide is converted to the product.

Take Care! Wear gloves and avoid contact with NaOH.

Take Care! Wear gloves, avoid contact with hydrochloric acid and acetic acid, and do not breathe their vapors.

Stop and Think: What should you do if the product dissolves?

Stop and Think: What do your observations tell you about the reaction?

Waste Disposal: Unless your instructor directs otherwise, wash all filtrates down the drain.

Exercises

1. What gas was responsible for the foaming when you acidified the reaction mixture? Write a balanced equation for the reaction that liberated the gas.
2. (a) May Bobble misread the directions; she acidified the reaction mixture to a pH of 2 with HCl and was surprised when there was no precipitate to filter. Explain what went wrong and write an equation for the reaction that caused the problem. (b) How could she have recovered the product and salvaged the experiment?
3. Describe and explain the possible effect (if any) on your results of the following experimental errors or variations. (a) The phthalimide wasn't dried completely and was allowed to sit for a week before it was used in the reaction. (b) The laundry bleach came from an old bottle and its NaOCl concentration was about 4%. (c) The lab assistant put out a

bottle of Clorox 2 Ultra bleach rather than standard Clorox (check the labels at a local store). (d) You used 3.0 M acetic acid rather than glacial acetic acid, and there was no foaming after you added 3.3 mL of it.

4. (a) Calculate the atom economy and reaction efficiency of your synthesis. (b) Describe some green features of your synthesis, and any that aren't so green.

5. Following the format in the "Planning an Experiment" appendix, construct a flow diagram for this experiment (excluding the preparation of phthalimide).

6. (a) When 35 mg of the product from this experiment was mixed with 0.46 g of camphor, the melting point of the mixture was found to be 157°C. Calculate the approximate molecular weight of the product if the melting point of pure camphor is 179°C and its freezing-point depression constant (K_f) is 40°C·kg·mol^{-1}. (b) Show how the molecular formula $C_7H_7NO_2$ can be derived using this result and data from the Scenario.

7. When 9-fluorenone hydrazone is treated with sodium nitrite in aqueous sulfuric acid, it rearranges to form phenanthridone. Propose a detailed mechanism that explains this reaction, showing the transition state for the rearrangement step. (*Hint*: What happens to amino groups in an acidified solution of sodium nitrite?)

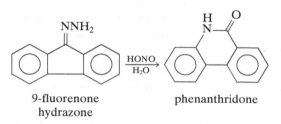

9-fluorenone   phenanthridone
hydrazone

8. (a) When a certain German chemist warmed a solution of N-bromoacetamide in base, he recognized an unmistakable pungent odor that slowly faded and was replaced by the strong ammonia-like odor of an escaping gas. What were the two substances that his nose told him were there? Write a mechanism explaining the formation of both. (b) Who was the chemist, and what reaction had he discovered?

Other Things You Can Do

(Starred items require your instructor's permission.)

*1. Record the infrared spectrum [OP-39] of the product and use it to assist you in identifying the product. Compare its spectrum with that of phthalimide in Figure 2, and interpret it as completely as you can.

*2. Carry out a molecular rearrangement of benzophenone oxime as described in the "Beckmann Rearrangement of Benzophenone Oxime" minilab.

3. Starting with sources listed in the Bibliography, write a research paper about the use of potassium phthalimide in the synthesis of amines and amino acids. Include a discussion of the phthalimidomalonic ester method and the Gabriel synthesis, and illustrate synthetic routes to specific products using each method.

Identification of an Unknown Amine

Reactions of Amines. Infrared Spectrometry. Qualitative Analysis.

Operations

OP-26 Washing and Drying Solids
OP-28 Recrystallization
OP-30 Simple Distillation
OP-33 Melting Point
OP-34 Boiling Point
OP-39 Infrared Spectrometry

Before You Begin

1. Read the experiment, read or review the operations as necessary, and write an experimental plan.
2. Read or review "Qualitative Organic Analysis," except for the "Directions" sections.

Scenario

The city health department of Arkham, Massachusetts, has been deluged with reports of bad-tasting city water, which may have been responsible for several reported cases of illness. Arkham's municipal water supply comes from the Miskatonic River, which winds through the town. A routine water analysis indicates the presence of a basic, nitrogen-containing compound, apparently an amine. The three most likely sources of the pollution, all upstream of the town, are:

- A dye factory that uses aniline and other aromatic amines as raw materials
- A chemical specialties company that synthesizes aliphatic amines for the manufacture of surfactants, corrosion inhibitors, and antioxidants
- An abandoned graveyard on Hangman's Hill, overlooking the river

With some help from the alchemy faculty at nearby Miskatonic University, health department personnel have obtained a sample of the unknown amine, and the Arkham town council has now asked your institute for help in identifying the source of this water contaminant. Your assignment is to identify the unknown amine and determine its probable source.

Applying Scientific Methodology

As you carry out the experiment, you should develop provisional hypotheses about the nature and identity of the unknown amine, which you will test—and perhaps reject or revise—as you gather additional experimental

From *Operational Organic Chemistry: A Problem Solving Approach to the Laboratory*, Fourth Edition, John W. Lehman. Copyright © 2009 by Pearson Education. Published by Prentice Hall. All rights reserved.

evidence. Your conclusion should, if possible, be consistent with all of the experimental evidence you obtain. Once you have identified the unknown, you should be able to deduce its probable source.

Biological Amines

Certain families of organic compounds, such as aldehydes and esters, tend to be associated with the pleasant aromas of fruits and perfumes. Amines, on the other hand, are more often associated with the unpleasant smells of body wastes, not-so-fresh fish, and decaying flesh. The amine family includes deadly poisons such as coniine, a component of the poison hemlock that killed Socrates, and dangerous drugs such as LSD, heroin, and methamphetamine. But the same family also includes some highly beneficial members that we couldn't get along without.

Some amines are produced by the enzyme-catalyzed breakdown of proteins and their component amino acids in decaying plant or animal material. For example, bacteria containing the enzymes called amino acid decarboxylases bring about the degradation of the amino acids ornithine and lysine to putrescine (1,4-butanediamine) and cadaverine (1,5-pentanediamine), respectively.

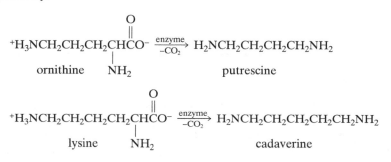

As their common names suggest, these amines are responsible for much of the objectionable odor of decaying flesh. The next homolog in this family of diamines, 1,6-hexanediamine, is more often associated with hosiery, camping gear, and outdoor clothing. Along with hexanedioic acid (adipic acid), it is a monomer used in the preparation of nylon 6,6, a commercially important polyamide.

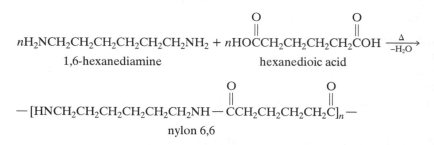

The family of amines called *phenethylamines*, whose parent compound is 2-phenylethylamine ($C_6H_5CH_2CH_2NH_2$), has many biologically active members, including body regulators such as epinephrine (adrenaline), useful drugs such as pseudoephedrine, and dangerous street drugs such as

430

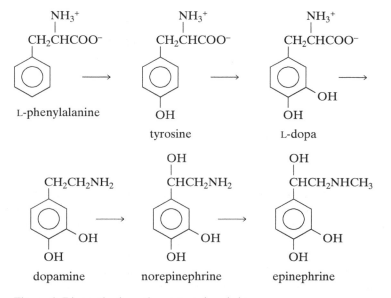

Figure 1 Biosynthetic pathway to epinephrine

methamphetamine. Epinephrine is synthesized in the body as the end product of an important biosynthetic pathway that starts with the amino acid L-phenylalanine (see Figure 1). Along this pathway are two other amino acids, tyrosine and L-dihydroxyphenylalanine (L-dopa), and the three *catecholamines* dopamine, norepinephrine, and epinephrine. Catecholamines are so named because they can be regarded as derivatives of the phenol 1,2-dihydroxybenzene, whose common name is catechol. L-Dopa, which is converted to dopamine in brain tissue, is used to help reduce the tremors and other abnormal movements characteristic of Parkinson's disease. The disease is apparently associated with a deficiency of dopamine in the brain, which causes an imbalance of the chemicals responsible for transmitting nerve impulses.

Norepinephrine is one of the body's major neurotransmitters and is responsible for the transmission of nerve impulses along the sympathetic (adrenergic) nervous system. Epinephrine, a hormone produced in the adrenal gland, increases the heart rate and blood pressure by constricting blood vessels, and also dilates bronchial passageways to permit free breathing. In this way, epinephrine prepares the body for "fright, flight, or fight," giving rise to the adrenaline rush sometimes experienced by athletes and people in stressful situations. Both norepinephrine and epinephrine have been used therapeutically, the former to maintain blood pressure for persons in shock and the latter to treat allergies and stimulate the heart during heart attacks.

Another phenethylamine, ephedrine, occurs naturally in several species of leafless green-stemmed shrubs of the genus *Ephedra*. Twigs from the Chinese shrub ma huang (*Ephedra sinica*) have been used for more than 5000 years to treat asthma and a variety of other ailments. Like epinephrine, ephedrine can constrict the walls of blood vessels and dilate bronchial tubes. Such properties have led to the widespread use of ephedrine and its diastereomer pseudoephedrine as decongestants for people suffering from asthma, sinus congestion, allergies, and even the common cold.

catechol

In 2006 a U.S. statute put strict limitations on the sale of products that contain pseudoephedrin—such as the nasal decongestant Sudafed—because it can be converted to the illicit drug methamphetamine.

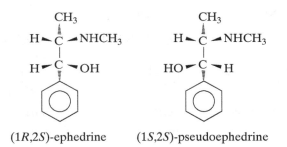

(1R,2S)-ephedrine   (1S,2S)-pseudoephedrine

Ephedrine has also been used widely in dietary supplements that are claimed to help people lose weight, feel more energetic, and develop their muscles. However, overdoses of ephedrine can cause heart attacks, strokes, seizures, and sometimes death, so the U.S. Food and Drug Administration has limited the amount of ephedrine that can be included in any dietary supplement and has banned its use in weight loss and bodybuilding products.

Methamphetamine has a structure very similar to that of ephedrine but is considerably more dangerous. Before its addictive potential was recognized, methamphetamine—also known as "speed"—was prescribed as an appetite suppressant and to treat depression. It is a nervous system stimulant said to generate a feeling of confidence and mental alertness, but its side effects include hallucinations, paranoia, and death. Epinephrine and methamphetamine both appear to stimulate the release of norepinephrine in the body, thereby increasing the transmission of nerve impulses.

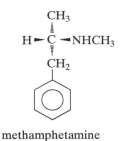

methamphetamine

Understanding the Experiment

This section provides a general discussion of most of the procedures you will follow to identify your unknown. For more detailed information about the interpretation of test results, see the appropriate sections in "Qualitative Organic Analysis." For information about the interpretation of infrared spectra, see Operation 39.

Because an unknown liquid amine may be impure, you should purify it by distillation before you perform any chemical tests or record its spectra. Solid amines can be purified by recrystallization, but see your instructor first to find out if an unknown solid requires purification. Measure the boiling point or melting point of your unknown as accurately as you can, because your list of possibilities will be based on the value you obtain. A preliminary examination of your unknown may provide some clues that will help you identify it, as will its solubility behavior in water and 5% HCl.

Tertiary amines are listed on a different table and have different derivatives than primary or secondary amines, so it is important to classify your amine correctly. Many amines can be classified with reasonable accuracy using a simple color test, the quinhydrone test. Before you can interpret this test, you must know whether your amine is aromatic or aliphatic; aliphatic amines are basic enough to dissolve in a buffer solution having a pH of 5.5, while most aromatic amines are not. To confirm your tentative classification, you should carry out Hinsberg's test, which is based on the properties of the products formed when an amine reacts with an arenesulfonyl chloride in aqueous NaOH. The arenesulfonamide formed by a primary amine

Key Concept: Because tertiary amines have no N—H bonds, they don't undergo many of the reactions of primary and secondary amines, which require loss of H⁺ from N to form the desired product.

is soluble in the reagent and precipitates when HCl is added. The arenesulfonamide formed by a secondary amine is insoluble in the reagent and doesn't dissolve when HCl is added. Most tertiary amines leave an insoluble residue that dissolves when HCl is added.

You can also classify an amine and characterize it further from its infrared (IR) spectrum. A typical primary amine has a medium-intensity, two-pronged N—H stretching band near 3350 cm^{-1}, a medium to strong N—H bending band near 1615 cm^{-1}, and a strong, broad N—H bending band in the vicinity of 800 cm^{-1}. A typical secondary amine has a single, weak N—H stretching band near 3300 cm^{-1} and a strong, broad N—H bending band around 715 cm^{-1}. A tertiary amine has no N—H bonds, so its IR spectrum shows none of these bands, but it may have a recognizable C—N stretching band in the 1340–1020 cm^{-1} region. The position of the C—N band, which is present for primary and secondary amines as well, depends on the structure of the amine; for aromatic amines, it is around 1340–1250 cm^{-1}, and for aliphatic amines, it is around 1250–1020 cm^{-1}. The IR spectrum of an aromatic amine should also exhibit characteristic Ar—H stretching and bending bands, as described in the "Characteristic Infrared Bands" section of OP-39.

Your unknown amine will be one of the amines listed in Tables 5 and 6 in the "Properties of Organic Compounds" appendix. After performing the classification tests and interpreting your IR spectrum, you should be able to prepare a short list of possibilities from the appropriate tables. You should then be able to identify your unknown by preparing a derivative whose melting point will distinguish it from all other amines with similar boiling or melting points. If possible, avoid preparing derivatives whose melting points for the compounds on your list are too low, too close together, or not listed for some of the possibilities. Keep in mind that incomplete purification and insufficient drying of the derivative can lower its melting point, so follow the directions for preparing the derivative carefully, and be sure that the product is completely dry before you measure its melting point. If you have difficulty preparing a certain derivative, or if the melting point of the derivative you prepare doesn't eliminate all of the possibilities but one, you should prepare a second derivative.

When you think you have gathered enough evidence to identify your unknown with some certainty, you are free to write down your conclusion. But keep in mind that your evidence should be sufficient to convince your instructor—and yourself—that your conclusion is justified.

Most aliphatic amines biodegrade rapidly when released into the environment, but some aromatic amines are highly toxic to aquatic life and may be hazardous air pollutants. Some of the reagents used in classification tests and derivative preparations may be harmful to the environment.

Reactions and Properties

General equations for the classification tests are given in the "Classification Tests" section of "Qualitative Organic Analysis." General equations for derivative preparations for amines are given in the "Derivatives of Primary and Secondary Amines" and "Derivatives of Tertiary Amines" sections. Physical properties of amines and the melting points of their derivatives are listed in Tables 5 and 6 of the "Properties of Organic Compounds" appendix.

DIRECTIONS

Safety Notes

Aromatic amines are very harmful if inhaled, ingested, or absorbed through the skin. Many aliphatic amines are flammable and corrosive, and are harmful if inhaled, ingested, or absorbed through the skin. Some amines are suspected carcinogens. Avoid contact with your unknown, do not inhale its vapors, and keep it away from flames.

Safety information for chemicals used in classification tests and derivative preparations are included with the corresponding procedures in "Qualitative Organic Analysis."

Take Care! Wear gloves, avoid contact with the amine, and do not breathe its vapors.

Preliminary Work. Obtain an unknown amine from your instructor and record its identification number in your laboratory notebook. If the unknown is a liquid, purify it by simple distillation [OP-30]; record its distillation boiling range and median boiling point. Then measure the boiling point [OP-34] of the purified liquid using a capillary-tube method. If it is a solid, purify it by recrystallization [OP-28], if necessary, and measure its melting point [OP-33]. Describe the physical state, general appearance, and any other notable characteristics of the compound in your lab notebook. Carry out an ignition test as described in "Preliminary Work" in "Qualitative Organic Analysis."

Stop and Think: Why might its odor disappear?

Solubility Tests. Test the solubility of the unknown in water as described in "Solubility Tests" in "Qualitative Organic Analysis." If it is soluble, test its aqueous solution with red litmus paper, and then add 5% HCl dropwise to see whether its odor (if any) disappears. If it is insoluble in water, test its solubility in 5% HCl as described in "Solubility Tests."

Classification of the Amine. Refer to the "Classification Tests" section in "Qualitative Organic Analysis" for procedures. Classify the unknown amine as aliphatic or aromatic using the basicity test (classification test C-4). Then classify it as primary, secondary, or tertiary using the quinhydrone test (C-20) or Hinsberg's test (C-15), or both. Obtain an infrared spectrum [OP-39] of your unknown and use it to see if your classifications are correct.

Waste Disposal: Dispose of all wastes as directed by your instructor.

Detection of Structural Features. In your lab notebook, list all compounds from the appropriate table (Table 5 or 6) in the "Properties of Organic Compounds" appendix that have melting or boiling points within ±10°C of your observed value; record their melting or boiling points and the melting points of the derivatives listed. At your instructor's discretion, show him or her your list; the instructor may approve the list if it includes your unknown or suggest additional work if it doesn't. Write the structure of every compound on your list and consider whether additional classification tests, such as Beilstein's test (C-5), would help you select the most likely possibilities. Inspect your IR spectrum to find out what you can about any structural features or secondary functional groups, such as aromatic rings, alkoxyl groups, or nitro groups. At this point, you should be able to prepare a short list of compounds by eliminating the least likely possibilities. Keep in mind, however, that classification tests and IR wave numbers are not infallible indicators of molecular structure, so it may be necessary later to reconsider some of the compounds that you eliminated from your short list.

Preparation of a Derivative. Refer to the "Preparation of Derivatives" section in "Qualitative Organic Analysis" for procedures. Select the derivative that should best differentiate the compounds on your short list. If your amine is primary or secondary, you can prepare one or more of the following derivatives for which reagents are available: benzamide (derivative D-8), *p*-toluenesulfonamide (D-9), phenylthiourea (D-10), or picrate (D-12). If your amine is tertiary, you can prepare a methiodide (D-11) or picrate (D-12). Purify the derivative by recrystallization [OP-28] as described in the appropriate procedure, dry [OP-26b] it thoroughly, and measure its melting point [OP-33]. Deduce the identity of your unknown from the derivative melting point and all other relevant evidence; justify your conclusion based on the evidence. Then deduce the probable source of the amine based on information given in this experiment.

Waste Disposal: Dispose of all wastes as directed by your instructor. Return any unused unknown to your instructor in its original vial.

Exercises

1. Interpret the infrared spectrum you obtained as completely as you can.
2. (a) Write balanced equations for the reactions involved in all of the classification tests for which you obtained a positive result. (b) Write balanced equations for the reaction(s) involved in your derivative preparation(s).
3. Describe and explain the possible effect on your results of the following experimental errors or variations. (a) When you carried out Hinsberg's test, you inadvertently used 3 M HCl in place of 3 M NaOH. (b) You mistakenly classified a tertiary amine as secondary and tried to prepare a *p*-toluenesulfonate derivative. (c) While performing the basicity test on a water-insoluble unknown, you inadvertently used a sodium acetate solution rather than the acetate–acetic acid buffer.
4. Calculate the atom economy of your derivative preparation.
5. Construct a flow diagram showing the process you followed to identify your unknown.
6. The basicity test differentiates aromatic and aliphatic amines based on their solubility in a pH 5.5 buffer. Given that K_b for aniline is 4.2×10^{-10} and K_b for cyclohexylamine is 5.0×10^{-4}, calculate the ratio of amine salt to dissolved amine for both compounds in such a buffer, and explain the difference in their solubility behavior.
7. An unknown liquid boiling around 185 ± 5°C dissolves in 5% HCl but is insoluble in water and in a pH 5.5 buffer. Shaking the unknown with *p*-toluenesulfonyl chloride in aqueous NaOH produces a clear solution that, when acidified, yields a white precipitate. Assuming that the unknown is listed in the "Properties of Organic Compounds" appendix, give its name and draw its structure.
8. An unknown liquid boiling around 185 ± 5°C dissolves in 5% HCl and in a pH 5.5 buffer but is insoluble in water. Shaking the unknown with *p*-toluenesulfonyl chloride in aqueous NaOH produces a white precipitate that doesn't dissolve in dilute HCl. Assuming that the unknown is listed in the "Properties of Organic Compounds" appendix, give its name and draw its structure.
9. Write mechanisms for the following reactions, which are used in chemical tests and derivative preparations: (a) the reaction of aniline with benzoyl chloride in aqueous NaOH; (b) the formation of the methiodide of triethylamine; (c) the reaction of diethylamine with benzenesulfonyl chloride in aqueous NaOH.

435

Other Things You Can Do

(Starred items require your instructor's permission.)

*1. Obtain and interpret an ^{1}H or ^{13}C NMR spectrum [OP-40] of your unknown.
2. Starting with sources listed in the Bibliography, write a research paper describing the structures, biological functions, and therapeutic uses (if any) of some phenethylamines.

Preparation and Mass Spectrum of 2-Phenylindole

Reactions of Carbonyl Compounds. Preparation of Heterocyclic Amines. Fischer Indole Synthesis. Phenylhydrazones. Mass Spectrometry.

Operations

OP-42 Mass Spectrometry
OP-7 Heating
OP-9 Temperature Monitoring
OP-10 Mixing
OP-15 Gravity Filtration
OP-16 Vacuum Filtration
OP-26 Washing and Drying Solids
OP-28 Recrystallization
OP-29 Sublimation (optional)
OP-33 Melting Point

Before You Begin

1. Read the experiment and OP-42, read or review the operations as necessary, and write an experimental plan.
2. Calculate the mass and volume of 10.0 mmol of acetophenone, and the theoretical yield of 2-phenylindole.

Scenario

The indole family of heterocyclic amines has a shady reputation because many of its members, such as psilocybin and LSD, have mind-altering properties that have made them popular—but illegal—recreational drugs. But other indoles, such as tryptophan (an essential amino acid) and serotonin (a brain-regulating chemical), are necessary for normal body functioning. The Pharmstead Company is interested in developing new synthetic indole derivatives for use as legitimate drugs. To better focus their search for promising pharmaceuticals, they are conducting a preliminary study of the effect of ring substitution on physiological activity. Virtually all physiologically active natural indole derivatives have a substituent at the #3 position and none at the #2 position of the indole ring system, so the physiological effects of 2-substituted indoles haven't been thoroughly explored. This may be because they *have* no significant physiological effects, but before coming to that conclusion, the drug development division at Pharmstead wants to obtain and test a representative sample of 2-substituted indoles whose structures are known with certainty. Your assignment is to prepare a sample of 2-phenylindole and confirm its structure using its mass spectrum.

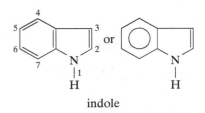

indole

From *Operational Organic Chemistry: A Problem Solving Approach to the Laboratory*, Fourth Edition, John W. Lehman. Copyright © 2009 by Pearson Education. Published by Prentice Hall. All rights reserved

Applying Scientific Methodology

After reading the experiment, you should be able to predict some features of the mass spectrum of 2-phenylindole, including the relative intensities of the M + 1 and M + 2 peaks. Such predictions can be incorporated into a hypothesis, which will be tested when you obtain its mass spectrum.

Of Toads and Toadstools

The indoles constitute a large family of natural and synthetic compounds with extraordinary properties and functions. Indoles as a group display an ambivalent nature, as illustrated by the parent compound, indole, which has an odor of fine jasmine in dilute solutions but a fecal smell when undiluted. 3-Methylindole is a major product of the digestive putrefaction of proteins and is mainly responsible for the repulsive odor of feces, giving rise to its common name, skatole—from *scat*, meaning animal droppings. However, skatole is also found in cabbage sprouts, tea, and even lilies!

In Mexico during the sixteenth century, Spanish conquistadors observed the Aztecs using some little brown mushrooms called *teonanacatl* ("flesh of the gods") in their religious ceremonies. According to the Spanish friar Bernardino de Sahagun, "They ate these little mushrooms with honey, and when they began to be excited by them, they began to dance, some singing, others weeping.... Some saw themselves dying in a vision and wept; others saw themselves being eaten by a wild beast; others imagined that they were capturing prisoners in battle, that they were rich, that they possessed many slaves, that they had committed adultery and were to have their heads crushed for the offense." Naturally, the Spanish friars disapproved of these ceremonies and banned them. This only led to the formation of cults that consumed the mushrooms in secret, until ethnomycologist R. Gordon Wasson revealed the existence of such practices in the 1930s. The little brown mushrooms are from several different species of the genus *Psilocybe*. Their hallucinogenic constituents include psilocin and psilocybin, both of which are derivatives of tryptamine, the parent compound of many physiologically active indoles. A similar tryptamine derivative, bufotenin, is the active principle of cohoba snuff, which is inhaled by certain Indians of South America and the Caribbean area to produce hallucinations. Bufotenin has also been isolated both from toads of the genus *Bufo* and from "toadstools" such as the poisonous mushroom *Amanita porphyria*.

magic mushrooms

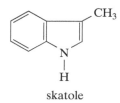

skatole

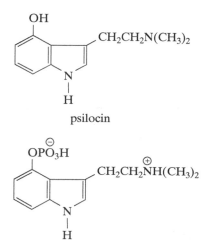

psilocin

psilocybin

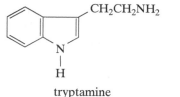

tryptamine

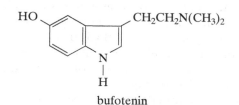

bufotenin

Other indole derivatives are more beneficial, such as the essential amino acid tryptophan, the plant-growth hormone 3-indoleacetic acid (also called heteroauxin), the beautiful dye indigo, and the bioregulator serotonin. Tryptophan is important as a source of serotonin and the B-vitamin nicotinamide, both of which are formed during its metabolism. Because the human body cannot biosynthesize aromatic compounds, tryptophan and the other aromatic amino acids, phenylalanine and tyrosine, must be obtained from food. Indoleacetic acid promotes the enlargement of plant cells and is the principal natural growth regulator for many plants. Indigo was one of the first natural dyes to be prepared synthetically, and it is still used to dye blue jeans and other textiles. Indigo's structure was determined in 1883 by German organic chemist Adolph von Baeyer after 18 years of research. Although the function of serotonin in the human body isn't fully understood, it appears to play an important role in mental processes. Some researchers see it as a mind stabilizer that helps to preserve sanity. The resemblance between serotonin and such mind-altering drugs as bufotenin is striking; some of the psychological activity of these drugs may arise from their interference with the action of serotonin.

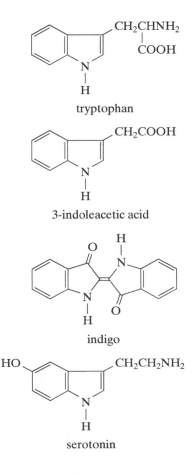

tryptophan

3-indoleacetic acid

indigo

serotonin

Understanding the Experiment

The preparation of 2-phenylindole by the Fischer indole synthesis involves the acid-catalyzed cyclization of a phenylhydrazone with the loss of a molecule of ammonia.

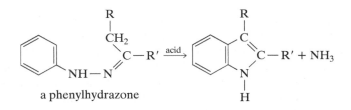

a phenylhydrazone

The phenylhydrazone can be prepared by combining phenylhydrazine or a substituted phenylhydrazine with an aldehyde or ketone having the structure RCH_2COR', where the R groups can be alkyl, aryl, or hydrogen. The generally accepted mechanism for this indolization reaction, first proposed by Robinson and Robinson in 1918, includes the following steps:

1. A tautomeric shift of a proton from carbon to the β-nitrogen
2. Protonation of that nitrogen
3. A concerted electron shift that forms a C—C bond to the ring and breaks the N—N bond
4. Another tautomeric shift of a proton from carbon to nitrogen
5. Nucleophilic attack by nitrogen on a doubly bonded carbon atom, followed by the loss of a proton
6. Loss of ammonia to yield an aromatic pyrrole ring

Robinson mechanism

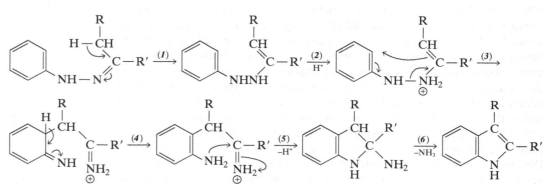

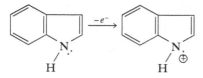

formation of the molecular ion

Key Concept: *The molecular weight of an amine, and thus the* m/e *value of its molecular ion peak, is usually an odd number.*

See OP-42 if you aren't familiar with the principles and terminology of mass spectrometry.

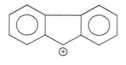

fluorenyl cation

In this experiment, you will synthesize 2-phenylindole by first converting acetophenone to acetophenone phenylhydrazone, then heating acetophenone phenylhydrazone with the acid catalyst polyphosphoric acid. Because acetophenone phenylhydrazone is sensitive to heat and light, you should dry it at room temperature and store it in the dark. Its reaction in polyphosphoric acid is exothermic and requires only a few minutes to go to completion, after which the reaction mixture is poured into water to dissolve the acid catalyst and precipitate crude 2-phenylindole. You can purify 2-phenylindole by recrystallization from 95% ethanol/water mixed solvent, followed by vacuum sublimation if desired. Recrystallization is complicated by the fact that the crystals dissolve quite slowly in 95% ethanol, so you will need to use a condenser to keep the solvent from boiling away.

The mass spectrum of indole (Figure 1) is characterized by an intense molecular ion peak ($M\cdot^+$, $m/e = 117$), which is also the base peak. The molecular ion is probably formed by loss of a nonbonded electron from the nitrogen atom. Most substituted indoles, like indole itself and other aromatic amines, have strong molecular ion peaks. Neutral fragments lost from the molecular ions of indoles include HCN and CH_2N, forming ions with m/e values of $M - 27$ and $M - 28$, respectively. The loss of CH_2N from 1-, 2-, and 3-phenylindoles leaves a $C_{13}H_9^+$ ion, which could be a fluorenyl cation. If so, the molecular ion must undergo considerable "scrambling" (intramolecular rearrangement) before it ejects CH_2N. Phenylindoles may lose the phenyl-substituted analogs of HCN (C_6H_5CN) and CH_2N (C_6H_5CHN) to form additional daughter ions. Because the molecular ion peak of 2-phenylindole is quite strong, its M + 1 and M + 2 peaks are also prominent, making it easy to compare their intensities with the expected values. The mass spectra of some indoles also show "half-mass" peaks that result from the formation of ions that have a 2+ charge. For example, the doubly charged molecular ion of indole itself gives an M^{++} peak with an m/e value of 58.5.

The infrared (IR) spectra of heteroaromatic compounds (see "Other Things You Can Do") are similar to those of analogous aromatic compounds, with some additional bands arising from the heteroatoms. Thus, pyrroles and indoles, like other aromatic compounds, show ring-stretching bands in the $1650-1300$ cm^{-1} region and C—H out-of-plane bending bands in the $910-665$ cm^{-1} region. Most pyrrole rings are distinguished

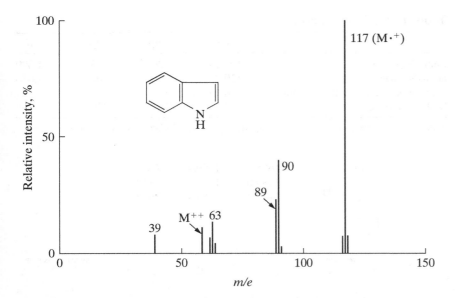

Figure 1 Mass spectrum of indole. (Reproduced from *Mass Spectrometry of Heterocyclic Compounds,* by Q. N. Porter and J. Baidas. Copyright © 1971 by John Wiley & Sons, Inc. This material is used by permission of John Wiley & Sons, Inc.)

by a characteristically strong, broad C—H bending band near 740 cm^{-1}. Heteroaromatic amines with N—H bonds absorb in the 3500−3220 cm^{-1} region. The N—H stretching band of indoles occurs near 3450 cm^{-1}.

Phenylhydrazine is toxic to aquatic organisms. Acetic acid occurs naturally in living organisms and readily breaks down to carbon dioxide and water in the environment.

pyrrole

Reactions and Properties

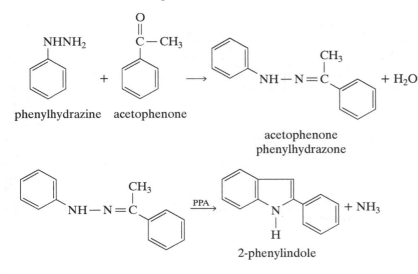

Table 1 Physical properties

	mol wt	mp	bp	d
phenylhydrazine	108.15	20	243	1.099
acetophenone	120.2	20.5	202	1.028
acetophenone phenylhydrazone	210.35	106		
2-phenylindole	193.25	189	250^{10}	

Note: mp and bp are in °C; density is in g/mL; superscripts indicate pressure in torr.

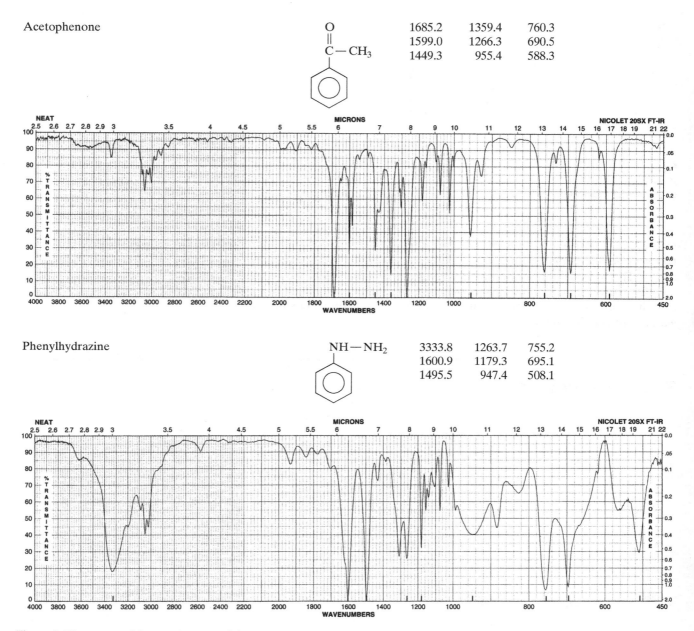

Acetophenone

1685.2	1359.4	760.3
1599.0	1266.3	690.5
1449.3	955.4	588.3

Phenylhydrazine

3333.8	1263.7	755.2
1600.9	1179.3	695.1
1495.5	947.4	508.1

Figure 2 IR spectra of the starting materials

DIRECTIONS

> Phenylhydrazine is corrosive and very toxic if inhaled, ingested, or absorbed through the skin; contact may cause painful skin eruptions in sensitive individuals. It is also a suspected carcinogen. Use gloves, dispense under a hood, avoid contact, and do not breathe its vapors.
> Acetic acid causes chemical burns that can seriously damage skin and eyes; its vapors are highly irritating to the eyes and respiratory tract. Dispense under a hood, avoid contact, and do not breathe its vapors.
> Polyphosphoric acid can cause serious burns, particularly to the eyes, so avoid contact with skin and eyes.
> Some indoles are suspected of causing cancer; minimize your contact with the product.

Safety Notes

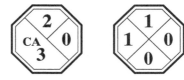

phenylhydrazine   acetophenonone

Preparation of Acetophenone Phenylhydrazone. In a small round-bottom flask, dissolve 10.0 mmol of acetophenone in 5.0 mL of 95% ethanol. Add 1.0 mL (~10 mmol) of freshly distilled phenylhydrazine, followed by 2 drops of glacial acetic acid; swirl to mix. Add boiling chips or a stir bar [OP-10], attach a condenser, and heat the reaction mixture under reflux [OP-7] for 15 minutes, using a steam bath or boiling-water bath. Transfer the warm reaction mixture to a small Erlenmeyer flask and cool it in an ice/water bath. Scratch the sides of the flask, if necessary, to promote crystallization. When crystallization is complete, collect the acetophenone phenylhydrazone by vacuum filtration [OP-16]. Wash the product on the filter with 4 mL of 1 M hydrochloric acid, followed by 2 mL of ice-cold 95% ethanol, and let it air-dry. If there isn't sufficient time to dry the product, blot it as dry as possible between large filter papers (wear protective gloves!). Acetophenone phenylhydrazone should be used soon after it is prepared, or else stored in a cool, dark place.

Impure phenylhydrazine is dark reddish-brown and will give an inferior product.

Take Care! Wear gloves, avoid contact with phenylhydrazine and acetic acid, and do not breathe their vapors.

Stop and Think: What is the purpose of the 1 M HCl?

Waste Disposal: Unless your instructor directs otherwise, wash the filtrate down the drain.

Reaction. Measure 10 mL of polyphosphoric acid into a dry 20-cm test tube. (Polyphosphoric acid can be warmed gently over a steam bath to make it easier to pour.) Clamp the tube so that the portion containing the liquid extends inside a steam bath, removing enough rings to let the test tube just slip through. Clamp a thermometer [OP-9] in the liquid, near one wall of the test tube but not touching it, to allow room for manual stirring (don't use the thermometer as a stirring rod!). Heat the polyphosphoric acid to 50°C, then mix in the acetophenone phenylhydrazone with a stirring rod. Heat [OP-7] the reactants on the steam bath, stirring until the solid dissolves. When the temperature of the reaction mixture rises to 100°C, turn off the steam. Have a cold-water bath handy to keep the temperature below 125°C. When the temperature begins to drop, turn on the steam and heat the mixture for 10–15 minutes, with occasional stirring.

Take Care! Avoid contact with polyphosphoric acid.

Observe and Note: Look for and record any evidence for a chemical reaction.

Separation. Cautiously pour the warm reaction mixture into 30 mL of ice water, using more water for the transfer, and stir until all of the polyphosphoric acid has dissolved. Collect the crude 2-phenylindole by vacuum filtration [OP-16], wash it on the filter with cold methanol, and let it air-dry on the filter.

Waste Disposal: Unless your instructor directs otherwise, wash the filtrate down the drain.

Purification and Analysis. Recrystallize [OP-28] the product from 95% ethanol/water mixed solvent, using a 50-mL round-bottom flask fitted with a reflux condenser. Start with 15 mL of 95% ethanol and boil the mixture for about 10 minutes, with stirring or shaking [OP-10]; if the solid doesn't dissolve completely, add more solvent in small portions, boiling for several minutes after each addition. When the product is completely dissolved, use Norit to partly decolorize the solution (unless your instructor suggests otherwise) and filter [OP-15] the hot solution by gravity. (Filtration shouldn't be necessary if you don't use Norit.) With the solution boiling, add hot water to the cloud point and continue as described in OP-28b. Dry [OP-26b] the 2-phenylindole at room temperature. At your instructor's request, purify the product (or part of it) further by vacuum sublimation [OP-29]. Measure the mass and melting point [OP-33] of the purified 2-phenylindole. Record a mass spectrum [OP-42] of the product or obtain one from your instructor. Tabulate the m/e values and intensities of the molecular ion peak, the M + 1 and M + 2 peaks, and all other peaks whose intensities are 10% or more of the base peak intensity. Derive the molecular formula of 2-phenylindole from its structure, use the formula to calculate the expected intensities of the M + 1 and M + 2 peaks, and compare the experimental and theoretical values. Characterize as many of the other peaks as you can, in each instance giving the formula of the species lost from the molecular ion and the formula of the resulting daughter ion.

Exercises

1. (a) Rewrite the general mechanism given in the "Understanding the Experiment" section so that it applies to the synthesis of 2-phenylindole, and sketch the activated complexes for steps **3** and **5** of the Robinson mechanism. (b) Write a mechanism for the reaction that forms acetophenone phenylhydrazone, showing the role of acetic acid.

2. Outline syntheses of 1-phenylindole and 3-phenylindole from appropriate starting materials.

3. Describe and explain the possible effect on your results of the following experimental errors or variations. (a) You rinsed the test tube used for the preparation of acetophenone phenylhydrazone with acetone and failed to remove all the acetone. (b) You used benzophenone rather than acetophenone. (c) You used phenylhydrazine hydrochloride ($C_6H_5NHNH_3^+Cl^-$) rather than phenylhydrazine.

4. (a) Calculate the atom economy and reaction efficiency of your synthesis of 2-phenylindole. (b) Describe some green features of your synthesis, and any that aren't so green.

5. Following the format in the "Planning an Experiment" appendix, construct a flow diagram for this experiment.

6. Draw structures for the indoles that would be obtained from the phenylhydrazones of the following carbonyl compounds: (a) acetone; (b) phenylacetaldehyde (2-phenylethanal); (c) cyclopentanone; (d) pyruvic acid ($CH_3COCOOH$); (e) camphor.

7. When the phenylhydrazone of isobutyrophenone (2-methyl-1-phenyl-1-propanone) is heated to 150°C with polyphosphoric acid, it yields a mixture of the two compounds shown. Propose a mechanism that explains the formation of each product.

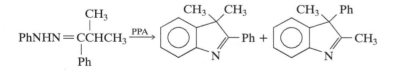

8. The total synthesis of strychnine, accomplished by Robert B. Woodward in 1954, began with the preparation of 2-(3,4-dimethoxyphenyl)indole. Show how this compound can be prepared starting with catechol (1,2-dihydroxybenzene).

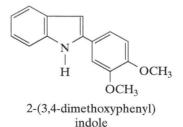

2-(3,4-dimethoxyphenyl)
indole

Other Things You Can Do

(Starred items require your instructor's permission.)

*1. Record the IR spectrum of 2-phenylindole. Interpret this spectrum as completely as you can, compare it with the spectra of the starting materials shown in Figure 2, and describe the evidence suggesting that the expected reaction has taken place.

*2. Prepare some indigo and use it to dye cloth as described in the "Dyeing with Indigo" minilab.

3. Starting with sources listed in the Bibliography, write a research paper about natural and synthetic plant-growth hormones (auxins), describing their sources and chemical structures and giving examples of their applications.

Nucleophilic Strength and Reactivity in S_NAr Reactions

EXPERIMENT

Reactions of Aryl Halides. Nucleophilic Aromatic Substitution.
Reaction Kinetics.

Operations

OP-41b Colorimetry
OP-5 Measuring Volume
OP-10 Mixing

Before You Begin

Read the experiment, read OP-41b, read or review the other operations as necessary, and write an experimental plan.

Scenario

Organic chemists rely on handbooks and other sources of compiled chemical information to help them design their experiments. For example, a nucleophile's *nucleophilic constant*, which measures the nucleophile's ability to displace a leaving group from a specific kind of substrate, could help a chemist estimate how long it would take to carry out a given nucleophilic substitution reaction. Minnie Colfax, a chemical information specialist for the Fulcourt Press, is compiling a list of nucleophiles for the next edition of a chemistry reference book. She wants to list them in order of nucleophilic strength, as indicated by the values of their nucleophilic constants, but some of the nucleophilic constants were measured many years ago by questionable methods and may not be accurate. Your project group's mission is to measure the nucleophilic constants for morpholine and piperidine in an S_NAr reaction, and from your results determine which is the stronger nucleophile.

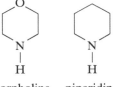

morpholine   piperidine

Applying Scientific Methodology

After reading the experiment, you should formulate a hypothesis predicting which of the two heterocyclic amines, morpholine or piperidine, should be the stronger nucleophile in S_NAr reactions. Your hypothesis will be tested when you determine and compare the nucleophilic constants of the two amines.

Nucleophilicity and the S_NAr Reaction

Nucleophilic aromatic substitution can occur by

- An S_N1 mechanism, as in some substitution reactions of aryldiazonium salts
- An elimination–addition mechanism involving an aryne intermediate
- A bimolecular addition–elimination route called the S_NAr reaction

From *Operational Organic Chemistry: A Problem Solving Approach to the Laboratory*, Fourth Edition, John W. Lehman. Copyright © 2009 by Pearson Education. Published by Prentice Hall. All rights reserved.

447

Key Concept: *In different kinds of nucleophilic substitution reactions, the leaving group can leave* before *the nucleophile attacks (S_N1), as the nucleophile attacks (S_N2), or* after *the nucleophile attacks (S_NAr and nucleophilic acyl substitution).*

In an S_NAr reaction, the nucleophile attacks an activated aromatic ring to form an intermediate complex, which then loses a leaving group to yield the product. The nature of that intermediate complex has long been the subject of speculation. The first evidence of its structure was obtained in 1898, when Jackson and Boos mixed picryl chloride (2,4,6-trinitrochlorobenzene) with sodium methoxide in methanol and isolated a red salt, which was converted by ethanol to another red salt. Jakob Meisenheimer prepared the second salt by two different methods, treating either 2,4,6-trinitroanisole with potassium ethoxide or 2,4,6-trinitrophenetole with potassium methoxide. He was then able to assign it the structure labeled *1* in the following reaction scheme:

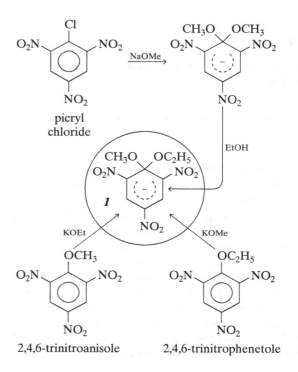

2,4,6-trinitroanisole   2,4,6-trinitrophenetole

Negatively charged aromatic species analogous to structure *1* are called *Meisenheimer complexes,* and many such complexes have been prepared and characterized. A large body of experimental evidence indicates that the intermediates in S_NAr reactions are Meisenheimer complexes, explaining why only aromatic compounds that are activated by electron-withdrawing substituents, such as nitro groups, undergo S_NAr reactions easily. Such substituents remove excess electron density from the aromatic ring, stabilizing the intermediate complex and thus facilitating its formation.

The mechanism of most S_NAr reactions appears to be a simple two-step process involving the initial addition of the nucleophile to form a Meisenheimer complex, followed by the departure of the leaving group. The first step of the reaction is ordinarily rate limiting, so the nucleophilic strength of the reactant—its ability to donate its electron pair to the substrate and form a sigma bond—affects the reaction rate. Equation **1**, which

General S_NAr mechanism

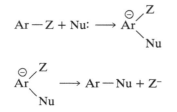

Note: Ar must be activated by electron-withdrawing groups; Z is the leaving group and Nu: the nucleophile.

is called the *Swain–Scott equation,* relates a reaction rate to the strength of the nucleophile (n) and the sensitivity of the substrate to nucleophilic substitution (s).

$$\log\frac{k}{k_0} = ns \qquad (1)$$

It has been applied widely to nucleophilic substitution reactions with aliphatic substrates, and some values of the nucleophilic constant n for reactions of various nucleophiles with methyl iodide are given in Table 1.

Attempts to use such correlations for S_NAr reactions have met with less success because changing the substrate or the solvent often changes the order of nucleophilic strength. However, an equation similar to Equation 1 can be useful in comparing the nucleophilic strengths of various reactants with reference to the same class of substrates. For this experiment, we define a nucleophilic constant (n_{Ar}) for the S_NAr reaction as follows:

$$n_{Ar} = \frac{1}{s}\log\frac{k}{k_0} \qquad (2)$$

The reaction of 2,4-dinitrochlorobenzene with ammonia in absolute ethanol, for which the rate constant (k_0) is 4.0×10^{-6} L mol^{-1} s^{-1} at 25°C, is used as the reference reaction for Equation 2. For this substrate and nucleophile, s is 1 and n_{Ar} is zero by definition. The rate constant k is for a reaction involving the nucleophile whose n_{Ar} value is being determined.

Understanding the Experiment

In this experiment, you and your coworkers will measure the rates of the reactions of piperidine and morpholine with 2,4-dinitrochlorobenzene and use the rate constants to calculate their nucleophilic constants, as defined by Equation 2. The reaction of 2,4-dinitrochlorobenzene with an amine is second order in both substrate and nucleophile, and follows the general rate equation

$$\frac{dx}{dt} = k(S_0 - x)(N_0 - 2x) \qquad (3)$$

where x is the concentration of the product at time t, and S_0 and N_0 are the initial concentrations of substrate and nucleophile, respectively. The computations can be simplified considerably if the experiment is carried out with the initial concentration of nucleophile being just twice that of 2,4-dinitrochlorobenzene. Equation 3 then becomes $dx/dt = 2k(S_0 - x)^2$, and the integrated rate equation is

$$\frac{1}{(S_0 - x)} = 2kt + \frac{1}{S_0} \qquad (4)$$

By measuring the concentration of the product, x, at regular intervals during the reaction, you can calculate the term on the left side of Equation 4. Graphing this expression versus time should then yield a straight line with slope $2k$.

The products of the S_NAr reactions are yellow-orange and absorb strongly in the visible region around 380 nm, so the concentration of each

Table 1 Nucleophilic constants for various nucleophiles

Nucleophile	n
CH_3OH	0.00
F^-	2.7
Cl^-	4.37
pyridine	5.23
NH_3	5.50
aniline	5.70
Br^-	5.79
CH_3O^-	6.29
$(CH_3CH_2)_3N$	6.66
$(CH_3CH_2)_2NH$	7.0
pyrrolidine	7.23
piperidine	7.30
I^-	7.42

Note: n values are measured relative to methanol, with methyl iodide as the substrate.

product will be determined indirectly by measuring the absorbance of 380-nm light by aliquots that are removed from the reaction mixture at various times. Because the absorbances are determined at a single wavelength, you can use a nonrecording spectrophotometer (colorimeter). Each aliquot must first be *quenched* by adding dilute acid to stop the reaction; this is done so that the product concentration will remain constant until you are ready to take the absorbance readings. The concentration term in Equation **4**, $S_0 - x$, is proportional to $A_\infty - A$, where A_∞ is the absorbance when the reaction is 100% complete and A is the absorbance at time t. Therefore,

$$\frac{1}{(S_0 - x)} = \frac{q}{(A_\infty - A)} \qquad \textbf{(5)}$$

where q is a proportionality constant. The "infinity" value of the absorbance A_∞ will be obtained by warming the reaction mixture to complete the reaction and measuring the absorbance of the resulting solution. The value of q can then be calculated from the relationship $q = A_\infty/S_0$. Note that S_0 is the initial substrate concentration in the *reaction mixture,* not in the stock solution you will use to prepare the reaction mixtures.

Because of their different reaction rates, the amines will be used in different initial concentrations so that both reactions will be about half complete after 30 minutes. The absorbance values of the quenched products are too high to measure, so you will have to dilute these solutions to obtain readings in a convenient range.

2,4-Dinitrochlorobenzene, morpholine, and piperidine may be harmful to aquatic life.

Reaction and Properties

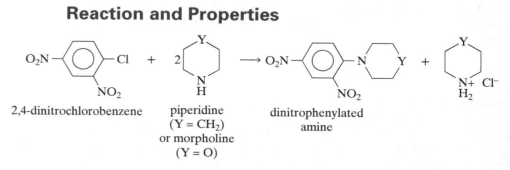

2,4-dinitrochlorobenzene piperidine (Y = CH₂) or morpholine (Y = O) dinitrophenylated amine

The extra mole of amine combines with the HCl liberated during the reaction.

Table 2 Physical properties

	mol wt	mp	bp	d
2,4-dinitrochlorobenzene	202.6	53	315	
morpholine	87.1	−5	128	1.000
piperidine	85.2	−9	106	0.861

Note: mp and bp are in °C; density is in g/mL.

DIRECTIONS

All glassware must be clean and dry. If equipment is limited, you may be asked to work in pairs or larger groups. Each student or group should have a timer or a watch that measures seconds. Stock solutions should be dispensed from burets or bottle-top dispensers.

> 2,4-Dinitrochlorobenzene is poisonous; skin contact may cause unpleasant and persistent dermatitis. Wear gloves and avoid contact with the 2,4-dinitrochlorobenzene solution.
> Morpholine and piperidine are toxic and corrosive, capable of causing severe damage to the skin, eyes, and respiratory system. Avoid contact with their solutions.
> Ethanol is very flammable, so keep ethanolic solutions away from flames and hot surfaces.

Safety Notes

2,4-dinitro-chlorobenzene

morpholine   piperidine

A. *Reaction of 2,4-Dinitrochlorobenzene with Piperidine*

Label seven clean, dry 4-dram screw-cap vials (or 15-cm test tubes) from A1 to A7. Using a 10-mL volumetric pipet, accurately measure [OP-5] 10.0 mL of the quenching solution (0.5 *M* sulfuric acid in 50% ethanol) into each vial and cap the vials. Measure about 20 mL of absolute ethanol into a 25-mL volumetric flask; then accurately measure 2.00 mL of the 0.20 *M* stock solution of 2,4-dinitrochlorobenzene in ethanol and add it to the flask. Have your stopwatch or timer ready. Measure 2.00 mL of the 0.40 *M* piperidine/ethanol stock solution into the volumetric flask and start the timer (or record the starting time) when about half of the solution has drained from the pipet. Without delay, fill the flask to the mark with absolute ethanol, stopper and shake it, and pour the contents into a 50-mL Erlenmeyer flask (the reaction flask). Use a clean, dry 1-mL volumetric pipet to withdraw a 1.00-mL aliquot of the reaction mixture, and transfer it to vial A1 as you record the quenching time to the nearest second. Cap the vial and seal the reaction flask with Parafilm.

Stir or occasionally swirl [OP-10] the contents of the reaction flask during the reaction period. Approximately every 5 minutes, rinse the 1-mL volumetric pipet with the reaction mixture, withdraw a 1.00-mL aliquot, and transfer it to the next quenching vial, recording the quenching time accurately. Repeat this process until you have withdrawn and quenched a total of six aliquots. Then warm the reaction flask (still sealed with Parafilm) in a 50°C water bath for at least 2 hours, or let it stand for at least 48 hours at room temperature, to bring the reaction to completion. Pipet a final 1.00-mL aliquot into vial A7 for the A_∞ solution.

B. *Reaction of 2,4-Dinitrochlorobenzene with Morpholine*

Label seven clean, dry 4-dram screw-cap vials (or 15-cm test tubes) from B1 to B7. Using a 10-mL volumetric pipet, accurately measure 10.0 mL of the quenching solution (0.5 *M* sulfuric acid in 50% ethanol) into each vial and cap the vials. Measure about 17 mL of absolute ethanol into a 25-mL volumetric flask; accurately measure 5.00 mL of the 0.20 *M* stock solution of 2,4-dinitrochlorobenzene in ethanol and add it to the flask. Have your watch or timer ready. Measure 2.00 mL of the 1.0 *M* morpholine/ethanol

Take Care! Do not pipet by mouth. Wear gloves and avoid contact with the stock solutions.

Stop and Think: Why does this stop the reaction?

Observe and Note: Look for and record any evidence for a chemical reaction.

Waste Disposal: Dispose of the remaining reaction mixture as directed by your instructor.

Take Care! Do not pipet by mouth. Wear gloves and avoid contact with the stock solutions.

stock solution into the volumetric flask, and start the timer (or record the starting time) when about half the solution has drained from the pipet. Without delay, fill the flask to the mark with absolute ethanol, stopper and shake it, and pour the contents into a 50-mL Erlenmeyer flask (the reaction flask). Use a clean, dry 1-mL volumetric pipet to withdraw a 1.00-mL aliquot of the reaction mixture and transfer it to vial B1 as you record the quenching time to the nearest second. Cap the vial and seal the reaction flask with Parafilm.

Observe and Note: Look for and record any evidence for a chemical reaction.

Stir or occasionally swirl [OP-10] the contents of the reaction flask during the reaction period. Approximately every 5 minutes, rinse the 1-mL volumetric pipet with the reaction mixture, withdraw a 1.00-mL aliquot, and transfer it to the next quenching vial, recording the quenching time. Repeat this process until you have withdrawn and quenched a total of six aliquots. Then warm the reaction flask (still sealed with Parafilm) in a 50°C water bath for at least 2 hours, or let it stand for at least 48 hours at room temperature, to bring the reaction to completion. Pipet a final 1.00-mL aliquot into vial B7 for the A_∞ solution.

Waste Disposal: Dispose of the remaining reaction mixture as directed by your instructor.

C. *Absorbance Measurements*

Obtain as many clean, dry 4-dram screw-cap vials (or 15-cm test tubes) as you have solutions to analyze, and number them to correspond to the quenched solutions. Using a volumetric pipet, accurately measure [OP-5] 10.0 mL of 95% ethanol into each one. Then accurately measure 0.40 mL of each quenched solution into the corresponding vial, swirl to mix the contents, and cap the vial.

Stop and Think: Why is this step necessary?

Zero the colorimeter [OP-41b] at 380 nm and set the 100%-transmittance control using a cuvette filled with 95% ethanol. Make sure the sample cuvette is positioned correctly, then record the transmittance of each solution from each vial. Use the same instrument and cuvette to analyze all of your solutions, including the A_∞ solution. Calculate the absorbance of each solution and use your data to compute $1/(S_0 - x)$ for each aliquot. For each amine, plot these values versus time and determine the slope of the line, or use a linear-regression program to calculate the slope. Calculate the second-order rate constant for each reaction and the n_{Ar} value for each amine. Arrange morpholine, piperidine, and ammonia ($n_{Ar} = 0$) in order, according to their n_{Ar} values, and try to explain their relative nucleophilicities.

Waste Disposal: Dispose of all solutions as directed by your instructor.

Exercises

1. (a) Write a detailed mechanism for the reaction of piperidine with 2,4-dinitrochlorobenzene. (b) The rate constants for the reactions of piperidine with 2,4-dinitrochlorobenzene and with 2,4-dinitrobromobenzene are virtually identical. Identify the rate-determining step in your mechanism from (a) and explain your reasoning.

2. Explain why the reaction of 2,4-dinitrochlorobenzene with piperidine or morpholine is second order even though there are three reactant molecules in the overall equation for the reaction.

3. Describe and explain the possible effect on your results of the following experimental errors or variations. (a) The reaction flask you used in the kinetic runs was rinsed with water and not dried. (b) The stockroom

was out of 2,4-dinitrochlorobenzene, so the lab assistant substituted chlorobenzene. (c) The lab assistant who prepared the stock solutions couldn't find any piperidine, so she used piperidine hydrochloride instead.

4. Describe some green features of this experiment, and any that aren't so green.

5. (a) Derive Equation **5** using Beer's law and evaluate the constant q in terms of Beer's law parameters. (b) Derive Equation **4** from Equation **3**.

6. A *spiro* species contains two rings that have one carbon atom in common. Outline a synthesis of the spiro Meisenheimer complex shown, starting with 1-chloro-2,4,6-trinitrobenzene.

7. (a) Calculate the concentrations of the dinitrophenylamines in the solutions used for the spectrophotometry infinity reading. (b) If you know the path length of the cuvette you used, calculate the molar absorptivities of these products at 380 nm.

8. Explain why quenching the reaction mixture with H_2SO_4 stops the S_NAr reaction, and give equations for any reactions involved.

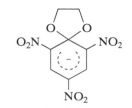

a spiro Meisenheimer complex

Other Things You Can Do

(Starred items require your instructor's permission.)

*1. Measure the reaction rates for one of the amines at different temperatures (0°C, 20°C, and 40°C, for example). Then plot ln k versus $1/T$ to determine the activation energy of the reaction, based on the following form of the Arrhenius equation:

$$\ln k = -\frac{E_{act}}{RT} + \ln A \qquad (R = 8.31 \text{ J mol}^{-1} \text{ K}^{-1})$$

*2. Carry out one of the reactions in other solvents, such as 2-propanol and aqueous ethanol, to measure the effect of solvent polarity on the rate constants. If you make up your own solutions, it is essential to wear protective gloves and to avoid contact with 2,4-dinitrochlorobenzene and the amines.

3. Read the paper by Bunnett, Garbisch, and Pruitt, *J. Am. Chem. Soc.* **1957**, *79*, 385. Then tell what is meant by the "element effect" in reactions of 1-substituted 2,4-dinitrobenzenes, and explain how it was used to elucidate the mechanism of the S_NAr reaction.

Structure of an Unknown
D-Hexose

Reactions of Monosaccharides. Preparation of Alditols. Reduction Reactions.
Structure Determination.

Operations

OP-7   Heating
OP-8   Cooling
OP-10 Mixing
OP-16 Vacuum Filtration
OP-26 Washing and Drying Solids
OP-28 Recrystallization
OP-33 Melting Point
OP-36 Optical Rotation

Before You Begin

1. Read the experiment, read or review the operations as necessary, and write an experimental plan.
2. Calculate the mass of 20.0 mmol of $C_6H_{12}O_6$ and the mass of 8.0 mmol of sodium borohydride. Calculate the theoretical yield of the alditol from part **A**.

Scenario

S. A. Tucker, a food chemist working for the Global Food Research Foundation, collects and analyzes foods from around the world. From Hunza, an isolated state in a high valley of the Hindu Kush mountains, Tucker obtained a yogurt made from yak's milk that is said to contribute to the exceptional longevity of the valley's inhabitants. Now he wants to isolate and identify the major constituents of the yogurt to see whether any of them exhibits life-extending properties. He has already isolated a simple sugar—a D-hexose that has the same molecular formula as glucose, $C_6H_{12}O_6$, but is only half as sweet. Your assignment is to determine the structure of this unknown sugar.

Applying Scientific Methodology

After reading the experiment, you may be able to venture an "educated guess" about the identity of the unknown D-hexose and express it as a hypothesis. You should then be able to predict the results of each experimental procedure you will carry out and see whether your actual results agree with your predictions.

From *Operational Organic Chemistry: A Problem Solving Approach to the Laboratory*, Fourth Edition, John W. Lehman. Copyright © 2009 by Pearson Education. Published by Prentice Hall. All rights reserved.

Sweet Molecules

One of the most apparent properties of the sugars is their sweetness. Fructose is the sweetest known sugar—1.8 times sweeter (in its crystalline form) than sucrose—but many other substances are sweeter than any of the sugars. Among synthetic sweeteners, cyclamates are approximately 45 times sweeter than sucrose, aspartame is 180 times sweeter, saccharin is 300 times sweeter, sucralose is 600 times sweeter, and a second-generation aspartame relative called neotame is about 13,000 times sweeter. But the natural substance thaumatin is even sweeter; it's about 100,000 times as sweet as sucrose.

A number of theories and models have been devised to explain the sweet taste sensation. Molecules that taste sweet are able to bind to a certain kind of receptor site on our taste buds. Recent studies have shown that there is only one kind of sweet taste receptor (compared to more than 30 bitter taste receptors), and that each receptor has two binding sites that can be activated by different molecules. This explains why certain sweeteners can amplify one another; for example, a mixture of saccharin and cyclamate is sweeter than would be expected from the sweetening power of the individual substances.

In order to bind to a receptor site, a molecule must have certain structural features that allow it to fit into the site. According to the so-called AH,B theory, all sweet molecules contain an AH,B couple, where A and B are electronegative atoms such as oxygen or nitrogen (but sometimes halogen or even carbon). According to this theory, A and B must be 0.25–0.40 nm apart in order to interact (by hydrogen bonding) with the receptor site, which is assumed to possess a similar AH,B couple. In sugars, AH and B are assumed to be an OH group and the oxygen atom of an adjacent OH group, respectively. For effective interaction, the OH groups should be in a *gauche* conformation, because in an *anti* conformation they would be too far apart to interact with the receptor site, and in a *syn* conformation they would tend to hydrogen bond intramolecularly rather than with the receptor site. Proposed AH and B sites for several sweet molecule are illustrated in Figure 1.

Another possible requirement for the sweet taste sensation is a hydrophobic or "greasy" site, X, on the sweet molecule. In the Keir tripartite model, this site is estimated to be about 0.35 nm from A and 0.55 nm from B in the triangular grouping illustrated.

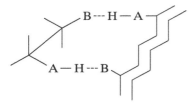

Interaction of a sweet molecule with the receptor site, according to the AH,B theory

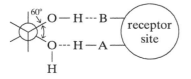

Gauche conformation of a sugar molecule

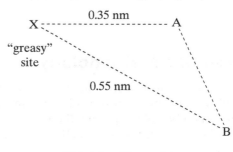

Keir tripartite model

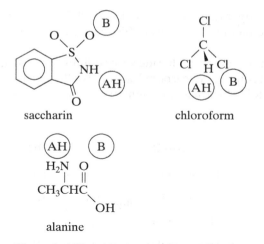

saccharin

chloroform

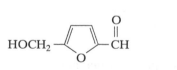

alanine

Figure 1 AH and B sites in sweet molecules

In the crystalline form of fructose, β-D-fructopyranose, the AH, B, and X sites are believed to be the C-1 OH, the CH_2OH oxygen atom, and the ring methylene group, respectively. An even more complex model, the Tinti–Nofre model, postulates no fewer than eight sites, including the three of the Keir tripartite model. Not all of the sites are utilized by every sweet molecule, but it is assumed that the more sites a molecule occupies, the greater its potential for sweetness.

Unfortunately, models proposed to explain the sweet taste sensation tend to be so general that they predict sweetness for many compounds that are actually tasteless or bitter, or so specific that only a few related molecules can satisfy their requirements for sweetness. Clearly, scientists do not yet have a complete understanding of the origin of the sweet taste sensation.

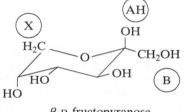

β-D-fructopyranose

See an illustration of the Tinti–Nofre model in J. Chem. Educ. **1995**, *72*, 671.

Understanding the Experiment

In this experiment, you will determine the structure of an unknown D-hexose by

- Using a simple chemical test that distinguishes aldohexoses from ketohexoses
- Reducing the unknown with sodium borohydride and measuring the optical rotation of the product
- Converting the unknown to a phenylosazone and measuring its melting point

Both aldohexoses and ketohexoses are dehydrated in dilute acid to 5-(hydroxymethyl)-2-furaldehyde, which reacts with resorcinol to form a red condensation product.

5-(hydroxymethyl)-2-furaldehyde   resorcinol

Ketohexoses dehydrate more rapidly than aldohexoses, making it possible to differentiate them using Seliwanoff's reagent, a solution of resorcinol in dilute HCl.

Reduction of a monosaccharide with sodium borohydride converts it to an alditol by reducing its carbonyl group. D-Glucose is converted to the alditol D-glucitol, which has no symmetry plane and is therefore optically active.

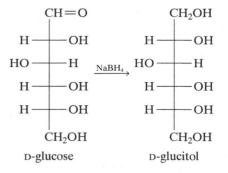

Key Concept: *Compounds that have a symmetry plane are achiral, meaning that they cannot exist in unique "left-handed" and "right-handed" forms. Achiral compounds do not rotate plane-polarized light, so they are optically inactive.*

D-Allose is converted to D-allitol, which has a symmetry plane and is therefore optically inactive.

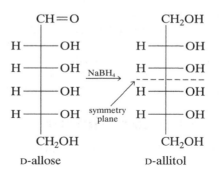

Thus, the optical activity or inactivity of the alditol formed from reduction of a monosaccharide can yield structural information about the monosaccharide itself, thereby narrowing down the number of possible structures.

Converting monosaccharides to their phenylosazones in effect destroys any differences at the #1 and #2 carbon atoms of their molecules by changing both —CHOH—CHO and —CO—CH$_2$OH to the same structural unit:

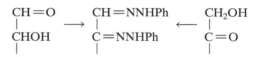

For example, D-glucose, its epimer D-mannose, and D-fructose are all converted to the same phenylosazone by phenylhydrazine.

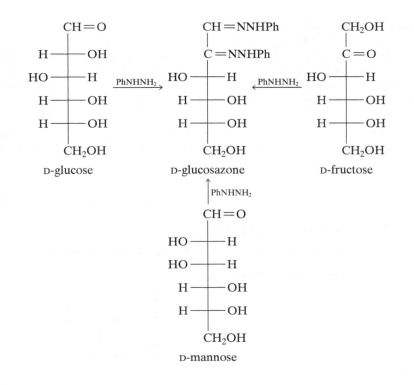

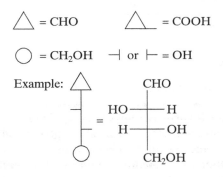

Only compounds that differ in structure from carbon #3 on down the chain will yield different phenylosazones. Among the D-hexoses, there are four C-3 to C-6 structural units that yield different phenylosazones; these are illustrated in Figure 2 using Rosanoff symbols.

Figure 2 C-3 to C-6 structural units of D-hexoses

Thus, D-glucose, D-mannose, and D-fructose yield the same phenylosazone because they all contain the same C-3 to C-6 structural unit, **B**.

In part **A** of this experiment, you will reduce your unknown D-hexose to an alditol by adding an excess of sodium borohydride in aqueous NaOH to an aqueous solution of the unknown. Like many sugars, the alditol tends to form supersaturated solutions and crystallizes slowly from solution. If your alditol refuses to crystallize after you cool the reaction mixture in ice water and rub the inside surface of its container with a stirring rod, you may be able to obtain a seed crystal from your instructor to help induce crystallization.

Measuring the alditol's optical rotation in water will tell you whether it is optically active or optically inactive.

You will carry out Seliwanoff's test in part **B**. In part **C**, you will prepare the phenylosazone of the unknown monosaccharide by a simple test-tube reaction. Because phenylosazones decompose near the melting point, you will use a special technique to measure the melting point of your phenylosazone.

Seliwanoff's reagent contains resorcinol, which is expected to be slightly toxic to aquatic life, and hydrochloric acid, which is toxic to aquatic life. Phenylhydrazine is also toxic to aquatic organisms.

Reactions and Properties

See "Understanding the Experiment" for reactions of representative hexoses.

Table 1 Physical properties

	mol wt	mp	bp
sodium borohydride	37.8	37	400d
phenylhydrazine hydrochloride	144.6	244d	sub

Note: mp and bp are in °C; density is in g/mL; d = decomposes; sub = sublimes.

Table 2 Phenylosazone melting points

Structural unit	Phenylosazone mp
A	178
B	205
C	173
D	201

Note: melting points are in °C.

DIRECTIONS

A. *Preparation of the Alditol*

Safety Notes

> **Sodium borohydride is corrosive and can react violently with concentrated acids, oxidizing agents, and other chemicals. Aqueous sodium borohydride solutions with pH values below 10.5 have been known to decompose violently, so be sure that your reaction mixture is sufficiently alkaline. Keep NaBH₄ away from other chemicals; avoid contact and do not breathe its dust.**

Reaction. Dissolve 20.0 mmol of the unknown D-hexose in 10 mL of water in a 25-mL Erlenmeyer flask, with stirring or swirling [OP-10] and gentle heating. Dissolve 8.0 mmol of sodium borohydride in 4.0 mL of 1 *M* NaOH in a test tube. Cool [OP-8] both mixtures in an ice/water bath for 5 minutes or more. Remove the beaker from the cold bath; use a Pasteur pipet to add the cold sodium borohydride solution to the D-hexose solution, drop by drop with stirring or swirling, for a period of about 10 minutes. If the temperature of the reaction mixture rises above 25°C, cool it in the cold bath for a minute or so before continuing. When the addition is complete, let the reaction mixture stand at room temperature, with stirring or occasional swirling, for 20 minutes. *Under the hood,* add 6 *M* HCl, drop by drop, until foaming stops and the reaction mixture turns blue litmus paper red.

Separation and Purification. Cool the reaction mixture in an ice/water bath and induce crystallization of the product, if necessary. Seal the flask with Parafilm and leave the reaction mixture in the cold bath while you complete the rest of the experiment. (For a better yield, leave it in a cool place overnight or longer.) Collect the product by vacuum filtration [OP-16] and wash it on the filter [OP-26a] with two portions of cold 95% ethanol. Dry [OP-26b] the product and measure its mass.

Analysis. Prepare an aqueous solution containing about 0.5 g of the alditol (weighed to the nearest milligram) per 25 mL of solution. You may have to heat the mixture gently to dissolve the alditol. Measure the optical rotation [OP-36] of this solution in a 2-dm polarimetry cell, using pure water as the blank. If the optical rotation of the alditol is essentially equal to that of the blank (plus or minus 0.2°), assume that it is optically inactive; otherwise, calculate its specific rotation.

B. Seliwanoff's Test
Dissolve 10 mg of the D-hexose in 1.0 mL of water in a small test tube. Then add 2.0 mL of Seliwanoff's reagent, swirl to mix, and heat the test tube in a boiling-water bath for 2 minutes (no longer). Development of a deep red color within 2 minutes is a positive test for a ketose. Aldoses give a red color with additional heating or after standing for some time.

C. *Preparation of the Phenylosazone*

Phenylhydrazine hydrochloride is very toxic by ingestion, inhalation, and skin absorption; it is a suspected carcinogen. Wear gloves, avoid contact, and do not breathe its dust.

Dissolve 0.10 g of the unknown D-hexose in 2 mL of water in a test tube. Stir in 0.20 g of phenylhydrazine hydrochloride, 0.30 g of sodium acetate trihydrate (or 0.18 g of anhydrous sodium acetate), and 0.20 mL of saturated aqueous sodium bisulfite. Seal the test tube with Parafilm and heat [OP-7] it in a boiling-water bath for 30 minutes, with occasional shaking. Add 3 mL of water and cool the reaction mixture in an ice/water bath. Collect the phenylosazone by vacuum filtration [OP-16], washing it on the filter with a little ice-cold methanol. Recrystallize [OP-28b] the product from an ethanol/water mixture, dissolving it in the ethanol first. When you collect it by vacuum filtration, wash it on the filter [OP-26a] with ice-cold methanol. Dry [OP-26b] the phenylosazone thoroughly at room temperature. Pulverize enough of the dry solid for two melting-point tubes [OP-33] and measure the temperature, T_1, at which the first sample melts with rapid heating (a rise of 10–20°C per minute). After the melting-point apparatus has cooled below T_1, adjust it for a temperature rise of 3–6°C per minute, and insert the second sample just as the temperature reaches T_1. Record the temperature

Take Care! Hydrogen is evolved, so keep flames away.

Stop and Think: What is the source of the hydrogen?

Waste Disposal: Unless your instructor directs otherwise, wash the filtrate and the used polarimetry solution down the drain.

Take Care! The reagent is acidic, so avoid contact.

Stop and Think: Is the D-hexose an aldohexose or a ketohexose?

Waste Disposal: Dispose of the solution as directed by your instructor.

Safety Notes

phenylhydrazine

Take Care! Wear gloves and avoid contact with phenylhydrazine hydrochloride.

Waste Disposal: Unless your instructor directs otherwise, wash the filtrates down the drain.

Stop and Think: Which two C-3 to C-6 structural units might the D-hexose contain? Which one can you eliminate based on your results in part **A**?

at which this sample becomes completely liquid as the melting point of the phenylosazone (see Table 2).

Deduce the structure of the D-hexose, draw its Haworth (flat-ring) projection, and use the formula index of *The Merck Index* or another reference work to find its common name.

Exercises

1. (a) Draw structures of all the monosaccharides that would yield the same alditol as your D-hexose. (b) Draw structures of all the monosaccharides that would yield the same phenylosazone as your D-hexose. (c) Draw structures of all the alditols that would be obtained by reduction of all possible D-hexoses, and indicate whether each one is optically active or optically inactive.

2. It is believed that the C-4 OH group and the C-3 oxygen atom of an aldopyranose, or the C-1 OH group and the CH_2OH oxygen atom of a ketopyranose, can interact as an AH,B couple with the sweet taste receptor site. Build molecular models of β-D-glucopyranose and the most stable pyranose ring form of the D-hexose that you identified. Use them to explain why your D-hexose isn't as sweet as glucose.

3. Describe and explain the possible effect on your results of the following experimental errors or variations. (a) In part **A**, you dissolved the $NaBH_4$ in 1.0 *M* HCl rather than 1.0 *M* NaOH. (b) You had to leave the lab while the Seliwanoff test solution was in a boiling-water bath, and when you returned the test solution was red. (c) In part **C**, you rinsed the test tube with acetone and didn't dry it out completely.

4. (a) Calculate the atom economy and reaction efficiency of your synthesis of the alditol. (b) Describe some green features of your synthesis, and any that aren't so green.

5. Following the format in the "Planning an Experiment" appendix, construct a flow diagram for the synthesis of the alditol in part **A**.

6. α-D-Mannose has a specific rotation of $+29.3°$, and β-D-mannose has a specific rotation of $-17.0°$. If either anomer is dissolved in water and allowed to stand until equilibrium is reached, the specific rotation of the equilibrium mixture is $+14.2°$. Calculate the percentage of each anomer in the equilibrium mixture.

7. (a) Draw the structures of the other D-hexoses that will yield the same phenylosazone as D-allose. (b) Draw the structures of the L-hexoses that will yield the same alditol as D-glucose.

Other Things You Can Do

(Starred items require your instructor's permission.)

*1. Draw chair-form pyranose rings for both anomers of the D-hexose you identified and predict which one should be more stable. Measure the optical rotation of a solution containing about 1 g (accurately weighed) of the D-hexose in 25 mL of aqueous solution. *Under the hood*, mix

2 drops of concentrated aqueous ammonia into the solution, and again measure its optical rotation. If the optical rotation changes with time, wait until it equilibrates before taking a final reading, then calculate the specific rotation of the equilibrium mixture. Using *The Merck Index* or another reference book, look up the specific rotations in water of the α and β anomers of the D-hexose and calculate the percentage of each in the equilibrium mixture. Decide whether or not the calculated composition of the equilibrium mixture verifies your prediction.

Take Care! Avoid contact with aqueous ammonia and do not breathe its vapors.

*2. Carry out some colorful reactions of monosaccharides with phenols as described in the "Reactions of Monosaccharides with Phenols" minilab.

3. After referring to articles in *J. Chem. Educ.* **1995**, *72*, pages 671–683, write a research paper about sweet compounds and the theory of the sweet taste sensation.

Fatty Acid Content of Commercial Cooking Oils

Reactions and Preparation of Carboxylic Esters. Transesterification. Fats and Oils.

Operations

OP-7   Heating
OP-18 Extraction
OP-19 Evaporation
OP-25 Drying Liquids
OP-37 Gas Chromatography

Before You Begin

Read the experiment, read or review the operations as necessary, and write an experimental plan.

Scenario

The Consumers Advocate (TCA) publishes *Caveat Emptor*, a periodical that rates consumer products and exposes inaccurate or misleading advertising. This organization is currently conducting a study of commercial vegetable oils to see whether their composition is consistent with advertising claims and to assess their relative dietary quality in terms of their effect on blood cholesterol. TCA's technical director, Patsy Haven, has asked your institute for help in evaluating some of the vegetable oils sold in your geographic area. Your project group's assignment is to determine the fatty acid composition of each vegetable oil provided and to calculate the ratio of unsaturated to saturated fatty acids as a measure of their potential effect on cardiovascular health.

Applying Scientific Methodology

If you are given the names of the vegetable oils in advance of the lab period, try to predict their relative desirability with respect to cardiovascular health. Express your predictions as a hypothesis, to be tested when you obtain the results of your project group's analyses.

Fatty Acids and Health

Cooking fats and oils are glyceryl esters of long-chain carboxylic acids called *fatty acids*. An "oil" in this sense is essentially a fat that is liquid at room temperature. Fats and oils have been put to many uses throughout human history. Excavation of an Egyptian tomb more than 5000 years old

From *Operational Organic Chemistry: A Problem Solving Approach to the Laboratory*, Fourth Edition, John W. Lehman. Copyright © 2009 by Pearson Education. Published by Prentice Hall. All rights reserved.

yielded several earthenware vessels containing substances identified as palmitic acid and stearic acid, most likely formed by the breakdown of palm oil and beef or mutton tallow, which were placed there as provisions for the deceased.

$$CH_3(CH_2)_{14}COOH$$

palmitic acid

$$CH_3(CH_2)_{16}COOH$$

stearic acid

The Egyptians used olive oil as a lubricant when moving huge stones for their building projects, and a mixture of fat and lime as axle grease for their war chariots. They may also have originated the art of painting with oils or waxes, using pigments mixed with natural waxes to paint portraits on their mummy cases.

The Roman scholar Pliny the Elder described a process for making soap by boiling goat fat with wood ashes, then treating the pasty mass with sea water to harden it. But the art of making soap from animal fats must have originated much earlier; the Phoenicians of 600 B.C. were already trading soap to the Gauls, who later introduced it to Rome. Soap factories have been excavated at Pompeii, a Roman city that was buried under a blanket of volcanic ash during an eruption of Vesuvius. The same eruption killed Pliny, whose scientific curiosity motivated him to study the erupting volcano up close.

Modern research has revealed the importance of fats and oils in nutrition and is just beginning to clarify their role in human disease. Linoleic acid, for example, is an essential component of the human diet because it is not synthesized in the body. Polyunsaturated fatty acids (PFAs) such as linoleic acid are believed to be involved in the biosynthesis of the prostaglandins, which help control blood pressure and muscle contraction.

$$CH_3(CH_2)_4\overset{\overset{\displaystyle H}{|}}{C}=\overset{\overset{\displaystyle H}{|}}{C}CH_2\overset{\overset{\displaystyle H}{|}}{C}=\overset{\overset{\displaystyle H}{|}}{C}(CH_2)_7\overset{\overset{\displaystyle O}{||}}{C}OH$$

linoleic acid

Polyunsaturated fatty acids also play a vital role in the functioning of biological membranes and have been implicated in the occurrence or prevention of such illnesses as atherosclerosis, cancer, and multiple sclerosis. Recent research suggests that PFAs of the $\omega 3$ and $\omega 6$ families are especially effective in preventing the buildup of cholesterol in arteries, which is a major cause of heart disease. The ω (omega) designation here refers to the distance of the last double bond from the methyl end of the fatty acid chain, as illustrated in the margin. Two $\omega 3$ PFAs found in fish oils, eicosapentaenoic acid (EPA) and docosahexaenoic acid (DHA), appear to be even more beneficial than the PFAs in vegetable oils. Besides lowering serum cholesterol levels, they also reduce the tendency of blood to clot, and thus help prevent strokes as well as heart attacks.

With respect to cardiovascular health, the desirability of a fat or oil is related to the kinds and proportions of fatty acid residues that are incorporated into its triglyceryl ester molecules. Animal fats, coconut oil, and

$$CH_3CH_2CH=CH\ldots$$
$$\textcircled{\omega 1}\textcircled{\omega 2}\textcircled{\omega 3}$$

palm oil contain a relatively high proportion of saturated fatty acids (SFAs), which raise blood cholesterol levels in humans and are believed to increase the risk of heart disease. Vegetable oils and fish oils that are high in polyunsaturated fatty acids can have the opposite effect, lowering the amount of cholesterol in the blood by hastening its excretion. Monounsaturated fatty acids (MFAs), which are abundant in olive oil and certain other vegetable oils, also help lower total cholesterol and may be even more healthful than the PFAs. Recent studies suggest that, unlike PFAs, MFAs lower total cholesterol without lowering high-density lipoprotein (HDL) levels. HDL is known as "good cholesterol" because it appears to reduce the risk of heart disease.

By contrast, *trans*-fatty acids raise total cholesterol levels and also lower HDL levels; thus, they may be even more harmful to human health than saturated fatty acids. *trans*-Fatty acids, which form during the partial hydrogenation of vegetable oils, are identical to the natural mono- and polyunsaturated acids except that they have *trans* double bonds where the natural acids have *cis* double bonds. They occur in most margarines and are used in a large number of processed food products.

Fatty acids are named and symbolized by several different systems. Most of the common fatty acids have trivial names that are still widely used, in part because of their simplicity compared to the systematic names. Linoleic acid, for example, is named *cis*-9-*cis*-12-octadecadienoic acid under the IUPAC system. Trivial names don't reveal the structures of the corresponding fatty acids, however, so shorthand notations are often used. For example, oleic acid can be represented by *c*-9-18:1, where *c* means *cis*, 9 refers to the position of the double bond (numbering from the COOH group), 18 is the total number of carbon atoms in the chain, and 1 is the number of double bonds. Linoleic acid is represented by *c*,*c*-9,12-18:2 using this system. Because all of the acids to be studied in this experiment have *cis* double bonds, the *c* prefix will be omitted here.

Key Concept: The effect of a fatty acid on cardiovascular health is apparently related to its shape. Saturated fatty acids and trans-*fatty acids have more-or-less straight molecules, whereas natural monounsaturated and polyunsaturated fatty acids have molecules with kinks where their* cis *double bonds occur.*

$$CH_3(CH_2)_7 - \overset{\overset{\displaystyle H}{|}}{C} = \overset{\overset{\displaystyle H}{|}}{C} - (CH_2)_7COOH$$

oleic acid (*c*-9-18:1)

Understanding the Experiment

The cooking oils to be analyzed in this experiment are triglycerides; that is, esters of the trihydroxy alcohol glycerol containing three fatty acid residues. An example of a triglyceride is tristearin, the stearic acid ester of glycerol. A mixture of fatty acid salts can be obtained by hydrolyzing a triglyceride in the presence of a base. This is the process used in soap formation, with the acid salts comprising the soap. Alternatively, a triglyceride can be transesterified with an alcohol such as methanol to yield a mixture of fatty acid methyl esters (FAME). Because the esters are much more suitable for analysis by gas chromatography than are the acid salts or the free acids themselves, the second method will be used in this experiment. The fatty acid composition of each cooking oil can then be derived from the percentages of the corresponding esters.

When methyl esters of saturated fatty acids are analyzed on a suitable gas chromatography column, their retention times (T_r) increase with the length of the carbon chain according to the relationship $\log T_r \propto$ number of carbons. The retention times of unsaturated fatty acid esters do not coincide

$$
\begin{array}{ll}
CH_3(CH_2)_{16}COOCH_2 & CH_2OH \\
\quad\quad\quad\quad\quad\quad | & | \\
CH_3(CH_2)_{16}COOCH & CHOH \\
\quad\quad\quad\quad\quad\quad | & | \\
CH_3(CH_2)_{16}COOCH_2 & CH_2OH \\
\text{a triglyceride,} & \text{glycerol} \\
\text{tristearin} &
\end{array}
$$

$$CH_3(CH_2)_{16}COO^-Na^+$$

a soap, sodium stearate

$$CH_3(CH_2)_{16}COOCH_3$$

methyl ester of stearic acid
(methyl stearate)

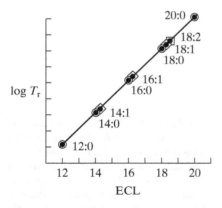

Figure 1 Plot of log T_r versus equivalent chain length for fatty acid methyl esters on a DEGS liquid phase

with those of saturated esters. On a nonpolar liquid phase, their retention times are shorter than those of the saturated esters of the same chain length, whereas on a polar liquid phase, they are longer. The actual value of T_r depends on the number and positions of the double bonds. By comparing the retention times of a large number of such esters, a series of equivalent chain-length (ECL) values has been worked out for various esters on different liquid phases. The ECL for a *saturated* ester is the same as its actual chain length—for instance, 14.0 for myristic acid (as the methyl ester), 18.0 for stearic acid, and so forth. The ECL for an *unsaturated* ester on a polar liquid phase is greater than its actual chain length—for instance, 18.43 for methyl oleate (9-18:1) and 19.22 for methyl linoleate (9,12-18:2), both analyzed on a diethylene glycol succinate (DEGS) liquid phase. If the retention times for two or more saturated esters are known, a calibration curve can be constructed by plotting the logarithms of their retention times against their equivalent chain lengths, as shown in Figure 1.

To identify an unknown fatty acid ester, one can calculate the logarithm of its retention time, read its ECL value from the graph, and compare that value with the ECL values of known methyl esters (see Table 1).

Table 1 Shorthand notation and ECL values (on DEGS liquid phase) for representative fatty acids

Fatty acid	Shorthand notation	ECL	Type
lauric	12:0	12.00	SFA
myristic	14:0	14.00	SFA
myristoleic	9-14:1	14.71	MFA
palmitic	16:0	16.00	SFA
palmitoleic	9-16:1	16.55	MFA
stearic	18:0	18.00	SFA
oleic	9-18:1	18.43	MFA
linoleic	9,12-18:2	19.22	PFA
linolenic	9,12,15-18:3	20.12	PFA
behenic	22:0	22.00	SFA

Note: ECL values are for the corresponding methyl esters.

In order for ECL values to provide an accurate means of identifying the esters, the same type of column and carrier gas should be used in all cases. Even then, the experimental values may not correspond exactly to literature values because of differences in such factors as the kind of column support, the amount of liquid phase, the age of the column, and the experimental conditions. In addition, some peaks may overlap in complex mixtures, so that two or more columns must be used for their separation, and deviations from linearity in the log T_r plot may occur when short-chain fatty acids are analyzed. The relatively simple mixtures of fatty acids that you will encounter in this experiment shouldn't present any serious experimental difficulties, however.

The transesterification of an oil to its methyl esters will be carried out by hydrolyzing it in methanolic sodium hydroxide and esterifying the resulting fatty acids in methanol with a boron trifluoride catalyst. After the methyl esters have been isolated from the reaction mixture, they will be mixed with an internal standard, methyl heptadecanoate, and analyzed by gas chromatography. Heptadecanoic acid (17:0) doesn't occur naturally, so the 17:0 peak from its ester won't interfere with other component peaks. To minimize the effect of retention-time drift due to changes in operating parameters, relative retention values should be calculated by dividing the retention time for each peak by that of the 17:0 peak. Once the 17:0 peak has been located, those of the 16:0 and the 18:0 esters can be identified by the fact that the log T_r interval between their peaks and 17:0 is the same. (The 16:0 ester often gives the first strong peak on the chromatogram, making it easy to recognize.) Then a log T_r versus ECL plot can be prepared, from which the other peaks can be identified. Because the peak area for each component should be proportional to its mass, the percentage composition of the mixture can be determined from peak areas with good accuracy.

Assuming that saturated fatty acids have a negative effect on cardiovascular health, and that both monounsaturated and polyunsaturated fatty acids have a positive effect, you can use the ratio (MFA + PFA)/SFA as a rough indicator of the "healthfulness" of your cooking oil compared to the other oils analyzed in your laboratory section.

Methanol is slightly toxic to aquatic organisms but biodegrades readily in water and soil. Sodium hydroxide may be harmful to the environment, especially with respect to aqueous organisms. Boron trifluoride isn't known to have significant harmful effects on the environment.

Reactions and Properties

$$\begin{array}{l} R'COOCH_2 \\ | \\ R''COOCH + 3CH_3OH \xrightarrow[BF_3]{NaOH} \\ | \\ R'''COOCH_2 \end{array} \quad \begin{array}{l} R'COOCH_3 \\ + \\ R''COOCH_3 \\ + \\ R'''COOCH_3 \end{array} + \begin{array}{c} H \; H \; H \\ O \; O \; O \\ | \; | \; | \\ CH_2CHCH_2 \end{array}$$

(R groups can be alike or different.)

Table 2 Physical properties

	mol wt	mp	bp	d
methanol	32.0	−94	65	0.791
boron trifluoride–methanol complex	131.9		59^4	
boron trifluoride	67.8	−127	−100	

Note: mp and bp are in °C; density is in g/mL. Superscripts indicate pressure in torr. The complex has the composition $BF_3 \cdot 2CH_3OH$.

Methyl stearate

$$CH_3(CH_2)_{16}\overset{\displaystyle O}{\overset{\displaystyle \|}{C}}OCH_3$$

2925.2	1360.7	1169.8
1744.9	1302.8	1117.3
1465.8	1247.5	721.3

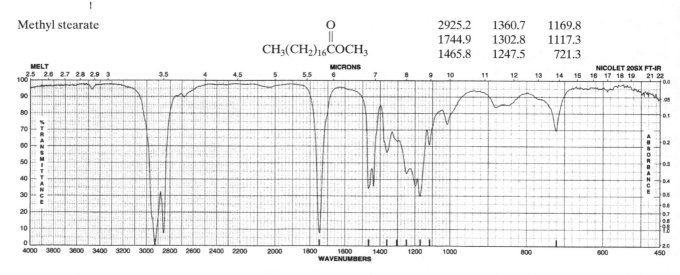

Figure 2a IR spectrum of a saturated 18-carbon methyl ester, methyl stearate

Methyl linolenate

$$CH_3(CH_2CH=CH)_3(CH_2)_7\overset{\displaystyle O}{\overset{\displaystyle \|}{C}}OCH_3$$

2930.3	1361.7	1171.7
1742.7	1308.2	1103.8
1435.7	1245.5	722.4

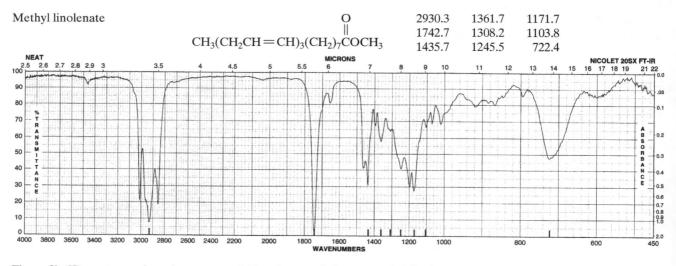

Figure 2b IR spectrum of a polyunsaturated 18-carbon methyl ester, methyl linolenate

DIRECTIONS

A selection of commercial cooking oils may be provided, or students may be asked to bring their own cooking oils. Different kinds of oils should be analyzed, such as canola, corn, olive, peanut, rice bran, safflower, soybean, and sunflower oils. All glassware and reagents should be dry for this experiment.

The methanolic sodium hydroxide solution is flammable and toxic. Avoid contact, do not breathe its vapors, and keep it away from flames.
The boron trifluoride/methanol solution is flammable, corrosive, and toxic, and it can cause severe damage to the eyes, skin, and respiratory tract. Use gloves and a hood; avoid contact and do not breathe its vapors.
Petroleum ether is extremely flammable. Keep it away from flames and hot surfaces.

Safety Notes

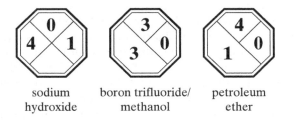

sodium   boron trifluoride/   petroleum
hydroxide   methanol   ether

Reaction. In a clean, *dry* 15-cm test tube, combine 0.15 g of a commercial cooking oil with 5.0 mL of 0.5 M sodium hydroxide in methanol. Add a boiling chip or two and heat [OP-7] the reaction mixture at a gentle boil over a steam bath or in a boiling-water bath until the oil has completely dissolved (about 3–5 minutes). *Under the hood,* add 6.0 mL of a 12.5% (weight/volume) solution of boron trifluoride in methanol, seal the test tube with Parafilm, and boil the mixture gently over the steam bath or in a hot-water bath for 2 minutes.

Separation. Transfer the reaction mixture to a separatory funnel using 30 mL of low-boiling (~35–60°C) petroleum ether and rinsing out the test tube with some of the solvent. Add 20 mL of saturated aqueous sodium chloride and shake to extract [OP-18] the methyl esters into the petroleum ether layer. Dry [OP-25] the petroleum ether layer with anhydrous sodium sulfate or magnesium sulfate and evaporate [OP-19] the solvent completely.

Analysis. Obtain a gas chromatogram [OP-37] of the fatty acid methyl ester mixture on a DEGS/Chromosorb W or similar column. Add a drop of a 50% solution of methyl heptadecanoate in dichloromethane to the remaining mixture and obtain its gas chromatogram. Measure the areas of all peaks on the first gas chromatogram. Identify the 17:0 peak and measure the relative retention times of all peaks on the second gas chromatogram. Calculate relative retention times and log T_r values for all the components; use these data to tentatively identify several of the methyl esters. For these esters, plot log T_r versus their ECL values and try to fit the rest of your data to the plot, redrawing it as necessary to get the best straight line. (If your data points don't fit the plot, you probably misidentified the esters. Make another guess and try again.) Identify the esters; then calculate the total percentages of saturated, monounsaturated, and polyunsaturated fatty acids and the ratio of unsaturated to saturated fatty acids. Tabulate the class results and rank the different oils according to their expected effect on cardiovascular health.

Take Care! Wear gloves, avoid contact with the methanolic NaOH and BF₃ solutions, and do not breathe their vapors.

Stop and Think: What is left behind in the aqueous layer?

Waste Disposal: Unless your instructor directs otherwise, wash the aqueous layer down the drain. Place any recovered petroleum ether in a designated solvent recovery container.

Exercises

1. Write the structures of the fatty acids whose triglycerides were in the oil you analyzed and give their IUPAC names.

2. On the gas chromatogram of a mixture of methyl esters, methyl palmitate had a retention time of 150 seconds and methyl heptadecanoate had a retention time of 198 seconds. What is the probable identity of a methyl ester with a retention time of 363 seconds on the same chromatogram?

3. Describe and explain the possible effect on your results of the following experimental errors or variations: (a) The reaction test tube contained water. (b) You heated the oil with methanolic sodium hydroxide, but you forgot to add the boron trifluoride/methanol solution. (c) You didn't evaporate all of the petroleum ether from your reaction mixture.

4. (a) Calculate the atom economy for the reaction of tristearin by the procedure used in this experiment. (b) Describe some green features of this experiment, and any that aren't so green.

5. (a) Following the format in the "Planning an Experiment" appendix, construct a flow diagram for this experiment. (b) Explain why there was no glycerol peak on the gas chromatogram of the methyl ester mixture, even though glycerol was a product of the hydrolysis.

6. Why was the Lewis acid boron trifluoride, rather than hydrochloric acid, used to catalyze the transesterification reaction?

7. Calculate the (MFA + PFA)/SFA ratio for palm oil, whose fatty acid content is approximately 9% linoleic, 2% myristic, 40% oleic, 45% palmitic, and 4% stearic acid.

8. (a) Neat's-foot oil consists almost entirely of the triglycerides of oleic and palmitic acids. How many different triglycerides of these two acids can it contain? (b) Draw structures for the triglycerides that contain two oleic acid units and one palmitic acid unit.

9. Outline a synthesis of the detergent sodium lauryl sulfate from glyceryl trilaurate (trilaurin).

$$CH_3(CH_2)_{10}CH_2OSO_2O^-Na^+$$

sodium lauryl sulfate

Other Things You Can Do

(Starred items require your instructor's permission.)

*1. Record an infrared spectrum [OP-39] of your methyl ester mixture and compare it with the spectra of the 18-carbon methyl esters in Figure 2. Try to account for significant similarities and differences in the spectra, and point out any bands that show evidence of unsaturation.

*2. Extract the fat trimyristin from nutmeg as described in the "Isolation of Trimyristin from Nutmeg" minilab.

*3. Make some soap using a phase-transfer catalyst as described in the "Preparation of a Soap using a Phase-Transfer Catalyst" minilab.

4. Starting with sources listed in the Bibliography, write a research paper about the health implications of various types of fats and oils. Include a description of the HDL and LDL forms of cholesterol and a discussion of the role they play in heart disease.

Structure of an Unknown Dipeptide

EXPERIMENT

Reactions of Peptides. Nucleophilic Aromatic Substitution. Amino Acids. Structure Determination.

Operations

OP-23 Paper Chromatography
OP-3 Using Glass Rod and Tubing
OP-18 Extraction
OP-19 Evaporation
OP-22 Thin-Layer Chromatography
OP-24 Washing Liquids

Before You Begin

Read the experiment and operation OP-23, read or review the other operations as necessary, and write an experimental plan.

Scenario

Snake venoms have been used in medicine as anticoagulants, which help dissolve blood clots or prevent their formation. Natural Nostrums, a pharmaceutical company that manufactures drugs based on natural substances, anticipates some medical uses for the venom of the black boomslang, a deadly African tree snake. Their native snake hunter recently had an unfortunate accident, so the supply of natural boomslang venom has dried up. Before they can prepare a synthetic version of the venom, which is a polypeptide, they need to determine the sequence of amino acids in its polypeptide chain. Ferdie Lance, the company's snake-venom expert, has used an enzyme called cathepsin C to break down the boomslang venom into dipeptide units. Now each dipeptide unit has to be identified so that Dr. Lance can reconstruct the amino acid sequence in the polypeptide. Your project group's assignment is to determine the structures of the unknown dipeptides.

Applying Scientific Methodology

After you analyze the hydrolysis mixture from your assigned dipeptide using paper chromatography, you can formulate a tentative hypothesis about the structure of the dipeptide. Your hypothesis will be tested by thin-layer chromatography (TLC) analysis of a hydrolysis mixture from the dinitrophenylated dipeptide.

From *Operational Organic Chemistry: A Problem Solving Approach to the Laboratory*, Fourth Edition, John W. Lehman. Copyright © 2009 by Pearson Education. Published by Prentice Hall. All rights reserved.

Mushrooms, Black Mambas, and Memory Molecules

The naturally occurring polypeptides and proteins range in size from tripeptides such as glutathione to complex proteins that have molecular weights on the order of 1 million; their variations in structure and function cover just as broad a range.

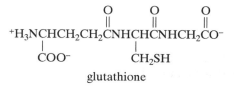

glutathione

Stop and Think: What is unusual about the structure of glutathione?

Some of them, such as the keratins of hair, horns, nails, and claws, act as biological building materials and have little or no biological activity. Others function as hormones, enzymes, antibiotics, or toxins, exerting a profound effect on biochemical reactions.

Bradykinin, known as the "pain molecule," is released by enzymatic cleavage of plasma glycoprotein whenever tissues are damaged.

Arg — Pro — Pro — Gly — Phe — Ser — Pro — Phe — Arg

bradykinin

It causes the sensation of pain by bonding to certain receptors on nerve endings. Peptides similar to bradykinin are present in wasp venom; other kinins act as hormones and stimulate a variety of physiological responses, such as the contraction or relaxation of smooth muscles and the dilation of blood vessel walls.

See Table 1 for the names and abbreviations of some amino acids. The textbook for your lecture course should contain abbreviations for amino acids not listed in the table.

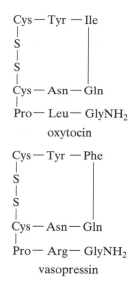

oxytocin

vasopressin

Oxytocin and vasopressin are both secreted by the posterior pituitary gland. Their structures are identical except for two amino acid residues, but their functions are entirely different. Vasopressin increases retention of water in the kidneys and is used as an antidiuretic in treating a form of diabetes that is characterized by excessive urine flow. Oxytocin intensifies uterine contractions during childbirth and is used clinically to induce labor. Both are cyclic compounds (cyclopeptides) that have a tripeptide side chain.

Poisonous mushrooms of the genera *Amanita* and *Galerina* contain cyclopeptides known as amatoxins and phallotoxins. These toxins are extremely potent; as little as one "death cap" mushroom, *Amanita phalloides*, can kill an adult. The Hollywood version of mushroom poisoning—in which the unlucky victim eats a serving of stewed mushrooms, turns pale, rises from the table clutching his throat, and immediately drops dead—is a myth. The victim may not even be aware that he or she has been poisoned for 8–24 hours after eating the mushrooms. Following a day or so of violent cramps, nausea, vomiting, and other unpleasant symptoms, the patient appears to recover and may even be sent home from the hospital. Death from kidney or liver failure often follows in several days. α-Amanitin and the other amatoxins are believed to attack the nuclei of liver and kidney cells, depleting their nuclear RNA and inhibiting the synthesis of more RNA so that protein synthesis stops and the cells die.

The Roman emperor Claudius died soon after eating mushrooms, but they were probably edible Amanita caesarea *mushrooms that had been laced with poison by his wife, Agrippina. She wanted him out of the way so that her son, Nero, would become emperor.*

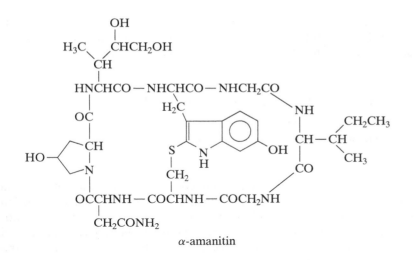

α-amanitin

Larger polypeptides, containing from 60 to 74 amino acid residues, are found in snake venoms such as those of the African black mamba, which can kill a mouse in less than 5 minutes, and the Indian cobra.

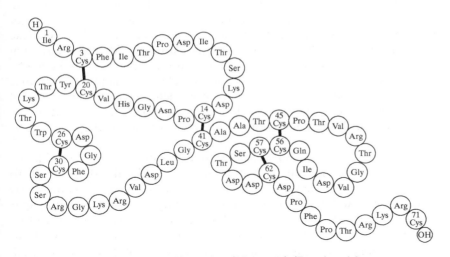

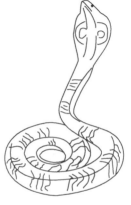

Indian cobra

Figure 1 Venom toxin of the Indian cobra (*Naja naja*) (Reprinted from *Biochemical and Biophysical Research Communications,* **1973**, *55*, 435, by permission.)

Most of these venom toxins have long chains that are cross-linked by four or more cystine disulfide bridges, as shown for the cobra's venom toxin in Figure 1.

One of the most exciting areas of polypeptide biochemistry is the study of "memory molecules." Researchers have discovered that an animal's learned behavior can be forgotten when a substance that interferes with peptide synthesis is injected into the animal's brain at a certain time. This suggests that peptide synthesis is involved in the consolidation of long-term memory. For example, a peptide called scotophobin was isolated from the brains of rats that had been conditioned to fear the dark.

$$Ser-Asp-Asn-Gln-Gln-Gly-Lys-Ser-Ala-Gln-Gln-Gly-Gly-TyrNH_2$$

scotophobin

(from the Greek *scotos,* dark; and *phobos,* fear)

When scotophobin was injected into unconditioned rats, they also became afraid of the dark. This raises the intriguing possibility that breaking the chemical memory code could enable chemists to synthesize the peptides corresponding to any kind of learning experience. Perhaps someday it will be possible to get an injection of Biology 101 or Philosophy 416 rather than absorbing the subject matter in the classroom!

Understanding the Experiment

The structures of long-chain polypeptides, such as those found in the venom of poisonous snakes, can be determined by breaking them down into shorter chains of amino acids and analyzing the fragments. For example, an enzyme called cathepsin C hydrolyzes a polypeptide into dipeptide units starting at the *N*-terminal amino acid residue (the one at the chain end terminated by an amino group), and the enzyme trypsin breaks a polypeptide chain after each lysine or arginine residue. By analyzing each fragment from these and other reactions, a biochemist can locate overlapping sequences of amino acids, from which the entire primary structure of the polypeptide can be deduced.

In this experiment, you will determine the structure of an unknown dipeptide that contains one or more of the amino acids listed in Table 1. To do so, you will first identify the amino acids your dipeptide contains by hydrolyzing it and analyzing the resulting amino acid mixture by paper chromatography. The dipeptides and amino acid derivatives you will be using are quite expensive; therefore, the experiment will be carried out on an ultramicro scale, using only a milligram of the dipeptide for each reaction. You will use Pasteur pipets for volume measurements and solvent extractions, and sealed capillary tubes for the hydrolysis reactions. It takes some practice to fill and seal a capillary tube properly, so it is recommended that you practice the technique with water before using the dipeptide and DNP–dipeptide solutions. The capillary method is very reliable when performed correctly, but there is always the chance that an improperly sealed tube will break or leak during the overnight hydrolysis period. To prevent the considerable loss of time that would result from a ruined sample, you will prepare at least three tubes for each hydrolysis reaction.

The paper chromatography of amino acids can be carried out in a multitude of developing solvents; no one solvent system is the best under all circumstances. The 2-propanol/formic acid/water (16:1:4) solvent system used

Table 1 Names and abbreviations of selected amino acids

Name	Abbreviation
histidine	His
lysine	Lys
serine	Ser
aspartic acid	Asp
glycine	Gly
threonine	Thr
alanine	Ala
proline	Pro
tyrosine	Tyr
valine	Val
phenylalanine	Phe
leucine	Leu

in this procedure is suitable for most amino acids, but certain combinations of amino acids may be separated more readily with a different solvent system, such as 1-propanol/ammonia (7:3) or 2-butanone/propionic acid/water (15:5:6). The amino acids are colorless, so their spots will be made visible by spraying them with a solution of ninhydrin, which reacts with most amino acids (proline is an exception) to form a blue-violet product.

To work out the complete structure of your dipeptide, you must determine the sequence in which the amino acids appear in the dipeptide. This can be done using a dinitrophenylation procedure developed by Frederick Sanger, who won the chemistry Nobel Prize in 1956 for determining the structure of insulin and again in 1980 for his work on nucleic acid structures. 2,4-Dinitrofluorobenzene (DNFB) is an unusually reactive aryl halide that undergoes nucleophilic substitution reactions with unprotonated amino groups. Because most peptides exist as zwitterions in neutral solutions, sodium bicarbonate is used to raise the pH of the peptide solution enough to deprotonate the amino group, allowing it to react with DNFB. This reaction yields a dipeptide that has a dinitrophenyl (DNP) substituent attached to the *N*-terminal amino acid residue, as shown in the "Reactions and Properties" section. In effect, the DNP group functions as a label for the *N*-terminal residue.

In the alkaline reaction mixture, the DNP-substituted dipeptide exists in the anionic form, with a polar —COO⁻ group. Extracting this solution with ether therefore removes the less polar DNFB but leaves the DNP–dipeptide in the aqueous layer. Lowering the pH with hydrochloric acid then protonates the carboxyl group, allowing the DNP–dipeptide to be extracted from the aqueous layer by diethyl ether and isolated by evaporating the ether. It is important to remove the last traces of ether before hydrolysis, so the residue is dissolved in acetone, which is also evaporated. The DNP–dipeptide is then hydrolyzed in aqueous hydrochloric acid, yielding the free *C*-terminal amino acid (the one from the chain end terminated by a carboxyl group) and a dinitrophenyl derivative of the *N*-terminal amino acid.

DNP–amino acids are more easily separated on silica gel than on paper, so your product mixture will be analyzed by thin-layer chromatography, using known DNP–amino acids as standards and chloroform/acetic acid/*t*-pentyl alcohol (23:1:10) as the developing solvent. Because the DNP derivatives are light sensitive, their chromatograms should be developed in a location away from strong light. The yellow spots formed by the DNP–amino acids are easy to locate, but they fade with time, so you should circle them in pencil soon after the TLC plate is developed. Dinitrophenol is a possible by-product of the dinitrophenylation procedure. However, its yellow spot is usually evident only when an alkaline developing solvent is used. If TLC analysis of your unknown produces two or more distinct spots, exposing the chromatogram to vapors of hydrochloric acid should bleach out the dinitrophenol spot.

Diethyl ether is not considered toxic to aquatic organisms and doesn't persist for long in either air or water. Chloroform is toxic to aquatic organisms, and acetic acid is expected to be slightly toxic to aquatic life, so the chloroform/acetic acid/*t*-pentyl alcohol developing solvent should not be released into the environment. 2-Propanol and formic acid are not expected to be toxic to aquatic life.

The solvent ratios are volume ratios. Thus, a 1-propanol/ammonia (7:3) solvent system can be prepared by mixing 70 mL of 1-propanol with 30 mL of concentrated aqueous ammonia.

ninhydrin

Key Concept: *The structures of amino acids and peptides are pH dependent. At low pH they exist as cations of the type* ⁺H₃N~COOH, *at high pH as anions of the type* H₂N~COO⁻, *and at intermediate pH as zwitterions of the type* ⁺H₃N~COO⁻.

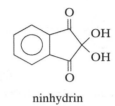

2,4-dinitrophenyl substituent
(DNP)

Reactions and Properties

(a) Dinitrophenylation of dipeptide

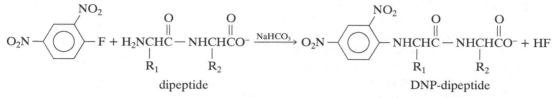

R_1, R_2 = amino acid side chains

(b) Hydrolysis of dipeptide and DNP-dipeptide

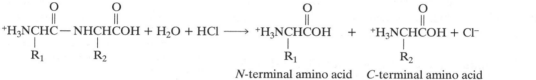

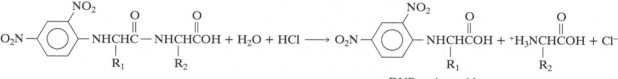

Table 2 Physical properties

	mol wt	mp	bp
2,4-dinitrofluorobenzene	186.1	27.5–30	178^{15}

Note: mp and bp are in °C; superscripts indicate the pressure in torr.

DIRECTIONS

Use a Pasteur pipet for all volume measurements; the pipet should deliver 35–45 drops per milliliter. Organize your time efficiently so that you can have your hydrolysis tubes prepared and in the oven by the end of the first laboratory period.

Safety Notes

2,4-Dinitrofluorobenzene is very toxic if ingested, inhaled, or absorbed through the skin. It can cause severe dermatitis in sensitive individuals and it is a suspected carcinogen. Wear gloves and avoid contact with the DNFB reagent.
Diethyl ether is extremely flammable and may be harmful if inhaled. Do not breathe its vapors; keep it away from flames and hot surfaces.

A. *Dinitrophenylation of the Dipeptide*

Reaction. In a 7.5-cm test tube, combine about 1 mg of your unknown dipeptide with 4 drops of distilled or deionized water, 1 drop of aqueous 4% sodium bicarbonate, and 8 drops of the DNFB reagent (a 5% solution of 2,4-dinitrofluorobenzene in ethanol). Cover the tube with Parafilm and shake it occasionally during a 1-hour period. Every 10 minutes, check the pH by dipping the closed end of a melting-point capillary into the solution and touching it to a strip of narrow-range pH paper. As necessary, add a drop or two of 4% sodium bicarbonate solution to keep the pH between 8 and 9.

Separation. Add 10 drops of water and 10 drops of aqueous 4% sodium bicarbonate to the reaction mixture. Wash [OP-24] the reaction mixture two or three times with diethyl ether, each time using a volume of ether approximately equal to the total volume of solution. Carry out each washing operation as described here.

- Add the ether to the reaction vessel.
- Draw both layers into a Pasteur pipet and eject the mixture forcefully into the reaction vessel to mix the layers; repeat a half-dozen times or more.
- Cool the mixture in ice water and wait for any emulsion to settle.
- Remove the ether (top) layer with the Pasteur pipet.

The last ether layer should be colorless; wash the reaction mixture with more ether if it is not. Add enough 6 M hydrochloric acid (2 or 3 drops are usually sufficient) to the aqueous layer to bring its pH down to 1 or 2. Then extract [OP-18] the aqueous solution with two portions of diethyl ether by the same technique you used to wash it; combine and save the extracts. Be careful not to include any of the aqueous layer when you withdraw the ether layers.

B. *Hydrolysis of the Dipeptide and DNP–Dipeptide*

Use a dry Pasteur pipet to distribute the ether solution equally among three wells on a porcelain spot plate and let the ether evaporate *completely* under the hood. Dissolve each residue in 2 drops of acetone and let the acetone evaporate under the hood. Then dissolve each residue in 4 drops of 6 M hydrochloric acid, using the closed end of a capillary melting-point tube for stirring. Prepare at least three hydrolysis tubes by method **1** if you are using capillary tubes that are sealed at one end, or by method **2** if you are using open-ended capillary tubes.

Method 1. Warm a capillary melting-point tube by holding it near its open end and moving it in and out of the "cool" part of a Bunsen burner flame for several seconds, then immediately insert the open end into the liquid in one of the wells. As the tube cools (blowing on it may help), it should begin to fill with liquid. When 2 to 3 cm of liquid are inside the tube, remove it; holding the open end just above horizontal, cool the closed end under a cold-water tap. Holding the tube upright near the open end, carefully strike it at a point below the liquid level with your fingernail until virtually all of the liquid is in the bottom of the tube. Capillary tubes are fragile, so don't tap the tube too hard or it will break. Holding the closed end so that your fingers just cover the liquid, rotate the tube as you move it rapidly in and out of the cool part of the burner flame for several seconds. (The tube should be

Take Care! Wear gloves and avoid contact with the DNFB reagent.

Stop and Think: Why is important to keep the pH in this range?

Take Care! Keep diethyl ether well away from flames.

Stop and Think: What is being removed by the ether?

Take Care! Avoid contact with the ether layers.

Waste Disposal: Place the wash ether layers in a designated solvent recovery container.

Waste Disposal: Unless your instructor directs otherwise, wash the aqueous layer down the drain.

Take Care! Don't burn yourself!

inserted lengthwise into the flame so that most of the empty part is heated.) Immediately seal [OP-3] the open end by rotating it in the flame until that end closes. Because of the vacuum created by preheating the tube, its end should collapse and bend over as it seals.

Method 2. Insert one end of an open capillary tube into one of the wells and draw in (by capillary action) about 2–3 cm of liquid. Hold the tube horizontally and tap it so that the liquid is near the middle, then seal one end by rotating it in the outermost edge of the flame. When that end has cooled, hold the open end up and strike the lower part of the tube with your fingernail until nearly all of the liquid is in the bottom. Seal the other end as described for method **1**.

Put the capillary tubes in a small test tube labeled with your name and "DNP–amino acid." Leave the test tube in a 100–110°C oven overnight or longer.

Dissolve about 1 mg of your unknown dipeptide in 10 drops of 6 *M* hydrochloric acid. Use this solution to prepare three or more capillary tubes by one of the previous methods. Put the capillary tubes in a small test tube labeled with your name and "amino acids." Leave this test tube in the 100–110°C oven overnight or longer.

C. *Separation and Analysis of the Amino Acids and the DNP–Amino Acid*

Safety Notes

> **Both chromatographic developing solvents contain flammable or toxic liquids with harmful vapors, and chloroform is a suspected carcinogen. Use a hood, avoid contact, do not breathe their vapors, and keep flames away.**

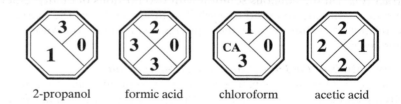

2-propanol   formic acid   chloroform   acetic acid

Remove the hydrolysis tubes from the oven and let them cool. *Under a hood*, prepare a large beaker (or another suitable developing chamber) for paper chromatography [OP-23] by adding enough of the 2-propanol/formic acid/water (16:1:4) solvent system to form a 1-cm layer on the bottom. Cover the beaker with plastic wrap and let the system equilibrate for at least 1 hour before using it.

Take Care! Avoid contact with the developing solvents and do not breathe their vapors.

Prepare a developing chamber for the TLC analysis [OP-22], using enough of the chloroform/acetic acid/*t*-pentyl alcohol (23:1:10) solvent system to form a 5-mm layer on the bottom. Cover the developing chamber with plastic wrap and let the system equilibrate for at least 30 minutes before using it.

Use a sharp triangular file or another glass cutter to open one of the cooled amino acid capillary tubes just above the liquid level, and empty it into one well of a spot plate. Evaporate [OP-19] the solvent under the hood and dissolve the residue in 1 drop of water. Obtain a sheet of Whatman #1 chromatography paper that is at least 12 cm long (in the direction of development) and wide enough to accommodate the standard amino acid solutions as well as your unknown solution. Spot the paper in two (or more) places with the amino acid solution, then spot it with the amino acid standards. Develop the chromatogram under a hood in the 2-propanol/formic acid/water solvent system and let it dry under the hood. Then spray the paper lightly with the ninhydrin spray reagent. Develop the color by heating the paper in a 100–110°C oven for about 10 minutes. Measure the R_f values of all the spots.

Open one of the DNP–amino acid capillary tubes and empty the contents into a small test tube, washing it down with 10–15 drops of water. Extract [OP-18] the aqueous solution twice with diethyl ether as described in part **A**, using a volume of ether equal to the volume of the solution for each extraction. Combine the extracts. Transfer the ether solution to a well on a spot plate and let the ether evaporate under the hood. Dissolve the residue in 3 drops of acetone and immediately use this solution to spot a silica gel TLC plate in two places. Spot the plate with the standard solutions of DNP–amino acids and develop it under a hood with the chloroform/acetic acid/*t*-pentyl alcohol solvent system in a location away from strong light. Let the developed TLC plate dry under the hood. If your unknown solution forms more than one yellow spot, momentarily hold the chromatogram over an open bottle of concentrated HCl *under a hood*. Circle the yellow spots as soon as the developed plate is dry; you can use an ultraviolet lamp to make them more clearly visible. Measure the R_f values of all the spots. Tabulate the R_f values from your chromatograms; identify the two amino acids and the DNP–amino acid. Draw the structure of the unknown dipeptide and name it.

Waste Disposal: Place the chromatography solvent in a designated solvent recovery container.

Waste Disposal: Unless you plan to confirm the identity of the *C*-terminal amino acid (see "Other Things You Can Do"), the aqueous layer can be washed down the drain (with your instructor's permission).

Waste Disposal: Place the chromatography solvent in a designated solvent recovery container. Place any unused capillary tubes in a sharps collector.

Take Care! Do not look directly at the lamp.

Exercises

1. Write equations for the reactions undergone by your dipeptide during the dinitrophenylation and hydrolysis steps.
2. Tell whether the dipeptide you identified could be obtained by using cathepsin C to break down the polypeptide from the cobra venom illustrated in Figure 1, and explain your answer. The *N*-terminal amino acid is the one that is labeled "1."
3. Describe and explain the possible effect on your results of the following experimental errors or variations: (a) You failed to check the pH of the dinitrophenylation reaction mixture, and it fell below 6. (b) You didn't add 6 *M* HCl to the dinitrophenylation reaction mixture before extracting it with diethyl ether. (c) You dissolved the DNP–dipeptide in 6 *M* NaOH rather than 6 *M* HCl before transferring it to the hydrolysis tubes.
4. Describe some green features of this experiment, and any that aren't so green.
5. Following the format in the "Planning an Experiment" appendix, construct a flow diagram for the synthesis and hydrolysis of the DNP-dipeptide.
6. When you extracted the DNP–dipeptide hydrolysate with diethyl ether, why wasn't your *C*-terminal amino acid extracted along with your DNP–amino acid? Write equations explaining your answer.
7. (a) Propose a detailed mechanism for the reaction of 2,4-dinitrofluorobenzene with the dipeptide you identified. (b) With reference to the mechanism, explain why the reaction wouldn't take place at low pH.
8. Will Bobble accidentally added aqueous sodium bisulfate instead of sodium bicarbonate to the dinitrophenylation reaction mixture just before

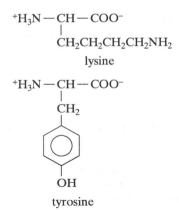

lysine

tyrosine

the first ether extraction. His DNP–dipeptide hydrolysate produced no spots when analyzed by TLC. What happened to his product, and why?

9. Bea Wilder decided to save time by adding a large excess of sodium bicarbonate at the beginning of the dinitrophenylation reaction instead of adding smaller amounts during the reaction. When she developed her TLC plate with a solvent system containing butanol and ammonia, a large yellow spot showed up that didn't match any of the DNP–amino acid standards. What compound formed the yellow spot? Write an equation for its formation.

10. (a) Some amino acids, such as lysine and tyrosine, yield dinitrophenylated derivatives even when they aren't at the end of a peptide chain. Explain, giving structures for the DNP derivatives. (b) Such derivatives don't usually interfere with the identification of the *N*-terminal DNP–amino acids because they aren't extracted from the aqueous hydrolysis mixture at pH 1 by diethyl ether. Explain.

Other Things You Can Do

(Starred items require your instructor's permission.)

*1. To confirm the identity of the *C*-terminal amino acid, evaporate the reserved aqueous layer from the DNP–dipeptide hydrolysate, add a drop of water to the residue, and identify the *C*-terminal amino acid by paper chromatography as described in the Directions.

*2. Isolate the protein casein from milk as described in the "Isolation of a Protein from Milk" minilab.

3. Starting with sources listed in the Bibliography, write a research paper about primary structure determination of polypeptides and proteins, describing the applications of such reagents and enzymes as phenyl isothiocyanate, dansyl chloride, trypsin, chymotrypsin, cathepsin C, and cyanogen bromide.

Multistep Synthesis of Benzilic Acid from Benzaldehyde

EXPERIMENT

Reactions of Carbonyl Compounds. Preparation of Carboxylic Acids.
Nucleophilic Addition. Oxidation. Molecular Rearrangements.

Operations

OP-7   Heating
OP-10 Mixing
OP-15 Gravity Filtration
OP-16 Vacuum Filtration
OP-26 Washing and Drying Solids
OP-28 Recrystallization
OP-33 Melting Point
OP-39 Infrared Spectrometry

Before You Begin

1. Read the experiment, read or review the operations as necessary, and write an experimental plan.
2. Calculate the mass and volume of 150 mmol of benzaldehyde, and the theoretical yields of benzoin, benzil, and benzilic acid expected from that much benzaldehyde.

Scenario

The α-hydroxy acids (AHAs) include lactic acid, which forms in milk as it sours and is also produced in muscles and blood after vigorous physical activity. Certain AHAs, such as glycolic acid ($HOCH_2COOH$), are used in anti-aging "wrinkle creams" that soften the skin and smooth out fine wrinkles and roughness. Golden Age Sundries is an organization that develops and markets various consumer goods for older people, and the success of AHAs in combating some effects of aging has led them to support research exploring the possible anti-aging benefits of other α-hydroxy acids. Your supervisor has just received a grant from them to investigate one of the AHAs, benzilic acid.

Benzilic acid can be prepared from an inexpensive starting material, benzaldehyde, by a three-step synthesis that involves a reaction called the benzoin condensation, an oxidation step, and a molecular rearrangement (see the "Reactions and Properties" section for equations). The benzoin condensation has traditionally been carried out using cyanide ion as a catalyst, but because of the toxicity of cyanide, your supervisor has decided to use vitamin B_1 instead. Your assignment is to find out whether or not the vitamin is a suitable catalyst for the benzoin condensation and, if it is, to convert the benzoin you obtain to benzilic acid.

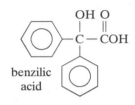

lactic acid

benzilic acid

From *Operational Organic Chemistry: A Problem Solving Approach to the Laboratory*, Fourth Edition, John W. Lehman. Copyright © 2009 by Pearson Education. Published by Prentice Hall. All rights reserved.

Applying Scientific Methodology

The scientific problem is outlined in the Scenario. You can solve it by the successful completion of the multistep synthesis described.

Justus von Liebig and the Bitter Almond Tree

Chemical warfare is generally thought of as being a recent and uniquely human invention, but, as with many such inventions, nature beat us to it. An otherwise unexceptional insect, the millipede *Apheloria corrugata*, discourages predators with a dose of poison gas powerful enough to kill a mouse. Many trees in the rose family, such as cherry, apple, peach, plum, and apricot trees, ensure their continued survival by protecting their seeds and foliage with cyanide-containing substances. There are cases on record of human fatalities from eating the seeds of these species; one man who considered apple seeds a delicacy died after eating a cup of them at one sitting. The chemical weapon in each of these examples is a natural cyanohydrin, mandelonitrile, which can be decomposed by enzymes or stomach acid into benzaldehyde and lethal hydrogen cyanide.

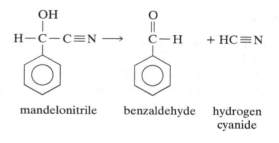

mandelonitrile   benzaldehyde   hydrogen cyanide

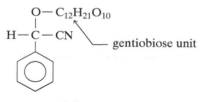

amygdalin

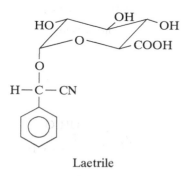

Laetrile

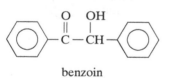

benzoin

In most cyanogenetic (cyanide-forming) plants, mandelonitrile is present as a carbohydrate derivative called a *glycoside*. The most common of these glycosides is amygdalin, which is an acetal of mandelonitrile and the carbohydrate gentiobiose. Amygdalin can be broken down enzymatically under certain conditions to yield mandelonitrile and its decomposition product, hydrogen cyanide. Closely related to amygdalin is the controversial cancer drug Laetrile, which allegedly kills malignant cells by releasing hydrogen cyanide (or possibly mandelonitrile) at the site of the malignancy. One of the most prolific sources of amygdalin is the bitter almond, which—unlike the sweet varieties used for human consumption—is grown for the oil that can be pressed from its seed kernels. The familiar "maraschino cherry" odor of almond oil comes from benzaldehyde formed by the breakdown of amygdalin. Both synthetic benzaldehyde and natural almond oil are used to flavor such food and beverage products as amaretto, cappuccino, and marzipan.

In the early 1800s, distilled almond oil was treated with aqueous alkali to remove hydrogen cyanide and other impurities. This process yielded a small amount of a white solid that was subsequently identified as benzoin. Friedrich Wöhler and Justus von Liebig studied the reaction in 1832 and discovered that benzoin formation results from the catalytic action of sodium cyanide (formed when HCN from amygdalin reacted with the base) on benzaldehyde. Surprisingly, cyanide ion is almost the only substance that catalyzes this reaction, so the early discovery of the benzoin condensation depended on the coincidental production of both cyanide and benzaldehyde when bitter almond oil was washed with an alkaline solution.

Not long after his work on the benzoin condensation, von Liebig discovered yet another unusual reaction. Benzoin can be oxidized to the diketone benzil by a variety of oxidizing agents. When benzil is treated with potassium hydroxide, it rearranges to yield (upon acidification) benzilic acid. This reaction, called the benzilic acid rearrangement, is the oldest known molecular rearrangement, the prototype of a general class of rearrangements to electrophilic carbon atoms.

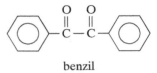

benzil

Understanding the Experiment

In this experiment, you will convert benzaldehyde to benzoin by the benzoin condensation, oxidize benzoin to benzil, and then convert benzil to benzilic acid. Because this is a multistep synthesis, you should try to keep material losses at a minimum in each step; otherwise, your overall yield will be quite low. It is essential that the benzaldehyde be pure, because impure benzaldehyde contains benzoic acid, which inhibits the condensation reaction. Unless the benzaldehyde is from a previously unopened bottle or one that has been stored under nitrogen, it must be distilled before use.

For many years, it was believed that only cyanide ion could catalyze the benzoin condensation, but recently thiamine hydrochloride (vitamin B_1) has proven to be an effective catalyst as well.

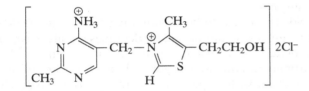

thiamine hydrochloride

It has the considerable advantage of being relatively hazard free, unlike the very poisonous cyanides. In the presence of sodium hydroxide, thiamine hydrochloride loses two protons to form a nucleophilic species that adds (with a proton) to the carbonyl group of benzaldehyde. The thiamine residue is sufficiently electron withdrawing to increase the acidity of the adjacent hydrogen atom, allowing its removal by the base to yield a resonance-stabilized carbanion, which undergoes nucleophilic addition to the carbonyl group of another benzaldehyde molecule. Loss of the thiamine residue from the product then yields benzoin.

Key Concept: Nucleophilic addition to an aldehyde or ketone involves nucleophilic attack at the carbonyl carbon, followed by addition of a proton to the carbonyl oxygen.

Major steps in the mechanism of the thiamine-catalyzed benzoin condensation

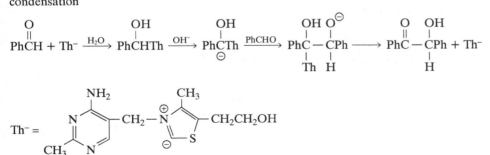

The benzoin condensation is carried out by heating a solution of benzaldehyde, sodium hydroxide, and thiamine hydrochloride in ethanol. To obtain a reasonable yield of benzoin, it is best to carry out the reaction for as long as possible (2–3 hours or more) during one lab period and let the reaction mixture stand until the next.

Benzoin can be converted to benzil by ammonium nitrate in the presence of a catalytic amount of copper(II) acetate. The benzoin is apparently oxidized by the direct action of copper(II) ions, which are reduced to copper(I) ions in the process. The ammonium nitrate then oxidizes the resulting copper(I) back to copper(II).

When treated with alcoholic potassium hydroxide, benzil undergoes the molecular rearrangement that was discovered by von Liebig. This rearrangement involves nucleophilic attack by hydroxide ion on one carbonyl carbon, followed by migration of the adjacent phenyl group to the other carbonyl carbon (see Exercise 2). The reaction initially yields a suspension of potassium benzilate, which should dissolve when the reaction mixture is heated. Benzilic acid is precipitated from the filtered solution by hydrochloric acid and purified by recrystallization from water.

You can gain additional experience in spectral interpretation by analyzing and comparing the infrared (IR) spectra of benzaldehyde and the products. These IR spectra should show bands from several different kinds of O—H, C—O, and C=O bonds, and in most of them you can observe aromatic C—H stretching vibrations with no interference from aliphatic C—H stretching bands.

Acetic acid is expected to be slightly toxic to aquatic life. Methanol is slightly toxic to aquatic organisms but biodegrades readily in water and soil. Copper(II) acetate is very toxic to aquatic life and should not be released into the environment. Potasssium hydroxide may be harmful in the environment, particularly with respect to aquatic organisms. Hydrochloric acid is expected to be toxic to aquatic life.

Reactions and Properties

A. Benzoin condensation

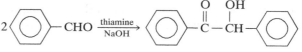

benzaldehyde   benzoin

B. Oxidation of benzoin

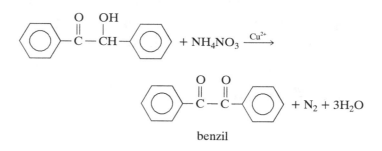

benzil

Multistep Synthesis of Benzilic Acid from Benzaldehyde

C. Benzilic acid rearrangement

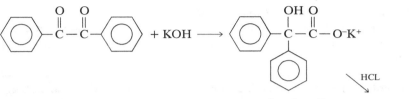

potassium benzilate

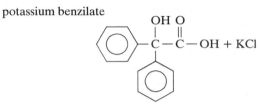

benzilic acid

Table 1 Physical properties

	mol wt	mp	bp	d
benzaldehyde	106.1	−26	178	1.042
thiamine hydrochloride	337.3	248d		
benzoin	212.2	137		
benzil	210.2	95–6		
benzilic acid	228.2	151		
ammonium nitrate	80.0	170		
potassium hydroxide	56.1			

Note: mp and bp are in °C; density is in g/mL; d = decomposes.
Potassium hydroxide pellets are about 85% KOH.

Benzaldehyde

1702.5	1310.7	745.4
1596.9	1203.7	688.3
1455.7	827.9	650.0

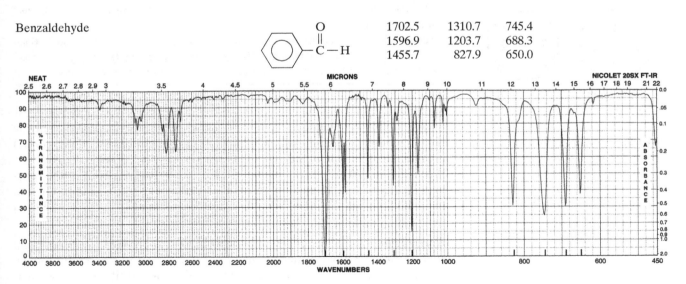

Figure 1 IR spectrum of benzaldehyde

DIRECTIONS

A. *Preparation of Benzoin from Benzaldehyde*

The reaction should be started at the beginning of a lab period when a different experiment is being performed, and allowed to proceed for as long as possible.

Safety Notes

benzaldehyde   methanol

Stop and Think: What impurity might benzaldehyde contain?

Waste Disposal: Dispose of the filtrate as directed by your instructor.

Methanol is flammable and harmful if ingested, inhaled, or absorbed through the skin. Avoid contact with the liquid and do not breathe its vapors.

Reaction.   Dissolve 5.0 g of thiamine hydrochloride in 8 mL of water in a 125-mL Erlenmeyer flask. Add 50 mL of 95% ethanol and cool the solution in an ice/water bath. Add 10 mL of 3 *M* aqueous sodium hydroxide solution, drop by drop with stirring [OP-10], slowly enough that the temperature doesn't exceed 20°C. Test the pH of the mixture; if it is not strongly alkaline (9 or higher), add more 3 *M* NaOH dropwise until it is. Add 150 mmol of *pure* benzaldehyde to this solution. Cover the mouth of the flask with Parafilm, and heat [OP-7] the mixture in a 60°±5°C hot-water bath until the end of the lab period. Then allow it to stand undisturbed in a dark place until the next lab period.

Separation and Analysis.   Scratch the inside of the flask to induce crystallization, if necessary, and then cool the reaction mixture in an ice/water bath until crystallization is complete. Collect the benzoin by vacuum filtration [OP-16]. Wash it on the filter [OP-26a] with cold water, then with two 10-mL portions of ice-cold methanol. Dry [OP-26b] and weigh the product before proceeding to part **B**. Measure its melting point [OP-33] and record its infrared spectrum [OP-39], or save enough product to do both later.

B. *Preparation of Benzil from Benzoin*

Safety Notes

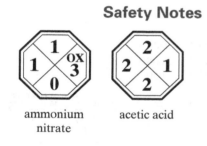

ammonium   acetic acid
nitrate

Take Care! Avoid contact with acetic acid and do not breathe its vapors.

Stop and Think: What is the gas, and where did it come from?

Ammonium nitrate may cause a fire or explosion if it is heated strongly or allowed to contact combustible materials. Keep it away from other chemicals and combustibles.
Acetic acid causes chemical burns that can seriously damage skin and eyes. Its vapors are highly irritating to the eyes and respiratory tract. Wear gloves and dispense under a hood; avoid contact and do not breathe its vapors.

Reaction.   Multiply the mass of dry benzoin by 0.5 and combine that mass of ammonium nitrate with 35 mL of aqueous 80% (volume/volume) acetic acid in a round-bottom flask. Mix in the benzoin and 0.15 g of copper(II) acetate. Drop in a few boiling chips or a stir bar and attach a condenser. With stirring [OP-10] or occasional shaking, heat the flask to start the reaction, which should be accompanied by vigorous evolution of a gas. When the gas evolution subsides, heat the solution to the boiling point, and then heat it under gentle reflux [OP-7] for an hour or more.

Separation.   Cool the reaction mixture to 50°C and pour it, with manual stirring, onto 75 g of crushed ice in a beaker. Allow it to stand until the ice melts. Then collect the benzil by vacuum filtration [OP-16] and wash it twice with cold water.

Purification and Analysis. Recrystallize [OP-28] the benzil from 95% ethanol, washing the yellow crystals with cold 50% aqueous ethanol. Dry [OP-26b] the product at a low temperature (50°C or less), and measure its mass. Measure its melting point [OP-33] and record its IR spectrum [OP-39], or save enough product to do both later.

C. *Preparation of Benzilic Acid from Benzil*

> The solution of potassium hydroxide in ethanol is flammable, toxic, and corrosive; it can cause severe damage to the eyes, skin, and respiratory tract. Wear gloves, avoid contact, and do not breathe its vapors. Concentrated hydrochloric acid is poisonous and corrosive. Contact or inhalation can cause severe damage to the eyes, skin, and respiratory tract. Wear gloves and dispense under a hood; avoid contact and do not breathe its vapors.

Waste Disposal: Unless your instructor directs otherwise, wash all filtrates down the drain.

Safety Notes

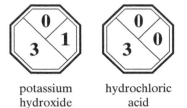

potassium   hydrochloric
hydroxide   acid

Reaction. Multiply the mass (in grams) of dry benzil by 2.5 and measure out that *volume,* in milliliters, of 6 *M* potassium hydroxide. Then multiply the mass of benzil by 3.0 and measure out that *volume,* in milliliters, of 95% ethanol. Combine the benzil with these liquids in a round-bottom flask, add boiling chips or a stir bar, and attach a condenser. Heat the mixture under gentle reflux [OP-7] for 15 minutes.

Separation. Pour the *hot* reaction mixture, with manual stirring, into 100 mL of water in a beaker and let the mixture stand for a few minutes. Then heat it to 50°C, with stirring [OP-10], to dissolve the potassium benzilate. There may be a colloidal suspension of unreacted benzil or by-products at this point, but most of the solid should dissolve. If it doesn't, add more warm water. Add about 0.5 g of decolorizing carbon (preferably pelletized Norit) and 0.25 g of filtering aid (Celite), stir or swirl the mixture at 50°C for 2 minutes, and filter the warm solution by gravity [OP-15] into a suitable container. *Under the hood,* carefully add 15 mL of concentrated hydrochloric acid to 100 g of crushed ice in a beaker. Add 10–15 mL of the potassium benzilate solution to the cold HCl solution, with manual stirring, and scratch the sides of the beaker until crystals begin to form. Then add the rest of the solution slowly, with continuous stirring. When the addition is complete, test the solution with pH paper. If the pH is higher than 2, add enough HCl to bring it down to 2. Cool the solution in ice water and collect the benzilic acid by vacuum filtration [OP-16], washing it on the filter [OP-26a] with cold water.

Take Care! Wear gloves, avoid contact with HCl, and do not breathe its vapors.

Purification and Analysis. Purify the benzilic acid by recrystallization [OP-28] from boiling water. It may be necessary to filter the hot solution by gravity to remove undissolved impurities. Dry [OP-26b] and weigh the purified product. Measure the melting point [OP-33] of the benzilic acid and record its IR spectrum [OP-39], or obtain the spectrum from your instructor. Calculate the percent yield for each step of the synthesis and the overall percent yield of benzilic acid.

Waste Disposal: Unless your instructor directs otherwise, wash all filtrates down the drain.

Exercises

1. Interpret the IR spectra of the products as completely as you can and describe the evidence suggesting that each reaction step has taken place as expected.
2. Propose a mechanism for the rearrangement of benzil to potassium benzilate in the presence of potassium hydroxide.
3. Describe and explain the possible effect on your results of the following experimental errors or variations: (a) The bottle of benzaldehyde for part **A** contained some white solid. (b) The label on the copper acetate bottle for part **B** read "cuprous acetate." (c) The pH of the solution in part **C** was 6 when you vacuum filtered it.
4. (a) Calculate the atom economy and reaction efficiency of each step in the synthesis and the overall synthesis. (b) Describe some green features of this experiment, and any that aren't so green.
5. Following the format in the "Planning an Experiment" appendix, construct a flow diagram for this experiment.
6. Write a detailed mechanism for the cyanide-catalyzed condensation of benzaldehyde, and explain the role played by the cyanide.
7. Using the reactions described in this experiment, write a synthetic pathway that illustrates the preparation of Compound **1** from a suitable five-carbon starting material.
8. Benzil reacts with urea in the presence of sodium hydroxide to form the sodium salt of 5,5-diphenylhydantoin (Dilantin), a powerful anticonvulsant used to treat epilepsy. By analogy with the benzilic acid rearrangement, propose a mechanism for this reaction.
9. In the presence of sulfuric acid, benzilic acid reacts with acetone to form a compound with the molecular formula $C_{17}H_{16}O_3$. Propose a structure for this product and write a balanced equation for the reaction.

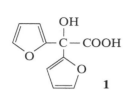

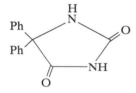

1

5,5-diphenylhydantoin

Other Things You Can Do

(Starred items require your instructor's permission.)

*1. Test both your crude and purified benzil for the presence of unreacted benzoin by dissolving a few crystals of each in 1 mL of ethanol and adding a drop of dilute sodium hydroxide solution. Test a small amount of benzoin in the same way and compare the results. Shake the solutions with air, let them stand, and record your observations.
*2. Carry out another reaction of benzaldehyde as described in "A Spontaneous Reaction of Benzaldehyde" minilab.
3. Starting with sources listed in the Bibliography, write a research paper about the use of α-hydroxy acids, Retin-A, and other skin care products to treat skin conditions, giving some of the advantages and disadvantages of each.

Using the Chemical Literature in an Organic Synthesis

Multistep Synthesis. Searching the Chemical Literature.

Before You Begin

1. Read the experiment and "The Chemical Literature" appendix, and familiarize yourself with the layout of the Bibliography.
2. In your laboratory notebook, outline a synthetic pathway leading to the target compound from readily available starting materials or the starting material(s) recommended by your instructor. For the chemicals you will be using and the target compound, list information concerning their physical properties, purification, safety and health hazards, and disposal. If the synthesis requires laboratory techniques with which you are not familiar, find information about these techniques in the literature, describe them, and sketch any special apparatus required for them. Locate any published spectra or other data that will help you characterize the target compound, and list their sources.
3. In your laboratory notebook, write a complete description of your plan for the synthesis, including a detailed procedure for each synthetic step (with safety precautions) and a description of the methods you propose to use to analyze the purity and verify the structure of the product. The procedure should be designed to yield about 3–5 g of the final product, unless your instructor indicates otherwise. Your write-up should also include a concise description of the experimental methodology. Submit your laboratory notebook (or duplicate pages) to your instructor for approval well in advance of the scheduled starting date. You should also discuss your plans with the instructor to make sure that the necessary chemicals and equipment are available, that the procedure can be carried out safely under the existing conditions, and that you have a good understanding of the experiment and any problems that might arise.

Scenario

Your supervisor has a backlog of chemicals that need to be prepared for various clients but doesn't have time to write up the procedures for you. You are on your own!

Applying Scientific Methodology

For this experiment, you will have to operate like a research chemist—find a suitable scientific problem to work on, plan a course of action, work out detailed experimental procedures, carry out your experimental plan in the laboratory, and evaluate your results. Throughout, you will be expected to apply what you have already learned about organic synthesis in this course and what you can learn from the chemical literature.

Planning Your Synthesis

Your instructor will either suggest a target compound for you to synthesize or allow you to choose your own, subject to approval. Your instructor will also inform you whether you will work individually or in teams. If you are to select your own target compound, you should consult your instructor before coming to a final decision, because your plans may be either too ambitious or not challenging enough. You can search for ideas in chemical periodicals such as the *Journal of Chemical Education,* in other laboratory manuals, or in many of the sources described herein (see "The Chemical Literature" appendix for more detailed information on these and other sources). Preferably, the target should be a compound that you have an interest in and really *want* to synthesize, such as an artificial flavor ingredient, a cosmetic ingredient, a perfume ingredient, an insect repellent, a plant-growth hormone, an analgesic drug, a pheromone, an artificial sweetener, a sunscreen, an antibiotic drug, a local anesthetic, a fluorescent dye, a chemoluminescent compound, and so forth—the possibilities are limitless!

Once you have selected a target compound, you will have to outline a synthetic pathway for making it from some readily available starting material. To help you work out a synthetic pathway, you can consult your lecture textbook or refer to "The Chemical Literature" appendix and the Bibliography to find such sources as *Organic Synthesis: The Disconnection Approach* [B30] and *Principles of Organic Synthesis* [B18]. After you develop one or more promising synthetic pathways, you should learn more about the reactions required for the synthesis. *Modern Synthetic Reactions* [B12], *Advanced Organic Chemistry* [H1], and *March's Advanced Organic Chemistry* [H11] describe a number of synthetic reactions and provide literature references to specific synthetic procedures. *Organic Reactions* [B19] is a comprehensive source of information about specific reactions and also includes some representative synthetic procedures, as well as numerous references to literature procedures. It describes the applications and limitations of many synthetic reactions and may help you tailor a synthetic procedure to fit the particular starting materials you will be working with. Many reactions and compound types are described in depth in review articles from such journals as *Chemical Reviews* and *Angewandte Chemie (International Edition in English)*.

There are many useful collections of detailed synthetic procedures. One of the best (and the first you may want to consult) is *Organic Syntheses* [B20], which provides a representative selection of carefully tested procedures. Other useful, if less comprehensive, sources include *Vogel's Textbook of Practical Organic Chemistry* [B31], *Organic Functional Group Preparations* [B27], and other works from Category B of the Bibliography, as well as a variety of basic and advanced organic chemistry lab textbooks. References to literature procedures for organic syntheses are given in many of the sources mentioned previously, such as *Organic Reactions* and the two advanced organic chemistry textbooks [H1, H11]. *Theilheimer's Synthetic Methods of Organic Chemistry* [B32] is an extensive guide to synthetic procedures that is updated each year. Each entry gives a brief outline of the

Sources from the Bibliography are referred to herein by category and number. For example, Organic Syntheses *[B20] is the twentieth entry under Category B, "Organic Reactions and Syntheses."*

procedure and cites its source. Other useful, if less complete, sources include *Synthetic Organic Chemistry* [B34], which covers many of the older reactions, *Comprehensive Organic Transformations* [B13], and *Compendium of Organic Synthetic Methods* [B11].

The most comprehensive guides to the chemical literature are *Chemical Abstracts* (*CA*) [J3] and *Beilstein* [A3]. With some practice, you can use them to find information about every aspect of your synthesis. For example, to find out more about your target compound, you should first find its *CA* index name and registry number in the *Index Guide*, which appears with the collective indexes that are published periodically by *Chemical Abstracts*. Then you can conduct a search of *Chemical Abstracts*—from an on-line database, if one is available—to locate articles that refer to your compound. See "The Chemical Literature" appendix for more information about the use of *CA*, *Beilstein*, and on-line searches. For more information about these and other useful sources on organic reactions and syntheses, as well as suggested literature searching strategies, read the three-part series "Information Sources for Organic Chemistry" [K7].

If you locate a specific procedure for the synthesis of your target compound in the chemical literature, you shouldn't assume that it will be suitable for your purposes as written. It may call for unavailable or excessively hazardous chemicals, or suggest techniques and apparatus that aren't appropriate to your laboratory situation. Primary literature procedures tend to be rather condensed, so you will probably have to "fill in the blanks" from your own experience or by consulting other sources.

If you want to prepare a target compound using a certain amount of starting material but can only find procedures that require more or less starting material than you expect to use, you will have to scale up or scale down the procedure for your use. For example, if a literature procedure calls for 24 g of acetophenone and you want to use only 3.6 grams, you should multiply the quantities of all reactants, reagents, catalysts, solvents, or other chemicals by the *scaling factor* 0.15, which is the ratio of 3.6 g to 24 g. You will need to reduce the size of the apparatus accordingly, and you may be able to reduce the reaction time as well. (Of course, it can't hurt to use the reaction time specified.) When you are scaling down a very large-scale procedure, such as one published in *Organic Syntheses* [B20], you should use somewhat larger volumes of most organic solvents (such as extraction and reaction solvents) than the scaling factor would indicate, because solvent losses due to evaporation, transfer, and other processes are proportionately greater with smaller volumes of a solvent. You may then have to use larger glassware than the scaling factor would indicate to accommodate the larger solvent volumes. On the other hand, don't use glassware that is too large for the volume of the materials you are using; larger glassware has more surface area, which leads to greater losses.

Most scaled-down syntheses don't give as high a percent yield as the original procedure. For example, losing 0.1 g of product during a transfer has a greater effect on the percent yield of a small-scale experiment than it does when you have more product to work with. Other factors, such as differences in surface-contact area or the rate of heat transfer, may also cause differences in the outcome of a scaled-down experiment, but most procedures can be scaled down to a moderate extent without difficulty.

Scaling up a procedure will ordinarily require larger glassware, and it may be advisable to increase the reaction time by 25–50%. If the scaling factor is quite large, you may want to increase the solvent volumes and container capacities somewhat less than the scaling factor would indicate. Keep in mind that an exothermic reaction run on a small scale may present no problems, but the same reaction run on a larger scale may become violent. So carrying out a scaled-up reaction may require taking some additional precautions, such as adding a reactant more slowly or cooling the reaction mixture while adding it.

If you can't locate a synthetic procedure for a specific synthetic conversion you plan to carry out, you may have to adapt a procedure for the same reaction of a closely related compound. Adapting a procedure is sometimes just a matter of recalculating the masses of the reactants. For example, suppose you want to adapt a literature procedure for the $NaBH_4$ reduction of cyclohexanone to the same reaction of 4-methylcyclohexanone. If the original procedure used 3.00 g (30.5 mmol) of cyclohexanone (mol wt = 98.2), you will need to use about 3.43 g (30.5 mmol) of 4-methylcyclohexanone (mol wt = 112.2) while keeping the quantities of other reactants the same. Such an adaptation may also require changes in such things as the size of the glassware you use, the amount or kind of recrystallization solvent needed, and the boiling range for a distillation, so it is important to identify changes in the properties of the reactants and products that necessitate procedural changes.

An organic synthesis ordinarily requires the use of one or more reagents, where a *reagent* is a chemical designed to bring about a specific kind of molecular transformation, such as the conversion of a carbonyl group to a hydroxyl group. Two excellent sources of detailed information about chemical reagents are *Fiesers' Reagents for Organic Synthesis* [B7] and *Encyclopedia of Reagents for Organic Synthesis* [B21]. General reference books, such as *The Merck Index* [A11], *Lange's Handbook of Chemistry* [A6], the *CRC Handbook of Chemistry and Physics* [A15], the *Dictionary of Organic Compounds* [A12], and the *Aldrich Catalog* [A1], can be consulted for information about the physical properties of the reagents, as well as other chemicals (including solvents) involved in your synthesis.

Before you carry out any chemical synthesis, you must learn how to handle the necessary chemicals safely. Detailed information about chemical hazards can be found in *Sax's Dangerous Properties of Industrial Materials* [C5], the *Sigma-Aldrich Library of Regulatory and Safety Data* [C4], and other sources from Category C of the Bibliography. You should also obtain and read the Material Safety Data Sheet (MSDS) for any hazardous chemical you will be working with (see "Finding and Using Chemical Safety Information" in the "Laboratory Safety" section). Information about safe laboratory practices may be found in *Prudent Practices in the Laboratory* [C7], which also provides guidelines for dealing with laboratory wastes.

If you are unfamiliar with some of the more advanced laboratory techniques required for a synthesis, consult *Guide for the Perplexed Organic Experimentalist* [D3], the appropriate volume in Weissberger's *Technique of Organic Chemistry* [D7], *Encyclopedia of Separation Science* [D10], or other references from Categories D and E of the Bibliography. If you need to purify a solvent or another common chemical, see *Purification of Laboratory Chemicals* [D1].

Once you have synthesized your target compound (or what you think is your target compound), you will have to confirm its identity by measuring one or more physical properties, such as its melting point or boiling point, and obtaining and interpreting at least one kind of spectrum. Refer to the appropriate sources in Category F if you need information about spectral analysis and the interpretation of spectra. *Spectrometric Identification of Organic Compounds* [F20] is a good place to start. There are many sources of published spectra, such as the *Aldrich Library of FT-IR Spectra* [F18] and the *Aldrich Library of ^{13}C and ^1H FT-NMR Spectra* [F16], Electronic libraries of spectra are available at most universities as well. Additional information about spectrometric and "wet" chemical methods for identifying organic compounds can be found in sources from Category G. You may also need to assess the purity of your product by gas chromatography, thin-layer chromatography (TLC), high-performance liquid chromatography (HPLC), or another method. Refer to Category E of the Bibliography for appropriate sources. For additional help in carrying out a literature search, consult "The Chemical Literature" appendix and appropriate sources listed in Category K of the Bibliography.

DIRECTIONS

Independent synthesis projects are intended for advanced or honors students who have mastered the necessary laboratory operations. These directions only furnish general guidelines regarding your synthesis. You must provide the procedural details and have them approved by your instructor. Keep detailed notes of your work and observations.

Safety Notes

> **Except when you have reliable information to the contrary, assume that all chemicals you will use are flammable and are hazardous by ingestion, inhalation, and skin absorption. Wear gloves and use a hood whenever possible, avoid contact with the chemicals, do not breathe their dust or vapors, and keep them away from ignition sources and other chemicals that might react with them.**

If necessary, purify any starting materials, reagents, or solvents that appear to be insufficiently pure. Carry out the synthesis in the laboratory according to the procedure you have developed. Purify the product, weigh the thoroughly dried product, and calculate the percent yield. Measure appropriate physical constants of the product and assess its purity by an appropriate chromatographic method, if requested. Confirm the identity of the product by one or more spectrometric methods, or by preparing one or more derivatives, or both.

Waste Disposal: Dispose of wastes as directed by your instructor.

Report. Write up your report as if it were a scientific paper being submitted to a professional publication, such as the *Journal of Organic Chemistry*. Such papers are traditionally written in an impersonal, objective style using the passive voice (for instance, "The solution was stirred" rather than "I stirred the solution"). Your report should include the following items, unless your instructor directs otherwise:

1. A brief but descriptive title
2. Your name and affiliation
3. A brief abstract that summarizes the principal results of the work
4. An introductory section (usually untitled) that provides a concise statement of the purpose and possible applications of the work, supported by

descriptions of related work from the literature. If your synthesis differs significantly from those reported in the literature, tell how and why.

5. A section titled "Experimental Methods" that gives enough detail about your materials and methods that another experienced worker could repeat your work. Give current *Chemical Abstract* index names and registry numbers (see "The Chemical Literature" appendix) for important starting materials and the product, and provide information about their purity, if possible. Note any significant hazards and safety precautions in a separate paragraph labeled "Caution."

6. A section titled "Results and Discussion" (or two separate "Results" and "Discussion" sections) that summarizes the important experimental results and points out any special features, limitations, or implications of your work. You should include any data (including spectral parameters) that will help justify your conclusion. You may also wish to suggest different approaches to the problem or areas that require further study.

7. A section titled "Conclusions" that states any conclusions you can draw from your work, based on the evidence presented

8. A section titled "References" that gives complete citations for all literature sources referred to in the report

Your instructor may suggest additions to, or modifications of, this list. *The ACS Style Guide* [L16] provides a more detailed discussion of these components, as well as helpful suggestions about writing style.

Exercises

1. (a) Calculate the atom economy and reaction efficiency of your synthesis. (b) Describe some green features of your synthesis, and any that aren't so green.

2. Herbert C. Brown was a corecipient (with Georg Wittig) of the 1979 chemistry Nobel Prize for his work with reagents for organic syntheses, principally organoboranes. Give the structure of Brown's reagent 9-BBN (9-borabicyclo[3.3.1]nonane), and describe some of its applications and characteristics, giving equations where appropriate. Cite several papers reporting the use of 9-BBN.

3. The synthesis of dodecahedrane has been described as the "Mount Everest of alicyclic chemistry." (a) Give its *Chemical Abstracts* index name and registry number, and draw its structure. (b) Locate the paper in which the synthesis of dodecahedrane was first reported. Give its title, the authors and their affiliation, and a standard literature citation showing where and when the paper appeared. (c) Summarize the salient points of the synthesis in your own words, specifying the starting material, the number of synthetic steps required, the yield of dodecahedrane, and the purification method. Tell how dodecahedrane was characterized, and report any spectral parameters. (d) Find a systematic name for dodecahedrane that is different from its *Chemical Abstracts (CA)* index name. (e) Quote and explain the reference, in the paper, to an ancient Greek philosopher.

4. (a) Cite the paper in which the use of pyridinium chlorochromate to oxidize alcohols to carbonyl compounds was first reported. (b) Tell how

pyridinium chlorochromate is prepared, describe a typical experimental procedure for oxidation of a primary alcohol to an aldehyde, and discuss the stoichiometry of the reaction. (c) Report on any hazards associated with the use of pyridinium chlorochromate, and describe safe disposal procedures for the reagent.

5. (a) Give a concise definition of the Knoevenagel condensation. (b) Describe typical experimental conditions for conducting a Knoevenagel condensation between an aldehyde and diethyl malonate. (c) Find and summarize a detailed procedure for the synthesis of ethyl coumarin-3-carboxylate using this reaction. (d) Describe the Doebner modification of the Knoevenagel condensation, and give at least one example.

6. (a) Describe any hazards associated with the use of thionyl chloride, and describe proper handling precautions and disposal procedures for this reagent. (b) Tell how thionyl chloride can be purified for use as a chemical reagent. (c) Cite a paper in which thionyl chloride was used to convert an amino acid to an ester in one step, and briefly describe the experimental conditions.

7. (a) Give the current *Chemical Abstracts* index name and registry number for (+)-camphor. (b) Draw a structure for (+)-camphor that shows its absolute configuration. (c) What is the melting point of the oxime of (+)-camphor? (d) Find an infrared spectrum for camphor and give the wave numbers of the major absorption bands. (e) Tell where you can find information about camphor in *Beilstein*. (f) Tell how most synthetic camphor is currently produced, giving equations for the reactions.

8. (a) Give the *Chemical Abstracts* index name of the compound whose CA registry number is [5543-57-7]. (b) Give the trivial name of this compound and describe its major application. (c) Tell where information about this compound can be found in *Beilstein*.

9. For each of the following abbreviated names, provide the full name of the journal, any names under which it was previously published, the year in which it was first published (as volume 1, under a current or previous name), the language or languages in which it is published, and a nearby library that carries it. (a) *Acc. Chem. Res.* (b) *Helv. Chim. Acta.* (c) *Dokl. Akad. Nauk SSSR.* (d) *Chem. Ber.*

10. Find detailed synthetic procedures for the following compounds, briefly describe the experimental conditions, and write equations for the relevant reactions: (a) hexaphenylbenzene; (b) vanillic acid; (c) 1,2-cyclononadiene; (d) octadecanedioic acid.

11. For each of the following compounds, find and reproduce as many different kinds of published spectra (or spectral parameters) as you can: (a) mandelic acid; (b) resorcinol; (c) exaltone; (d) bourbonal; (e) testosterone.

A Research Project in Organic Chemistry

EXPERIMENT

Research in Organic Chemistry.

Before You Begin

1. Read the experiment and review the "Scientific Methodology" section of the Introduction. Review "The Chemical Literature" appendix as necessary.
2. Write a research proposal based on one of the projects discussed in this - experiment or on a project that you or your research mentor has developed.
3. In your laboratory notebook, write a complete description of your research plans, including a detailed procedure for each experiment you intend to perform, with safety precautions. Submit your research proposal and lab notebook (or duplicate pages) to your research mentor.

Scenario

Your job with the Consulting Chemists Institute is nearly at an end. Your supervisor, who has a high regard for your abilities and potential, has encouraged you to consider making chemistry your career. To obtain employment as a professional chemist, you will probably have to earn a master's degree or a Ph.D. in chemistry. One of the requirements for your degree is the completion of an independent research project. You have decided to get a head start by carrying out an undergraduate research project under the direction of your supervisor or another faculty mentor. Now you must select a project to work on.

Applying Scientific Methodology

For this experiment, you will have to operate like a professional chemist—find a suitable scientific problem to work on, develop a hypothesis, plan a course of action, work out detailed experimental procedures, follow your experimental plan in the laboratory, evaluate your results, and arrive at a conclusion. Throughout, you will be expected to apply what you have already learned about organic chemistry in this course and what you can learn from the chemical literature.

Conducting Scientific Research

Conducting worthwhile research in chemistry requires a curious and logical mind, efficient work habits, superior laboratory skills, a good understanding of chemical concepts, and a great deal of perseverance. There is no single method to be followed in scientific research; different scientists often

From *Operational Organic Chemistry: A Problem Solving Approach to the Laboratory*, Fourth Edition, John W. Lehman. Copyright © 2009 by Pearson Education. Published by Prentice Hall. All rights reserved.

employ vastly different approaches. But the outline of scientific methodology in the Introduction lists the important steps in a scientific research project.

- Define the problem.
- Plan a course of action.
- Gather evidence.
- Evaluate the evidence.
- Develop a hypothesis.
- Test the hypothesis.
- Reach a conclusion.
- Report the results.

First, you need to decide what problem to investigate. Some examples of possible research problems are discussed in the next section, but you may wish to select your own problem to work on, after consultation with your mentor. It should, above all, be some aspect of organic chemistry that interests you intensely; without such motivation, it will be difficult for you to expend the time and effort required to complete a research project successfully. If possible, it should be in an area in which your mentor or other chemists at your institution have considerable interest and expertise. That will enable you to benefit from the guidance and enthusiasm they can provide. One way to come up with ideas for a research project in organic chemistry is to think about things that puzzled you during the lab or lecture course, such as unexpected lab results, incomplete or inconsistent explanations of phenomena, and gaps in textbook descriptions of some aspect of organic chemistry. After consulting the chemical literature, you may find that there are already explanations for such phenomena—no textbook or course can cover the entire field of organic chemistry—but in the process of looking for explanations, you may find other problems worth exploring. You can also get ideas by looking through chemistry periodicals such as the *Journal of Chemical Education*—which occasionally contains articles that describe potential research projects—and review journals or research reports, such as *Angewandte Chemie (International Edition in English)*, *Chemical Reviews*, or *Annual Reports on the Progress of Chemistry, Section B* [J2]. When you do find an article dealing with a subject that interests you, be sure to check the citations in that article to locate more articles on the same subject. The important thing is to read and learn as much as you can about the areas that interest you; the more you learn, the easier it is to select a worthwhile problem.

Sources from the Bibliography are referred to herein by category and number. For example, Organic Syntheses *[B20] is the twentieth entry under Category B, "Organic Reactions and Syntheses."*

Before you start working on any kind of scientific problem, you need to find out what research has already been carried out that is related to the problem. Therefore, you should do a thorough search of *Chemical Abstracts* [J3], and perhaps of other sources as well (such as *Beilstein* [A3]). See "The Chemical Literature" appendix for information about both of these references and about on-line searches of *Chemical Abstracts*. If, after a literature search, you learn that a problem you were planning to work on has already been "solved" satisfactorily, there is little point in working on the same problem. If only certain aspects of a problem have been investigated, you may decide to modify your objectives and concentrate on the areas in which original research can still be performed. Learning what has already been done on problems related to your own will help you fine-tune your objectives and plan your course of action.

The course of action you develop will depend on the kind of problem you select. If the problem requires a multistep synthesis, for example, you can refer to the "Using the Chemical Literature in an Organic Synthesis" experiment, if included, for help. In any case, you will need to consult the chemical literature to help you design your experimental approach and work out detailed procedures for all experimental work. Start by reading the appropriate sections of "The Chemical Literature" appendix and consulting the Bibliography to find out about some of the sources that are available to you. You may also want to consult one or more of the sources in Category K of the Bibliography for more complete and detailed information about the chemical literature. If you will need special chemicals, supplies, or equipment, first check with your mentor or the stockroom manager to find out if they are available. If chemicals must be purchased, check *Chem Sources*, which lists the chemicals manufactured by hundreds of chemical companies, or consult the *Aldrich Catalog* [A1] or another chemical catalog. If supplies need to be purchased, check *The VWR Scientific Products Catalog*, the *Fisher Catalog*, or another chemical supplies catalog. Your plans and procedures should be written up in detail in your laboratory notebook, summarized on a form like the one in Figure 1, and submitted to your instructor for approval.

Other aspects of scientific methodology previously listed—gathering and evaluating evidence, developing and testing hypotheses, and arriving at a conclusion—are described in the "Scientific Methodology" section of the Introduction

Your plans, ideas, experimental work, significant observations, results, and other aspects of your research should be recorded faithfully in your laboratory notebook.

Unless your instructor indicates otherwise, you should report your results as if they were to be published in a scientific journal—and they could be, since the results of undergraduate research projects are sometimes accepted for publication.

Suggested Research Projects

Many of these projects are open ended and can lead to further investigations not suggested in the outlines. Although some of them may not lead directly to new or unique contributions to the sum of chemical knowledge, others could yield hitherto unknown facts and new discoveries. Each project is outlined only briefly, so that you will have considerable latitude in developing and pursuing a course of action. Each project names one or more key references that will often include citations to other articles on the same subject.

1. Isolating and Testing a Natural Growth Inhibitor
Key Reference: *J. Chem. Educ.* **1977**, *54*, 156.

It has been speculated that juglone, a natural quinone that occurs in walnut trees, acts as a chemical defense agent for walnut seedlings, favoring their growth at the expense of competing species, particularly plants of the heath family (genus *Ericaceae*). You could isolate juglone or another substance that affects plant growth from a natural source and test its effect on the growth of various species or varieties of plants. Such substances could also be modified chemically to see what effect, if any, the modifications have on their growth-regulating properties.

juglone

Name _____ Date Submitted _____

Name of Project _____

Describe the scientific problem and indicate its significance.

State what you expect to accomplish and, in general terms, how you plan to accomplish it.

Describe, in approximate chronological order, specific experiments you expect to perform. In each case, give a rough estimate of the time you expect each experiment to take.

Describe any special chemicals, supplies, and equipment that will be needed. If any must be purchased, estimate their cost.

Approved by (mentor) _____ on (date) _____

Figure 1 Research project summary page

2. Analysis of an Essential Oil

Key References: *J. Chem. Educ.* **1994**, *71*, A146. *J. Chem. Educ.* **1969**, *46*, 846.

Essential oils can be obtained from many plants by steam distillation, expression, and other isolation techniques. They can also be purchased in some health food stores and other stores that sell herbs and new-age supplies. You could obtain an essential oil and analyze it by gas chromatography to see if it contains a few major components that might be easily separated and identified. Its components could be separated by preparative gas chromatography, preparative high-performance liquid chromatography (HPLC), or another method. You may then be able to identify one or more components by infrared (IR) spectrometry, nuclear magnetic resonance (NMR) spectrometry, gas chromatography–mass spectrometry (GC–MS), or some other spectrometric method.

3. Medicinal Components of Indigenous Wild Plants

Key References: S. Foster and J. A. Duke, *A Field Guide to Medicinal Plants: Eastern and Central North America* (Boston: Houghton Mifflin, 1990). R. Ikan, *Natural Products: A Laboratory Guide,* 2nd ed. (San Diego: Academic Press, 1991).

Many indigenous wild plants were used by Native Americans for medicine, and some still have medicinal uses. You could select a plant that appears to show significant pharmacological activity and attempt to isolate and identify one or more of its components. Keep in mind that the plant you select must be abundant enough to provide the large amounts of plant material that may be needed. In some cases, it may be possible to isolate major components by extraction or steam distillation, analyze them by gas chromatography, separate one or more components using basic laboratory operations, and identify them by IR or NMR spectrometry. But because most plants contain many diverse and complex constituents, it may be necessary to use advanced instrumental methods, such as HPLC or GC–MS, to separate and identify the components of a species you have selected. Unless you have access to such instruments, you may have to analyze the essential oils or extracts of several different species using gas chromatography or HPLC until you find one that is simple enough to work with.

4. The Effect of Molecular Modification on Odor

Key References: *J. Chem. Educ.* **1992**, *69*, A43. R. W. Moncrieff, *The Chemical Senses,* 3rd ed. (Cleveland, Ohio: CRC Press, 1967).

Relatively minor modifications in molecular structure can have drastic and often unpredictable effects on odor. Select an organic compound that has a discernible odor and two or more functional groups, such as *trans*-cinnamaldehyde or 4'-hydroxyacetophenone, and modify its molecules in various ways to find out how such modifications affect its odor.

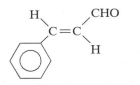

trans-cinnamaldehyde

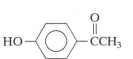

4'-hydroxyacetophenone

$$CH_3$$
$$|$$
$$CH_3OCCH_3$$
$$|$$
$$CH_3$$
MTBE

Note that the presence of several functional groups may cause complications in certain reactions unless one of them is protected. See *Protective Groups in Organic Synthesis* [B10] or a related source for information about the use of protective groups.

5. Gas Chromatographic Analysis of Gasoline
Key References: *J. Chem. Educ.* **1998**, *75*, 1595. *J. Chem. Educ.* **1976**, *53*, 51.

The compositions of different grades of gasoline and gasoline from different suppliers can vary considerably. Most gas stations label their gasoline accurately, but a few have been known to sell unleaded regular gasoline as premium gasoline, at premium prices. Some suppliers add certain oxygenates (oxygen-containing components) to their gasoline, such as methyl *t*-butyl ether (MTBE), which is a subject of environmental concern. You can analyze samples of gasoline from different sources by gas chromatography to look for oxygenates or for differences in their gas chromatographic hydrocarbon profile.

6. Stereochemistry of Addition Reactions
Key Reference: *J. Chem. Educ.* **1990**, *67*, 554.

Most bromine addition reactions appear to proceed through a bromonium ion intermediate that yields *anti* addition exclusively, but certain unsaturated substrates, such as *trans*-anethole, yield substantial amounts of *syn* addition products. You can investigate the effect of substrate structure on stereochemistry by selecting one or more unsaturated compounds, carrying out a bromine addition reaction, and analyzing the product. You can explore the effect of reaction conditions on stereochemistry by using different brominating reagents, varying the solvent, or varying the reaction temperature. You might also extend your study to stereoselective reactions other than bromine addition.

7. Alkylation of a Bidentate Nucleophile
Key Reference: *J. Chem. Educ.* **1990**, *67*, 611.

Under different reaction conditions, the alkylation of sodium saccharin with ethyl iodide can yield varying proportions of *N*-ethylsaccharin and *O*-ethylsaccharin.

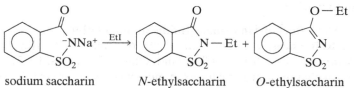

sodium saccharin   *N*-ethylsaccharin   *O*-ethylsaccharin

You can explore the effects of different factors, such as the metal cation, alkylating agent, substrate, reaction temperature, and use of a phase-transfer catalyst, on the product composition. You should analyze the product by HPLC, NMR, or some other instrumental method.

Bridged intermediate in
the pinacol rearrangement

8. Migratory Aptitudes of Aryl Groups
Key Reference: *J. Chem. Educ.* **1971**, *48*, 257.

The pinacol rearrangement involves the migration of an alkyl or aryl group, presumably by means of a bridged intermediate. You can investigate the factors that contribute to migratory aptitude by preparing pinacols in which either of two different groups (R and R′) can migrate and analyzing the products of their pinacol rearrangement reactions. By carrying out a reasonable number of reactions using carefully selected substrates, you should be able to arrange different groups in order of their migratory aptitude. The pinacols can be prepared from appropriate ketones and the products analyzed by NMR, gas chromatography, or another instrumental method.

9. Stability of Endocyclic and Exocyclic Double Bonds
Key Reference: *J. Chem. Educ.* **1973**, *50*, 372.

The stability of an alkene depends on the number of alkyl substituents attached to the double-bonded carbon atoms. In general, the more alkyl substituents there are, the more stable the alkene. The stability of a cyclic alkene can also vary with the location of the double bond; in general, double bonds that are within the ring (*endo*) are more stable than those external to the ring but involving a ring carbon (*exo*). You can investigate the stability of *exo* double bonds in one or more ring systems by carrying out elimination reactions (such as dehydration or dehydrohalogenation) on *tertiary* substrates (**1**) that can yield both *endo* and *exo* double bonds without rearrangement. By varying certain features of the substrate, such as the ring size and the kinds of substituents on the starred carbon atom, you can explore the factors that affect double-bond stability. Alcohol substrates can be made by Grignard reactions with cyclic ketones; alkyl halides and other substrates can be made from the alcohols. The products can be analyzed by gas chromatography, HPLC, NMR, or another appropriate method.

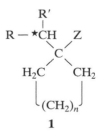

1

Note: R, R′ can be alkyl, aryl, or hydrogen; Z is a leaving group such as OH or Br.

10. Synthesis and Activity of an Insect Pheromone
Key References: *J. Chem. Educ.* **1991**, *68*, 71. *J. Chem. Educ.* **1986**, *63*, 1014. *J. Chem. Educ.* **1984**, *61*, 927.

Insect pheromones are "chemical messengers" that attract other insects for mating, inform them of danger, help them find their way, and perform a variety of other functions. A number of pheromone syntheses are reported in the chemical literature. You can select a pheromone that interests you, synthesize it, and test its effect on the target insect (if you can obtain specimens). You may also be able to determine whether one stereoisomer is more effective than another or than a racemic mixture of the pheromone, and you can investigate the effect of impurities or molecular modifications on the activity of a pheromone.

11. Effect of Phase-Transfer Catalysts on a Reaction
Key References: E. V. Dehmlow and S. S. Dehmlow, *Phase Transfer Catalysis,* 3rd ed. (New York: VCH, 1993). W. P. Weber and G. W. Gokel, *Phase Transfer Catalysis in Organic Synthesis* (New York: Springer-Verlag, 1977).

Phase-transfer catalysts accelerate many two-phase reactions by helping reactants or intermediates cross the phase boundary and come into contact with one another. You should select an organic reaction that is carried out in two phases, preferably one for which phase-transfer catalysis hasn't been investigated extensively. Perform one or more examples of the reaction, with and without a quaternary ammonium or phosphonium salt, to see whether or not the onium salt catalyzes the reaction. If it does, you can use different onium salts and observe their effects on the reaction rate to determine their relative catalytic effectiveness. You can also vary substrates, solvents, and other factors to observe the effect of such changes.

12. Synthesis of a New Organic Compound
Key Reference: *J. Amer. Chem. Soc.* **1974**, *94*, 4024.

To prove the structure of α-pinene, Adolf von Baeyer started by oxidizing it to pinonic acid with potassium permanganate. This reaction has been shown to proceed in high yield using "purple benzene," a solution of potassium permanganate in benzene that contains a crown ether.

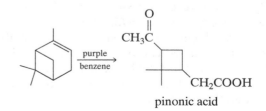

pinonic acid

Pinonic acid is a relatively uncommon compound containing two reactive functional groups. It should therefore be possible, using it as the starting material, to prepare a completely new organic compound—one that has never been reported in the chemical literature (you will need to conduct a thorough literature search to establish this). Benzene is hazardous, and the crown ether needed to make purple benzene is quite expensive, so you should develop an alternative procedure for preparing pinonic acid. Note that some reagents may react with both of its functional groups unless one of them is protected. See *Protective Groups in Organic Synthesis* [B10] or a related source for information about the use of protective groups. Your new compound should not be a simple functional-group derivative (such as an ester or a phenylhydrazone) of pinonic acid; its preparation should require at least two synthetic steps. Once you have synthesized and purified the new compound, you will need to prove its structure by spectrometric or chemical methods, or both.

DIRECTIONS

Research projects are intended for advanced or honors students who have mastered the major laboratory operations required. These directions only furnish general guidelines to help you complete your project. You must provide the procedural details and have them approved by your instructor. Keep detailed notes of your work and observations.

Safety Notes

Except when you have reliable information to the contrary, assume that all chemicals you will use are flammable and are hazardous by ingestion, inhalation, and skin absorption. Wear gloves and use a hood whenever possible, avoid contact with the chemicals, do not breathe their dust or vapors, and keep them away from ignition sources and other chemicals that might react with them.

Begin your research project by following the plan and procedures you have developed. Keep in mind that you are venturing into unknown territory, so your results may not turn out as you planned. If so, try to benefit from unexpected outcomes by considering what you might learn from them. You may then decide to revise your research objectives in order to investigate your findings. In any case, be flexible enough to follow new leads or even switch to a different research project if your original research plan seems unproductive. Meet with your mentor regularly to discuss your findings and receive guidance. Provide him or her with duplicate copies of your lab notebook pages. Continue to read everything you can find that relates to your research; this may help you overcome a difficulty that has hampered your research or suggest new avenues for you to explore.

Waste Disposal: Dispose of wastes as directed by your instructor.

Report. Write up your report as if it were a scientific paper being submitted to a professional publication, such as the *Journal of Organic Chemistry*. Such papers are traditionally written in an impersonal, objective style using the passive voice (for instance, "The solution was stirred" rather than "I stirred the solution"). Your report should include the following items, unless your instructor directs otherwise:

1. A brief but descriptive title
2. Your name and affiliation
3. A brief abstract that summarizes the principal results of the work
4. An introductory section (usually untitled) that provides a concise statement of the purpose and possible applications of the work, supported by descriptions of related work from the literature
5. A section titled "Experimental Methods" that gives enough detail about your materials and methods that another experienced worker could repeat your work. Give current *Chemical Abstract* index names and registry numbers (see "The Chemical Literature"appendix) for important starting materials and the product, and provide information about their purity, if possible. Note any significant hazards and safety precautions in a separate paragraph labeled "Caution."
6. A section titled "Results and Discussion" (or two separate "Results" and "Discussion" sections) that summarizes the important experimental results and points out any special features, limitations, or implications of your work. You should include any data (including spectral parameters) that will help justify your conclusion. You may also wish to suggest different approaches to the problem or areas that require further study.
7. A section titled "Conclusions" that states any conclusions you can draw from your work, based on the evidence presented
8. A section titled "References" that gives complete citations for all literature sources referred to in the report

Your instructor may suggest additions to, or modifications of, this list. *The ACS Style Guide* [L16] provides a more detailed discussion of these components, as well as helpful suggestions about writing style.

Cleaning and Drying Glassware

Cleaning Glassware

Clean glassware is essential for good results in the organic chemistry laboratory. Even small amounts of impurities can sometimes inhibit chemical reactions, catalyze undesirable side reactions, or invalidate the results of chemical tests or rate studies. Always clean dirty glassware at the end of each laboratory period, or as soon as possible after the glassware is used. This way, your glassware will be clean and dry for the next experiment, and you will be ready to start work when you arrive. If you wait too long to clean glassware, residues may harden and become more resistant to cleaning agents; they may also attack the glass itself, weakening it and making future cleaning more difficult. It is particularly important to wash out strong bases such as sodium hydroxide promptly, because they can etch the glass permanently and cause glass joints to "freeze" tight. When glassware has been thoroughly cleaned, water applied to its inner surface should wet the whole surface and not form droplets or leave dry patches. However, used glassware that has been scratched or etched may not wet evenly.

You can clean most glassware adequately by vigorous scrubbing with hot water and a laboratory detergent such as Alconox, using a brush of appropriate size and shape to reach otherwise inaccessible spots. A plastic trough or another suitable container can serve as a dishpan. A tapered centrifuge-tube brush can be used to clean centrifuge tubes. A nylon mesh scrubber is useful for cleaning spatulas, stirring rods, beakers, and the outer surfaces of other glassware. Pipe cleaners or cotton swabs can be used to clean narrow funnel stems, eyedroppers, and so on.

Organic residues that can't be removed by detergent and water will often dissolve in organic solvents such as technical-grade acetone. (Never use reagent-grade solvents for washing.) For example, it is difficult—if not impossible—to scrub the inside of a porcelain Buchner or Hirsch funnel, but squirting a little acetone around the inside of the funnel stem and letting it drain through the porous plate should remove chemical residues that may have lodged there. Use acetone sparingly and recycle it after use (don't pour it down the drain), as it is much more costly than water and may harm the environment. Be certain that acetone is completely removed from glassware before you return it to a lab kit, because it will dissolve a foam lab-kit liner.

After washing, always rinse glassware thoroughly with water (a final distilled-water rinse is a good idea) and check it to see if the water wets its surface evenly rather than forming separate beads of water. If it doesn't pass this test, scrub it some more or use a cleaning solution such as Nochromix. Note that some well-used glassware may not pass the test because of surface damage, but it may still be clean enough to use after thorough scrubbing.

Drying Glassware

Always dry glassware thoroughly if it will be used with organic reactants and solvents under nonaqueous conditions. Don't waste time drying wet

From *Operational Organic Chemistry: A Problem Solving Approach to the Laboratory*, Fourth Edition, John W. Lehman. Copyright © 2009 by Pearson Education. Published by Prentice Hall. All rights reserved.

glassware if it will come into contact with water or an aqueous solution during an experiment. Just let it drain for a few minutes before you use it.

The easiest (and cheapest) way to dry glassware is to let it stand overnight in a position that allows easy drainage. You can dry the outer surfaces of glassware with a cloth or paper towel, but don't use a towel to dry any surfaces that will be in contact with chemicals because of the likelihood of contamination. If a piece of glassware is needed shortly after washing, drain it briefly to remove excess water, then rinse it with one or two small portions of wash acetone. Dry it in a stream of clean, dry air or put it in a drying oven for a few minutes. Compressed air from an air line may contain pump oil, moisture, and dirt, so don't use it directly from the line for drying. Air can be cleaned and dried as described in OP-27.

Take Care! Use tongs or heat-resistant gloves when handling hot glass.

Glassware that is to be used for a moisture-sensitive reaction must be dried very thoroughly before use. If possible, clean the glassware during the previous lab period, let it dry overnight or longer, and then dry it in an oven set at about 110°C for 20 to 30 minutes. Assemble the apparatus and attach one or more drying tubes (see OP-12a) as soon as possible after oven-drying; otherwise, moisture will condense inside it as it cools. If the glassware must be cleaned the same day it is used, rinse it with acetone after washing and flush it with clean, dry air before you put it in the oven. You can also dry glassware by passing a "cool" Bunsen burner flame over the surface of the assembled apparatus, but this practice should never be used in laboratories where volatile solvents such as diethyl ether are in use. It should be done only with the instructor's permission and according to his or her directions.

Using Specialized Glassware

Most specialized glassware components used in organic chemistry have rigid ground-glass joints called *standard-taper* joints. The size of a tapered joint is designated by two numbers, such as 19/22, in which the first number is the diameter at the top of the joint and the second is the length of the taper, measured in millimeters (see Figure A1).

Glassware from a commercial organic lab kit, or its equivalent purchased as separate parts, can be used to construct apparatus for many different laboratory operations. The glassware provided in a typical standard scale lab kit is illustrated in the "Laboratory Equipment" appendix. Setups for the various operations are illustrated in the appropriate operation descriptions in this book. For example, to find an illustration of a setup for fractional distillation, refer to operation OP-32.

Figure A1 19/22 standard-taper joint

Lubricating Joints

For some operations, such as vacuum distillation, glass joints should be lubricated with a suitable joint grease. For most other operations, lubrication of glass joints is unnecessary and may be undesirable. Your instructor should inform you if lubrication will be necessary. To lubricate a ground-glass joint, apply a thin layer of joint grease completely around the top half of the inner (male) joint. Do not lubricate the outer (female) joint. Be careful to keep grease away from the open end of the joint, where it may come into contact with and contaminate your reaction mixture or product. When you assemble the components, press the outer and inner joints together firmly, with a slight twist, to form a seal around the entire joint with no gaps. Grease should never extend beyond the joint inside the apparatus.

After disassembling the apparatus, remove the grease completely by using a suitable organic solvent. You can remove petroleum-based greases with petroleum ether or hexanes, and silicone greases by thorough cleaning with dichloromethane. An inner joint can be cleaned by wrapping a small amount of cotton loosely around the end of an applicator stick, dipping it in the solvent, and wiping the joint with the moist cotton.

Take Care! Keep flames away from petroleum ether and hexanes. Avoid contact with dichloromethane and do not breathe its vapors.

Assembling Glassware

Standard-taper joints are rigid, so a glassware apparatus must be assembled carefully to avoid strain that can result in breakage. First, place the necessary clamps and rings at appropriate locations on the ring stand (use two ring stands for distillation setups). Then assemble the apparatus *from the bottom up, starting at the heat source.* Position the heat source on a ring or other support so that it can be removed easily when the heating period is over; otherwise, it may continue to heat a reaction mixture or an empty distilling flask even after it is switched off, causing a danger of

From *Operational Organic Chemistry: A Problem Solving Approach to the Laboratory*, Fourth Edition, John W. Lehman. Copyright © 2009 by Pearson Education. Published by Prentice Hall. All rights reserved.

breakage, tar formation, or even an explosion. Clamp the reaction flask or boiling flask securely at the proper distance from the heat source.

As you add other components, clamp them to the ring stand(s), but don't tighten the clamp jaws completely until all of the components are in place and aligned properly. Use as many clamps as are necessary to provide adequate support for all parts of the apparatus. A vertical setup, such as the one for addition under reflux [OP-11], requires at least two clamps for security—if the setup is bumped, the clamp holding the reaction flask may rotate and deposit your glassware on the lab bench, with expensive consequences. Some vertical components, such as Claisen connecting tubes, need not be clamped if they are adequately supported by the component below. Non-vertical components, such as distillation condensers, should be clamped; otherwise, they may be jarred loose and fall. Clamping condensers and other components at an angle to a ring stand require an adjustable clamp with a wing nut on the shaft. This wing nut is tightened after the apparatus is aligned. Distillation receivers should be supported by a ring and wire gauze or another suitable support. They should not be clamped, because they may have to be replaced quickly during a distillation.

Some joints, such as the joint that connects a condenser to a vacuum adapter, tend to separate easily, so they should be held together with joint clips or strong rubber bands. For example, you can secure a vacuum adapter to a condenser by stretching a rubber band around the tubulation on both or by snapping a joint clip around the joint rim. Condensers and vacuum adapters should never be allowed to hang unsupported, even momentarily while you are assembling the apparatus.

Position the clamps so that all parts are aligned correctly and their glass joints slide together easily. Then seat the joints firmly—with a slight twist, if necessary—and tighten all the clamps. Examine the joints for gaps, then check to make sure that the apparatus is held securely by the clamp jaws and that the clamp holders are secured tightly to the ring stand(s).

Figure A2 summarizes the steps followed in assembling one kind of ground-glass apparatus. (Most of the glassware setups you will be using are less complex than the one illustrated.)

Disassembling Glassware

Disassemble (take apart) ground-joint glassware promptly after use, because joints that are left coupled for an extended period of time may freeze together and become difficult or impossible to separate without breakage. Ground joints can usually be separated by pulling the components apart with a twisting motion. If a joint is frozen, you can sometimes loosen it by tapping it gently with the handle of a wooden-handled spatula or by applying steam to the joint while rotating the apparatus slowly, and then pulling the components apart with a twisting motion. If this doesn't work, see your instructor. Clean [OP-1] the glassware thoroughly and return each component to its proper location in the lab kit or to the stockroom.

Take Care! The glass may break, so protect your hands with heavy gloves.

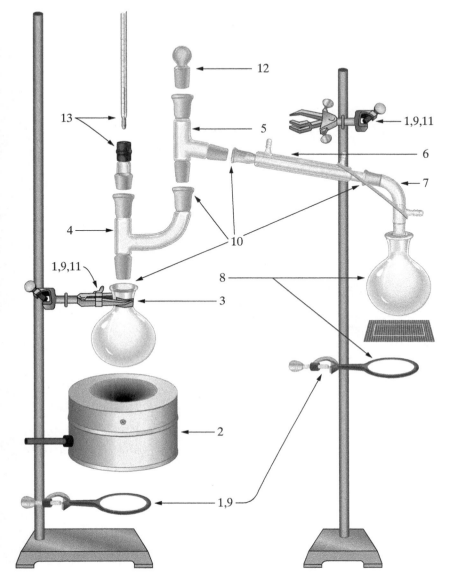

12

13

1,9,11

5

6

7

4

10

1,9,11

8

3

2

1,9

Steps

1. Position clamps, rings.
2. Position heat source.
3. Clamp boiling flask securely.
4., 5. Add Claisen adapter and connecting adapter.
6. Clamp West condenser in place.
7. Attach vacuum adapter with rubber band or spring clamp.
8. Attach receiving flask, support with ring and wire gauze.
9. Readjust all clamps to align parts.
10. Press joints together.
11. Tighten clamps.
12. Add stopper.
13. Add thermometer adapter and position thermometer.

Figure A2 Steps in the assembly of a ground-glass apparatus

Using Glass Rod and Tubing

Glass connecting tubes, stirring rods, and other simple glass items are required for certain operations in organic chemistry. Soft-glass rod and tubing can be worked easily with a Bunsen burner, but borosilicate glass (Pyrex, Kimax, etc.) requires the hotter flame provided by a Meker-type burner or an oxygen torch. To distinguish borosilicate from soft glass, dip the glass into anhydrous glycerol; most (but not all) borosilicate glass will seem to disappear in the liquid because it has nearly the same refractive index (see OP-35) as glycerol ($n_D^{20} = 1.475$).

Cutting Glass Rod and Tubing

Glass rods and tubes are cut by scoring them at the desired location and snapping them in two. Score the rod or tube by drawing a sharp triangular file (or other glass-scoring tool) across the surface at a right angle to the axis of the tubing. Often, only a single stroke is needed to make a deep scratch in the surface; don't use the file like a saw. To cut a thin, fragile glass tube, such as a melting-point tube or the capillary tip of a Pasteur pipet, it's best to use a special glass scorer, but a sharp triangular file may work if applied carefully so as not to crush the glass. Moisten the scratch with water or saliva. Using a towel or gloves to protect your hands, place your thumbs about 1 cm apart on the side opposite the scratch and, while holding the glass firmly in both hands, press forward against the glass with your thumbs as you rotate your wrists outward (Figure A3).

Working Glass Rod and Tubing

The cut ends of a glass rod or tube should always be *fire-polished* to remove sharp edges and prevent accidental cuts. To fire-polish a glass rod or tube, hold it at a 45° angle to a burner flame (see OP-7a for directions on using a burner) and rotate its cut end slowly in the flame until the edge becomes rounded and smooth (Figure A4).

To round the cut end of a glass rod, rotate the rod in a burner flame, holding it at a 45° angle with its tip at the inner blue cone of the flame. The end should be hemispherical in shape, not rounded only at the edges and flat on the bottom.

To flatten one end of a glass rod, rotate it with its tip at the inner blue cone of the flame until it is incandescent and very soft, but not starting to bend. Then press the softened end straight down onto a hard surface, such as the base of a ring stand. The flattened end should be well centered and about twice the diameter of the rod.

To seal one end of a glass tube, hold the tube at a 45° angle to the burner, with its end just above the inner blue cone of the flame, and rotate it until the soft edges come together and eventually merge. Remove the tube from the flame as soon as it is closed and immediately blow into the open end to obtain a sealed end of uniform thickness. Let the tube cool to room temperature. Then check it for leaks by connecting the open end to an aspirator or

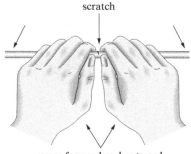

Figure A3 Breaking glass tubing

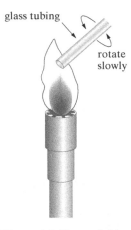

Figure A4 Fire polishing

Take Care! Don't burn yourself on the hot end of a glass rod or tube, or lay the glass onto combustible materials.

From *Operational Organic Chemistry: A Problem Solving Approach to the Laboratory*, Fourth Edition, John W. Lehman. Copyright © 2009 by Pearson Education. Published by Prentice Hall. All rights reserved.

Take Care! Avoid contact with dichloromethane and do not breathe its vapors.

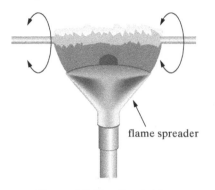

Figure A5 Bending tubing

Safety Notes

Cork borer

Figure A6 A cork borer

Take Care! Don't grasp the tube too far from the stopper. The glass may break and lacerate your hand.

a vacuum line with a length of rubber tubing, placing the closed end in a test tube that contains a small amount of dichloromethane, and turning on the vacuum. If the tube isn't properly sealed, the liquid will leak into it when you apply suction. To seal the end of a thin, fragile tube such as a melting-point capillary, rotate its open end in the *outer* edge of the flame.

To bend glass tubing, first place a flame spreader on the barrel of a Bunsen burner (or use a Meker-type burner). Hold the tubing over the burner flame parallel to the long axis of the flame spreader, and rotate it constantly at a slow, even rate until it is nearly soft enough to bend under its own weight (see Figure A5). (The flame will turn yellow as the glass begins to soften.) Remove the hot tubing from the flame and immediately bend it to the desired shape with a firm, even motion and a minimum of force (if much force is required, the glass isn't soft enough). Bend it in a vertical plane, with the ends up and the bend at the bottom; the bend should follow a smooth curve with no constrictions.

Inserting Glass Items into Stoppers

Improper insertion of glass tubes and thermometers through stoppers is one of the most frequent causes of laboratory accidents. The resulting cuts and puncture wounds can be severe, requiring medical treatment and sometimes causing the victim to go into shock. Thermometers are particularly easy to break, especially at the scored immersion line.

Sometimes you may have to insert a glass tube through a hole bored in a cork or rubber stopper. To bore a hole in a solid stopper, obtain a *sharp* cork borer (Figure A6) that is slightly smaller in diameter than the object to be inserted in the stopper. (If the borer is dull, use a special cork-borer sharpener to sharpen it.) Lubricate its cutting edge with a small amount of glycerine, and then *twist* it through the stopper using a minimum of force (don't try to "punch" out the hole). Rotate the borer and stopper in opposite directions, checking the alignment frequently to make sure that the borer is going in straight. When the borer is about halfway through, twist it out and start boring from the opposite end of the stopper until the holes meet. You can remove the plug left inside the cork borer with a rod that comes with a set of cork borers.

To insert a glass tube into a rubber stopper, first lubricate the hole lightly with glycerol or another suitable lubricant; water may work if the hole is not too tight. You can use a cotton swab or an applicator stick to apply the lubricant evenly. Protect your hands with gloves or a towel, then grasp the tube close to the stopper and twist it through the hole with firm, steady pressure. Apply force directly along the axis of the tube, because any sideways force may cause it to break. Using excessive force or forcing the tube through a hole too small for it can also cause it to break. After the tube is correctly positioned, rinse off any glycerol with water. Follow the same directions to insert a thermometer through a rubber stopper or a thermometer adapter cap.

To remove a glass tube from a stopper, lubricate the part of the glass that will pass through the stopper with water or glycerol, protect your hands with gloves or a towel, and twist the tube out with a firm, continuous motion. Hold the tube close to the stopper or cap and avoid applying any sideways force that could cause it to break. If you can't remove the tube by this method, obtain a cork borer of a size that will just fit around it, lubricate the borer's cutting edge, and twist it gently through the stopper until the tube can be pulled out easily. (Follow the same directions to remove a thermometer from a thermometer adapter cap.)

Weighing

Most chemistry laboratories are equipped with electronic balances that display the mass directly, without any preliminary adjustments (Figure A7). If you will be using a different type of balance, your instructor will demonstrate its operation. For many organic chemistry experiments, balances that measure to the nearest centigram (0.01 g) are acceptable, but milligram balances are preferable. Most products obtained from a preparation are transferred to vials or other small containers, which should be *tared*—weighed empty—and

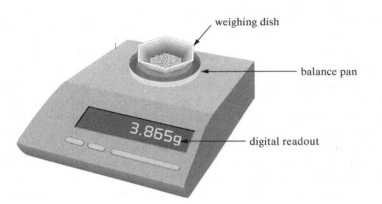

weighing dish

balance pan

3.865g

digital readout

Figure A7 An electronic balance

then reweighed after the product has been added. As a rule, the container should be weighed with its cap and label on, and this *tare mass* recorded.

A balance is a precision instrument that can easily be damaged by contaminants, so avoid spilling chemicals on the balance pan or on the balance itself. If spillage does occur, *clean it up immediately*. If you spill a liquid or corrosive solid on any part of the balance, notify your instructor as well. Before you leave the balance area, replace the caps on all reagent bottles, return them to their proper locations (if you obtained them elsewhere), and ensure that the area around the balance is clean and orderly.

Weighing Solids

Solids can be weighed in glass containers (such as vials or beakers), in aluminum or plastic weighing dishes, or on glazed weighing papers. Solid reactants are usually weighed on glazed paper or in weighing dishes and then transferred to the reaction flask. When it is important to avoid losses, however, solids should be measured directly into the reaction vessel. Hygroscopic solids, those that absorb moisture from the atmosphere, should be weighed in screw-cap vials or other containers that can be capped immediately after the solid is added. Filter paper and other absorbent papers should not be used for weighing, because a few particles will always remain in the fibers of the paper.

From *Operational Organic Chemistry: A Problem Solving Approach to the Laboratory*, Fourth Edition, John W. Lehman. Copyright © 2009 by Pearson Education. Published by Prentice Hall. All rights reserved.

To weigh a sample of a solid that is in a tared container, such as a preweighed screw-cap vial, set the digital readout to zero by pressing the appropriate button, and then place the container on the balance pan. Be sure that the draft shield (if there is one) is in place, then read the mass of the container and its contents from the digital display. Wait until the reading remains constant, and then record the mass in your laboratory notebook; include all digits after the decimal point. For example, if the balance reads 3.610 g, don't record the mass as 3.61 g, because zeroes following the decimal point are significant. Then subtract the tare mass to obtain the mass of the solid.

To weigh a sample of a solid that is to be transferred to another container, such as a weighing dish or a storage vial, place the container on the balance pan, press the tare button to zero the digital display, and transfer the solid to the container. With the draft shield in place, wait until the reading has stabilized and then read the mass of the sample directly from the digital display.

To measure out a specific quantity of a solid—such as a solid reactant—into a reaction flask or another container, first support the container on the balance pan and press the tare button to zero the digital display. Then use a spatula or Scoopula to add the solid in small portions until the desired mass appears on the digital display. With the draft shield in place, wait until the reading has stabilized and then read the mass of the sample directly from the digital display. Ordinarily you need not measure out the exact mass specified in a procedure, but try not to deviate from the specified mass by more than 2% or so, especially for a limiting reactant. Because the theoretical yield of a preparation is based on the actual mass of a starting material, always use your measured mass—not the mass you calculated for the prelab assignment—for yield calculations.

For example, if a procedure requires 2.50 g of a limiting reactant, you should measure out between 2.45 g and 2.55 g of the reactant.

Weighing Liquids

Organic liquids should be weighed in screw-cap vials or other closed containers to prevent damage to the balance from accidental spillage and losses by evaporation. If liquid must be added to or removed from a weighed container, the container should be removed from the balance pan first. Any excess liquid should be placed in a waste container or otherwise disposed of—*not* returned to a stock bottle.

To measure the mass of a liquid sample in a tared or untared container, follow the directions for solids, but be sure to keep the container capped while it's on the balance pan. When using a tared container, subtract the tare mass to obtain the mass of the liquid.

To measure out a specific mass of a liquid from a reagent bottle, you should first measure the approximate quantity of the liquid by volume and then weigh that quantity accurately in an appropriate closed container. For example, if you need 3.71 g of 1-butanol (d = 0.810 g/mL) for an experiment, you can use a small graduated cylinder or a measuring pipet to measure [OP-5] about 4.6 mL (3.71 g ÷ 0.810 g/mL) of the liquid into a tared container, then cap and weigh the container and liquid. (The balance can first be zeroed with the container and its cap on the balance pan—don't forget to include the cap!) If the measured mass isn't close enough to 3.71 g, add or remove liquid with a clean Pasteur pipet or medicine dropper.

Take Care! Be careful not to spill liquids on the balance pan. If you do, clean up the spill immediately and inform your instructor.

Always weigh liquid limiting reactants! Volume measurements are far less accurate than weight measurements.

Measuring Volume

Several different kinds of volume-measuring devices are used in the undergraduate organic chemistry laboratory. Relatively large volumes of liquids are generally measured using graduated cylinders whose capacity may vary from 10 mL to 100 mL or more. Smaller volumes of liquids can be measured using various kinds of pipets and syringes. Reagent bottles containing liquids may be provided with bottle-top dispensers that measure out a preset volume of the liquid. For a few experiments, you may use a buret or a volumetric flask; their use is described in most general chemistry laboratory manuals.

Graduated Cylinders

Graduated cylinders aren't highly accurate, but they are often used to measure specified quantities of solvents and wash liquids, or even some liquid reactants that are used in excess.

To use a graduated cylinder, transfer the liquid being measured to the cylinder—by pouring it or by using a Pasteur pipet—until the cylinder is filled to the graduation mark corresponding to the desired volume. Read the liquid volume from the bottom of the meniscus, as shown in Figure A8. If necessary, add or remove liquid with a Pasteur pipet.

Bottle-Top Dispensers

A typical adjustable bottle-top dispenser (see Figure A9) has a moveable plunger that pumps liquid into a glass cylinder, from which it is dispensed through a discharge tube. The cylinder is usually surrounded by a protective sleeve that is raised to fill the cylinder and lowered to dispense the liquid. The dispenser is screwed onto a bottle containing the liquid and adjusted to dispense a specified volume of liquid, which is read from a scale on the sleeve or cylinder. Before its initial use, the dispenser must be *primed* by pumping it several times to fill the cylinder and discharge tube, and to expel any air bubbles.

To use a bottle-top dispenser, first check to see that there are no air bubbles in the discharge tube (if there are, prime the dispenser or inform your instructor). Then hold your container underneath the discharge tube outlet and raise the sleeve as high as it will go. Release the sleeve so that it drops by gravity, and then push it down gently until it moves no further. Touch the tip of the discharge tube to an inside wall of your container to remove the last drop of liquid. If the liquid is the limiting reactant for a preparation, you should then weigh it accurately (as described in OP-4).

Measuring Pipets and Volumetric Pipets

A *measuring pipet* has a graduated scale and is used to measure liquid volumes within a range of values; for example, a typical 1-mL measuring pipet can measure volumes up to 1.00 mL to the nearest 0.01 mL. A *volumetric pipet* measures only a single volume, but it is more accurate than a measuring

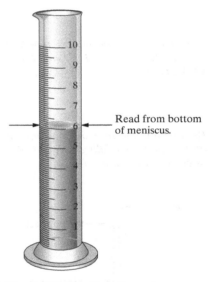

Read from bottom of meniscus.

Figure A8 Reading the volume contained in a graduated cylinder—in this case, 6.0 mL

Pipets and syringes are a common cause of contamination, so never allow a liquid to be sucked into a rubber bulb or pipet pump, and clean [OP-1] all pipets and syringes thoroughly after use.

From *Operational Organic Chemistry: A Problem Solving Approach to the Laboratory*, Fourth Edition, John W. Lehman. Copyright © 2009 by Pearson Education. Published by Prentice Hall. All rights reserved.

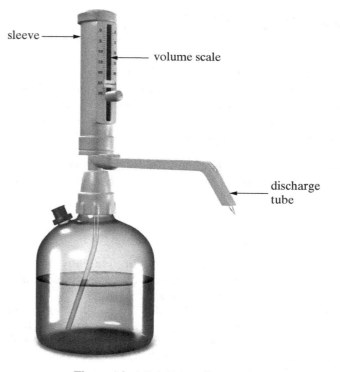

Figure A9 A bottle-top dispenser

A convenient "homemade" pipetting bulb is described in J. Chem. Educ. **1974**, *51*, 467.

Be careful not to raise the pipet tip out of the liquid while filling a pipet by this or any other method.

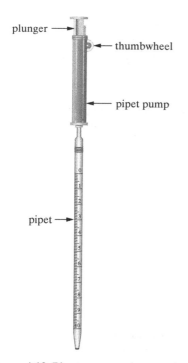

Figure A10 Pipet pump and measuring pipet

pipet. Suction is required to draw the liquid into a measuring or volumetric pipet, but you should never use mouth suction because of the danger of ingesting toxic or corrosive liquids. A pipet pump is a simple and convenient suction device for filling such pipets. Other pipet fillers, such as large rubber bulbs, can also be used.

To use a measuring pipet with a pipet pump of the type shown in Figure A10, first see that the plunger is as far down as it will go. Then insert the wide (untapered) end of the pipet firmly into the opening at the bottom of the pump. Place the tip of the pipet in the liquid and rotate the front of the thumbwheel downward (moving your thumb back toward you) until the liquid meniscus rises a few millimeters above the zero graduation mark; be careful not to draw any liquid into the pump itself. Slowly rotate the front of the thumbwheel upward (moving your thumb away from you) until the meniscus drops just to the zero mark. Measure the desired volume of liquid into a clean container by placing the pipet tip over the container and rotating the thumbwheel upward until the meniscus drops to the graduation mark corresponding to the desired volume (Figure A11). Touch the tip of the pipet to the inside of the container to remove any adherent drop of liquid. If the pipet is one dedicated for use with a particular reagent bottle, the excess liquid can be drained into the bottle by depressing the pump's quick-release lever (if it has one) or by rotating the thumbwheel upward as far as it will go. Otherwise, the excess liquid should be drained into another container or disposed of as directed by your instructor.

To use a volumetric pipet, obtain a bulb-type pipet filler or a pipet pump with a quick-release lever that allows the liquid to drain by gravity.

Use the bulb or pump to fill the volumetric pipet to its calibration mark, hold the pipet tip over a receiving container, and use the quick-release lever or another device to let the liquid drain out until only a small amount of liquid is left in the tip. Touch the tip of the pipet to the inside of the container to remove any adherent drop of liquid, but do *not* expel the liquid in the pipet tip—its volume is accounted for when the pipet is calibrated.

Automatic Pipets

Automatic pipets (also called *pipetters*) provide a quick, convenient way to deliver a specified volume of liquid with a high degree of reproducibility (Figure A12). Most automatic pipets measure comparatively small volumes of liquids and are therefore most useful for small-scale experiments. A variable-volume automatic pipet can be set to a specified volume within a certain range of volumes, such as 100–1000 μL (0.100–1.000 mL). The volume is displayed on a digital display or an analog scale, usually in microliters (μL) To prevent contamination, liquid is drawn into a disposable tip and never inside the pipet itself. Whenever the pipet is used for a different liquid, the volume is reset (if necessary) and a new pipet tip is installed. The instructor or a lab assistant will ordinarily set the volume of an automatic pipet and designate it for a specific liquid. Do *not* try to reset the volume or use the pipet for a different liquid without explicit permission from your instructor.

To use an automatic pipet, depress the plunger to the first *detent* (stop) position, when you will feel resistance to further movement. (Using excessive force will move the plunger to its second detent position, causing an inaccurate measurement.) Insert the pipet tip into the liquid to a depth of

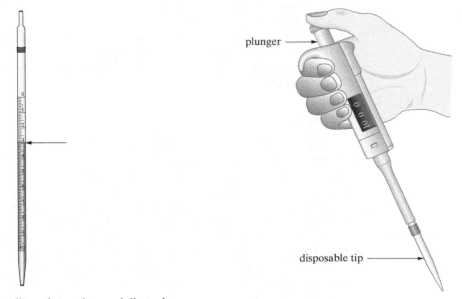

plunger

disposable tip

Figure A11 Reading the volume delivered from a measuring pipet—in this case, 3.0 mL

Figure A12 An automatic pipet

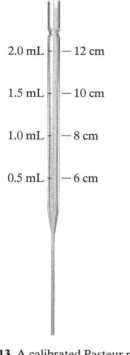

2.0 mL — 12 cm

1.5 mL — 10 cm

1.0 mL — 8 cm

0.5 mL — 6 cm

Figure A13 A calibrated Pasteur pipet

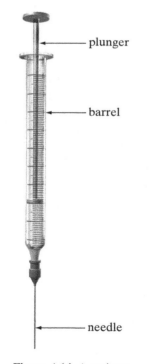

plunger

barrel

needle

Figure A14 A syringe

Take Care! Don't stick yourself with the needle!

about 1 cm or less; don't let it touch the bottom of the liquid's container, where impurities may be concentrated. Slowly release the plunger to draw liquid into the pipet tip. Place the tip inside the receiving container and depress the plunger to the first detent position; pause for a second or two, then push the plunger down to the second detent position and touch the tip to the inner wall of the receiving container to expel the last droplet of liquid.

Calibrated Pasteur Pipets

A calibrated Pasteur pipet (Figure A13) can be used for very approximate measurements of small volumes of liquids. To calibrate a Pasteur pipet, first attach a latex rubber bulb to its wide end. Measure 0.50 mL of water into a small test tube using a measuring pipet or another accurate measuring device. Carefully draw all the liquid into the Pasteur pipet so that there are no air bubbles in its tip (if necessary, squeeze the bulb *gently* to expel any air) and mark the position of the meniscus with an indelible glass-marking pen. Expel all the water and repeat this operation using 1.00 mL of water, and other volumes as desired.

A quicker but less accurate way to calibrate a short ($5\frac{3}{4}$ inch) Pasteur pipet is to use a ruler to mark lines at distances of 6 cm, 8 cm, 10 cm, and 12 cm from the narrow (capillary) tip of the pipet. These lines mark volumes of approximately 0.5 mL, 1.0 mL, 1.5 mL, and 2.0 mL. Make sure that the capillary tip is intact; if part of it is broken off, this calibration method won't work.

To use a calibrated pipet, hold the pipet (with its attached bulb) vertically over the liquid to be measured, squeeze the bulb to expel some of the air (ideally, an amount of air nearly equal to the volume of liquid required), and insert the tip in the liquid. With practice, you should learn how far to squeeze the bulb in order to draw in the desired amount of liquid. Then release the bulb until the liquid meniscus is at the level of the appropriate calibration mark. Without delay, raise the pipet tip out of the liquid, move it into position over the receiving container, and squeeze the bulb to expel all the liquid into the container. It takes practice to transfer the liquid without losing some in the process, so read OP-6 for additional tips about the use of Pasteur pipets.

Syringes

A syringe (Figure A14) can be used to measure and deliver small volumes of liquid, often by inserting its needle through a *septum*—a rubber or plastic disk that can be penetrated by a needle but that remains more-or-less airtight after the needle is withdrawn. Syringes of appropriate sizes can be used to inject liquid samples into a gas chromatograph, and to introduce liquids into some types of sample cells for infrared spectrometry.

To fill a syringe, hold it vertically, with the needle pointing down; then place the needle tip in the liquid and slowly pull out the plunger until the barrel contains a little more than the required volume of liquid. If there are air bubbles in the liquid, remove them by holding the syringe vertically—with the needle pointing up—and tapping the barrel with your fingernail, or by expelling the liquid and filling the syringe again, more slowly. Hold the syringe so that the needle is pointing up; slowly push in the plunger to eject the excess liquid until the bottom of the liquid column is at the appropriate graduation mark. Wipe off the tip of the needle with a tissue, place the needle tip into the receiving vessel or through a septum, and expel the liquid by gently pushing the plunger in as far as it will go. Clean the syringe immediately after use by flushing it repeatedly with an appropriate solvent, such as acetone, or a soap solution. If you use soap for washing, rinse the syringe thoroughly with water afterward. Dry the syringe by pumping the plunger several times to expel excess solvent. Then remove the plunger to let the barrel dry. If the syringe is to be used again soon you can dry it by drawing air through the barrel with an aspirator or a vacuum line.

Take Care! Don't bend the plunger.

Making Transfers

In many organic syntheses, losses during transfers constitute a substantial part of the total product loss, so they can have a major impact on your yield. Such losses can occur whenever you transfer a liquid or a solid from one container to another, whether the original container is a stock bottle, reaction flask, beaker, or funnel.

Transferring Solids

Bulk solids (such as those from a lab stock bottle) can be transferred from one container to another using spatulas of various shapes and sizes (Figure A15). A Scoopula is usually preferred because it is curved to help keep the solid from sliding off. A flat-bladed spatula will also work, but unless you are careful, some of the solid may spill over its sides.

Solids can be conveniently transferred to small-mouthed containers such as test tubes and storage vials using a folded square of weighing paper or a square plastic weighing dish as a makeshift funnel. To transfer a solid from a plastic weighing dish, hold opposite corners of the dish between your thumb and middle finger and bend the dish to form a "spout" from which you can pour out or scrape out the solid. During such transfers, place the receiving container on a square of weighing paper or in a weighing dish (or clamp it above the paper or dish) so that any solid that misses the container can be recovered. If the solid you are transferring sticks to the sides of its container (such as a reaction vial or a Buchner funnel), use a flexible flat-bladed spatula to scrape as much as you can off the sides. If you need to transfer the last traces of a solid, you can dissolve the residual solid in a volatile solvent, make the transfer, and evaporate the solvent as described next for liquid transfers.

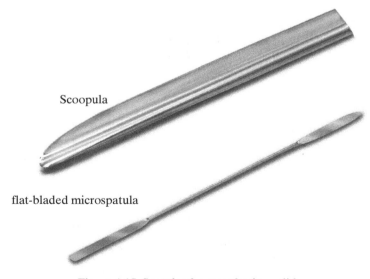

Scoopula

flat-bladed microspatula

Figure A15 Spatulas for transferring solids

From *Operational Organic Chemistry: A Problem Solving Approach to the Laboratory*, Fourth Edition, John W. Lehman. Copyright © 2009 by Pearson Education. Published by Prentice Hall. All rights reserved.

Transferring Liquids

In most standard scale work, liquid transfers are accomplished by *decanting* (pouring) the liquid from its original container into another container. When transferring small volumes of liquids, it may be preferable to use a Pasteur pipet fitted with a latex rubber bulb. Volatile liquids such as dichloromethane tend to partially vaporize during a transfer (especially on a warm day or when the pipet is warmed by your hand), causing some of the liquid to spurt out of the tip of the pipet. You should be able to avoid this problem by drawing in and expelling the liquid several times to fill the pipet with solvent vapors before you use it for the transfer. Alternatively, you can use a *filter-tip pipet*. To make a filter-tip pipet, obtain a *very* small wisp of clean cotton, roll it into a loose ball, and use a straight length of thin (~20 gauge) copper wire to push it past the narrow neck of a $5\frac{3}{4}$-inch Pasteur pipet into its capillary end. Hold the pipet with the capillary tip pointed up as you use the wire to push the cotton as close to the tip of the pipet as you can (see Figure A16). If the cotton ball is too large, it will get hopelessly stuck in the capillary and you will have to start over with another pipet and cotton ball. You may have to poke the cotton ball repeatedly with the wire to get it in place; the capillary is very fragile, so be careful you don't break it.

A filter-tip pipet is useful for transferring all types of liquids, not just volatile ones, because its cotton plug helps remove solid impurities from the

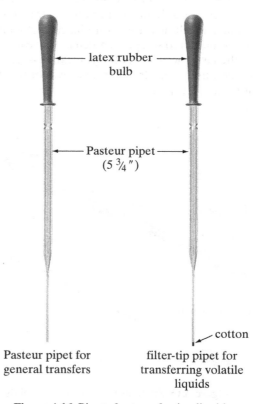

Pasteur pipet for general transfers

filter-tip pipet for transferring volatile liquids

Figure A16 Pipets for transferring liquids

liquid (if any are present). It also gives you better control over the transfer process, reducing the likelihood that some of your product will drip onto the benchtop on the way to the collecting container.

When you are transferring a liquid from one container to another with a Pasteur pipet, you can avoid losses by keeping the containers as close together as possible. For example, if you are transferring a liquid from a flask to a screw-cap storage vial, hold the containers together in the same hand—with their mouths at the same level—and then use your free hand to make the transfer. This way, any dripping liquid should be caught by one or the other container rather than ending up on the benchtop. Even after a careful transfer, an appreciable amount of liquid may remain behind in the original container. When it is important to avoid losses, you can recover that liquid by adding a small amount of a volatile solvent to the original container, tilting and rotating the container to wash all the liquid off its sides, transferring the resulting solution to the receiving container, and evaporating [OP-19] the solvent. The volatile solvent must be one in which the liquid is appreciably soluble. Dichloromethane and diethyl ether are suitable solvents for most organic liquids.

Heating

a. Heat Sources

Chemical reactions are accelerated by heat, because heat (thermal energy) speeds up the reactant molecules so that they collide more often, and increases the energy of those collisions so that they are more likely to generate product molecules. Therefore, most organic reactions are performed using some kind of heat source so that they can be carried out in a reasonable period of time. Heating devices are used for other purposes as well, such as distilling liquid mixtures and evaporating volatile solvents.

A variety of heat sources are used in the organic chemistry laboratory. The choice of a heat source for a particular application depends on such factors as the temperature required, the flammability of a liquid being heated, the need for simultaneous stirring, and the cost and convenience of the heating device. Of the heat sources described here, heating mantles, steam baths, hot-water baths, and oil baths are generally used for heating reaction mixtures, but burners, hot plates, and heat lamps have some applications as well. For example, burners can be used for glass working [OP-3] and hot plates for heating recrystallization solvents that won't boil on a steam bath. Heating blocks and sand baths, if available, can be used for some minilabs and qualitative analysis procedures.

When a reaction mixture is being heated, there is always a chance that an exothermic reaction will "take off" (become too vigorous), in which case the reaction mixture may spew out of the reaction apparatus and create a potentially dangerous situation. For that reason, it is always a good idea to have a container with cold water handy so that you can chill the reaction flask (after separating it from the heat source) to bring the reaction under control. If that can't be done safely and the reaction is being carried out under a fume hood, close the hood sash to isolate the reaction mixture and turn off the heat source by pulling the plug or by any other appropriate means. If a reaction becomes too vigorous while a reagent is being added [OP-11], the addition should be stopped or the rate of addition reduced. Some reaction mixtures will boil up vigorously if boiling chips (see part **b** of this Operation) haven't been added or if the stirring rate [OP-10] is too slow. If you forgot to use boiling chips, be sure to cool the reaction mixture well below the boiling point before adding them.

Heating Mantles. A heating mantle (Figure B1) is generally used to heat a round-bottom flask during a reaction or distillation. It is always used in conjunction with a voltage-regulating or time-cycling ("on–off") heat control to vary its heat output. A mantle can be used with a magnetic stirrer (see OP-10), and its heat output can be varied over a wide range, but its operating temperature can't easily be monitored with a thermometer. Certain heating mantles, such as Thermowell ceramic flask heaters, are designed to heat round-bottom flasks over a range of sizes. For example, a 100-mL ceramic mantle can be used to heat 25-mL, 50-mL, and 100-mL round-bottom flasks efficiently. Most other mantles are designed for a specific flask size, so a 100-mL fiberglass heating mantle should only be used to heat a 100-mL round-bottom flask; the mantle won't heat efficiently and could even burn

From *Operational Organic Chemistry: A Problem Solving Approach to the Laboratory*, Fourth Edition, John W. Lehman. Copyright © 2009 by Pearson Education. Published by Prentice Hall. All rights reserved.

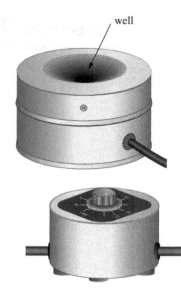

Figure B1 Heating mantle and heat control

A Thermowell mantle should not be operated directly on the desktop unless a sheet of aluminum is placed under it to act as a heat sink.

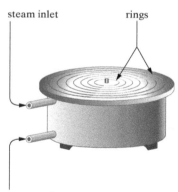

Figure B2 Steam bath

out if used with a flask of another size. Don't turn on an empty heating mantle or use it to heat an empty flask, because that might burn out its heating element. If you spill any chemicals into the well of a heating mantle, particularly if it's hot, unplug it and notify your instructor.

To operate a heating mantle, first support it on a ring support or a set of wood blocks so that it can be lowered and removed quickly if the heating rate becomes too rapid. If one is available, you can use a *lab jack* instead. A lab jack is an adjustable platform that can be raised or lowered by rotating a knob. Clamp the flask in place so that its bottom is in direct contact with the well of the heating mantle. See that the heat-control dial is set to zero, then plug the mantle into it—*never* directly into an electrical outlet—and adjust the heat-control dial until the desired rate of heating is attained. Note that the dial controls only the rate of heating and cannot be set to a specific temperature. Because a heating mantle responds slowly to changes in the control setting, it is easy to exceed the desired heating rate by setting the dial too high at the start. If that happens, lower the mantle so that it is no longer in contact with the flask, reduce the dial setting, and allow sufficient time for the temperature to drop before raising the mantle again. Further adjustments may be needed to maintain heating at the desired rate. When you are done heating, lower the mantle, adjust the heat-control dial to its lowest or "off" setting, and let the mantle cool down before you attempt to remove it.

Steam Baths. A steam bath (Figure B2) is a metal container with metal rings that can be removed or added to accommodate glassware of different sizes. It uses externally generated steam for heating, so it has only one operating temperature, 100°C. This limits its usefulness somewhat (e.g., a steam bath can't be used to boil water or an aqueous solution), but the relatively low temperature helps prevent decomposition of heat-sensitive substances. Steam baths are often used to heat recrystallization mixtures, evaporate volatile solvents, and heat low-boiling liquids under reflux. Condensation of steam in the vicinity of a steam bath may be a nuisance, but it can be reduced by maintaining a slow rate of steam flow and by using enough rings to bridge any gaps between a flask (or another container) and the steam bath. Beyond a certain point, there is no advantage to increasing the steam flow rate since the steam temperature is constant. If the flask and rings are positioned correctly, heating is quite uniform and efficient.

To use a steam bath, obtain two lengths of rubber tubing, attach one to the steam bath's *water outlet* tube and the other to the steam valve over the sink, and place the open ends of both rubber tubes in the sink. (If your steam bath has no water outlet tube, you will have to turn off the steam periodically to empty it of water.) Remove inner rings from the steam bath, leaving enough rings to safely support the container you wish to heat (unless it's supported by a clamp), but providing an opening large enough so that the steam will contact most of the container's bottom. If the container is a round-bottom flask that is clamped to a ring stand, remove enough rings so that the flask can be lowered through the rings to about its midpoint, leaving the smallest possible gap between the innermost ring and the flask. Directing the steam into the sink drain, open the steam valve fully and let it run until little or no water drips from the end of the rubber tube. Close the steam valve, connect it to the steam bath's *steam inlet* tube, and then open it just enough to maintain the desired rate of heating with the container in place. You can adjust the heating rate somewhat by adding or removing rings, raising or lowering a clamped flask, or changing the steam flow rate. When you are done heating, turn off the steam valve completely and let the steam bath cool down. Then remove the rubber tubes, drain any water that remains in the steam bath, and put it and the rubber tubes back where you found them. (Don't leave rubber tubing in the sink!)

Oil Baths. An oil bath (Figure B3) provides very uniform heating and precise temperature control, thereby reducing the likelihood of decomposition and side reactions caused by local overheating, and its operating temperature can be measured with a thermometer. But oil baths are messy to work with, difficult to clean, and potentially hazardous. Hot oil can cause severe injury if accidentally spilled on the skin—the oil, which is difficult to remove and slow to cool, remains in contact with the skin long enough to produce deep, painful burns. An oil bath liquid can suddenly burst into flames if it is heated above its *flash point* when an ignition source, such as a spark or burner flame, is present. Hot oil can also catch fire if it splatters onto a hot surface, such as the top of a hot plate. Most oil fires can be extinguished by dry-chemical fire extinguishers or powdered sodium bicarbonate. Water must be kept away from most oil baths, because spilling water into a hot oil bath causes dangerous splattering. Oil that contains water shouldn't be used until the water is removed, and a bath liquid that has darkened or contains gummy residues should be replaced.

Mineral oil is probably the most commonly used oil bath liquid, but it presents a potential fire hazard and is hard to clean up. High molecular-weight polyethylene glycols such as Carbowax 600 are water soluble, which makes cleanup much easier, and they can be used at comparatively high temperatures without appreciable decomposition. Some silicone oils can be used at even higher temperatures, but they are considerably more expensive than the other bath liquids. Flash points and other information about selected oil bath liquids are given in the margin. Note that flash points may vary with composition; check the label or ask your instructor if you aren't sure about the flash point of a specific oil bath liquid.

An oil bath is ordinarily heated by a removable heating element, such as a coil of resistance wire or an immersion heater. (A hot plate can also be used, but it may cause a fire if any bath liquid spills onto the hot surface.) The output of the heating element is controlled by a variable transformer, and the temperature of the bath is measured with a thermometer suspended in the liquid. A large porcelain casserole (see Figure B3) makes a convenient bath container, because it's less easily broken than a glass container and has a handle for convenient placement and removal.

To use an oil bath, first place it on a lab jack, a set of wood blocks, or some other support that will allow it to be removed from contact with the reaction apparatus quickly in case a reaction becomes violent. If that isn't possible, be sure that the reaction apparatus can be raised out of the oil bath quickly. Don't set it on a ring support, because of the danger of spilling hot oil when the ring is raised or lowered. See that the apparatus containing the reaction flask or boiling flask is clamped securely to a ring stand. Then loosen (at the ring stand) the clamp holding the flask and lower the flask into the bath so that the liquid level inside it is 1 to 2 mm below the oil level.

Take Care! Avoid contact with the steam, which can cause serious thermal burns.

The flash point of a liquid is the minimum temperature at which its vapors can be ignited by a small flame.

Oil bath liquids

Mineral oil
Flash point ~190°C, but varies with composition
Potential fire hazard

Glycerol
Flash point 160°C
Water soluble, viscous

Dibutyl phthalate
Flash point 171°C
Viscous at low temperatures

Triethylene glycol
Flash point 165°C
Water soluble

Polyethylene glycols (Carbowaxes)
Flash point varies with molecular weight
Water soluble, some are solids at room temperature

Silicone oil, high temperature
Flash point 315°C; usable range −40°C to 230°C
Expensive; decomposition products are very toxic

Heating

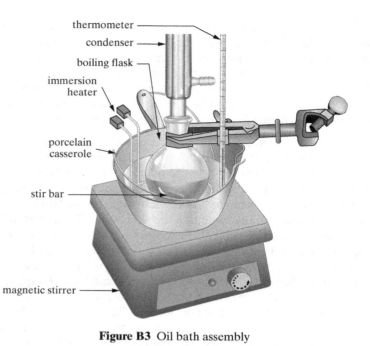

thermometer
condenser
boiling flask
immersion heater
porcelain casserole
stir bar
magnetic stirrer

Figure B3 Oil bath assembly

Take Care! If the oil bath liquid starts smoking, discontinue heating and use fresh oil or an oil bath liquid with a higher flash point.

Take Care! Keep flames away from petroleum ether. Avoid contact with and inhalation of dichloromethane.

Clamp a thermometer so that its bulb is immersed in the oil but doesn't touch anything else in the oil bath. Drop a stir bar into the bath, if desired, and stir [OP-10] the bath gently to ensure more uniform heat distribution. If boiling chips (see OP-7b) are not used, a smaller stir bar should be used to stir the flask contents. Switch on the variable transformer, adjust it until the desired temperature is obtained, and then readjust it as needed to maintain that temperature.

When you are done heating, turn off the heat, lower the oil bath (or raise the apparatus out of it), and allow the oil bath to cool nearly to room temperature. Transfer the oil to an appropriate container for reuse. Clean the bath container using a suitable solvent, such as petroleum ether for mineral oil, dichloromethane for silicone oil, or water for glycerol and polyethylene glycol.

Burners. Bunsen-type burners are simple and convenient to operate, but they present a serious risk of fire in an organic chemistry lab, in which highly flammable solvents are often used. For that reason, burners should be used mainly for operations that can't be conducted with flameless heat sources, such as bending and fire-polishing glass tubing.

Safety Notes

Always check to see that there are no flammable liquids in the vicinity before you light a burner. Never use a burner near a heated oil bath or to heat a flammable liquid in an open container. Never leave a burner flame unattended; it may go out and cause an explosion due to escaping gas.

534

To operate a typical burner with a needle valve at the base, connect it to a gas outlet with a rubber hose and make sure that the valve at the gas outlet is turned off. Close the needle valve on the burner by rotating the knurled wheel clockwise until you feel resistance (don't close it tightly), and then open it a turn or two. Open the gas valve and—without delay—ignite the burner with a burner lighter. If it doesn't light, rotate the barrel of the burner clockwise (or close the sleeve-type regulator, if it has one) and try again. When the burner is lit, adjust the needle valve and rotate the barrel or sleeve to obtain a flame of the desired size and intensity. Rotating the barrel counterclockwise or opening the sleeve regulator to introduce more air produces a hotter, bluer flame. If you are using a burner to heat a non-flammable liquid in a beaker or other container, place the container on a ring support using a ceramic-centered wire gauze to spread out the flame and prevent superheating. The ring support should be positioned so that the bottom of the wire gauze is at the top of the inner blue cone of the flame, where it is hottest.

Hot Plates. A hot plate (Figure B4) can be used to heat most liquids and solutions in flat-bottomed containers, such as Erlenmeyer flasks and beakers. It should *not* be used to heat low-boiling, flammable liquids that could splatter on the hot surface and ignite, or to heat round-bottom flasks directly. Hot plates can also be used to heat water baths, sand baths, and heating blocks, which are in turn used to heat reaction mixtures and other liquids or solutions. A hot plate with a built-in magnetic stirrer (see OP-10) can be used when a reaction mixture or another liquid mixture is to be simultaneously heated and stirred.

To use a hot plate, plug it into an electrical outlet and adjust the heat-control dial to obtain the desired temperature or heating rate. Keep tongs, heat-resistant gloves, or other insulating materials handy so that you can quickly remove the container being heated when necessary. For example, you can fold a rectangle of paper towel lengthwise several times and loop it around the neck of a hot Erlenmeyer flask to remove the flask from a hot plate.

Hot-Water Baths. Hot-water baths are useful for heating low-boiling reaction mixtures, evaporating [OP-19] volatile solvents, and in other applications that require gentle heating. Although special metal water baths that resemble steam baths are available, a beaker can be used for most purposes.

Take Care! A heated hot plate looks just like a cold one, so never touch its platform unless you are sure it is cold.

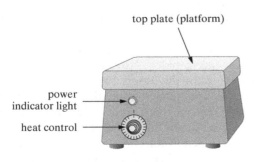

Figure B4 Hot plate

The water should fill the water-bath container about three-fourths full when the container being heated is immersed in it.

To prepare a hot-water bath, measure an appropriate amount of water into the bath container and set it on a the platform of a hot plate or hot plate–stirrer. Secure the container being heated inside the water bath so that the liquid level in the container is below the water level. Clamp a thermometer with its bulb beneath the water surface and at the same level as the mixture to be heated; its bulb shouldn't touch the bath container or the container being heated. If you are using a magnetic stirrer [OP-10], the stirring device inside the container should be close enough to the center of the platform to allow efficient stirring. If a specific bath temperature is required, adjust the heat setting and observe the thermometer reading until that temperature is reached. If the bath temperature rises above the specified value by 5°C or more, withdraw some of the bath water and replace it by an equal volume of cold water. A 10-mL (or larger) pipet equipped with a pipet pump can be used for this purpose. For most purposes, the bath temperature can be allowed to vary by ±5°C or so from the specified value. If a boiling-water bath is required, add boiling chips or a stir bar to the water before you heat it to boiling. A stir bar is desirable even when the water isn't boiling, because it ensures more uniform heat distribution.

If precise temperature control isn't necessary, you can fill a beaker with preheated water from a hot-water tap or another source and adjust the temperature by adding hot or cold water. As the bath cools, withdraw some of the bath water and replace it by fresh heated water.

Heating Blocks. Aluminum heating blocks with holes or wells designed to accommodate small test tubes and other containers can be used to conduct small-scale reactions when a high temperature is required. Although heating blocks and sand baths (described next) are not essential for standard scale work, a heating block can be used, for example, to synthesize the dye fluorescein and to prepare nitrobenzoate derivatives of alcohols. Heating blocks are also convenient for testing recrystallization solvents [OP-28c] and conducting small-scale recrystallizations [OP-28].

To use a heating block, set it on a hot plate or hot plate–stirrer and insert a thermometer (such as a mercury-free glass thermometer or a bimetallic dial thermometer with a metal probe) to monitor its temperature. If you will be using a magnetic stirrer [OP-10], position the heating block so that the well holding the container being heated is close to the center of the hot plate–stirrer. A mercury-free glass thermometer should be secured by a three-finger clamp on a ring stand and *carefully* lowered into a small hole (one drilled in the face of the block to accommodate it) until its bulb just rests on the bottom of the hole. Position a glass thermometer in the block *before* you begin heating, or the thermometer bulb may break. The metal probe of a dial thermometer can be inserted into a small hole drilled in one corner of a typical heating block. Note that it isn't always necessary to monitor the temperature of the block, which is invariably higher than the temperature inside the container it is heating—but by knowing the block temperature, you can control the heating rate more accurately and avoid overheating. Because a heating block takes some time to reach a desired temperature, it's a good idea to start heating it well before it will be needed.

Place the container to be heated in a well of the appropriate size. For the most uniform heating, the liquid level in the container should be just

Take Care! Do not use a mercury thermometer to measure the temperature of a heating block. If the bulb breaks it will release toxic mercury vapor into the atmosphere and the lab will have to be evacuated.

Take Care! A hot metal block looks just like a cold one, so never touch a heating block unless you are sure it is cold.

Take Care! Wear gloves while handling glass wool.

Take Care! Do not use an unshielded mercury thermometer to measure the temperature of a sand bath. If the bulb breaks it will release toxic mercury vapor into the atmosphere and the lab will have to be evacuated.

below the top of its well. If the liquid level is above the well top, you can insulate the container with glass wool held in place by aluminum foil. Adjust the heat control on the hot plate so that the temperature of the heating block is at least 20°C higher than the temperature you wish to attain inside the container you are heating. Then readjust the heat control, as necessary, until the desired heating rate is attained. For example, if you want to boil a mixture in which water is the solvent, first raise the block temperature to ~120°C. If the reaction mixture doesn't boil when the block is at that temperature, advance the heat control gradually until it does boil. You can control the heating rate to some extent by raising and lowering a container in its well without changing the heat setting. If you need to lower the temperature quickly, as when a recrystallization mixture threatens to boil over, raise the container out of its well first and *then* lower the heat setting or clamp the container at a higher level.

Sand Baths. A sand bath is easy to set up, and it can be used for the same kind of small-scale operations as a heating block. It has the disadvantage of being somewhat messier to use, since sand spills are not uncommon. Sand baths heat and cool more slowly than aluminum blocks, but it's easier to observe changes in a reaction mixture and to swirl or shake a mixture in a sand bath. A sand bath provides a temperature gradient, with lower temperatures near the top of the sand layer and higher temperatures near the bottom. Thus, it shouldn't be necessary to measure the temperature of a sand bath, because you can vary the temperature of the container being heated by varying its depth in the sand.

A convenient sand bath can be prepared by filling the ceramic well of a 100-mL Thermowell heating mantle (see Figure B1) 60–85% full with good-quality sand.

To use such a sand bath, set the heat control to 40% of maximum power at least 15 minutes before the sand bath will be used. Lower the container being heated far enough into the sand so that the liquid level in the container is below the top of the sand. Control the heating rate by changing the depth of the container in the sand. For example, you can bring a reaction mixture to the boiling point quickly by immersing its container deep in the sand, and then raise the container just enough to keep it boiling gently. If necessary, you can also vary the power level, but do not exceed 40% of the heat control's maximum power; higher levels can produce dangerously high temperatures and damage the heating mantle.

Other Heat Sources. Heating devices such as infrared heat lamps (see Figure B5) and electric forced-air heaters (heat guns) can be used in some heating applications. A heat lamp plugged into a variable transformer provides a safe and convenient way to heat comparatively low-boiling liquids. The boiling flask is usually fitted with an aluminum foil heat shield to concentrate the heat on the reaction mixture.

Take Care! Do not touch a sand bath or its container unless you are sure it is cold.

Figure B5 Heat lamp bulb

b. Smooth Boiling Devices

When a liquid is heated at its boiling point, it may erupt violently as large bubbles of superheated vapor are discharged from the liquid; this phenomenon is called *bumping. Boiling chips* prevents bumping by providing nucleating sites on which smaller bubbles can form. Boiling chips (also called boiling stones) are made from porous pieces of alumina, carbon, glass, marble (calcium carbonate), Teflon, and other materials. Alumina and calcium carbonate boiling chips may break down in strongly acidic or alkaline solutions, so boiling chips made of carbon, Teflon, or other chemically resistant materials should be used with such solutions. Microporous carbon boiling chips work very well for most purposes. Teflon chips are suitable with most organic solvents, but they float on water and other dense solvents, making them ineffective in such solvents. Wooden applicator sticks can be broken in two and the broken ends used to promote smooth boiling in nonreactive solvents; they shouldn't be used in reaction mixtures because of the possibility of contamination. Boiling chips aren't needed when a liquid being heated is stirred at a moderate rate with a magnetic stir bar, because stirring [OP-10] causes turbulence that breaks up the large bubbles responsible for bumping.

Unless you are instructed differently, always add several boiling chips to any liquid or liquid mixture that will be boiled without stirring, such as a liquid to be distilled [OP-30] or a reaction mixture to be heated under reflux (see OP-7c). It is important to add boiling chips *before* heating begins, because the liquid may froth violently and boil over if you add them when it's hot. If you let a boiling liquid cool below its boiling point, add a fresh boiling chip if you reheat it later, because liquid fills the pores of a boiling chip and reduces its effectiveness when boiling stops.

c. Heating Under Reflux

Most organic reactions are carried out by heating the reaction mixture to increase the reaction rate. The temperature of a reaction mixture can be controlled in several ways, the simplest and most convenient being to use a reaction solvent that has a boiling point within the desired temperature range for the reaction. Sometimes a liquid reactant itself may be used as the solvent. The reaction is conducted at the boiling point of the solvent, using a *condenser* to return solvent vapors to the reaction vessel so that no solvent is lost. This process of boiling a reaction mixture and condensing the solvent vapors back into the reaction vessel is known as *heating under reflux* (or more informally as "refluxing"), where the word reflux refers to the "flowing back" of the solvent. Usually a reaction time is specified for a reaction conducted under reflux. That interval should be measured from the time the reaction mixture begins to boil, *not* from the time heating is begun.

Round-bottom flasks are used as the reaction vessels for most of the synthetic experiments in this book. A typical standard scale lab kit contains round-bottom flasks with capacities of 25, 50, 100, 250, and 500 mL. As a rule, the reaction vessel should be the smallest appropriate container that will be about half-full or less when all of the reactants have been added. For example, if you will be dissolving 8 mL of reactant A in 20 mL of solvent before starting a reaction, and adding 6 mL of reactant B during the reaction, the maximum volume of liquid in the reaction vessel will be approximately 34 mL. Because that volume would fill a 50-mL flask more than half full, a 100-mL round-bottom flask should be used.

Rule of Thumb: Total volume of reaction mixture $\leq \frac{1}{2} \times$ *volume of reaction flask.*

Several different kinds of reflux condensers are available. A *water-cooled condenser* consists of two concentric tubes, with cold tap water

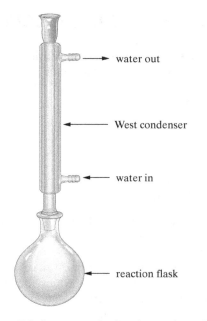

Figure B6 Apparatus for heating under reflux

circulating through the outer tube and solvent vapors from a boiling reaction mixture rising up the inner tube. The circulating water cools the walls of the inner tube, cooling the vapors and causing them to condense to liquid droplets that flow back into the reaction vessel. A water-cooled West condenser is used for most standard scale reactions conducted under reflux (see Figure B6).

An *air condenser* can be a single- or double-walled tube whose walls transfer heat to the surrounding air, cooling and condensing the vapors of a boiling liquid. A distilling column is sometimes used as an air condenser, but no water is circulated through its jacket, if it has one. Because of their more efficient cooling action, water-cooled condensers are used for most standard scale reactions conducted under reflux, although air condensers can be used with solvents that boil at 150°C or above.

Small amounts of reactants can be heated under reflux using a cold-finger condenser inserted into a test tube or small flask (Figure B7). As water passes through the condenser, it cools the surrounding area enough to condense the rising vapors. To prevent pressure buildup in the container, a stopper with a groove in one side, a two-hole stopper, or a sidearm test tube is used. The reflux ring that appears on the sides of the container should be kept well below the top of the test tube or flask so that vapors don't escape. Although the following general procedure specifies a West condenser, a small-scale reflux apparatus is used in essentially the same way except that cooling water goes into the upper connector of a cold-finger condenser and comes out the lower one.

Don't mistake a jacketed distilling column for a West condenser; the condenser has a smaller inner diameter.

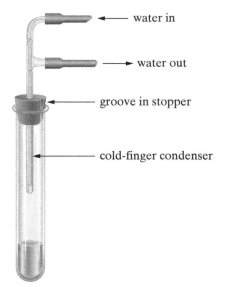

Figure B7 Small-scale apparatus for heating under reflux

DIRECTIONS FOR HEATING UNDER REFLUX

Safety Notes

> **Never heat the reaction flask before the condenser water is turned on; solvent vapors may escape and cause a fire or health hazard.**

Equipment and Supplies

> heat source
> round-bottom flask
> West condenser
> boiling chips or stir bar
> two lengths of rubber tubing

Select an appropriate heat source, such as a heating mantle or steam bath. Position the heat source so that it can be removed quickly if the flask should break or the reaction become too vigorous. Select a round-bottom flask of a size such that the reactants fill it about half full or less. Clamp this *reaction flask* securely to the ring stand at the proper location in relation to the heat source. Transfer [OP-6] the reactants and any specified solvent to the reaction flask. Solids should be added through a powder funnel or with a weighing dish or a square of weighing paper, and liquids should be added through a stemmed funnel. Add a few boiling chips or a magnetic stir bar (see OP-10); mix the reactants by swirling or stirring. Insert a West condenser into the flask, making sure that the joint is tight. Do *not* stopper the condenser—that will create a closed system, which may shatter violently when heated. Put a clamp near the top of the condenser to keep the apparatus from toppling over if jarred, but don't tighten its jaws completely.

Take Care! Never heat a closed system.

Connect the water inlet (the lower connector) on the condenser jacket to a cold-water tap with a length of rubber tubing, and run another length of tubing from the water outlet (the upper connector) to a drain, making sure that it is long enough to prevent splashing when the water is turned on. If the rubber tubing slips off when pulled with moderate force, replace it by tubing of smaller diameter or secure it with wire or a tubing clamp. Turn on the water carefully so that the condenser jacket slowly fills with water from the bottom up, and adjust the water pressure so that a narrow stream flows from the outlet. The flow rate should be just high enough to (1) maintain a continuous flow of water in spite of pressure changes in the water line and (2) keep the condenser at the temperature of the tap water during the reaction. Excessively high water pressure may force the tubing off the condenser and spray water on you and your neighbors.

If you are using a stir bar, begin stirring at a moderate rate (unless the experiment's directions specify a more vigorous stirring rate). Turn on the heat source and adjust it to keep the solvent boiling gently; measure the reaction time from the time that boiling begins, when a continuous stream of bubbles will rise through the liquid. Reflux has begun when liquid begins to drip into the flask from the condenser. The vapors passing into the condenser will then form a *reflux ring* of condensing vapors that should be clearly visible. Below this point, liquid will be seen flowing back into the flask; above it, the condenser should be dry. If the reflux ring is more than halfway up the condenser, reduce the heating rate or increase the water flow rate to prevent the escape of solvent vapors.

At the end of the reaction period, turn off the heat source and remove it from contact with the flask. Let the apparatus cool; then turn off the condenser water. Unless the next operation will be carried out in the reaction flask, decant the reaction mixture into a container suitable for that operation, leaving any boiling chips behind. Clean [OP-1] the reaction flask as soon as possible so that residues don't dry on the glass.

Summary

1. Position heat source.
2. Clamp flask in or over heat source.
3. Add solvent and reactants.
4. Add boiling chips or a stir bar.
5. Insert condenser, clamp in place, and attach tubing.
6. Turn on condenser water and adjust flow rate.
7. Start stirrer (if used); adjust heat control so that reaction mixture boils gently.
8. Readjust water flow or heating rate as necessary; boil gently until end of reflux period.
9. Turn off and remove heat source, let flask cool, and transfer reaction mixture.
10. Disassemble and clean apparatus.

When Things Go Wrong

If, when you turn on the cooling water, the condenser fills from the top down rather than the bottom up, you connected the rubber tubes to the wrong hose connectors. Turn off the water, reattach the tube from the water tap to the condenser's bottom connector and the other tube to its top connector, and turn on the water again.

If, as you heat a reaction mixture, the liquid bumps or foams up, you probably forgot to add boiling chips or to use a magnetic stirrer. Drop in a stirring device and start stirring, or let the apparatus cool for several minutes and then drop one or more boiling chips down the top of the condenser. If you were already using boiling chips or a stirrer, you are probably heating the reaction mixture too strongly. Reduce the heating rate by raising the apparatus or lowering the heat source a few millimeters (for rapid cooling) or by turning down the heat control (for slower cooling), or both. You can always return the apparatus to its original location once the heating rate has decreased.

If, as you heat a reaction mixture, the liquid level in the reaction vessel goes down or the reflux ring of condensing vapors rises above the midpoint of the condenser, either the cooling water isn't flowing fast enough (or at all), you are heating the reaction mixture too strongly, or you are using an air condenser when you should be using a water-cooled condenser. A water-cooled condenser should be cool to the touch. If it isn't, adjust (or turn on) the cooling water so that a steady stream flows through the condenser—not a strong stream that may force the hose off the condenser. If the reflux ring is still too high, reduce the heating rate as described previously until the reflux ring stays in the bottom half of the condenser. If you are using an air condenser, replace it with a water-cooled condenser (let the reaction mixture cool down before switching condensers). If the liquid level in the reaction vessel has gone down, add more solvent to replace any that boiled away.

If, when you are taking the apparatus apart, you can't separate the condenser from the reaction flask, the glass joints have probably frozen. See "Disassembling Glassware" in OP-2.

Cooling

Some reactions proceed too violently to be conducted safely at room temperature, or involve reactants or products that decompose at room temperature. In such cases, the reaction mixture is cooled with some kind of cold bath, which can be anything from a beaker filled with cold water to an electrically refrigerated device. Cold baths are also used to increase the yield of crystals from a reaction mixture or recrystallization mixture.

A cold bath can be prepared using any suitable container, such as a beaker of suitable size, a crystallization dish, an evaporating dish, or a pair of nested Styrofoam cups. A beaker can be wrapped with glass wool or another insulating material and placed inside a larger beaker to keep it cold longer, if necessary.

A number of cooling media are used for cold baths. A mixture of crushed ice (or snow) and water can be used for cooling in the 0–5°C range. Enough water should be present to just cover the ice, because ice alone isn't an efficient heat-transfer medium. An ice–salt bath consisting of three parts of finely crushed ice or snow to one part of sodium chloride can attain temperatures down to −20°C, and mixtures of $CaCl_2 \cdot H_2O$ containing up to 1.4 g of the calcium salt per gram of ice or snow can provide temperatures down to −55°C. In practice, these minimum values may be difficult to attain, because the actual temperature of an ice–salt bath depends on such factors as the fineness of the ice and salt and the insulating ability of the container. Temperatures down to −75°C can be attained by mixing small chunks of dry ice (solid carbon dioxide) with acetone, ethanol, or another suitable solvent in a vacuum-jacketed container such as a Dewar flask.

Take Care! Wear gloves while handling glass wool.

Temperatures below −40°C can't be measured using a mercury thermometer, because mercury freezes at that temperature.

Take Care! Never handle dry ice with bare hands.

DIRECTIONS FOR COOLING

Equipment and Supplies

    cold bath container
    cooling medium
    thermometer

Obtain a suitable cold bath container and fill it with the cooling medium to a level depending on the size of the container to be cooled. When this container is immersed in the cold bath, the cooling medium should fill the cold bath container about three-fourths full. Clamp a thermometer [OP-9] so that its bulb is entirely immersed in the cooling medium but not touching either container. If you are using an ice–salt bath, mix in the appropriate salt in small portions—waiting for the temperature to equilibrate after each addition—until the desired temperature is attained. Lower the container to be cooled into the cooling bath so that the liquid level in that container is below the cooling fluid level. Keep the contents of the cold bath mixed by occasional stirring or swirling. The contents of the container being cooled can also be swirled or stirred for more efficient cooling. Add small portions of ice, as needed, to keep the temperature in the desired range, removing an equal amount of water (with a pipet, etc.) to make room for it.

Summary

1. Fill container with cooling medium.
2. Insert thermometer in cooling medium.
3. Insert container to be cooled.
4. Keep contents of container and cooling bath mixed; adjust temperature as needed.

Temperature Monitoring

In the organic chemistry lab, thermometers are used to monitor the temperatures of heating devices, cooling baths, reaction mixtures, distillations, and for many other purposes. Such thermometers should have a range of at least −10°C to 260°C, and a wider range is desirable for some purposes. Most broad-range glass thermometers contain mercury, which is toxic and presents a safety hazard if a thermometer is broken, but broad-range mercury-free thermometers are also available. For the most accurate temperature readings, a thermometer should be *calibrated* and an *emergent stem correction* applied as described in OP-33, but this is generally not necessary for routine temperature monitoring.

To read a thermometer accurately, rotate it so that its liquid column is adjacent to its graduation marks, and view it with your line of sight perpendicular to the thermometer and extending to the top of the mercury column. If the thermometer is vertical, for example, your eyes should be at about the same level as the top of the mercury column. You should then be able read the temperature to at least the nearest half degree.

You can monitor the temperature of a heating medium (such as water, oil, or sand) using a thermometer clamped with its bulb entirely immersed in the heating medium. It should be held in place by a three-fingered clamp or a special thermometer clamp, or inserted into a stopper that is held by a utility clamp. The thermometer shouldn't touch the side or bottom of the container.

To monitor the temperature of a reaction mixture that will be stirred [OP-10] in an open container such as an Erlenmeyer flask, clamp a thermometer so that its bulb is completely immersed in the mixture but doesn't contact the stirring device (a large stir bar could break the thermometer bulb). If a magnetic stirrer isn't available, you may have to hold a thermometer inside the reaction vessel as it is being swirled or shaken. Do this by holding the neck of the flask and nesting the thermometer stem in the "vee" between your thumb and index finger, so that the bulb of the thermometer is held securely inside the flask and continuously immersed in the liquid. With a little practice, you should be able to mix the contents of the flask quite vigorously without damage to the thermometer. If continuous mixing isn't necessary, you can insert the thermometer each time you stop shaking or swirling the reaction flask, read it when the temperature has stabilized, then remove it and resume mixing. Never use the thermometer itself for stirring, because the bulb is fragile and breaks easily.

Using a Thermometer Adapter

You will ordinarily need a *thermometer adapter* (Figure B8) to monitor the temperature of an operation (such as distillation) conducted in a jointed glassware setup. Be certain that the thermometer adapter, when inserted in the apparatus, does not create a closed system. For example, never put a sealed thermometer adapter assembly on top of a reflux condenser that is

Figure B8 Thermometer adapter

From *Operational Organic Chemistry: A Problem Solving Approach to the Laboratory*, Fourth Edition, John W. Lehman. Copyright © 2009 by Pearson Education. Published by Prentice Hall. All rights reserved.

attached directly to a reaction flask, because heating such a system may cause it to shatter.

To use a thermometer adapter, carefully insert the bulb of the thermometer through the rubber cap of the adapter using an appropriate lubricant (see OP-3). Then secure the adapter in the appropriate joint on the apparatus and carefully raise or lower the thermometer so that its bulb is positioned correctly. To prevent accidental breakage, remove the thermometer assembly from the apparatus before repositioning the thermometer.

Mixing

Reaction mixtures are often stirred, shaken, or agitated in some other way to promote efficient heat transfer, prevent bumping, increase contact between the components of a heterogeneous mixture, or mix in a reactant as it is being added.

Manual Mixing

If you are carrying out a reaction in an Erlenmeyer flask or a test tube, the reactants can be mixed using a stirring rod or spatula, or by manual shaking or swirling. A motion that combines shaking with swirling is more effective than swirling alone. If you are carrying out a reaction under reflux, you may be able to mix the reactants adequately by clamping the apparatus *securely* to a ring stand and carefully sliding the base of the ring stand back and forth. But when more efficient and convenient mixing is required, particularly over a long period of time, you should use a mechanical or magnetic stirrer, as described next.

Manual mixing may be used at other times than during reactions. For example, liquids can be dried [OP-25] by swirling the liquid with a drying agent in an Erlenmeyer flask. This increases the amount of contact between the liquid and the particles of drying agent, increasing drying efficiency.

Mechanical Stirring

A mechanical stirrer (Figure B9) consists of a stirring motor connected to a paddle or agitator by means of a shaft that extends through the neck of

stirring motor

shaft

Teflon stirring paddle

Figure B9 Mechanical stirrer

From *Operational Organic Chemistry: A Problem Solving Approach to the Laboratory*, Fourth Edition, John W. Lehman. Copyright © 2009 by Pearson Education. Published by Prentice Hall. All rights reserved.

A slurry is a thick suspension of solid in a liquid.

the reaction vessel. A sleeve or bearing is used to align the shaft, which is ordinarily made of glass to reduce the likelihood of contamination. Mechanical stirrers exert more torque than magnetic stirrers and are preferred when viscous liquids or slurries must be stirred. A variety of stirring paddles made of Teflon, glass, and chemically resistant wire are available.

Magnetic Stirring

A *magnetic stirrer* (Figure B10) is an enclosed unit containing a motor that rotates a bar magnet underneath a metal or ceramic platform. As the bar magnet rotates, it spins a Teflon-coated stirring device inside a container placed on or above the platform. The most common stirring device, called a *stir bar,* is an oblong (usually cylindrical) Teflon-coated magnet. Because no moving parts extend outside of the container in which stirring occurs, a reaction assembly that is to be stirred magnetically can be completely enclosed if necessary. The rate of stirring is controlled by a dial on the magnetic stirrer. For efficient stirring, the vessel (flask, beaker, etc.) containing the stirring device should be positioned near the center of the stirring unit and as close to its platform as practicable.

Magnetic stirrers can be used in conjunction with heating mantles, oil baths, steam baths, and other heat sources that are constructed of nonferrous materials. A *hot plate–stirrer* has a heating device in the same unit that houses the magnetic stirrer, so it has two dials: one to control the heating unit and the other to control the stirrer. Hot plate–stirrers can be used to heat and stir flat-bottomed containers such as Erlenmeyer flasks directly, but they are also used in conjunction with heating devices that require an external heat source, such as hot-water baths and some oil baths.

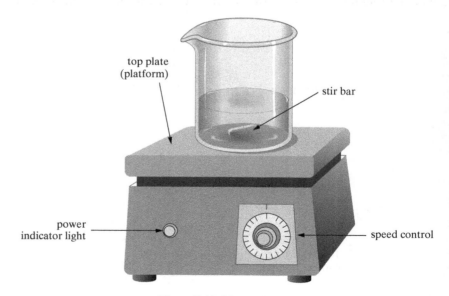

top plate (platform)

stir bar

power indicator light

speed control

Figure B10 Magnetic stirrer

DIRECTIONS FOR STIRRING A REACTION MIXTURE MAGNETICALLY

Equipment and Supplies

> stirrer or hot plate–stirrer
> heating device
> reaction vessel
> stir bar

Set the heating device (heating mantle, hot-water bath, etc.), if any, directly on the platform of the magnetic stirrer or hot plate–stirrer. Position the reaction vessel in the heating device so that it's close to the center of the stirring unit's platform, secure it with a clamp (if necessary), and drop in a stir bar. (Don't add boiling chips; the stirring action prevents bumping.) If you need to stir a heating bath as well, use a stir bar that is larger than the one in the reaction mixture. If necessary, attach a condenser or other device to the reaction vessel. Start circulating water through a water-cooled condenser, if you are using one. Start the magnetic stirrer and adjust the stirring rate dial carefully so that the stirring action is vigorous (you should see a vortex in the middle of the container) but smooth. If the stirring rate is too high or the reaction vessel isn't positioned correctly, the stir bar will flop around erratically rather than rotate smoothly. If that happens, reset the dial to a low value and increase it gradually until a suitable rate is attained, or reposition the reaction vessel to bring it closer to the top and center of the stirring unit's platform. High stirring rates may be needed for heterogeneous reaction mixtures, such as those involving two immiscible liquids, but in most cases a moderate stirring rate is suitable. If you are to heat the stirred reaction mixture, adjust the heating rate as described in OP-7a for the heating device you are using.

Summary

1. Place heating device (if used) on stirring unit.
2. Secure reaction vessel on or inside heating device.
3. Drop in stir bar or spin vane.
4. Adjust stirrer for appropriate stirring rate.

When Things Go Wrong

If, as you increase the spinning rate of a stir bar, it wobbles or otherwise moves erratically, try the following remedies in order. Make sure you're not using a ferrous container, such as a stainless-steel beaker for an oil bath. Reduce the stirring rate and move the reaction flask (or other container) that contains the stir bar horizontally until it is centered over the platform; then advance the speed control *slowly* until you attain a suitable stirring rate. If the stir bar still turns erratically, try lowering the reaction flask so that it is closer to the top of the platform. If that doesn't help, try a different magnetic stirrer or stir bar.

If the stir bar you are using for a reaction that requires thorough mixing (such as a heterogeneous reaction) isn't stirring the reaction mixture vigorously enough (it should produce a vortex in the liquid at high speed), switch to a larger stir bar.

Addition of Reactants

In many organic preparations, the reactants are not all combined at the start of the reaction. Instead, one or more of them is added during the course of the reaction. This is necessary when the reaction is strongly exothermic or when one of the reactants must be kept in excess to prevent side reactions. Solid reactants can be added slowly or at regular intervals from a plastic weighing dish that is bent to form a pouring spout. Solids can also be divided into small portions that are added at regular intervals. Liquids are usually added in portions or drop by drop using a separatory funnel or a special addition funnel.

An *addition funnel* has a cylindrical body, a drain tube controlled by a stopcock, and a pressure-equalizing tube to equalize the pressure in the reaction vessel and addition funnel, allowing its contents to flow freely into the reaction vessel. A *separatory funnel* usually has a pear-shaped body attached to a similar drain tube but lacks a pressure-equalizing tube (see Figure B11). Because addition funnels are seldom available in undergraduate labs, a separatory funnel (which we will call a separatory–addition funnel here) is generally used for that purpose. An opening must be left at the top of the funnel for air to enter; otherwise, the liquid out-flow will create a vacuum and the flow will eventually stop. If a reaction is run in an open container, such as an Erlenmeyer flask, the separatory–addition funnel can simply be clamped to a ring stand above the flask, which is swirled or stirred during the addition. An apparatus like the one in Figure B11 is used for a reaction conducted under reflux; see the directions that follow.

Some reactions involving addition under reflux require that the temperature of the reaction mixture be monitored [OP-9] or that the mixture be stirred with a mechanical stirrer (see OP-10), in which case the flask and Claisen adapter shown in Figure B11 are replaced by a three-necked flask (Figure B12). For temperature monitoring, the addition funnel should be inserted in the middle neck, and the reflux condenser and thermometer in the outer necks. For mechanical stirring, the stirrer shaft is inserted in the middle neck, and the addition funnel and reflux condenser in the outer necks.

Small amounts of reactants can be added to a reaction mixture using a measuring pipet or volumetric pipet. A setup suitable for this purpose is illustrated in Figure B13. The pinchcock valve is constructed by inserting a solid glass bead into a length of thin-walled rubber tubing. The valve is then attached to the top of the pipet, and the pipet's other end is inserted into a lubricated rubber stopper. To fill a measuring pipet or volumetric pipet with the liquid to be added, insert the wide end of a medicine-dropper tip into the pinchcock valve, squeeze a large rubber bulb to drive out its air, and place it over the narrow end of the medicine dropper tip. Insert the tip of the pipet into the liquid, and then fill the pipet slowly to the appropriate calibration mark by pinching the valve at the glass bead. Remove the rubber bulb and place the pipet assembly in a sidearm test tube or another suitable reaction vessel. (An ordinary test tube can be used if the stopper is notched for pressure release.) The assembly can be modified for addition under

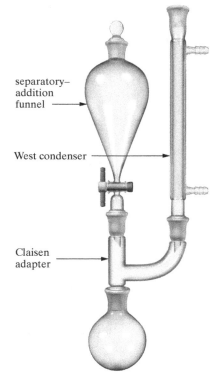

separatory–
addition
funnel

West condenser

Claisen
adapter

Figure B11 Apparatus for addition under reflux

From *Operational Organic Chemistry: A Problem Solving Approach to the Laboratory*, Fourth Edition, John W. Lehman. Copyright © 2009 by Pearson Education. Published by Prentice Hall. All rights reserved.

Figure B12 Three-necked flask

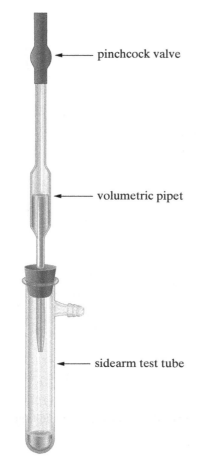

pinchcock valve

volumetric pipet

sidearm test tube

Figure B13 Apparatus for small-scale addition

reflux by using a two-holed rubber stopper with a cold-finger condenser [OP-7c] in one hole, and a gas trap [OP-14] or drying tube [OP-12a] can be attached to the sidearm.

The following directions are for addition with a separatory–addition funnel to a reaction mixture being heated under reflux, but they can be adapted for conducting such a reaction with the small-scale apparatus as well.

DIRECTIONS FOR ADDITION UNDER REFLUX

Equipment and Supplies

> round-bottom reaction flask
> Claisen adapter
> separatory–addition funnel
> West condenser
> stopper (can be omitted for most aqueous solutions or other nonvolatile liquids)

Measure the appropriate reactants into the flask and assemble the apparatus shown in Figure B11, placing the separatory–addition funnel on the straight arm of the Claisen adapter so that it is directly over the reaction flask. Clamp the flask and the Claisen adapter securely to a ring stand. Make sure the stopcock is closed; then place the liquid to be added in the separatory–addition funnel. Unless this liquid must be protected from atmospheric moisture, place a strip of filter paper between the stopper and the funnel's ground-glass joint. (If the liquid is moisture sensitive, insert a drying tube [OP-12a] filled with drying agent in the top of the funnel.) Add the liquid either in portions or continuously, as directed in the experiment. For portionwise addition, add small portions of the liquid at regular intervals by opening the stopcock momentarily while stirring magnetically or shaking to mix the reactants. For continuous addition, open the stopcock just far enough so that the liquid drips or drizzles slowly into the reaction flask; adjust the stopcock position to provide the desired rate of addition. Continuous addition is usually carried out dropwise (drop by drop), with magnetic stirring or periodic shaking [OP-10] to keep the reactants mixed.

When Things Go Wrong

If the liquid you are adding stops draining from a separatory–addition funnel, its stopper may be inserted too tightly. Remove the stopper and place a folded piece of paper between it and the joint.

If the liquid still doesn't drain, close the stopcock and pour the liquid out the top of the funnel into another container. Filter [OP-15] the liquid if it contains solid impurities. Remove the stopcock, use a piece of wire (or a toothpick, etc.) to clean any debris out of the hole, rinse the hole with distilled water or an appropriate organic solvent, and let it dry. Then insert the stopcock in the separatory–addition funnel, return the liquid to the funnel, and continue.

Excluding Water from Reaction Mixtures

a. Using Drying Tubes

Some chemicals react with water vapor from the air, and some reactions are inhibited or prevented by traces of water. Water-sensitive reactions can be carried out and water-sensitive chemicals protected by attaching *drying tubes* (see Figure B14) wherever an apparatus is open to the atmosphere. The drying tube is filled with a suitable desiccant (drying agent) such as calcium chloride, calcium sulfate (Drierite), granular alumina, or silica gel. Calcium chloride is the least efficient of these, but it's adequate in many cases. When a very dry atmosphere is required, the apparatus should be swept out by passing dry nitrogen or another dry gas through it as described in Operation 13. Unless your instructor directs otherwise, put used desiccant in a designated container (*not* the container you got it from) when you are done. If you leave calcium chloride in a drying tube exposed to the atmosphere, its granules will eventually clump together in a solid mass that can only be removed by immersing the drying tube in water overnight or longer until the solid dissolves.

To prepare a drying tube, use a glass rod or applicator stick to push a small plug of dry cotton into the drying tube until it covers the narrow opening; tamp it down gently to hold it in place. Add calcium chloride or another drying agent through the top of the drying tube until it is filled to within a few centimeters of the top; then insert another plug of cotton in the top to keep the desiccant in place. Push the connector at the bottom of the drying tube into a thermometer adapter and insert the adapter into the top of a reflux condenser (or into any other part of an apparatus that is open to the atmosphere), as shown in Figure B14. If the apparatus includes a vacuum adapter, the drying tube can be attached to its sidearm using a short length of rubber tubing.

b. Water Separation

During some reactions that yield water as a by-product, it may be necessary to remove the water to prevent the decomposition of a water-sensitive product or to increase the yield. This is sometimes done by codistilling (see OP-20b) the water with an organic solvent that forms a low-boiling azeotrope (see OP-32) with water. This process is known as *azeotropic drying.* The solvent used must be less dense than water and immiscible in it. For example, a mixture of water and toluene (bp = 111°C, d = 0.866 g/mL) yields an azeotrope containing 13.5% water by mass that distills at 84°C, so toluene is often used to remove water from reaction mixtures.

The codistillation can be accomplished with an ordinary simple distillation apparatus [OP-30a], but it is more convenient to use a *water separator,* such as the Dean–Stark trap shown in Figure B15. The

Take Care! Never stopper a drying tube, as this will result in a closed system that might explode or fly apart when heated.

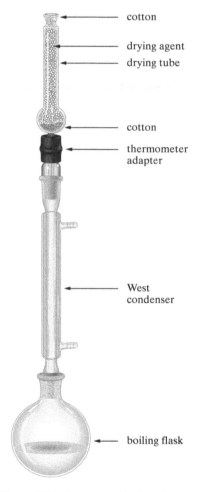

— cotton
— drying agent
— drying tube
— cotton
— thermometer adapter
— West condenser
— boiling flask

Figure B14 Apparatus for heating under reflux in a dry atmosphere

A "homemade" Dean–Stark trap can be constructed as described in J. Chem. Educ. **1963,** *40,* 349.

From *Operational Organic Chemistry: A Problem Solving Approach to the Laboratory*, Fourth Edition, John W. Lehman. Copyright © 2009 by Pearson Education. Published by Prentice Hall. All rights reserved.

Figure B15 Dean–Stark trap

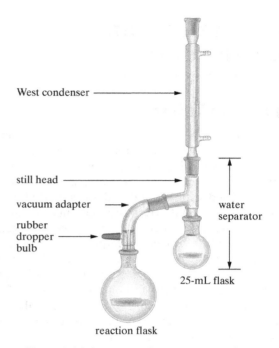

Figure B16 Apparatus for water separation

Dean–Stark trap is inserted in the reaction flask, filled to the level of its sidearm with the reaction solvent, and fitted with a reflux condenser. As water forms during the reaction, its vapors and those of the reaction solvent condense inside the reflux condenser and drip down into the water separator. The organic solvent, which separates on top of the water layer, overflows through the sidearm and returns to the reaction flask, while the water stays in the bottom of the separator. The theoretical yield of water from the reaction can be calculated, so the volume of water in the separator is monitored to determine when the reaction is nearing completion.

If a Dean-Stark trap is not available, the parts from an organic lab kit can be assembled as shown in Figure B16 so that the 25-mL flask, still head, and vacuum adapter together function like a Dean–Stark trap. When you assemble this apparatus, clamp both flasks securely and close the vacuum adapter outlet with a rubber bulb from a medicine dropper. Use a funnel to fill the water separator with the organic solvent to a level just below the bottom of the sidearm. Heat the reaction mixture under gentle reflux, being careful that the adapter's drip tip doesn't become flooded with liquid (an adapter with a missing drip tip works better). When disassembling the apparatus after the reaction, leave the water separator clamped while the other components are removed, then tilt it carefully to pour liquid from its sidearm into a beaker.

Excluding Air from Reaction Mixtures

Some chemicals react readily with oxygen from the air, so reactions using such chemicals must be conducted in an inert (oxygen-free) atmosphere. The simplest and least expensive way to provide an inert atmosphere is to flush all parts of a reaction apparatus with nitrogen. This process also removes water vapor and thus provides a dry atmosphere as well.

To flush a reflux assembly with nitrogen, first assemble the apparatus pictured in Figure B17. Use glassware components that have been oven-dried and then cooled. Coat all the joints with a thin layer of joint grease (see OP-2) and use joint clips to keep them from separating. Fold a rubber septum over the straight arm of the Claisen adapter and another rubber septum over the top of the condenser. Insert syringe needles (but not the syringes) through

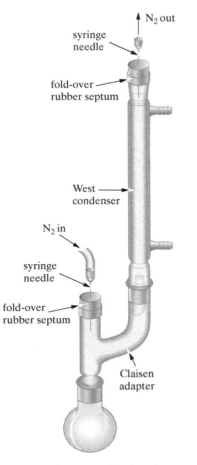

Figure B17 Apparatus for conducting a reaction in a dry, oxygen-free atmosphere

From *Operational Organic Chemistry: A Problem Solving Approach to the Laboratory*, Fourth Edition, John W. Lehman. Copyright © 2009 by Pearson Education. Published by Prentice Hall. All rights reserved.

both septa. To make a gas bubbler that will monitor the nitrogen flow, attach a short Pasteur pipet to one end of a length of rubber or plastic tubing and clamp it over a test tube partly filled with mineral oil, inserting its narrow end in the oil; then attach the other end of the tubing to the base of the syringe needle at the top of the condenser. Use another piece of tubing to attach the needle on the Claisen adapter to a nitrogen source. Open the nitrogen flow valve just far enough to produce a gentle stream of bubbles in the mineral oil. After a few minutes, reduce the flow to maintain a small positive nitrogen pressure in the apparatus, and then carry out the reaction. If the reaction mixture is being heated, increase the flow rate at the end of the heating period to maintain a positive pressure while the flask cools down.

Trapping Gases

The best way to keep toxic and smelly gases out of the laboratory air is to conduct all reactions under an efficient fume hood. If that isn't possible, or if the hood is not adequate, gases can be removed using either a gas trap or a water aspirator.

A gas trap containing a suitable gas-absorbing liquid or solid will remove most gases effectively. Water alone will dissolve some gases, but dilute aqueous sodium hydroxide (about 5% or 1 M) is generally used for acidic gases, such as HBr or SO_2. It converts them to salts that dissolve in the water.

$$HBr + NaOH \longrightarrow NaBr + H_2O$$
$$SO_2 + NaOH \longrightarrow NaHSO_3$$

Similarly, dilute aqueous HCl can be used to trap ammonia and other alkaline gases. A drying tube (see OP-12a) filled with cotton that is carefully moistened with water can trap some gases and remove some odors, but it is only effective for water-soluble gases and organic vapors, and precautions must be taken to keep water from dripping into the apparatus.

You can construct a simple gas trap by clamping an inverted narrow-stemmed funnel over a beaker that contains a suitable gas-absorbing liquid and then lowering the funnel so that its rim just touches the surface of the liquid, as shown in Figure B18. Connect the gas trap to the reaction apparatus at any point that is open to the atmosphere (usually the top of a reflux condenser) using rubber tubing and a short length of fire-polished glass tubing (see OP-3) that is inserted into a thermometer adapter or rubber stopper.

You can remove water-soluble gases such as hydrogen halides by using a water aspirator. Attach a vacuum adapter to the top of your reflux condenser, or any other part of your apparatus that is open to the atmosphere, and use a length of heavy-walled rubber tubing to connect the sidearm of the adapter to the aspirator. Turn on the aspirator while the gas is being generated. The gas should be drawn into the aspirator, dissolve in the water, and pass down the drain. Before using an aspirator for this purpose, make sure that it is legally permissible in your city or state to flush such gases into the wastewater system.

For small amounts of gases, a straight glass tube inserted into a test tube containing the gas-absorbing liquid may be adequate (Figure B19). Clamp the outlet of the glass tube about a millimeter *above* the surface of the liquid to keep it from backing up into the reaction apparatus when gas evolution ceases or heating is discontinued. Connect it to the reaction apparatus as shown in Figure B18, using a thermometer adapter or rubber stopper.

From *Operational Organic Chemistry: A Problem Solving Approach to the Laboratory*, Fourth Edition, John W. Lehman. Copyright © 2009 by Pearson Education. Published by Prentice Hall. All rights reserved.

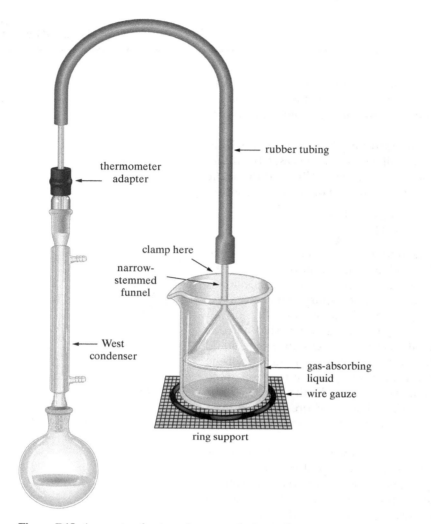

Figure B18 Apparatus for trapping gases during reflux

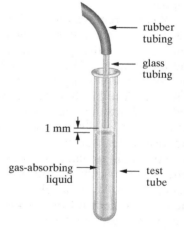

Figure B19 Small-scale gas trap

Gravity Filtration

Filtration is used for two main purposes in organic chemistry:

- To remove solid impurities from a liquid or solution
- To separate an organic solid from a reaction mixture or a crystallization solvent

Gravity filtration is generally used for the first purpose, and *vacuum filtration* [OP-16] for the second. *Centrifugation* [OP-17] can be used for either. In a gravity filtration, the liquid component of a liquid–solid mixture drains through a filtering medium (such as filter paper or cotton) by gravity alone, leaving the solid on the filtering medium. The filtered liquid, called the *filtrate,* is collected in a flask or another container. Gravity filtration is often used to remove drying agents from dried organic liquids or solutions and solid impurities from hot recrystallization solutions.

If the solid being removed is coarse and quite dense, it can sometimes be removed from a liquid by letting it settle to the bottom of the container (preferably an Erlenmeyer flask) and then slowly and carefully pouring the liquid into another container, leaving the solid behind. Some of the liquid may remain behind in the flask, but it can be transferred [OP-6] using a Pasteur pipet or a filter-tip pipet, if necessary. This process, called *decanting,* should not be used with finely divided solids, because some of the solid will inevitably be poured out with the liquid and contaminate it.

Gravity filtration of moderate to large volumes of organic liquids can be carried out using a funnel with a short, wide stem (such as a powder funnel) and a relatively fast, fluted filter paper (Figure C1). Circles of ordinary

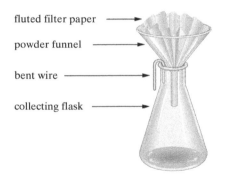

Figure C1 Apparatus for gravity filtration

Take Care! Wear gloves when handling glass wool.

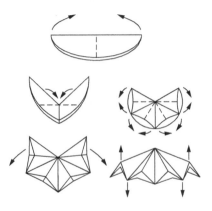

Figure C2 Making a fluted filter paper

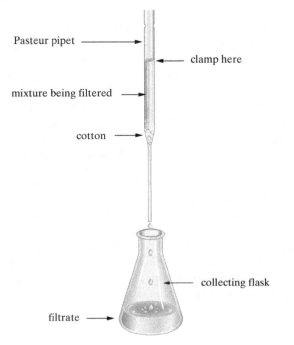

Figure C3 Filtration with a filtering pipet

From *Operational Organic Chemistry: A Problem Solving Approach to the Laboratory*, Fourth Edition, John W. Lehman. Copyright © 2009 by Pearson Education. Published by Prentice Hall. All rights reserved.

filter paper, such as 12.5 cm Whatman #1 (for fine particles) or Whatman #4 (for coarser particles), can be fluted (folded) as shown in Figure C2, but commercial fluted filter papers are available from chemical supply houses. Glass wool is sometimes used for very fast filtration of coarse solids. A thin layer of glass wool is placed inside the cone of a short-stemmed funnel, covering the outlet hole, and the mixture to be filtered is poured directly onto the glass wool. Because fine particles will pass through glass wool fibers, this method is most often used for prefiltration of mixtures that will be filtered again.

Small amounts of solid–liquid mixtures (~10 mL or less) can be filtered using a *filtering pipet*—a $5\frac{3}{4}$-inch Pasteur pipet that contains a small plug of cotton (see Figure C3). A filtering pipet with a somewhat larger capacity can be constructed by cutting the rounded top off the bulb of a plastic Beral-type pipet and packing some cotton or glass wool in its neck (see *J. Chem. Educ.* **1993**, *70*, A204). The plastic may not be compatible with some organic solvents, however.

DIRECTIONS FOR GRAVITY FILTRATION WITH A FUNNEL

Equipment and Supplies

> powder funnel
> fluted filter paper
> bent wire or paper clip
> Erlenmeyer flask or other collecting container

If you are filtering the solid–liquid mixture into a narrow-necked container such as an Erlenmeyer flask, support the funnel on the neck of the flask, placing a bent wire or a paper clip between them to leave a gap for pressure equalization (Figure C1). Alternatively, you can set the funnel in a ring support or funnel support positioned directly over the collecting container. Open the fluted filter paper to form a cone and insert it snugly into the funnel, trying not to flatten out any of its folds. If the solid is not finely divided or if there is not much of it, decant (pour) the mixture directly into the filter paper cone. If the mixture contains a considerable amount of finely divided solid, let the solid settle first, and then carefully decant the liquid into the filter paper cone so that most of the solid remains behind until the end of the filtration (this helps keep the fine solid from clogging the pores of the filter paper and slowing the filtration). In either case, add the mixture fast enough to keep the filter paper cone about two-thirds full, without allowing any liquid to rise above the top of the filter paper, until it has all been added. Swirl a small amount of an appropriate pure solvent (usually the solvent present in the mixture being filtered) in the decanting container to wash any residual solid, then pour it into the filter paper cone and let it drain into the receiving container. Wash the solid on the filter paper with this solvent by stirring gently as the solvent drains, but be careful not to tear the filter paper with your stirring rod. This washing step should reduce losses due to adsorption of dissolved organic materials on the solid.

Unless you need to save the solid as well as the filtrate, there is no need to transfer all of the solid to the filter paper.

Summary

1. Support funnel over collecting container.
2. Insert fluted filter paper.
3. Pour mixture being filtered into filter cone and let drain.
4. Wash solid in decanting vessel and on filter paper.
5. Clean up.

DIRECTIONS FOR GRAVITY FILTRATION WITH A FILTERING PIPET

Equipment and Supplies

two $5\frac{3}{4}$-inch Pasteur pipets

rubber bulb (2-mL capacity)

cotton

applicator stick or stirring rod

collecting containers

Roll a small amount of cotton between your fingers to form a loose ball and insert it in the top of a $5\frac{3}{4}$-inch Pasteur pipet. (Alternatively, use a Beral-type pipet with the top cut off.) Then use a small stirring rod or a wooden applicator stick to push it down the body of the pipet, forming a cotton plug that ends about where the capillary section of the pipet begins, as shown in Figure C3. Don't pack it too tightly, because that will slow down the filtration. Clamp the resulting filtering pipet vertically over a small beaker. Rinse the plug with a suitable wash solvent (usually the solvent present in the mixture being filtered) by using a second Pasteur pipet to transfer about 0.5 mL of the solvent to the top of the filtering pipet, letting it drain, and using a rubber bulb to force any remaining solvent through. Replace the beaker by another collecting container, such as a small flask, and use the second Pasteur pipet to transfer the mixture being filtered—in several portions, if necessary—to the top of the filtering pipet. Let the liquid drain by gravity into the collecting container. If the filtration rate is very slow, you can use a pipet pump (see OP-5) to apply a gentle, constant pressure to the top of the filtering pipet (a rubber bulb may also work). Don't use excessive pressure, because that may force particles into the filtrate. Depress the pipet pump's quick-release lever (if it has one) before you remove it. Wash the solid and the plug with a small amount of wash solvent as described previously, collecting the solvent in the container that holds the filtrate. Use a rubber bulb or a pipet pump to force out the last few drops of liquid. If you wish to reuse the Pasteur pipet, remove the plug (when it is dry) either by pulling it out with a wooden applicator stick (twirl it to snag the fibers) or by snagging it with a copper wire bent to form a "J" at one end.

Summary

1. Prepare filtering pipet by inserting cotton plug in Pasteur pipet.
2. Clamp filtering pipet over beaker and rinse with solvent.
3. Replace beaker with collecting container.

4. Transfer mixture being filtered to filtering pipet and let drain.

5. Wash filtering pipet with solvent.

6. Clean up.

When Things Go Wrong

If a liquid is filtering very slowly, the filter paper or other filtering medium may be too retentive or the particles may be so fine that they plug the pores in the filter paper. Try using a coarser filtering medium, such as a coarse fluted filter paper for a funnel or a glass wool plug (wear gloves) for a filtering pipet. If necessary, you can *gently* force solvent through a filtering pipet with a rubber bulb or a pipet pump. If fine particles pass into the filtrate, refilter using a more retentive filtering medium.

Vacuum Filtration

Vacuum filtration (also called suction filtration) provides a fast, convenient method for isolating a solid from a liquid–solid mixture and for removing solid impurities from a relatively large quantity of liquid. In a typical vacuum filtration involving moderate to large amounts of solids, a circle of filter paper is laid flat on a perforated plate inside a porcelain *Buchner funnel,* which is attached by an airtight connector to a thick-walled *filter flask* that has a sidearm on its neck (see Figure C4). The filter flask's sidearm is connected to the inlet of a *water aspirator* or to a vacuum line, ordinarily by way of a trap (described in the "Experimental Considerations" section), with a short length of thick-walled rubber tubing. In the water aspirator, a rapid stream of water flows past a small hole at the inlet, creating a vacuum there and in the attached filter flask, and exits into a sink. An aspirator should always be run "full blast," because its efficiency decreases and the likelihood of water backup increases at lower flow rates. When the mixture being filtered is poured into the Buchner funnel, the liquid is forced through the paper by the unbalanced external pressure and collects in the filter flask, while the solid remains on the filter paper as a compact *filter cake.*

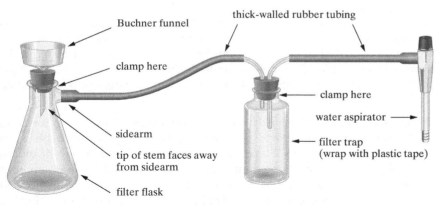

Figure C4 Apparatus for vacuum filtration

Smaller quantities of solids can be filtered by essentially the same method using a *Hirsch funnel* attached to a small filter flask or a sidearm test tube (see Figure C5). A porcelain Hirsch funnel contains an integral perforated plate about 1–2 cm in diameter; plastic Hirsch-type funnels with separate fritted disks (which don't require filter paper) are also available. Hirsch funnels use very small filter paper circles. These are available commercially, but they can also be cut from ordinary filter paper using a sharp cork borer (see OP-3) on a flat cutting surface, such as the bottom of a large cork. For a porcelain Hirsch funnel, the filter paper should be about equal in size to the perforated plate or slightly smaller, but large enough to completely cover all of its holes.

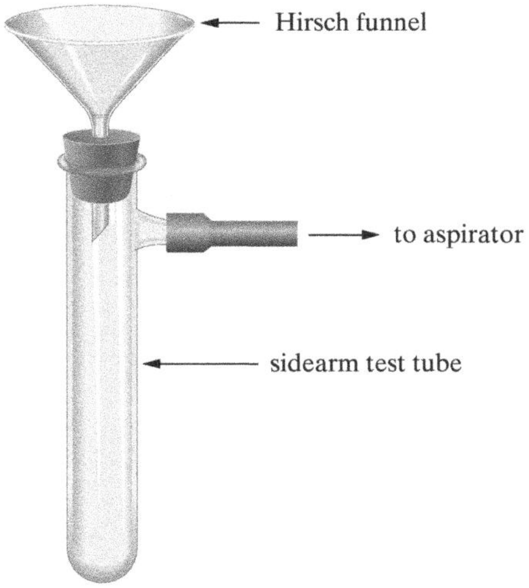

Experimental Considerations

Filter Traps and Cold Traps. You should ordinarily interpose a *filter trap* between the filter flask (or sidearm test tube) and a water aspirator to keep

Figure C5 Apparatus for small-scale vacuum filtration

From *Operational Organic Chemistry: A Problem Solving Approach to the Laboratory,* Fourth Edition, John W. Lehman. Copyright © 2009 by Pearson Education. Published by Prentice Hall. All rights reserved.

water from backing up into the flask when the water pressure changes, as it often does. Using a filter trap is most important when the filtrate is to be saved, because any backed-up water will contaminate the filtrate, but it's a good idea to use the trap for all vacuum filtrations involving an aspirator. A suitable filter trap can be constructed by wrapping a thick-walled Pyrex jar with transparent plastic tape (to reduce the chance of injury in case of implosion) and inserting a rubber stopper fitted with two L-shaped connecting tubes. Note that one of the connecting tubes should be longer than the other (see Figure C4). A filter trap with a pressure-release valve is illustrated in Figure E11 of OP-31.

Take Care! Never use a thin-walled container, such as an Erlenmeyer flask, as a trap; it may shatter under vacuum.

If you are using a vacuum line connected to a central mechanical vacuum pump, you may need to use a *cold trap* to protect the pump from solvent vapors that might damage it (your instructor will inform you if this is necessary). A filter trap can function as a cold trap if it is immersed in an appropriate cold bath [OP-8].

Filtering Media. Because of the external pressure on the mixture being filtered, solid particles are more likely to pass through the filter paper than with gravity filtration, so a slower (finer-grained) grade of filter paper should be used. An all-purpose filter paper, such as Whatman #1, is adequate for filtration of most solids. When filtering a finely divided solid impurity from a liquid, you may need to use a *filtering aid* (such as Celite) to keep the solid from plugging the pores in the filter paper. In a stoppered flask, shake the filtering aid vigorously with a suitable solvent to form a slurry (a thick suspension). Without delay, pour the slurry onto the filter paper—while applying a vacuum—until a bed about 2–3 mm thick has been deposited. Remove the solvent from the filter flask before continuing with the filtration. This method can't be used when the solid is to be saved, because it would be contaminated with the filtering aid.

Washing. Unless otherwise instructed, you should always *wash* the solid on the filter paper with an appropriate solvent—usually the same solvent as the one from which it was filtered. To reduce losses, the wash solvent should be cooled in ice water. For example, if you filter a solid from an aqueous solution, use cold distilled water as the wash solvent. If you filter a solid from a mixture of solvents, as in a mixed-solvent recrystallization [OP-28b], you should ordinarily use the solvent in which the solid is least soluble. For more information about washing solids, see OP-26a.

Drying. A solid that has been collected by vacuum filtration is usually *air-dried* after the last washing by leaving it on the filter for a few minutes with the vacuum turned on. The vacuum draws air through the solid, which increases the drying rate. If the solid is still quite wet, you can place a *rubber dam* (a thin, flexible rubber sheet) or a sheet of plastic wrap over the mouth of the funnel. The vacuum should cause the sheet to flatten out on top of the filter cake, forcing water out of it. Unless a solid is filtered from a very low-boiling solvent, it should be dried further by one of the methods described in OP-26b.

DIRECTIONS FOR VACUUM FILTRATION

Equipment and Supplies

Buchner funnel or Hirsch funnel
filter flask (or sidearm test tube)
1-hole rubber stopper or neoprene adapter

filter trap
filter paper
thick-walled rubber tubing
flat-bottomed stirring rod (optional)
flat-bladed microspatula
wash solvent

Clamp the filter flask and trap (if you are using one) securely to a ring stand, and connect them to an aspirator or a vacuum line as shown in Figure C4. Use thick-walled rubber tubing that will not collapse under vacuum for all connections. If you are using a water aspirator, connect the longer glass tube on the filter trap (the tube that extends farther into the trap) to the aspirator, and the shorter glass tube to the filter flask. If you are using a vacuum line that must be protected by a cold trap, connect the trap to the vacuum line and filter flask; secure it inside a cooling bath as directed by your instructor. Insert a Buchner or Hirsch funnel into the filter flask using a neoprene filter adapter or a snug-fitting rubber stopper to provide a tight seal. Obtain a circle of filter paper of the correct diameter and place it inside the funnel so that it covers all of the holes in the perforated plate but doesn't extend up the sides of the funnel.

Replace the term filter flask *by* sidearm test tube *if you are using the latter.*

Moisten the filter paper with a few drops of wash solvent—a solvent that is present in the mixture being filtered or one that is miscible with it. Open the aspirator tap or vacuum-line valve as far as it will go. Direct the water stream from an aspirator into a large beaker or another container to prevent splashing. If the solid is finely divided, let it settle before you decant the liquid into the funnel, and transfer the bulk of the solid near the end of the filtration. Otherwise, stir or swirl the mixture just before decanting to transfer more of the solid and leave less behind in the decanting vessel. If the volume of the filtration mixture is greater than the capacity of the funnel, add the mixture rapidly enough to keep the funnel about two-thirds full throughout the filtration, until it has all been added. Transfer any remaining solid to the filter paper with a flat-bladed spatula, using a small amount of the filtrate or some cold wash solvent to facilitate the transfer. Leave the vacuum on until only an occasional drop of liquid emerges from the stem of the funnel. If there is a possibility that water collecting in a trap will back up into the filter flask, or if you are using an aspirator with no filter trap, break the vacuum using a pressure-release valve or disconnect the rubber tubing at the vacuum source before you turn off the vacuum.

Do not attach a rubber tube to the aspirator outlet to reduce splashing, because it will also reduce the aspirator's effectiveness.

With the vacuum off, add enough previously chilled wash solvent to cover the solid. Being careful not to disturb the filter paper, stir the mixture *gently* with a spatula or a flat-bottomed stirring rod until the solid is suspended in the liquid. Without delay, turn on the vacuum to drain the wash liquid. Work quickly to avoid dissolving an appreciable amount of solid in the wash solvent. It's usually best to repeat the washing step with at least one more portion of chilled wash solvent. After the last washing, leave the vacuum on for 3–5 minutes (longer if the solvent is water) to air-dry the solid on the filter and make it easier to handle. Run the tip of a flat-bladed microspatula (see OP-6) around the circumference of the filter paper to dislodge the filter cake; then invert the funnel carefully over a square of glazed paper, a watch glass, a weighing dish, or another suitable container to remove the filter cake and filter paper. Use your spatula to scrape any remaining particles onto the paper or into the container. Dry

Rule of Thumb: *Use about 1–2 mL of wash solvent per gram of solid unless directed otherwise.*

Waste Disposal: Dispose of the filtrate as directed by your instructor or as indicated in an experiment's directions.

the solid by one of the methods described in OP-26b. To reduce losses, dry the filter paper along with the filter cake and scrape off any additional solid after it is dry, being careful not to scrape any filter paper fibers into your product.

Summary

1. Assemble apparatus for vacuum filtration.
2. Position and moisten filter paper, and turn on vacuum.
3. Add mixture being filtered to funnel.
4. Transfer any remaining solid to funnel.
5. Wash solid on filter with chilled wash solvent.
6. Air-dry solid on filter paper.
7. Transfer solid to container and remove filtrate from filter flask.
8. Disassemble and clean apparatus.

When Things Go Wrong

If a liquid is filtering very slowly, the filter paper may be too retentive or its pores may be plugged with fine particles. Replace the used filter paper with a new one (keep any solid you collected on the used one), let the solid settle to the bottom of the mixture you are filtering, then carefully decant the liquid into the filtering funnel and wait until the end of the filtration process to transfer the solid (with any remaining liquid). Also consider switching to a larger filtering device, such as a Buchner funnel rather than a Hirsch funnel. If filtration is still too slow, try using a coarser filtering medium, such as a circle of Whatman #4 paper rather than Whatman #1 (you may have to refilter the filtrate if fine particles pass through the paper). If you don't need to save the solid, you can use a filtering aid such as Celite. (See "Filtering Media.") Slow filtration rates with a water aspirator may also be caused by low water pressure when too many aspirators are running at the same time. Be patient, or wait until later to compete your filtration.

If water backs up into the filter flask when you turn off an aspirator, you probably didn't use a filter trap. Remove the water, and then connect a trap between the filter flask and the aspirator as shown in Figure C4. Alternatively, pull off the tubing at the aspirator before you turn it off. (See "Filter Traps and Cold Traps.")

If an appreciable amount of solid product disappears when you wash it, the wash solvent may not have been adequately chilled, you may have used too much of it, or it may be inappropriate for washing your product. If the filtrate contains a relatively low-boiling solvent, you should be able to recover the solid by evaporating [OP-19] the solvent, but it should then be purified and washed more carefully. Alternatively, some solid may have passed under the filter paper and into the filtrate. Try refiltering the filtrate, being careful not to displace the filter paper when you wash the recovered solid. (See "Washing.")

Centrifugation

Centrifugation is used to separate different phases from one another by centrifugal force. When a mixture in a centrifuge tube is placed inside a *centrifuge* (Figure C6) and whirled around a circular path at high speed, the denser phase (usually a solid) is forced to the bottom of the tube, leaving the other phase on top. Centrifugation can also be used to ensure complete separation between two immiscible liquids after an extraction [OP-18a] and to collect small amounts of liquids that have been separated by preparative gas chromatography [OP-37].

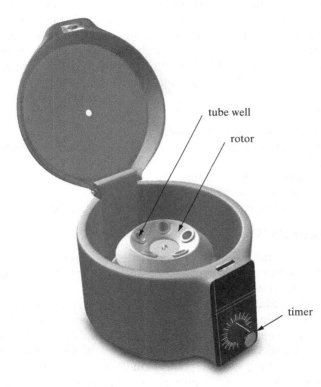

tube well

rotor

timer

Figure C6 A benchtop centrifuge

DIRECTIONS FOR CENTRIFUGATION

Equipment and Supplies

  benchtop centrifuge
  two centrifuge tubes
  Pasteur pipet (for liquid–liquid mixtures)
  flat-bladed microspatula (for liquid–solid mixtures)

Transfer the mixture to be centrifuged to a conical centrifuge tube with a capacity of ~15 mL, or another centrifuge tube specified by your instructor or the experimental procedure. Obtain an empty matched centrifuge tube

From *Operational Organic Chemistry: A Problem Solving Approach to the Laboratory*, Fourth Edition, John W. Lehman. Copyright © 2009 by Pearson Education. Published by Prentice Hall. All rights reserved.

Alternatively, find another student who is doing the same operation and use his or her centrifuge tube to balance your own. Label the tubes so you don't mix them up.

and add enough water to it so that the two tubes, with their contents, have approximately equal masses. Usually you can estimate the amount of water by volume, but you may have to weigh the tubes to ensure proper balance. Place the two centrifuge tubes directly opposite each other in the centrifuge's rotor; they fit into tube wells, which may be cushioned to help prevent breakage. Close and lock the centrifuge lid, set the centrifuge's timer (if it has one) to 3–5 minutes, and start the centrifuge. When the time is up (or when you switch off the centrifuge), the rotor will slowly come to a stop. Wait until its whirring sound has stopped; then open the lid and remove the centrifuge tubes. If you are centrifuging a liquid–solid mixture and the solid is not firmly packed in the bottom of the tube, continue centrifuging until the solid is compacted and there are no floating particles. Then carefully decant the liquid or remove it with a Pasteur pipet or a filter-tip pipet, leaving the solid behind. Use the pointed end of a flat-bladed microspatula to remove the solid. If you are centrifuging a mixture of two immiscible liquids, separate the liquids after centrifugation by removing the lower layer with a Pasteur pipet, as described in OP-18a. Use a tapered centrifuge brush, if one is available, to clean the centrifuge tube.

Summary

1. Transfer mixture to centrifuge tube.
2. Place centrifuge tube and a second tube of comparable mass in opposite tube wells.
3. Run centrifuge for 3–5 minutes.
4. Let centrifuge stop, and remove tubes.
5. Separate liquid layer from solid or second liquid layer.

When Things Go Wrong

If the centrifuge vibrates badly, rattles loudly, or stops before the time is up, the centrifuge tubes are not properly balanced. Remove and balance them, and then resume centrifugation.

If a centrifuge tube breaks while the centrifuge is operating, the broken tube may have been faulty, it may have been the wrong kind for the centrifuge you are using, it may not have been balanced properly, or the tube wells may not be adequately cushioned. Clean up the mess and try to identify the problem so that it doesn't happen again. If there is little or no cushioning in the wells, you may be able to push in some Styrofoam that has been cut to fit. See your instructor first, because the padding may raise the tubes so high that they contact the lid of the centrifuge when it spins.

Extraction

If you shake a bromine/water solution with some dichloromethane, the red-brown color of the bromine fades from the water layer and appears in the dichloromethane layer as you shake. The color changes show that the bromine has been transferred from one solvent (water) to another (dichloromethane). The process of transferring a substance from a liquid or solid mixture to a solvent is called *extraction,* and the solvent is called the *extraction solvent.* An extraction solvent is usually a low-boiling organic solvent that can be evaporated [OP-19] after extraction to isolate the desired substance.

Extraction is used for the following purposes in organic chemistry:

- To separate a desired organic substance from a reaction mixture or some other mixture
- To remove impurities from a desired organic substance, which is usually dissolved in an organic solvent

The second process is described in OP-24, "Washing Liquids."

a. Liquid–Liquid Extraction

Principles and Applications

Liquid–liquid extraction is based on the principle that if a substance is soluble to some extent in two immiscible liquids, most of it can be transferred from one liquid to the other by a process that involves thorough mixing of the liquids. For example, acetanilide is partly soluble in both water and dichloromethane. If a solution of acetanilide in water is shaken with a portion of dichloromethane, some of the acetanilide will be transferred to the organic (dichloromethane) layer (see Figure C7). The organic layer, being denser than water, separates below the water layer and can be removed and replaced with another portion of dichloromethane. When that portion of dichloromethane is shaken with the aqueous solution, more acetanilide passes into the new organic layer. This new layer can then be removed and combined with the

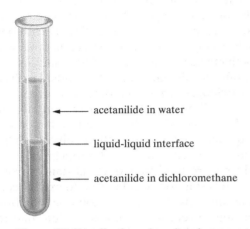

acetanilide in water

liquid-liquid interface

acetanilide in dichloromethane

Figure C7 Distribution of a solute between two liquids

From *Operational Organic Chemistry: A Problem Solving Approach to the Laboratory*, Fourth Edition, John W. Lehman. Copyright © 2009 by Pearson Education. Published by Prentice Hall. All rights reserved.

first. By repeating this process enough times, virtually all of the acetanilide can be transferred from the water to the dichloromethane.

The ability of an extraction solvent (S_2) to remove a solute (A) from another solvent (S_1) depends on the partition coefficient (K) of solute A in the two solvents, as defined in Equation **1**:

$$K = \frac{\text{concentration of A in } S_2}{\text{concentration of A in } S_1} \qquad \textbf{(1)}$$

In the example of acetanilide in water and dichloromethane, the partition coefficient is given by

$$K = \frac{[\text{acetanilide}]_{\text{dichl.}}}{[\text{acetanilide}]_{\text{water}}}$$

The larger the value of K, the more solute will be transferred to the organic layer with each extraction, and the fewer portions of dichloromethane will be required for essentially complete removal of the solute. A rough estimate of K can be obtained by using the ratio of the solubilities of the solute in the two solvents—that is,

$$K \sim \frac{\text{solubility of A in } S_2}{\text{solubility of A in } S_1}$$

This approximate relationship can be helpful in choosing a suitable extraction solvent.

Extraction Solvents

Most extraction solvents are organic liquids that are used to extract nonpolar and moderately polar solutes from aqueous solutions. A good organic extraction solvent should be immiscible with water, dissolve a wide range of organic substances, and have a low boiling point so that it can be removed by evaporation after the extraction. The substance being extracted should be more soluble in the extraction solvent than in water; otherwise, too many steps will be required to extract it.

Diethyl ether and dichloromethane (methylene chloride) are the most commonly used organic extraction solvents. Diethyl ether (also called ethyl ether or simply "ether") has a very low boiling point (35°C) and can dissolve both polar and nonpolar organic compounds, but it is extremely flammable and tends to form explosive peroxides on standing. Dichloromethane is denser than water, which usually simplifies the extraction process, and it isn't flammable. Dichloromethane has a tendency to form emulsions, which can make it difficult to separate cleanly, and it must be handled with caution because it is a suspected carcinogen. These and other extraction solvents and their properties are listed in Table C1. Organic extraction solvents that are less dense than water ($d = 1.00$ g/mL) will separate as the top layer during the extraction of an aqueous solution; extraction solvents that are more dense than water will ordinarily separate as the bottom layer.

Just as organic solvents are used to extract substances from aqueous solutions, water and aqueous solutions can be used to extract certain polar substances from organic solutions. An aqueous solution may function as a *chemically active* extraction solvent if it contains a solute that reacts with the substance to be extracted, thus changing its distribution between the

Table C1 Properties of commonly used extraction solvents

Solvent	bp, °C	d, g/mL	Comments
water	100	1.00	for extracting polar compounds, generally using a reactive solute such as NaOH or HCl
diethyl ether	35	0.71	good general solvent; absorbs some water; very flammable
dichloromethane	40	1.33	good general solvent; suspected carcinogen
toluene	111	0.87	for extracting aromatic and nonpolar compounds; difficult to remove
petroleum ether	~35–60	~0.64	for extracting nonpolar compounds; very flammable
*hexane	69	0.66	for extracting nonpolar compounds; flammable

*The mixture of C_6H_{14} isomers called hexanes is cheaper than pure hexane and is often used in place of it.

aqueous and organic layers. For example, dilute aqueous sodium hydroxide can be used to extract carboxylic acids from organic solvents by first converting them to carboxylate salts, which are much more soluble in water and less soluble in organic solvents than are the original carboxylic acids.

$$RCOOH + NaOH \longrightarrow RCOO^- Na^+ + H_2O$$

If the carboxylic acid is sufficiently insoluble in water, it can be recovered by acidifying the aqueous extract to precipitate the acid, which is then collected by vacuum filtration [OP-16]. Similarly, dilute hydrochloric acid is used to extract basic solutes such as amines from organic solvents by converting the amines to ammonium salts, which are much more soluble in water and less soluble in organic solvents than are the amines themselves.

$$RNH_2 + HCl \longrightarrow RNH_3^+Cl^-$$

Potential hazards should be considered when selecting and using an extraction solvent. For example, solvents such as benzene, trichloromethane (chloroform), and tetrachloromethane (carbon tetrachloride) should not be used as extraction solvents in an undergraduate laboratory because of their toxicity and carcinogenic potential. Precautions must be taken with all organic solvents to minimize skin and eye contact and inhalation of vapors. Flames must not be allowed in the laboratory when highly flammable solvents, such as diethyl ether and petroleum ether, are in use.

Experimental Considerations

Extraction Methods. A standard scale liquid–liquid extraction is ordinarily carried out by shaking the liquids in a *separatory funnel* (see Figure C9), allowing time for the liquid layers to separate sharply, and opening the separatory funnel's stopcock to drain the lower layer into a separate container. The extraction is usually repeated several times to transfer most of the desired substance to the extraction solvent.

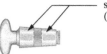

stopcock grease
(on both sides)

Figure C8 Lubricating a glass stopcock

Separatory funnels are expensive and break easily. Never prop a separatory funnel on its base; set it in a ring support or some other stable support. If your separatory funnel has a glass stopcock, lubricate it by applying thin bands of stopcock grease on both sides, leaving the center (where the drain hole is located) free of grease to prevent contamination (see Figure C8). A glass stopcock is secured to the separatory funnel by a compression clip or a rubber ring, which should be tight enough to keep it from leaking. A Teflon stopcock (which should *not* be lubricated) is secured by a Teflon washer, rubber O-ring and Teflon nut, in that order. The nut is screwed in tightly enough to prevent leakage, but not so tightly as to prevent smooth rotation of the stopcock.

A small-scale liquid–liquid extraction can be performed by shaking the liquids in a conical centrifuge tube and separating them with a Pasteur pipet. A 15-mL centrifuge tube can be used with liquid volumes up to ~12 mL. A screw-cap centrifuge tube is preferable to one with a snap-on cap, because it's less likely to leak. Always check a centrifuge tube for leaks by shaking some water in the capped tube. If it leaks, replace the tube if it has nicks or other damage on the rim, and replace the cap if its liner is missing or damaged. After an extraction, the liquid layers are separated by removing the *lower* layer with a Pasteur pipet and transferring it to another container. This way, the interface between the layers is at the narrowest part of the container when the last of the lower layer is removed, making a sharp separation possible. It takes some practice and a steady hand to remove all of the bottom layer without including any of the top layer, but it's important that you learn how to do so. Otherwise, you will lose part of your product, or the product will be contaminated with material from the layer being extracted. Most extraction solvents have a high vapor pressure, which may cause them to spurt out of the tip of a Pasteur pipet during transfer. Spurting can usually be prevented by making sure that the extraction solvent, the liquid being extracted, and the Pasteur pipet are at room temperature or below; and by rinsing the Pasteur pipet with the extraction solvent two or three times to fill it with solvent vapors just before use.

For either extraction method, accurate separation of layers is most important for the last extraction step, because any extraction solvent that isn't recovered during earlier steps can be recovered in the last one.

Volume of Extraction Solvent.

The volume of extraction solvent and the number of extraction steps are sometimes specified in an experimental procedure. If they are not, use a volume of extraction solvent about equal to the volume of liquid being extracted, divided into at least two portions. For example, you can extract 12 mL of an aqueous solution with two successive 6-mL (or three 4-mL) portions of extraction solvent. Note that it is more efficient to use several small portions of extraction solvent rather than one large portion of the same total volume.

Rule of Thumb: Total volume of extraction solvent ≈ volume of liquid being extracted.

Getting Good Separation.

Under some conditions, the liquid layers do not separate sharply, either because an *emulsion* forms at the interface between the two liquids or because droplets of one liquid remain in the other liquid layer. Emulsions can often be broken up by using a wooden applicator stick to stir the liquids gently at the interface. If that doesn't work, mix in some saturated aqueous sodium chloride solution (or enough

An emulsion usually contains microscopic droplets of one liquid suspended in another.

solid NaCl to saturate the aqueous layer) and allow the extraction container to stand open and undisturbed for a time.

To consolidate the liquid layers, use an applicator stick to rub or stir any liquid droplets that form on the sides or bottom of the extraction container. You can also use an applicator stick to remove small amounts of insoluble "gunk" that sometimes form near the interface. Larger amounts of insoluble material can be removed by filtering [OP-15] the mixture through a loose pad of glass wool in a powder funnel. If you are using a centrifuge tube rather than a separatory funnel, you can spin it in a centrifuge [OP-17] to help separate the layers cleanly.

Saving the Right Layer. *Always keep both layers until you are certain which layer contains the desired product!* All too often, a student will unthinkingly discard the extraction layer that contains the product and will have to repeat an experiment from the beginning. The safest practice is to keep both layers until you have actually isolated the product from one of them, but you can usually determine which is the right layer before then. In most extractions, the product is extracted from an aqueous solution into an organic solvent such as dichloromethane or diethyl ether. If you make careful observations when you add the extraction solvent, you can usually tell whether it floats on top of the aqueous layer or sinks below it. Because diethyl ether is less dense than water, it will form the upper layer when it is used to extract an aqueous solution. Dichloromethane is denser than water, so it will ordinarily form the lower layer with an aqueous solution (but see "When Things Go Wrong").

DIRECTIONS FOR EXTRACTION WITH A SEPARATORY FUNNEL

These directions apply to the use of an organic extraction solvent. If you are using an aqueous solvent to extract an organic solution, follow the same procedure but save the aqueous layer.

Equipment and Supplies

separatory funnel with stopper
ring stand
support for separatory funnel
narrow-stemmed funnel
extraction solvent
graduated cylinder
wooden applicator stick
2 flasks

Support a separatory funnel on a ring support of suitable diameter or another appropriate support. Close the stopcock by turning its handle to a horizontal position. Pour the liquid to be extracted into the separatory funnel, preferably using a stemmed funnel to avoid getting liquid on the glass joint. The liquid should be at or below room temperature to prevent vaporization of the extraction solvent. Measure the required volume of extraction solvent using a graduated cylinder (the exact volume isn't crucial)

If you use a metal ring support, cushion it with three short lengths of split rubber tubing to prevent damage to the separatory funnel.

and pour it through the stemmed funnel into the separatory funnel. The total volume of both liquids should not exceed three-quarters of the separatory funnel's capacity. If it does, obtain a larger separatory funnel or carry out the extraction in two or more steps, using a portion of the liquid to be extracted in each step.

Moisten the stopper with water and insert it firmly with a twisting motion. Then pick up the funnel in both hands and partly invert it, with your right hand holding the stopcock (or your left hand, if you're a southpaw) and the first two fingers of your left hand holding the stopper in place (see Figure C9). Holding the separatory funnel with its outlet above the liquid level and its stem pointed away from you and your neighbors, *vent* it by slowly opening the stopcock to release any pressure buildup. Close the stopcock, shake the separatory funnel gently for a few seconds (still keeping its stem end higher than its stoppered end), and vent it as before. Then shake the funnel more vigorously, with occasional venting, for 2–3 minutes. As you shake the funnel, rotate the wrist holding its stem end so that its contents are swirled as well as shaken; this motion is more efficient than shaking alone. Avoid overly vigorous mixing if the solvent tends to form emulsions.

Replace the funnel on its support, remove the stopper, and allow the funnel to stand until there is a sharp dividing line between the two layers. Use a wooden applicator stick to help consolidate the layers, if necessary. Begin to drain the bottom layer into a labeled Erlenmeyer flask (flask **A**) by opening the stopcock fully. As the interface approaches the bottom of the funnel, partly close the stopcock to slow the drainage rate. Close it completely, separating the layers cleanly, just as the interface reaches the

Take Care! Wear gloves during an extraction to protect your hands in case of leakage.

Venting should not be necessary once there is no longer an audible hiss of escaping vapors when the stopcock is opened.

Separation Operations

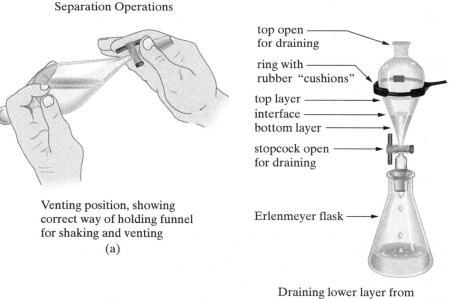

Venting position, showing correct way of holding funnel for shaking and venting
(a)

top open for draining

ring with rubber "cushions"

top layer
interface
bottom layer

stopcock open for draining

Erlenmeyer flask

Draining lower layer from separatory funnel
(b)

Figure C9 Extraction techniques

stopcock. Follow method **1** if the extraction solvent is *more* dense than the liquid being extracted (forming the lower layer) and method **2** if it is *less* dense than the liquid being extracted (forming the upper layer).

1. Extract the liquid that remains in the separatory funnel (the original top layer) with a fresh portion of the same extraction solvent; then drain the bottom layer into container **A** as before, combining the extracts. Repeat the process, as necessary, with fresh extraction solvent. After the bottom layer has been removed following the last extraction, pour the remaining liquid out of the *top* of the separatory funnel into a separate labeled container (**B**), and retain it for later disposal.
2. Pour the liquid that remains in the separatory funnel (the original top layer) out of the *top* of the separatory funnel into a separate labeled container (flask **B**). Then return the liquid in **A** to the separatory funnel and extract it with a fresh portion of extraction solvent. Again drain the bottom layer into **A** and pour the top layer into **B**. Repeat the process, as necessary, with fresh extraction solvent, combining all extracts in **B**. Retain the liquid in flask **A** for later disposal.

Summary

1. Add liquid to be extracted to separatory funnel.
2. Add extraction solvent, stopper funnel, invert, and vent.
3. Shake and swirl funnel, with venting, to extract solute into extraction solvent.
4. Remove stopper and let layers separate.
5. Drain lower layer into flask **A**.
   IF extraction solvent was lower layer, GO TO 6.
   IF extraction solvent was upper layer, GO TO 7.
6. Stopper flask **A**.
   IF another extraction step is needed, GO TO 2.
   IF extraction is complete, empty and clean separatory funnel; STOP.
7. Pour remaining layer into flask **B** and stopper it.
   IF another extraction step is needed, return contents of **A** to separatory funnel; GO TO 2.
   IF extraction is complete, clean separatory funnel; STOP.

DIRECTIONS FOR EXTRACTION WITH A CENTRIFUGE TUBE

Equipment and Supplies

centrifuge tube with cap
support for extraction container
Pasteur pipet with bulb
10-mL graduated cylinder
extraction solvent
wooden applicator stick
1–2 containers (screw-cap vials, test tubes, etc.)

Obtain a 15-mL conical centrifuge tube with a screw cap and test it for leakage, then set it in a test-tube rack or another suitable support. Add the

Waste Disposal: Dispose of the extracted liquid as directed by your instructor or as indicated in an experiment's directions.

liquid to be extracted, which should be at room temperature or below. Use a small graduated cylinder (or other measuring device) to add a measured portion of the extraction solvent and cap the container tightly. Shake the extraction container gently and unscrew the cap slightly after 5–10 shakes to release any pressure inside the container. Tighten the cap and shake the mixture vigorously for at least 1 minute, with occasional venting. Shake less vigorously but for a longer time if the extraction solvent is dichloromethane, which tends to form emulsions. Loosen the cap and let the mixture stand until there is a sharp interface between the layers. Use a wooden applicator stick to help consolidate the layers, if necessary. Follow method **1** if the extraction solvent is *more* dense than the liquid being extracted (forming the lower layer) and method **2** if it is *less* dense than the liquid being extracted (forming the upper layer).

To facilitate layer separation, the tube can be spun in a centrifuge [OP-17] for several minutes.

1. Squeeze the bulb of a Pasteur pipet to expel air and insert the pipet vertically so that its tip barely touches the bottom of the centrifuge tube. Slowly withdraw the *bottom* (organic) layer, taking care not to mix the layers, and transfer it to a labeled test tube or another small container (container **A**). Add another measured portion of pure extraction solvent to the liquid that remains in the centrifuge tube (the original top layer) and shake to extract as before, transferring the extract (the bottom layer) to **A**. If another extraction is necessary, repeat the process, combining all of the extracts in **A**. Retain the liquid in the centrifuge tube for later disposal.

2. Squeeze the bulb of a Pasteur pipet to expel air and insert the pipet vertically so that its tip barely touches the bottom of the centrifuge tube. Slowly withdraw the *bottom* (aqueous) layer, taking care not to mix the layers, and transfer it to a labeled test tube or another small container (**A**). Transfer the contents of the centrifuge tube to a different labeled container (**B**) and return the contents of **A** to the centrifuge tube. Add another measured portion of pure extraction solvent and shake to extract as before, then transfer the lower layer to **A** and combine the upper layer with the extract in **B**. If another extraction is necessary, return the contents of **A** to the centrifuge tube and repeat the process. Retain the liquid in **A** for later disposal.

Waste Disposal: Dispose of the extracted liquid as directed by your instructor or as indicated in an experiment's directions.

Summary

1. Add liquid to be extracted to centrifuge tube.
2. Add extraction solvent to centrifuge tube and cap tightly.
3. Shake gently, vent, and continue shaking to extract solute into extraction solvent.
4. Loosen cap and let layers separate.
5. Uncap centrifuge tube; transfer lower layer to container **A**.
   IF extraction solvent was lower layer, GO TO 6.
   IF extraction solvent was upper layer, GO TO 7.
6. Cap or stopper container **A**.
   IF another extraction step is needed, GO TO 2.
   IF extraction is complete, clean up; STOP.
7. Transfer remaining layer to container **B** and cap it.
   IF another extraction step is needed, transfer contents of container **A** to centrifuge tube; GO TO 2.
   IF extraction is complete, clean up; STOP.

When Things Go Wrong

If there is bubbling or foaming when you mix a chemically active extraction solvent with the liquid to be extracted, the extraction solvent is reacting with a component of the liquid to yield a gas, usually carbon dioxide. Don't shake the mixture yet; stir it until the reaction has subsided and then begin shaking *gently,* with frequent venting.

If you're not sure which layer is the organic one, test the one you think is organic by adding a drop or two of water to a drop or two of that layer. If the water doesn't mix to give a homogeneous liquid, you've selected the organic layer; if the water mixes completely, you've got the aqueous layer. It's a good idea to label the containers for the extraction layers so you won't lose track of what's in them. (See "Saving the Right Layer.")

If the organic and aqueous layers don't separate cleanly, see "Getting Good Separation."

If you are draining the bottom layer from a separatory funnel and it stops draining, you forgot to take out the stopper. Close the stopcock and remove the stopper; then continue draining.

Suppose you are trying to extract a substance from an aqueous solution with two portions of diethyl ether. You carried out the extraction with the first portion of ether and transferred the bottom layer to a different container, leaving the top layer in the separatory funnel or centrifuge tube. Then you poured the second portion of ether into the extraction vessel and no layer separated. This is one of the most common extraction errors—adding the second portion of extraction solvent to the first portion of the *same* solvent rather than to the aqueous solution being extracted. Keep in mind that the combined ether layers still contain all of the product that was extracted by the first portion of ether. All you have to do is transfer the combined layers to another container, return the former bottom layer to the extraction vessel, extract it with a third portion of ether, and combine that portion with the rest of the ether. If you then evaporate [OP-19] the solvent, it will take a little longer to remove the extra ether, but that's better than starting over.

Suppose you saturated an aqueous reaction mixture with potassium carbonate to salt out [OP-18b] the organic product and then extracted the mixture with dichloromethane. Because dichloromethane ($d = 1.33$ g/ml) is denser than water ($d = 1.00$ g/ml), you saved the bottom layer, only to discover that the solvent in that layer wouldn't evaporate [OP-19] under the usual conditions. Although *pure* water is less dense than dichloromethane, adding a solute increases its density, and saturated aqueous potassium carbonate has a density of 1.56 g/mL—so the layer you saved was actually the aqueous layer. You could still salvage the situation by evaporating the solvent from the top (dichloromethane) layer, unless you discarded it, in which case you're out of luck.

In the James Bond movies, Bond always insists that his martinis be "shaken, not stirred." He's just being contrary; according to tradition, a good martini should be stirred, not shaken.

b. Salting Out

Adding an inorganic salt (such as sodium chloride or potassium carbonate) to an aqueous solution that contains an organic solute usually reduces the solubility of the organic compound in the water and thus promotes its separation. This *salting-out* technique is often used to separate a sparingly soluble organic liquid from its aqueous solution. For example, when an ester is hydrolyzed, the product mixture may be distilled to remove the alcohol, which can then be recovered by saturating the aqueous distillate with potassium carbonate and extracting it with diethyl ether. Salting out can also be used during an extraction to increase the amount of organic solute transferred from the aqueous to the organic layer and to remove excess water from the organic layer.

To salt out an organic liquid from an aqueous solution containing the liquid, add enough of the salt to saturate the aqueous solution, and then stir or shake it to dissolve the salt. You can estimate the amount of salt needed by using its water solubility or data from the "Saturated Solutions" table in *The Merck Index*. If you don't know how much salt to use, add it in small portions until a portion no longer dissolves completely. If any undissolved salt remains, filter the mixture through a plug of glass wool. Transfer the mixture to a separatory funnel or centrifuge tube for separation or extraction.

To improve separation during an extraction, add enough of the salt to the extraction vessel to saturate the aqueous layer, and shake to dissolve the salt. (You can also add a saturated solution of the salt, rather than the pure salt, to the extraction mixture, but the salting-out process is less complete because the resulting salt solution is more dilute.) If necessary, filter [OP-15] the contents of the extraction container through a plug of glass wool to remove any undissolved salt. Then proceed as for a normal extraction.

The 14th edition of The Merck Index *doesn't include this table, but it can be found in earlier editions.*

Take Care! Wear gloves when handling glass wool.

c. Liquid–Solid Extraction

Liquid–solid extraction involves the removal of one or more components of a solid by mixing the solid with an extraction solvent and separating the resulting solution from the solid residue. This method is often used to separate substances from natural products and other solid mixtures. For example, the red-orange pigment lycopene can be extracted from tomato products by petroleum ether and other solvents.

To perform a liquid–solid extraction, mix the solid intimately with the extraction solvent in a beaker or another suitable container, using a flat-bottomed stirring rod or a flexible flat-bladed spatula. Press or crush the solid against the bottom and sides of the container with the flat end of the stirring rod or spatula to extract as much of the solute as you can. Filter the mixture by gravity filtration [OP-15] or vacuum filtration [OP-16] and return any solid that collects on the filter to the beaker for the next extraction. Repeat the extraction as many times as necessary and combine the liquid extracts in a single collecting container.

For smaller amounts of extraction solvent, shake the solid vigorously with the solvent in a capped centrifuge tube or another suitable container, and then use a flat-bladed microspatula to crush and rub the solid against the sides of the tube. Repeat the shaking and crushing sequence several times. Centrifuge [OP-17] the mixture and transfer [OP-6] the extract to a suitable container, leaving the residue in the centrifuge tube. Repeat the extraction as many times as necessary and combine the liquid extracts in a single collecting container.

Liquid–solid extractions can also be carried out by treating the solid with hot or boiling solvent—often under reflux [OP-7c]—and filtering the mixture by gravity [OP-15].

Evaporation

Evaporation is the conversion of a liquid to vapor at or below the boiling point of the liquid. Evaporation can be used to remove a volatile solvent, such as diethyl ether or dichloromethane, from a comparatively involatile liquid or solid. Complete solvent removal is used to isolate an organic solute after such operations as extraction [OP-18] or column chromatography [OP-21]. Partial solvent removal, or *concentration,* can be used to bring a recrystallization solution to its saturation poin t (see OP-28).

Experimental Considerations

Because of possible health and fire hazards, you should never evaporate an organic solvent by heating an open container outside a fume hood. Even when using the methods described here, you should know and allow for the hazards associated with each solvent. In standard scale work, solvents are generally removed by distillation or under vacuum, but small amounts of solvents can be evaporated under a stream of nitrogen or dry air, or by leaving them under a fume hood. With any evaporation method, it is important to make sure that all of the solvent has evaporated. This can be done by weighing the evaporation container after evaporation, as described in "Directions for Evaporation Under Vacuum."

Evaporation Under a Fume Hood. The easiest (but slowest) way to evaporate small quantities of a volatile solvent from a solution is to put the solution in a tared wide-mouth container, such as an evaporating dish or a small beaker, and to leave the container under a fume hood for several hours or overnight. It's a good idea to protect the solution from contamination by airborne particles by supporting a circle of filter paper on a ring clamped several centimeters above the evaporation container. The process can be accelerated by clamping an inverted stemmed funnel over the container and drawing air through it with an aspirator or vacuum pump. Solvents evaporated by this method end up in the environment, so it should not be used for large quantities of solvents.

Take Care! Make sure that the hood is turned on.

Whenever possible, it is best to use an evaporation method that allows recovery of the evaporated solvent.

Evaporation Under Nitrogen or Dry Air. Relatively small quantities of a volatile solvent can be evaporated by passing a slow stream of nitrogen or dry air over the solution. Nitrogen is preferred, because the oxygen in air may react with easily oxidized solutes, but clean, dry air is suitable for most purposes. If you are using air from an air line, clean and dry it as described in OP-27. The gas stream sweeps solvent molecules away from the surface of the liquid, accelerating the evaporation rate. Evaporation cools the remaining liquid, however, so heating may be needed to maintain a rapid evaporation rate and to prevent condensation of water vapor in the product. This operation must be carried out under a fume hood to keep solvent vapors out of the laboratory. The solution to be evaporated is placed in a beaker or another suitable container, the gas delivery tube (which can be a Pasteur pipet) is clamped vertically a centimeter or two above the liquid, and a stream of the dry gas is directed over the surface of the liquid, which can be protected from

From *Operational Organic Chemistry: A Problem Solving Approach to the Laboratory*, Fourth Edition, John W. Lehman. Copyright © 2009 by Pearson Education. Published by Prentice Hall. All rights reserved.

airborne particles by supporting a filter paper several centimeters above it (see Figure C10). The container can be heated gently in a hot-water bath or over a steam bath to increase the evaporation rate, but heating it too strongly may cause the product to decompose.

Both this and the previous method have the disadvantage that the solvent ends up in the environment. Whenever possible, it is better to use one of the following methods and to save the solvent for recycling or later disposal.

Waste Disposal: Place the solvent in a designated solvent recovery container.

Distillation. High-boiling solvents and relatively large quantities of low-boiling solvents can be removed by simple distillation [OP-30] or vacuum distillation [OP-31]. This procedure is often used when a reaction mixture contains a liquid product in a volatile solvent. After the solvent has distilled, the product of the reaction can be purified by distillation in the same apparatus.

Evaporation Under Vacuum. Solvents can be evaporated under vacuum using one of the setups pictured in Figure C11. The test tube or flask containing the liquid to be evaporated is heated [OP-7a] gently with a hot-water bath or steam bath, and an aspirator or vacuum line is used to reduce the pressure inside the apparatus, thereby increasing the evaporation rate. Swirling or stirring the solution continuously during evaporation speeds up the process and reduces foaming and bumping.

Evaporation under vacuum requires constant attention, because excessive heat or a sudden pressure decrease may cause liquid to foam up and out of the container. One way to control the vacuum and reduce the likelihood of boilover is to replace the stopper shown in Figure C11b with a Hirsch funnel assembly. If you hold your thumb over the holes in the porcelain plate of the Hirsch funnel, you can decrease the internal pressure by pressing down with your thumb or increase the pressure by raising it.

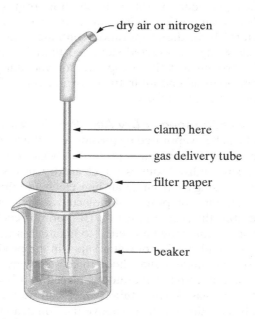

Figure C10 Apparatus for evaporation with nitrogen or dry air

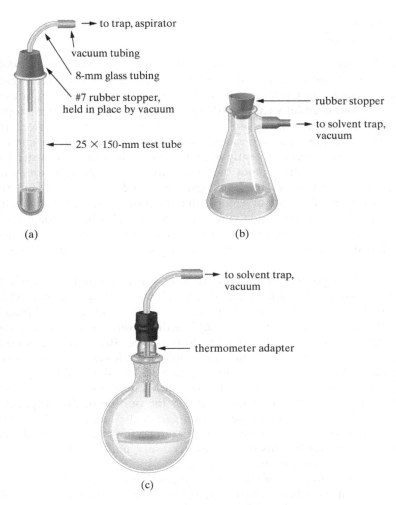

(a)

(b)

(c)

Figure C11 Apparatus for evaporation under vacuum

A trap similar to the one pictured in Figure C4 of OP-16 should be interposed between the evaporation container and the aspirator to collect the evaporated solvent, which should then be put in a solvent recovery container. To recover a low-boiling solvent such as diethyl ether, the solvent trap should be immersed in an appropriate cold bath (see OP-8).

Commercial *flash evaporators* are used to evaporate solvents rapidly under reduced pressure, but they are seldom available in undergraduate organic chemistry labs because of their high cost.

DIRECTIONS FOR EVAPORATION UNDER VACUUM

Equipment and Supplies

evaporation container (Figure C11)
rubber tubing
solvent trap

aspirator

heat source

Assemble one of the setups pictured in Figure C11 using heavy-walled rubber tubing that won't collapse under vacuum. Be sure to check all glassware for cracks, star fractures, and other imperfections that might cause them to implode under vacuum. Add the solution to be evaporated, stopper the evaporation container, and connect the apparatus to a solvent trap (see OP-16) and the trap to a vacuum source. Turn on the vacuum and heat the evaporation container gently over a steam bath or in a hot-water bath [OP-7a], swirling it throughout the evaporation to minimize foaming and bumping. (In some cases, the liquid can be stirred magnetically [OP-10].) Adjust the steam flow rate or water bath temperature to attain a satisfactory rate of evaporation; the liquid may boil gently but should not foam up. Be ready to remove the evaporation container from the heat source immediately if it starts to foam up; otherwise, your product may be carried over to the trap.

Continue evaporating until the residue, if it is a liquid, no longer appears to decrease in volume with time, or, if it is a solid, appears dry. At this time, boiling should have stopped and the odor of the solvent should be gone. When evaporation appears complete, discontinue heating and remove the evaporation container from the heat source. Break the vacuum by detaching the vacuum hose, opening a pressure-release valve on the trap (if it has one) or—for the apparatus in Figure C11a—sliding the stopper off the mouth of the test tube. Then turn off the vacuum source. To make sure that all of the solvent has evaporated, dry the outside of the evaporation container thoroughly to remove moisture from the heating bath, weigh it when it has cooled, and resume evaporation for a few minutes; then dry and weigh it again. Repeat this process, as necessary, until the mass no longer decreases significantly between weighings.

If you need to transfer the residue to another container, let the evaporation container cool down first. You can transfer the last traces of residue by rinsing the container with a small amount of a volatile solvent (such as diethyl ether or dichloromethane) and allowing the solvent to evaporate under a hood or in a stream of nitrogen or dry air.

If you are using a steam bath, wear gloves or use a towel to protect your hands.

If you only need to concentrate the solution, stop the evaporation when sufficient solvent has been removed.

Waste Disposal: Dispose of the recovered solvent as directed by your instructor or as indicated in an experiment's directions.

Summary

1. Assemble apparatus for evaporation under vacuum.
2. Add liquid; connect evaporation container to trap and vacuum source.
3. Turn on vacuum.
4. Apply heat with swirling or stirring until evaporation is complete.
5. Discontinue heating and turn off vacuum.
6. Transfer residue and recover solvent.
7. Disassemble and clean apparatus.

When Things Go Wrong

If you are evaporating a solution under vacuum and it keeps foaming up, see "Evaporation Under Vacuum."

If you are evaporating a solution and some of the liquid foams out of the evaporating flask, you can return it directly to the flask from the trap. If the trap isn't clean, you should purify the residue after the solvent has evaporated (you may be doing this anyway).

Suppose you are trying to isolate a solid by heating a solution under vacuum to evaporate the solvent, but no solid appears; you obtain only a liquid that doesn't decrease in volume with further heating. Remove the flask from the heat source and cool it under cold tap water to see if the liquid solidifies. If it doesn't, try to induce crystallization by rubbing the tip of a glass stirring rod against the inside of the container—as directed in the "Inducing Crystallization" section in OP-28—or use another appropriate technique described there. If that doesn't work, your solution may contain a high-boiling solvent along with the more volatile solvent. You may be able to evaporate it by stronger heating under vacuum (using a hot plate rather than a steam bath, for example), or by distillation [OP-30], but be careful that you don't evaporate or decompose the desired product.

Steam Distillation

Distillation of a mixture of two (or more) immiscible liquids is called *codistillation*. When one of the liquids is water, the process is usually called *steam distillation*. *External steam distillation* is carried out by passing externally generated steam (usually from a steam line) into a boiling flask that contains the organic material (see Figure C12). The vaporized organic liquid is carried over into a receiver along with the condensed steam. *Internal steam distillation* can be carried out by boiling a mixture of water and an organic material in a distillation setup, such as the apparatus in Figure C13, causing vaporized water (steam) and organic liquid to distill into a receiver.

Both kinds of steam distillation are used to separate organic liquids from reaction mixtures and natural products, leaving behind high-boiling residues such as tars, inorganic salts, and other relatively involatile components. Steam distillation is particularly useful for isolating the volatile oils of plants from various parts of the plant. Steam distillation is not useful for the final purification of a liquid, however, because it cannot effectively separate components that have similar boiling points.

Principles and Applications

When a *homogeneous mixture* of two liquids is distilled, the vapor pressure of each liquid is lowered by an amount proportional to the mole fraction of the other liquid present. This usually results in a solution boiling point that is somewhere between the boiling points of the separate components. For example, a solution containing equal masses of cyclohexane (bp = 81°C) and toluene (bp = 111°C) boils at 90°C.

If you aren't familiar with the principles of distillation, see OP-30.

When a *heterogeneous mixture* of two immiscible liquids, A and B, is distilled, each liquid exerts its vapor pressure more or less independently of the other. The total vapor pressure over the mixture (P) is thus approximately equal to the sum of the vapor pressures that would be exerted by the separate pure liquids (P_A° and P_B°) at the same temperature.

$$P \approx P_A^\circ + P_B^\circ$$

This has several important consequences. First, the vapor pressure of a mixture of immiscible components will be *higher* than the vapor pressure of its most volatile component. Because raising the vapor pressure of a liquid or liquid mixture lowers its boiling point, the boiling point of the mixture will be *lower* than that of its most volatile (lowest-boiling) component. Because the vapor pressure of a pure liquid is constant at a constant temperature, the vapor pressure of the mixture of liquids will be constant as well. Thus, the boiling point of the mixture will remain constant throughout its distillation as long as each component is present in significant quantity.

For example, suppose you are distilling a mixture of the immiscible liquids toluene and water at standard atmospheric pressure (760 torr, 101.3 kPa). The mixture will start to boil when the sum of the vapor pressures of the two liquids is equal to the external pressure, 760 torr. This

From *Operational Organic Chemistry: A Problem Solving Approach to the Laboratory*, Fourth Edition, John W. Lehman. Copyright © 2009 by Pearson Education. Published by Prentice Hall. All rights reserved.

Table C2 Boiling points and compositions of heterogeneous mixtures of various organic compounds, with water as Component B

Component A	bp of A (°C)	bp of A/B mixture (°C)	mass % of A in distillate
toluene	111°	85°	80%
chlorobenzene	132°	90°	71%
bromobenzene	156°	95°	62%
iodobenzene	188°	98°	43%
quinoline	237°	99.6°	10%

These calculations are approximate, because the vapors are not ideal gases.

occurs at 85°C, where the vapor pressure of water is 434 torr and that of toluene is 326 torr. Because the vapor pressures of the two components are additive, the mixture distills well below the normal boiling point of either toluene (bp = 111°C) or water. According to Avogadro's law, the number of moles of a component in a mixture of ideal gases is proportional to its partial pressure in the mixture, so the mole fraction of toluene in the vapor should be about 0.43 (326/760), and that of water should be about 0.57 (434/760). In other words, about 43% of the molecules in the vapor are toluene molecules. Because toluene (mol wt = 92) molecules are heavier than water (mol wt = 18) molecules, they make a greater contribution to the total mass of the vapor. In 1.00 mol of vapor, there will be 0.43 mol of toluene and 0.57 mol of water, so the mass of toluene in the vapor will be about 40 g (0.43 mol × 92 g/mol), and the mass of water will be about 10 g (0.57 mol × 18 g/mol). The mass of one mole of the vapor is thus about 50 g, of which toluene makes up 40 g (80%). The liquid that collects in the receiver during a distillation—the *distillate*—is merely condensed vapor, so distilling a mixture of toluene and water will yield a distillate that contains about 80% toluene, by mass.

Because of its comparatively low molecular weight and its immiscibility with many organic compounds, water is nearly always one of the liquids used in a codistillation involving an organic liquid. The organic liquid must be insoluble enough in water to form a separate phase, and it must not react with hot water or steam. As shown in Table C2, the higher the boiling point of the organic liquid, the lower will be its proportion in the distillate, and the closer the mixture boiling point will be to 100°C.

Because the distillation boiling point is never higher than 100°C at 1 atm—well below the normal boiling points of most water-immiscible organic liquids—thermal decomposition of the organic component is minimized.

a. External Steam Distillation

Externally generated steam is preferred for most standard scale steam distillations, especially those involving solids or high-boiling liquids, because external steam produces a rapid distillation rate and helps prevent bumping caused by solids and tars. The steam is usually obtained from a steam line; if another kind of steam generator is to be used, your instructor will show you how to use it. A *steam trap* is needed to remove condensed water and

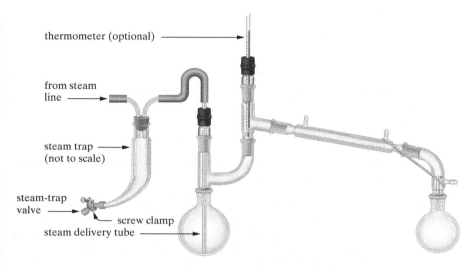

thermometer (optional)

from steam
line

steam trap
(not to scale)

steam-trap
valve

screw clamp

steam delivery tube

If the thermometer is not used, replace it and the thermometer adapter with a stopper.

Figure C12 Apparatus for external steam distillation

foreign matter, such as grease or rust, from externally generated steam. A steam trap that includes a valve for draining off excess water, such as the one illustrated in Figure C12, works best. With other kinds of traps (such as the one in Figure E11 of OP-32), distillation may have to be interrupted periodically to drain the trap.

The capacity of the boiling flask should be at least three times the volume of the liquid being distilled, so that it won't become much more than half full throughout the distillation. Some steam will condense during the distillation, raising the water level in the boiling flask; during an extended distillation, excessive water can be removed by external heating, if necessary. A Claisen adapter is used to help prevent mechanical transfer of liquids or particles from the boiling flask to the receiver. If the organic distillate is quite volatile, a thermometer can be used to indicate when the end of the distillation is near. For example, with a toluene–water mixture, the temperature will rise rather rapidly—from 85°C to about 100°C—when the toluene is nearly gone. With liquids that have boiling points of 200°C or higher, a thermometer is of little use because the vapor temperature will be close to 100°C throughout the distillation. The distillation should be carried out rapidly to reduce condensation in the boiling flask and to compensate for the large volume of water-laden distillate that may have to be collected to yield much of the organic component. Owing to the rapid distillation rate and the high heat content of steam, efficient condensing is essential. The vacuum adapter should be cool to the touch throughout the distillation, and no steam should escape from its outlet.

DIRECTIONS FOR EXTERNAL STEAM DISTILLATION

Equipment and Supplies

heat source
ring stand, ring supports, clamps
rubber tubing

> steam delivery tube
> large round-bottom flask
> Claisen adapter
> still head (connecting adapter)
> thermometer and thermometer adapter, or stopper
> West condenser
> vacuum adapter
> receiving flask
> steam trap (bent adapter, two-hole rubber stopper, bent glass tubes, rubber tubing, screw clamp)

Assemble the apparatus pictured in Figure C12 using a large round-bottom boiling flask and, as the steam delivery tube, a 6-mm o.d. (outer diameter) glass tube extending to within about 0.5 cm of the bottom of the flask (it must not touch the bottom). Use a stopper in place of the thermometer adapter and thermometer if the component being separated boils above ~200°C. Position the boiling flask high enough so that external heat can be applied, if necessary. Use a length of rubber tubing to connect the steam delivery tube to a bent glass tube on the steam trap, which should be clamped to a ring stand over a beaker. See that the screw clamp on the steam trap is closed. Add the organic mixture and a small amount of water (unless the mixture already contains water) to the boiling flask, which should be no more than one-third full at the start. Be sure that the condenser hoses fit tightly before you turn on the condenser water; the water should flow at a comparatively rapid rate. Connect a rubber hose to the steam valve and turn it on to purge the steam line, directing the steam into the sink, until only a little water drips from the end of the hose. Turn off the steam and connect the hose to the other bent tube on the steam trap.

Take Care! Don't burn yourself with the steam.

Open the steam valve cautiously so that the liquid in the flask is agitated, but not too violently. The liquid should soon begin to boil, after which distillate will begin to pass over into the receiver. Adjust the steam flow to maintain a rapid rate of distillation without causing liquid in the flask to splash up into the condenser. Check the vacuum adapter periodically; if it becomes warm, and especially if vapor begins to escape from its outlet, you should increase the cooling water flow rate, cool the receiver in an ice/water bath, or reduce the steam flow rate. Check the connection between the condenser and still head frequently to make sure that no vapor is escaping; this joint sometimes separates because of the violent action of the steam (you can use a rubber band or a joint clip to prevent this). Drain the trap periodically to remove condensed water. If you must interrupt the distillation for any reason, open the steam-trap valve (if there is one) or raise the steam delivery tube out of the liquid *before* you turn off the steam; otherwise, liquid in the boiling flask may back up into the steam trap.

When the distillate appears clear *and* the temperature is near 100°C (if you used a thermometer), collect and examine a few drops of fresh distillate on a watch glass. Continue distilling if the fresh distillate is cloudy, contains oily droplets, or has a pronounced odor, and collect and examine more distillate at 5- or 10-minute intervals. When the distillate is water clear and distillation appears complete, open the steam-trap valve fully (or raise the steam delivery tube out of the liquid) and then turn off the steam.

The organic liquid can be separated from the distillate using a separatory funnel or by extraction [OP-18] with diethyl ether or another suitable solvent. Extraction is advisable if the volume of the organic liquid is small compared to that of the water. If the aqueous layer is cloudy, you can saturate it with sodium chloride or another salt to salt out [OP-18b] the organic liquid.

Waste Disposal: Dispose of the aqueous layer as directed by your instructor.

Summary

1. Assemble apparatus for external steam distillation.
2. Add organic mixture and water (if necessary) to boiling flask.
3. Turn on condenser water.
4. Purge steam line, connect to steam trap, and turn on steam.
5. Distill rapidly until distillate is clear; drain trap periodically.
6. Open steam-trap valve and turn off steam.
7. Separate organic liquid from distillate.
8. Disassemble and clean apparatus.

When Things Go Wrong

Most of the things that go wrong during a simple distillation can also go wrong during an external steam distillation, so you can refer to "When Things Go Wrong" in OP-30 for help. The following cases apply only to external steam distillation.

If, during a steam distillation, the water level in the boiling flask rises well above its midpoint, check to make sure that water from the steam trap isn't passing over into the distillation flask. If it is, drain the steam trap and monitor its water level more carefully. If not, heat the boiling flask externally with a steam bath or heating mantle to reduce condensation.

If, during a steam distillation, vapor escapes from the vacuum adapter outlet, first check to see that the condenser is cool to the touch; if it isn't, increase the cooling water's flow rate. If that doesn't help, cool the receiver in an ice/water bath. It may also be necessary to reduce the steam flow rate.

b. Internal Steam Distillation

An organic liquid can sometimes be separated from a reaction mixture or another mixture by internal steam distillation (codistillation with water). The procedure is essentially the same as that for simple distillation [OP-30], except that more water may need to be added during the distillation, using the apparatus in Figure C13. If the organic distillate is quite volatile, a thermometer can be used to indicate when the end of the distillation is near.

DIRECTIONS FOR INTERNAL STEAM DISTILLATION

See OP-30 for more detailed directions for conducting a distillation.

Equipment and Supplies

heat source
ring stand, ring supports, clamps
condenser tubing
round-bottom flask

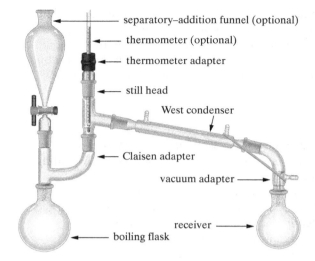

Figure C13 Apparatus for internal steam distillation

If the thermometer is not used, replace it and the thermometer adapter with a stopper.

boiling chips or stir bar
still head (connecting adapter)
thermometer and thermometer adapter, or stopper
West condenser
vacuum adapter
receiver
Claisen adapter (optional)
separatory–addition funnel (optional)

If it will be necessary to add more water during the distillation, assemble the apparatus shown in Figure C13; otherwise, assemble the apparatus pictured in Figure E6 of OP-30. Replace the thermometer adapter and thermometer by a stopper if the component being separated boils above ~200°C. Add the mixture to be steam distilled, boiling chips or a stir bar, and enough water to fill the boiling flask about one-third to one-half full (unless enough water is already present). Turn on the condenser water and the stirrer (if you are using one), and heat the flask with an appropriate heat source [OP-7a] to maintain a rapid rate of distillation. If necessary, add water to replace that lost during the distillation. When the distillate appears clear *and* the temperature is near 100°C (if you used a thermometer), collect and examine a few drops of fresh distillate on a watch glass. Continue distilling if the fresh distillate is cloudy, contains oily droplets, or has a pronounced odor, and collect and examine more distillate at 5- or 10-minute intervals. When the distillate is water clear and distillation appears complete, discontinue heating. Separate the organic liquid from the distillate as described for external steam distillation.

Waste Disposal: Dispose of the aqueous layer as directed by your instructor.

Summary

1. Assemble apparatus for internal steam distillation.
2. Add organic mixture and water to boiling flask.

3. Turn on stirrer (if used) and condenser water.
4. Distill until distillate is clear, adding water as necessary.
5. Separate organic liquid from distillate.
6. Disassemble and clean apparatus.

When Things Go Wrong

Most of the things that go wrong during a simple distillation can also go wrong during an internal steam distillation, so you can refer to "When Things Go Wrong" in OP-30 for help.

Column Chromatography

If you touch the tip of a felt-tip pen to a piece of absorbent paper, such as a coffee filter, and then slowly drip isopropyl rubbing alcohol onto the spot with a medicine dropper, the spot will spread and separate into rings of different color—the dyes of which the ink is composed. This is a simple example of *chromatography,* the separation of a mixture by distributing its components between two phases. The *stationary phase* (the coffee filter, in this example) remains fixed in place, while the *mobile phase* (the rubbing alcohol) flows through it, carrying components of the mixture along with it. The stationary phase acts as a "brake" on most components of a mixture, holding them back so that they move along more slowly than the mobile phase itself. Because of differences in such factors as the solubility of the components in the mobile phase and the strength of their interactions with the stationary phase, some components move faster than others, and the components therefore become separated from one another.

Different types of chromatography can be classified according to the physical states of the mobile and stationary phases. In *liquid–solid* chromatography, which is applied in column chromatography [OP-21] and thin-layer chromatography [OP-22], a liquid mobile phase filters down or creeps up through the solid phase, which may be cellulose, silica gel, alumina, or some other *adsorbent.* The adsorbent is a finely divided solid that attracts solute molecules from the mobile phase onto its surface. In *liquid–liquid chromatography,* which is used in high-performance liquid chromatography [OP-38], the mobile phase is usually an organic solvent and the stationary phase can be a high-boiling liquid that is adsorbed by or chemically bonded to a solid *support.* In *gas–liquid chromatography*—the most common type of gas chromatography [OP-37]—the mobile phase is a gas that passes through a hollow or packed column containing a high-boiling liquid on a solid support. Gas chromatography (GC) and high-performance liquid chromatography (HPLC) are instrumental methods that are used primarily for analyzing mixtures, so they will be discussed in the "Instrumental Analysis" section of the operations.

a. Liquid–Solid Column Chromatography

Principles and Applications

The usual stationary phase for liquid–solid column chromatography is a finely divided solid adsorbent, which is packed into a glass tube called the *column.* The mixture to be separated (the *sample*) is placed on top of the column and *eluted*—washed down the column—by the mobile phase, which is a liquid solvent or solvent mixture. Different components of the sample are attracted to the surface of the adsorbent more or less strongly, depending on their polarity and other structural features. The more strongly a component is attracted to the adsorbent, the more slowly it will move down the column. So, as the mobile phase—also called the *eluant*—filters down through the adsorbent, the components of the sample spread out to form separate *bands* of solute, some passing down the column rapidly and others lagging behind.

From *Operational Organic Chemistry: A Problem Solving Approach to the Laboratory*, Fourth Edition, John W. Lehman. Copyright © 2009 by Pearson Education. Published by Prentice Hall. All rights reserved.

Carvone and limonene are major constituents of spearmint oil.

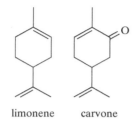

limonene   carvone

For example, consider a separation of carvone and limonene on a silica gel adsorbent using hexane as the eluant. At any given time, a molecule of one component will either be adsorbed on the silica gel stationary phase or dissolved in the mobile phase. While it's adsorbed, the molecule will stay put; while it's dissolved, it will move down the column with the eluant. Molecules with polar functional groups are attracted to polar adsorbents such as silica gel and are relatively insoluble in nonpolar solvents such as hexane. So a molecule of carvone, with its polar carbonyl group, tends to spend more time adsorbed on the silica than dissolved in the hexane. It will therefore pass down the column very slowly with this solvent. On the other hand, a nonpolar molecule of limonene is quite soluble in hexane and only weakly attracted to silica gel, so it will spend less time sitting still and more time moving than will a carvone molecule. As a result, limonene molecules pass down the column rapidly and are soon separated from the slow-moving carvone molecules.

The separation attained by column chromatography depends on a number of factors, including the nature of the components in the mixture, the quantity and kind of adsorbent used, and the polarity of the mobile phase. The lists that follow show how strongly different functional groups are attracted to polar adsorbents and how strongly different adsorbents attract polar molecules.

Approximate strength of adsorption of different functional groups on polar adsorbents

COOH	strongest
OH	
NH_2	
SH	
CHO	
$C=O$	
COOR	
OR	
$C=C$	
Cl, Br, I	weakest

Common chromatography adsorbents in approximate order of adsorbent strength

Alumina (Al_2O_3)	strongest
Activated carbon (polar) (C)	
Silica gel (SiO_2)	
Magnesia (MgO)	weakest

Note: Adsorbent strength varies with grade, particle size, and other factors.

Experimental Considerations

Adsorbents. A number of different adsorbents are used for column chromatography, but alumina and silica gel are the most popular. Adsorbents are available in a wide variety of activity grades and particle size ranges; alumina can be obtained in acidic, basic, and neutral forms as well. The *activity* of an adsorbent is a measure of its attraction for solute molecules, the most active grade of a given adsorbent being one from which all water has been removed. The most active grade may not be the best for a given application, because too active an adsorbent may catalyze a reaction or cause bands to move down the column too slowly. Less active grades of alumina, for example, are prepared by adding different amounts of water to the most active grade (see Table C3), stirring thoroughly to mix in the alumina, and letting the mixture stand for at least 24 hours. Since all polar adsorbents are deactivated by water, it is important to keep their containers tightly closed and to minimize their exposure to atmospheric moisture.

Some samples shouldn't be separated on certain kinds of adsorbents. For example, basic alumina would be a poor choice to separate a mixture containing aldehydes or ketones, which might undergo aldol reactions on the column. Neutral alumina of activity II or III is a suitable adsorbent for most purposes. Silica gel, which is less active than alumina, is a good all-purpose adsorbent that can be used with most organic compounds.

The amount of adsorbent required for a given application depends on the sample size and the difficulty of the separation. If the components of a mixture differ greatly in polarity, a long column of adsorbent should not be necessary, because the separation will be easy. The more difficult the separation, the more adsorbent will be needed. About 20 to 50 g of adsorbent per gram of sample is recommended for most separations, but easy separations may require less adsorbent and difficult separations may require more.

The particle size of the adsorbent is also important, because the flow rate will be too slow if the particles are too small and the separation will be poor if the particles are too large. Particle size is often indicated by a range of mesh numbers, where the *mesh number* is the number of openings per linear inch in the finest screen that will allow the particles to pass through. Thus, a higher mesh number indicates smaller particles. Typical particle sizes for column chromatography are 70–230 mesh for silica gel and ~150 mesh for alumina.

Eluants. In a column chromatography separation, the eluant acts primarily as a solvent to differentially remove molecules of solute from the surface of the adsorbent. In some cases, polar solvent molecules will also *displace* solute molecules from the adsorbent by becoming adsorbed themselves. If the solvent is too strongly adsorbed, the components of a mixture will spend most of their time in the mobile phase and won't separate efficiently. For this reason, it is usually best to start with a solvent of low polarity, and then (if necessary) increase the polarity gradually to elute the more strongly adsorbed components. Table C4 lists a series of common chromatographic solvents, in order of increasing eluting power, for alumina and silica gel. Such a listing is called an *eluotropic series.*

Table C3 Alumina activity grades (Brockmann scale)

Grade	Mass % water
I	0
II	3
III	6
IV	10
V	15

The eluotropic series for a non-polar adsorbent is nearly the reverse of the one for alumina; less polar solvents are more effective eluants with such adsorbents.

Table C4 Eluotropic series for alumina and silica gel

Alumina	Silica gel
pentane	cyclohexane
petroleum ether	petroleum ether
hexane	pentane
cyclohexane	trichloromethane
diethyl ether	diethyl ether
trichloromethane	ethyl acetate
dichloromethane	ethanol
ethyl acetate	water
2-propanol	acetone
ethanol	acetic acid
methanol	methanol
acetic acid	

Elution Techniques. Many chromatographic separations can't be performed efficiently with a single solvent, so several solvents or solvent mixtures are used in sequence, starting with the weaker eluants—those near the top of the eluotropic series for the adsorbent being used. Such eluants will wash down only the most weakly adsorbed components, while strongly adsorbed solutes remain near the top of the column. The remaining solute bands can then be washed off the column by more powerful eluants.

In practice, it is best to change eluants gradually by using solvent mixtures of varying composition, rather than to change directly from one solvent to another. In *stepwise elution,* the strength of the eluting solvent is changed in stages by adding varying amounts of a stronger eluant to a weaker one. The proportion of the stronger eluant is increased more or less exponentially. For example, 5% dichloromethane in hexane may be followed by 15% and 50% mixtures of these solvents. According to one rule of thumb, the eluant composition should be changed after about three column volumes of the previous eluant have passed through. For example, if the packed volume of the adsorbent is 15 mL, the eluant composition should be changed with every 45 mL or so of eluant.

Columns. There are many different kinds of chromatography columns, ranging from a simple glass tube with a constriction at one end to an elaborate column with a detachable base and a porous plate to support the adsorbent. A 25-mL to 100-mL buret, preferably one with a Teflon stopcock, is adequate for many separations, but the lack of a detachable base makes it difficult to remove the adsorbent afterward. A 10-mL microburet is suitable for small-scale separations. If a column doesn't have a stopcock, the tip can be closed with a piece of flexible tubing equipped with a screw clamp. Unless the tubing is resistant to the eluants (polyethylene and Teflon won't contaminate most solvents), it should be removed before elution begins.

In selecting a column for a chromatographic separation, first estimate the amount of adsorbent needed for the sample you will be separating. Then choose a column of such a size that, after it has been packed with adsorbent, the adsorbent's surface will be about 10 cm or more below the top of the column and the height of the adsorbent column will be at least 10 times its diameter. If the column contains a porous plate to support the packing, no additional support is necessary; otherwise, the column packing should be supported on a layer of glass wool and clean sand.

Figure C14 shows a packed chromatography column with a continuous-feed reservoir: a separatory–addition funnel with its outlet at the desired eluant level in the column (the funnel should be secured in a ring support). As eluant flows down the column, liquid from the separatory–addition funnel replaces it. This method requires a stemmed (not jointed) separatory funnel having a wide-bore stopcock. For most purposes, you can support an ordinary jointed separatory funnel directly over the column, and add eluant periodically to keep the eluant level fairly constant.

Flow Rate.   The rate of eluant flow through the column should be slow enough that the solute can attain equilibrium, but not so slow that the solute bands will broaden appreciably by diffusion. For most purposes, a flow rate of between 5 and 50 drops per minute should be suitable; difficult separations require the slowest rates. The flow rate can be reduced by partly closing the stopcock or pinch clamp on the column (if it has either) or by reducing the *solvent head*—the depth of the eluant layer above the adsorbent. The flow rate can be increased by opening the stopcock or pinch clamp fully and by maintaining a high solvent head.

Packing a Column.   To achieve good separation with a chromatographic column, it must be packed properly. The packing must be uniform, without air bubbles or channels, and its surface must be even and horizontal. Columns using alumina can be packed by pouring the dry adsorbent through a layer of solvent. Columns using silica gel are usually packed with a slurry containing the adsorbent suspended in a solvent. Once a column's adsorbent is moistened with solvent, it must be kept covered with the solvent at all times; allowing it to dry out creates channels that lead to uneven bands and poor separation.

DIRECTIONS FOR LIQUID–SOLID COLUMN CHROMATOGRAPHY

These directions are for a 25–50 mL column; adjust the quantities for smaller or larger columns.

Equipment and Supplies

chromatography column
buret funnel (or small powder funnel)
column-packing solvent
glass wool
clean sand
tapper (pencil and one-hole stopper)
adsorbent
collectors (flasks, test tubes, vials, etc.)
Pasteur pipet with bulb
eluant(s)
separatory–addition funnel

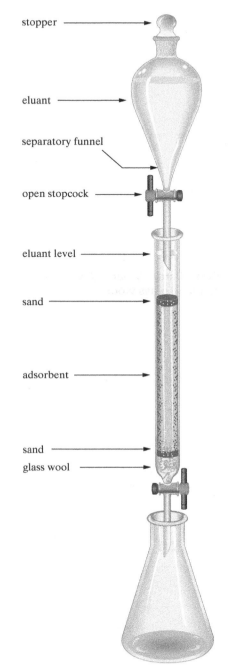

stopper
eluant
separatory funnel
open stopcock
eluant level
sand
adsorbent
sand
glass wool

Figure C14 Packed column with continuous-feed reservoir

Packing the Column. Obtain an appropriate column and clamp it securely to a ring stand so that it is as nearly vertical as possible. Use a buret clamp if one is available. Be sure that the stopcock or screw clamp at the outlet of the column is closed. Construct a "tapper" by, for example, inserting one end of a pencil into a small, one-hole rubber stopper. Measure out the amount of adsorbent you will need to prepare the column and keep it in a tightly closed container. Number and weigh the collectors you will be using to collect the eluant fractions. Then pack the column with adsorbent by one of the following methods (omit the glass wool and sand support if it has a porous plate). Method **1** is generally used for silica gel and method **2** for alumina.

1. *Slurry-packing the column.* Using a funnel, fill the column about half full with the least polar eluting solvent to be used in the separation, or a solvent recommended in the experimental procedure. Use a long glass rod to push a plug of glass wool to the bottom of the column; tamp the glass wool down gently to form a level surface and press out any air bubbles. Using a *dry* funnel, slowly pour in enough clean sand to form a 1-cm layer at the bottom of the column. As the sand filters down through the solvent, tap the column gently and continuously with the tapper so that the sand layer is uniform and level. The column should be tapped near its center, where it is clamped, to avoid displacing it from the vertical.

   Mix the measured amount of silica gel (or another suitable adsorbent) thoroughly with enough of the column-packing solvent to make a fairly thick, but pourable, slurry. With the column outlet closed, slowly pour part of this slurry through a funnel, with tapping, until the adsorbent forms a layer about 2 cm thick at the bottom of the column. With a flask under the column outlet, open the outlet so that the solvent drains slowly as you add the rest of the slurry, tapping constantly to help settle and pack the adsorbent. If the slurry becomes too thick to pour, add more solvent to it. There should be enough solvent in the column so that the solvent level is well above the adsorbent level at all times; if necessary, add more solvent. When all of the adsorbent has been added, close the outlet. The surface of the adsorbent should be as even and horizontal as possible, so continue tapping until it has settled. Gently stirring the top of the solvent layer as the adsorbent is settling can also help form a level surface. Use a Pasteur pipet containing the solvent to rinse down any adsorbent that adheres to the sides of the column. Add enough clean sand to form a protective layer about 0.5 cm thick on top of the adsorbent; the sand surface should also be level. Open the outlet until the solvent surface drops to within 1–2 cm of the sand surface, then close the outlet and stopper the column tightly. Keep the adsorbent covered with solvent at all times; allowing it to dry out creates channels that lead to uneven bands and poor separation. Save the drained solvent, which can be reused.

2. *Packing the column with dry adsorbent.* Use a funnel to fill the column about two-thirds full with the least polar eluting solvent to be used in the separation, or a solvent recommended in the experimental procedure. Use a long glass rod to push a plug of glass wool to the bottom of the column; tamp the glass wool down gently to form a level surface and press out any air bubbles. Using a *dry* funnel, slowly pour in enough clean sand

Take Care! Wear gloves when handling glass wool.

Take Care! Wear gloves when handling glass wool.

to form a 1-cm layer at the bottom of the column. As the sand filters down through the solvent, tap the column gently and continuously with the tapper so that the sand layer is uniform and level. The column should be tapped near its center, where it is clamped, to avoid displacing it from the vertical.

With the column outlet closed, slowly pour enough alumina (or another suitable adsorbent) through a *dry* funnel, while tapping, until the adsorbent forms a layer about 2 cm thick at the bottom of the column. With a flask under the column outlet, open the outlet and add the rest of the dry alumina as the solvent drains, tapping constantly to help settle and pack the adsorbent. There should be enough solvent in the column so that the solvent level is well above the adsorbent level at all times; if necessary, add more solvent. When all of the adsorbent has been added, close the outlet. The surface of the adsorbent should be as even and horizontal as possible, so continue tapping until it has settled. Gently stirring the top of the solvent layer as the adsorbent is settling can also help form a level surface. Use a Pasteur pipet containing the solvent to rinse down any adsorbent that adheres to the sides of the column. Add enough clean sand to form a protective layer about 0.5 cm thick on top of the adsorbent; the sand surface should also be level. Open the outlet until the solvent surface drops to within 1–2 cm of the sand surface, then close the outlet and stopper the column tightly. Keep the adsorbent covered with solvent at all times. Save the drained solvent, which can be reused.

Separating the Sample. If the sample is a solid, dissolve it in a minimum amount of a suitable nonpolar solvent; use liquid samples without dilution. Open the column outlet until the solvent surface comes down *just* to the top of the sand layer, and then close it. Use a Pasteur pipet to apply the sample around the circumference of the sand so that it spreads evenly over the surface. Open the outlet until the sample's surface comes down to the top of the sand layer, and then close it. Pipet a small amount of the initial eluant around the inside of the column to rinse down any adherent sample. Open the outlet again until the eluant's surface comes down to the top of the sand layer, and then close it.

Clamp a solvent reservoir such as a separatory–addition funnel over the column and measure the initial eluant into it. (Alternatively, you can add the eluants through an ordinary funnel or use a continuous-feed reservoir as shown in Figure C14, moistening the stopper with solvent to provide an airtight seal.) Add enough eluant to nearly fill the column. Place a tared collector at the column outlet, open the outlet, and continue adding eluant as needed to keep the liquid level near the top of the column throughout the elution. If you need to change eluants during the elution, let the previous eluant drain to the top of the sand layer before adding the next one.

If the components are colored or can be observed on the column by some visualization method (such as irradiation with ultraviolet light), change collectors each time a new band of solute begins to come off the column *and* when it has almost disappeared from the column. If two or more bands overlap, collect the overlapping regions in separate collectors to avoid contaminating the purer fractions. Unless directed otherwise, evaporate [OP-19] the solvent from any fractions that contain the desired component(s).

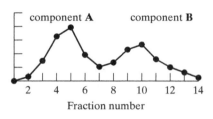

Figure C15 Elution curve

Waste Disposal: Dispose of unused and recovered solvents as directed by your instructor or as indicated in an experiment's directions.

If the components aren't visible and the procedure doesn't specify the fraction volumes, collect equal-volume fractions in tared collectors. Each fraction can be roughly 1/10 or less of the total eluant volume; use more fractions for more difficult separations. Evaporate the solvent from each fraction, weigh the collectors and their contents, and plot the mass of each residue versus the fraction number to obtain an elution curve such as the one illustrated in Figure C15. From the elution curve, you should be able to identify separate components and decide which fractions can be combined.

To remove the contents of the column, let it dry completely, then invert it over a beaker and tap it as needed to dislodge the adsorbent. If necessary, attach the column outlet to an air line, hold its other end over the beaker, and *slowly* open the air valve to blow out the glass-wool plug and any remaining adsorbent.

Summary

1. Pack column using appropriate adsorbent, solvent, and packing method.
2. Drain column to top of sand layer; add sample, drain, rinse, and drain again.
3. Add eluant, put collector in place, and open column outlet.
4. Elute sample, keeping eluant level nearly constant.
5. To change eluants, drain current eluant to top of sand and add next eluant.
   IF components are visible, GO TO 6.
   IF components are not visible, GO TO 7.
6. Change collectors when new band starts or ends and where bands overlap. GO TO 8.
7. Change collectors after a predetermined volume has been collected.
8. Stop elution after last fraction has been collected.
9. Evaporate and weigh appropriate fractions.
10. Disassemble and clean apparatus; dispose of solvents.

When Things Go Wrong

Suppose you are separating the components of a reaction mixture by column chromatography, but analysis of the product shows that it is still impure. To find out what went wrong, ask yourself the following questions. If the answer to a question is yes, consult the paragraph indicated, reread the directions more carefully, and repeat the chromatographic separation. (1) Was the amount of sample too large for the amount of adsorbent used? (See "Adsorbents.") (2) Was the flow rate too slow, causing broad or diffuse bands? (See "Flow Rate.") (3) Was the column unevenly packed or was its surface disturbed, causing channeling, uneven bands, or non-horizontal bands? (See "Packing a Column.") (4) Did you change the eluant polarity too rapidly, resulting in channeling or cracks in the column? (See "Elution Techniques.")

b. Flash Chromatography

Flash chromatography is a variation of liquid–solid column chromatography that uses a single elution solvent and takes less time than the standard method. Pressurized nitrogen, air, or another gas is applied to the top of the column to force eluant through the adsorbent, which is usually finely divided (~230–400 mesh) silica gel. The eluant must be selected carefully to ensure good separation. Mixtures of low-boiling petroleum ether with ethyl acetate or dichloromethane work for many separations. A prospective solvent system can be tested by spotting a silica-gel thin-layer chromatography (TLC) plate [OP-22] with the sample and developing it with the solvent system; a suitable solvent system should move the desired component at least a third of the way from the starting line to the solvent front, and it should give good separation between the desired component and any impurities. Separation is poor if the sample size is too large; the following procedure works best with 0.25 g of sample or less. Larger samples usually require more eluant and a column of greater diameter.

Commercial flash chromatography systems may require expensive columns, pumps, and flow controllers, so they are seldom available for use in undergraduate laboratories. An inexpensive flash chromatography system can be constructed using the "homemade" flow controller shown in Figure C16.

This flash chromatography apparatus is described in J. Chem. Educ. **1992**, *69, 939.*

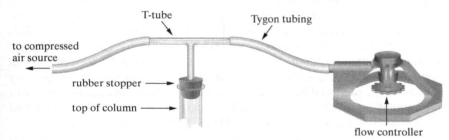

Figure C16 Flow controller for flash chromatography

The flow controller is assembled by inserting the bottom of a small plastic T-tube into a one-hole rubber stopper that fits into the top of the column, and then attaching two lengths of $\frac{3}{8}$-inch i.d. (inner diameter) Tygon tubing to the straight ends of the T and securing them with copper wire. One tube is attached to the gas inlet on a Bunsen burner base (the barrel can be removed) and the other to a source of clean, dry, compressed air. The column can be a 50-mL buret packed to a depth of 15 cm or so with adsorbent, but a 12 × 1.5-cm polypropylene column packed with 5–6 g of adsorbent has also been used successfully and is less likely to break under pressure.

The pressure can also be controlled, but less precisely, by the user's thumb rather than the burner base.
See J. Chem. Educ. **2000**, *77, 263.*

You should have read OP-21a before attempting to carry out a flash chromatography separation, since the apparatus and procedures are similar. Pack an appropriate column no more than half full with finely divided silica gel while tapping the column gently; then add a uniform 1-cm layer of clean sand. Fill the column with eluant, open the column outlet (with a receiving flask in place), and apply pressure with dry air or nitrogen to saturate the adsorbent with solvent. Save the drained solvent, which can be reused. Drain the solvent to the top of the sand layer; immediately introduce the sample, as a 25% solution in the eluant, onto the sand layer with a long Pasteur pipet. When all of the sample is within the sand layer (pressure can be applied to force it down), close the column outlet and carefully fill the column to within 1–2 cm of the top with eluant. Insert the stopper of the flow controller into the top of the column with a firm twist to keep it from popping out (it should stay in place at the desired pressure). Open the needle valve on the burner base, then open the column's stopcock with a collector in place. Carefully turn on the air valve to pressurize the system and adjust the needle valve so that the eluant level decreases at a rate of ~5 cm per minute. Collect and evaporate the fractions as described in OP-21a. If the separation is unsatisfactory, try using a longer column and a larger volume of eluant, or change to a more suitable eluant.

Waste Disposal: Dispose of excess and unused solvents as directed by your instructor.

c. Reversed-Phase Column Chromatography

Adsorbents are polar solids that attract polar compounds more strongly than nonpolar ones, so nonpolar solutes are eluted from adsorbent-packed columns more rapidly than polar ones. Another kind of stationary phase can be prepared by coating particles of silica gel with a high-boiling nonpolar liquid. With such a stationary phase, components of the sample are partitioned between the liquid mobile phase and the liquid layer of the stationary phase, where to *partition* a solute means to distribute it between two phases. If the mobile phase is more polar than the stationary phase, the usual order of elution will be reversed; that is, polar compounds will be eluted before nonpolar ones. This general method is called *reversed-phase chromatography*. The mobile phases for reversed-phase column chromatography are usually polar solvents such as water, methanol, and acetonitrile, or mixtures of such solvents. Stationary phases can be prepared by coating a specially treated (silanized) silica gel with a nonpolar liquid phase, such as a hydrocarbon or silicone. Bonded liquid phases, such as the ones described for HPLC [OP-38], can also be used.

To prepare a column using coated silica gel, the liquid mobile and stationary phases are shaken together in a separatory funnel to saturate each phase with the other, and the layers are separated. The stationary phase is then stirred with the silica gel, and the coated support is made into a slurry with the saturated mobile phase. The column is slurry packed, usually with stirring to make it more uniform and to remove air bubbles. A separation is carried out by eluting with the saturated mobile phase, essentially as described previously for normal-phase column chromatography.

Thin-Layer Chromatography

Principles and Applications

Like column chromatography, thin-layer chromatography (TLC) utilizes a solid adsorbent as the stationary phase and a liquid solvent as the mobile phase, but the mobile phase creeps *up* the adsorbent layer by capillary action rather than filtering down through it by gravity. A *TLC plate* consists of a thin layer of the adsorbent on an appropriate *backing* (solid support) made of plastic, aluminum, or glass. The sample (or several samples) is dissolved in a suitable solvent and applied near the lower edge of the TLC plate as small spots. The plate may also be spotted with a selection of standard solutions for comparison. The TLC plate is *developed* by immersing its lower edge in a suitable mobile phase, the *developing solvent.* As this solvent moves up the adsorbent layer, it carries with it the components of each spot, which are separated by the mechanism described in OP-21 for column chromatography.

Although TLC is not useful for separating large quantities of material, it is much faster than column chromatography and can be carried out with very small sample volumes, so that little is wasted. TLC provides better separation than the related technique of paper chromatography [OP-23], and it can be applied to a wider range of organic compounds. Although TLC is categorized under separation operations in this book, it is also used for qualitative and quantitative analysis of organic compounds.

Applications of TLC include the following:

- To identify unknown substances and unknown components of mixtures
- To monitor the course of a reaction and assess the purity of its product by comparing the relative amounts of product, reactants, and by-products on successive chromatograms
- To determine the best solvent for a column chromatography separation (see "Choosing a Developing Solvent")
- To determine the composition of each fraction from a column chromatography separation, so that fractions containing the same component can be detected and combined
- To determine whether a substance purified by recrystallization or another method still contains appreciable amounts of impurities

Experimental Considerations

Adsorbents. The most commonly used adsorbents for TLC are silica gel, alumina, and cellulose. The adsorbent is more finely divided than that used in column chromatography, and it is provided with a *binder*—such as polyacrylic acid—to make it stick to the backing. It may also contain a *fluorescent indicator,* which makes most spots visible under ultraviolet (UV) light.

TLC Plates. Small "do-it-yourself" TLC plates can be prepared by dipping glass microscope slides into a slurry of the adsorbent and binder in a suitable solvent and allowing the solvent to evaporate. Such plates may give inconsistent results because of variations in the thickness of the adsorbent layer. More uniform TLC plates (measuring 20×20 cm or larger) are

From *Operational Organic Chemistry: A Problem Solving Approach to the Laboratory*, Fourth Edition, John W. Lehman. Copyright © 2009 by Pearson Education. Published by Prentice Hall. All rights reserved.

commercially available with a wide variety of adsorbents, backings, and layer thicknesses. For example, a typical TLC plate suitable for use in undergraduate laboratories has a flexible plastic backing coated with a 200-μm-thick layer of silica gel mixed with a binder, and possibly a fluorescent indicator as well. The adsorbent layer of a TLC plate is easily damaged, so it is important to avoid unnecessary contact with its coated surface and to protect the plate from foreign materials. Like adsorbents for column chromatography, TLC adsorbents pick up moisture when exposed to the atmosphere, making them less active. TLC plates can be activated by heating them in a 110°C oven for an hour or so.

Spotting. A TLC plate is prepared for development by applying solutions of the sample(s) to be analyzed and any reference standards as small spots; this process is known as *spotting*. The sample is dissolved in a suitable solvent to make an approximately 1% solution. Ordinarily, the solvent should be quite nonpolar and have a boiling point in the 50–100°C range. Column chromatography fractions and other solutions can often be used as is, if the solute is present at a concentration in the 0.2–2.0% range.

It is best to wear thin disposable gloves while spotting a TLC plate, because if you touch the surface of the adsorbent with your bare fingers, your fingerprints may hinder development or obscure developed spots. Position the spots accurately, because incorrectly placed spots may run into one another or onto the edge of the adsorbent layer. This can be done with a transparent plastic ruler supported just above the surface of the plate so that it doesn't touch the adsorbent. Mark the starting line with a pencil on both edges, about 1.5 cm from the bottom of the plate (or 1.0 cm for a microscope-slide plate), and position the spots along the starting line at least 1.5 cm from each edge of the plate and 1.0 cm from each other. Thus, a 10 × 10-cm TLC plate can accommodate up to eight spots, as shown in Figure C17.

Large, diffuse spots spread out too much for accurate results, so each spot should be as small and concentrated as possible. The spots are best applied with a microliter syringe or a capillary micropipet. Capillary micropipets such as Drummond Microcaps are commercially available, but suitable micropipets can be prepared by heating an open-ended melting-point capillary in the middle over a small flame, drawing it out to form a fine capillary about 4–5 cm long, allowing the tube to cool, and then scoring it and snapping it apart in the middle to form two micropipets (see Figure C18).

To spot a TLC plate with a micropipet, dip the narrow tip into the solution to draw in a small amount of liquid, and then gently touch the tip to the surface of the TLC plate, at the proper location, for only an instant. Be careful not to dig a hole in the adsorbent surface, because this will obstruct solvent flow and distort the chromatogram. Make several successive applications at each location, letting the solvent dry each time, to form a spot 1–3 mm in diameter. It may be worthwhile to try one, two, and three applications of a sample at three separate locations on the TLC plate to determine which quantity gives the best results. Too much solution can result in "tailing" (a zone of diffuse solute following the spot), "bearding" (a zone of diffuse solute preceding the spot), and overlapping of components. Too little solution makes it difficult to detect some of the components. Capillary micropipets can be reused a few times, but a different micropipet should be used for each different solution to avoid cross-contamination.

You can practice your spotting technique on a used or damaged TLC plate.

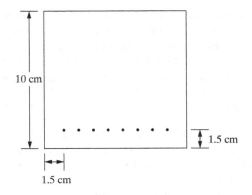

Figure C17 Spotted 10 × 10-cm TLC plate

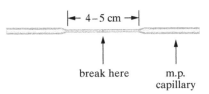

Figure C18 Drawing out a capillary micropipet (not to scale)

To spot a TLC plate with a microliter syringe, deliver about 1 μL of solution with each application and make two to three applications for each spot, letting the solvent dry between applications. Take care not to touch the adsorbent surface with the syringe needle. Before you fill the syringe with a different solution, rinse it with a suitable solvent and remove excess solvent by pumping the plunger gently a few times. After the last application, clean the syringe with more solvent, remove the plunger, and let it dry.

Choosing a Developing Solvent. Solvents that are suitable eluants for column chromatography are equally suitable as TLC developing solvents; the eluotropic series in Table C4 of OP-21 may help you choose a solvent for a particular application. A quick way to find a suitable solvent is to spot a TLC plate with the sample, applying as many spots as you have solvents to test (you can use a grid pattern with the spots 1.5–2.0 cm apart), and then to apply enough solvent directly to each spot to form a circle of solvent 1–2 cm in diameter. Mark the circumference of each circle before the solvent dries. A solvent whose chromatogram (after visualization) shows well-separated rings, with the outermost ring about 50–75% of the distance from the center to the solvent front, should be satisfactory. It is preferable to use the least polar solvent that gives good separation. Hexane, toluene, dichloromethane, and methanol or ethanol (alone or in binary combinations) are suitable for most separations. If no single solvent is suitable, choose two miscible solvents whose outermost rings bracket the 50–75% range (one with too little solute migration, the other with too much), and test them in varying proportions.

Development. TLC plates are developed by placing them in a *developing chamber* that contains the developing solvent. A paper wick can be used to help saturate the air in the developing chamber with solvent vapors, which improves reproducibility and increases the rate of development. The developing chamber can be a jar with a screw-cap lid, a beaker covered with plastic film or aluminum foil, or a commercial developing tank with a lid. You should use the smallest available container that will accommodate the TLC plate, because a larger container takes longer to fill with solvent vapors. Development should be carried out in a place away from direct sunlight or drafts to prevent temperature gradients. It may take 20 minutes or more to develop a 10 × 10-cm TLC plate; a microscope-slide plate can often be developed in 5–10 minutes.

The solvent should not be allowed to reach the top edge of the plate, because the spots will spread by diffusion once the solvent has stopped advancing. When the *solvent front*—the boundary between the wet and dry parts of the adsorbent—is within 5 mm or so of the top of the plate, remove the TLC plate from the developing chamber and mark the solvent front and spots with a pencil, as described in the directions, before the plate has had time to dry. Then let the plate dry, preferably under a hood.

Visualization. If the spots are colored, they can be observed immediately; otherwise, they must be *visualized* (made visible) by some method. The simplest way to visualize many spots is to observe the TLC plate under ultraviolet light. Handheld ultraviolet lamps used for this purpose may have a switch to select either short-wave (254 nm) or long-wave (365 nm) radiation. If the TLC adsorbent contains a fluorescent indicator, compounds that quench fluorescence will show up as dark spots on a light background when the plate is irradiated with 254-nm UV light. Fluorescent compounds will produce bright spots when irradiated with UV light of an appropriate wavelength. Mark the center of each spot immediately with a pencil, because the spots will disappear when the ultraviolet light is removed. If a spot is irregular, instead mark its center of concentration—the midpoint of its most densely shaded region. It is also a good idea to outline each spot with your pencil.

See J. Chem. Educ. **1985**, *62, 156 for an alternative method of visualizing TLC plates with iodine.*

Another general visualization procedure is to place the *dry* plate in a closed chamber (such as a wide-mouthed jar with a screw-cap lid), add a few crystals of iodine, and heat the chamber gently (preferably on a steam bath) so that the iodine vapors sublime onto the adsorbent. Most organic compounds, except saturated hydrocarbons and halides, form brown spots with iodine vapor. Unsaturated compounds may show up as light spots against the dark background. The iodine color fades in time, so mark the spots shortly after visualization. It is important that the TLC plate be completely dry; otherwise, the residual solvent will pick up the iodine color, resulting in a dark background that may obscure the spots.

See J. Chem. Educ. **1996**, *73, 358 for a description of the cotton-ball procedure.*

Spots can also be made visible by applying a *visualizing reagent* to the TLC plate. The visualizing reagent can be applied by spraying it onto the *dry* plate, dipping the plate into the reagent, or wiping the plate with a cotton ball that has been saturated with a noncorrosive reagent. A 20% (mass/volume) solution of phosphomolybdic acid in ethanol can be used to visualize most organic compounds; the spots appear after the plate is heated with a heat gun or in an oven. Other visualizing reagents are used for specific classes of compounds, such as ninhydrin reagent for amino acids and 2,4-dinitrophenylhydrazine reagent for aldehydes and ketones. All spraying should be done under a hood in a "spray box," which can be made from a large cardboard box with the top and one side removed. A thin spray is applied to the TLC plate from about 2 feet away, using an aerosol can or spraying bottle that contains the visualizing reagent. Large plates are sprayed by crisscrossing them with horizontal and vertical passes. As for the previous method, the TLC plate must be completely dry before the visualizing reagent is applied, because residual solvent may otherwise inhibit the visualization reaction.

Analysis. The ratio of the distance a component travels up a TLC plate to the distance the solvent travels is called its R_f *value.*

$$R_f = \frac{\text{distance traveled by spot}}{\text{distance traveled by solvent}}$$

The R_f (ratio to front) value of a spot is determined by measuring the distance from the starting line to the center of the spot and dividing that value by the distance from the starting line to the solvent front, both distances being measured along a line extending from the starting point of the spot to its final location. If the spot is irregular, its center of concentration (the midpoint of its most densely shaded region) is used instead.

The R_f value of a substance with a given mobile and stationary phase depends on the polarity of its functional groups and other structural features, so it is a physical property of the substance that can be used in its identification. R_f values for some compounds, using specified mobile and stationary phases, have been reported in the literature. Reported R_f values alone can seldom be used to establish the identity of a substance, however, because they depend on a number of factors that are difficult to standardize, such as the sample size, the thickness and activity of the adsorbent, the purity of the solvent, and the temperature of the developing chamber. The only way to be reasonably sure that a TLC unknown is identical to a known compound is to spot a solution of the known compound on the same TLC plate as the unknown. Even then, the identity of the unknown may have to be confirmed by an independent method. An unknown substance or mixture is often analyzed on the same plate with a series of standard solutions, each containing a substance that may be identical to the unknown—or to one of its components, if it is a mixture.

DIRECTIONS FOR PREPARING MICROSCOPE-SLIDE TLC PLATES

Several students should work together so that they can use the same slurry. For each TLC plate, clean a microscope slide with detergent and water, and then rinse it with distilled water and 50% aqueous methanol. After a slide has been cleaned, don't touch the surface that will be coated; hold the slide by its edges or at the top. *Under the hood,* measure 100 mL of dichloromethane into a 4-oz (125-mL) screw-cap jar, add 35 g of Silica Gel G, with vigorous stirring or swirling, and shake the capped jar vigorously for about a minute to form a smooth slurry. Stack two clean microscope slides back to back, holding them together at the top. Without allowing the slurry to settle (shake it again, if necessary), dip the stacked slides into the slurry for about 2 seconds, using a smooth, unhurried, paddle-like motion (see Figure C19) to coat them uniformly with the adsorbent. Immerse the slides deeply enough so that only the top 1 cm or so remains uncoated.

Take Care! Avoid contact with dichloromethane and do not breathe its vapors.

Touch the bottom of the stacked slides to the jar to drain off excess slurry, and let them air-dry for a minute or so to evaporate the solvent. Then separate them and wipe off the excess adsorbent from the edges with a piece of tissue paper. Repeat with more slides, as needed; if the slurry becomes too thick, dilute it with dichloromethane. Activate the coated slides by heating them in a 110°C oven for 15 minutes. Slides that have streaks, lumps, or thin spots in the coating should be wiped clean and re-dipped. If the coating is too fragile, try adding some methanol (up to one-third by

Waste Disposal: Dispose of the slurry as directed by your instructor.

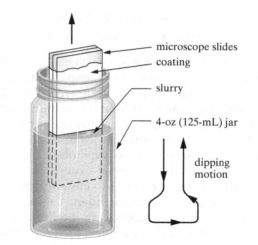

microscope slides
coating
slurry
4-oz (125-mL) jar
dipping motion

Figure C19 Dipping a pair of stacked microscope slides

volume) to the slurry. Coated slides can be stored in a microscope-slide box inside a desiccator.

DIRECTIONS FOR THIN-LAYER CHROMATOGRAPHY

Equipment and Supplies

TLC plate(s)
developing chamber
paper wick
developing solvent
pencil and ruler
capillary micropipets or microliter syringe
solutions to be spotted
visualizer (sprayer, iodine chamber, UV lamp, etc.)

The wick may not be necessary if the developing chamber is allowed to stand for an hour or more after the developing solvent has been added.

Do not use aluminum foil if the developing solvent contains a volatile acid or another corrosive liquid.

Obtain a beaker, screw-cap jar, or another container large enough to hold the TLC plate. A 4-oz screw-cap jar is suitable for a microscope-slide TLC plate, a 400-mL beaker will hold a 6.7 × 10-cm plate, and a 1-L beaker will hold a 10 × 10-cm plate. If necessary, prepare and insert a paper wick made from filter paper or chromatography paper. The wick can be prepared by cutting a rectangular strip of paper 3–5 cm wide and long enough to extend in a "U" down one side of the developing chamber, along the bottom, and up the opposite side (see Figure C20). Pour in enough developing solvent to form a liquid layer about 5 mm deep on the bottom of the developing chamber. Cover the chamber with a screw cap, a square of aluminum foil or plastic food wrap, or another suitable closure. Tip the chamber and slosh the solvent around to soak the wick with developing solvent; then put it in a place where it can sit undisturbed, away from drafts and direct sunlight. Let the developing chamber stand for 30 minutes or more to saturate the atmosphere inside the chamber with solvent vapors.

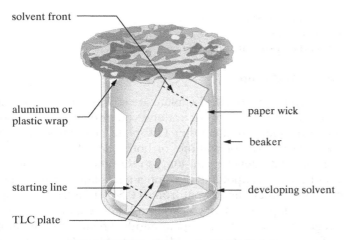

Figure C20 Development of a TLC plate

Mark the starting line on a TLC plate and spot it with (1) the solution(s) to be analyzed and (2) any standard solutions required, making spots 1–3 mm in diameter. Except on a microscope-slide TLC plate, which can accommodate up to three evenly spaced spots, the spots should be at least 1.0 cm apart and the outermost spots should be 1.5 cm from the edges of the plate. When the spots are dry, place the TLC plate in the developing chamber—spotted end down—so that it leans *across* the wick with its top against the glass wall of the chamber. No part of a plastic- or aluminum-backed TLC plate should touch the exposed part of the wick, because solvent can diffuse onto the adsorbent at that point. Cover the developing chamber without delay and don't move it during development.

Observe the development frequently. When the solvent front is within about 5 mm of the top of the plate, remove the plate from the developing chamber. Before the solvent evaporates, use a pencil to trace a line along the solvent front and mark the centers (or centers of concentration) of any visible spots. It is advisable to outline each spot with your pencil as well. Let the plate dry thoroughly, preferably under a hood. If necessary, visualize the spots by one of the methods described in "Visualization," and then use a pencil to outline any previously unseen spots and mark their centers (or centers of concentration). Keeping your ruler parallel to the edges of the plate along the line of development, measure the distance in millimeters from the starting line to the solvent front and from the starting line to the center of each spot. Calculate the R_f value for each spot. If requested, make a permanent record of the chromatogram by photocopying or photographing it.

Waste Disposal: Dispose of the developing solvent as directed by your instructor or as indicated by an experiment's directions.

The distance from the starting line to the solvent front may vary, so measure that distance for each spot along an imaginary vertical line that goes through the spot.

Summary

1. Put wick and developing solvent in developing chamber, cover, and let stand.
2. Obtain or prepare TLC plate.
3. Spot TLC plate with solutions of the unknown(s) and any standards.
4. Place TLC plate in developing chamber, cover, and observe.
5. Remove TLC plate when solvent front nears top of plate.
6. Mark solvent front and visible spots, and let plate dry.

7. Visualize and mark spots, as needed.

8. Measure R_f values.

9. Clean up and dispose of solvent.

When Things Go Wrong

If the spots on your developed TLC plate are so large or irregular that you can't measure their R_f values accurately, you probably used too much sample to spot the plate. Spot another TLC plate, applying smaller spots or making fewer successive applications, or both. (See "Spotting.") You may also have let the plate develop too long, so that the solvent front reached the top end of the plate. Spot and develop a new plate, taking it out of the developing solvent when the solvent front is 0.5–1.0 cm from the top of the plate. (See "Development.") If you used a "do-it-yourself" plate, it may have an irregular surface; if so, prepare another plate, more carefully this time. (See "Directions for Preparing Microscope-Slide TLC Plates.")

If the spots for some components are too close together to identify from their R_f values, try another developing solvent or solvent mixture. Be sure that the solvents aren't contaminated by water or other impurities. (See "Choosing a Developing Solvent.")

It's also possible that the plate has an organic binder, in which case a different type of TLC plate or a different visualization method should be used.

If you used iodine vapor for visualization and the entire TLC plate has become quite dark, you probably didn't let it dry long enough. If you can't locate all of the expected spots, you will have to prepare, develop, thoroughly dry, and visualize another plate. (See "Visualization.")

If you don't see the expected spots on your developed TLC plate, think about what you might have done wrong. Were your spots so small or diffuse that they could no longer be seen after development? (See "Spotting.") Did you use too much developing solvent or draw your starting line too low on the TLC plate, so that the solvent covered the starting line and washed out the components of the spots? (See "Development.") If you used a UV lamp to visualize the spots, did you irradiate the wrong side of the TLC plate or use the wrong UV wavelength? (See "Visualization.") If you put your TLC plate in an iodine–vapor chamber, did you set the plate aside for so long that the iodine spots faded before you examined it? (See "Visualization.") If you used a visualizing reagent such as phosphomolybdic acid, did you fail to dry the plate completely before applying the reagent, or did you not heat the plate long enough for the spots to appear? (See "Visualization.") If you think you may have done (or not done) any of these things, read the indicated section carefully, then prepare, develop, and visualize another plate, taking steps to correct any possible mistakes.

Paper Chromatography

Principles and Applications

Paper chromatography is similar to thin-layer chromatography [OP-22] in practice but quite different in principle. A square or rectangle of chromatography paper is spotted with solutions of the sample and standards, and the chromatogram is developed with a suitable mobile phase. Although paper consists mainly of cellulose, the stationary phase is not cellulose itself but the water that is adsorbed by it. Chromatography paper can adsorb up to 22% water, and the developing solvents usually contain enough water to keep it saturated. During development, a comparatively nonpolar mobile phase seeps up through the cellulose fibers, partitioning the solutes between the bound water and the mobile phase. Paper chromatography thus operates by a liquid–liquid partitioning process rather than by adsorption on the surface of a solid.

Because only polar compounds are appreciably soluble in water, paper chromatography is most frequently used to separate polar substances such as amino acids and carbohydrates. Manufactured chromatography paper is quite uniform, and the activity of cellulose doesn't vary as much as the activity of most TLC adsorbents, so R_f values obtained by paper chromatography may be more reproducible than those from thin-layer chromatography. However, the resolution of spots is often poorer and the development times are usually much longer. Nevertheless, paper chromatography is an inexpensive and convenient analytical technique that can accomplish a variety of separations.

Experimental Considerations

Because many of the experimental aspects of paper chromatography are similar or identical to those for thin-layer chromatography, you should read the appropriate parts of OP-22 for additional information about experimental techniques.

Paper. Various grades of chromatography paper, such as Whatman #1 Chr, are manufactured in rectangular sheets, strips, and other convenient shapes. For good results, the chromatography paper must be kept clean. The benchtop or other surface on which the paper is handled should be covered with a sheet of freezer paper or some other liner. The chromatography paper should be held only by the edges or along the top; alternatively, an extra strip of paper can be left on one or both ends of the chromatography paper, used for handling it, and then cut off just before development. The paper should be cut so that its grain is parallel to the direction of development. For most purposes, the paper should be 10–15 cm high (in the direction of development) and wide enough to accommodate the desired number of spots.

Spotting. As for thin-layer chromatography, the substance(s) to be analyzed should be dissolved in a suitable solvent, usually at a concentration of about 1% (mass/volume). The starting line should be marked with a pencil about 2 cm above the bottom edge of the chromatography paper; the positions of the spots can also be marked lightly with a pencil. The spots tend to spread out more with paper chromatography than with TLC, so they should

It is advisable to wear thin disposable gloves while handling chromatography paper.

From *Operational Organic Chemistry: A Problem Solving Approach to the Laboratory*, Fourth Edition, John W. Lehman. Copyright © 2009 by Pearson Education. Published by Prentice Hall. All rights reserved.

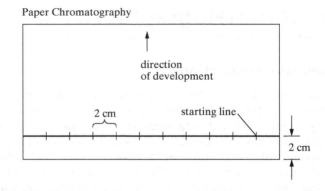

Figure C21 11 × 22-cm chromatography paper marked for spotting

be applied farther apart—about 1.5–2.0 cm from each other and 2.0 cm from the edges of the paper, as shown in Figure C21. Make sure that the chromatography paper is not on an absorbent surface that might soak up or distort the spots. Spotting can be performed using a capillary micropipet or a microsyringe (see OP-22), but a round wooden toothpick is adequate for most purposes. Each spot should be 2–5 mm in diameter. It should be made using several consecutive applications, and the solvent should be allowed to evaporate after each application. Use no more than 10 µL of solution, in all, per spot; too little is better than too much. You can practice your spotting technique on a piece of filter paper before attempting to spot the chromatogram. It is important that the spots be completely dry before development. If necessary, leave the chromatography paper under the hood or carefully blow clean air on the spots until they are dry.

Developing Solvents. As a rule, paper chromatography developing solvents contain water, which is needed to maintain the composition of the aqueous stationary phase on the cellulose. They also contain an organic solvent and (if necessary) one or more additional components to increase the solubility of the water in the organic solvent or provide an acidic or basic medium. A developing solvent for paper chromatography may be prepared by saturating the organic solvent(s) with water in a separatory funnel, separating the two phases, and using the organic phase for development. Alternatively, a monophase (single-phase) mixture with essentially the same composition as the organic phase of the corresponding saturated mixture can be used. Some typical monophase solvent mixtures are listed in Table C5. Most solvent mixtures should be made up fresh each time they are used and not kept for more than a day or two.

Table C5 Some monophase solvent mixtures for paper chromatography

Solvents	Composition
2-propanol/ammonia/water	9:1:2
1-butanol/acetic acid/water	12:3:5
phenol/water	500 g phenol, 125 mL water
ethyl acetate/1-propanol/water	14:2:4

Note: All solvent ratios are by volume.

Development. Narrow paper strips accommodating two or more spots can be developed in test tubes, bottles, cylinders, or Erlenmeyer flasks. A wider sheet can be rolled into a cylinder and developed in a beaker. A typical paper chromatogram is developed in much the same way as for TLC, but more time is required to saturate the developing chamber with solvent vapors.

Visualization. Visualization of spots by ultraviolet light is quite useful in paper chromatography, because paper fluoresces dimly in a dark room and many organic compounds will quench its fluorescence, yielding dark spots on a light background. Paper chromatograms can also be visualized by spraying them or by dipping them into a solution of a suitable visualizing reagent.

Analysis. A substance responsible for a spot on a developed chromatogram is characterized by its R_f value, which is determined as illustrated in Figure C22. Spot migration distances are customarily measured from the starting line to the front of each spot, rather than to its center as for TLC. It is usually necessary to run one or more standards along with an unknown to identify the unknown. Whenever possible, the solvent and concentration should be the same for the standard as for the unknown.

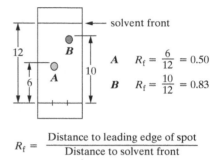

$A \quad R_f = \dfrac{6}{12} = 0.50$

$B \quad R_f = \dfrac{10}{12} = 0.83$

$$R_f = \frac{\text{Distance to leading edge of spot}}{\text{Distance to solvent front}}$$

Figure C22 Measuring R_f values on a paper chromatogram

DIRECTIONS FOR PAPER CHROMATOGRAPHY

Equipment and Supplies

chromatography paper
developing chamber
developing solvent
pencil and ruler
capillary micropipets (or toothpicks, etc.)
solutions to be spotted
visualizer (sprayer, UV lamp, etc.)

The following procedure can be used when up to 13 spots are to be applied. (For just a few spots, a strip of chromatography paper can be spotted, folded in the middle or hung from a wire embedded in a cork, and developed in a test tube, a jar, or another appropriate container.)

Add enough developing solvent to a 600-mL beaker (or another suitable developing chamber) to provide a liquid layer about 1 cm deep (see Figure C23). Cover the chamber tightly with plastic food wrap (or cap it), slosh the solvent around in it for about 30 seconds, and then put it in a place where it can sit undisturbed, away from drafts and direct sunlight. Allow sufficient time (usually an hour or more) for the solvent to saturate the developing chamber. While the developing chamber is equilibrating, obtain a sheet of chromatography paper and cut it to form an 11×22-cm rectangle (or another appropriate size). Without touching the surface of the paper with your fingers, use a pencil to draw a starting line 2 cm from one long edge (the bottom edge) and lightly mark the positions for spots with a pencil, spacing them about 2 cm from each side and 1.5–2.0 cm apart. Spot the paper with all of the solutions to be analyzed and let the spots dry completely. Then roll it into a cylinder and staple the ends together, leaving a small gap between them (see Figure C23). Uncover the developing chamber, place the

(cover omitted for clarity)

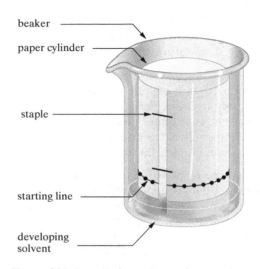

beaker

paper cylinder

staple

starting line

developing solvent

Figure C23 Developing a paper chromatogram

paper cylinder inside (spotted end down), and cover it without delay. The paper must not touch the sides of the chamber and the chamber should not be moved during development. Development may take an hour or more, depending on the developing solvent and the distance traveled.

When the solvent front is a centimeter or less from the top of the paper, remove the cylinder and separate its edges; then accurately draw a line along the entire solvent front with a pencil. If any spots are visible at this time, outline them with a pencil (carefully, to avoid tearing the wet paper), as they may fade in time. Again bend the paper into a cylinder and stand it on edge to air-dry, preferably under a hood. When it is completely dry, visualize the spots by an appropriate method, if necessary, and outline any previously unseen spots with a pencil. Keeping your ruler parallel to the edges of the paper along the line of development, measure the distance in millimeters from the starting line to the solvent front and from the starting line to the leading edge of each spot. Calculate the R_f value of each spot.

Waste Disposal: Dispose of the developing solvent as directed by your instructor or as indicated by an experiment's directions.

The distance from the starting line to the solvent front may vary, so measure that distance for each spot along an imaginary vertical line that goes through the spot.

Summary

1. Add developing solvent to developing chamber, cover, and let stand.
2. Obtain chromatography paper and cut it to size.
3. Spot chromatography paper with solutions and roll into cylinder.
4. Place paper in developing chamber, cover, and observe.
5. Remove paper chromatogram when solvent front nears top of paper.
6. Mark solvent front and any visible spots; let chromatogram dry.
7. Visualize and mark spots, as needed.
8. Measure R_f values.
9. Clean up; dispose of solvent as directed.

When Things Go Wrong

Most of the things that go wrong during TLC analysis can also go wrong during a paper chromatography analysis (with minor modifications), so you can refer to "When Things Go Wrong" in OP-22 for help.

Washing Liquids

In practice, the process of washing liquids is identical to liquid–liquid extraction [OP-18a], but its purpose is different. *Extraction* separates a desired substance (such as the product of a reaction) from an impure mixture; *washing* removes impurities from a desired substance. The liquid being washed may be a neat liquid (one without solvent) or a solution that contains the desired substance. In either case, the substance must not dissolve appreciably in the wash liquid or it will be extracted along with the impurities.

The *wash liquid* is usually water or an aqueous solution, although organic solvents such as diethyl ether can be used to remove low-polarity impurities from aqueous solutions that contain polar solutes. Both water and saturated aqueous sodium chloride remove water-soluble impurities, such as salts and polar organic compounds, from organic liquids. Saturated sodium chloride is frequently used for the last washing before a liquid is dried [OP-25], because it removes excess water from the organic liquid by the salting-out effect described in OP-18b. It is preferred to water in some other cases because it helps prevent the formation of emulsions at the interface between liquids.

Some aqueous wash liquids contain chemically reactive solutes that convert water-insoluble impurities to water-soluble salts, which then dissolve in the wash solvent. Aqueous solutions of bases remove acidic impurities, as illustrated for sodium bicarbonate.

A stronger base, such as sodium hydroxide, is needed to remove phenols and other weak acids.

$$NaHCO_3 + HA \text{ (acidic impurity)} \longrightarrow Na^+A^- \text{ (soluble salt)} + H_2O + CO_2$$

Aqueous solutions of acids remove alkaline impurities, as illustrated for hydrochloric acid.

$$HCl + B \text{ (alkaline impurity)} \longrightarrow BH^+Cl^- \text{ (soluble salt)}$$

When a chemically reactive wash liquid is used, it is usually advisable to perform a preliminary washing with water or aqueous NaCl to remove most of the water-soluble impurities. This may prevent a potentially violent reaction between the reactive wash liquid and the impurities. A follow-up washing with water or aqueous NaCl is often used to remove traces of the chemically reactive solute from the product.

The effectiveness of washing with a given volume of wash liquid increases if it is carried out in several steps. Unless otherwise indicated in the experimental procedure, a liquid should be washed in two or three stages, using equal volumes of wash liquid for each stage, and the total volume of wash liquid should be roughly equal to the volume of the liquid being washed. For example, if you are washing 6 mL of a liquid, you can use two 3-mL or three 2-mL portions of the wash liquid. When several different wash liquids are used in succession, one or two washings with each wash liquid may be sufficient, but the total volume of all of the wash liquids should usually equal or exceed the volume of the liquid being washed.

Rule of Thumb: Total volume of wash liquid ≈ volume of liquid being washed.

The procedure for washing liquids is essentially the same as that for liquid–liquid extraction [OP-18a], except that the extraction solvent (the wash liquid) is discarded and the liquid being extracted is saved. As for extraction,

From *Operational Organic Chemistry: A Problem Solving Approach to the Laboratory*, Fourth Edition, John W. Lehman. Copyright © 2009 by Pearson Education. Published by Prentice Hall. All rights reserved.

it is important to save *both* layers until you are absolutely certain you are working with the right layer. Refer to the directions in OP-18a for illustrations and experimental details.

DIRECTIONS FOR WASHING LIQUIDS

If you are washing only a small amount of liquid, use the method described in "Directions for Extraction with a Centrifuge Tube" in OP-18a.

Combine the wash liquid and the liquid being washed in a separatory funnel. If the wash liquid contains sodium carbonate, sodium bicarbonate, or another reactive solute that generates a gas, use a glass stirring rod to stir it vigorously with the liquid being washed until gas evolution subsides. Otherwise, a pressure buildup might cause the stopper to pop out and your product to spray all over the lab. Then stopper the separatory funnel and shake it, very gently at first, with frequent venting. When you no longer hear a "whoosh" of escaping vapors upon venting, shake the separatory funnel more vigorously for 1–2 minutes, with occasional venting. Then remove the stopper and set it on a support until the layers separate sharply.

If the liquid being washed is *less* dense than the wash liquid (for example, if it's an ether solution), drain the lower layer (the wash liquid) into a flask or beaker after each washing. Then add the next portion of wash liquid to the liquid being washed, which remains in the separatory funnel, and repeat the washing as needed. Set the wash liquid aside for later disposal.

If the liquid being washed is *more* dense than the wash liquid (for example, if it's a dichloromethane solution), drain the lower layer into a flask and pour the wash liquid out the top of the separatory funnel into another container after each washing. Return the lower layer to the separatory funnel, add the next portion of wash liquid, and repeat the washing as needed. Set the wash liquid aside for later disposal.

Waste Disposal: Dispose of the wash liquid as directed by your instructor or as indicated by an experiment's directions.

When Things Go Wrong

Most of the things that go wrong during a liquid–liquid extraction can also go wrong when you are washing a liquid, so you can refer to "When Things Go Wrong" in OP-18a for help.

Drying Liquids

When an organic substance (or a solution containing it) is extracted from an aqueous reaction mixture, washed with an aqueous wash liquid, steam distilled from a natural product, or comes into contact with water in some other way, the substance or its solution will retain traces of water that must be removed before such operations as evaporation and distillation are carried out. Organic liquids and solutions can be dried in bulk by allowing them to stand in contact with a *drying agent*, which is then removed by decanting or filtration. Small amounts of liquids can be dried by passing them through a *drying column*, such as a Pasteur pipet packed with a suitable drying agent.

Drying Agents

Most drying agents are anhydrous (water-free) inorganic salts that form hydrates by combining chemically with water. For example, a mole of anhydrous magnesium sulfate can combine with up to seven moles of water to form hydrates of varying composition.

$$MgSO_4 + nH_2O \rightleftharpoons MgSO_4 \cdot nH_2O \qquad (n = 1\text{--}7)$$

The effectiveness and general applicability of a drying agent depends on the following characteristics:

- Speed—how fast drying takes place
- Capacity—the amount of water absorbed per unit of mass
- Intensity—the degree of dryness attained
- Chemical inertness—unreactivity with the substances being dried
- Ease of removal

Ideally, a drying agent should be very fast and have both a high capacity and a high intensity. It should not react with (or dissolve in) a substance being dried, and it should be easy to remove when drying is complete. Table D1

Table D1 Properties of commonly used drying agents

Drying agent	Speed	Capacity	Intensity	Comments
magnesium sulfate	fast	medium	medium	good general drying agent, suitable for nearly all organic liquids
calcium sulfate (Drierite)	very fast	low	high	fast and efficient, but low capacity; may contain a blue indicator that turns pink when hydrated
sodium sulfate	slow	high	low	suitable when thorough drying isn't necessary; easy to remove
calcium chloride	slow to fast	low to medium	medium	removes traces of water quickly, larger amounts slowly; reacts with many organic compounds
silica gel	medium	medium	high	good general drying agent, more expensive than most
potassium carbonate	fast	low	medium	cannot be used to dry acidic compounds
potassium hydroxide	fast	very high	high	used to dry amines, reacts with many other compounds; caustic

From *Operational Organic Chemistry: A Problem Solving Approach to the Laboratory*, Fourth Edition, John W. Lehman. Copyright © 2009 by Pearson Education. Published by Prentice Hall. All rights reserved.

summarizes the properties of some common drying agents. As you can see in the table, there is no ideal drying agent, but anhydrous magnesium sulfate is perhaps the best all-around drying agent.

The choice of a drying agent depends, in part, on the properties of the liquid being dried and the degree of drying required. Solvents such as diethyl ether and ethyl acetate retain appreciable quantities of water, so their solutions are often washed [OP-24] with saturated aqueous sodium chloride to salt out some of the water before further drying. They should then be dried by a drying agent with a relatively high capacity, such as magnesium sulfate or sodium sulfate. Powdered anhydrous magnesium sulfate tends to adsorb organic solutes onto its surface, so it should always be washed with a suitable pure solvent to recover adsorbed material. Granular anhydrous sodium sulfate doesn't adsorb much of the substance being dried and is easy to remove, so it's often used when thorough drying isn't necessary.

Relatively nonpolar solvents, such as petroleum ether and dichloromethane, retain little water and can be dried with lower-capacity drying agents such as calcium sulfate (Drierite) or calcium chloride. Calcium chloride reacts with many organic compounds that contain oxygen or nitrogen, including alcohols, aldehydes, ketones, carboxylic acids, phenols, amines, amides, and some esters, so it shouldn't be used to dry such compounds or their solutions. To dry a dichloromethane solution that will later be evaporated, it may be sufficient to filter the solution through a cotton plug to remove water droplets (if there are any). The remaining water forms an azeotrope (see OP-32) with dichloromethane and evaporates along with it.

Drying agents come in different particle sizes. Finer particles dry liquids more effectively, but coarser particles make it easier to separate the dried liquid. Anhydrous magnesium sulfate is usually finely powdered, so it should be removed by gravity filtration [OP-15]. Anhydrous sodium sulfate can be obtained in coarse particles similar to those of granulated sugar, and calcium chloride comes in coarse granules with mesh numbers of 20 or lower, so these drying agents are often removed by decanting (see OP-15).

The mesh number of a granular substance is the number of openings per linear inch in the finest screen that will allow the substance's particles to pass through. The finer the particles, the higher the mesh number.

Small quantities of neat (undiluted) liquids should be dissolved in a *carrier solvent*, such as diethyl ether or dichloromethane, before drying. Otherwise, you may lose much of your product by adsorption on the drying agent. After drying, the carrier solvent is removed by evaporation [OP-19].

Pre-Drying

Saturated aqueous sodium chloride is often used to pre-dry a wet solution obtained by extraction, especially when the extraction solvent is diethyl ether. (Most other common extraction solvents, including dichloromethane and all hydrocarbons, dissolve little water and don't require pre-drying.) When diethyl ether is used to extract an aqueous solution, the resulting ether layer contains about 1.5% by mass of dissolved water. Washing it with saturated aqueous sodium chloride draws most of the dissolved water out of the ether solution, in part because dilution of a concentrated salt solution is energetically favorable. This reduces the amount of drying agent needed to dry it efficiently. The washing is carried out as described in OP-24, using a volume of saturated sodium chloride that is 50–100% that of the ether solution being washed.

Because of its high capacity, anhydrous sodium sulfate is sometimes used to pre-dry very wet solutions that are later dried thoroughly with a high-intensity drying agent such as calcium sulfate.

Drying Liquids in Bulk

Amount of Drying Agent. The amount of drying agent needed for bulk drying depends on the capacity and particle size of the drying agent and on the amount of water present. Usually, about 1 g of drying agent should be used for every 25 mL of liquid. More may be needed if the drying agent has a low capacity or large particle size, or if the liquid has a high water content. It is best to start with a small amount of drying agent and then add more, if necessary—using too much results in excessive losses by adsorption of liquid on the drying agent. The appearance of the drying agent when the drying time is up often suggests whether more drying agent is needed. As they become hydrated, sodium sulfate and magnesium sulfate particles clump together, calcium chloride displays a glassy surface appearance, and blue indicating Drierite changes color to pink. If most of a drying agent has changed as described after the initial drying period, more drying agent should be added or the spent drying agent should be removed and replaced with fresh drying agent.

Rule of Thumb: Use about 1 g of drying agent per 25 mL of liquid.

Drying Time. The time required for bulk drying depends on the speed of the drying agent and the amount of water present. Most drying agents attain at least 80% of their ultimate drying capacity within 15 minutes, so longer drying times are seldom necessary—5 minutes is usually sufficient for magnesium sulfate or Drierite, and 15 minutes is recommended for calcium chloride or sodium sulfate. When more complete drying is required, it's better to replace the spent drying agent or use a more efficient drying agent than to extend the drying time.

Spent drying agent contains hydrates that reduce drying efficiency.

Removal of the Drying Agent. A drying agent should be removed as completely as possible when the drying period is over. Most drying agents are removed by gravity filtration [OP-15] through a coarse fluted filter paper or a filtering pipet. A coarse-grained drying agent, such as granular sodium sulfate, calcium chloride, or Drierite, can sometimes be removed by carefully decanting the liquid (see OP-15), but granular calcium chloride often contains a fine powder that requires filtration. The spent drying agent should ordinarily be washed with a small amount of a suitable solvent, which is then combined with the dried liquid, to recover adsorbed solute that would otherwise be discarded with the drying agent.

DIRECTIONS FOR BULK DRYING

Equipment and Supplies

Erlenmeyer flask
drying agent
funnel and fluted filter paper

If you are drying a small amount of a neat liquid, it is advisable to dissolve the liquid in a carrier solvent, such as diethyl ether or dichloromethane, and to evaporate the solvent after drying. If the liquid to be dried contains water droplets or a separate aqueous layer, remove the water using a Pasteur pipet or a separatory funnel.

Select an Erlenmeyer flask that will hold the liquid with plenty of room to spare, and add the liquid. Measure out the estimated quantity of a suitable drying agent, being sure to cap its original container tightly. Protect it from atmospheric moisture until you are ready to use it. Add the drying agent to the liquid, stopper the flask, and swirl or shake it for a few seconds. Let the liquid dry for 5–15 minutes (use the longer drying time for calcium chloride, sodium sulfate, and other slow drying agents). Swirl, stir, or shake the mixture occasionally during the drying period. If a second (aqueous) phase forms during drying, remove it with a Pasteur pipet and add more drying agent.

When the drying period is over, examine the drying agent carefully. If most of it is spent, add more drying agent (or remove it and replace it with fresh drying agent), and continue drying for 5 minutes or more. When drying appears to be complete, separate the dry liquid from the drying agent by filtering the liquid by gravity [OP-15] through coarse fluted filter paper (for small amounts you can use a filtering pipet). If the drying agent is anhydrous sodium sulfate or another granular solid, you may be able to decant the liquid into another container, leaving all of the drying agent behind. If you are drying a solution, wash the drying agent with a small volume of the pure solvent and combine the rinse liquid with the dried liquid. If you are drying a neat liquid, you can wash the drying agent with a suitable solvent, combine the solvent with the dried liquid, and evaporate the solvent.

Summary

1. Select drying agent and measure estimated quantity needed.
2. Add drying agent to liquid in Erlenmeyer flask.
3. Stopper flask and mix contents, then set aside.
4. Shake, stir, or swirl occasionally until drying time is up.
IF drying agent is spent or aqueous phase separates, GO TO 5.
IF not, GO TO 6.
5. Remove aqueous phase or spent drying agent, if necessary; add fresh drying agent; GO TO 3.
6. Separate liquid from drying agent.
IF liquid being dried is a neat liquid, GO TO 7.
IF liquid being dried is a solution, GO TO 8.
7. Wash drying agent with solvent, combine with dried liquid, and evaporate solvent.
8. Wash drying agent with appropriate solvent and combine with dried solution.
9. Clean up.

Drying Columns

Small quantities of wet liquid (~10 mL or less) can be dried using a drying column (Figure D1), which can be constructed by supporting the drying agent on a cotton plug inside a Pasteur pipet or another suitable column. Granular anhydrous sodium sulfate is the preferred drying agent; it comes in relatively large grains, allowing liquids to flow through easily. A sodium sulfate column can absorb relatively large amounts of water without plugging up.

Waste Disposal: Dispose of the spent drying agent as directed by your instructor.

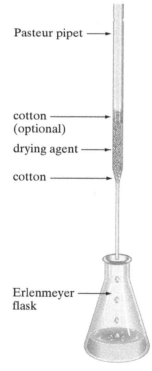

Pasteur pipet

cotton (optional)

drying agent

cotton

Erlenmeyer flask

Figure D1 A drying column

DIRECTIONS FOR USING A DRYING COLUMN

Equipment and Supplies

two $5\frac{3}{4}$-inch Pasteur pipets
latex rubber bulb
cotton
applicator stick or stirring rod
drying agent
collecting container

If you are drying a neat liquid, dissolve it in 5 mL or more of a carrier solvent, such as diethyl ether or dichloromethane. (You will need to evaporate the solvent after drying.) To prepare a drying column, obtain a $5\frac{3}{4}$-inch Pasteur pipet and use an applicator stick or a thin glass stirring rod to gently tamp a small ball of clean cotton into the column, until it lodges where the pipet narrows. Add enough anhydrous sodium sulfate through the top of the Pasteur pipet to provide a 2–3-cm layer of the drying agent. If the liquid to be dried contains visible water droplets or a separate aqueous layer, remove most of the water with a Pasteur pipet, and then tamp a loose plug of cotton into the drying column so that it rests on top of the layer of drying agent. Clamp the drying column vertically to a ring stand, place a suitable collecting container under the outlet, and transfer the liquid being dried to the column with a Pasteur pipet. If the liquid flow stops or becomes very slow, attach a latex rubber bulb or a pipet pump to the top of the column and use it to force the liquid *slowly* through the column. When all of the liquid has passed through the drying agent, add about 0.5 mL of fresh solvent (the solvent present in the liquid being dried) to the top of the drying column and let it drain into the container holding the dried liquid. Use a latex rubber bulb to gently expel any liquid remaining on the column into the container. For a neat liquid, evaporate [OP-19] any added solvent.

Waste Disposal: Dispose of the spent drying agent as directed by your instructor.

Summary

1. Select drying agent and measure quantity needed.
2. Prepare drying column containing drying agent supported on cotton plug.
3. Clamp drying column to ring stand over collecting container.
4. Transfer liquid to column with Pasteur pipet and drain into collecting container.
5. Rinse drying agent with fresh solvent and combine with dried liquid.
6. Clean up.

When Things Go Wrong

If most or all of the drying agent you used for bulk drying has clumped together or (in the case of calcium chloride) has a glassy appearance, try adding roughly half as much fresh drying agent as you used initially (this assumes that you followed the rule of thumb given previously). If, after swirling and standing, the added drying agent has about the same appearance as the drying agent already there, decant (see OP-15) the liquid from the spent drying agent (it doesn't matter if a little drying agent goes with the liquid) and add fresh drying agent. After swirling and standing, most of the fresh drying agent should have the same granular or powdery appearance as it has in the dry form; if not, repeat this process until it does. If you have to add a large amount of drying agent to get to this point, you may want to add more solvent (if you're drying a solution) to minimize product losses. If you're drying a neat (undiluted) liquid, you can add a low-boiling solvent, such as dichloromethane, and then evaporate it after the drying agent has been removed.

If, after you add a drying agent to the liquid being dried, you observe a separate water layer (usually cloudy), you may not have separated the organic layer cleanly from the aqueous layer during a previous extraction or washing process, or you may not have dried your glassware carefully. Remove the aqueous layer with a Pasteur pipet [OP-6] (try not to remove any of the organic layer) and then add more drying agent.

If the liquid flow through a drying column stops or becomes very slow, attach a latex rubber bulb to the top of the column and squeeze it just enough to force the liquid *slowly* through the column. If that doesn't work, pull out the plunger of a pipet pump, attach it to the top of the column, and rotate the thumbwheel enough to force the liquid through the column.

The location of the water band can vary with the sampling method used. In a CCl₄ solution, it occurs around 3700 cm⁻¹.

If you record an infrared spectrum of your dried product and it shows a broad absorption band centered near 3500 cm^{-1}, it's probably not dry enough, because that is the usual frequency of the O—H stretching vibration of water. Similarly, a ^{1}H NMR singlet at $\delta = 1.55$ ppm in CDCl$_3$ may indicate the presence of dissolved water. Unless there is another good explanation for such a result, you should re-dry your product with fresh drying agent for at least 10 minutes and then repeat the analysis.

Solids that have been collected by vacuum filtration [OP-16] tend to retain traces of impurities on the surfaces of their crystals, which can be washed with an appropriate solvent. Solids obtained by other operations, such as evaporation [OP-19] of a solvent, may also benefit from careful washing.

Solids that have been separated from a reaction mixture or isolated from other sources usually retain traces of water or other solvents used in the separation. The solvent can be removed by a number of drying methods, depending on the nature of the solvent, the amount of material to be dried, and the melting point and thermal stability of the solid compound.

a. Washing Solids

Solid products obtained from a reaction or a recrystallization [OP-28] operation are ordinarily collected by vacuum filtration [OP-16] and washed directly on the filter. The wash solvent should be chosen carefully, because one in which the solid is appreciably soluble will reduce the amount of product you recover. To minimize losses due to solubility, the wash solvent should ordinarily be chilled in ice water before use.

The solvent from which a solid was originally filtered is usually a suitable wash solvent, because the solid shouldn't be very soluble in it—otherwise, there wouldn't be much solid to filter. For example, a solid that was recrystallized [OP-28] from 95% ethanol can be washed with fresh portions of cold 95% ethanol. Because most organic compounds are less soluble in water than in ethanol, using a wash solvent that contains a higher percentage of water—such as 50% ethanol—should reduce its solubility even further (but make sure that the solid isn't one of the few organic compounds that is more soluble in water than in ethanol). If you filter a solid from a mixture of two solvents, as in a mixed-solvent recrystallization [OP-28b], wash it with the solvent in which it is *least* soluble or with an appropriate mixture of the two solvents. For example, aspirin can be recrystallized from a mixture of ethanol and water that contains about twice as much water as ethanol, so it can be washed with an ethanol–water mixture that contains at least that much water, or with water alone.

Solids that are filtered and washed are ordinarily dried afterward, so if a solid was originally filtered from a high-boiling solvent, washing it with a lower-boiling solvent that has similar properties will help it dry faster. For example, a solid that was filtered from a toluene (bp = 111°C) solution can be washed with low-boiling petroleum ether (bp = ~35–60°C), because the components of petroleum ether, like toluene, are hydrocarbons. Of course the wash solvent must be miscible with the original solvent, so never use petroleum ether, for example, to wash a solid that was filtered from an aqueous solution.

When a solid contains appreciable amounts of one or more impurities, it may be advantageous to wash it in a separate container before filtration. For example, the alcohol triphenylmethanol is often contaminated by the hydrocarbon biphenyl when it is prepared as described in Experiment 30.

From *Operational Organic Chemistry: A Problem Solving Approach to the Laboratory*, Fourth Edition, John W. Lehman. Copyright © 2009 by Pearson Education. Published by Prentice Hall. All rights reserved.

To remove the impurity, a hydrocarbon solvent such as high-boiling petroleum ether is added to a flask containing the impure triphenylmethanol, which is then rubbed and ground against the side of the flask with the tip of a glass stirring rod to remove the biphenyl. This rubbing and grinding process is called *trituration*.

To wash a solid that has been collected in a Buchner or Hirsch funnel, first cool the solvent in ice water for 10 minutes or more. With the vacuum turned off, add enough of the solvent to completely cover the solid. Stir the mixture *gently* with a spatula or stirring rod to suspend the solid in the liquid, being careful not to disturb the filter paper. Without delay, turn on the vacuum to drain the wash liquid. The washing is usually repeated with fresh chilled solvent. After the last washing, leave the vacuum turned on for several minutes to partially dry the solid.

To wash a solid by trituration, place it in a glass container (such as a beaker or Erlenmeyer flask) and add enough of the wash solvent to completely cover the solid, or the amount of solvent specified by the procedure you are following. Using the tip of a glass stirring rod, rub and grind the solid against the sides of the container for several minutes. It is important to grind the solid finely to increase the amount of its surface area exposed to the solvent. Then remove the solvent by vacuum filtration [OP-16].

When Things Go Wrong

If an appreciable amount of solid product disappears when you wash it, the wash solvent may not have been adequately chilled, you may have used too much of it, or it may be inappropriate for washing your product. If the filtrate contains a relatively low-boiling solvent, you should be able to recover the solid by evaporating [OP-19] the solvent, but it should then be purified and washed more carefully. Alternatively, some solid may have passed under the filter paper and into the filtrate. Try refiltering the filtrate, being careful not to displace the filter paper when you wash the recovered solid.

b. Drying Solids

Experimental Considerations

Solids that have been collected by vacuum filtration [OP-16] are usually air-dried on the filter by leaving the vacuum on for a few minutes after filtration is complete. Unless the solvent is very volatile, further drying is required. Comparatively volatile solvents can be removed by simply spreading the solid on a watch glass or evaporating dish (covered to keep out airborne particles) and placing the container in a location with good air circulation, such as a hood, for a sufficient period of time (Figure D2). Clamping an inverted funnel above the watch glass or evaporating dish and passing a gentle stream of dry air or nitrogen over it will accelerate the drying rate.

A very wet solid can be partially dried by transferring it to a filter paper on a clean surface and blotting it with another filter paper to remove excess solvent. The solid is then rubbed against the filter paper with the blade of a flat-bladed spatula until it is finely divided and friable, using fresh filter paper if necessary. It should then be dried completely by one of the methods described next.

Many wet solids can be spread out in a shallow ovenproof container and dried in a laboratory oven set at 110°C or another suitable temperature. The

Waste Disposal: Dispose of the wash liquid as directed by your instructor or as indicated by an experiment's directions.

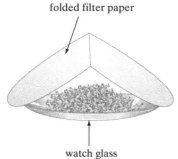

folded filter paper

watch glass

Figure D2 Covered watch glass for drying solids

Take Care! Don't blow the crystals away.

expected melting point of the solid should be at least 20°C above the oven temperature, and the solid should not be heat sensitive or sublime readily at the oven temperature. It isn't unusual for a student to open an oven door and discover that the product he or she worked many hours to prepare has just turned into a charred or molten mass, or disappeared entirely. Aluminum weighing dishes and other commercially available containers made of heavy aluminum foil are usually suitable for oven drying, because the aluminum conducts heat well, cools quickly, and isn't likely to burn your fingers. Aluminum reacts with acids and bases, so acidic and basic solids (or solids that may be wet with acidic or basic liquids) should be oven-dried in Pyrex or porcelain containers, such as watch glasses or evaporating dishes.

If you aren't sure whether your product can be oven-dried safely, consult your instructor.

A *vacuum oven* combines the use of heat with low pressure for very fast, efficient drying. A simple vacuum oven can be constructed by clamping a sidearm test tube horizontally and connecting it to a vacuum source (see *J. Chem. Educ.* **1988**, *65*, 460). The sample, in an open vial, is inserted in the sidearm test tube, which is stoppered and heated with a heat lamp while the vacuum is turned on.

When time permits, the safest way to dry a solid is to leave it in a *desiccator* overnight or longer. A desiccator consists of a tightly sealed container partly filled with a *desiccant* (drying agent) that absorbs water vapor, creating a moisture-free environment in which the solid should dry thoroughly. Desiccators such as the one shown in Figure D3 are available commercially. A simple "homemade" desiccator for drying small amounts of solid can be constructed using an 8-oz (~250-mL) wide-mouth jar with a screw cap (see Figure D4). Enough of a solid desiccant (about 50 mL, measured in a graduated beaker) is added to form a 1-cm layer of desiccant on the bottom. The wet solid, in an appropriate container, is set inside the desiccator, which is capped and allowed to stand undisturbed until drying is complete. If there is any danger of the container tipping over, a wire screen can be cut to fit on top of the desiccant layer and provide a more stable surface. Except when a product is being added or removed, the desiccator must be kept tightly closed at all times to keep the dessicant active.

A similar desiccator with a polyethylene storage rack is available commercially.

Anhydrous calcium chloride is a good (if rather slow-working) desiccant because it's inexpensive and has a high water capacity. Drierite (anhydrous calcium sulfate) is faster and more efficient than calcium chloride, but it has

desiccator

porcelain plate

desiccant

solid being dried

drying pan

Figure D3 Commercial desiccator

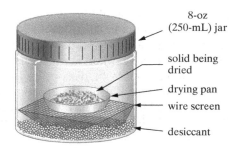

Figure D4 "Homemade" desiccator

a much lower capacity. A combination of calcium chloride with a small amount of indicating (blue) Drierite works better than either desiccant separately. The blue Drierite removes traces of moisture that calcium chloride cannot, and it turns pink when the desiccant is spent and needs to be replaced. Unless your instructor indicates otherwise, spent desiccant should be placed in a designated container for reactivation. Drierite can be reactivated by heating it in a 225°C oven overnight; calcium chloride should be heated overnight at 250–350°C.

DIRECTIONS FOR DRYING SOLIDS IN AN OVEN

Be sure that the oven temperature is at least 20°C below the expected melting point of your compound.

Obtain a wide, shallow, ovenproof container, such as a small evaporating dish or an aluminum weighing dish. Weigh it and label it to prevent mix-ups. Spread the solid on the bottom of the container in a thin, uniform layer and place it in the oven, preferably where it is well separated from other containers. After 30 minutes or so, remove the container (wear gloves when handling a glass container), let it cool to room temperature, and weigh it. Then put it back in the oven for 5–10 minutes, let it cool, and weigh it again. If the mass has decreased by 1% or more, repeat this process until the mass doesn't change significantly between weighings.

DIRECTIONS FOR DRYING SOLIDS IN A DESICCATOR

If the sample will remain in the desiccator until the next lab period, you can dry it in a tared, labeled storage vial with the cap removed. (At the beginning of the next lab period, you should cap the vial and weigh it.) If the sample will only be in the desiccator overnight or for a day or two, spread it out in a shallow, tared container, such as a polystyrene or aluminum weighing dish or a drying tray made by folding a square of heavy aluminum foil. Label the container with the name of the compound, your name or initials, and the tare mass. Set the container inside a desiccator provided with fresh desiccant, taking care to place it securely so that it won't tip over. With a homemade desiccator, vials can be pushed down into the desiccant layer and low containers can be set on a rack made of wire screen or another material (see Figure D4). A commercial desiccator has a porcelain plate or another kind of rack to hold the samples. Cap or cover the desiccator securely and let it stand overnight or longer (preferably longer). Remove and weigh the container with the sample in it. If you're not certain that the solid is completely dry, return it to the desiccator and reweigh it after several hours. If the mass has decreased by 1% or more, return the container to the desiccator and leave it there until the mass doesn't change significantly between weighings.

When Things Go Wrong

If a solid being dried in an oven begins to discolor, it's probably beginning to decompose. Dry it at a lower temperature or by a different method.

If a solid being dried in an oven is decreasing in volume, it's probably undergoing sublimation (conversion from a solid to a vapor). Dry it by a different method.

If a solid being dried in a desiccator doesn't dry overnight or after several days, check the appearance of the desiccant. Calcium chloride granules and some other desiccants clump together when exhausted, and indicating Drierite turns pink. If the desiccant appears to be exhausted, remove the old desiccant, clean and dry the inside of the desiccator, and add fresh desiccant. Then resume drying.

Cleaning and Drying Gases

Air and nitrogen are often used to evaporate [OP-19] a solvent from a desired product, nitrogen and other inert gases are used to provide an inert atmosphere [OP-13] for reactions of oxygen-sensitive compounds, and reactive gases such as carbon dioxide are used in certain chemical syntheses. Gases must ordinarily be clean and dry for such applications. Gases can be dried and moisture can be excluded from reaction mixtures using desiccants like the ones described in OP-26b for drying solids.

Many gases, such as nitrogen, are available in cylinders and can be purchased in a form that is pure enough for most applications. Other gases, especially compressed air obtained from a laboratory air line, may have to be cleaned and dried before use. For most purposes, air from an air line and other impure gases can be cleaned and dried by passing the gas slowly through a drying tube or a U-tube filled with a suitable desiccant (drying agent) and plugged with a layer of cotton at both ends (read about the use of drying tubes in OP-12a). Indicating silica gel and granular alumina are very efficient desiccants; indicating Drierite and calcium chloride are satisfactory for many purposes. Silica gel has the advantage of being chemically inert, but calcium chloride is cheaper and easier to use. The cotton plugs remove most particles, grease, and other impurities from the air line. One end of the drying tube should have a connector that is inserted in a rubber or plastic tube going to the air line; the other end should have a connecter that is inserted in a similar flexible tube going to a Pasteur pipet or a gas delivery tube. If necessary, you can make a connector by inserting a short length of fire-polished glass tubing (see OP-3) into a one-hole rubber stopper of a size that will fit in the drying tube.

When it is important that a gas be very clean and dry, it can be bubbled through a gas-washing bottle such as the one in Figure D5. The bottle is

gas in ⟶   ⟶ gas out

concentrated
sulfuric acid

Figure D5 Gas-washing bottle

From *Operational Organic Chemistry: A Problem Solving Approach to the Laboratory*, Fourth Edition, John W. Lehman. Copyright © 2009 by Pearson Education. Published by Prentice Hall. All rights reserved.

Take Care! Avoid contact with sulfuric acid and use it under a fume hood.

partly filled with concentrated sulfuric acid or another suitable liquid. The gas is bubbled into the liquid through the long glass tube and exits through the short tube, from which it is conveyed through a flexible tube to wherever it's needed. To make sure that the acid isn't carried with the airstream into a reaction flask or another vessel, it's a good idea to attach an empty trap (see Figure C4, OP-16) at the outlet of the gas-washing bottle. The acid should be replaced after extended use. Note that many reactive gases, such as ammonia, can't be dried in sulfuric acid.

Recrystallization

The simplest and most widely used operation for purifying organic solids is *recrystallization*. Recrystallization is so named because it involves dissolving a solid that (in most cases) had originally crystallized from a reaction mixture or another solution, and then causing it to *again* crystallize from solution. In a typical recrystallization procedure, the crude solid is dissolved by heating it in a suitable *recrystallization solvent*. The hot solution is then filtered by gravity and the filtrate is allowed to cool to room temperature or below, whereupon crystals appear in the saturated solution and are collected by vacuum filtration. The crystals are ordinarily much purer than the crude solid, because most of the impurities either fail to dissolve in the hot solution, from which they are separated by gravity filtration or transfer, or remain dissolved in the cold solution, from which they are separated by vacuum filtration or centrifugation.

Recrystallization is based on the fact that the solubility of a solid in a given solvent increases with the temperature of the solvent. Consider the recrystallization from boiling water of a 5.00-g sample of salicylic acid contaminated by 0.25 g of acetanilide. The solubility of salicylic acid in water at 100°C is 7.5 g per 100 mL, so the amount of water required to just dissolve 5.00 g of salicylic acid at the boiling point of water is 67 mL.

$$5.00 \text{ g} \times \frac{100 \text{ mL}}{7.5 \text{ g}} = 67 \text{ mL of water}$$

All of the acetanilide impurity will also dissolve in the boiling water. If the solution is cooled to 20°C, at which temperature the solubility of salicylic acid is only 0.20 g per 100 mL, about 0.13 g of salicylic acid will remain dissolved.

$$67 \text{ mL} \times \frac{0.20 \text{ g}}{100 \text{ mL}} = 0.13 \text{ g of salicylic acid}$$

The dissolved salicylic acid will end up in the filtrate during the vacuum filtration; the remaining 4.87 g will crystallize from solution (if sufficient time is allowed) and will be collected on the filter. The solubility of acetanilide in water is 0.50 g per 100 mL at 20°C, so up to 0.35 g of acetanilide can dissolve in 67 mL of water at 20°C.

$$67 \text{ mL} \times \frac{0.50 \text{ g}}{100 \text{ mL}} = 0.35 \text{ g of acetanilide}$$

This means that all 0.25 g of acetanilide in the crude product should remain in solution and end up in the filtrate. Therefore, under ideal conditions, the recrystallization should yield a 97% recovery of salicylic acid uncontaminated by acetanilide.

$$\frac{4.87 \text{ g}}{5.00 \text{ g}} \times 100 = 97\% \text{ recovery}$$

The recovery could be increased by cooling the mixture in an ice/water bath to further lower the solubility of salicylic acid, but even then, some of

From *Operational Organic Chemistry: A Problem Solving Approach to the Laboratory*, Fourth Edition, John W. Lehman. Copyright © 2009 by Pearson Education. Published by Prentice Hall. All rights reserved.

the salicylic acid would remain in solution. You can never recover all of your product after a recrystallization, but by allowing plenty of time for the product to crystallize and making careful transfers, you should be able to minimize your losses.

This is a simplified description of a rather complex process. A number of factors may bring about results different from those calculated.

- Crystals of the desired solid may adsorb impurities on their surfaces or trap them within the crystal lattice.
- The solubility of a solute in a saturated solution of a different solute may not be the same as its solubility in the pure solvent.
- Using only enough recrystallization solvent to dissolve a solid can result in premature crystallization, so additional solvent may be added to prevent this.

a. Recrystallization from a Single Solvent

Experimental Considerations

Most experimental procedures that involve recrystallization specify a suitable recrystallization solvent in the directions. If the solvent isn't specified, see section **c**, "Choosing a Recrystallization Solvent."

In its simplest form, the recrystallization of a solid is carried out by dissolving the impure solid in the hot (usually boiling) recrystallization solvent and letting the resulting solution cool to room temperature or below to allow crystallization to occur. Additional steps, such as filtering or decolorizing the hot solution, may also be necessary. Sometimes it is desirable to collect a second or third crop of crystals by concentrating (see OP-19) the *mother liquor* (the liquid from which the crystals are filtered) from the previous crop. These crystals will contain more impurities than the first crop and may require recrystallization from fresh solvent. A melting-point determination [OP-33] or thin-layer chromatography (TLC) analysis [OP-22] can be used to assess the purity of a recrystallized solid.

Recrystallization of a gram or more of solid is usually carried out in an Erlenmeyer flask, which—depending on the boiling point of the solvent—can be heated using a steam bath or hot plate. If necessary, the hot solution is filtered by gravity through fluted filter paper to remove insoluble impurities. After crystallization is complete, the product is collected by vacuum filtration on a Buchner funnel.

Recrystallization of about 0.1 g to 1 g of solid can be carried out using test tubes. Depending on the boiling point of the solvent, a hot-water bath, sand bath, or heating block can be used for heating [OP-7a]. If necessary, the hot solution is filtered using a preheated filter-tip pipet, and the crystals are collected by vacuum filtration with a Hirsch funnel.

Dissolving the Impure Solid. The impure solid is usually dissolved by heating it with a sufficient amount of recrystallization solvent at the boiling point of the solvent. Except with very small amounts of solvent, the recrystallization solvent should be heated to the boiling point and kept hot while it is being added to the solid. If you know the solubility of the solid substance at the boiling point of the solvent you are using, you can calculate the approximate volume of boiling solvent that will be needed to dissolve it. Otherwise, you will have to determine the necessary amount of recrystallization solvent by trial and error—adding a measured amount of the hot solvent, boiling the mixture for a minute or so to see if it dissolves, adding more solvent if it doesn't, and continuing to add and boil fresh portions of hot solvent until it eventually goes into solution. Because the solid is most soluble at the boiling point of the solvent, it is important to bring the mixture back to the boiling point after each solvent addition and to boil it for a minute or so before making the next addition. Most solids dissolve fairly rapidly in a boiling solvent, but some do not. Slow-dissolving solids will usually dissolve when heated under reflux (to prevent solvent loss) for 5–10 minutes after each addition of fresh solvent.

Filtering the Hot Solution. Some impurities in a substance being crystallized may be insoluble in the boiling solvent and should be removed after the desired substance has dissolved. Don't mistake such impurities for the substance being purified and add too much solvent in an attempt to dissolve them, because the excess solvent will reduce the yield of crystals and may even prevent the substance from crystallizing at all. If, after most of the solid has dissolved, addition of another portion of hot solvent does not appreciably reduce the amount of solid in the flask, that solid is probably an impurity—particularly if it is different in appearance from the solid that dissolved.

Excess solvent can be removed by evaporation [OP-19], if necessary.

For most recrystallizations, you can remove undissolved impurities by filtering the hot solution through coarse fluted filter paper, using the procedure for gravity filtration [OP-15]. To help prevent premature crystallization, you should use at least 10% more recrystallization solvent than the minimum amount needed to dissolve the crude solid, and carry out the filtration as rapidly as possible. You should also preheat the filtration apparatus by, for example, setting the funnel on an Erlenmeyer flask containing the boiling recrystallization solvent so that it is heated by hot solvent vapors; this flask is then used as the collecting flask after unused solvent has been removed. (Alternatively, you can preheat the funnel in an oven or invert it inside a large beaker set on a steam bath.) If a few crystals form on the filter paper or in the funnel stem during filtration, dissolve them by pouring a small amount of hot recrystallization solvent over them. If a relatively large quantity of solid crystallizes in the filter or funnel stem, scrape it into the filtrate and redissolve it by adding about 10% more recrystallization solvent and heating the mixture to boiling. Then refilter the hot solution and dissolve any precipitate or cloudiness that forms in the collecting flask by heating it before you set it aside to cool. If the particles of the solid impurity are relatively large, you may be able to remove them by letting them settle to the bottom of the recrystallization flask and then decanting (pouring) the liquid into another container without disturbing the solid.

For small-scale recrystallization, filtering the hot solution is complicated by the fact that small quantities of liquid and small-scale filtering devices cool more rapidly than larger ones, making premature crystallization much more likely. To prevent it, you should dilute the hot solution with about 30–50% more recrystallization solvent than was needed to dissolve the solid, and preheat everything that will contact the solution when it is being filtered. You can then filter the diluted solution with a shortened filter-tip pipet—one that has all but ~5 mm of the capillary tip cut off [OP-3]. Preheat the filter-tip pipet by drawing in and expelling several portions of the boiling recrystallization solvent (*not* the solution you are filtering). Without delay, use it to transfer the hot solution, while it is just below its boiling point, to another test tube. To remove the excess solvent, continuously twirl the rounded end of a microspatula in the tube as you boil the resulting solution. Stop boiling when solid begins to form on the spatula just above the liquid level, indicating that the solution is near the saturation point. Then set the solution aside to cool and crystallize (as described later).

If premature crystallization occurs in the filter-tip pipet, you may be able to redissolve the crystals in the solvent by blowing hot air from a heat gun over the pipet while its outlet is over the crystallization tube, adding a little more solvent if necessary. Otherwise, return the contents of the pipet to the hot recrystallization mixture, add more recrystallization solvent, and try again. If necessary, use a freshly prepared and preheated filtering device to complete the filtration.

Removing Colored Impurities. If a crude sample of a compound known to be white or colorless yields a recrystallization solution with a pronounced color, activated carbon (Norit) can often be used to remove the colored impurity. Pelletized Norit, which consists of small cylindrical pieces of activated carbon, is usually preferable to finely powdered Norit. Powdered Norit, although it is somewhat more efficient than the pelletized form, obscures the color and is difficult to filter out completely.

To use pelletized Norit, let the boiling recrystallization solution cool down for a minute or so, and then stir in a *small* amount of the Norit. Unless otherwise directed, start with about 0.1 g or so. Stir or swirl the mixture for a few minutes, keeping it hot enough to prevent your product from crystallizing, but not boiling it. Then let it settle; observe the color of the solution. If much color remains, you can add more pelletized Norit and repeat the process. Avoid adding too much, because any excess Norit can adsorb your product as well as the impurities, and some color may remain no matter how much you use. Then heat the solution just to boiling and separate it from the Norit by one of the methods described in the "Filtering the Hot Solution" section.

Powdered Norit can be used in much the same way as pelletized Norit, except that less is needed and you won't be able to see whether the decolorization was successful until the solution is filtered. If Norit particles pass through the filter during gravity filtration of the hot solution, they can be removed (with some product loss) by vacuum filtration through a bed of a filtering aid such as Celite. To prepare such a bed, mix the filtering aid with enough low-boiling solvent (such as diethyl ether or dichloromethane) to form a thin slurry; then pour it onto the filter paper in a Buchner or Hirsch funnel, with the vacuum turned on, until it forms a layer about 3 mm thick. When the bed is dry, remove the solvent from the filter flask. Quickly filter the hot solution under vacuum and wash the filtering aid with a small amount of hot recrystallization solvent. Turn off the vacuum without delay to prevent evaporation of the filtrate. Redissolve any solid that forms in the

Take Care! Never add Norit to a solution at or near the boiling point—it may boil up violently.

filtrate by heating it and, as necessary, adding more hot solvent. Then let it cool and crystallize (as described later).

Cooling the Hot Solution. The size and purity of the crystals formed depends on the rate of cooling; rapid cooling yields small crystals and slow cooling yields large ones. The medium-sized crystals obtained from moderately slow cooling are usually the best, because larger crystals tend to *occlude* (trap) impurities, whereas smaller ones adsorb more impurities on their surfaces and take longer to filter and dry. You can reduce the rate of cooling by setting the recrystallization container on a surface that is a poor heat conductor and inserting it inside or covering it with another container. For example, a recrystallization flask can be set on the benchtop and covered with a large beaker. A test tube used for recrystallization can be supported in a small Erlenmeyer flask, which is then covered with an inverted beaker.

You can increase the yield of crystals somewhat by cooling the mixture in an ice/water bath once a good crop of crystals is present, but their purity may decrease slightly as a result. Cooling the mixture before well-formed crystals are present may result in small, impure crystals that take longer to filter and dry.

Inducing Crystallization. If no crystals form after a hot recrystallization solution is cooled to room temperature, the solution may be supersaturated. If so, crystallization can often be induced by one or more of the following methods:

- Dip the end of a glass stirring rod into the liquid; then remove it and let the solvent evaporate to leave a thin coating of the solid. Reinsert the glass rod into the liquid and stir gently.
- Rub the tip of a glass stirring rod against the inside of the recrystallization container, just above the liquid surface, for a minute to two. Use an up-and-down motion with the rod tip just touching the liquid on the downstroke.
- Cool the solution in an ice/water bath, and then continue rubbing (as described previously) for several minutes.
- If any *seed crystals* (crystals of the pure compound) are available, drop a few into the solution with cooling and stirring.

A glass rod that has not been fire-polished works best, but it will also scratch the glass, so don't use one without your instructor's permission.

If crystals still don't form, you may have used too much recrystallization solvent. In that case, try one or both of the following procedures, in order:

- Concentrate the solution by evaporation [OP-19] until it becomes cloudy or crystals appear, heat it until the cloudiness or crystals disappear (add a little more recrystallization solvent, if necessary), and then let it cool. If necessary, use one or more of the previous methods to induce crystallization.
- Heat the solution back to boiling; then add another solvent that is miscible with the first, and in which the compound should be less soluble (for example, try adding water to an ethanol solution). Add just enough of the second solvent to induce cloudiness or crystal formation at the boiling point. Next, add enough of the original solvent to cause the cloudiness or crystals to disappear from the boiling solvent, and let it cool.

As a last resort, remove all of the solvent by evaporation and try a different recrystallization solvent—but see your instructor for advice first.

Dealing with Oils and Colloidal Suspensions. When the solid being recrystallized is quite impure or has a low melting point, it may separate as an *oil* (a second liquid phase) upon cooling. Oils are undesirable because, even if they solidify on cooling, the solid retains most of the original impurities.

Using a lower-boiling solvent usually results in a lower percent recovery.

If the solid to be purified has a melting point below the boiling point of the recrystallization solvent, it may be possible to prevent oiling by substituting a lower-boiling solvent with similar properties. For example, methanol (bp 65°C) might be substituted for ethanol (bp 78°C), or acetone (bp 57°C) for 2-butanone (bp 80°C). Oiling may also be prevented by using more recrystallization solvent, adding seed crystals, or both. Seed crystals can sometimes be obtained by dissolving a small amount of the oil in an equal volume of a volatile solvent in a small, open test tube and letting the solvent evaporate slowly.

If oiling occurs, try the following remedies, in order:

1. Heat the solution until the oil dissolves completely—adding more solvent, if necessary—and then cool it slowly while rubbing the inside of the container (see "Inducing Crystallization").
2. Add an amount of pure recrystallization solvent equal to about 25% of the total solvent volume and repeat the process described in step **1**.
3. Follow the procedure in step **1**, but add a seed crystal or two at the approximate temperature where oiling occurred previously.
4. Try to crystallize the oil by either (a) cooling the solution in an ice–salt bath, rubbing the oil with a stirring rod and adding seed crystals, if necessary, or (b) removing all of the oil with a Pasteur pipet, dissolving it in an equal volume of a volatile solvent, and letting the solvent evaporate slowly in an open test tube. Then collect the solid by vacuum filtration and recrystallize it from the same solvent or a more suitable one. If necessary, use one or more of the previous methods to prevent further oiling.

A *colloid* is a suspension of very small particles dispersed in a liquid or another phase. Colloids generally have a cloudy appearance and cannot be filtered through ordinary filtering media because the particles pass right through. If a solid separates from a cooled solution as a colloidal suspension, the colloid can often be coagulated to form normal crystals by extended heating in a hot-water bath, or (if the solvent is polar) by adding an electrolyte such as sodium sulfate. Colloid formation can sometimes be prevented by treating a recrystallization solution with Norit, as described previously, or by cooling the solution very slowly.

DIRECTIONS FOR SINGLE-SOLVENT RECRYSTALLIZATION

Safety Notes

Unless you are informed otherwise, consider all recrystallization solvents (except water) to be flammable and harmful by ingestion, inhalation, and contact. Avoid contact with and inhalation of such solvents; keep them away from flames and hot surfaces.

Use this method (illustrated in Figure E1) when you have approximately 1 g or more of crude solid.

Equipment and Supplies

2 Erlenmeyer flasks
recrystallization solvent
graduated cylinder
heat source
boiling (applicator) stick or boiling chips
flat-bottomed stirring rod
small watch glass
Buchner funnel with filter paper
filter flask

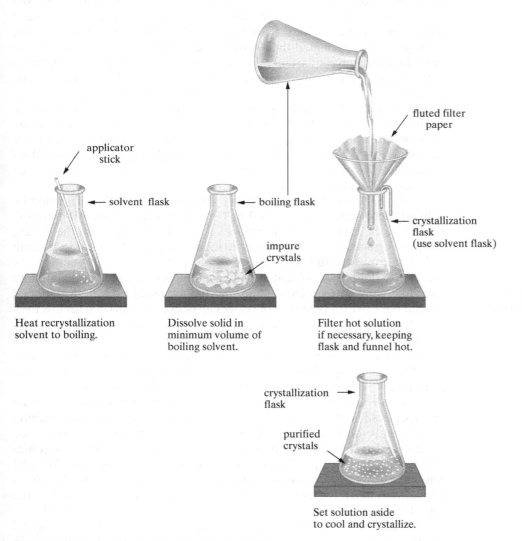

applicator
stick

← solvent flask

Heat recrystallization
solvent to boiling.

← boiling flask

impure
crystals

Dissolve solid in
minimum volume of
boiling solvent.

fluted filter
paper

crystallization
flask
(use solvent flask)

Filter hot solution
if necessary, keeping
flask and funnel hot.

crystallization →
flask

purified
crystals

Set solution aside
to cool and crystallize.

Figure E1 Steps in the recrystallization of a solid

cold washing solvent

watch glass or beaker (to cover crystallization flask)

powder funnel (optional)

fluted filter paper (optional)

Norit (optional)

If you know the solubility of the solid in the boiling recrystallization solvent, calculate the approximate volume of solvent that you will need to recrystallize it; measure out that amount plus 10–20% extra. Otherwise, start with about 10 mL per gram of solid and use more if needed. Measure the solvent into an Erlenmeyer flask—the *solvent flask*. Add a boiling stick or a few boiling chips, insert a powder funnel in the flask mouth, and heat the solvent to boiling with an appropriate heat source [OP-7a]. A steam bath is often preferred for organic solvents that boil below 100°C; a hot plate can be used for water and higher-boiling organic solvents. Place the solid to be purified in a second Erlenmeyer flask—*the boiling flask*—and add about one-quarter of the hot liquid in the solvent flask to the boiling flask (if you've calculated the approximate volume of solvent needed, you can add about three-quarters of the calculated amount). Heat the mixture *at the boiling point,* with continuous swirling or stirring; break up any large particles with a spatula or flat-bottomed stirring rod, until it appears that no more solid will go into solution. If undissolved solid remains, add more portions of hot solvent—about 10% of the total each time—and heat the solution *at the boiling point,* with swirling or stirring after each addition. Continue this process until (1) the solid is completely dissolved *or* (2) no more solid dissolves when a fresh portion of solvent is added and it appears that only solid impurities remain.

If the solution has an intense color but the pure product shouldn't be colored, decolorize it as directed in the "Removing Colored Impurities" section. If the boiling solution contains no solid impurities, use the boiling flask as a crystallization flask and go to the next paragraph. If it does contain solid impurities (including Norit for decolorizing), add about one-tenth as much recrystallization solvent as you have used so far and heat the mixture back to boiling. Put a preheated powder funnel on the neck of the emptied solvent flask (with a bent wire or paper clip between them) and set this flask (which is now the *crystallization flask*) on the heat source. Insert a coarse fluted filter paper in the funnel, and rapidly filter the hot solution while it is still near the boiling point, keeping any unfiltered solution hot throughout the filtration. If any solid crystallizes on the filter paper or inside the funnel, redissolve it as described in the "Filtering the Hot Solution" section.

Set the crystallization flask on the benchtop, cover it with a watch glass or an inverted beaker, and let the solution cool slowly to room temperature. If no crystals form by the time the solution reaches room temperature, see "Inducing Crystallization." If an oil separates or the solution becomes cloudy but no solid precipitates, see "Dealing with Oils and Colloidal Suspensions." Once crystals have begun to form, allow at least 15 minutes (sometimes much longer) for complete crystallization. If desired, cool the flask further in an ice bath for 5 minutes or more to improve the yield.

Collect the crystals by vacuum filtration [OP-16] on a Buchner funnel (or Hirsch funnel) of appropriate size. Transfer any crystals remaining in the crystallization flask to the funnel with a small amount of ice-cold

See "Filtering the Hot Solution" for additional information about removing solid impurities.

recrystallization solvent (or another appropriate solvent) and use more of the cold solvent to wash the solid on the filter [OP-26a]. Air-dry the crystals by leaving the vacuum on for a few minutes after the last washing, and then dry [OP-26b] them further as necessary.

Summary

1. Measure recrystallization solvent into solvent flask; heat to boiling.
2. Add some hot solvent to solid in boiling flask; boil with stirring.
3. Add more hot solvent in portions (as necessary) until solid dissolves.
   IF solution contains colored impurities, GO TO 4.
   IF solution contains undissolved impurities, add more hot solvent; GO TO 5.
   IF not, GO TO 6.
4. Cool below boiling point, stir in Norit, and heat to boiling.
5. Filter hot solution by gravity.
6. Cover flask and set aside to cool until crystallization is complete.
7. Collect crystals by vacuum filtration; wash and air-dry on filter.
8. Clean up and dispose of solvent.

DIRECTIONS FOR SMALL-SCALE RECRYSTALLIZATION

Use this method (illustrated in Figure E2) when you have approximately 0.1 g to 1 g of crude solid.

Equipment and Supplies

2 test tubes, 13 × 100 mm or 15 × 125 mm

recrystallization solvent

calibrated Pasteur pipet

heat source

boiling stick or boiling chip

flat-bladed microspatula

Hirsch funnel with filter paper

small filter flask

cold washing solvent

small Erlenmeyer flask (to hold test tube)

beaker (to cover flask and test tube)

shortened filter-tip pipet (optional)

pelletized Norit (optional)

If you know the solubility of the solid in the boiling recrystallization solvent, calculate the approximate volume of solvent you will need to recrystallize it; measure out that amount plus 20–50% extra (use the higher value if you think you will need to filter the hot solution). Otherwise, start with about 1 mL per 0.1 g of solid and use more if needed. Obtain a test tube large enough that the solvent will fill it no more than half full. Measure the recrystallization solvent into the test tube (the *solvent tube*) with a calibrated Pasteur pipet, add a boiling chip or boiling stick, and heat it to boiling using an appropriate heat source [OP-7a]. Place the solid to be purified in an identical test tube

Waste Disposal: Dispose of the filtrate as directed by your instructor or as indicated in an experiment's directions.

If you will need less than ~2 mL of recrystallization solvent, it isn't necessary to preheat the solvent.

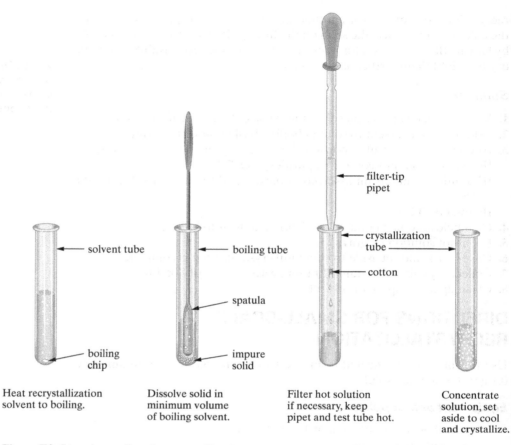

| Heat recrystallization solvent to boiling. | Dissolve solid in minimum volume of boiling solvent. | Filter hot solution if necessary, keep pipet and test tube hot. | Concentrate solution, set aside to cool and crystallize. |

Figure E2 Steps in small-scale recrystallization

(the *boiling tube*) and clamp this test tube *above* the heat source (not in it, because the solid may melt) so that you can control the heating rate quickly by raising or lowering it. Use the calibrated Pasteur pipet to transfer about one-quarter of the liquid in the solvent tube to the boiling tube (if you've calculated the approximate volume of solvent needed, you can add about three-quarters of the calculated amount). Lower the boiling tube and heat the mixture *at the boiling point* while continuously stirring it by twirling the rounded end of a flat-bladed microspatula in the test tube, until it appears that no more solid will go into solution. If undissolved solid remains, add more portions of hot solvent—about 10% of the total each time—and heat the solution *at the boiling point,* with swirling or stirring after each addition. Continue this process until (1) the solid is completely dissolved *or* (2) no more solid dissolves when a fresh portion of solvent is added and it appears that only solid impurities remain.

If the solution has an intense color but the pure product shouldn't be colored, see the "Removing Colored Impurities" section. If the boiling solution contains no solid impurities, use the boiling tube as a crystallization tube and go to the next paragraph. If it does contain solid impurities (including Norit used for decolorizing), add 30–50% as much recrystallization solvent as you used to dissolve the solid and heat the mixture back to boiling. Use a pre-heated filter-tip pipet to transfer the hot solution to a *crystallization tube* (use the emptied solvent tube), leaving the solid impurities behind. If crystals begin to form in the pipet, redissolve them as described in the "Filtering the Hot Solution" section. Concentrate the filtered solution (see OP-19) by boiling it while stirring with a flat-bladed microspatula until traces of solid begin to form on the microspatula just above the solvent level.

See "Filtering the Hot Solution" for additional information about removing solid impurities.

Set the crystallization tube in a small Erlenmeyer flask, cover it with an inverted beaker, and let the solution cool slowly to room temperature. If no crystals form by the time the solution reaches room temperature, see "Inducing Crystallization." If an oil separates or the solution becomes cloudy but no solid precipitates, see "Dealing with Oils and Colloidal Suspensions." Once crystals have begun to form, allow at least 10 minutes (sometimes much longer) for complete crystallization. If desired, cool the test tube further in an ice bath for 5 minutes or more to increase the yield.

Collect the product by vacuum filtration [OP-16] on a Hirsch funnel. Transfer any crystals remaining in the crystallization flask to the funnel with a small amount of ice-cold recrystallization solvent (or another appropriate solvent) and use more cold solvent to wash the solid on the filter [OP-26a]. Air-dry the crystals by leaving the vacuum on for a few minutes after the last washing, and then dry [OP-26b] them further as necessary.

Waste Disposal: Dispose of the filtrate as directed by your instructor or as indicated in an experiment's directions.

Summary

1. Measure recrystallization solvent into solvent tube; heat to boiling.
2. Add some hot solvent to solid in boiling tube; boil with stirring.
3. Add more hot solvent in portions (as necessary) until solid dissolves.
   IF solution contains colored impurities, GO TO 4.
   IF solution contains undissolved impurities, add more hot solvent; GO TO 5.
   IF not, GO TO 6.
4. Cool below boiling point, stir in pelletized Norit, and heat to boiling.
5. Filter and concentrate hot solution.
6. Cover hot solution and set aside to cool until crystallization is complete.
7. Collect crystals by vacuum filtration; wash and air-dry on filter.
8. Clean up and dispose of solvent.

When Things Go Wrong

If you are attempting to dissolve a solid product in a hot recrystallization solvent but no more solid appears to dissolve with each addition of fresh solvent, ask yourself the following questions. (1) Do the crystals that remain in solution look different from those that already dissolved? If the crystals look different from the ones that dissolved, they probably belong to an impurity. Follow the directions in "Filtering the Hot Solution." (2) Does the volume of the solution stay about the same each time you add fresh solvent and bring the mixture back to the boiling point? If the volume is not increasing significantly, you must be boiling away solvent about as fast as you are adding it. You should be using an Erlenmeyer flask, a test tube, or another narrow-mouthed vessel for recrystallization—never a beaker or similar container that allows rapid evaporation. If you are using an appropriate container, try turning down the heat to the lowest setting that keeps the solvent boiling. It may also help to reduce the time you allow the solution to boil after each addition of fresh solvent.

Suppose you cool the recrystallization solution by putting it in a container of ice and water that is too big for it, so that—as the ice melts—the flask tips over and fills with water. Because most organic solids are even less soluble in water than in the common recrystallization solvents, you may be able to recover your product by waiting until the ice has completely melted and then removing the liquid with a vacuum filtration apparatus [OP-16]. The solid that collects on the filter will be wet and impure, so it will have to be dried [OP-26b] and recrystallized again, but at least you won't have to start from square one.

Suppose you carry out the recrystallization of a solid product and let the solution cool to room temperature, but no solid crystallizes. This usually implies one of three things: (1) the solution is supersaturated, (2) you used too much recrystallization solvent, or (3) you used an inappropriate recrystallization solvent. The "Inducing Crystallization" section tells you how to deal with each of these situations. In case you used too much solvent, refer to "Dissolving the Impure Solid" before you attempt another recrystallization.

If you filter a hot recrystallization solution by vacuum filtration [OP-16] and your product crystallizes in the filtrate (which is very likely), transfer the mixture in the filter flask to a suitable recrystallization vessel (don't use the filter flask), heat it with enough additional recrystallization solvent to get the solid back into solution, and then filter the hot solution by gravity [OP-15]. Vacuum filtration should ordinarily *not* be used to filter recrystallization solutions, because the hot solvent vaporizes rapidly under vacuum.

If, after cooling the recrystallization solution, you obtain considerably less solid product than you started with, you may have used too much recrystallization solvent or an inappropriate solvent. Collect the product that has already crystallized, using vacuum filtration [OP-16], and then follow the appropriate directions in the second part of "Inducing Crystallization" to obtain another crop of crystals. The crystals you collected first should be purer than the second crop, so they should be used for any melting-point measurement or spectral analysis.

If you are recrystallizing a solid product from water and obtain a low yield of crystals on cooling, you can try dissolving some sodium chloride in the cold solution to salt out (see OP-18b) more of the product. Don't use more than about 3 g of salt per 10 mL of solution. Make sure all of it dissolves; otherwise, your product will be contaminated with salt, which you will have to wash out [OP-26a] with fresh water.

If, after your impure solid has dissolved, a liquid separates or a suspension of fine particles forms on cooling, see "Dealing with Oils and Colloidal Suspensions."

If the solid that crystallizes is colored but your product is supposed to be colorless or a different color, see "Removing Colored Impurities."

If the crystals that form on cooling are very fine or very coarse, you may have cooled the recrystallization solution too rapidly or too slowly. See "Cooling the Hot Solution."

b. Recrystallization from Mixed Solvents

Solids that cannot be recrystallized readily from any single recrystallization solvent can usually be purified by recrystallization from a mixture of two compatible solvents, such as those listed in the margin. The solvents must be miscible (mutually soluble in all proportions), and the solid compound should be quite soluble in one solvent and relatively insoluble in the other. If the composition of a suitable solvent mixture is known beforehand (such as 40% ethanol in water), the recrystallization can be carried out with the premixed solvent in the same way as for a single-solvent recrystallization. But a mixed-solvent recrystallization is usually performed by heating the compound in the solvent in which it is most soluble (which we will call solvent A) until it dissolves, and then adding enough of the second solvent (solvent B) to bring the solution to the saturation point.

Some compatible solvent pairs

ethanol–water
methanol–water
acetic acid–water
acetone–water
ethyl ether–methanol
ethanol–acetone
absolute ethanol–petroleum ether
ethyl acetate–cyclohexane

If the compound is *very* soluble in solvent A, the total volume of solvent may be quite small compared to that of the crystals, which may then separate as a dense slurry. In such a case, you should use more of solvent A than is needed to just dissolve the compound, and add correspondingly more of solvent B to bring about saturation. Be careful to avoid adding so much of solvent A that *no* amount of solvent B will result in saturation. If that occurs, you will have to concentrate the solution (see OP-19) or remove all of the solvent and start over.

DIRECTIONS FOR MIXED-SOLVENT RECRYSTALLIZATION

Most of the steps in a mixed-solvent recrystallization are the same as for single-solvent recrystallization; refer to the previous directions for experimental details.

Place the crude solid in a boiling flask or tube. Add solvent A (previously heated to boiling) in portions, while boiling and stirring, until the solid dissolves or only undissolved impurities remain. If necessary, the solution can be decolorized with Norit at this point. If the hot solution contains undissolved impurities (including Norit), add enough solvent A to prevent premature crystallization, heat it to boiling, and filter it. For small-scale work, concentrate the solution after filtration to remove most of the excess solvent. Add hot solvent B in small portions, with stirring; keep the mixture boiling after each addition, until a persistent cloudiness appears or a precipitate starts to form. Then add just enough hot solvent A to the boiling mixture—drop by drop, with stirring—to clear it up or dissolve the precipitate. Set the mixture aside to cool to room temperature, allow sufficient time for crystallization, and cool it further in an ice/water bath if desired. When crystallization is complete, collect the product by vacuum filtration [OP-16] and wash the product on the filter [OP-26a] with cold solvent B or another suitable solvent.

Waste Disposal: Dispose of the filtrate as directed by your instructor or as indicated in an experiment's directions.

When Things Go Wrong

Most of the things that can go wrong during a single-solvent recrystallization can also go wrong during a mixed-solvent recrystallization, so you can refer to the previous "When Things Go Wrong" section for help. The following case applies only to mixed-solvent recrystallization.

Suppose you have dissolved the impure solid in solvent A, added enough B to produce cloudiness or a precipitate, and are now adding more A—drop by drop—at the boiling point of the mixture to clear it up, but it doesn't clear up. You may be boiling away solvent A (which is often the more volatile solvent) faster than solvent B, thereby preventing the solid material from dissolving. Turn down the heat to the lowest setting that will keep the solvent boiling. Continue adding solvent A, perhaps at a faster rate than before, until the solution is clear; then remove it from the heat source without delay.

c. Choosing a Recrystallization Solvent

A solvent suitable for recrystallization of a given solid should meet the following criteria, or as many of them as is practical:

- Its boiling point should be in the 60–100°C range.
- Its freezing point should be well below room temperature.
- It must not react with the solid.
- It should not be excessively hazardous to work with.
- It should dissolve between 5 g and 25 g of the solid per 100 mL at the boiling point, and less than 2 g per 100 mL at room temperature, with at least a 5:1 ratio between the two values.

As a rule, the recrystallization solvent should be either somewhat more or somewhat less polar than the solid, because a solvent of very similar polarity will dissolve too much of it. Solubility information from reference books listed in Category A of the Bibliography, if included, may help you choose a suitable solvent. For example, a solvent in which the compound is designated as *sparingly soluble* or *insoluble* when cold and *very soluble* or *soluble* when hot may be suitable for recrystallization. If solubility data for the compound are not available, a solvent may have to be chosen by trial and error from a selection such as that in Table E1. Once you have identified some possible solvents, test them as described next. You can test several solvents at the same time and choose the best one.

DIRECTIONS FOR TESTING RECRYSTALLIZATION SOLVENTS

Weigh about 0.1 g of the finely divided solid into a small test tube and add 1 mL of the solvent. Stir the mixture by twirling the round end of a flat-bladed microspatula in it; carefully observe what happens. If the solid dissolves in the cold solvent, the solvent is unsuitable. If the solid doesn't dissolve, heat the mixture to boiling, with stirring. If it dissolves after heating, try to induce crystallization as described next. If it doesn't dissolve completely, add more solvent in 0.5-mL portions, gently boiling and stirring after each addition, until it dissolves *or* until the total volume of added solvent is about 3 mL. If the solid *does not* dissolve in that amount of hot solvent, the solvent is probably not suitable. If it *does* dissolve at any point, record the volume of boiling solvent required to dissolve it. Let the solution cool while rubbing the inside of the tube with a glass rod to see whether crystallization occurs. If crystals separate, examine them for apparent yield and evidence of purity (absence of extraneous color and good crystal structure).

Table E1 Properties of common recrystallization solvents

Solvent	bp	fp	Comments
water	100	0	solvent of choice for polar compounds; crystals dry slowly
methanol	65	−94	good solvent for relatively polar compounds; easy to remove
95% ethanol	78	−116	excellent general solvent; usually preferred over methanol because of higher boiling point
2-butanone	80	−86	good general solvent; acetone is similar, but its boiling point is lower
ethyl acetate	77	−84	good general solvent
toluene	111	−95	good solvent for aromatic compounds; high boiling point makes it difficult to remove
petroleum ether (high boiling)	~60–90	low	a mixture of hydrocarbons; good solvent for less polar compounds;
hexane	69	−94	good solvent for less polar compounds; easy to remove
cyclohexane	81	6.5	good solvent for less polar compounds; freezes in some cold baths

Note: bp and fp (freezing point) are in °C. Solvents are listed in approximate order of decreasing polarity.

If no single solvent is satisfactory, choose one solvent in which the compound is quite soluble and another in which it is comparatively insoluble (the two solvents must be miscible). Dissolve the specified amount of solid in the first solvent, with stirring and boiling, and record the amount of solvent required. Add the second hot solvent, drop by drop while boiling and stirring, until saturation occurs. Then cool the mixture and try to induce crystallization.

Once a suitable solvent or solvent pair has been identified, estimate the volume of solvent needed to dissolve all of the solid to be purified, based on the volumes of solid and solvent you used in the test.

Sublimation

Sublimation is a phase change in which a solid passes directly into the vapor phase without going through an intermediate liquid phase. Many solids that have appreciable vapor pressures below their melting points can be purified by (1) heating the solid to sublime it (convert it to a vapor), (2) condensing the vapor on a cold surface, and (3) scraping off the condensed solid. This method works best if impurities in the crude solid do not sublime appreciably. Sublimation isn't as selective as recrystallization or chromatography, but it has some advantages in that no solvent is required and losses in transfer can be kept low.

Experimental Considerations

Sublimation is usually carried out by heating the *sublimand* (the solid before it has sublimed) with a suitable heat source and collecting the *sublimate* (the solid after it has sublimed and condensed) on a cool surface. For best results, the sublimand should be dry and finely divided, and the distance between the sublimand and the condensing surface should be minimized. A simple but effective sublimator consists of two nested beakers of appropriate sizes. For example, a 250-mL beaker can be nested inside a 400-mL beaker, with the inner beaker rotated so as to leave a gap of about 1 cm at the bottom. In some cases, it may be necessary to place separators made of folded-over strips of filter paper or paper towel between the beakers to get the right spacing. Good beaker combinations are 100 mL/150 mL, 250 mL/400 mL, and 400 mL/600 mL. The sublimand is spread out on the bottom of the outer beaker, and the condensing (inner) beaker is partially filled with cold water, with or without added ice. As the outer beaker is heated, crystals of sublimate collect on the bottom of the condensing beaker. Figure E3 illustrates a sublimator operating on the same principle, except that an Erlenmeyer flask is used as a condenser and the temperature is controlled by flowing water.

On humid days, using ice may cause condensation of moisture on the sublimate.

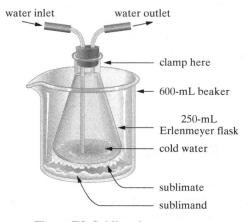

Figure E3 Sublimation apparatus

From *Operational Organic Chemistry: A Problem Solving Approach to the Laboratory*, Fourth Edition, John W. Lehman. Copyright © 2009 by Pearson Education. Published by Prentice Hall. All rights reserved.

Sublimation

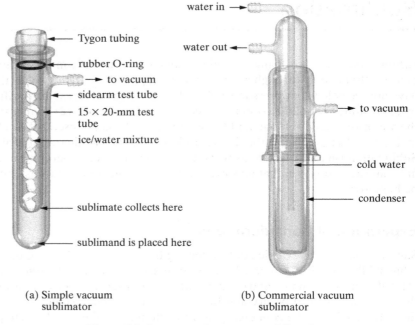

(a) Simple vacuum
    sublimator

(b) Commercial vacuum
    sublimator

Figure E4 Apparatus for vacuum sublimation

See J. Chem. Educ. **1991**, *68*, A63 for a description of such a sublimator.

Solids that don't sublime rapidly at atmospheric pressure may do so under vacuum. Figure E4a illustrates a vacuum sublimator that can be assembled by fitting a 15 × 125-mm test tube snugly inside an 18 × 150-mm sidearm test tube, using a rubber O-ring to act as a vacuum seal. A short section of 15-mm i.d. Tygon tubing (or several layers of masking tape) is placed around the lip of the inner tube to keep it from slipping inside the sidearm test tube. A commercial vacuum sublimator, such as the one in Figure E4b, is more efficient because the condenser has a flat, wide bottom that is close to the sublimate.

Depending on the temperature required and the nature of the sublimation apparatus, heat sources such as hot-water baths, oil baths, steam baths, hot plates (for nested beakers), heating blocks, and sand baths can be used for sublimation. An oil bath provides the most uniform heating, but oil baths are messy and somewhat hazardous to work with. With some of these heat sources, crystals tend to collect on the sides of the sublimation container as well as on the condenser. Wrapping the base of the sublimation container with aluminum foil or other insulation will help prevent this.

DIRECTIONS FOR SUBLIMATION

Safety Notes

Because of the possibility of an implosion, safety glasses must be worn during a vacuum sublimation. It is best to work behind a hood sash or safety shield while the apparatus is under vacuum.

Equipment and Supplies

sublimation apparatus
heat source
cooling fluid
flat-bladed spatula

Assemble one of the sublimation setups described or one suggested by your instructor. Powder the dry sublimand finely and spread it in a thin, uniform layer over the bottom of the sublimation container. If you are using a vacuum sublimator, attach the apparatus to a trap and vacuum source (see OP-16), and then turn on the vacuum. Turn on the cooling water *or* partly fill the condensing tube or beaker with cold water or ice water (use ice water for a vacuum sublimator). Heat the sublimation container with an appropriate heat source until some sublimate begins to collect on the condenser, and then adjust the temperature to attain a suitable rate of sublimation without melting or charring the sublimand. If necessary, add small pieces of ice to the condenser—if you are using one—to replace melted ice. When the condenser is well covered with sublimate (but before sublimate crystals begin to drop into the sublimand), stop the sublimation, remove the sublimate as described in the next paragraph, and then resume sublimation, if necessary. If the sublimand hardens or becomes encrusted with impurities, stop the sublimation, grind it to a fine powder, and then resume sublimation (if necessary).

When all of the compound has sublimed or only a nonvolatile residue remains, remove the apparatus from the heat source, break the vacuum (if you are using a vacuum sublimator), and let the apparatus cool. Carefully remove the condenser (avoid dislodging any sublimate) and scrape the crystals into a suitable tared container using a flat-bladed spatula.

Summary

1. Assemble sublimation apparatus; add sublimand.
2. Turn on vacuum if necessary; add cooling mixture or turn on cooling water.
3. Heat until sublimation begins; adjust heat to maintain good sublimation rate.
4. When sublimation is complete, stop heating, break vacuum (if necessary), and let cool.
5. Scrape sublimate into tared container.
6. Clean sublimation apparatus.

When Things Go Wrong

Suppose you carried out a sublimation but the sublimate was wet when you removed it. You may have used ice water in a nested-beaker sublimator on a humid day; use cold water without ice instead. If you used a vacuum sublimator, you may have added ice to the inner tube before you turned on the vacuum, causing moisture to condense inside the apparatus. If your product seems pure except for the moisture, you may be able to dry it [OP-26b] without repeating the sublimation.

If you are carrying out a sublimation and the sublimand begins to melt, turn dark, or char, you are overheating it. Disassemble the apparatus, let the liquid (if any) solidify, and break up the solid (which may have a hard crust) with a stirring rod. Then resume sublimation using a lower heat setting or a low-intensity heat source, such as a steam bath.

Simple Distillation

a. Distillation of Liquids

A pure liquid in a container open to the atmosphere boils when its vapor pressure equals the external pressure, which is usually about 1 atm (760 torr, 101.3 kPa). The vapor contains the same molecules as the liquid, so its composition is identical to that of the pure liquid. A mixture of two (or more) liquids with different vapor pressures will boil when the total vapor pressure over the mixture equals the external pressure, but the composition of the vapor will be different than that of the liquid itself, being richer in the more volatile component (the one with the higher vapor pressure). If this vapor is condensed into a separate receiving vessel, the condensed liquid will have the same composition as the vapor; that is, it will also be richer in the more volatile component.

The process of vaporizing a liquid mixture in one vessel and condensing the vapors into another is called *distillation*. The liquid mixture being distilled, the *distilland,* can be heated in a boiling vessel—sometimes called the *pot*—using an apparatus such as the one shown in Figure E6 on a following page. The vapors are condensed on a cool surface, such as the inside of a water-cooled condenser, and the resulting liquid, the *distillate*, is collected in a suitable *receiver*. If the components of the distilland have sufficiently different vapor pressures, most of the more volatile component will end up in the receiver and most of the less volatile component(s) will remain in the pot.

The distilland is usually a solution of two or more miscible liquids, but it may also be a liquid–solid solution. The distillation of immiscible liquids is discussed in OP-20.

The purity of the distillate increases with the number of vaporization–condensation cycles it experiences—the number of times it is vaporized and condensed on its way to the receiver. *Simple distillation* involves only a single vaporization–condensation cycle. It is most useful for purifying a liquid that contains either nonvolatile impurities or small amounts of higher- or lower-boiling impurities. *Fractional distillation* [OP-32] allows for several vaporization–condensation cycles in a single operation. It can be used to separate liquids with comparable volatilities and to purify liquids that contain relatively large amounts of volatile impurities. *Vacuum distillation* [OP-31] is carried out under reduced pressure, which reduces the temperature of the distillation. It is used to purify high-boiling liquids and liquids that decompose when distilled at atmospheric pressure.

Principles and Applications

To understand how distillation works, consider a mixture of two ideal liquids with ideal vapors, which obey both Raoult's law (Equation **1**) and Dalton's law (Equation **2**).

$$\text{Raoult's law: } P_A = X_A \cdot P_A^o \qquad \textbf{(1)}$$

$$\text{Dalton's law: } P_A = Y_A \cdot P \qquad \textbf{(2)}$$

In these expressions, P_A is the partial pressure of component A over the mixture, P_A^o is the equilibrium vapor pressure of pure A at the same temperature, X_A is the mole fraction of A in the liquid, and Y_A is the mole fraction of A in the vapor. Unfortunately, no real liquids obey these laws perfectly,

From *Operational Organic Chemistry: A Problem Solving Approach to the Laboratory*, Fourth Edition, John W. Lehman. Copyright © 2009 by Pearson Education. Published by Prentice Hall. All rights reserved.

Presumably, entane and orctane exist only in J. R. R. Tolkien's Middle-Earth, where they are used for fuel by Ents and Orcs, respectively.

so we shall consider the behavior of two imaginary hydrocarbons, *entane* (bp = 50°C) and *orctane* (bp = 100°C), which obey them both. If a mixture of entane and orctane is heated at normal atmospheric pressure, it will begin to boil at a temperature that is determined by the composition of the liquid mixture, producing vapor of a different composition. For example, an equimolar mixture of entane and orctane will start to boil at a temperature just above 66°C, and the vapor will contain more than four moles of entane for every mole of orctane. The liquid and vapor composition of an entane–orctane mixture at any temperature can be calculated using Equations **3** and **4**, which are derived from Dalton's law and Raoult's law.

P is the total pressure over the mixture, assumed here to be 1 atm (760 torr).

$$X_A = \frac{P - P_B^o}{P_A^o - P_B^o} \tag{3}$$

$$Y_A = \frac{P_A^o}{P} X_A \tag{4}$$

For example, at 70°C the vapor pressure of orctane is 315 torr, and that of entane is 1370 torr (see Table E2), so the mole fraction of entane in a distilland that boils at 70°C will be (from Equation **3**)

$$X_{entane} = \frac{760 - 315}{1370 - 315} = 0.422$$

Its mole fraction in the vapor will be (from Equation **4**)

$$Y_{entane} = \frac{1370}{760} \times 0.422 = 0.761$$

showing that the vapor (and thus the distillate) is considerably richer in entane than is the liquid. The vapor pressures and approximate liquid–vapor compositions for entane and orctane at this and other temperatures are given in Table E2.

The key to an understanding of distillation is this: *The vapor over any mixture of volatile liquids contains more of the lower-boiling component than does the liquid mixture itself.* So, at any time during a distillation, the liquid condensing into the receiver contains more of the lower-boiling component than does the liquid in the pot. As more of the lower-boiling

Table E2 Equilibrium vapor pressures and mole fractions of entane and orctane at different temperatures

	Entane			Orctane		
T, °C	$P°$, torr	X	Y	$P°$, torr	X	Y
50°	760	1.00	1.00	160	0.00	0.00
60°	1030	0.67	0.90	227	0.33	0.10
70°	1370	0.42	0.76	315	0.58	0.24
80°	1790	0.24	0.57	430	0.76	0.43
90°	2300	0.11	0.32	576	0.89	0.68
100°	2930	0.00	0.00	760	1.00	1.00

Note: $P°$ = equilibrium vapor pressure of the pure liquid; X = mole fraction in liquid mixture; Y = mole fraction in vapor.

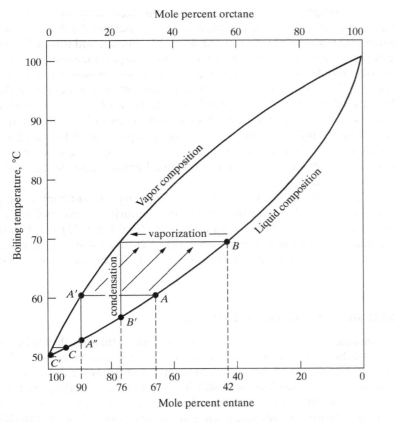

Figure E5 Temperature–composition diagram for entane–orctane mixtures

component distills away, the pot liquid becomes richer in the higher-boiling liquid, so, by the end of the distillation, most of the lower-boiling liquid is in the receiver and most of the higher-boiling liquid is in the pot.

The purification process is shown by Figure E5, in which the liquid and vapor compositions are plotted against the boiling temperatures of entane–orctane mixtures. Suppose we distill a mixture that contains 2 moles of entane for every mole of orctane (67 mole percent entane). From the graph and Table E2, you can see that such a mixture will boil at 60°C (point A) and that its vapor will contain 90 mole percent (mol%) entane (point A′). Thus, the distillate that is condensed from this vapor (point A″) will be much richer in entane than was the original mixture in the pot. As the distillation continues, however, the more volatile component will boil away faster and the pot will contain progressively less entane. Therefore, the vapor will also contain less entane and the boiling temperature will rise. When the percentage of entane in the pot has fallen to 42 mol% (point B), the boiling temperature will have risen to 70°C and the distillate will contain only 76 mol% entane (point B′). Only if the distillation were to be continued after nearly all of the entane had distilled would the distillate contain more of the less volatile component; at 90°C, for example, more than two-thirds of the molecules in the distillate would be orctane molecules.

This example shows that the purification effected by simple distillation of a mixture of volatile liquids may be very imperfect. In the example, the distillate never contains more than 90 mol% entane, and it may be considerably less pure than that, depending on the temperature range over which it is collected. If we start with a mixture that contains only 5 mol% orctane (point C), however, considerably better purification can be accomplished. The initial distillate will be 99 mol% entane (point C') at 51°C, and, if the distillation is continued until the temperature rises to 55°C, the final distillate will be 95 mol% entane. The average composition of the distillate will lie somewhere between these values, so most of the orctane will remain in the boiling flask along with some undistilled entane, and the distillate will be relatively pure entane.

Thus, simple distillation can be used to purify a liquid containing *small* amounts of volatile impurities if (1) the impurities have boiling points appreciably higher or lower than that of the liquid, and (2) the distillate is collected over a narrow temperature range (usually 4–6°C), starting at a temperature that is within a few degrees of the liquid's normal boiling point.

Experimental Considerations

Apparatus. The size of the glassware used for distillation should be consistent with the volume of the distilland; otherwise, excessive losses will occur. For example, suppose you recovered 18 mL of crude isopentyl acetate from Experiment 5 and decided to distill it from a 250-mL boiling flask over a 137–143°C boiling range. At the end of the distillation, the flask would be filled with 250 mL of undistilled vapor at a temperature of 143°C (416 K). An ideal gas law calculation shows that this is about 0.0073 mol of vapor.

$$n = \frac{PV}{RT} = \frac{(1.00 \text{ atm})(0.25 \text{ L})}{(0.0821 \text{ L atm mol}^{-1} \text{ K}^{-1})(416 \text{ K})} = 0.0073 \text{ mol}$$

Isopentyl acetate has a molecular weight of 130 and a liquid density of 0.876 g/mol, so this is about 1.1 mL of the liquid.

$$0.0073 \text{ mol} \times \frac{130 \text{ g}}{1 \text{ mol}} \times \frac{1 \text{ mL}}{0.876 \text{ g}} = 1.1 \text{ mL}$$

Thus, the vapor would condense to about 1.1 mL of liquid isopentyl acetate, which would not be recovered. By comparison, a 50-mL boiling flask will retain only one-fifth as much condensed vapor. Liquid can also be lost by surface adsorption on glass, so the lower surface area of the smaller boiling flask will reduce losses as well. Additional liquid losses occur in the still head, condenser, and any other parts of the apparatus that can trap vapors or adsorb liquid. As a rule, you should use the smallest boiling flask for which the liquid volume will be roughly half (or less) of the flask's capacity; for example, use a 50–mL round-bottom flask if the liquid volume is 13–25 mL, and use a 25 mL flask if it is less than 13 mL.

Figure E6 illustrates a typical setup for simple distillation. The boiling flask should be no more than half full and should contain several boiling chips or a magnetic stir bar to prevent bumping [OP-7b]. A thermometer

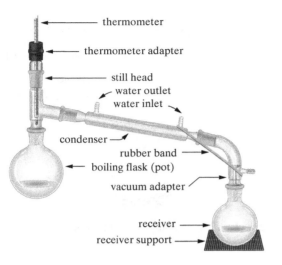

Figure E6 Conventional apparatus for simple distillation

is used to monitor the temperature [OP-9] of the distillate vapors during a distillation, both to ensure that the right substance is being collected and to provide an estimate of its boiling point. The thermometer is inserted into the *still head* (a connecting adapter) through a stopper or thermometer adapter. It should be well centered in the still head (not closer to one wall than another), with the entire bulb below an imaginary line extending from the bottom of the sidearm. In other words, the *top* of the bulb should be aligned with the *bottom* of the sidearm, as illustrated in Figure E7. In this way, the entire bulb will become moistened by the condensing vapors of the distillate. The placement of the thermometer is extremely important. If the thermometer is too high, the temperature reading will be too low and much of the desired product may be discarded. If the thermometer is only a few millimeters below the sidearm, its reading shouldn't be affected, but if it is quite close to the boiling liquid, its reading will be too high.

The condenser should have a straight inner section of comparatively small diameter. A West condenser of the type used for heating under reflux can also be used for distillation, but a jacketed distillation column should not be used for that purpose; its larger inner diameter provides less efficient condensation. The vacuum adapter (and sometimes the still head as well) should be secured to the condenser by a joint clip or a rubber band. An open container such as a tared vial can be used as a receiver unless the distillate is quite volatile or has vapors that might represent a health hazard. In that case, a ground-joint flask that fits snugly on the vacuum adapter should be used. When a ground-joint receiver is used, the vacuum adapter's sidearm must never be plugged up—otherwise, heating the system will build up pressure that could result in an explosion and severe injury from flying glass.

If you distill a comparatively small quantity of a liquid (~1–10 mL) in a conventional distillation apparatus, a large fraction of your product mass may be lost due to trapping of vapors and adsorption of liquid in the apparatus. You can reduce such losses by assembling the compact distillation

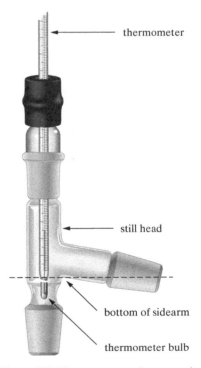

Figure E7 Thermometer placement in still head

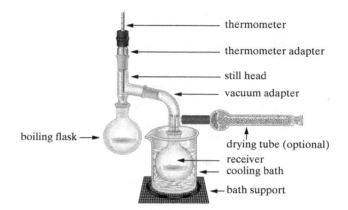

Figure E8 Compact apparatus for simple distillation

Both flasks must be clamped or otherwise supported.

apparatus shown in Figure E8, in which the distillate is condensed by a cold bath surrounding the receiver rather than a West condenser. As a rule, you should use the smallest round-bottom flask available (usually 25 mL) as the boiling flask and another small flask for the receiver. The vacuum adapter should be secured by a wire or joint clip, because a rubber band exposed to the heat of the vapors may break. If a bulky heat source is used, it may be necessary to twist the vacuum adapter and receiver at an angle to the still head to allow room for the heat source.

In order for the cooling bath to work properly, the ground-glass joint between the receiver (which cannot be an open container) and vacuum adapter must be tight, so the receiving flask should be clamped in place or secured by a joint clip. The type of coolant needed depends on the boiling point of the distillate. The following coolants should be suitable for the distillate boiling-point ranges indicated:

<50°C	ice–salt
50–100°C	ice/water
101–150°C	cold tap water
>150°C	no coolant if receiver is well insulated from heat source

When an ice/water or ice–salt bath is used, the vacuum adapter sidearm should be connected to a drying tube [OP-27] so that moisture won't condense inside the receiver.

With the two following qualifications, distillation with the compact apparatus is carried out as described in the "Directions for Simple Distillation" section. (1) If vapors begin to come out of the vacuum adapter outlet, use a colder bath or add ice (or salt) to the one you are already using. (2) If you need to change receivers, stop the distillation and remove the heat source first.

Heating. Almost any of the heat sources described in OP-7a can be used for simple distillation. Heating mantles and oil baths are preferred because they provide reasonably constant, even heating over a wide temperature range. Such a heat source should be positioned so that it can be easily lowered and removed at the end of the distillation.

The heating rate should be adjusted to maintain gentle boiling in the pot and a suitable distillation rate. For most distillations, a distillation rate of 1–3 drops per second (about 3–10 mL of distillate per minute) is recommended. Distilling at higher rates will decrease the purity of the product and may make it difficult to record the boiling range accurately.

If you are distilling a liquid over a wide boiling range, it may be necessary to increase the heating rate gradually to maintain the same distillation rate. Otherwise, the temperature at the heat source should be kept relatively constant throughout a simple distillation. An excessive heating rate, in addition to reducing distillation efficiency, may cause mechanical carryover or decomposition of the distilland. An insufficient heating rate during distillation can cause the still-head temperature to fluctuate and distillation to slow down or stop altogether.

Boiling Range. An approximate boiling range for a distillation may be specified in an experimental procedure. For example, when isopentyl acetate is prepared by the reaction of isopentyl alcohol and acetic acid in Experiment 5, the product is collected over a boiling range of 137°C to 143°C.

$$
\underset{\substack{\text{acetic acid}}}{CH_3\overset{\overset{\displaystyle O}{\|}}{C}OH} + \underset{\substack{\text{isopentyl alcohol} \\ \text{b.p. 130°C}}}{HOCH_2CH_2\overset{\overset{\displaystyle CH_3}{|}}{C}HCH_3} \rightleftharpoons \underset{\substack{\text{isopentyl acetate} \\ \text{b.p. 142°C}}}{CH_3\overset{\overset{\displaystyle O}{\|}}{C}OCH_2CH_2\overset{\overset{\displaystyle CH_3}{|}}{C}HCH_3} + H_2O
$$

Because the major impurity in this case is the more volatile isopentyl alcohol, most of the isopentyl acetate should distill below its normal boiling point of 142°C; using 143°C as the end of the range allows for experimental error. If the boiling range for a distillation is not specified, you should collect the *main fraction* (the distilled liquid that contains the desired component) over a relatively narrow boiling range—usually 4–6°C—that brackets the boiling point of the desired component. A liquid fraction that distills below the expected boiling range for the main fraction is called a *forerun*. It should be collected in a different container than the main fraction, saved until distillation is complete, and then disposed of as directed. Sometimes, because of improper thermometer placement or an excessive heating rate, the internal thermometer will record a temperature lower than the actual vapor temperature. In that case, some or all of the liquid collected as forerun will actually be part of the expected main fraction and should *not* be discarded. So if you collect more "forerun" than expected, save it and redistill it later, after readjusting the heating rate or thermometer position. It may be advisable to redistill *all* of the liquid that distilled previously, because the rest of the distillate may also have been collected over the wrong temperature range.

DIRECTIONS FOR SIMPLE DISTILLATION

Equipment and Supplies

heat source

supports for heat source and receiver

clamps, ring stands

round-bottom flask (pot)

boiling chips *or* stir bar and magnetic stirrer

connecting adapter (still head)

thermometer adapter

thermometer

condenser

condenser tubing

vacuum adapter

receiver(s)

joint clip(s) or rubber band

stemmed funnel

For distilling ~10 mL of liquid or more, assemble [OP-2] the conventional distillation apparatus pictured in Figure E6. As the pot, use the smallest round bottom flask for which the liquid volume will be roughly half (or less) of the flask's capacity. For distilling less than 10 mL of liquid, assemble the compact apparatus pictured in Figure E8 and use a 25-mL round bottom flask as the pot. Be sure to position the thermometer correctly in the still head (see Figure E7). If you are using the compact apparatus, or the liquid being distilled is quite volatile or hazardous, use a round-bottom flask as the receiver; otherwise, you can use an open container (usually tared), such as an Erlenmeyer flask, a graduated cylinder, or a large vial. Remove the thermometer assembly, add the distilland to the boiling flask through a stemmed funnel, and then drop in a few boiling chips or a stir bar. Replace the thermometer assembly and—if you are using the conventional apparatus—turn on the condenser water to provide a slow but steady stream of coolant. Note that the condenser water should flow *in* the lower end of the condenser and *out* the upper end. If you are using the compact apparatus, immerse the receiver in a suitable cooling bath.

Start the stirrer—if you are using one—and turn on the heat source, adjusting the heating rate so that the liquid boils gently and a reflux ring of condensing vapors rises slowly into the still head. Shortly after the reflux ring reaches the thermometer bulb, the temperature reading should rise rapidly and vapors should begin passing through the sidearm into the condenser or vacuum adapter, coalescing into droplets that run into the receiving flask. As the first few droplets come over, the thermometer reading should rise to an equilibrium value and stabilize at that value. At this time, the entire thermometer bulb should be covered by a thin film of condensing liquid, which will drip off the end of the bulb and into the pot. Record the temperature at which the thermometer reading stabilizes; if it is lower than expected, check the thermometer placement and adjust it if necessary. Distill the liquid at a rate of 1–3 drops per second for the conventional apparatus, or about 1 drop per second using the compact apparatus, and monitor the temperature frequently throughout the distillation.

If the initial thermometer reading is below the expected boiling range, carry out the distillation until the lower end of the range is reached, collecting the forerun in the receiver; then replace the receiver by another one. Save any forerun for later disposal or possible redistillation. Try to make the switch quickly enough so that no distillate is lost. (Stop the distillation before changing receivers if you are using the compact apparatus.) If the initial thermometer reading is within the expected boiling range, there is no need to change receivers. Continue distilling until the upper end of the expected boiling range is reached or until only a small volume of liquid remains—enough to just moisten the bottom of the boiling flask. Turn off and remove the heat source before the boiling flask is completely dry; heating a dry flask might cause tar formation or even an explosion. Disassemble and clean the apparatus as soon as possible after the distillation is completed.

Waste Disposal: Dispose of the residue from the pot and any forerun as directed by your instructor or as indicated in an experiment's directions.

Summary

1. Assemble distillation apparatus.
2. Add distilland and boiling chips or stir bar.
3. Turn on condenser water and stirrer (if used).
4. Start heating; adjust heat so that vapors rise slowly into still head.
5. Record temperature after distillation begins and thermometer reading stabilizes.
   IF initial temperature is below expected boiling range, GO TO 6.
   IF initial temperature is within expected boiling range, GO TO 7.
6. Collect forerun and change receivers at low end of boiling range.
7. Distill until temperature reaches high end of boiling range or until pot is nearly dry.
8. Turn off and remove heat source.
9. Disassemble and clean apparatus; dispose of forerun (if any) and residue in pot.

When Things Go Wrong

If the liquid in the flask is boiling but the thermometer records a temperature well below its expected boiling point, don't worry. The temperature is probably low because the product's vapors haven't reached the still head yet. When they do, you'll see the temperature rise rapidly.

If a substantial amount of liquid has distilled but the thermometer at the still head records a temperature below the expected boiling range, the thermometer is probably positioned incorrectly. Refer to Figure E7 and move the thermometer farther down (or, rarely, farther up) if it isn't positioned as shown in the illustration. Then return all of the distilled liquid to the boiling flask and begin the distillation again. If the thermometer was originally positioned correctly, your product must contain a substantial amount of low-boiling impurity (forerun). Continue distilling until the temperature nears the expected boiling range, transfer the forerun to a separate container (or change receivers), and begin collecting the main fraction when the temperature reaches the lower end of its boiling range.

If, after the expected product begins distilling, the temperature drops below the product's boiling range, either (1) the heating rate isn't high enough to maintain distillation, or (2) all of the product that can distill has distilled. Try increasing the heat setting to see whether the temperature will rise again (vapors should be rising into the still head, in this case). If raising the heat over a period of several minutes has no effect on the still-head temperature and vapors are no longer rising toward the still head, the distillation is over; continue as described in the directions.

Suppose your distillation is going well and product is dripping into the receiver at a gratifying rate when suddenly the vacuum adapter slips off the condenser and goes crashing onto the desktop—along with the receiver and the product you distilled up to that point. Because you failed to secure your vacuum adapter to the apparatus, you have just lost a battle with gravity. There isn't much you can do to get out of this situation gracefully; trying to recover a spilled liquid from a flat (and probably contaminated) surface is like trying to shovel water out of a flooded basement. You will probably have to rely on whatever liquid is left in the pot, or start over.

Suppose you carry out a distillation until all (or nearly all) of the liquid in the pot is gone, but shortly after you remove the heat source, you notice some liquid that wasn't there before. The extra liquid came from vapors that didn't make it into the receiver and condensed into the pot instead. Trying to get the undistilled liquid into the receiver by boiling it again is pointless, because its vapors will only condense into the pot again when the apparatus cools. You might recover more product by using a chaser, as described in OP-32, but that's usually not worth the trouble for a simple distillation.

b. Distillation of Solids

A "cool" burner flame can be used if no flammable liquids are in the vicinity.

Low-melting solids can be distilled using the apparatus pictured in Figure E8 or with a special apparatus designed for that purpose. Unless the solid has a boiling point below 150°C, a cooling bath shouldn't be necessary. Use a vacuum adapter with the drip tip (outlet tube) removed, if any are available; otherwise, have a heat gun or heat lamp handy to melt any solid that forms in the outlet tube. When distillation is complete, melt the solid (unless it is still liquid) by heating the receiving flask and transfer it to a tared vial or another container. The last traces of solid can be transferred with a small amount of diethyl ether or another volatile solvent, which is then evaporated under a hood.

Vacuum Distillation

Principles and Applications

The boiling point of a liquid decreases when the external pressure is reduced, so under reduced pressure a liquid distills at a temperature that is lower than its normal boiling point. For example, a liquid that boils at 200°C at a pressure of 1 atm (760 torr) will boil near 100°C at 25 torr, as shown in Table E3. Carrying out a distillation well below atmospheric pressure, by reducing the boiling point of the liquid being distilled, reduces the likelihood that it will be degraded by thermal decomposition or other high-temperature processes. Distillation under reduced pressure is usually called *vacuum distillation*. As a rule, vacuum distillation is used for purifying most liquids that are heat sensitive or have boiling points of 200°C or higher at atmospheric pressure.

Vacuum distillation has certain inherent features that can potentially cause hazards and experimental difficulties. According to Boyle's law ($V \propto 1/P$), the volume of vapor generated by boiling a given amount of liquid increases when the pressure is reduced. For example, a vapor bubble that occupies a volume of 1 μL (0.001 mL) at 760 torr will expand to 0.3 mL at 25 torr. This can cause excessive bumping in the boiling flask and mechanical carryover of liquid to the receiver. Capillary bubblers, which produce a stream of very fine bubbles, are often used to maintain smooth boiling, but using microporous boiling chips or magnetic stirring should also work. Carryover can be reduced by interposing a Claisen adapter between the pot and still head. Reducing the pressure also increases the vapor velocity, because there are fewer molecules around to bump into. This can cause superheating of the vapor at the still head and produce a pressure differential throughout the system, making the observed distillation temperature too high and the pressure reading too low. These problems can be circumvented by using the right kind of apparatus and by carrying out the distillation slowly. Even then, the separation attainable under vacuum distillation does not equal that possible at atmospheric pressure, and there is always the danger that the apparatus may implode because of the unbalanced external pressure on the system. Accordingly, a vacuum distillation must be performed with great care and attention to detail to obtain satisfactory results and prevent accidents.

Table E3 Approximate boiling points of liquids at 25 torr

Normal bp	bp at 25 torr
150°C	60°C
200°C	100°C
250°C	140°C
300°C	180°C

Experimental Considerations

Apparatus. A typical setup for vacuum distillation is shown in Figure E11, which follows. The glassware used to assemble it must be free of cracks, star fractures, and other imperfections that might cause the apparatus to shatter under reduced pressure. All rubber connecting tubing should be thick walled to prevent collapse under vacuum and as short as possible to reduce the pressure differential between the vacuum source and the system. The rubber tubes should be stretched or bent to see that they are pliable and free of cracks. Connections between rubber and glass, as well as ground-joint connections, must be secure and airtight. If the distilland may contain a volatile impurity, at least two receivers should be available to collect the impurity and the main fraction. It is usually necessary to remove the heat source and break

From *Operational Organic Chemistry: A Problem Solving Approach to the Laboratory*, Fourth Edition, John W. Lehman. Copyright © 2009 by Pearson Education. Published by Prentice Hall. All rights reserved.

the vacuum before changing receivers. Although commercially available rotating receivers (sometimes called "cows" because of their udderlike appearance) make it possible to switch receivers without breaking the vacuum, they are seldom available in undergraduate laboratories.

Before assembly of an apparatus such as the one in Figure E11, the ground glass joints should be lubricated with vacuum grease to prevent leaks (be sure to clean the joints afterward, as described in OP-2). For small quantities of distilland, the compact apparatus for simple distillation pictured in Figure E8 of OP-30 can be used under reduced pressure if its vacuum adapter sidearm is connected to a vacuum line through a trap, as illustrated in Figure E11. The procedure is essentially the same as that used for a conventional vacuum distillation, except that a cooling bath is used instead of condenser water. It may be necessary to insert a Claisen adapter between the boiling flask and the still head to prevent mechanical carryover of the distilland or to allow for insertion of a bubbler.

Vacuum Sources. Most organic chemistry laboratories are provided with either water aspirators or vacuum lines that are connected to a remote vacuum pump. In principle, an aspirator should be able to attain a reduced pressure equal to the vapor pressure of the water flowing through it, which is a function of the water temperature, as shown in Table E4. In practice, the pressure is often 5–10 torr higher because of insufficient water pressure, leaks in the system, or deficiencies of the aspirator itself. Thus, with cold tap water at a temperature of 14°C running through it, a typical aspirator may provide a vacuum of around 20 torr. Because the water flow rate in your laboratory probably varies with the number of people using aspirators, the pressure will also vary as aspirators are turned on and off. An aspirator must be provided with a trap to prevent backup of water into the receiving flask during changes of water pressure and to reduce pressure fluctuations throughout the system. A thick-walled filter flask of the largest convenient size makes a good trap, although a Pyrex glass bottle wrapped with plastic tape (see OP-16) may also be adequate. The trap should be provided with a pressure release valve and hooked up to the aspirator and distillation apparatus, as illustrated in Figure E11.

Most lab systems with vacuum lines connected to a central vacuum pump attain reduced pressures that don't vary significantly and are comparable to those attained by water aspirators. All vacuum pumps must be protected from condensable vapors that might damage them. A central vacuum system should have its own purge assembly to remove such vapors, but it's not a bad idea to interpose a cold trap between the vacuum line and your apparatus, just in case the purge assembly is inadequate or poorly maintained. A cold trap can be assembled by immersing an ordinary aspirator trap (or a commercial cold trap) in an ice–salt bath, dry ice in acetone, or some other efficient coolant, and clamping the trap to a ring stand. A trap should always be used with any free-standing vacuum pump that isn't equipped with a purge system.

Pressure Measurement. To know with any certainty when the desired substance is distilling, you need to know (or be able to estimate) the pressure inside the vacuum distillation system so that you can estimate the boiling point of the desired component at that pressure. Devices called *manostats* can be used to maintain a desired pressure in a system, but they are seldom available in undergraduate laboratories. More often, you must work with the pressure provided by your aspirator or other vacuum system and use a *manometer*

Silicone grease has a tendency to creep under vacuum, causing contamination of glassware, so other types of vacuum grease may be preferable.

Table E4 Vapor pressure of water below 30°C

T, °C	P, torr	T, °C	P, torr
30	31.8	18	15.5
28	28.3	16	13.6
26	25.2	14	12.0
24	22.4	12	10.5
22	19.8	10	9.2
20	17.5	8	8.0

Take Care! Never use a thin-walled container, such as an Erlenmeyer flask, as a trap; it may shatter under vacuum.

A manometer measures the pressure inside a system; a manostat controls it.

to measure that pressure. For example, if the closed-end manometer shown in Figure E9 is attached to an evacuated system, the pressure (in torr) inside the system will be equal to the vertical distance (Δh, in millimeters) between the mercury levels in the inner tube and the cylinder. Another kind of closed-end manometer is shown in Figure E11; its pressure reading (in torr) is the difference in height (in millimeters) between the mercury levels in the two arms of the bent tube. The mercury in a manometer can present a hazard if the vacuum is broken suddenly—air rushing in can push the mercury column forcefully to the closed end of the tube, breaking it and releasing toxic mercury into the laboratory. For this and other reasons, the vacuum must always be released *slowly*. It is advisable to open the valve connecting a manometer to an evacuated system only while a pressure reading is being made.

When the boiling points of any impurities are quite different from that of the main fraction, you may get by without a manometer if you can make a rough estimate of the pressure. For example, if you are using a water aspirator, you can measure the temperature of the water, estimate its vapor pressure from Table E4, and estimate the minimum boiling temperature of the liquid as described in the next paragraph. The product should distill somewhat *above* that temperature; its actual boiling range will depend on the efficiency of the aspirator and the airtightness of your apparatus. You can also use a vacuum gauge to measure the pressure at the outlet of an aspirator or vacuum line, keeping in mind that the pressure in your distillation apparatus will be somewhat higher than the measured pressure.

Boiling Points Under Reduced Pressure. If the boiling point of a substance at a given pressure isn't known, it can be estimated using the vapor pressure–temperature nomograph shown in Figure E10. More precise estimates can be made using tables such as those in R. R. Dreisbach, *Pressure–Volume–Temperature Relationships of Organic Compounds* (New York: McGraw-Hill, 1952), or by using various empirical relationships. The main fraction should be collected over a range that brackets the expected boiling point, keeping in mind that the distillation temperature of a liquid may vary by 10°C or more under vacuum because of pressure fluctuations and other factors.

Heat Sources. The heat source should be capable of providing constant, uniform heating to prevent bumping and superheating and to maintain a constant distillation rate. For a typical vacuum distillation, an oil bath or a good heating mantle should be suitable. See OP-7a for information about the use of these heat sources.

Smooth-Boiling Devices. You can reduce bumping and foaming during a vacuum distillation by using microporous boiling chips, a magnetic stirring device, or a bubbler. Your lab kit may contain a narrow-tipped tube with a very fine hole at the outlet, which can be used as a bubbler. Otherwise, you can construct a flexible capillary bubbler, about as fine as a cat's whisker, by drawing it from a length of *thick-walled* capillary tubing (capillary bubblers drawn from thin-walled tubing break easily). See your instructor for help in constructing a capillary bubbler. A short rubber tube with a screw clamp should be placed at the top of either kind of bubbler to control the rate of bubbling. The bubbler is inserted through a thermometer adapter (or a rubber stopper, if necessary) so that its tip extends to within a millimeter or

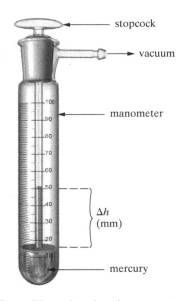

Figure E9 A closed-end manometer

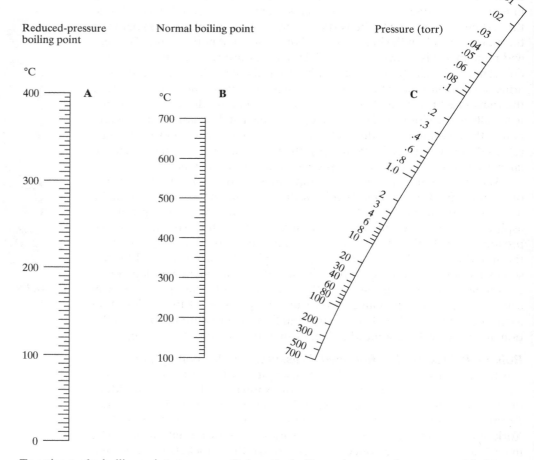

To estimate the boiling point at pressure P given the boiling point at another pressure P': (a) connect pressure P' in **C** with the boiling point at that pressure in **A** using a ruler, and place a sharp pencil point where the ruler intersects line **B**; (b) pivot the ruler around the pencil point until it reaches the desired pressure (P) in **C**, and then read the boiling point at that pressure from **A**.

Example: To estimate the boiling point of dibutyl phthalate at 10 torr from its reported boiling point of 236°C at 40 torr, place a ruler at 40 torr in **C** and 236° in **A**, causing it to intersect line **B** at about 345°. Then hold a pencil point at 345° on **B**, pivot the ruler about that point to 10 torr in **C**, and read the boiling point from **A**. This yields an estimated boiling point of 197°C at 10 torr.

Figure E10 Reduced-pressure boiling-point nomograph

two of the bottom of the boiling flask. Under vacuum, this device should deliver a very fine stream of air bubbles, preventing development of large bubbles that cause bumping. However, a bubbler has several drawbacks. Air entering the system raises the pressure slightly and may oxidize the product at high temperatures, and a capillary bubbler may plug up when the vacuum is broken. Nevertheless, a well-constructed capillary bubbler works better than any other smooth-boiling device.

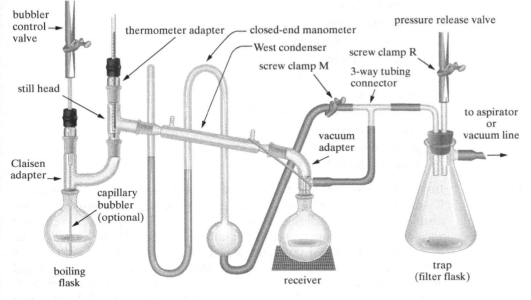

Figure E11 Apparatus for vacuum distillation

DIRECTIONS FOR VACUUM DISTILLATION

Safety Notes

Because of the possibility of an implosion, safety glasses *must* be worn during a vacuum distillation. Work behind a hood sash or safety shield while the apparatus is under vacuum. A rapid pressure increase, accompanied by a thick fog in the distilling flask, indicates decomposition of the distilland. If this occurs, unplug the heat source *immediately* and get away (warning others to do so also) until the flask cools. Report the incident to your instructor.

Before beginning a vacuum distillation, you should make a rough estimate of the boiling temperature of your sample under vacuum, or be ready to estimate it using the nomograph in Figure E10 once you obtain a manometer reading. Italicized instructions apply only if you are using a manometer; otherwise, disregard them.

Equipment and Supplies

heat source
rings, clamps, supports
round-bottom flask (pot)
bubbler or other smooth-boiling device
Claisen adapter
connecting adapter (still head)
stopper (if bubbler is not used)
thermometer
thermometer adapter
condenser

vacuum adapter
receiving flask(s)
joint clips (or wire, etc.)
condenser tubing
thick-walled rubber tubing
screw clamps
trap with pressure-release valve
manometer (optional)
glass tee (optional)
stemmed funnel

Inspect all glassware and rubber tubing, and replace any damaged items; if you have any doubt about their condition, see your instructor. For distilling ~10 mL of liquid or more, assemble [OP-2] the conventional vacuum-distillation apparatus as pictured in Figure E11. Be sure that the thermometer is placed correctly, as shown in Figure E7 of OP-30. For distilling less than 10 mL of liquid, assemble the compact apparatus pictured in Figure E8 but connect it to the rest of the system, as shown in Figure E11; interpose a Claisen head between the boiling flask and still head if you will be using a capillary bubbler or if carryover may be a problem. Apply vacuum grease at all joints, as described in OP-2. If you aren't using a manometer, omit the three-way tubing connector shown. Connect the vacuum adapter to a trap with a pressure-release valve, and connect the trap to the vacuum source. If you are using a capillary bubbler, provide it with a screw clamp on a short length of rubber tubing to control the bubbling rate. If you are using microporous boiling chips or a stir bar to prevent bumping, drop the chips or stir bar into the reaction flask and insert a ground-glass stopper into the short arm of the Claisen adapter (if your apparatus has one). If you are using a vacuum line rather than an aspirator, cool the trap if directed to do so by your instructor.

Make sure that all joints and connections are tight; then add the liquid to be distilled through a funnel. (If the liquid contains a volatile solvent, remove it first by distilling at atmospheric pressure, and then let the apparatus cool before proceeding.) If you are using a bubbler, open its screw clamp a turn or two. Raise the heat source into position, but don't begin heating yet. Turn on the condenser cooling water (or immerse the receiving flask of the compact apparatus in a suitable cooling bath), open screw clamp R, and turn on the vacuum fully. Slowly close clamp R and adjust the screw clamp on the bubbler (if you are using one) so that it emits a fine stream of bubbles. (If bumping and foaming occur, there may be some residual solvent in the distilland; open clamp R slowly and then close it down to a point at which the solvent will evaporate without excessive bumping. If a rubber tube collapses under vacuum, open clamp R slowly to break the vacuum and replace it with sturdier tubing.) *Slowly open clamp M, wait a minute or two until the pressure equilibrates, then read the manometer and close clamp M. If the observed pressure is more than ~10 torr above the estimated pressure, check the system for leaks caused by loose joints, cracked tubing, and so on. If you find any leaks, release the vacuum by slowly opening clamp R and fix them. If the pressure is satisfactory, use the nomograph shown in Figure E10 to estimate the boiling range at that pressure.*

If you are using a magnetic stirrer, turn it on. Begin heating to bring the mixture to the boiling point. If you are using a bubbler, adjust the bubbler clamp as necessary to maintain a very fine stream of bubbles as the temperature rises. If excessive foaming occurs on boiling, reduce the heating rate. If bubbles form around any joint during the distillation, that joint is leaking air into the system; remove the heat source, release the vacuum, and regrease the joint or replace the glassware part by another one. When liquid begins to condense into the receiver, record the temperature reading. *Slowly open clamp M, let the pressure equilibrate, and record the pressure reading; then close clamp M and leave it closed, except when you need to make another pressure reading. If the pressure differs substantially from the first reading, estimate the boiling range at the current pressure.* Adjust the heat source so that a distillation rate of about one drop per second or less is attained. If the temperature at the still head jumps up or down while the liquid is distilling, the pressure may be fluctuating because of changes in the aspirator flow rate; adjust the heating rate as necessary to maintain a suitable distillation rate. (To minimize such fluctuations, only a few students should use aspirators at the same time.)

If the initial distillation temperature is markedly lower than the estimated boiling range for the product, you are probably distilling a volatile forerun. Continue distilling until the temperature reaches the low end of the expected boiling range. Then change receivers without turning off the vacuum using the following procedure:

1. Lower the heat source and let the system cool down.
2. Open the bubbler clamp (if you are using one); then open clamp R slowly to bring the system to atmospheric pressure.
3. Replace the receiver with another one. If you are using microporous boiling chips, add another chip or two.
4. Slowly close clamp R and adjust the bubbler (if used).
5. Heat until distillation resumes.
6. Record the boiling temperature.

A capillary bubbler will sometimes plug up when the vacuum is broken; if that happens, you will have to replace it with a new one. Continue distilling until the upper end of the estimated boiling range is reached or until a significant drop in temperature indicates that the product is completely distilled. Stop the distillation before the boiling flask is completely dry.

When the distillation is complete, follow steps **1** and **2** for bringing the system back to atmospheric pressure, and then turn off the vacuum. Disassemble the apparatus and clean the glassware promptly.

Waste Disposal: Dispose of the residue and any forerun as directed by your instructor or as indicated in an experiment's directions.

Summary

1. Inspect glassware and tubing, assemble apparatus, and check connections and joints.
2. Add distilland and smooth-boiling device.
3. Position heat source, start cooling water, open clamp R, and turn on vacuum.
4. Close R and let pressure equilibrate.
5. *Open M, read pressure, close M, and estimate boiling range.*
6. Heat until distillation begins; adjust bubbler (if used).

7. Record temperature *and pressure*.
   IF temperature is below estimated range, GO TO 8.
   IF temperature is within estimated range, GO TO 12.
8. Adjust heat and distill until temperature reaches lower end of expected boiling range.
9. Lower heat source, let cool, open bubbler clamp, and clamp R.
10. Change receiver and close R.
11. Adjust bubbler (if used), heat until distillation resumes, and record temperature.
12. Distill until upper end of temperature range is attained or only a little distilland remains.
13. Lower heat source, let cool, and open R.
14. Turn off vacuum and remove distillate.
15. Disassemble and clean apparatus; dispose of residue and forerun.

When Things Go Wrong

Most of the things that go wrong during a simple distillation can also go wrong during a vacuum distillation, so you can refer to "When Things Go Wrong" in OP-30 for help. The following cases apply only to vacuum distillation.

Suppose you are performing a vacuum distillation using an aspirator (no manometers are available), but when liquid begins to distill, the still-head temperature is well above the estimated boiling point at 20 torr. Although a typical aspirator may provide a 20 torr vacuum, that is only a rough estimate—aspirators vary in efficiency, and their efficiency decreases as the number of aspirators in use increases. Leaks in the apparatus will also reduce the vacuum attainable. Check for leaks by looking for bubbles that form around the inside of joints under vacuum, and repair any leaks as described in the directions. If there are no leaks, continue collecting the liquid until the temperature either rises or drops markedly. You can check to make sure your product is the right one by obtaining an infrared (IR) spectrum or analyzing it in some other way.

If severe bumping occurs in the pot during a vacuum distillation, your smooth-boiling device isn't working properly (see "Smooth Boiling Devices"). Depending on the device you are using, you can either prepare a new bubbler, replace boiling chips with fresh ones, or stir faster, using a larger stir bar if necessary. The stir bar should rotate smoothly, without hopping or wobbling.

Fractional Distillation

Principles and Applications

Although simple distillation can purify organic liquids that contain small amounts of volatile impurities, it isn't a very effective means of separating the components of a mixture when each component makes up a substantial fraction of the mixture, unless the boiling points of the components are far apart. With mixtures of closer-boiling liquids, the distillate composition and boiling point will change continually throughout the distillation, as illustrated in Figure E12, and most of the distillate will be a relatively impure mixture of the components.

The separation could be improved by redistilling portions of the initial distillate and subsequent distillates. Such a process is diagrammed in Figure E13, in which the initial distillate is delivered directly to a second distilling flask, which redistills the condensed vapors and delivers its distillate to a third distilling flask, which distills that liquid into a receiver. This process can be understood by referring to the temperature–composition diagram in Figure E14 for the imaginary entane–orctane mixture discussed in OP-30.

When the mixture that contains 50.0 mol% of both entane (bp = 50°C) and orctane (bp = 100°C) is boiled in flask **A** (point *A* on the diagram in Figure E14), the vapor over the mixture has a composition of 81.4 mol% entane and only 18.6 mol% orctane (point *A′*). This is because entane has a considerably higher vapor pressure at the boiling point of the mixture (66.5°C) than does orctane. The vapor is condensed into flask **B** (line *A′ − B*), where it boils at 55°C to yield a vapor that contains 95.3 mol% entane (line *B − B′*), which is condensed (line *B′ − C*) into flask **C**. The condensed liquid in **C** boils at 51°C to yield a vapor that is 99.0 mol% entane (line *C − C′*), which is delivered to receiver **R** as a liquid of the same composition (line *C′ − R*).

Only the first few drops of distillate will attain this degree of purity, because as the more volatile entane is removed, the less volatile orctane will accumulate in the distilling flasks, reducing the proportion of entane in the vapor. The efficiency of the hypothetical apparatus would be improved considerably if some of the orctane-enriched liquid in each flask were drained back into the preceding flask through an overflow tube so that orctane did not accumulate as rapidly in the upper stages. Even then, the purity of the distillate would decrease with time. For example, when the amount of entane in flask **A** had decreased to 25 mol% (point *A″*), the vapor condensing into the receiver (point *R″*) would be only 96.6 mol% entane, as shown by the broken lines in Figure E14. In other words, during a distillation, the distilland climbs inexorably up the temperature–composition graph, and the distillate composition changes accordingly. Nevertheless, the separation effected by several distillation stages is considerably better than that effected by only one, as can be seen by comparing the curves for simple distillation and fractional distillation in Figure E12.

Fractional distillation refers to a distillation process that involves several concurrent vaporization–condensation cycles. During a fractional distillation,

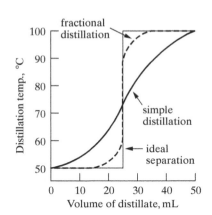

Figure E12 Separation efficiency of simple and fractional distillations

The process illustrated in Figure E13 is purely hypothetical; there are more practical ways of accomplishing the same result.

The boiling point decreases with each subsequent distillation because the distilland has become richer in the more volatile component.

From *Operational Organic Chemistry: A Problem Solving Approach to the Laboratory*, Fourth Edition, John W. Lehman. Copyright © 2009 by Pearson Education. Published by Prentice Hall. All rights reserved.

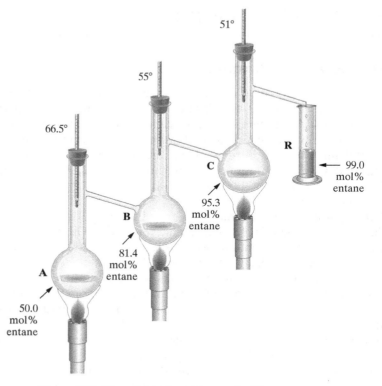

Figure E13 Hypothetical multistage distilling apparatus

the distillate is usually collected in several separate *fraction collectors* (receivers), the contents of each being a different *fraction*. Each fraction is collected over a different temperature range, with the lower-boiling fractions containing a greater percentage of the more volatile component and the higher-boiling fractions containing more of the less volatile component. For a fractional distillation having the distillation curve illustrated by the broken line in Figure E12, the first 30% (15 mL) or so of distillate would be nearly pure entane and the last 30 percent would be nearly pure orctane. The middle fraction would be a mixture of the two, which could be redistilled if desired.

Like the hypothetical distillation diagrammed in Figure E13, fractional distillation is a multistage distillation process performed in a single operation. A vertical *distilling column* performs the function of boiling flasks **B** and **C** in the hypothetical apparatus—in effect, redistilling the original distillate from flask **A**. The column is filled with some kind of *column packing*, which provides a large surface area from which repeated vaporization and condensation cycles can take place.

Suppose our 50.0 mol% mixture of entane and orctane is distilled through such a column, as diagrammed in Figure E15. The vapor leaving the pot will have the same composition (81.4 mol% entane) as it did in the hypothetical apparatus, but as it passes onto the column, it will cool, condense onto the packing surface, and begin to trickle down the column on its way back to the pot. Because the temperature is higher near the pot, part of the condensate will vaporize on the way down, yielding a vapor richer in

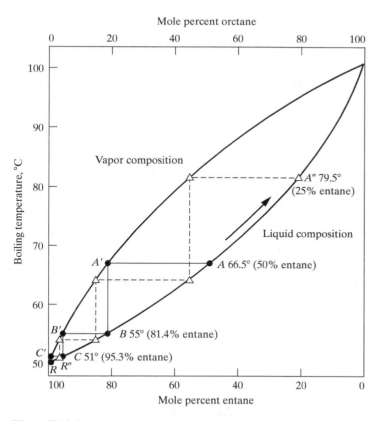

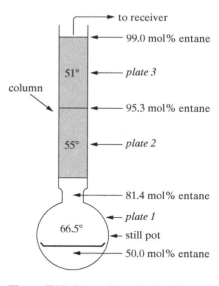

Figure E15 Operation of a fractionating column

Figure E14 Temperature–composition diagram for fractional distillation of entane–orctane mixture

entane. This vapor will rise up the column until—at a higher level than before (because its boiling point is lower)—it cools enough to recondense. This process of vaporization and condensation may be repeated a number of times on the way to the top of the column so that, when the vapor finally arrives at that point, it is nearly pure entane. Although this is a continuous process involving the simultaneous upward flow of vapor and downward flow of liquid, the net result is the same as that produced by successive discrete distillations.

Each section of the distillation apparatus that provides a separation equivalent to one cycle of vaporization and condensation (one "step" on the temperature–composition graph) is called a *theoretical plate*. The first cycle occurs in the pot, which provides one theoretical plate; the column illustrated in Figure E15 contributes two more. Note that there is a continuous variation in both temperature and vapor composition as one proceeds up the column, and that the temperature is fixed by the liquid–vapor composition. For instance, the entane-rich liquid near the top of the column boils at a lower temperature than the original mixture, so the average temperature of plate 3 is lower than that of the plates below it.

Column Efficiency. The efficiency of a fractional-distillation apparatus can be determined using the *Fenske equation*,

In certain multistage columns, the "theoretical" plates are real. A Bruun column consists of a series of horizontal plates stacked at intervals inside a vertical tube, and one vaporization–condensation cycle occurs on each plate.

$$n = \frac{\log\dfrac{Z_A}{X_A} - \log\dfrac{Z_B}{X_B}}{\log \alpha}$$

where n is the total number of theoretical plates, X_A and X_B are the mole fractions of liquids A and B in the distilland, and Z_A and Z_B are the mole fractions of the same components in the vapor that emerges from the top of the column. The term α is the *relative volatility* of the two liquids, where the volatility of a liquid in a mixture is the ratio of its mole fraction in the vapor to its mole fraction in the liquid. The pot provides one theoretical plate, so the number of theoretical plates provided by the column is $n - 1$. The efficiency of a particular kind of column or column packing is given by its *Height Equivalent to a Theoretical Plate (HETP),* which is equal to the height of the column divided by the number of theoretical plates it provides. For example, a 24-cm column that provides four theoretical plates has an HETP of 6 cm. The lower its HETP, the more efficient the column.

In practice, a number of factors limit the efficiency of a given column. Efficiency is highest under the equilibrium condition of *total reflux,* in which all of the vapors are returned to the pot. In practice, some of the vapors are continuously distilling into the receiver, which disturbs the equilibrium and reduces the column's efficiency. To maintain a high efficiency, the *reflux ratio (R)* — the ratio of liquid returned to liquid distilled measured over the same time interval — should be kept reasonably high by keeping the distillation rate low.

$$R = \frac{\text{liquid volume returning to pot}}{\text{liquid volume distilled}}$$

According to one rule of thumb, the reflux ratio should at least equal the number of theoretical plates for efficient operation. Reflux ratios of 5 to 10 are common for routine separations. To a lesser extent, the distillation rate and the *holdup* of a column (the amount of liquid that adheres to a column's surface and packing) can also affect the efficiency of a distillation.

Azeotropes. In discussing the principles of simple distillation and fractional distillation, we considered only the imaginary ideal liquids, entane and orctane. No real liquid displays ideal behavior, although some may come very close. Nonideal behavior arises from intermolecular interactions, with the greatest deviations from ideality occurring in liquids that have strong intermolecular forces. Thus, water, whose molecules exhibit hydrogen bonding, behaves much less ideally than cyclohexane, whose molecules are held together by weak dispersion forces.

Large deviations from ideal behavior in liquid mixtures may result in the formation of azeotropes, where an *azeotrope* is a solution of two or more liquids whose composition does not change during distillation. Azeotrope formation can make it difficult or impossible to purify certain liquids by distillation. For example, ethanol and water form a *minimum-boiling azeotrope* called (inaccurately) 95% ethanol, which contains 95.6% ethanol and 4.4% water by mass and boils at 78.15°C — a temperature lower than the boiling point of either ethanol (78.5°C) or water. Distilling ethanol–water mixtures that contain a higher percentage of water eventually yields 95.6% ethanol, but it is impossible to obtain pure ethyl alcohol by distilling 95.6%

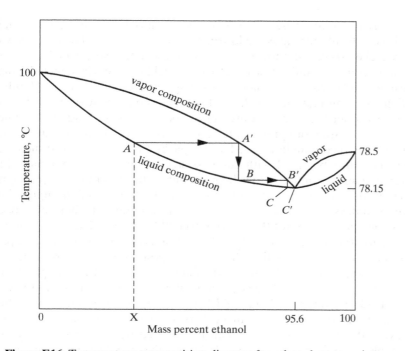

Figure E16 Temperature–composition diagram for ethanol–water mixtures

ethanol, as illustrated by the phase diagram in Figure E16. Suppose we start with a mixture that contains X% ethanol (by mass), with X being less than 95.6%. The liquid will initially boil at the temperature shown by point A, and its vapor (point A') can be condensed and revaporized in a column until it eventually reaches point C' on the diagram. At that point, the liquid and vapor composition are the same, so the liquid 95.6% ethanol will yield a vapor that is also 95.6% ethanol, and no further purification will occur.

In this case, the problem caused by an azeotrope can be solved by a different azeotrope. Benzene and water form an azeotrope with ethanol that boils at a lower temperature (64.9°C) than the ethanol–water azeotrope, so by distilling 95% ethanol with some benzene, the benzene–water–ethanol azeotrope can be distilled off until all of the water is removed and absolute (100%) ethanol is obtained. This is an example of *azeotropic drying,* the removal of water from an organic liquid by distillation with another liquid that forms a low-boiling azeotrope with water.

Experimental Considerations

Apparatus. The column is the most important part of any fractional-distillation apparatus. The *Vigreux column* illustrated in Figure E17a has a series of indentations to provide more surface on which the liquid can condense. Nevertheless, the total surface area is still quite small, so Vigreux columns aren't very efficient, with HETP values in the 8–12-cm range.

Another type of fractional distillation column is a straight tube (usually jacketed) filled with a suitable packing material (Figure E17b). Packed

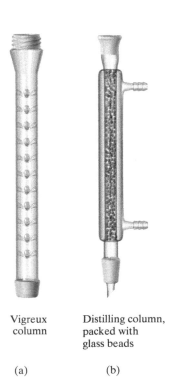

Vigreux
column

Distilling column,
packed with
glass beads

(a)　　　　(b)

Figure E17 Some columns for
fractional distillation

**Take Care: Stainless steel sponge
has sharp edges; wear gloves while
handling it.**

columns are more efficient than Vigreux columns, but their holdup is higher and their distillation rates are lower. The packing is introduced into a wide-bore jacketed column (not the narrower West condenser), which can be obtained from a standard scale lab kit. Packing materials include metal turnings and glass or porcelain beads, rings, helices, and saddles. Highly efficient packing materials such as glass helices may provide HETP ratings down to about 1 cm, but they are quite expensive. Glass beads and stainless-steel sponge are more practical for use in most undergraduate laboratories. The jacketed column in Figure E17b is packed with glass beads; such a column can also be filled with stainless-steel sponge pads that have been stretched and cut into sections long enough to fill the column from approximately the top of the lower glass joint to the bottom of the upper joint. With stainless-steel packing, the column is sometimes deliberately flooded by strong heating to wet the packing (see "Flooding"). Then the heat is reduced to drain the column before distillation is begun. Stainless-steel packing shouldn't be used to distill halogen compounds, which corrode it.

The apparatus for fractional distillation is like that for simple distillation, except that a distilling column is interposed between the pot and the still head, as shown in Figure E18. For high-boiling liquids, the column should be insulated to prevent heat losses that may reduce efficiency or prevent distillation entirely. It can be covered by one or more layers of crumpled aluminum foil (shiny side in), or glass wool (wear gloves) can be wrapped around it and held in place by aluminum foil. The insulation should provide "windows" that can be opened for observation of the vapors in the still head and the packing near the bottom of the column. The still head can be insulated with the same materials as the column.

Heat Sources.　For good results, the heat source should provide constant, uniform heating. An oil bath works best, but a heating mantle will suffice if its heat output is adjusted carefully to bring about the desired distillation rate. See OP-7a for information about the use of these heat sources.

Flooding.　One problem often encountered during a fractional distillation is *flooding,* in which the column becomes partly or entirely filled with liquid. Flooding is usually caused by an excessive heating rate, but it may also be caused by poor insulation, an unsuitable packing support, or improper packing. For example, sponge packing that is too tightly compressed or a glass-wool plug used as a packing support may hold up enough liquid to cause flooding. If flooding occurs, the apparatus must be separated from the heat source until all of the excess liquid has returned to the pot. Heating can then be resumed at a slower rate. Flooding will greatly decrease the efficiency of a separation, because it reduces the surface area of packing available for the separation.

Chasers.　A column with a high holdup will retain a relatively large amount of distillate. To improve the distillate recovery, the held-up liquid can be driven off the column and into the receiver by a suitable high-boiling substance, called a *chaser*. For example, *p*-xylene (bp 138°C) is a good chaser for liquids that boil around 100°C or below. After the last fraction has distilled, the chaser is added to the pot and heated to boiling, and the temperature is monitored as it climbs up the column. When the temperature begins to rise sharply, indicating that the chaser has reached the still head, distillation is stopped immediately and the recovered distillate is collected.

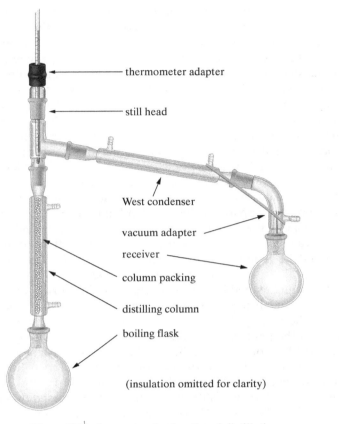

thermometer adapter

still head

West condenser

vacuum adapter

receiver

column packing

distilling column

boiling flask

(insulation omitted for clarity)

Figure E18 Apparatus for fractional distillation

DIRECTIONS FOR FRACTIONAL DISTILLATION

Equipment and Supplies

heat source
clamps, rings, supports
boiling flask (pot)
boiling chips *or* stir bar and stirrer
distilling column
column packing
insulating material (optional)
connecting adapter (still head)
thermometer
thermometer adapter
condenser
condenser tubing
vacuum adapter
fraction collectors
joint clips or rubber bands
stemmed funnel

If you are using column packing, pack the column to within a centimeter or so of the upper ground joint. To pack a column with stainless-steel sponge, *pull* it into the column using a copper wire bent into a hook at one end, making sure that it is as uniform as possible. Wear gloves, or you might cut yourself on the sharp edges of the packing. To pack a column with glass beads, hold the column nearly horizontal with your hand over the bottom opening and place a few large beads in the top of the column. Then quickly pivot the column to an upright position so that (with a little luck) the beads will jam together at the constriction and support the remainder of the packing. (A small plug of stainless-steel sponge can also serve as a support.) Slowly pour in the rest of the packing from a beaker, with continuous shaking, so that it is as uniform as possible. Other packing can be added similarly, except that glass helices should be dropped in one at a time, with shaking.

Assemble the apparatus illustrated in Figure E18, using a boiling flask large enough that it will be no more than half full of distilland. The fraction collectors can be screw-cap vials or other containers of an appropriate size; they should be numbered and tared. For very volatile distillates, small ground-joint flasks can be used as fraction collectors. The vacuum adapter drip tube should extend into the collector to reduce losses by evaporation. Make sure that all joints are tight, the column is perpendicular to the benchtop, the boiling flask and fraction collector are supported properly, and none of the joints is under excessive strain. If the boiling temperature will exceed 100°C or so during the distillation, it is advisable to insulate the apparatus from the bottom of the column to the top of the still head. Position the thermometer correctly, as illustrated in Figure E7 of OP-30. Add the distilland to the distilling flask through a stemmed funnel and drop in a few boiling chips or a stir bar. Start cooling water flowing through the condenser, but *not* through the column jacket.

Position the heat source, start the stirrer (if you are using one), and begin heating to bring the mixture to the boiling point. When it boils, adjust the heating rate so that the reflux ring of condensing vapor passes up the column at a slow, even rate—it should take 5–10 minutes or more to reach the top of the column. Watch the packing at the bottom of the column closely for evidence of flooding. If flooding occurs, remove the heat source immediately and let the liquid drain into the boiling flask; then resume heating at a lower rate. If flooding is still a problem, you may need to reinsulate or repack the column. When the vapors rise above the column packing, adjust the heat to keep the reflux ring between the packing and the sidearm for a minute or so, giving the column time to equilibrate. After vapors begin to condense into the collector, read the thermometer when the temperature reading stabilizes. Distill at a rate of about 1 drop every 1–3 seconds, or at a rate that gives the desired reflux ratio. (Estimate the reflux ratio by counting the drops that drip into the pot and those that drip into the receiver during a short time period.) If the initial distillate is cloudy (due to dissolved water), change receivers when it becomes clear.

If the column is not very efficient or the components' boiling points are close together, the temperature may rise only gradually throughout the distillation. In that case, it is best to collect fractions continuously at regular temperature intervals and redistill them as needed. Otherwise, continue distilling until the still-head temperature begins to rise sharply or until a predetermined target temperature is reached; then change fraction collectors and record the temperature. Change collectors again when the temperature begins to stabilize at a higher value, or when the next target temperature is reached, and record the temperature. Increase the heating rate as necessary to maintain a suitable distillation rate. Continue to collect fractions over the appropriate temperature ranges until the pot is nearly dry, the temperature drops sharply, or the final target temperature is reached. (Note that the temperature may drop if the heating rate is too low, so that the hot vapors no longer reach the thermometer bulb.) Then lower and turn off the heat source and let the column drain. Any fractions collected while the temperature was rising rapidly are impure; unless you wish to redistill them, they should be placed in a solvent recovery container. Disassemble and clean the apparatus; if stainless steel packing was used, remove and clean it without delay.

Waste Disposal: Dispose of the residue and any impure fractions as directed by your instructor or as indicated in an experiment's directions.

Summary

1. Pack column and assemble apparatus.
2. Add distilland and boiling chips or stir bar.
3. Turn on cooling water, stirrer (if used), and heat source.
4. Adjust heat so that reflux ring passes slowly up the column.
5. Record temperature after distillation begins, when thermometer reading stabilizes.
6. Distill until temperature rises sharply or target temperature is reached; record temperature.
   IF more fractions are to be collected, change collector; REPEAT 6.
   IF you are distilling the last (or only) fraction, CONTINUE.
7. Distill until temperature drops sharply or final target temperature is reached.
8. Remove heat source and drain column.
9. Disassemble and clean apparatus; dispose of residue and any impure fractions.

When Things Go Wrong

Most of the things that go wrong during a simple distillation can also go wrong during a fractional distillation, so you can refer to "When Things Go Wrong" in OP-30 for help. The following cases apply only to fractional distillation.

If, while you're collecting a fraction, the temperature drops below that fraction's boiling range when there is still liquid in the pot, it's likely that all of the liquid making up that fraction has distilled but the vapors of the next fraction have not yet reached the still head. Keep heating, increasing the heating rate as necessary, so that the next fraction will start distilling. It is also possible that the heat setting wasn't high enough to maintain distillation of the first fraction, in which case it should resume distilling after you turn up the heat.

Suppose that, when you assembled your apparatus, you were careful to connect the cooling-water tap to all of the available hose connections. Now the liquid in the pot is boiling, but none of its vapors are reaching the still head, where the temperature is still below 30°C. By connecting your distilling column to the cooling water, you have turned it into a reflux condenser; any vapors that enter it will condense and drip back into the pot. Yes, a distilling column does look a lot like a condenser, but it's not to be used as one during a fractional distillation.

Melting Point

Principles and Applications

The *melting point (mp)* of a pure substance is defined as the temperature at which the solid and liquid phases of the substance are in equilibrium at a pressure of 1 atmosphere. At a temperature slightly below the melting point, a mixture of the two phases solidifies; at a temperature slightly above the melting point, the mixture liquefies. Melting points can be used to characterize organic compounds and to assess their purity. The melting point of a pure compound is a unique property of that compound, which is essentially independent of its source and method of purification. This is not to say that no two compounds will have the same melting point; many compounds have melting points that differ by no more than a fraction of a degree. If two pure samples have *different* melting points, however, they are almost certainly different compounds.

The melting point of an organic solid is usually measured by grinding the solid to a powder and packing the powder inside a *melting-point tube*, a capillary tube that is closed at one end. The melting-point tube is then placed in an appropriate heating device, and the *melting-point range* of the sample — the range of temperatures over which the solid is converted to a liquid—is observed and recorded. A pure substance usually melts within a range of no more than 1–2°C; that is, the transition from a crystalline solid to a clear, mobile liquid occurs within a degree or two if the rate of heating is sufficiently slow and the sample is properly prepared.

The presence of impurities in a substance *lowers* its melting point and *broadens* its melting-point range. To better understand the effects of impurities on melting points, consider the phase diagram for phenol (*P*) and diphenylamine (*D*) in Figure F1. Pure phenol melts at 41°C and pure diphenylamine at 53°C. If a sample of phenol contains diphenylamine as an impurity, its melting point will be lower than 41°C by an amount that depends on the mole percent of diphenylamine present. Similarly, the melting point of diphenylamine will be lower than 53°C if it contains phenol as an impurity. For example, the melting point of phenol containing 10 mol% diphenylamine is given by point *M* on the phase diagram, and that of diphenylamine containing 20 mol% phenol is given by point *N*.

Pure phenol and pure diphenylamine both have sharp melting points, meaning that the transition from solid to liquid occurs over a narrow temperature range. Mixtures of the two (except the *eutectic mixture* at the minimum in the diagram) exhibit broader melting-point ranges that depend on their composition. The approximate melting-point range for a mixture is given by the distance between the broken lines connecting points *P* and *E* or points *E* and *D* and the solid lines connecting the same points on the phase diagram. For example, the melting-point range of phenol containing 10 mol% diphenylamine is given by the distance between *M'* and *M*, and the melting-point range of diphenylamine containing 20 mol% phenol is given by the distance between *N'* and *N*.

Because the melting point decreases in a nearly linear fashion as the amount of impurity increases (until the eutectic point, *E*, is reached), the difference between the observed and expected values can make it possible to

Melting-point tubes are available commercially, but they can also be constructed by sealing open-ended capillary tubes.

From *Operational Organic Chemistry: A Problem Solving Approach to the Laboratory*, Fourth Edition, John W. Lehman. Copyright © 2009 by Pearson Education. Published by Prentice Hall. All rights reserved.

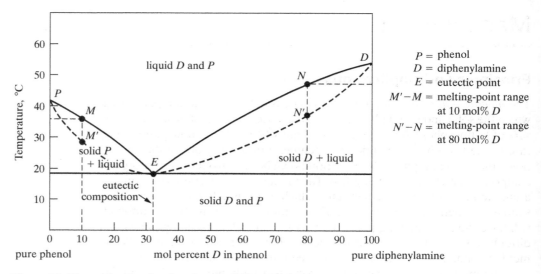

Figure F1 Phase diagram for the phenol–diphenylamine system

estimate a compound's purity. The melting-point lowering effect can also be used to confirm the identity of a substance, such as the product of a reaction, when it is thought to be a certain known compound. The compound in question is mixed with a sample of the known compound and the melting point of the mixture is measured. If the two compounds are identical, the mixture melting point will be essentially the same as that of the known compound. If they are not identical, the known compound will act as an impurity in the unknown, so the melting point of the mixture will be lower and its range broader than for the known compound.

Experimental Considerations

Melting Behavior. The melting-point range of a sample is reported as the range between (1) the temperature at which the sample first begins to liquefy and (2) the temperature at which it is completely liquid, called the *liquefaction point*. When a single melting point is to be reported, the liquefaction point is generally used. A compound may also be characterized by its *meniscus point*, the temperature at which the liquid meniscus is barely clear of the solid below it. Some automatic melting-point devices report melting points that are closer to the meniscus point than to the liquefaction point.

If traces of solvent remain in a sample because of insufficient drying or other causes, you may observe "sweating" of solvent from the sample or bubbles in the molten sample, which may resolidify when all of the solvent is driven off. If a sample does show this behavior, it should be dried and the melting point remeasured. Even a dry sample will tend to soften and shrink before it begins to liquefy; this process begins at the *eutectic temperature* (point *E* in Figure F1). In any case, softening, shrinking, and sweating should not be mistaken for melting behavior. The melting-point range does not begin until the first free liquid is clearly visible, at which time you should see movement of both solid and liquid in the melting-point tube.

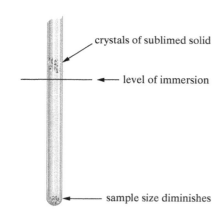

crystals of sublimed solid

level of immersion

sample size diminishes

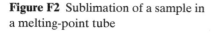

Figure F2 Sublimation of a sample in a melting-point tube

Some compounds sublime—change directly from the solid to the vapor state—when they are heated in an open container. Sublimation can be detected during a melting-point determination by a pronounced shrinking of the sample, accompanied by the appearance of crystals higher up inside the melting-point tube (Figure F2). The melting point of a sample that sublimes at or below its melting temperature can be measured using a sealed melting-point tube. An ordinary melting-point tube should be cut (see OP-3) short enough so that it doesn't project above the block of a melting-point apparatus (see Figure F4), or so that it can be entirely immersed in a heating-bath liquid. The sample is introduced and the open end is sealed in a burner flame (see OP-3). Then the melting point is measured by one of the methods described in the "Directions" section.

If a sample becomes discolored and liquefies over an unusually broad range during a melting-point determination, it is probably undergoing thermal decomposition. Compounds that decompose on heating usually melt at temperatures that vary with the rate of heating. The approximate melting point (also called the *decomposition point*) of such a compound should be measured by heating the melting-point apparatus to within a few degrees of the expected melting temperature before inserting the sample, and then raising the temperature at a rate of about 3–6°C per minute.

Apparatus for Measuring Melting Points. Melting points can be determined with good accuracy using a Thiele tube or Thiele–Dennis tube filled with a heating-bath liquid such as mineral oil, as illustrated in Figure F5 (which follows) for a Thiele–Dennis tube. The design of such tubes promotes good circulation of the heating liquid without stirring. A melting-point tube containing the solid is secured to a thermometer, which is then immersed in the bath liquid. The solid is observed carefully for evidence of melting as the apparatus is heated. Melting points can also be measured in an ordinary beaker if the bath liquid is stirred constantly (Figure F3), either manually or with a magnetic stirrer [OP-10].

Melting-point instruments that use capillary melting-point tubes, such as the Mel-Temp illustrated in Figure F4, are available commercially. As a rule, they are more accurate and easier to use than melting-point baths. The Mel-Temp and similar devices can be used to make several measurements at once, which is convenient when a mixture melting point is being determined, because it allows the melting points of the unknown compound, the known, and the mixture to be measured and compared at the same time. The heating rate is adjusted by a dial that controls the voltage input to a heating coil. The dial reading required to attain the desired heating rate at the sample's melting point can be estimated from a heating-rate chart furnished with the instrument. The dial is initially set higher than this to bring the temperature to within 20°C or so of the expected melting point, and then reset to the value estimated from the chart.

Thermometer Corrections. The observed melting point of a compound may be inaccurate because of defects in the thermometer used or because of the *emergent stem error* that results when a thermometer is not immersed to its intended depth in a heating bath. Many thermometers are designed to be immersed to the depth indicated by an engraved line on the stem, usually 76 mm from the bottom of the bulb; slight deviations from this depth won't result in serious error. Other thermometers are designed for total immersion; if

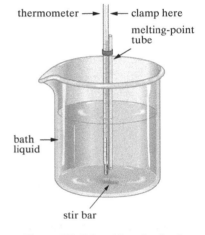

Figure F3 Stirred heating bath

Newer Mel-Temp models are provided with mercury-free precision digital thermometers.

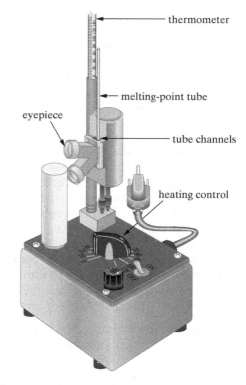

Figure F4 Apparatus for measuring melting points (Mel-Temp method)

Small melting-point errors may result from reading the thermometer incorrectly. View the mercury column with your line of sight perpendicular to the thermometer and level with the top of the column.

they are used under other circumstances, the temperature readings will be in error. An emergent stem error can be compensated for by placing the bulb of a second thermometer opposite the middle of the exposed part of the thermometer's mercury column when the sample is melting, recording the temperature readings of both thermometers, and calculating an *emergent stem correction* with the following equation:

$$\text{emergent stem correction} = 0.00017 \cdot N(t_1 - t_2)$$

N = length in degrees of exposed mercury column
t_1 = observed melting temperature
t_2 = temperature at middle of exposed column

The emergent stem correction is added to the observed melting temperature, t_1. Melting points that have been corrected in this way should be reported as, for example, "mp 123–124° (corr.)."

Errors that arise from thermometer defects as well as an emergent stem can be corrected by *calibrating* the thermometer under the conditions in which it is to be used. A thermometer used for melting-point determinations, for example, is calibrated by measuring the melting points of a series of known compounds, subtracting the observed melting point from the true melting point of each compound, and plotting this difference—the *melting-point correction*—as a function of temperature. The correction at the melting point of any other compound can then be read from the graph and added to its observed melting point, taking into account the sign (+ or −) of the correction. A list of pure compounds that can be used for melting-point calibrations is given in Table F1. Sets of pure calibration substances are available from chemical supply houses.

Mixture Melting Points. A mixture melting point is obtained by grinding together approximately equal quantities of two solids (a few milligrams of each) until they are thoroughly intermixed, then measuring the melting point of the mixture by the usual method. Usually one of the compounds, X, is an unknown that is believed to be identical to a known compound, Y. A sample of pure Y is mixed with X, and the melting points of this mixture and of pure Y (and sometimes of X as well) are measured. If the melting points of pure Y and of the mixture are the same, to within a degree or so, then X is probably identical to Y. If the mixture melts at a lower temperature and over a broader range than pure Y, then X and Y are different compounds.

Table F1 Substances used for melting-point calibrations

Substance	mp, °C
ice	0
diphenylamine	54
m-dinitrobenzene	90
benzoic acid	122.5
salicylic acid	159
3,5-dinitrobenzoic acid	205

DIRECTIONS FOR MELTING-POINT MEASUREMENT

Mineral oil begins to smoke and discolor below 200°C and can burst into flames at higher temperatures. Oil fires can be extinguished with solid-chemical fire extinguishers or powdered sodium bicarbonate.

Safety Notes

Equipment and Supplies

(Starred items are for method **B** only):

Mel-Temp (method **A** only)
watch glass
flat-bottomed stirring rod or flat-bladed spatula
1-m length of glass tubing
thermometer
capillary melting-point tube
*Thiele tube or Thiele–Dennis tube
*clamp, ring stand
*heating oil
*burner
*cutaway cork or thermometer clamp
*3-mm rubber ring

Put a few milligrams of the dry solid on a small watch glass and grind it to a fine powder with a flat-bottomed stirring rod or a flat-bladed spatula. Use a spatula to make a small pile of powder near the middle of the watch glass. Press the open end of a capillary melting-point tube into the pile until enough has entered the tube to form a column 1–2 mm high. Using too much sample can result in a melting-point range that is too broad and a melting-point value that is too high. Tap the closed end of the tube gently on the benchtop (or rub its sides with a small file); then drop it (open end up) through a 1-m length of small-diameter glass tubing onto a hard surface, such as a benchtop or a ceramic tile. Repeat this process several times to pack the sample firmly into the bottom of the tube. Use one of the methods that follow

A melting-point tube can be constructed by sealing one end of an open-ended capillary tube that is approximately 10 cm long and 1 mm in diameter.

to measure the melting-point range of the sample. If you don't know the sample's expected melting point, you can determine its approximate value with rapid heating (6°C per minute or more), and then carry out a more accurate melting-point measurement with a second sample, as described here.

A. Mel-Temp Method.   Place the melting-point tube (sealed side down) in one of the channels on the Mel-Temp's heating block (Figure F4). Use the heating-rate chart to estimate the heat-control dial setting that will cause the temperature to rise at a rate of 1–2°C per minute at the expected melting point of the sample. Set the dial to a higher value at first, so that the temperature rises quite rapidly to about 20°C below the expected melting point, and then reduce the dial setting to the value that you estimated. As the temperature nears the expected melting point, adjust the dial as necessary so that the temperature rises at a rate of 1–2°C per minute while the sample is melting. Observe the sample through the eyepiece and record (as the limits of the melting-point range) the temperatures (1) when the first free liquid appears in the melting-point tube and (2) when the sample is completely liquid. For best results, let the block cool to 15–20°C below the melting point and repeat the measurement. Cooling can be accelerated by passing an air stream over the block.

B. Thiele-Tube Method.   Clamp the Thiele tube or Thiele–Dennis tube securely to a ring stand and add enough mineral oil (or another appropriate bath liquid) to just cover the top of the sidearm outlet, as shown in Figure F5a. (Refer to OP-7a for precautions to be followed when using oil baths.) Secure the melting-point tube to a broad-range thermometer as follows:

You can use a similar method with other melting-point baths, such as the one shown in Figure F3, but a hot plate-stirrer or another flameless heat source will be required in that case.

1. Cut a 3-mm-thick rubber ring from $\frac{1}{4}$-inch i.d. thin-walled rubber tubing (rubber rings may be provided).
2. Place the rubber ring around the thermometer, about 9 cm from its bulb end.
3. Pinch the rubber ring between your fingers to create a gap; insert the open end of the melting-point tube through the gap.
4. Move the melting-point tube until the sample is adjacent to the middle of the thermometer bulb (see Figure F5c).

The cork is bored out to accommodate the thermometer, and then cut with a single-edged razor blade or a sharp knife so that the thermometer can be snapped into place from the side rather than inserted from the top.

Snap the thermometer into the center of a cutaway cork (Figure F5b) at a point above the rubber ring, with the melting-point tube and the degree markings on the same side as the opening in the cork. Insert this assembly into the bath liquid and move the thermometer, if necessary, so that its bulb is centered in the tube about 3 cm below the sidearm junction and the temperature can be read through the opening in the cork (Figure F5a). The rubber ring should be 2–3 cm above the liquid level so that the bath liquid, as it expands on heating, won't come in contact with it. If the hot oil meets the rubber, it may soften and allow the melting-point tube to drop out.

Heat the bottom of the Thiele tube with a burner flame (or use a microburner for more precise heat control) until the temperature is about 15°C below the expected melting point. Reduce the heating rate by turning down the flame and applying it at the sidearm, so that the temperature rises at a rate of 1–2°C per minute at the melting point. Continue heating at that rate as you observe the sample closely, and record (as the limits of the melting-point range) the temperatures (1) when the first free liquid appears in the melting-point tube and (2) when the sample is completely liquid.

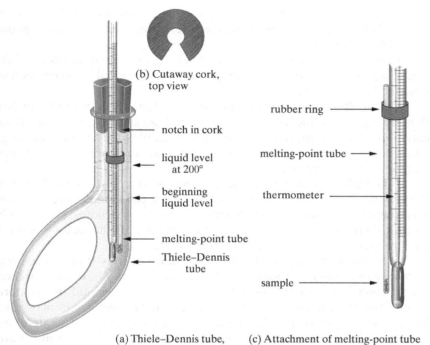

You can use a thermometer clamp instead of a cutaway cork to hold the thermometer in place.

(b) Cutaway cork, top view

notch in cork

liquid level at 200°

beginning liquid level

melting-point tube

Thiele–Dennis tube

rubber ring

melting-point tube

thermometer

sample

(a) Thiele–Dennis tube, assembled

(c) Attachment of melting-point tube

Figure F5 Apparatus for measuring melting points (Thiele-tube method)

For best results, let the heating bath cool to 15–20°C below the melting point and repeat the measurement. Cooling can be accelerated by passing an air stream over the tube.

Clean up the apparatus and either place the oil in a designated container or store it in the Thiele tube. Mineral oil can be removed from glassware by rinsing the glassware with petroleum ether, followed by acetone, and then washing it with a detergent and water.

Summary

1. Assemble apparatus for melting-point determination.
2. Grind solid to a powder and fill melting-point tube(s) to depth of 1–2 mm. IF you are using method **B**, GO TO 4.
3. Insert sample in Mel-Temp heating block; GO TO 5.
4. Secure melting-point tube to thermometer; insert assembly in heating bath.
5. Heat rapidly to ~15–20°C below mp; then reduce heating rate to 1–2°C/min.
6. Observe and record melting-point range.
7. Disassemble apparatus as needed and clean up.

When Things Go Wrong

If, during a melting-point determination, the solid sample begins to shrink before any liquid appears, don't assume that it is melting. The melting-point range doesn't begin until there is some liquid with the solid. But if the sample shrinks until there is little (if any) solid left at the bottom of the melting-point tube, your sample is subliming and may completely disappear before it starts to melt. In that case, you should prepare a new sample tube and seal it as described in "Melting Behavior."

If your sample discolors significantly during a melting-point determination, it is probably decomposing. Prepare a new sample tube and proceed as described in "Melting Behavior."

If the melting point you measure for a substance is substantially higher than its expected value, you may have heated the sample too rapidly. If so, carry out another measurement using a new sample (don't re-melt the original sample), with the temperature rising at a rate of no more than 2°C per minute at the melting point.

If the melting point you measure for a substance is substantially lower than its expected value, you may have recorded the temperature before it was completely melted. Try again with a new sample, making sure that it is entirely liquid before your record its melting point. If the melting point is still low, your product is probably wet or impure.

If the substance appears to melt over an excessively broad range, you may have used too much sample or the sample may not have been packed tightly enough; the sample in the melting-point tube should be no more than 2 mm high. If you used the right amount of sample, you may have heated the sample too rapidly; the temperature should rise at a rate of no more than 2°C per minute at the melting point. Otherwise, you may have recorded the initial temperature before the sample began to liquefy, or your product may have decomposed near its melting point (see "Melting Behavior"). If repeating the melting-point measurement more carefully with a new sample (don't re-melt the original sample) still gives a broad range, your product may be wet or impure.

The *boiling point (bp)* of a liquid is defined as the temperature at which the vapor pressure of the liquid is equal to the external pressure at the surface of the liquid, and also as the temperature at which the liquid is in equilibrium with its vapor phase at that pressure. These definitions are the basis for various standard scale and small-scale methods for measuring boiling points. For example, the boiling point of a liquid can be determined by distilling a small quantity of the liquid and observing the temperature at the still head, where the liquid and its vapors are assumed to be in equilibrium. It can also be determined by measuring the temperature at which the liquid's vapor, trapped inside a capillary tube immersed in the liquid, exerts a pressure equal to the external pressure. Like the melting point of a solid, the boiling point of a liquid can be used to help identify it and assess its purity.

Boiling-Point Corrections

The *normal boiling point* of a liquid is its boiling point at an external pressure of 1 atmosphere (760 torr, 101.3 kPa). Because the atmospheric pressure at the time of a boiling-point determination is seldom exactly 760 torr, observed boiling points may differ somewhat from values reported in the literature and should be corrected. If a laboratory boiling-point determination is carried out at a location reasonably close to sea level, atmospheric pressure will rarely vary by more than 30 torr from 760 torr. For deviations of this magnitude, a *boiling-point correction*, t, can be estimated using Equation **1**.

$$\Delta t \approx y(760 - P)(273.1 + t) \qquad (1)$$

Δt = temperature correction, to be added to the observed boiling point
P = barometric pressure, in torr
t = observed boiling point, in °C

The value 1.0×10^{-4} is used for the constant y if the liquid is water, an alcohol, a carboxylic acid, or another associated liquid; otherwise, y is assigned the value 1.2×10^{-4}. For example, the boiling point of water at 730 torr is 98.9°C. Use of Equation **1** leads to a correction factor of $[(1.0 \times 10^{-4})(760 - 730)(273.1 + 98.9)]°C = 1.1°C$, which yields the correct normal boiling point of 100.0°C.

At high altitudes, the atmospheric pressure may be considerably lower than 1 atmosphere, resulting in observed boiling points that are substantially lower than the normal values. For example, water boils at 93°C on the campus of the University of Wyoming at Laramie, which has an elevation of 2290 m (7520 ft). For major deviations from atmospheric pressure, Equation **2** can be used in conjunction with approximate entropy of vaporization values obtained from the "Correction of Boiling Points to Standard Pressure" section in older editions of the *CRC Handbook of Chemistry and Physics* [Bibliography, A15].

$$\Delta t \approx \frac{(273 + t)}{\varphi} \log \frac{760}{P} \qquad (2)$$

φ = (entropy of vaporization at normal boiling point)/$2.303R$

*Equation **2** is a simplified form of the Hass–Newton equation found in the CRC Handbook, 64th Edition, p. D-189.*

From *Operational Organic Chemistry: A Problem Solving Approach to the Laboratory*, Fourth Edition, John W. Lehman. Copyright © 2009 by Pearson Education. Published by Prentice Hall. All rights reserved.

For example, hexane boils at 49.6°C at 400 torr. The value of φ for alkanes is found (from the *CRC Handbook*) to be about 4.65 at that temperature. Substituting these values into Equation **2** yields a correction factor of

$$\Delta t \approx \frac{(273°C + 49.6°C)}{4.65} \log \frac{760 \text{ torr}}{400 \text{ torr}} = 19.3°C,$$

which gives a normal boiling point of 68.9°C. A second approximation using the value of φ at the corrected boiling point gives 68.8°C, which compares very favorably to the reported normal boiling point of 68.7°C. As for melting-point determinations, it may be necessary to correct a boiling point for thermometer error, especially when working with high-boiling liquids. See "Thermometer Corrections" in OP-33 for instructions.

a. Distillation Boiling Point

During a carefully performed distillation of a pure liquid, the vapors surrounding the thermometer bulb are in equilibrium (or nearly so) with the liquid condensing on the bulb. Thus, the vapor temperature recorded during the distillation of a pure liquid should equal its boiling point. If the liquid is contaminated by impurities, the distillation boiling point may be either too high or too low, depending on the nature of the impurity. Volatile impurities in a liquid lower its boiling point, whereas nonvolatile impurities raise it; in either case, its boiling point will vary throughout its distillation. Therefore, if there is any doubt about the purity of a liquid, it should be distilled or otherwise purified prior to a boiling-point determination.

DIRECTIONS FOR DISTILLATION BOILING-POINT MEASUREMENT

Assemble the compact distillation apparatus pictured in Figure E8 of OP-30 using a 25-mL round-bottom flask and placing the thermometer as shown in Figure E7. Add 5–10 mL of the liquid to the flask and drop in a boiling chip or two, or a stirring device. Distill the liquid slowly, recording the temperature readings when (1) the liquid has begun to collect in the well or receiver and the temperature has equilibrated; (2) about half of the liquid has distilled; and (3) the pot is nearly empty but the temperature hasn't begun to drop. The first and last readings represent the boiling-point range, and the middle reading is the *median boiling point*. The median value should provide the best estimate of the actual boiling point. A boiling-point range greater than 2°C suggests that the liquid may need to be purified before further work is done. Record the barometric pressure so that you can make a pressure correction, if necessary.

Waste Disposal: Dispose of the residue and any distillate that will not be used later as directed by your instructor or as indicated in an experiment's directions.

When Things Go Wrong

If your liquid distills at too low or too high a temperature, if it distills over a broad range, or if the still-head temperature rises or drops abruptly after only part of it has distilled, it is probably impure. Purify it by an appropriate distillation method and then repeat the measurement.

Most of the things that go wrong during a simple distillation can also go wrong during a distillation boiling-point measurement, so refer to "When Things Go Wrong" in OP-30 for help if you have other problems.

b. Capillary-Tube Boiling Point

When a liquid is heated to its boiling point, the pressure exerted by its vapor becomes just equal to the external pressure at the liquid's surface. If a tube that is closed at one end is filled with a liquid and immersed (open end down) in a reservoir containing the same liquid, the tube will begin to fill with vapor as the liquid is heated to its boiling point. At the boiling point, the vapor pressure inside the tube will balance the pressure exerted on the liquid surface by the surrounding atmosphere, so that the liquid levels inside and outside the tube will be equal (see Figure F6). If the temperature is raised above the boiling point, vapor will escape in the form of bubbles; if the temperature is lowered below the boiling point, the tube will begin to fill with liquid.

This behavior is the basis for a semi-microscale method for measuring boiling points. It requires a *bell*—a capillary tube sealed at one end—that is inverted inside a *boiling tube* containing the liquid. A bell can be made by cutting [OP-3] an ordinary capillary melting-point tube in half and saving the sealed half. A boiling tube is constructed by sealing an 8–10-cm length of 4–5-mm o.d. glass tubing at one end, as described in Minilab 1. The bell is inverted into the boiling tube, the liquid is added, and the assembly is secured to a thermometer and heated in a Thiele or Thiele–Dennis tube. Alternatively, you can use a stirred oil bath as illustrated in Figure F3 of OP-33.

It is important to avoid overheating during a boiling-point measurement; otherwise, the liquid will boil away. It may be necessary to add more liquid if the sample is very volatile. For best results, you should repeat the boiling-point measurement at least once with a fresh sample.

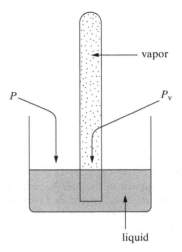

Figure F6 Boiling-point principle. At the boiling point, $P_v = P$, where P_v = pressure exerted by the vapor on the liquid surface and P = pressure exerted by the atmosphere on the liquid surface.

DIRECTIONS FOR CAPILLARY-TUBE BOILING-POINT MEASUREMENT

Equipment and Supplies

boiling tube
bell
thermometer
rubber ring
Thiele tube or Thiele–Dennis tube
mineral oil or other bath liquid
burner

Construct a boiling tube and a bell, if necessary. Add 2–4 drops of the liquid to a boiling tube and shake the tube to force the liquid to the bottom. Insert the bell into the boiling tube with its open end down. Secure the assembly to a thermometer by means of a rubber ring cut from thin-walled rubber tubing, as illustrated in Figure F7. Insert this assembly into a Thiele tube or Thiele–Dennis tube as for a melting-point determination (see Figure F5, OP-33), with the rubber ring 2 cm or more above the liquid level. (Refer to OP-7a for precautions to be followed when using oil baths.) Heat the tube with a burner flame (or use a microburner, for more precise heat control) until the temperature is within a few degrees of the expected boiling point of the liquid (if it is known). Then continue heating more slowly until you see a *rapid, continuous* stream of bubbles emerging from the bell. (The expansion of heated air in the bell will cause a *slow* evolution of bubbles; if you stop heating before rapid bubbling occurs, your reported boiling point will be too low.) Remove the heat source, let the bath liquid cool slowly until the bubbling stops, and record the temperature when liquid *just* begins to enter the bell. Let the temperature drop a few degrees so that the liquid partly fills the bell. Then heat very slowly until the first bubble of vapor emerges from the mouth of the bell. Record the temperature at this time also. The two temperatures represent the boiling-point range; they should be within a degree or two of each other. Record the barometric pressure so that you can make a pressure correction, if necessary. Clean and dry the boiling tube, and save it for future boiling-point measurements.

Summary

1. Construct boiling tube and boiling-point bell.
2. Add liquid to boiling tube and insert inverted bell.
3. Secure boiling tube assembly to thermometer.
4. Place assembly in heating bath.
5. Heat until continuous stream of bubbles emerges from bell, then stop heating.
6. Record temperature when liquid just enters bell.
7. Heat slowly until first vapor bubble emerges from bell; record temperature.
8. Let liquid cool below boiling point.
   IF another measurement is needed, replace liquid by fresh sample; GO TO 5.
   IF not, CONTINUE.
9. Record barometric pressure and correct observed boiling point.
10. Disassemble apparatus; clean up.

When Things Go Wrong

If, after seeing bubbles in the boiling tube, you remove the heat source but the liquid level in the bell doesn't change, you probably mistook air bubbles for vapor bubbles. Resume heating until you see a *rapid* stream of bubbles emerging from the bell (which should contain no liquid at that point), and then proceed as described in the directions.

If, after a while, you can't see any liquid in the boiling tube, it has probably boiled away. Add more liquid and heat the apparatus more carefully, making sure that you don't heat it too long and miss the actual boiling point.

If you just can't get the capillary-tube method to work for you and you have enough product, try this instead. Transfer 0.5 mL of your liquid to a 10×75-mm test tube, add a boiling chip, and clamp a thermometer inside

Sometimes the capillary tube will stick to the bottom of the boiling tube. This can be prevented by cutting a small nick in the open end of the capillary tube with a triangular file.

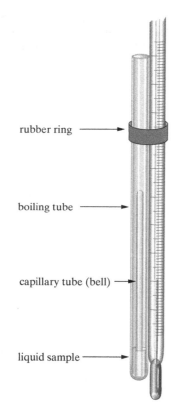

rubber ring

boiling tube

capillary tube (bell)

liquid sample

Figure F7 Semi-microscale boiling-point assembly

the tube so that its bulb is about 5 mm above the liquid surface. Heat the sample to boiling and continue heating (don't overheat) until the ring of condensing vapors is 1–2 cm above the *top* of the thermometer bulb. Keep the vapors at that level as you monitor the temperature. When it has stabilized at one value for at least a minute, record that value as your boiling point. Unless your liquid decomposes near its boiling point, the remaining liquid should be pure enough to put back with the rest of your product.

Refractive Index

The *refractive index* (index of refraction) of a substance is defined as the ratio of the speed of light in a vacuum to its speed in the substance in question. When a beam of light passes into a liquid, its velocity is reduced, causing it to bend downward. The refractive index (n) is related to the angles that the incident and refracted (bent) beams make with a line perpendicular to the liquid surface, as shown in Figure F8 and Equation **1**.

$$n^t_\lambda = \frac{c_{\text{vac}}}{c_{\text{liq}}} = \frac{\sin \theta_{\text{vac}}}{\sin \theta_{\text{liq}}} \tag{1}$$

n^t_λ = refractive index at temperature t using light of wavelength λ
c = speed of light

The refractive index is a unique physical property that can be measured with great accuracy (up to eight decimal places), so it is very useful for characterizing pure organic compounds. Refractive-index measurements are also used to assess the purity of known liquids and to determine the composition of solutions.

Experimental Considerations

It is much easier to make measurements in air than in a vacuum, so most refractive-index measurements are made in air, which has a refractive index of 1.0003; the small difference is corrected by the instrument. The refractive-index value for a liquid depends on both the wavelength of the light used for its measurement and the density of the liquid, which varies with its temperature. Most values are reported with reference to light from a yellow line in the sodium emission spectrum (called the D line), which has a wavelength of 589 nm. Thus, a refractive index value may be reported as $n_{\text{D}}^{20} =$ 1.3330, for example, where the superscript is the temperature in °C and "D" refers to the sodium D line. Because most refractive index readings are made at or corrected to this wavelength, the "D" is sometimes omitted. If another light source is used, its wavelength is specified in nanometers.

An Abbe refractometer (see Figure F9) is often used for measuring refractive indexes of liquids. It measures the *critical angle* (the smallest angle at which a light beam is completely reflected from a surface) at the boundary between the liquid and a glass prism, and converts it to a refractive-index value. The instrument employs a set of compensating prisms so that white light can be used to give refractive-index values corresponding to the sodium D line. A properly calibrated Abbe-3L refractometer should be accurate to within ±0.0002. The calibration of the instrument can be checked by measuring the refractive index of distilled water, which should be 1.3330 at 20°C and 1.3325 at 25°C.

The sample block of an Abbe refractometer can be kept at a constant temperature of 20.0°C by water pumped through it from a thermostatted water bath. If a refractive index is measured at a temperature other than 20.0°C, the temperature should be read from the thermometer on the instrument and the refractive index corrected by using the equation

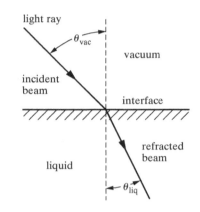

Figure F8 Refraction of light in a liquid

From *Operational Organic Chemistry: A Problem Solving Approach to the Laboratory*, Fourth Edition, John W. Lehman. Copyright © 2009 by Pearson Education. Published by Prentice Hall. All rights reserved.

$$\Delta n = 0.00045 \times (t - 20.0)$$

where t is the temperature of the measurement in °C. The correction factor (including its sign) is added to the observed refractive index. For example, if the refractive index of an unknown liquid is found to be 1.3874 at 25.1°C, its refractive index at 20.0°C should be about $1.3874 + [0.00045 \times (25.1 - 20.0)] = 1.3897$. Alternatively, the refractive index of a reference liquid similar in structure and properties to the unknown liquid can be measured at the same temperature (t) as the unknown, and a correction factor calculated from the equation

$$\Delta n = n^{20} - n^t$$

where n^t is the measured refractive index of the reference liquid at temperature t, and n^{20} is the reported value of its refractive index at 20°C. The correction factor is then added to the measured refractive index of the unknown liquid at temperature t. This method can correct for experimental errors (improper calibration of the instrument, etc.) as well as temperature differences.

Small amounts of impurities can cause substantial errors in the refractive index. For example, the presence of just 1% (by mass) of acetone in chloroform reduces the refractive index of the latter by 0.0015. Such errors can be critical when refractive-index values are being used for qualitative analysis, so it is essential that an unknown liquid be pure when its refractive index is measured.

DIRECTIONS FOR REFRACTIVE-INDEX MEASUREMENTS

These directions apply to an Abbe-3L refractometer; if you are using a different instrument, your instructor will demonstrate its operation.

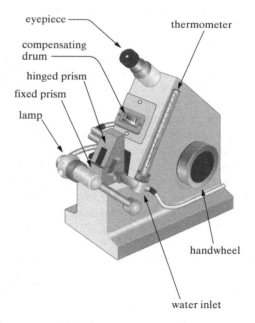

Figure F9 Abbe-3L refractometer

Equipment and Supplies

Abbe-3L refractometer
dropper
washing liquid
soft tissues

Raise the *hinged prism* of the refractometer and, using an eyedropper, place 2–3 drops of the sample in the middle of the *fixed prism* below it. Never allow the tip of a dropper or another hard object to touch the prisms—they are easily damaged. With the prism assembly closed, switch on the *lamp* and move it toward the prisms to illuminate the visual field as viewed through the eyepiece. Rotate the *handwheel* until two distinct fields (light and dark) are visible in the eyepiece, and reposition the lamp for the best contrast and definition at the borderline between the fields. Rotate the *compensating drum* on the front of the instrument until the borderline is sharp and achromatic (black and white) where it intersects an inscribed vertical line. (If the borderline can't be made sharp and achromatic, the sample may have evaporated.) Rotate the handwheel (or the fine adjustment knob, if there is one) to center the borderline exactly on the crosshairs (Figure F10).

Depress and hold down the *display switch* on the left side of the instrument to display an optical scale in the eyepiece. Read the refractive index from this scale (estimate the fourth decimal place). Record the temperature, if it is different from 20.0°C. Open the prism assembly and remove the sample by gently *blotting* it with a soft tissue (do not rub!). Wash the prisms by moistening a tissue or cotton ball with a suitable solvent (acetone, methanol, etc.) and blotting them gently. When the residual solvent has evaporated, close the prism assembly and turn off the instrument.

If the liquid is volatile and free flowing, it may be introduced into the channel alongside the closed prisms.

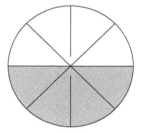

Figure F10 Visual field for a properly adjusted refractometer

Summary

1. Insert sample between prisms.
2. Switch on and position lamp.
3. Rotate handwheel until two fields are visible; reposition lamp for best contrast.
4. Rotate compensating drum until borderline is sharp and achromatic.
5. Rotate handwheel or fine adjustment knob until line is centered on crosshairs.
6. Depress display switch and read refractive index; record temperature.
7. Clean and dry prisms; close prism assembly.
8. Make temperature correction, if necessary.

When Things Go Wrong

If, while you are adjusting the refractometer for a reading, the borderline between the fields becomes fuzzy and colored or the fields seem to fade away, your sample is evaporating. Make sure the lamp is properly positioned; then add more sample (use an extra drop or two), adjust the instrument as quickly as you can, and take the reading. Repeat, if necessary.

If the refractive index you record is significantly different from the expected value, read the thermometer and, if the temperature is not

20°C, make a temperature correction (unless you already did). If the refractive index is still not close enough, repeat the measurement more carefully. If that doesn't help, check the calibration of the instrument using distilled water or another suitable liquid. If the instrument is calibrated correctly, your product is probably wet or otherwise impure. Purify it and try again.

Optical Rotation

Principles and Applications

Light can be considered a wave phenomenon with vibrations that occur in an infinite number of planes perpendicular to the direction of propagation. When a beam of ordinary light passes through a *polarizer*, such as a Nicol prism, only the light-wave components that are parallel to the plane of the polarizer can pass through. The resulting beam of *plane-polarized light* has light waves whose vibrations are restricted to a single plane (see Figure F11). When a beam of plane-polarized light passes through an optically active substance, molecules of the substance interact with the light so as to rotate its plane of polarization. The angle by which a sample of an optically active substance rotates the plane of that beam is called its *observed rotation*, α. Measurement of such angles of rotation is known as *polarimetry*, and the instrument that measures them is a *polarimeter*.

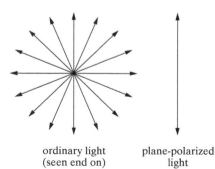

ordinary light (seen end on)   plane-polarized light

Figure F11 Schematic representations of ordinary and plane-polarized light

The observed rotation of a sample depends on the length of the light path through the sample and the concentration of the sample, as well as its identity. The first two variables are not intrinsic properties of the sample itself, so the observed rotation is divided by these variables to yield its *specific rotation*, $[\alpha]$, as shown in this equation.

$$[\alpha] = \frac{\alpha}{lc} \qquad (1)$$

$[\alpha]$ = specific rotation
α = observed rotation
l = length of sample, in decimeters (dm)
c = concentration of solution, in g solute per mL solution
  (for a neat liquid, substitute the density in g/mL)

The specific rotation of a pure substance is an intrinsic property of the substance and can be used to characterize it.

The *enantiomeric excess* (also called *optical purity*) of a chiral substance is calculated by dividing its observed specific rotation by the literature value for the appropriate pure enantiomer and multiplying by 100%.

$$\text{enantiomeric excess} = \frac{[\alpha]_{\text{observed}}}{[\alpha]_{\text{pure}}} \times 100\%$$

For example, the specific rotation of pure (–)-menthol is 50°, so the entamiomeric excess of a sample of (−)-menthol having a specific rotation of 30° is 60%:

$$\text{enantiomeric excess} = \frac{30°}{50°} \times 100\% = 60\%$$

This means that the sample contains the equivalent of 60% (−)-menthol (which produces all of the optical rotation) and 40% racemic (+/−)-menthol, half of which (or 20% of the sample) is (−)-menthol and half (+)-menthol. So the total percentage of (−)-menthol in the sample is 60% + 20%, or 80%.

From *Operational Organic Chemistry: A Problem Solving Approach to the Laboratory*, Fourth Edition, John W. Lehman. Copyright © 2009 by Pearson Education. Published by Prentice Hall. All rights reserved.

The composition of a mixture of two optically active substances can be calculated from its specific rotation, using the equation

$$[\alpha] = [\alpha]_A X_A + [\alpha]_B (1 - X_A) \qquad \textbf{(2)}$$

In this equation, $[\alpha]$ is the specific rotation of the mixture, $[\alpha]_A$ is the specific rotation of component A, X_A is the mole fraction of component A, and $[\alpha]_B$ is the specific rotation of component B. For example, an equilibrium mixture of α-D-glucose ($[\alpha] = 112°$) and β-D-glucose ($[\alpha] = 18.7°$) has a specific rotation of 52.7°. The mole fraction of α-D-glucose in the mixture can be calculated by substituting these values into Equation **2** and solving for X_A.

$$52.7° = (112°)X_A + (18.7°)(1 - X_A)$$

$$X_A = 0.364$$

Because both forms of glucose have the same molecular weight, the equilibrium mixture contains 36.4% α-D-glucose and 63.6% β-D-glucose by mass.

Experimental Considerations

The specific rotation of an optically active sample can be determined using a polarimeter such as the one illustrated in Figure F12. A polarimeter includes a light source, a polarizing prism called the *polarizer*, a sample cell to hold the sample, and a second polarizing prism called the *analyzer* (see Figure F13). The traditional light source is a sodium lamp, which produces monochromatic light with a wavelength of 589 nm, but modern polarimeters

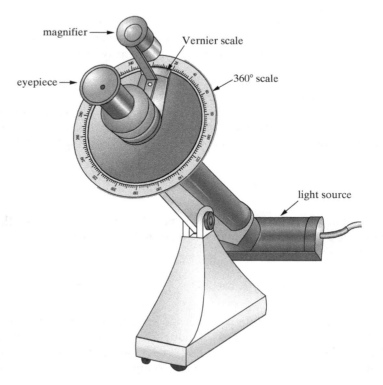

Figure F12 Cole–Parmer EW-81205 polarimeter

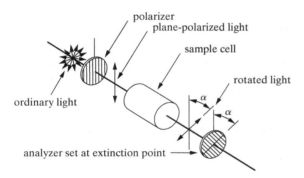

Figure F13 Schematic diagram of a polarimeter

may use a halogen lamp with an orange filter to provide light of that wavelength. The polarizer is fixed in place and light that passes through it is polarized in the plane of its vertical axis—in other words, all light waves *except* those parallel to the polarizer's axis are blocked out. The analyzer can be rotated so that its axis is at an angle to the polarizer's axis. When the axis of the analyzer is perpendicular to that of the plane-polarized light, the light is essentially blocked out so that its intensity is at a minimum; this condition is called the *extinction point.* It is easier for the human eye to match two intensities than to recognize a point of minimum intensity, so in a precision polarimeter, the analyzer contains two (or more) prisms set at a small angle to each other, and it is rotated until the prisms bracket the extinction point, transmitting dim light of equal intensity. The angle by which the analyzer must be rotated to reach this point equals the angle by which the sample rotated the beam of plane-polarized light—its observed rotation, α. Using Equation **1**, we can convert the observed rotation of the sample to its specific rotation, given the sample's concentration and the length of the sample cell. The most commonly used sample cells have lengths of 1 dm (10 cm) and 2 dm (20 cm).

The optical rotation of a substance is usually measured in solution. Water and ethanol are common solvents for polar compounds, and dichloromethane can be used for less polar ones. Often a suitable solvent will be listed in the literature, along with the light source and temperature used for the measurement. The volume of solution required depends on the size of the polarimeter cell, but 10–25 mL is usually sufficient. A solution for polarimetry ordinarily contains about 1–10 g of solute per 100 mL of solution and should be prepared using an accurate balance and a volumetric flask. If the solution contains particles of dust or other solid impurities, it should be filtered [OP-15]. When possible, the concentration should be comparable to that reported in the literature. For example, the *CRC Handbook of Chemistry and Physics* reports the specific rotation of (+)-menthol as "+49.2 (al, $c = 5$)," where the concentration (c) is given in grams per 100 mL of an alcoholic (al) solution (c is defined differently here than in Equation **1**). Thus, a (+)-menthol solution suitable for polarimetry can be prepared by accurately weighing about 1.25 g of (+)-menthol, dissolving it in ethyl alcohol in a 25-mL volumetric flask, adding more alcohol up to the calibration mark, and mixing the solution thoroughly.

Because the solvent you use or the polarimeter itself may cause variations in the observed rotation, you should always run a *solvent blank* by measuring the optical rotation of the pure solvent and subtracting its rotation from that of your sample. Be sure to take account of + and − signs; for example, if your sample's optical rotation is +20.5° and the blank's optical rotation is −0.3°, the corrected rotation is +20.5° − (−0.3°) = +20.8°.

DIRECTIONS FOR POLARIMETRY

Equipment and Supplies

polarimeter
light source
sample cell
volumetric flask
sample and solvent

This procedure applies to a Zeiss-type polarimeter with a split-field image. Experimental details may vary somewhat for different instruments. If the light source is a sodium lamp, make sure that it has ample time to warm up (some require 30 minutes or more). Weigh the sample accurately and use a volumetric flask (or another appropriate volumetric container) to prepare a solution of the sample in a suitable solvent. Ordinarily, you should prepare 25 mL of solution and use a 2-dm sample cell, but if quantities are limited you can prepare 10 mL of solution and use a 1-dm cell.

Remove the screw cap and the glass end plate from the wider end of a clean sample cell (don't get fingerprints on the end plate), and rinse the cell with a small amount of the solution to be analyzed. Stand the polarimeter cell vertically on the benchtop and fill it with the solution; rock the cell, if necessary, to shake loose any air bubbles. Add the last milliliter or so with a dropper so that the liquid surface is convex. Carefully slide on the glass end plate, trying not to leave any air bubbles trapped beneath it. If the cell has a bulge at one end, a small bubble can be tolerated; in that case, tilt the cell so that the bubble migrates to the bulge and stays out of the light path. Screw on the cap (don't forget to replace the end plate) just tightly enough to provide a leak-proof seal—overtightening it may strain the glass and cause erroneous readings. Place the sample cell in the polarimeter trough, close the cover, see that the light source is oriented to provide maximum illumination in the eyepiece, and focus the eyepiece (if necessary). Set the Vernier scale to zero (as read through the magnifier) and, if necessary, rotate it a few degrees in either direction until a dark and a light field are clearly visible. You may see a vertical bar down the middle and a background field on both sides, as shown in Figure F14, or two fields divided down the middle. Focus the eyepiece so that the line(s) separating the fields is as sharp as possible. Rotate the Vernier scale away from zero in a clockwise direction, and then (if necessary) in a counterclockwise direction, until you reach a point at which both fields are of nearly equal intensity. (If you have rotated it about 90° and see a very bright visual field, you have gone too far; return to zero and try again.) Then back off a degree or so toward zero and use the fine adjustment control (if there is one) to rotate the scale *away* from zero, until the entire visual field is as uniform as possible and the dividing lines

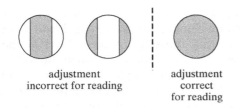

adjustment
incorrect for reading

adjustment
correct
for reading

Figure F14 Split-field image of polarimeter

between fields have all but disappeared. If you overshoot the final reading, move the scale back a few degrees so that you approach it again going away from zero. Read the rotation angle from the Vernier scale, estimating fractions of a degree, and record the direction of rotation: + for clockwise or − for counterclockwise. Obtain another reading of the rotation angle, this time approaching the final reading going *toward* zero. For accurate work, you should take a half-dozen readings or more—reversing the direction each time to compensate for mechanical play in the instrument—and average them.

Rinse the cell with the solvent used in preparing the solution. Fill the cell with that solvent (or use a solvent blank provided) and determine the solvent's rotation angle by the same procedure as before. Remove the solvent and let the cell drain dry, or clean it as directed by your instructor. Subtract the average observed rotation of the solvent blank (note + and − signs) from that of the sample to obtain the observed rotation of the sample, and calculate its specific rotation using Equation **1**. When reporting the specific rotation, specify the temperature, light source, solvent, and concentration.

Waste Disposal: Dispose of the solution and any solvents used as directed by your instructor or as indicated in an experiment's directions.

Summary

1. Prepare solution of compound to be analyzed.
2. Rinse sample cell and fill with solution; place in polarimeter.
3. Adjust light source; focus eyepiece.
4. Rotate Vernier scale until optical field is uniform; read rotation angle.
5. Repeat step **4** several times, reversing direction each time, and average readings.
   IF solvent blank has been run, GO TO 7.
   IF not, GO TO 6.
6. Place solvent blank in polarimeter; GO TO 4.
7. Clean cell, drain dry, and dispose of solution and solvent as directed.
8. Calculate observed rotation and specific rotation of sample.

When Things Go Wrong

If, when you look through the eyepiece of the polarimeter, you see a gap at the top of the visual field, there is an air bubble in the polarimeter tube. Tilt the tube until the bubble migrates to the bulge in the tube. If it has no bulge, add more solution as described in the directions until the tube is completely filled with liquid.

If, when you look through the eyepiece, the visual field is so dark that you can't compare the light intensities accurately, try the following remedies in order. Check to see that the sodium lamp (if you are using one) has warmed up enough to produce a bright light, and that it is positioned properly for maximum illumination of the visual field. Check to see whether there is a movable ring (possibly marked $+/-$) at the far end of the polarimeter that, when rotated, adjusts the light intensity; if so, adjust it for optimum intensity. Examine the sample in the polarimeter tube for turbidity (suspended solids); if it isn't water clear, filter it by gravity filtration [OP-15].

If the specific rotation you calculate from your observed value is significantly different than the expected value, make sure that you subtracted the observed rotation of a solvent blank from that of your sample and that your calculation is correct. Also check to see whether the solvent you used and the temperature of your measurement are similar enough to those used to obtain the expected value to make a comparison valid. If you were analyzing a chiral compound provided by a chemical supply company, it may not be enantiomerically pure, which would lead to a low specific rotation; check the label on the bottle the chemical came in (it should list the value of $[\alpha]$) or ask your instructor to do so. If you still think your result may be inaccurate, reread the directions and repeat the measurement more carefully. If necessary, prepare a fresh solution, making sure to weigh the sample and measure the solvent volume accurately.

Gas Chromatography

Gas chromatography (GC) affords a powerful method for the separation and analysis of volatile components of mixtures. Like all chromatographic methods, its operation is based on the distribution of the sample components between a mobile phase and a stationary phase. *Gas–liquid chromatography* is the most useful form of gas chromatography. The mobile phase for gas–liquid chromatography is an unreactive *carrier gas* such as helium, and the stationary phase consists of a high-boiling liquid on a solid support, contained within a heated column. The components of the sample must have reasonably high vapor pressures so that their molecules will spend enough time in the vapor phase to travel through the column with the carrier gas. Thus, gas chromatography can be used to separate gases, liquids that vaporize without decomposing when heated, and some volatile solids. (Solids must first be dissolved in a suitable solvent.) Less volatile liquids and solids can be separated by high-performance liquid chromatography [OP-38].

See OP-21 for a general introduction to chromatographic methods.

    Analytical gas chromatography can be used for both the qualitative and quantitative analysis of mixtures, that is, to identify the components of a mixture and find out how much of each component is present. An analytical gas chromatograph requires only a tiny amount of sample, usually a microliter or so. *Preparative gas chromatography* is used to separate the components of a mixture and recover the pure components, or to purify a major component of a mixture. Because even a large GC column will not accommodate sample sizes greater than about 0.5 mL, preparative GC cannot be used to separate large volumes of liquids. In the undergraduate organic chemistry lab, it is sometimes used to obtain small samples of pure compounds for spectral analysis.

Principles and Applications

In gas–liquid chromatography, the components of a mixture are partitioned between the liquid stationary phase and the gaseous mobile phase (the carrier gas). The time it takes for a component to pass through the column, called its *retention time,* depends on its relative concentrations in the liquid and gas phases. While the molecules of a component are in the gas phase, they pass through the column at the speed of the carrier gas. While they are in the liquid phase, they remain stationary. The more time a component spends in the gas phase, the sooner it will get through the column, and the lower its retention time will be. Conversely, the more time a component spends in the liquid phase, the longer its retention time will be. The time a component spends in the gas phase depends on its volatility (and thus on its boiling point) and the temperature of the column; the time it spends in the liquid phase depends on the strength of the attractive forces between its molecules and the molecules of the liquid phase.

    For any two components of a mixture to be separated sharply, they must have significantly different retention times, and their bands (the regions of the column they occupy) must be narrow enough so that they don't overlap appreciably as they exit the column. The degree of separation depends on a

From *Operational Organic Chemistry: A Problem Solving Approach to the Laboratory*, Fourth Edition, John W. Lehman. Copyright © 2009 by Pearson Education. Published by Prentice Hall. All rights reserved.

number of factors, including the length and efficiency of the column, the carrier gas flow rate, and the temperature at which the separation is carried out. Modern gas chromatographs provide the means to vary these factors precisely, and they offer an almost endless variety of applications, from analyzing automobile emissions for noxious gases to detecting polychlorinated biphenyls (PCBs) in lake trout.

There are several important differences between gas–liquid chromatography and liquid–solid chromatographic methods such as column chromatography [OP-21] and thin-layer chromatography (TLC) [OP-22]. Unlike the mobile phase in a liquid–solid separation, the mobile phase in gas chromatography doesn't interact with the molecules of the sample; its only purpose is to carry them through the column. Therefore, the separation of the components of a mixture depends mainly on (1) how strongly they are attracted to the stationary phase and (2) how volatile they are. If the components have similar polarities, they will be attracted to the stationary phase to about the same extent, so they will tend to be separated in order of relative volatility, with the lower-boiling components having the shorter retention times. If the components have different polarities, their retention times will depend on their relative polarities and the polarity of the stationary phase. A polar stationary phase will attract polar components more strongly than nonpolar ones, giving polar components longer retention times than nonpolar components. A nonpolar stationary phase will attract nonpolar components more strongly, giving them longer retention times.

A column chromatography or TLC separation is usually conducted at room temperature, and the temperature stays about the same throughout the separation. In contrast, a GC separation is usually carried out at an elevated temperature, and the temperature can be changed throughout the separation according to a preset program. Increasing the temperature of the column increases the fraction of each component in the gas phase, thus decreasing its retention time. The column temperature also affects the separation efficiency, because at excessively high temperatures, components will tend to spend most of their time in the vapor phase, causing their bands to overlap.

Instrumentation

In addition to the column and carrier gas, a gas chromatograph must have some means of vaporizing the sample, controlling the temperature of the separation, detecting each constituent of the sample as it leaves the column, and recording data from which the composition of the sample can be determined. A typical analytical gas chromatograph includes the components diagrammed in Figure G1 and described here.

Injection Port. The injection port is the starting point for a sample's passage through the column. The sample, in a microliter syringe, is injected into the column by inserting the needle through a rubber or silicone septum and depressing the plunger. The sample size for a packed column is typically about 1–2 μL, but it may vary from a few tenths of a microliter to 20 μL. With an open tubular column (described later), a sample splitter delivers about 1 nL (10^{-3} μL) of the injected sample to the column; the rest is discarded. The injector port is heated to a temperature sufficient to vaporize the sample, usually about 50°C above the boiling point of its least volatile component.

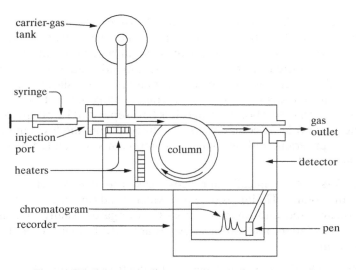

Figure G1 Schematic diagram of a gas chromatograph

Packed Columns. A packed column is a long tube packed with a finely divided solid support whose particles are coated with the high-boiling liquid phase. The tube is usually made of stainless steel or glass. A typical column may be 1.5–3.0 m long, with an inner diameter (i.d.) of 2–4 mm, and it is usually bent into a coil to fit inside a column oven, where its temperature is controlled. Although such columns can be packed by the user, most columns are purchased ready-made. The composition of the packing is described on a tag attached to each column. For example, a column packing described as "10% DEGS/Chromosorb W 80/100" contains 10% by mass of the liquid phase, diethylene glycol succinate, coated onto a Chromosorb W (crushed diatomaceous earth) support that has a particle-size range from 80 to 100 mesh (0.18 to 0.15 mm). As for a fractional distillation column [OP-32], the efficiency of a chromatography column can be measured in terms of the number of theoretical plates it provides. Most packed columns have efficiencies ranging from 500 to 1000 theoretical plates per meter.

The mesh number is the number of meshes per inch in the finest sieve that will let the particles pass through.

Open Tubular Columns. An *open tubular column* or *capillary column* consists of an open tube coated on the inside with the liquid phase. A very thin film of the liquid phase (ranging from 0.05 μm to 1.0 μm or more in thickness) is adsorbed on or chemically bonded to the inner wall of the column, which is a long capillary tube made of glass or fused silica. Fused silica open tubular (FSOT) columns are flexible enough to be bent into coils 15 cm or so in diameter. The columns range in size from microbore columns, which may have an i.d. of 0.05–0.10 mm and a length of 20 meters, to Megabore columns, which have an i.d. of about 0.50 mm and a length of 100 meters or more. Packed columns are generally cheaper, less fragile, and easier to use than open tubular columns, and they accommodate much larger sample sizes, but open tubular columns are faster and less likely to react with the sample, and they provide unparalleled resolution of sample components—a microbore column may have an efficiency of more than 10,000 theoretical plates per meter. Because an open tubular column may be 20–50 times longer than a typical packed column, it is usually hundreds of times more efficient than a packed column containing the same liquid phase.

Column Oven. The column is mounted inside a heated chamber—the *column oven*—that controls its temperature. For *isothermal operation,* the oven temperature is kept constant throughout a separation; for *program operation,* it is varied according to a programmed sequence. As a general rule, the column temperature for isothermal operation should be approximately equal to or slightly above the average boiling point of the sample. If the sample has a broad boiling range, it is best separated by program operation. The more volatile components are eluted during the low-temperature end of the program, and less volatile components are eluted at its high-temperature end.

Carrier Gas. A chemically unreactive gas is used to sweep the sample through the column. Helium is the most widely used carrier gas, but nitrogen and argon are used with some detectors. Carrier gases usually come in pressurized gas cylinders, and various devices are used to measure and control their flow rates.

Detector. The detector is a device that detects the presence of each component as it leaves the column and sends an electronic signal to a recorder or other output device. A separate oven is used to heat the detector enclosure so that the sample molecules remain in the vapor phase as they pass the detector. The most widely used detectors for routine gas chromatography are *thermal conductivity* (*TC*) detectors and *flame ionization* (*FI*) detectors. A TC detector responds to changes in the thermal conductivity of the carrier gas stream as molecules of the sample pass through. With an FI detector, the component molecules are pyrolyzed (transformed by heating) in a hydrogen-oxygen flame, producing short-lived ions that are captured and used to generate an electrical current. Thermal conductivity detectors are comparatively simple and inexpensive, and they respond to a wide variety of organic and inorganic species. Flame ionization detectors are much more sensitive than TC detectors, so they are used with open tubular columns (for which TC detectors are unsuited) as well as packed columns. An FI detector is somewhat inconvenient to use because it requires hydrogen and air to produce the flame. In addition, an FI detector can't be used for preparative gas chromatography because it destroys the sample.

Data Display. A typical gas chromatograph intended for student use may have a mechanical *recorder* that records a peak on moving chart paper as each component band passes the detector. The resulting *gas chromatogram* consists of a series of peaks of different sizes, each produced by a different component of the mixture. The recorder may be provided with an *integrator* that measures the area under each component peak. Most modern gas chromatographs are interfaced with computers and other hardware devices that display the peaks on a monitor screen, print or plot copies of the gas chromatogram, and provide digital readouts of peak areas, retention times, and various instrumental parameters.

Liquid Phases

The factor that most often determines the success or failure of a gas chromatographic separation is the choice of a liquid phase. In general, polar liquid phases are best for separating polar compounds, and nonpolar liquid phases

Table G1 Selected liquid phases for gas chromatography

Stationary phase	Maximum T, °C	X'	Y'	Z'
squalane	150	0	0	0
dimethylpolysiloxane (OV-1)	350	16	55	44
diphenyl/dimethylpolysiloxane (OV-17)	350	119	158	162
polyethylene glycol (Carbowax 20M)	250	322	536	368
diethylene glycol succinate (DEGS)	225	496	746	590
dicyanoallylpolysiloxane (OV-275)	275	629	872	763

Note: McReynold's numbers (X', Y', Z') apply to the commercial stationary phase in parentheses. Commercial designations for the same kind of stationary phase vary widely; for example, AT-1, DB-1, Rtx-1, SE-30, and DC-200 are all similar to OV-1.

are best for separating nonpolar compounds. However, there are hundreds of liquid phases available, and choosing the right one for a particular separation may not be easy. Some typical liquid phases and their maximum operating temperatures are listed in Table G1 in order of polarity (lower to higher). General-purpose liquid phases such as dimethylpolysiloxane (dimethylsilicone) can separate a variety of compounds successfully, usually in approximate order of their boiling points. Other liquid phases have more specialized applications; for example, diethylene glycol succinate is a high-boiling ester that is used mainly to separate the esters of long-chain fatty acids.

The selection of a liquid phase can be facilitated by the use of *McReynolds numbers,* which indicate the affinity of a liquid phase for different types of compounds; the higher the number, the greater the affinity. X' is a McReynolds number that measures the relative affinity of a liquid phase for aromatic compounds and alkenes; Y' measures its affinity for alcohols, phenols, and carboxylic acids; and Z' measures its affinity for aldehydes, ketones, ethers, esters, and related compounds (see Table G1). For example, the polar liquid phase DEGS has a much higher Z' value (590) than does OV-1 (44), so it will retain an ester much longer. McReynolds numbers are particularly useful for selecting a liquid phase to separate compounds of different chemical classes, such as alcohols from esters. For example, a Carbowax 20M column should separate isopentyl acetate from isopentyl alcohol satisfactorily because its Y' and Z' values are very different; but an OV-17 column would not be a good choice for such a separation. Chromatography supply companies often provide detailed information about the kinds of separations their columns can accomplish.

Qualitative Analysis

The retention time (R) of a component is the time it spends on the column, from the time of injection to the time its concentration at the detector reaches a maximum. The retention time corresponds to the distance on the chromatogram—along a line parallel to the baseline—from the injection point to the top of the component's peak, as shown in Figure G2. This distance can be converted to units of time if the chart speed is known. If all instrumental parameters (temperature, column, flow rate, etc.) are kept constant, the retention time of a component will be characteristic of that compound and may be used to identify it. You can seldom (if ever) identify

Heating a column above its maximum operating temperature will cause the liquid phase to vaporize.

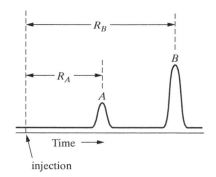
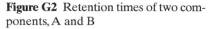

Figure G2 Retention times of two components, A and B

a compound with certainty from its retention time alone, but you can sometimes use retention times to confirm the identity of a compound whose identity you suspect. For example, if a known compound has the same retention times as an unknown compound on two or more different stationary phases under the same operating conditions, the compounds are likely to be identical.

When you carry out a reaction and obtain a gas chromatogram of the product mixture, you may be able to guess which GC peak corresponds to which reactant or product, especially if the components have significantly different boiling points and the stationary phase is known to separate compounds in order of boiling point. However, it is always a good idea to back up your guess with proof. One way to identify the components of a product mixture is to "spike" the mixture with an authentic sample of a possible component and see which GC peak increases in relative area after spiking. For example, suppose that you carry out a Fischer esterification of acetic acid by ethanol and record a gas chromatogram of the product mixture.

$$CH_3COOH + CH_3CH_2OH \rightleftharpoons CH_3COOCH_2CH_3 + H_2O$$
$$\text{acetic acid} \qquad \text{ethanol} \qquad \qquad \text{ethyl acetate}$$

Because this is an equilibrium reaction, the product mixture would be expected to contain some unreacted starting materials as well as the product. To detect the presence of unreacted ethanol, you can add a small amount of pure ethanol to the sample and record a second gas chromatogram. The peak that increases in relative area is the ethanol peak, as shown in Figure G3. The process could be carried out with different pure compounds to identify the other components, if necessary.

Another way to identify the components of a mixture using GC is to obtain the spectra of the components after they pass through the column.

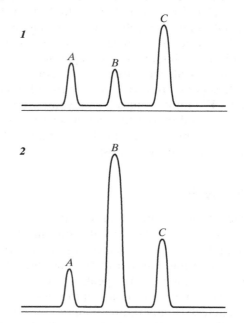

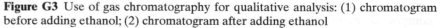

Figure G3 Use of gas chromatography for qualitative analysis: (1) chromatogram before adding ethanol; (2) chromatogram after adding ethanol

As described in OP-42, a mass spectrometer coupled to a gas chromatograph can act as a "superdetector," identifying the components as they come off the column. If the GC column has a large enough capacity that individual components can be collected at the column outlet, they can often be identified from their infrared (IR) or nuclear magnetic resonance (NMR) spectra.

Quantitative Analysis

The use of gas chromatography for quantitative analysis is based on the fact that, over a wide range of concentrations, a detector's response to a given component is proportional to the amount of that component in the sample. Therefore, the area under a component's peak can be used to determine its mass percentage in the sample. If a peak on a gas chromatogram is symmetrical, its area can be calculated with fair accuracy by multiplying its height (h) in millimeters (measured from the baseline) by its width at a point exactly halfway between the top of the peak and the baseline ($w_{\frac{1}{2}}$), as shown in Figure G4.

$$\text{approximate peak area} = h \times w_{\frac{1}{2}}$$

Many gas chromatographs are equipped with integrators that automatically calculate the peak areas and display them digitally. Peak areas can also be measured by making a photocopy of the chromatogram, accurately cutting out each peak with a sharp knife or razor blade (using a ruler to cut a straight line along the baseline), and weighing the peaks to the nearest milligram (or tenth of a milligram) on an accurate balance.

From the peak areas for a sample, you can sometimes estimate the percentage of each component in the mixture by dividing its area by the sum of the areas and multiplying by 100%. For example, suppose a gas chromatogram has three peaks, corresponding to three components, A, B, and C. If the area of peak A is 1227 mm^2, the area of peak B is 214 mm^2, and the area of peak C is 635 mm^2, the sum of the areas is 2076 mm^2, so the mass percentages of the components are approximately

$$\%A = \frac{1227}{2076} * 100\% = 59.1\%$$

$$\%B = \frac{214}{2076} * 100\% = 10.3\%$$

$$\%C = \frac{635}{2076} * 100\% = \frac{30.6\%}{100\%}$$

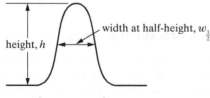

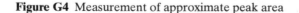
approximate area = $h \times w_{\frac{1}{2}}$

Figure G4 Measurement of approximate peak area

This kind of calculation is valid only if the detector responds similarly to each component, which may be the case if you are analyzing very similar compounds, as in a mixture of long-chain fatty acid esters. More often, however, a detector will respond differently to different compounds. Flame ionization detectors respond mainly to ions produced by certain reduced carbon atoms, such as those in methyl and methylene groups. For example, ethanol is only about 52% carbon by mass, whereas heptane is 84% carbon, so the response of an FI detector to a gram of ethanol is only about three-fifths as great as its response to a gram of heptane. Thermal conductivity detectors also respond differently to different substances, but the variations are usually not as large as with FI detectors.

For accurate quantitative analysis of most mixtures, you should multiply each component's peak area by a *detector response factor* to obtain a corrected area that is proportional to its mass. Detector response factors can be obtained from the literature (in some cases), or by direct measurement. For example, detector response factors for cyclohexane and toluene using a TC detector are reported to be 0.942 and 1.02, respectively (relative to benzene). Suppose that the gas chromatogram of a cyclohexane–toluene mixture is recorded using such a detector and has peak areas of 78.0 mm^2 for cyclohexane and 14.6 mm^2 for toluene. The corrected peak areas are then $(0.942 \times 78.0 \text{ mm}^2) = 73.5$ mm^2 for cyclohexane and $(1.02 \times 14.6 \text{ mm}^2) = 14.9$ mm^2 for toluene. Dividing each corrected area by the sum of the corrected areas and multiplying by 100 gives mass percentages of 83.1% for cyclohexane and 16.9% for toluene.

If detector response factors for the components of a mixture are not known, you can determine them by the following method, which is described for two components, A and R. Component R is a reference compound, arbitrarily assigned a detector response factor of 1.00.

- Obtain a gas chromatogram of a mixture containing carefully weighed amounts of A and R.
- Measure the peak area for each component.
- Calculate the detector response factor for A using the following relationship:

$$\text{detector response factor for A} = \frac{\text{mass}_A}{\text{area}_A} \times \frac{\text{area}_R}{\text{mass}_R}$$

This method can be used to calculate detector response factors for any number of components simultaneously if their peaks are well resolved. Each component (including the reference compound) is carefully weighed, a gas chromatogram of the mixture is recorded, all of the peak areas are measured, and the detector response factors are calculated from the resulting masses and areas using the previous equation.

Preparative Gas Chromatography

Most preparative gas chromatographs are too expensive to be used routinely in undergraduate laboratories, but some inexpensive analytical gas chromatographs, such as the Gow-Mac 69-350, can be operated with preparative columns using an adapter that is connected to the exit port on the gas chromatograph. A 2-mm outer diameter (o.d.) glass tube about 8 cm in length can be packed with glass wool and inserted into the GC exit port while the desired component's peak is being recorded. The component should condense on the surface of the glass wool, from which it can be washed off with a small amount of solvent (if the component is quite volatile, the tube should be chilled first). An IR or NMR spectrum of the compound can then be obtained in a solution of the solvent used, or the solvent can be evaporated.

DIRECTIONS FOR RECORDING A GAS CHROMATOGRAM

Equipment and Supplies

gas chromatograph and recorder
10-μL microsyringe
screw-cap vial containing sample
lab tissues
syringe-washing solvent

Do not attempt to operate the instrument without prior instruction and proper supervision. Do not adjust any of the controls on the gas chromatograph except with your instructor's permission. The directions that follow are for a typical student-grade gas chromatograph connected to a mechanical recorder. For other kinds of instruments, follow your instructor's directions. Consult the instructor if the instrument doesn't seem to be working properly or if you have questions about its operation. It will be assumed that all instrumental parameters have been preset, that an appropriate column has been installed, that the carrier gas is flowing at the right rate, and that the column oven will be operated isothermally. If not, the instructor will show you what to do. Before you begin, be sure you have read the section in OP-5 about the use of syringes.

If the sample is a volatile solid, dissolve it in the minimum volume of a suitable low-boiling solvent; otherwise, use the neat liquid. Rinse a microsyringe with the sample a few times, and then partially fill it with the sample. A microsyringe is a very delicate instrument, so handle it carefully and avoid using excessive force that might bend the needle or plunger. If there are air bubbles inside the syringe, tap the barrel with the needle pointing up, or eject the sample and refill the syringe more slowly. Hold the syringe with the needle pointing up and expel excess liquid until the desired volume of the sample (usually 1–2 μL) is left inside. Wipe the needle dry with a tissue and pull the plunger back a centimeter or so to prevent prevaporization of the sample.

Set the chart speed, if necessary, and switch on the recorder's chart drive (and the integrator, if there is one). Carefully insert the syringe needle into the injection port by holding the needle with its tip at the center of the septum and pushing the barrel slowly (but firmly) with the other hand, until the needle is as far inside the port as it will go. Inject the sample by *gently* pushing the plunger all the way in just as the recorder pen crosses a chart line (the starting line); use as little force as possible to avoid bending the plunger. Withdraw the needle and promptly mark the starting line, from which all retention times will be measured. Let the recorder run until all of the anticipated component peaks have been recorded. Then turn off the chart drive and tear off the chart paper using a straightedge. Inspect the

Take Care! The syringe is fragile and easily damaged.

Take Care! The injection port is hot! Don't touch it.

chromatogram carefully; if it is unsuitable because the significant peaks are too small, poorly resolved, or off-scale, repeat the analysis after taking measures to remedy the problem. If there is evidence of prevaporization (as indicated by an extraneous small peak preceding each major peak at a fixed interval), be sure that the plunger is pulled back before you inject the sample for the next run. Injecting the sample immediately after you insert the needle into the injector port will also prevent prevaporization, but this technique requires good timing.

Before you analyze a different sample, clean the syringe and rinse it thoroughly with that sample. When you are finished, rinse the syringe with an appropriate low-boiling solvent such as methanol or dichloromethane, remove the plunger, and set it on a clean surface to dry.

Don't store the syringe with the plunger inside.

Summary

1. Rinse syringe and fill with designated volume of sample.
2. Start chart drive and integrator (if applicable).
3. Insert syringe needle into injector port; inject sample when pen crosses chart line.
4. Withdraw needle; mark starting line.
5. Stop chart drive after last peak is recorded.
6. Remove chromatogram; clean and dry syringe.

When Things Go Wrong

See your instructor before you make any adjustments to the instrument as suggested here, or let the instructor make the adjustments.

If you have injected your sample in the gas chromatograph but no peaks have appeared after 10 minutes or so, consider the following possibilities and, if one seems likely, refer to the indicated section or sections. You didn't fill the syringe properly or its needle is plugged, and there is little if any sample in it. (See the directions.) You didn't insert the syringe needle far enough into the injection port, or the injection port isn't hot enough. (See "Injection Port" and the directions.) The column oven is not turned on or is not set to the right temperature. (See "Column Oven.") The carrier gas is not turned on or its flow rate has not been adjusted correctly. (See "Carrier Gas.") The filament current for a TC detector is not turned on, the flame of an FID detector is not lit, or the detector enclosure is not at the right temperature. (See "Detector.") The recorder is not turned on or its chart is not advancing. (See "Data Display" and the directions.) The liquid phase in the column is not appropriate for your sample. (See "Liquid Phases.")

If the peaks on your gas chromatogram are too small, you may not have injected enough sample. Try again, making sure that the liquid fills the syringe up to the desired mark, with no air bubbles (see OP-5). If that makes no difference, the recorder gain may have been set too low; see your instructor.

If the peaks on your gas chromatogram are too large—flattening out near the top of the chart paper—you may have injected too much sample or the recorder gain may have been set too high.

If you recorded a gas chromatograph but some of its peaks are "doubled"—with a small peak preceding a larger one at a fixed interval—you forgot to pull back the plunger of the syringe after you filled it, leaving sample in the needle that vaporized too soon. (See the directions.)

If you recorded a gas chromatograph but some of the peaks overlap significantly, consider the following possibilities and, if one seems likely, refer to the indicated section. You injected too much sample or injected the sample too slowly. (See the directions.) The column oven temperature is too high or the programmed temperature sequence is not appropriate. (See "Column Oven.") The carrier gas flow rate is too high. (See "Carrier Gas.") The liquid phase in the column is not appropriate for your sample. (See "Liquid Phases.")

Suppose you recorded a gas chromatogram but it has one or more extraneous peaks (peaks that you wouldn't expect to be there) that are not doubled as described previously. If the extraneous peaks are quite small, check to see whether several other students who are analyzing the same product have chromatograms with similar peaks; if so, they may have come from traces of impurities in chemicals that were used to prepare the product. If a small extraneous peak precedes all of your sample peaks, it may be an air peak, due to air that was in the syringe needle, or the peak of a volatile syringe-washing solvent (such as dichloromethane) that hadn't completely evaporated before you filled the syringe with your sample. If you think the peak is from a syringe-washing solvent, you should run another sample using a clean, completely dry syringe. If one or more extraneous peaks are quite large, you may have injected your sample before another student's sample completely passed out of the column. Wait a minute or so after the last peak of your chromatogram has appeared and then inject a fresh sample. If that doesn't make a difference and none of the previous possibilities seem likely, your product may need further purification.

High-Performance Liquid Chromatography

Principles and Applications

High-performance liquid chromatography (HPLC) can be regarded as a hybrid of column chromatography and gas chromatography, sharing some features of both methods. As in column chromatography, the mobile phase is a solvent or solvent mixture (the eluant) that carries the sample through a column packed with fine particles that interact with the components of the sample to different extents, causing them to separate. As in gas chromatography, the sample is usually injected onto the column and detected as it leaves the column, and its passage through the column is recorded as a series of peaks on a chromatogram. The stationary phase may be a solid adsorbent, as in column chromatography, but it is more often an organic phase that is bonded to tiny beads of silica gel. The silica beads are, in effect, coated with a very thin layer of a liquid organic phase. Each component of the sample is partitioned between a liquid mobile phase and the liquid stationary phase according to a ratio—the *partition coefficient*—that depends on its solubility in each liquid. The components of a mixture generally have different partition coefficients in a given liquid phase, so they pass down the column at different rates.

Unlike gas chromatography, HPLC can be used to separate nonvolatile solids and liquids as well as substances that decompose at elevated temperatures. Substances that are often analyzed by HPLC include proteins, amino acids, carbohydrates, nucleic acids, steroids, drugs, pesticides, natural products, and inorganic compounds.

Instrumentation

HPLC was developed as a means of improving the efficiency of a column chromatographic separation by reducing the particle size. Most column chromatography packings contain particles with diameters in the 75–175 μm range, whereas most modern HPLC packings have particle sizes in the 3–10 μm range, increasing separation efficiency dramatically. But solvents won't easily flow through such small particles by gravity alone, so a powerful pump is needed to force them through the column at pressures up to 6000 psi (~400 atm).

The basic components of an HPLC system are diagrammed in Figure G5. The instrument ordinarily has several large solvent reservoirs, each of which can be filled with a different eluting solvent. *Isocratic elution* is elution using a single solvent. *Gradient elution* utilizes two or more solvents of different polarity and varies the solvent ratio throughout a separation according to a programmed sequence. Gradient elution can reduce the time needed for a separation and increase the separation efficiency.

Preparative HPLC systems, which require special wide-bore columns, are equipped with fraction collectors to collect the eluant as it comes off the column; the fractions are evaporated to yield the pure components. Analytical HPLC systems, which are used to determine the compositions

From *Operational Organic Chemistry: A Problem Solving Approach to the Laboratory*, Fourth Edition, John W. Lehman. Copyright © 2009 by Pearson Education. Published by Prentice Hall. All rights reserved.

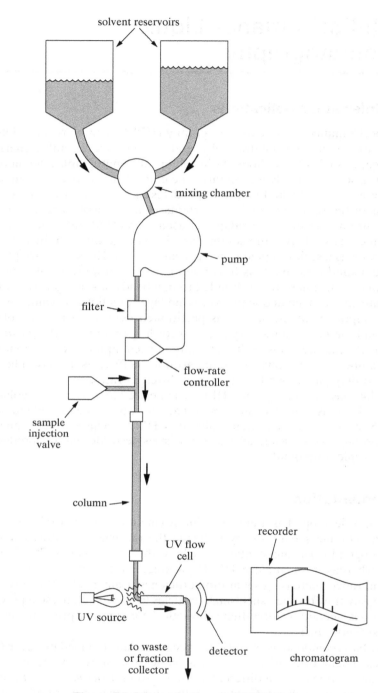

Figure G5 Schematic diagram of HPLC system

of mixtures, require much smaller samples and the components aren't recovered. A typical analytical HPLC column is a straight stainless-steel tube with a length of 10–25 cm and an i.d. of 2.1–4.6 mm. A microbore analytical column may have an i.d. of 1 mm, and a large preparative column may have an i.d. of 50 mm or so. Samples are introduced onto the column by means of a syringe or sampling valve and are carried through it by the pressurized eluant mixture. Because the particles of the stationary phase are so small, a column can easily be plugged by particulate matter or adherent solutes introduced by either the eluant or the sample. To remove anything that might harm the column, the eluant is forced through one or more filters and the sample may be introduced through a short *guard column*.

As each component of a sample leaves the column, the detector responds to some property of the component, such as its ability to absorb ultraviolet (UV) radiation. The detector then sends an electronic signal to a recorder, which traces the component's peak on a chart. The resulting chromatogram is a graph of some property of the components, such as UV absorbance, plotted against the volume of the mobile phase. Because different solutes may have greatly different UV absorptivities at the wavelength used by an *ultraviolet absorbance detector,* for example, a detector response factor (see OP-37) must be determined for each component before its percentage in the mixture can be calculated. Components that do not absorb UV radiation won't be detected by a UV detector; in that case, the components can be converted to derivatives that do absorb UV radiation, or a different type of detector can be used. Any component whose refractive index is different from that of the eluant can be detected by a *refractive index (RI) detector,* but RI detectors are less sensitive than UV detectors.

A high-performance liquid chromatograph will separate substances whose volatilities are too low for gas chromatography. Because HPLC separations can be run at room temperature, there is little danger of decomposition reactions or other chemical changes that sometimes occur in the heated column of a gas chromatograph. These advantages have made HPLC the fastest growing separation technique in chemistry, but its use in undergraduate laboratories is somewhat limited, in part because of the cost of the instruments, columns, and high-purity solvents required (HPLC-grade water costs about $50 a gallon!).

Stationary Phases

Some HPLC columns contain a solid adsorbent such as silica gel or alumina. Such a stationary phase is much more polar than the eluant, so nonpolar components are eluted faster than polar ones. Most modern HPLC columns contain a *bonded liquid phase*—an organic phase that is chemically bonded to particles of silica gel. Silica gel contains silanol (—Si—OH) groups to which long hydrocarbon chains, such as octadecyl groups, can be attached by reactions such as the following:

$$-\text{Si}-\text{OH} \xrightarrow{\text{R}_2\text{SiCl}_2} -\text{Si}-\text{O}-\underset{\underset{\text{R}}{|}}{\overset{\overset{\text{R}}{|}}{\text{Si}}}-\text{Cl} \xrightarrow{\text{H}_2\text{O}} \xrightarrow{(\text{CH}_3)_3\text{SiCl}}$$

$$-\text{Si}-\text{O}-\underset{\underset{\text{R}}{|}}{\overset{\overset{\text{R}}{|}}{\text{Si}}}-\text{O}-\text{Si}(\text{CH}_3)_3 \qquad \text{R} = \text{CH}_3(\text{CH}_2)_{17}- \text{ (octadecyl)}$$

717

The bonded stationary phase in this example is *less* polar than the eluant, which may be a mixture of water with another solvent such as methanol, acetonitrile, or tetrahydrofuran. Therefore, polar components will spend more time in the eluant than in the stationary phase and will be eluted faster than nonpolar ones, reversing the usual order of elution. This mode of separation is called *reversed-phase chromatography.*

Other stationary phases operate by still different mechanisms. The stationary phase for *size-exclusion chromatography* is a porous solid that separates molecules based on their effective size and shape in solution. Small molecules can enter even the narrowest openings in the porous structure, larger molecules find fewer openings they can get into, and still larger molecules may be completely excluded from the solid phase. As a result, large, bulky molecules pass down the column faster than smaller molecules. A stationary phase for *ion-exchange chromatography* has ionizable functional groups that carry a negative or positive charge and therefore attract certain ionic solutes. In organic chemistry, such stationary phases are used mainly to separate ionizable organic compounds such as carboxylic acids, amines, and amino acids. Chiral stationary phases that can separate enantiomers and determine their optical purity are also available.

Hundreds of different stationary phases are used for HPLC separations. Some of the most popular reverse-phase packings contain silica gel bonded to methyl ($-CH_3$), phenyl ($-C_6H_5$), octyl [$-(CH_2)_7CH_3$], octadecyl [$-(CH_2)_{17}CH_3$], cyanopropyl [$-(CH_2)_3CN$], and aminopropyl [$-(CH_2)_3NH_2$] groups. Size-exclusion stationary phases contain silica, glass, and polymeric gels of varying porosity. Ion-exchange stationary phases include (1) styrene–divinylbenzene copolymers to which ionizable functional groups (such as $-SO_3H$ and $-NR_4^+OH^-$) are attached; (2) beads with a thin surface layer of ion-exchange material; and (3) bonded phases on silica particles.

DIRECTIONS FOR HPLC

Do not attempt to operate the instrument without prior instruction and proper supervision. Do not adjust any controls on the HPLC system except with your instructor's permission. Because HPLC systems vary widely in construction and operation, only a very general outline of the procedure is provided here. It will be assumed that all instrumental parameters have been preset, that an appropriate reversed-phase column has been installed, and that the elution will be isocratic. If not, the instructor will provide additional directions.

Prepare an approximately 0.1% stock solution of the sample in the same solvent or solvent mixture as the one being used for the elution; dilute an aliquot of this solution further, if necessary. Be certain that you are using HPLC-grade solvents for preparing the solution and eluting it through the column. The solvents should be purged with helium prior to elution to remove dissolved gases. Filter the solution through a 1.0-μm membrane filter to remove any particulate matter. Degas it, if necessary, as directed by your instructor. Inject the sample through the injection port, or use a sampling valve to introduce it into the system. Wait until no more peaks appear on the chromatogram, and then inspect the chromatogram to see if the components are well resolved. If they are not, repeat the determination using a higher percentage of the more polar solvent (usually water) in the solvent mixture.

Infrared Spectrometry

Principles and Applications

The atoms of a molecule behave as if they were connected by flexible springs rather than by rigid bonds resembling the connectors of a ball-and-stick molecular model (see Figure G6). A molecule's component parts can oscillate in different *vibrational modes,* which are vividly described by such terms as stretching, rocking, scissoring, twisting, and wagging. When IR radiation is passed through a sample of a pure compound, its molecules can absorb radiation of the energy and frequency needed to bring about transitions between vibrational ground states and vibrational excited states. For example, if a molecule contains a C—H bond that vibrates 90 trillion times a second in its vibrational ground state, the molecule must absorb IR radiation having exactly that frequency $(9.0 \times 10^{13}$ Hz) to jump to an excited state in which the C—H bond vibrates twice as fast. The frequency of IR radiation is usually given in *wave numbers* $(\bar{\nu})$. The wave number in cm^{-1} of a vibration is the number of peak-to-peak waves per centimeter. The relationship between wave number and frequency (ν) in hertz (s^{-1}) is given by

$$\nu = c \cdot \bar{\nu}$$

where c is the speed of light ($\sim 3.0 \times 10^{10}$ cm s^{-1}). For example, the wave number of 9.0×10^{13} Hz radiation is

$$\bar{\nu} = \frac{\nu}{c} = \frac{9.0 \times 10^{13}\, s^{-1}}{3.0 \times 10^{10}\, cm\, s^{-1}} = 3000\ cm^{-1}$$

The wave number of an IR band is the inverse of its wavelength, which is generally measured in micrometers (μm); the two can be interconverted using the following relationship:

$$\text{wave number (in cm}^{-1}) = \frac{10^4\ \mu m/cm}{\text{wavelength (in } \mu m)}$$

For example, the wave number of a 5.85 μm C=O bond vibration is $(10,000/5.85)\ cm^{-1} = 1710\ cm^{-1}$.

The *infrared spectrum* of a compound plots the amount of IR radiation the compound absorbs over a broad range of wavelengths, usually about 2.5–17 μm (4000–600 cm^{-1}). An IR spectrum is obtained by placing a sample of the compound in an *infrared spectrometer,* which measures the sample's response to IR radiation of different wavelengths. On a typical IR spectrum, wavelengths increase and wave numbers decrease from left to right, so wave-number ranges are usually reported with the higher value first. When a sample absorbs IR radiation of a given wavelength, the recorder pen on one kind of spectrometer moves downward by a distance that depends on the amount of IR radiation absorbed. Therefore, an IR

Figure G6 "Ball-and-spring" model of a chemical bond

A spectrometer is an instrument that measures and records the components of a spectrum in order of wavelength, mass, or some other property.

From *Operational Organic Chemistry: A Problem Solving Approach to the Laboratory*, Fourth Edition, John W. Lehman. Copyright © 2009 by Pearson Education. Published by Prentice Hall. All rights reserved.

spectrum consists of a series of inverted peaks, with each peak corresponding to a different kind of bond vibration. Because vibrational transitions usually are accompanied by rotational transitions in the frequency region scanned, the inverted peaks appear as comparatively broad "valleys" called *IR bands*, rather than sharp peaks such as those seen in NMR spectra [OP-40].

Infrared spectrometry is most often used to detect the presence of specific functional groups and other structural features from band positions and intensities, and to show whether an unknown compound is identical to a known compound whose IR spectrum is reproduced in literature sources or computerized databases. The *fingerprint region* of an IR spectrum ($1250–670$ cm^{-1}) is best for establishing that two substances are identical, because the bands found in this region are often characteristic of the molecule as a whole and not of isolated bonds. IR spectrometry is particularly useful in synthetic organic chemistry—comparing the spectra of the reactant and product should show clearly whether or not a reaction took place, and will often reveal the identity of the product. IR spectrometry may also be used to assess the purity of a compound, monitor the rate of a reaction, measure the concentration of a solution, and study hydrogen bonding and other phenomena.

Instrumentation

In a conventional *dispersive infrared spectrometer,* IR radiation is broken down into its component wavelengths by a diffraction grating or prism and beamed through the sample, one wavelength interval at a time. As the spectrum is scanned from lower to higher wavelength (higher to lower wave number), the radiation that passes through the sample at each wavelength is detected and its intensity is recorded on a chart. The resulting IR spectrum is a graph of *percent transmittance* (the percentage of radiation that passes through the sample) on the *y*-axis versus wavelength and wave number on the *x*-axis (see Figure G15 for an example).

In a *Fourier-transform infrared (FTIR) spectrometer,* the sample is irradiated briefly with an intense beam that contains the entire spectrum of IR radiation in the instrument's range. The multiple-wavelength radiation that exits the sample is then converted by a microprocessor to an IR spectrum that closely resembles a scanned spectrum. To understand how an FTIR spectrometer works, refer to the diagram in Figure G7. The heart of the instrument is a *Michelson interferometer,* which causes two beams of IR radiation to interfere with each other. The radiation generated by a heated filament or other IR source passes through a *beam splitter* that sends half of the radiation to a fixed mirror and half to a moving mirror. The beam that reflects off the fixed mirror always travels the same distance from the source to the sample; the distance the other beam travels is varied continuously by the moving mirror. The beams from both mirrors are recombined before the IR radiation passes through the sample. Suppose for a moment that the IR beam coming from the source is of a single wavelength, λ. When the moving and fixed mirrors are the same distance from the beam splitter, both beams will travel the same distance before they recombine. As a result, the peaks and troughs of their waveforms will be aligned and will interfere constructively with one another, sending a beam of high intensity through

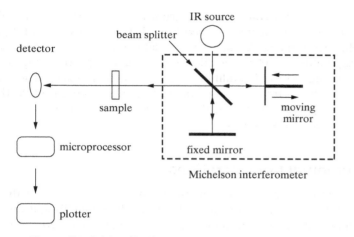

Figure G7 Schematic diagram of an FTIR spectrometer

the sample. When the moving and fixed mirrors are not the same distance from the beam splitter, the beams will travel different distances and their waveforms usually will not be aligned peak to peak when they recombine. For example, if the peaks of one beam exactly align with the troughs of the other, the beams will interfere destructively with each other, sending no radiation through the sample. In other alignments, the intensity of the combined beam will be somewhere between these two extremes.

As a result of constructive and destructive interference, the intensity of a light beam of wavelength λ will vary, with a sinusoidal wave pattern, at the frequency of the moving mirror. This pattern is called an *interferogram*. Because light beams of a different wavelength will align differently when they recombine, each different wavelength of IR radiation will generate a different interferogram. Interferograms are additive, so the interferogram that reaches the sample will be the sum of all the interferograms of all of the wavelengths. If IR radiation of a particular wavelength is absorbed as it passes through the sample, the intensity of that wavelength's interferogram — and thus its contribution to the overall interferogram — will decrease, changing the waveform of the overall interferogram that exits the sample. As a result, the interferogram that exits the sample will differ from the one that entered it in a way that depends on the amount by which the intensity of each of its component interferograms was reduced by the sample. In other words, this interferogram contains all of the intensity information for all of the different wavelengths that passed through the sample — there is no need to break down the IR radiation into its component wavelengths and measure the intensity of the transmitted radiation at each individual wavelength, as for a dispersive IR spectrometer. When the interferogram impinges on a detector, it generates an electronic signal that is sent to a microprocessor. The microprocessor uses a mathematical technique called *Fourier-transform analysis* to "decode" the interferogram and recover the intensity data for each wavelength. These data are then plotted as an FTIR spectrum.

Unlike a continuous-wave IR spectrometer, which takes 5 minutes or more to record a spectrum, an FTIR spectrometer can acquire a complete spectrum in a few seconds, making it possible to accumulate many spectra of the same sample in a minute or less. The data from these spectra are averaged to yield a composite spectrum that is much cleaner and better resolved than a spectrum obtained by a dispersive instrument, because it lacks the electronic background noise that can distort IR bands. This averaging capability makes it possible to obtain good spectra using very small samples (1 mg or less). In addition, a helium–neon laser is used as a standard against which the frequencies of the radiation are measured, so the wave numbers displayed by an FTIR spectrum are much more accurate than those on a scanned spectrum.

Experimental Considerations

An IR spectrometer is a precision instrument that may cost more than a Jeep Wrangler but doesn't respond as well to rough handling. Treat it with respect and follow instructions carefully to prevent damage and avoid the need for costly repairs. Never unplug or switch off the instrument unless directed otherwise—some IR spectrometers must be kept on continually to prevent damage to their optical parts. Keep water and aqueous solutions away from an IR spectrometer; some of its components may be water sensitive. Never move the chart holder, drum, or pen carriage on a dispersive instrument while the instrument is in operation or before it has been properly reset at the end of a run—this can damage mechanical components. Don't leave objects lying on the bed of a flat-bed recorder, because they might jam the chart drive.

Background Scans. Before running the IR spectrum of a sample in an FTIR spectrometer (see Figure G8 for a typical instrument), the instructor or user must perform a *background scan*, which is subtracted from the spectrum of the sample to remove IR bands (such as those from atmospheric CO_2) that don't belong to the sample. The same background scan can be used for many samples, but a new background should be recorded occasionally to compensate for changes in the lab's atmosphere. With some instruments, the background spectrum is automatically subtracted from the sample's spectrum; with others the subtraction must be carried out by the user. A spectrum that is stored and later subtracted from the sample's spectrum is also called a *reference scan.*

See the following section on sample preparation for information about the sampling devices mentioned here.

When a neat liquid sample is being analyzed in a sample cell, the background scan is run either with no cell in the sample compartment or (sometimes) with a cell containing the salt windows to be used with the sample. The background scan then contains signals due to carbon dioxide and water vapor from the atmosphere and certain optical components of the instrument. When a liquid sample is being analyzed using a disposable IR card, the blank card to which the liquid will be applied is used for the background scan. When a solution is to be analyzed, the background scan is run with a sample cell containing the pure solvent. When a KBr disk spectrum is being run in a Mini-Press, the empty press can be placed in the sample compartment for the background scan (this may not be necessary for routine spectra).

Dispersive IR spectrometers don't ordinarily require background scans. When a solution is analyzed, a sample cell containing the pure solvent is placed in the spectrometer's reference beam, and the solvent's spectrum is automatically subtracted from that of the sample as a spectrum is recorded.

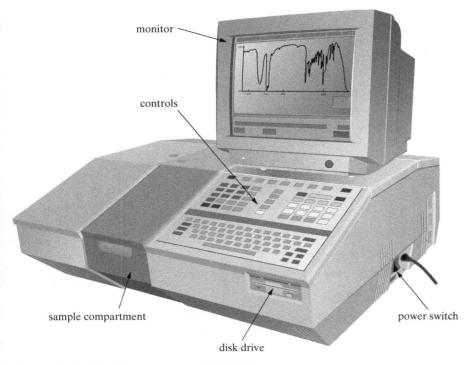

Figure G8 Perkin–Elmer Spectrum RXI FTIR spectrometer

Using an FTIR Spectrometer. To obtain an IR spectrum using an FTIR spectrometer (Figure G8), the user places a cell or other sampling device containing the sample into the sample compartment and selects the desired number of scans (usually 4–16). Unless a large number of scans is selected, the spectrum should appear on the monitor in a minute or so. A copy of the spectrum can then be obtained by using a plotter or a computer printer. Most instruments can print the wave number of each band directly on the spectrum; with some instruments, you may need to determine the wave numbers by using a cursor and then write them on the spectrum. FTIR spectrometers are often provided with a library of IR spectra that can be searched for comparison with the spectrum of a reaction product or an unknown compound.

Using a Dispersive IR Spectrometer. A typical dispersive IR spectrometer with a flat-bed recorder is shown in Figure G9. The chart paper on which spectra are recorded, which has wave number and wavelength values printed on it, is clipped to a moveable paper carriage. With other instruments, the chart paper may be wrapped around a moveable drum. The user may need to align the chart paper by matching a wave number on the chart (for instance, 4000 cm^{-1}) with an alignment mark on the recorder bed or drum. If it isn't aligned properly, the IR bands will appear at the wrong locations on the chart paper, and their wave numbers will be incorrect. The user then moves the paper carriage or drum to its initial position (with the pen at the far left of the chart paper), moves the pen to a point near the top of the chart paper with an attenuator control to set the baseline, and scans the spectrum.

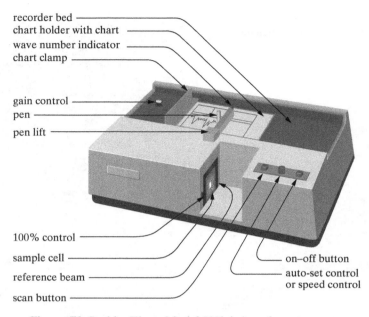

recorder bed
chart holder with chart
wave number indicator
chart clamp

gain control
pen
pen lift

100% control
sample cell
reference beam
scan button

on–off button
auto-set control
or speed control

Figure G9 Perkin–Elmer Model 710b infrared spectrometer

Sample Preparation

Most IR spectra are obtained by using sample cells into which the sample is introduced with a syringe or by some other means. Certain sampling accessories, such as attenuated total reflectance devices (ATRs), make it possible to record the IR spectrum of a liquid or solid without using a sample cell. Because sample cells and other sampling accessories vary widely in construction and application, most sampling techniques should be demonstrated by the instructor.

Care of Infrared Windows. In most sample cells, the sample is placed between two *windows* made by compressing a metal halide (sodium chloride, silver chloride, etc.) to form a transparent round or rectangular crystal. These windows are very fragile and most are water soluble. A window should be touched only on the edges with clean, dry hands or gloves and handled with great care to avoid damage. Sodium chloride and potassium chloride windows must not be exposed to moisture; even breathing on such a window can cause some etching because of moisture in your breath. Therefore, all samples and solvents that will come into contact with NaCl and KCl windows must be dry, and the windows must be stored in a dry atmosphere when not in use. After use, NaCl and KCl windows are washed with a dry, volatile solvent such as dichloromethane, sodium chloride-saturated absolute ethanol, or a 1:1 mixture of absolute ethanol and low-boiling petroleum ether. They are then either air-dried or carefully blotted dry with nonabrasive tissues, and stored in a desiccator. Silver chloride windows can be washed with ethanol or acetone. These windows are unaffected by water, but they must be stored in the dark because AgCl eventually turns black when exposed to light.

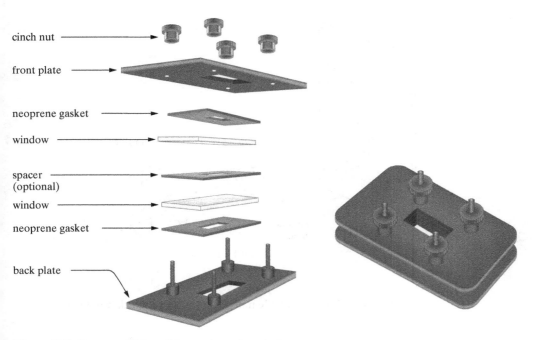

cinch nut

front plate

neoprene gasket

window

spacer
(optional)

window

neoprene gasket

back plate

Figure G10 Demountable cell for rectangular windows

Thin Films. Thin films cannot be used for very volatile liquids, such a diethyl ether, because they may evaporate before the spectrum is complete; with such liquids, use a spacer as described next. To prepare a thin film of a neat (undiluted) liquid using a *demountable cell* such as the one illustrated in Figure G10, layer a gasket and a window on the back plate and place 1–2 drops of the liquid on the window. (If the cell has round windows, use an O-ring rather than a gasket.) Then position the upper window by touching an edge to the corresponding edge of the lower window and carefully lowering it into place. Press the windows together so that the liquid fills the space between them, taking care to exclude air bubbles. Place another gasket (or O-ring) on the top window, add the front plate, and tighten the cinch nuts just enough to hold the cell components together securely. Be careful not to overtighten the nuts, because this may make the liquid film too thin or even break a window. After you have recorded a spectrum, disassemble the cell; then wash, dry, and store the windows as described previously.

Take Care! Hold the windows by their edges.

The demountable silver chloride mini-cell illustrated in Figure G11 is especially convenient for small-scale work, because less sample is required; a small drop from a Pasteur pipet is usually sufficient. After the sample is spread between the flat sides of the recessed AgCl windows, the cell is assembled by placing the windows, protected by two O-rings, inside the plastic window holder and carefully screwing on the plastic retainer. When an infrared spectrum is recorded, the cell is supported in the special cell holder shown.

Volatile Neat Liquids. If a liquid is very volatile, its spectrum can be run in a demountable, sealed, or sealed–demountable cell, using a spacer approximately 0.015–0.030 mm thick. Fill a demountable cell by placing the spacer

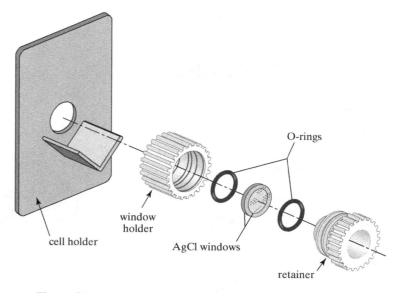

Figure G11 Demountable mini-cell for silver chloride windows

on the lower window, adding sufficient liquid to fill the cavity in the spacer, positioning the upper window, and reassembling the cell as described in the previous section. After you have recorded a spectrum, disassemble the cell; then wash, dry, and store the windows as described previously.

A *sealed cell* or *sealed–demountable cell* (Figure G12) is filled by injecting the sample into one of its filling ports with a Luer-Lok syringe body. If you are using a sealed–demountable cell that hasn't been assembled, assemble it using Figure G12 as a guide, starting with the back plate. Remove both plugs from the filling ports, draw about 0.5 mL of liquid into the syringe, and carefully insert the syringe tip into one of the ports with a slight twist. Holding the cell upright with the syringe port at the bottom, depress the syringe's plunger until the space between the windows is filled and a small amount of liquid appears at the upper port. If there is much resistance to filling, try the push–pull method described next. If there are air bubbles between the windows, they can sometimes be removed by tapping gently on the metal frame of the cell. Put the cell on a flat surface, remove the syringe, and insert a plug in the upper port with a slight twist. Remove any excess solvent in the lower port with a piece of tissue paper or cotton and close that port with another plug.

After the spectrum has been run, clean the cell by removing most of the liquid with a syringe and flushing the cell several times with a dry, volatile solvent. To flush a cell using the push–pull method illustrated in Figure G13, lay it on a flat surface and insert a syringe filled with solvent into one port and an empty syringe into the other port. Twist the syringes slightly as you insert them so that they won't pull out easily. Slowly push on one plunger while pulling on the other, as shown in the figure, to draw washing liquid through the cell from one syringe to the other. Do this several times; then remove the excess liquid with an empty syringe and dry the cell by passing clean, dry air or nitrogen between the windows. An ear syringe or a special cell-drying syringe can be used to force air through the cell, or it can be dried by

Take Care! These syringes are fragile and break easily.

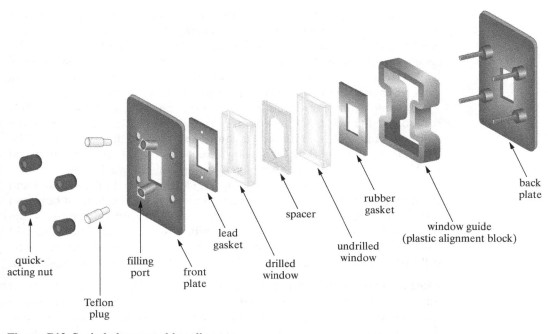

Figure G12 Sealed–demountable cell

quick-
acting nut

Teflon
plug

filling
port

front
plate

lead
gasket

drilled
window

spacer

undrilled
window

rubber
gasket

window guide
(plastic alignment block)

back
plate

attaching a trap and aspirator to one port and a drying tube filled with desiccant [OP-12a] to the other. Store the assembled cell in a desiccator [OP-26b].

Solutions. Solutions of solids or liquids in a suitable solvent can be analyzed in a sealed or sealed–demountable cell that has a spacer 0.1 mm or more in thickness. The solvent should be dry, relatively nonpolar, unreactive with the solute, and transparent to IR radiation in the regions of interest. It should ordinarily dissolve enough of the solute to yield a 5–10% solution; more dilute solutions can be used with FTIR spectrometers. Only a few solvents, such as carbon tetrachloride, chloroform, and carbon disulfide, meet these criteria with a wide range of solutes. These solvents (particularly carbon tetrachloride) are all hazardous to human health, and carbon disulfide is extremely flammable, so they are to be used only with appropriate safety equipment (hood, gloves, safety goggles, etc.) and under the supervision of an instructor. It is best to use spectral-grade solvents so that impurities will not give rise to extraneous peaks. When (or after) the sample's spectrum is recorded, the IR spectrum of the solvent is subtracted from the solution spectrum to give the spectrum of the solute. Even then, strong solvent peaks will obscure certain portions of the spectrum. For example, the spectrum of a solute run in chloroform will yield no useful information in the 1250–1200 cm^{-1} and 800–650 cm^{-1} regions, because chloroform absorbs nearly all of the IR radiation there. Sometimes spectra are run separately in two solvents that absorb at different wave numbers, such as chloroform and carbon disulfide, to obtain the equivalent of a complete spectrum.

With an FTIR spectrometer, an IR cell is first filled with the pure solvent, and the solvent's spectrum is run as a background scan. When the spectrum of the sample is run in the same cell, the background spectrum is

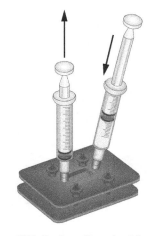

Figure G13 Push–pull method for flushing a sealed or sealed–demountable cell

An inexpensive solution cell that requires only a small volume of solution is described in J. Chem. Educ. **1991**, *68,* A124.

subtracted to yield the spectrum of the solute. The background spectrum is stored by the instrument or an attached computer, so a number of samples can be run in the same cell using the same background. With a dispersive IR spectrometer, one cell is filled with the solution and another (identical) cell is filled with the solvent, using spacers of the same thickness. The spectrum is then run with the solvent cell in the instrument's reference beam.

To prepare a sample cell for a solution spectrum, make up a 5–10% solution of the substance to be analyzed. Usually, 0.1–0.5 mL of solution will be required. A 0.1-mm spacer can be used unless the solution is quite dilute. If the cell is ported, fill it using a Luer-Lok syringe body as described in "Volatile Neat Liquids." (A silver chloride mini-cell can be used for solutions by filling the recessed side of one AgCl window with the solution and covering it with the flat side of the other window, so as to exclude air bubbles.) After the spectrum has been recorded, clean the cell by removing the excess solution and flushing it (as described in "Volatile Neat Liquids") with the pure solvent used in preparing the solution. If necessary, rinse the cell with a more volatile solvent before drying it, and store it in a desiccator.

Mulls. A solid sample can be prepared as a *mull* in Nujol (a kind of mineral oil) or another mulling oil. The sample spectrum should be compared with a spectrum of the mulling oil so that peaks due to the oil can be identified and disregarded during interpretation. When Nujol is used, the aliphatic C — H stretching and bending regions (3000–2850, 1470, 1380 cm^{-1}) cannot be interpreted, but most of the IR bands arising from functional groups and other structural features can be identified. If it is necessary to examine the entire spectrum, another sample can be prepared using a complementary mulling oil such as Fluorlube. Nujol is essentially transparent at wave numbers lower than 1300 cm^{-1}, and Fluorlube is transparent above 1300 cm^{-1}. Some scattering of IR radiation by particles of the solid will reduce transmittance at the high wave-number end of the spectrum, so the baseline of a dispersive IR spectrometer shouldn't be set at that end but wherever the transmittance is highest.

Preparing a usable mull takes some practice, so follow the directions carefully and be ready to prepare additional samples if the first one doesn't work out. Grind about 10–20 mg of the solid in an agate or mullite mortar until it coats the inner surface of the mortar and has a glossy appearance (at least 5 minutes of grinding is recommended). The particles must be ground to an average diameter of about 1 μm to avoid excessive radiation loss by scattering. Add a drop or two of mulling oil and grind the mixture for a minute or so after all of the solid that coated the inside of the mortar is incorporated into a paste. The paste should have about the consistency of petroleum jelly. Transfer most of the mull to the lower window of a demountable cell using a rubber policeman. Spread the mull into a uniform thin film by sliding or rotating the top window, taking care to exclude air bubbles. The mull, as viewed through the cell windows, should be translucent or transparent, not opaque or grainy. Assemble the cell, run the spectrum, and clean the windows as for a neat liquid, using low-boiling petroleum ether or another suitable solvent. Then dry and store the windows as described previously.

Potassium Bromide Disks. A potassium bromide (KBr) disk is prepared by mixing a solid with *dry* spectral-grade potassium bromide and using a die to press the mixture into a more-or-less transparent wafer. Potassium bromide absorbs moisture from the atmosphere, so it must be kept in a tightly capped container and stored in an oven or desiccator. It is advisable to dry it before use by heating it in a 110°C oven for several hours. Even then, it will usually pick up enough moisture during sample preparation to give rise to O—H bands around 3450 cm^{-1} and 1640 cm^{-1}.

It takes time and effort to prepare a usable KBr disk by manual grinding, because it is difficult to get the particles fine enough; even then, there may be some spectral degradation due to scattering of IR radiation in the sample. (A ball mill works better, as described in the next paragraph.) Grind 0.5–2.0 mg of the solid very finely in a dry agate or mullite mortar as if you were preparing a mull; then add about 100 mg of dry potassium bromide, mix it thoroughly with the sample, and grind it very finely. Use about half of this mixture to prepare a disk with a Mini-Press, as described next. If a pneumatic press will be used, a larger sample may be necessary.

If a small, vibrating ball mill is available, such as the Wig-L-Bug used by some dentists, mix about 1 mg of the solid with 200 mg of dry KBr (you can scale up the quantities, if necessary), put the mixture in the ball mill, and run the mill for 5 minutes. Use about one-quarter of this mixture to prepare a disk with a Mini-Press.

To use a Mini-Press (Figure G14), screw in its bottom bolt five full turns and introduce the indicated amount of sample mixture into the barrel. Keeping the open end of the barrel pointed up, tap it gently against the benchtop to level the mixture, brush down any material on the threads with a soft brush, and screw in the top bolt. Alternately tap the bottom bolt on the benchtop and screw in the top bolt with your fingers several times to level the sample further. When the bolt is finger tight, clamp the bottom bolt in a vise and gradually tighten the top bolt as far as you can with a heavy wrench (or to 20 ft-lbs with a torque wrench). Leave the die under pressure for a minute or two. Remove both bolts, leaving the KBr disk in the center of the barrel, and check to see that it is homogeneous and translucent or nearly transparent; if not, prepare a new disk. A disk may be cloudy or inhomogeneous because the sample is wet, not thoroughly ground, or not completely mixed. It is also possible that the disk is too thick, the sample size is too large, or the top bolt wasn't tightened enough.

Place the block containing the disk on a holder (provided with the Mini-Press) in the spectrometer sample beam. As for a mull, scattering will reduce transmittance at the left end of the spectrum, so for a dispersive instrument, set the baseline wherever the transmittance is highest. After you have run the spectrum, punch out the KBr disk using the eraser end of a pencil. Wash the barrel and bolts with water, rinse them with acetone or methanol, and store the clean, dry press in a desiccator.

Melts. IR spectra of low-melting solids can sometimes be obtained by one of the following procedures.

A. Spread a thin, uniform layer of the finely powdered solid on a silver chloride window, cover it with another silver chloride window, and heat the assembly *slowly* on a hot plate. As soon as the solid melts to produce a uniform film between the windows, remove the windows, press them together with forceps until the sample solidifies, install them in a demountable cell, and run the spectrum as for a thin film. If the spectrum is distorted because of excessive light scattering, try method **B**.

If another kind of press is to be used, follow the manufacturer's or your instructor's directions for preparing the disk.

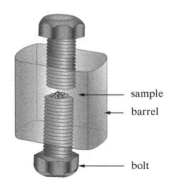

sample
barrel
bolt

Figure G14 Potassium bromide Mini-Press

See J. Chem. Educ. **1977**, *54*, 287 *for additional suggestions regarding the preparation of KBr disks.*

B. Heat a pair of sodium chloride windows in an oven to a temperature at least 20°C above the melting point of the solid, and then set one window on the back plate of a demountable cell (don't forget to use a gasket or an O-ring). Without delay, place about 0.1 g of the solid on that window; position the other window so that the solid, as it melts, fills the space between the windows; and assemble the cell. If possible, run the spectrum while the sample is still liquid. You may still be able to get a good spectrum if the liquid crystallizes as a glassy film or very small crystals, but larger crystals produce excessive light scattering.

Disposable IR Cards.   If your laboratory has disposable IR cards available, you can obtain a spectrum by using the blank card for a background scan and then applying the sample to the same card and scanning its spectrum. Apply the sample—as a neat liquid or a solution of a liquid or solid in a volatile solvent such as dichloromethane—to the matrix (a thin polymer film) in the middle of the card and allow the solvent (if any) to evaporate completely. If the initial spectrum isn't satisfactory, another spectrum can be recorded using the same card, after excess sample has been removed or more sample has been added. Excess sample may result from using a liquid neat rather than in solution. The excess can be removed by rinsing the matrix with a small amount of volatile solvent and letting the solvent evaporate. The card can be reused if it is rinsed with enough solvent to remove all traces of the previous sample (you may have to run another spectrum to be sure of that).

One disadvantage of this method is that the IR bands of the card's matrix—which is made of polyethylene (PE) or polytetrafluoroethylene (PTFE)—may alter or obscure some bands from your product, particularly those in the C—H region if a PE matrix is used. Also, low-boiling liquids may evaporate too fast to yield a satisfactory spectrum.

Attenuated Total Reflectance (ATR) Sampling.   Some FTIR instruments are equipped with ATR accessories that greatly simplify the process of recording an IR spectrum. The sample is placed on a crystal of zinc selenide, germanium, diamond, or some other material that has a high refractive index. An infrared beam is directed through the crystal at the angle at which total reflection occurs from both of its faces so that the beam, in effect, bounces off the sample numerous times to yield what is called an *evanescent wave*. At each point of contact, the wave penetrates a few micrometers into the sample. At frequencies where the sample absorbs energy, the IR beam is attenuated (reduced in intensity). It is then directed to the instrument's detector, where the spectrum is generated.

A typical ATR accessory suitable for liquid samples has a recessed crystal surface in a horizontal plate. After a background scan is performed, the crystal is covered with a thin layer of the liquid and the spectrum is recorded. Solids are best analyzed on an ATR accessory that has a diamond surface; the solid is forced onto the surface with a pressure tip that holds it in close contact with the crystal. In either case, the crystal surface must be cleaned thoroughly with a solvent-soaked tissue or cotton swab after a spectrum is run.

DIRECTIONS FOR RECORDING AN INFRARED SPECTRUM

Equipment and Supplies

Starred items are needed only for the sample types indicated in parentheses.

IR spectrometer

sample

Pasteur pipet

IR sample cell(s) and windows or other sampling device

*Luer-Lok syringe, spacer (volatile neat liquids)

*spectral-grade solvent, Luer-Lok syringe, spacer (solutions)

*mortar and pestle, mulling oil, glass rod with rubber policeman (mulls)

*dry potassium bromide, mortar and pestle, Mini-Press, vise, wrench (KBr disks)

*hot plate and forceps, or oven (melts)

*disposable IR card (IR cards)

solvent for cleaning windows, etc.

tissues

desiccator for storing windows

Do not attempt to operate the instrument without prior instruction and proper supervision. Do not make any adjustments to the controls, other than the ones specified here, except with the instructor's permission. The construction and operation of commercial IR spectrometers vary widely, so the following is meant only as a general guide to assist you in recording an IR spectrum. Specific operating techniques must be learned from the instructor, the operating manual, or both. It will be assumed that the necessary operational parameters have been set beforehand; if not, your instructor will show you what to do. If you are using an ATR accessory, your instructor should show you how to apply your sample. If you are using an FTIR spectrometer, follow Procedure **A**; for a dispersive IR spectrometer, follow Procedure **B**.

A. FTIR Spectrometer. Your instructor will tell you which keys or computer commands (if the spectrometer is controlled by a computer) to use for such processes as scanning a spectrum, using a cursor, subtracting a background scan, and printing or plotting a spectrum. If your compound is in solution, run a background spectrum with a cell containing the pure solvent in the sample compartment; use the same cell for the solution. If you are using a disposable IR card, scan its spectrum before you apply the sample. Otherwise, run the background spectrum (if one is necessary) with the sample compartment empty just before you record your spectrum. Prepare a sample cell, IR card, or KBr disk by one of the methods described previously and place the cell, card, or KBr disk holder in the sample cell holder. Select the desired number of scans (four are usually sufficient for a routine spectrum) and start scanning the spectrum. Wait until a spectrum appears on the monitor. If the instrument does not automatically subtract any background spectrum, do so as directed by your instructor. If the spectrum doesn't look right—for example, if the low or high wave-number end is missing or you are seeing only a small part of the total spectrum—display the "normal" spectrum using the appropriate key(s) (some instruments use *Rerange* and *Rescale* keys for this purpose) or computer commands. The strongest bands should extend nearly to the bottom of your spectrum; if they do not, use a vertical-scale expansion option to improve the appearance of the spectrum. See that the printer or plotter is turned on and properly adjusted, and then use the appropriate key or computer command to print or plot the spectrum. If the instrument you are using doesn't record wave numbers directly on the spectrum, use the cursor arrow keys to move the cursor to the significant bands and write the displayed wave numbers below the corresponding IR bands on your spectrum. Reset the instrument to display a normal spectrum, if necessary. Then remove the sample cell and close the sample compartment. Clean, dry, and store the cell windows (if you are using them) as described previously.

B. Dispersive IR Spectrometer. Prepare a sample cell or other sampling device by one of the methods described previously and place the sampling device in the sample cell holder. If you are running a solution spectrum, place an identical cell containing the solvent in the reference compartment; otherwise, leave it empty. If necessary, place chart paper on the paper carriage (or wrap it around a drum); then align the paper properly and move the carriage or drum to the starting position. Set the 100% transmittance control so that the pen is at 85–90% T, lower the pen onto the chart paper, and scan the spectrum. Examine the spectrum to see whether the absorption bands show satisfactory intensity and resolution. Ideally, the strongest absorption band should have a maximum transmittance of 5–10%. If your first spectrum is not acceptable, try varying the following parameters, depending on the sample preparation method:

Take Care! Make sure the instrument has been reset correctly before attempting to move the drum or carriage.

- *Neat liquid*—Vary cell path length or film thickness.
- *Solution*—Vary concentration or cell path length.
- *KBr disk*—Vary amount of sample or thickness of disk.
- *Mull*—Vary amount of sample or film thickness.

Remove the sample and spectrum; reset the instrument, if necessary. Clean, dry, and store the sample cell or cell windows as described previously.

Summary

1. Run background spectrum, if necessary.
2. Put sample in sample cell or prepare IR card or KBr disk.
3. Put sample cell, card, or KBr disk holder in instrument's sample holder. IF you are using an FTIR spectrometer, GO TO 7.
4. Align chart paper and move drum or carriage to starting position. IF you are not analyzing a solution, GO TO 6.
5. Put solvent cell in reference beam.
6. Adjust 100% transmittance control; lower pen to paper.
7. Scan spectrum; subtract any background spectrum, if necessary. IF you are using a dispersive IR spectrometer, GO TO 9.
8. Print or plot spectrum; record wave numbers, if necessary.
9. Disassemble cell; clean, dry, and store cell windows.
   Note: Additional steps are required for running solution spectra.

When Things Go Wrong

If you press the Scan key or another key on an FTIR spectrometer and nothing happens, the instrument probably needs to be operated using a computer. See your instructor for directions.

If you scan an IR spectrum and see significant absorption near 2350 cm^{-1} (due to CO_2 from the atmosphere), a background scan has probably not been run recently. Perform a background scan as described in the directions.

If you scan a spectrum and see nothing but a flat line near the 100% transmittance level, you (or someone else) probably ran a background scan with the sample in the cell compartment. Perform a background scan with nothing (or the solvent, if you are analyzing a solution) in the cell compartment, as described in the directions.

If you scan an FTIR spectrum and see only a partial spectrum or a display that doesn't look like a normal spectrum, use the scale- and range-setting options to display a normal spectrum.

If the baseline of your mull, KBr disk, or melt spectrum begins (on the high-frequency end) well below the 100% transmittance level and slopes upward before flattening out near the 2500 cm^{-1} region, and especially if your peaks "tail off" (are distorted along their trailing edges), your sample (for a mull or KBr disk) wasn't ground finely enough or the melt formed unsuitably large crystals. Prepare a new mull or KBr disk, or try method **B** for a melt. If you still can't get a good spectrum, you may have to use a different sampling method.

If your IR spectrum shows significant absorption bands near 3500 cm^{-1} and 1650 cm^{-1}, especially if your compound doesn't contain OH or NH bonds, your sample is probably wet. If you are running a liquid film, solution spectrum, or mull, clean the IR windows immediately and thoroughly so that they won't be etched by the water. Then dry your product and run another spectrum. If you are using a KBr disk, the presence of a little water may be unavoidable, but preparing a new disk using oven-dried KBr and avoiding extended exposure to the atmosphere should help.

If some bands on your IR spectrum "bottom out" near 0% transmittance (they will usually be somewhat flattened at the bottom), your sample film is too thick or (for a solution) the solution is too concentrated. On an FTIR spectrometer, you may be able to get a satisfactory spectrum by using a scale expansion control. Otherwise, you will have to prepare the sample cell again, using less sample or a less concentrated solution.

Suppose the peaks on your IR spectrum are broad and indistinct, lacking fine structure. If your sample is a neat liquid, it has probably been evaporating or leaking out of the infrared beam area. Look at the infrared windows to see if there are areas between them where there is no liquid. If so, prepare another sample cell, using a spacer or more liquid. (See "Volatile Neat Liquids"). If you prepared a mull or KBr disk with a solid sample, you probably didn't grind the solid finely enough. The spectrum of a mull may also have a sloping baseline in this case. See "Mulls" or "Potassium Bromide Disks" and prepare another mull or disk.

If you run a spectrum with a dispersive IR spectrometer and all of the wave numbers seem to vary by the same amount from the expected values, the chart paper wasn't aligned properly or the spectrometer wasn't calibrated properly. Check to see that the appropriate wave number on the chart paper is directly opposite the alignment mark on the instrument; if not, align it and run another spectrum. If the chart paper was aligned properly, ask your instructor to have the spectrometer recalibrated (or to help you do it), and then run another spectrum.

Interpretation of Infrared Spectra

Because most IR bands are associated with specific chemical bonds, it is usually possible to deduce the functional class of an organic compound from its IR spectrum. The *stretching* vibrations of chemical bonds resemble the vibrations of springs in that stronger bonds have higher vibrational energies and frequencies than weaker ones. Thus, triple bonds generally absorb at higher wave numbers than double bonds, and double bonds absorb at higher wave numbers than single bonds. However, because of the comparatively low mass of a hydrogen atom, single bonds to hydrogen (C—H, O—H, N—H, etc.) have even higher vibrational frequencies than double and triple bonds. Stretching bands involving single bonds to hydrogen occur at the high-frequency (left) end of an IR spectrum, in the region between 3700 and 2700 cm^{-1} (2.7–3.7 μm). Triple bonds usually absorb between 2700 and 1850 cm^{-1} (3.7–5.4 μm), and double bonds and aromatic bonds absorb between 1950 and 1450 cm^{-1} (5.1–6.9 μm). Most IR bands between 1500 and 600 cm^{-1} (6.7–16.7 μm) are produced by *bending* vibrations or single-bond stretching vibrations. It takes less energy to bend a bond than to stretch it, so bending vibrations tend to have comparatively low frequencies. An absorption band in the 1500–600 cm^{-1} region may be associated with more than one bond; for example, the so-called acyl–oxygen stretching band of an ester arises from the vibration of C—C—O units rather than isolated C—O bonds.

What to Look for in an IR Spectrum

The IR spectra in this book are reproduced from the Aldrich Library of FT–IR Spectra, Edition II, with permission.

Consider the IR spectrum of 2-methyl-1-propanol (isobutyl alcohol) in Figure G15. At first glance, it may seem indecipherable—just a series of dips and rises in a graph. But each "dip" (IR band) arises from a stretching or bending vibration of one or more bonds in the 2-methyl-1-propanol molecule, and some of the bands can tell you a great deal about the molecules that

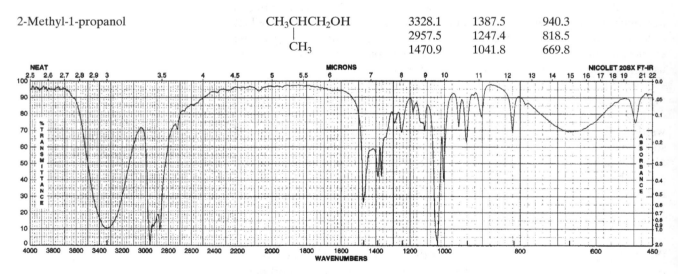

2-Methyl-1-propanol	CH$_3$CHCH$_2$OH	3328.1	1387.5	940.3
	$\mid$	2957.5	1247.4	818.5
	CH$_3$	1470.9	1041.8	669.8

Figure G15 Infrared spectrum of 2-methyl-1-propanol

gave rise to them. First look at the WAVENUMBERS scale at the bottom of the spectrum; from this scale, you can read off the wave number, in cm^{-1}, of each band. For example, the first large band in the spectrum is between 3600 and 3000 cm^{-1}, and its minimum is at approximately 3330 cm^{-1}. Bands designated by tick marks (short lines) at the bottom of a spectrum have their exact wave numbers listed, so you can find a more accurate wave number for this band, 3328.1 cm^{-1}, in the list of numbers above the right-hand end of the spectrum. Another numerical scale at the top of the spectrum indicates the wavelength in micrometers (microns).

The numbers on the left side of the spectrum are transmittance values. For example, the minimum in the 3328 cm^{-1} band has a transmittance of ~10%, meaning that only 10% of the 3328 cm^{-1} IR radiation passed through the sample. The other 90% was absorbed during a change in the bond vibrational frequency of some bond in the compound—but which bond? Because the band is at the left end of the spectrum, the bond must have a high vibrational energy, and we have already seen that bands in the 3700–2700 cm^{-1} region of the spectrum arise from vibrations of bonds to hydrogen atoms. There are only two bonds of this type in the molecule: C—H bonds and O—H bonds. Now note that there are two bands in the 3700–2700 cm^{-1} region—the strong, broad, symmetrical one on the left, and a rather ragged band with several minima (centered around 2900 cm^{-1}) on the right. The ragged band is actually composed of several overlapping bands, arising from vibrations of several different bonds of the same general type. There is only one O—H bond in the molecule, and there are nine C—H bonds, so it is reasonable to assume that the overlapping bands on the right arise from C—H stretching vibrations and that the band on the left is the O—H band. Note that the size of a band is not directly related to the number of bonds that give rise to it; the single O—H bond has a much broader band than the nine C—H bonds.

So the bond responsible for a given IR band can often be identified from its *location* on the spectrum (as indicated by its wave number), its *intensity* (relative strength), and its *shape*. Most O—H bands, like the one in the previous spectrum, are very broad and strong (a *strong* band is one whose minimum is near the bottom of the spectrum). Most C—H bands are relatively strong and give rise to a ragged array of overlapping bands.

Another very strong band appears at 1042 cm^{-1} in the Figure G15 spectrum. This band, which is in the wave-number region for single-bond stretching vibrations (other than those involving hydrogen), arises from stretching vibrations of the C—O bond. The presence of both a C—O and an O—H band in the IR spectrum of a compound is good evidence that the compound is an alcohol (or possibly a phenol), because all alcohols contain a C—O—H grouping in their molecules.

Although we have now located bands corresponding to every kind of bond in the 2-methyl-1-propanol molecule (except C—C single bonds, which don't give prominent bands), the spectrum contains a number of additional bands. This is because the same kind of bond can undergo different kinds of vibrations. For example, most of the bands just to the left of the C—O band arise from *scissoring, wagging,* and *twisting* vibrations of CH$_2$ and CH$_3$ groups (see Figure G16), and the very broad, weak band centered at 670 cm^{-1} arises from an O—H bending vibration.

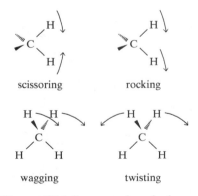

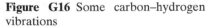

Figure G16 Some carbon–hydrogen vibrations

Spectral Regions

Some IR bands, particularly the stretching bands we have discussed, are more easily recognized than others and are more useful in revealing the presence of functional groups. Many of the other bands can be ignored for the time being, although they may provide useful information to a chemist skilled in spectral interpretation. The key to efficient IR spectral interpretation is *knowing where to look* for the more useful bands. Examining the following regions of the IR spectrum will help you locate the most useful IR bands quickly:

Region 1: 3600–3200 cm^{-1} (2.8–3.1 μm). Bands in this region can arise from O—H and N—H stretching vibrations of alcohols, phenols, amines, and amides. O—H bands are generally very strong and broad; N—H bands are somewhat weaker and, in the case of primary amines and amides, they have two peaks.

Region 2: 3100–2500 cm^{-1} (3.2–4.0 μm). This region contains most of the C—H stretching vibrations. A strong band in the 3000–2850-cm^{-1} region, arising from C—H bonds to sp^3 carbon atoms, is present for most organic compounds. The sp^2 C—H bonds associated with aromatic hydrocarbons and alkenes absorb at higher frequencies (3100–3000 cm^{-1}), and the C—H bonds of aldehyde (CHO) groups absorb at lower frequencies. The O—H bond of a carboxylic acid gives rise to a very broad absorption band in this region.

Region 3: 1750–1630 cm^{-1} (5.7–6.1 μm). This region contains most of the carbonyl (C=O) stretching bands of aldehydes, ketones, carboxylic acids, amides, and esters. The carbonyl band is usually strong and quite unmistakable. Unsaturated compounds may have a C=C stretching band in the 1670–1640-cm^{-1} region, but this band is nearly always weaker and narrower than a carbonyl band.

Region 4: 1350–1000 cm^{-1} (7.4–10.0 μm). This region is usually cluttered with many C—H bending bands and other bands, but it is often possible to identify the C—O stretching bands of alcohols, phenols, carboxylic acids, and esters, and some C—N stretching bands of amines and amides.

2981.9	1367.2	1108.5
1718.5	1275.8	1028.5
1451.4	1175.2	710.3

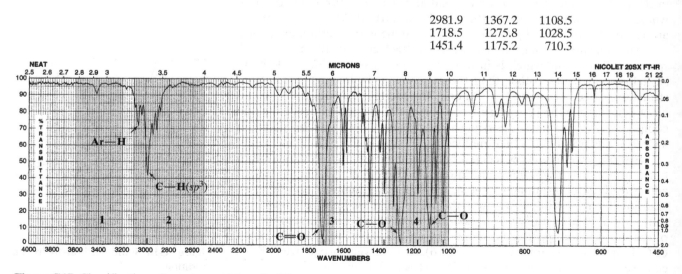

Figure G17 Classification of a compound from its IR spectrum

These four spectral regions are shaded in the IR spectrum illustrated in Figure G17. In this spectrum, the absence of any band in Region 1 (or a broad band in Region 2) eliminates from consideration all compounds that contain O—H and N—H bonds, including alcohols, phenols, and primary or secondary amines and amides. In Region 2, the appearance of a weak "shoulder" on the C—H band at 3050 cm^{-1} indicates an sp^2 C—H bond associated with either an aromatic ring or a carbon–carbon double bond. Region 3 has a strong C=O band at 1719 cm^{-1}, and Region 4 shows a strong C—O band at 1276 cm^{-1} as well as a weaker one at 1109 cm^{-1}. The absence of an O—H or N—H band and the presence of the C=O and two C—O bands suggest that the compound responsible for this spectrum is an ester. The compound is, in fact, the aromatic ester ethyl benzoate, whose structure and bond wave numbers are shown in the margin.

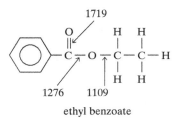

ethyl benzoate

Table G2 summarizes the locations and characteristics of important absorption bands from the four spectral regions and tells you where to look for other bands that may help you confirm the presence of a particular functional group.

Table G2 Important bands in Regions 1–4 of infrared spectra

Region	Frequency range (cm^{-1})	Bond type	Family	Comments
1	3500–3200	N—H	amine, amide	weak–medium. 1°: 2 bands; 2°: 1 band; 3°: no bands; see also Region 3.
	3600–3200	O—H	alcohol, phenol	broad, strong; see Region 4.
2	3300–2500	O—H	carboxylic acid	very broad, strong, centered around 3000; see Regions 3 and 4.
	3100–3000	C—H	aromatic hydrocarbon, alkene	may be shoulder on stronger sp^3 C—H band.
	2850–2700	C—H	aldehyde	weak to medium, usually two sharp bands; see Region 3.
3	1740–1685	C=O	aldehyde	strong; see Region 2.
	1750–1660	C=O	ketone	strong.
	1725–1665	C=O	carboxylic acid	strong; see Regions 2 and 4.
	1775–1715	C=O	ester	strong; see Region 4.
	1695–1615	C=O	amide	strong; see Region 1.
4	1350–1210	C—O	carboxylic acid	medium–strong; see Regions 1 and 3.
	1300–1180	C—O	phenol	strong; see Region 1.
	1200–1000	C—O	alcohol	strong; see Region 1. Wave numbers in order 3° > 2° > 1°.
	1310–1160	C—O	ester	strong; see Region 3. Accompanied by weaker C—O band as for alcohol.

Note: Tentative classifications must be confirmed by referring to the following descriptions of specific families.

The best way to become proficient at identifying IR bands is to study spectra that contain those bands, such as the spectra in your lecture textbook, in the "Characteristic Infrared Bands" section that follows, and in collections of spectra described in Category F of the Bibliography. When you have learned to recognize the most important IR bands, you can take some shortcuts that will help you identify functional groups quickly—or at least eliminate the functional groups that aren't there. The following flowchart should help you do that. Just start at the top and work your way down, following the yes–no arrow that answers each question.

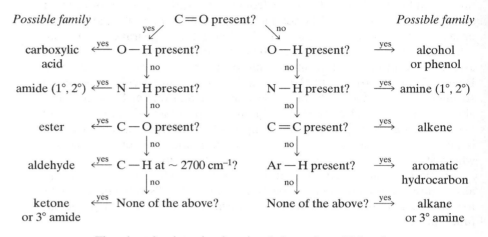

Flowchart for detecting functional classes from IR bands

This flowchart is intended as a rapid screening device and is not infallible; some bands (such as the C=C stretching band) are hard to identify with certainty, and the locations of other bands may vary widely. Moreover, some compounds may contain more than one functional group; thus, hydroxyacetone (CH_3COCH_2OH) has both an O—H and a C=O band in its spectrum, but it isn't a carboxylic acid, as you could tell from the location of its O—H band. When you arrive at a tentative conclusion about the nature of the compound responsible for an IR spectrum, you should refer to Table G2 to see whether other bands in the spectrum are consistent with your initial choice. Then study the spectral characteristics of the appropriate class of compounds to confirm (or disprove) your tentative classification. The IR correlation chart on a back endpaper of this book may also help you identify some infrared spectral bands.

For example, suppose that the flowchart suggests that your compound may be an alcohol or phenol. You can first check Table G2 to see if any other bands characteristic of alcohols and phenols appear in its spectrum, such as a C—O band. If so, you should read the "Characteristic Infrared Bands" sections about alcohols and phenols to find out whether your compound is an alcohol or a phenol. If you find that your compound is an alcohol, you should then study its spectrum for clues to its structure. The frequency of its C—O band may tell you whether it is primary, secondary, or tertiary. By consulting the sections on aromatic hydrocarbons and alkenes (which also apply to other compounds that contain aromatic rings and C=C bonds), you can find out whether your alcohol is aromatic or contains a carbon–carbon double bond. Of course, if you find that your compound is *not* an alcohol or a phenol, you should continue down the chart or start at the beginning.

Characteristic Infrared Bands

This section contains information about the most useful IR bands of the most commonly encountered kinds of organic compounds—alkanes, alkenes, aromatic hydrocarbons, alcohols, phenols, aldehydes, ketones, carboxylic acids, esters, amines, amides, and organic halides. Note that compounds other than hydrocarbons may contain bands characteristic of alkanes, alkenes, or aromatic hydrocarbons, so you can check the sections for these hydrocarbons when you are interpreting the spectra of other kinds of compounds. For each family of organic compounds, a summary of the main spectral features that characterize the family is followed by a description of individual bond vibrations and a representative IR spectrum. The wave-number ranges given are for solids (in Nujol mulls or KBr discs) or neat liquids; values for solutions may differ somewhat. Although the wave-number ranges apply to most of the organic compounds in each class, compounds with certain structural features (such as highly strained rings) may have bands outside of the ranges indicated. On the spectra, some absorption bands are designated either as stretching (ν) or bending (δ) bands. Only those bands that are most useful for identifying functional groups or structural features are labeled. Note that the exact wave numbers of significant bands (designated by tick marks along the lower edge of the spectra) are listed with each spectrum.

Alkanes. Alkanes are identified primarily by the absence of any IR bands characteristic of functional groups. Their spectra are quite simple, containing only the C—H stretching and bending vibrations characteristic of sp^3 hybridized carbon atoms. Because nearly all other organic compounds contain such C—H bonds, their spectra will also contain some or all of the bands described for alkanes. (See Figure G18.)

C—H *stretch:* 3000–2800 cm^{-1} (multiple overlapping bands, strong to weak). CH$_3$ bands are near 2960 cm^{-1} and 2870 cm^{-1}. CH$_2$ bands are near 2925 cm^{-1} and 2850 cm^{-1} (nearly always to the *right* of 3000 cm^{-1}).

C—H *bend:* 1465–720 cm^{-1} (moderate to weak). CH$_3$ bands are near 1450 cm^{-1} and 1375 cm^{-1}. CH$_2$ bands occur near 1465 cm^{-1}, between 1350 cm^{-1} and 1150 cm^{-1} (several weak bands), and sometimes around 720 cm^{-1}. The 720 cm^{-1} band is characteristic of unbranched alkanes that have seven or more carbon atoms.

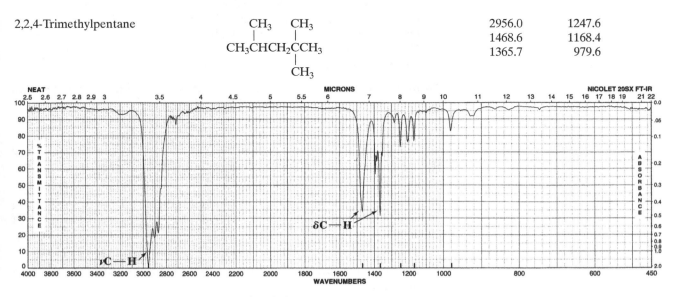

Figure G18 IR spectrum of an alkane, 2,2,4-trimethylpentane

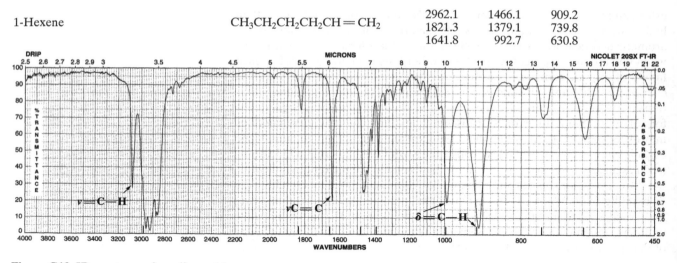

Figure G19 IR spectrum of an alkene, 1-hexene

Alkenes. Most alkenes contain the same kinds of bands as alkanes, plus additional bands associated with carbon–carbon double bonds and vinylic ($=C-H$) carbon–hydrogen bonds. The presence of one or two strong bands in the 1000–650 cm^{-1} region and a sharp band near 1650 cm^{-1} suggests an alkene functional group, especially if the compound is not aromatic. (See Figure G19.)

$=C-H$ *stretch:* 3125–3030 cm^{-1} (moderate to weak). May appear as a shoulder on a stronger sp^3 $C-H$ band, but nearly always to the *left* of 3000 cm^{-1}.

$C=C$ *stretch:* 1675–1600 cm^{-1} (moderate to weak, narrow). May be absent for symmetrical alkenes. Conjugation moves band to lower wavelengths.

$=C-H$ *out-of-plane bend:* 1000–650 cm^{-1} (usually strong). Position depends on type of substitution: $RCH=CH_2$ has bands at 995–985 and 915–905 cm^{-1}; *cis*-$RCH=CHR$ a band at 730–665 cm^{-1}; *trans*-$RCH=CHR$ a band at 980–960 cm^{-1}; and $R_2C=CH_2$ a band at 895–885 cm^{-1} (R = alkyl or aryl substituent).

Aromatic Hydrocarbons. Most compounds containing benzene rings are characterized by (1) aromatic $C-H$ ($Ar-H$) stretching bands near 3070 cm^{-1}, (2) a distinctive pattern of weak bands in the 2000–1650-cm^{-1} region, (3) two sets of bands near 1600 cm^{-1} and 1515–1400 cm^{-1}, and (4) one or more strong absorption bands in the 900–675-cm^{-1} region. The presence of such bands and the absence of absorption bands characteristic of functional groups suggest an aromatic hydrocarbon. (See Figure G20.)

$Ar-H$ *stretch:* 3100–3000 cm^{-1} (moderate to weak). May appear as a shoulder on a stronger sp^3 $C-H$ band, but nearly always to the *left* of 3000 cm^{-1}.

Overtone-combination vibrations: 2000–1650 cm^{-1} (multiple bands, weak). The band pattern is related to the kind of ring substitution, as shown in Figure G21.

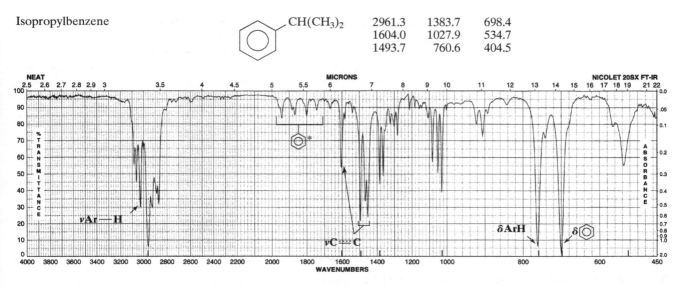

Figure G20 IR spectrum of an aromatic hydrocarbon, isopropylbenzene
Note: The bands marked are ⬡* aromatic overtone-combination bands.

C⁻⁻C *stretch:* 1615–1585 cm^{-1} and 1515–1400 cm^{-1} (variable).

Ar—H *out-of-plane bend:* 910–730 cm^{-1} (strong). The band frequency varies with the number of adjacent ring hydrogens:

> two adjacent hydrogens: 855–800 cm^{-1}
> three adjacent hydrogens: 800–765 cm^{-1}
> four or five adjacent hydrogens: 770–730 cm^{-1}

Monosubstituted, *meta*-disubstituted, and some trisubstituted benzenes show an additional ring-bending band around 715–680 cm^{-1}. For example, a *meta*-disubstituted benzene has three adjacent ring hydrogens, so it should have bands in the 800–765-cm^{-1} and 715–680-cm^{-1} regions.

Alcohols. The presence of a strong, broad band centered around 3300 cm^{-1} and a strong C—O band in the 1200–1000-cm^{-1} region is good evidence for an alcohol. (See Figure G22.) A C—O band above 1200 cm^{-1} may suggest a phenol, as described next.

O—H *stretch:* 3600–3200 cm^{-1} (strong, broad). Usually centered near 3300 cm^{-1}.

C—O *stretch:* 1200–1000 cm^{-1} (strong to moderate). Most saturated aliphatic alcohols absorb near 1050 cm^{-1} if they are primary, near 1110 cm^{-1} if they are secondary, and near 1175 cm^{-1} if they are tertiary. Alicyclic alcohols and alcohols with aromatic rings or vinyl groups on the carbon that is bonded to OH absorb at wave numbers about 25–50 cm^{-1} lower than these.

Phenols. Phenols are characterized by a strong, broad band centered around 3300 cm^{-1} and a strong band near 1230 cm^{-1}, accompanied by bands

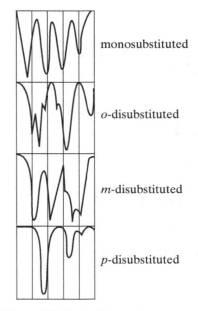

Figure G21 Typical absorption patterns of substituted aromatic compounds in the 2000–1650-cm^{-1} region

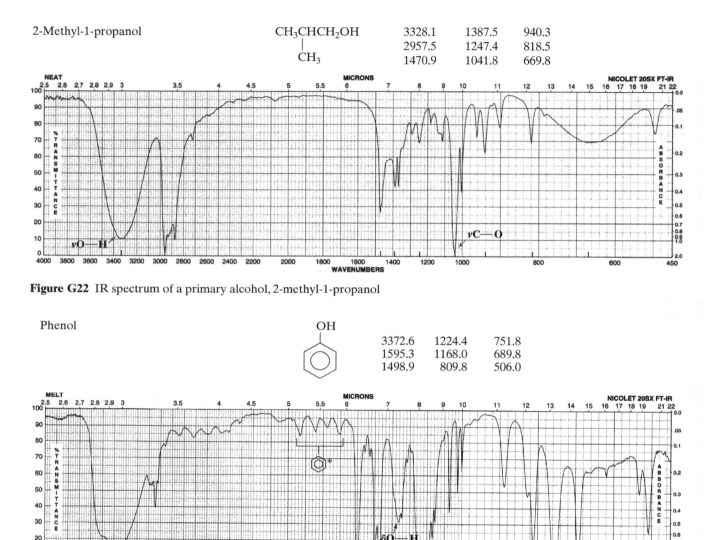

2-Methyl-1-propanol CH_3CHCH_2OH 3328.1   1387.5   940.3
                           | 2957.5   1247.4   818.5
                          CH_3 1470.9   1041.8   669.8

Figure G22 IR spectrum of a primary alcohol, 2-methyl-1-propanol

Phenol   OH   3372.6   1224.4   751.8
              1595.3   1168.0   689.8
              1498.9   809.8   506.0

Figure G23 IR spectrum of phenol
Note: The bands marked ⬡* are aromatic overtone-combination bands.

indicating an aromatic structure. (See "Aromatic Hydrocarbons" and Figure G23.)

O—H *stretch:* 3600–3200 cm^{-1} (strong, broad).

O—H *bend:* 1390–1315 cm^{-1} (moderate).

C—O *stretch:* 1300–1180 cm^{-1} (strong); usually close to 1230 cm^{-1}. This band may be split, with several distinct peaks.

Aldehydes. The presence of a sharp, medium-intensity band near 2720 cm^{-1} and a strong carbonyl band near 1700 cm^{-1} is good evidence for an aldehyde. (See Figure G24.)

3-Methylbutanal

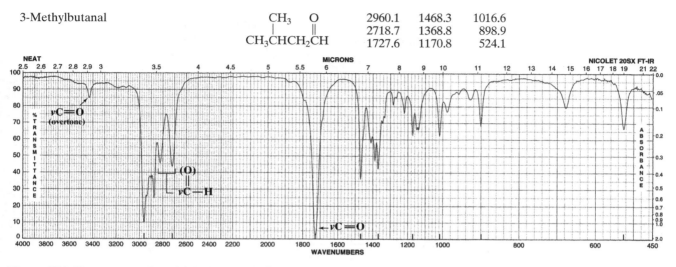

Figure G24 IR spectrum of an aldehyde, 3-methylbutanal

$$\underset{\|}{\overset{(O)}{C}}\!-\!H$$ *stretch:* 2850–2700 cm^{-1} (moderate to weak). From the carbonyl C—H bond; most aldehydes have two bands near 2850 and 2720 cm^{-1}, with the low-frequency band well separated from other aliphatic C—H bands.

C=O *stretch:* 1740–1685 cm^{-1} (strong). Most unconjugated aldehydes absorb near 1725 cm^{-1}; conjugation of the carbonyl group with an aromatic ring or another unsaturated system shifts the band to the 1700–1685-cm^{-1} region. A weak overtone of this band may appear near 3400 cm^{-1}.

Ketones. The presence of a strong carbonyl band around 1700 cm^{-1} is good evidence for a ketone if other bands described in Table G2 (O—H, N—H, C—O, and aldehyde C—H) are absent. One or more bands in the 1300–1100-cm^{-1} region arise from C—C—C vibrations involving the carbonyl carbon. Such bands are generally weaker and narrower than C—O bands, for which they might otherwise be mistaken. (See Figure G25.)

C=O *stretch:* 1750–1660 cm^{-1} (strong). Most unconjugated aliphatic ketones absorb around 1715 cm^{-1}, and conjugated ketones absorb near 1670 cm^{-1}. A weak C=O overtone band is usually evident near 3400 cm^{-1}.

$$\underset{\|}{\overset{(O)}{C}}\!-\!\underset{}{C}\!-\!C$$ *stretch–bend:* 1300–1100 cm^{-1} (moderate). Often multiple bands. Unconjugated ketones absorb around 1230–1100 cm^{-1}; conjugated ketones absorb around 1300–1230 cm^{-1}.

Carboxylic Acids. The presence of a very broad band centered near 3000 cm^{-1} and a carbonyl band around 1700 cm^{-1} is good evidence for a carboxylic acid. (See Figure G26.)

O—H *stretch:* 3300–2500 cm^{-1} (strong, very broad). C—H stretching bands are usually superimposed on this band.

2-Pentanone

O
‖
$CH_3CCH_2CH_2CH_3$

2963.9	1366.0	1170.7
1717.4	1295.5	727.0
1422.9	1235.5	591.9

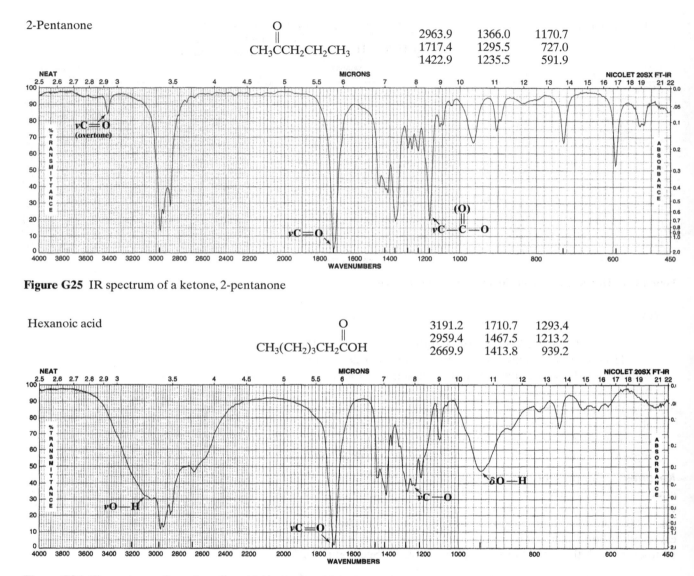

Figure G25 IR spectrum of a ketone, 2-pentanone

Hexanoic acid

O
‖
$CH_3(CH_2)_3CH_2COH$

3191.2	1710.7	1293.4
2959.4	1467.5	1213.2
2669.9	1413.8	939.2

Figure G26 IR spectrum of a carboxylic acid, hexanoic acid

$C=O$ *stretch:* 1725–1665 cm^{-1} (strong). Unconjugated acids absorb around 1725–1700 cm^{-1}; conjugated acids absorb around 1700–1665 cm^{-1}.

$C-O$ *stretch:* 1350–1210 cm^{-1} (strong). Long-chain acids may have a number of sharp peaks in this region.

$O-H$ *bend:* 950–870 cm^{-1} (moderate, broad).

Esters. The presence of a strong carbonyl band around 1740 cm^{-1} and an unusually strong $C-O$ band in the 1310–1160-cm^{-1} region is good evidence for an ester, especially if there is no $O-H$ band. (See Figure G27.)

$C=O$ *stretch:* 1775–1715 cm^{-1} (strong). Near 1770 cm^{-1} for phenyl esters (RCOOAr) and vinyl esters, 1740 cm^{-1} for most unconjugated esters, and 1730–1695 cm^{-1} for formates and conjugated esters.

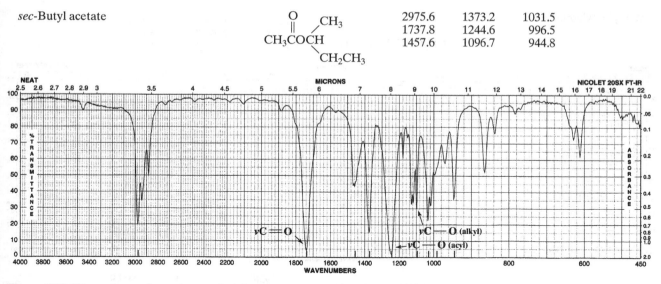

sec-Butyl acetate		2975.6	1373.2	1031.5
		1737.8	1244.6	996.5
		1457.6	1096.7	944.8

Figure G27 IR spectrum of an ester, *sec*-butyl acetate

C—O *stretch (acyl–oxygen):* 1310–1160 cm^{-1} (strong, broad). Occurs near 1310–1250 cm^{-1} for conjugated esters, 1240 cm^{-1} for unconjugated acetates, and 1210–1165 cm^{-1} for most other unconjugated esters. Both the acyl–oxygen and alkyl–oxygen bands arise from coupled vibrations involving C—C—O groupings.

C—O *stretch (alkyl–oxygen):* 1200–1000 cm^{-1} (moderate). Occurs in the same region as alcohol C—O bands and varies in the same way with changes in the alkyl group's structure. Esters of phenols absorb at higher wave numbers.

Amines. Primary amines are characterized by a medium-intensity, two-pronged band near 3350 cm^{-1} and two medium–strong bands near 1615 and 800 cm^{-1}, the latter one being very broad. Secondary amines have a single weak band near 3300 cm^{-1} and a broad band near 715 cm^{-1}. Tertiary amines can sometimes be distinguished by the presence of a C—N band. (See Figure G28.)

N—H *stretch:* 3500–3200 cm^{-1} (moderate to weak, broad). Primary aliphatic amines give rise to a two-pronged band centered near 3350 cm^{-1}, secondary aliphatic amines have one weak band near 3300 cm^{-1}, and tertiary amines have none. Primary and secondary aromatic amines absorb near 3400 and 3450 cm^{-1}, respectively.

N—H *bend (scissoring):* 1650–1500 cm^{-1} (strong to moderate). Usually near 1615 cm^{-1} for primary amines. Seldom observed for secondary aliphatic amines; secondary aromatic amines absorb near 1515 cm^{-1}.

N—H *bend (wagging):* 910–660 cm^{-1} (strong to moderate, broad). Often very broad; around 910–770 cm^{-1} for primary amines, and near 715 cm^{-1} for secondary amines.

C—N *stretch:* 1340–1020 cm^{-1} (strong to moderate). Around 1340–1250 cm^{-1} for aromatic amines, and 1250–1020 cm^{-1} for aliphatic amines. As with an alcohol C—O band, the frequency of an aliphatic C—N band varies with changes in the structure of the attached alkyl group.

3-Methylbutylamine

$$CH_3 \atop | \atop CH_3CHCH_2CH_2NH_2$$

3366.4	1384.1	847.7
2955.0	1066.7	815.5
1467.7	919.2	770.5

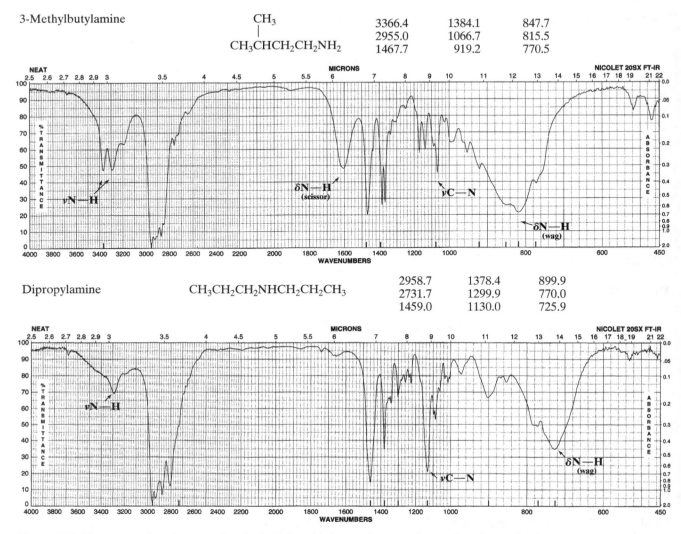

Dipropylamine $CH_3CH_2CH_2NHCH_2CH_2CH_3$

2958.7	1378.4	899.9
2731.7	1299.9	770.0
1459.0	1130.0	725.9

Figure G28 IR spectra of a primary amine, 3-methylbutylamine, and a secondary amine, dipropylamine

Amides. The presence of a carbonyl band near 1640 cm^{-1} and two bands (or peaks) in the 3500–3000 cm^{-1} region is good evidence for an amide. (See Figure G29.)

N—H *stretch:* 3450–3300 cm^{-1} and 3225–3180 cm^{-1} (one or two bands, strong to moderate). Primary amides have two bands (or two prongs on a broad band) near 3400 and 3200 cm^{-1}. Secondary amides have a single N—H stretching band near 3340 cm^{-1}, with an N—H bending overtone near 3080 cm^{-1}. Tertiary amides have no N—H stretching bands.

C═O *stretch:* 1695–1615 cm^{-1} (strong). Usually centered near 1640 cm^{-1}.

N—H *bend:* 1655–1615 cm^{-1} (primary) or 1570–1515 cm^{-1} (secondary) (strong to moderate). This band usually overlaps the carbonyl band on the spectra of primary amides obtained using KBr disks or mulls; it appears at lower frequencies on the spectra obtained in solution. The band is near 1540 cm^{-1} for most secondary amides, and an overtone can sometimes be seen at about 3080 cm^{-1}.

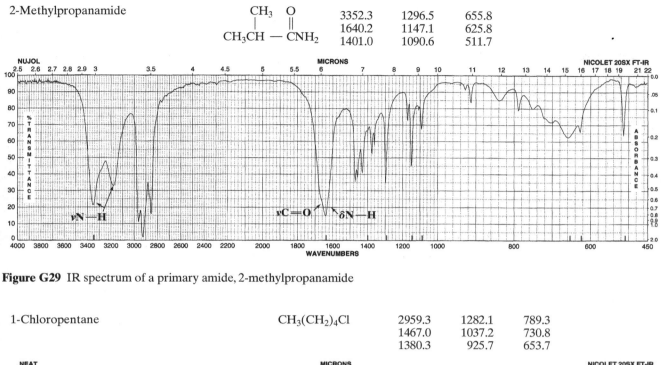

2-Methylpropanamide

$$CH_3CH(CH_3) — CNH_2$$ (with CH_3 and O shown)

3352.3	1296.5	655.8
1640.2	1147.1	625.8
1401.0	1090.6	511.7

Figure G29 IR spectrum of a primary amide, 2-methylpropanamide

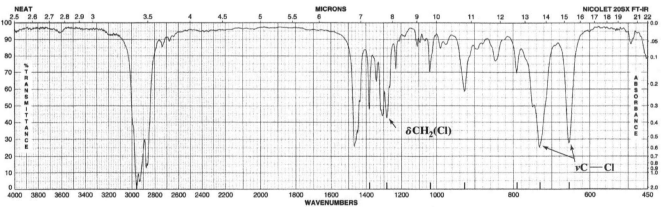

1-Chloropentane $CH_3(CH_2)_4Cl$

2959.3	1282.1	789.3
1467.0	1037.2	730.8
1380.3	925.7	653.7

Figure G30 IR spectrum of an alkyl chloride, 1-chloropentane

Organic Halides. Alkyl chlorides and bromides show fairly strong absorption between 800 and 500 cm^{-1}. Additional chemical evidence is usually needed to characterize organic halides. (See Figure G30.)

C(X)—H *bend:* 1300–1150 cm^{-1} (moderate). Observed only for halides with terminal halogen atoms (—CH$_2$X).

C—Cl *stretch:* 850–550 cm^{-1} (strong to moderate). Two bands near 725 and 645 cm^{-1} when the chlorine is terminal, and below 625 cm^{-1} otherwise—unless several chlorine atoms are on the same or adjacent carbons. Ar—Cl bonds absorb around 1175–1000 cm^{-1}.

C—Br *stretch:* 760–500 cm^{-1} (strong to moderate). Near 645 cm^{-1} when the bromine is terminal. Ar—Br bonds absorb around 1175–1000 cm^{-1}.

Nuclear Magnetic Resonance Spectrometry

The theoretical principles underlying nuclear magnetic resonance (NMR) spectrometry can be found in most textbooks of organic chemistry and in appropriate sources listed in Category F of the Bibliography, if included. Here, we will review only those principles that are needed to gain a working knowledge of NMR spectrometry.

Nuclear magnetic resonance spectrometry is based on the magnetic properties of certain nuclei that possess a quality known as *spin*. The nucleus of an ^{1}H atom, which is a single proton, has spin. The nuclei of ^{13}C atoms also have spin, but the nuclei of ^{12}C atoms, which are nearly 100 times more abundant than ^{13}C atoms, do not. An atom with spin behaves like a tiny bar magnet. When placed in a magnetic field, it tends to become aligned with the field. For convenience, we will refer to a nucleus that is aligned with the external magnetic field as being in an **up** spin state and a nucleus that is aligned against the field as being in a **down** spin state. If a sample containing magnetic nuclei is placed in a magnetic field and exposed to radio frequency (RF) radiation of just the right frequency, some of its **up** nuclei will flip over, into the **down** spin state. This transition is illustrated in Figure G31. Because a nucleus in the **down** state is less stable (contains more energy) than a nucleus in the **up** state, the spin transition results in an absorption of energy by the nucleus. Such a transition is possible only if the energy of an RF photon, $h\nu$, is exactly equal to the energy of the transition, ΔE, so that $\nu = \Delta E/h$. When this is the case, the *resonance condition*—the condition under which nuclei of a given kind can undergo spin transitions—is fulfilled. The transition energy, ΔE, is directly proportional to the strength of the external magnetic field, H_o, so ν is also proportional to H_o. This means that the resonance condition for a nucleus can be attained either by adjusting the frequency of the RF radiation or by adjusting the strength of the external field.

If you are not familiar with the principles and terminology of NMR spectrometry, read the section "Interpretation of ^{1}H NMR Spectra" or consult your lecture text.

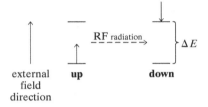

Figure G31 Spin transition of a magnetic nucleus

a. ^{1}H NMR Spectrometry

Instrumentation

There are two fundamentally different ways of obtaining an NMR spectrum. With a *continuous-wave (CW) NMR spectrometer,* the sample is irradiated continuously with RF waves as the magnetic field or RF frequency is varied, and the electromagnetic signals generated by nuclei as they change spin states are converted to peaks on a moving chart. With a *Fourier-transform NMR (FT–NMR) spectrometer,* the sample is irradiated with intense pulses of full-spectrum RF radiation that displace the nuclei from their equilibrium distribution. Their response to the displacement is monitored, generating data that is converted by a microprocessor to an NMR spectrum.

Continuous-Wave NMR. In a typical continuous-wave NMR spectrometer, a glass tube containing the sample is placed between the poles of a magnet and irradiated with RF radiation from a transmitter coil as the magnetic field is "swept" (varied continuously) over a preset range. In an instrument of the type diagrammed in Figure G32, the magnetic field is swept from low to high field

From *Operational Organic Chemistry: A Problem Solving Approach to the Laboratory*, Fourth Edition, John W. Lehman. Copyright © 2009 by Pearson Education. Published by Prentice Hall. All rights reserved.

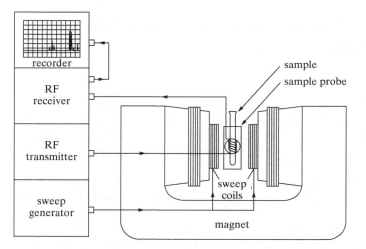

Figure G32 Schematic diagram of a continuous-wave NMR spectrometer

(*downfield* to *upfield*) by varying the strength of an electric current passing through the sweep coils. When the resonance condition for a particular kind of nucleus in the sample is met, nuclei of that kind flip from the **up** state to the **down** state. As they do so, they generate a small fluctuating magnetic field that can be detected by a receiver coil encircling the sample tube. The receiver coil sends an electronic signal to an RF receiver, which amplifies and modifies the signal so that it can be displayed by a recorder as part of an NMR spectrum.

An NMR spectrum is a record of all the signals generated by all of the different kinds of nuclei in the sample that absorb RF radiation over the range swept by the instrument. If the sweep range is one in which the resonance conditions for ^{1}H nuclei (protons) are met, the spectrum should display different signals for protons that are in different molecular environments. For example, protons on the benzene ring in *para*-xylene are in a different molecular environment than protons on the methyl groups, so the NMR spectrum of *p*-xylene will display two signals—one for each kind of proton—at different positions on the spectrum, as shown in Figure G33. The position of a signal relative to the position of a reference signal, usually that of tetramethylsilane (TMS), is called its *chemical shift*. A chemical shift,

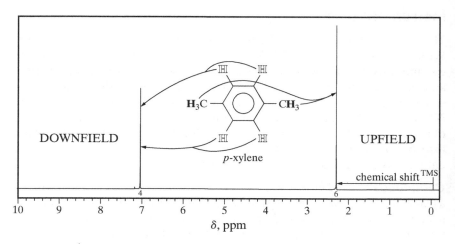

Figure G33 ^{1}H NMR spectrum of *p*-xylene

represented by the Greek letter δ, is ordinarily measured in parts per million (ppm). Because the TMS signal ($\delta = 0$) is on the right (upfield) side of a spectrum, chemical shifts increase from right to left.

A typical CW–NMR spectrometer suitable for use by undergraduate students may operate at a frequency of 60 MHz and a magnetic field strength of approximately 1.4 tesla (14,000 gauss). When an ^{1}H NMR spectrum is recorded using a 60-MHz spectrometer, the magnetic field is swept over a range of about 1.4×10^{-5} tesla (0.14 gauss), which is only 10 millionths of the external field strength, or 10 parts per million. This sweep range can be extended to 15 ppm or so to detect protons whose resonance conditions occur outside this range.

Fourier-Transform NMR. A Fourier-transform NMR spectrometer is capable of producing spectra with better resolution and a much higher signal-to-noise ratio than any CW instrument. In an FT–NMR instrument, the sample (in an appropriate sample tube) is placed between the poles of a powerful electromagnet and irradiated with a short ($\sim 10\,\mu s$) pulse of RF radiation that covers the entire frequency range of interest. The pulse is so intense that it raises all of the absorbing nuclei into the high-energy **down** state. As the high-energy nuclei return to their equilibrium state, they generate a *free induction decay (FID)* signal that contains information about the nuclei whose resonance conditions were met by any of the RF frequencies in the pulse. The FID signal, which is equivalent in information content to a complete NMR spectrum, is detected and sent to a microprocessor that accumulates and averages the FID signals from a series of pulses. The microprocessor then "decodes" the averaged FID signal by Fourier-transform analysis and converts it to a conventional NMR spectrum. The FID signal generated by one pulse takes less than a second to acquire, so an FT–NMR spectrometer can accumulate and average the equivalent of several hundred NMR spectra in the 2–5 minutes it takes a CW instrument to record a single spectrum. The resulting averaged spectrum has very little electronic noise and is thus much "cleaner" than a conventional CW spectrum.

A typical research-grade FT–NMR spectrometer uses an electromagnet whose components are cooled with liquid helium. At the temperature of liquid helium (4 K, $-269°C$), the coils of wire that generate the magnetic field are electrical superconductors, making it possible to attain very high field strengths of 14 tesla or more. Increasing the field strength of an NMR spectrometer causes the NMR signals to spread out, reducing overlap between adjacent signals. This and the high signal-to-noise ratio make complex ^{1}H NMR spectra generated on an FT instrument easier to interpret than those obtained with a CW instrument.

Adding the data generated by successive pulses improves the quality of the NMR spectrum because a signal increases in intensity with each addition, whereas electronic noise—being random—tends to cancel out.

Chemical-Shift Reagents

The amount of structural information that can be obtained from a CW–NMR spectrum is often limited by the presence of overlapping signals. Increasing the magnetic-field strength reduces overlapping by increasing the chemical shifts (in Hz) of all the signals by the same amount. Using a *chemical-shift reagent* also changes the chemical shifts of NMR signals, but it affects different signals differently; some are shifted more than others, and some may not be shifted at all. Nevertheless, an appropriate chemical-shift reagent can often be used to separate the signals of interest and facilitate spectral interpretation.

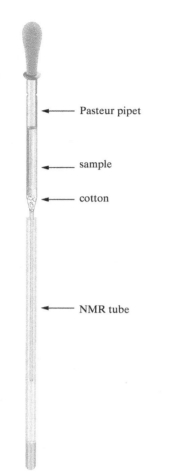

Pasteur pipet

sample

cotton

NMR tube

Figure G34 Filtering an NMR solution

Chemical-shift reagents are organometallic complexes of certain paramagnetic rare earth metals. These complexes can coordinate with the oxygen and nitrogen atoms of alcohols, amines, carbonyl compounds, and other Lewis bases. The local magnetic field produced by the paramagnetic metal atom shifts the signals of nearby protons to an extent that varies with distance; the closer a nucleus is to the metal atom, the more its chemical shift will change. Different chemical-shift reagents have different effects on a spectrum; thus, tris(dipivaloylmethanato)europium(III) [$Eu(dpm)_3$] causes signals to shift to the left (downfield) on an NMR spectrum, while the corresponding complex of praseodymium [$Pr(dpm)_3$] causes signals to shift to the right (upfield).

Sample Preparation

Most substances analyzed by NMR are first dissolved in a suitable solvent. Liquids that are no more viscous than water can sometimes be analyzed neat, but neat liquids may give broadened peaks and other spectral distortions due to intermolecular interactions. FT–NMR spectrometers yield good proton NMR spectra with solution concentrations as low as 0.1% (w/v). CW–NMR instruments usually require concentrations on the order of 5–20% (w/v), although satisfactory spectra may be obtained with lower concentrations when the amount of sample is limited. The liquid or solution is placed in a special thin-walled *NMR tube,* which is closed with a tight-fitting cap to prevent evaporation. A typical NMR tube has an o.d. of 5 mm, a length of 17.5 cm, and is both fragile and expensive. The NMR tube should be straight and uniform; a tube that wobbles when it is rolled down a slightly inclined glass plate will give large spinning sidebands, as discussed in "Sample Spinning." For a routine ^1H NMR analysis on a CW instrument, you can prepare the sample as described here.

- Dissolve 50–100 mg of your compound in 0.5–0.8 mL of a suitable solvent.
- Transfer the solution to the NMR tube with a Pasteur pipet. If the solution may contain solid impurities, use a filtering pipet (Figure G34).
- Add 5–15 μL of a reference standard, ordinarily TMS.
- Cap the NMR tube carefully.
- Invert the tube several times to mix the components thoroughly.

Some commercial deuterated solvents contain added TMS, in which case the third step is omitted. The NMR tube should be filled to a depth of at least 2.5 cm, but it should be no more than three-fourths full. TMS boils near room temperature, so it should be kept in a refrigerator and added with a *cold* syringe or fine-tipped dropper. For very high-resolution spectra, the sample should be *degassed* by bubbling a fine stream of pure nitrogen through it for one minute; degassing is not necessary for routine spectra.

NMR Solvents

A solvent suitable for ^1H NMR analysis should have no protons that produce intense signals of their own, because they might obscure signals from the sample. Therefore, hydrogen-containing solvents such as chloroform and acetone are used in their completely deuterated forms. Deuterium (^2H) undergoes resonance at about $6\frac{1}{2}$ times the field strength required for ^1H, so an isotopically pure deuterated solvent does not interfere with a proton

Table G3 Properties of some NMR solvents

Solvent	^{1}H δ, ppm	Solvent strength	Freedom from interactions	Viscosity
carbon disulfide	none	good	good	low
cyclohexane-d_{12}	1.4	poor	good	medium
acetonitrile-d_3	2.0	good	fair	low
acetone-d_6	2.1	good	poor	low
dimethyl-d_6 sulfoxide	2.5	very good	poor	high
1,4-dioxane-d_8	3.5	good	fair	medium
deuterium oxide	~5.2 (v)	good	poor	medium
chloroform-d	7.3	very good	fair	low
pyridine-d_5	7.0–8.7	good	poor	medium
trifluoroacetic acid-d	~12.5 (v)	good	poor	medium

Note: δ is the chemical shift of the protic form of the solvent; v = variable; solvent strength refers to the ability to dissolve a broad spectrum of organic compounds.

NMR spectrum. Most deuterated solvents, however, contain a significant amount of the protic form, giving rise to one or more small signals. For example, the NMR spectrum of a deuterochloroform (chloroform-d, CDCl$_3$) solution has a small CHCl$_3$ signal at 7.27 ppm, but this signal usually doesn't interfere with the solute's signals. A solvent for FT–NMR analysis *must* contain deuterium, because the instrument locks onto the resonance signal of deuterium to help the user adjust the controls for maximum spectral resolution.

A good NMR solvent should also have a low viscosity, a high solvent strength, and no appreciable interactions with the solute. Deuterochloroform is the most widely used NMR solvent because its polarity is low enough to prevent significant solute–solvent interactions, and most organic compounds are sufficiently soluble in it for NMR analysis. When a more polar solvent is required, dimethyl-d_6 sulfoxide can be used, often in mixtures with deuterochloroform. It is convenient to add 1–3% TMS to the bulk solvent so that it doesn't have to be added during sample preparation; as noted previously, some commercial solvents already contain TMS.

Table G3 compares the properties of some deuterated NMR solvents and gives the approximate chemical shifts (δ) of their ^{1}H NMR signals.

Instrumental Parameters

Spinning Rate. To minimize the effect of magnetic-field inhomogeneity, an NMR sample is rotated at a rate of 30–60 revolutions per second while its NMR spectrum is being recorded. It is important to use an appropriate spinning rate. Excessively high rates create a vortex that may extend into the region of the receiver coil—this is most likely when there isn't enough solution in the sample tube. Spinning rates that are too low can cause *spinning sidebands* or signal distortion (see Figure G35). Spinning sidebands are small peaks that are symmetrically spaced on either side of a main peak at a distance equal to the spinning rate; thus, an NMR tube spun at 30 cycles per second can give rise to sidebands 30 Hz from each main peak. Spinning sidebands can also be caused by field inhomogeneity and wobbling NMR

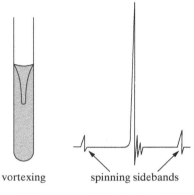

vortexing   spinning sidebands

Figure G35 Effects of spinning rate

tubes or sample spinners. To find out whether small signals are spinning sidebands or impurity peaks, change the spinning rate and scan over the peaks again to see if their positions change.

Field Homogeneity. Recording a good NMR spectrum requires that the magnetic field be homogeneous (uniform) at the sample. The most important homogeneity control, usually called the Y control, is adjusted to produce a uniform field along the axis of the sample tube. For routine work on a previously tuned CW–NMR spectrometer, the Y control can be set by placing a blank sheet of paper over the chart paper and repeatedly scanning a strong peak in the spectrum of the sample (or of a standard acetaldehyde solution), each time making small adjustments in the Y control until the peak is as tall and narrow as possible and shows a good "ringing" (beat) pattern. Figure G36 shows an excellent ringing pattern for the quartet (four-peak signal) of acetaldehyde, characterized by the high amplitude, long duration, and exponential decay of the "wiggles" following the main peaks. An FT–NMR spectrum does not show a ringing pattern; magnetic-field homogeneity is adjusted by maximizing the intensity of a deuterium lock signal. Ordinarily, the instructor or a lab technician performs such adjustments.

Signal Amplitude. With a typical CW–NMR spectrometer, the amplitude (height) of the signals is adjusted with two controls. The *spectrum amplitude* control changes the amplitude of both the signals and the baseline noise. The *RF power* control increases signal height without increasing baseline noise up to the point at which *saturation* begins. At that point, the number of nuclei in both spin states is so nearly equal that increasing the intensity of the RF radiation no longer increases the number of transitions; instead it can cause distortion and reduce the signal size. Unless high sensitivity is required, the RF power level is usually set to a value at which there is little likelihood of saturation (usually about midrange), and the spectrum amplitude control is then adjusted so that the strongest peak in the spectrum extends nearly to the top of the chart paper.

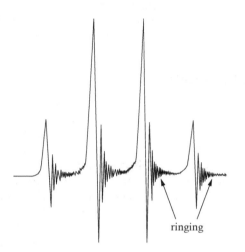

Figure G36 Ringing pattern for the quartet of acetaldehyde

Sweep. There are four sweep controls on a typical CW–NMR spectrometer; these control the reference point of the spectrum, the sweep width, the sweep time, and the portion of the spectrum to be scanned. The *sweep zero* control is used to set the signal for the reference compound to the proper value (zero for TMS). The *sweep width* control sets the total chemical-shift range to be scanned, usually 600–1000 Hz when the entire spectrum is being scanned on a 60-MHz instrument. A 600-Hz (10-ppm) range can be used if the sample is known to contain no protons that absorb downfield of 10 ppm. A CW–NMR spectrum is often scanned at a sweep rate (sweep width divided by sweep time) of 1 Hz per second, so the *sweep time* can be set numerically equal to the sweep width (for example, 600 s for a 600-Hz sweep width). The *sweep offset* control is used when only a specific portion of the spectrum is to be scanned; it sets the upfield limit of the scan. For example, if a scan between 350 and 500 Hz is desired, the sweep offset should be 350 Hz and the sweep range 150 Hz.

Phasing. The *phasing* control should be adjusted to obtain a straight baseline before and after a signal (see Figure G37). Correct phasing is much more important when an NMR spectrum is being integrated than when it is being recorded.

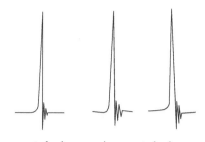
correct phasing   incorrect phasing

Figure G37 Effects of phasing on baseline

Integrating a Spectrum

An ¹H NMR spectrum is ordinarily *integrated* to measure the areas of its signals. With a typical CW–NMR instrument, the recorder pen traces a horizontal line until it reaches a signal; then it rises a distance that is proportional to the signal's area as it crosses the signal. Because the area of a signal on a proton NMR spectrum is proportional to the number of protons responsible for the signal, integrating the spectrum makes it possible to determine how many protons give rise to each signal.

    Following is a summary of the steps in the integration of a typical ¹H NMR spectrum. If you will be expected to integrate your NMR spectrum, your instructor will provide more detailed directions.

With an FT–NMR spectrometer, the signals are integrated electronically.

1. The RF power is optimized to provide an acceptable signal-to-noise ratio.
2. The instrument is switched to the integral mode.
3. While the spectrum is scanned rapidly, the integral amplitude control is adjusted until the integrator trace spans the vertical axis of the chart.
4. With the sweep offset and sweep width controls set to scan a region free from NMR signals, the balance control is adjusted during a slow scan of that region to give a horizontal line.
5. While scanning a signal, the phasing control is adjusted to make the integrator traces before and after the signal as nearly horizontal as possible.
6. The integral over the entire spectrum is recorded using a sweep time that is about one-fifth to one-tenth that for the normal spectrum. The pen should be returned to the baseline after the scan.
7. The relative peak areas are determined by measuring the vertical distances between the integrator traces before and after each signal (see Figure G38).

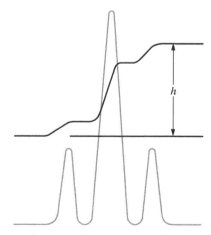
(*h* is proportional to the total area under the triplet)

Figure G38 Measuring signal areas

DIRECTIONS FOR RECORDING AN ¹H NMR SPECTRUM

These directions are for a typical CW-NMR instrument. If you will be using an FT-NMR instrument, your instructor will demonstrate its operation.

Equipment and Supplies

NMR spectrometer
sample
deuterated NMR solvent
TMS
NMR tube
Pasteur pipet
tissues
washing solvent

Do not attempt to operate the instrument without prior instruction and proper supervision. Do not make any adjustments other than the ones specified, except at the instructor's request and under his or her supervision. Some of the adjustments described here may be made in advance by the instructor or a lab technician.

Take Care! Handle NMR tubes with great care; they are fragile and may break.

Prepare a solution of the sample in a suitable NMR solvent as described in "Sample Preparation," and add 1–3% TMS, if necessary. Fill the NMR tube to a depth of about 3 cm with this solution and cap the tube. Wipe the outside of the NMR tube carefully with a tissue paper or lint-free cloth, insert it in the sample spinner using a depth gauge to adjust its position, wipe it again, and carefully place the assembly into the sample probe between the magnet pole faces. Adjust the air flow to spin the sample at 40–50 Hz; it may need to be readjusted later to minimize spinning sidebands. Align the chart paper on the recorder and cover it with a sheet of scrap paper. Set the sweep controls to scan the desired range at a suitable rate. Typical settings for a 60-MHz instrument are: sweep offset, 0; sweep width, 600 Hz; and sweep time, 600 s. Set the RF power to about midrange and the filter response time to 1 s or less. Set the spectrum amplitude control to about midrange, and scan the spectrum to find the tallest peak. Readjust the spectrum amplitude to keep that peak on scale near the top of the chart during a scan. If necessary, optimize peak shape and ringing and adjust the phasing as directed by your instructor. Set the TMS peak to δ 0.0 with the sweep zero control; you may have to sweep through the TMS signal several times, adjusting the control each time, until it is lined up with the zero on the chart paper. Set the recorder baseline, if necessary, to a convenient location near the bottom of the spectrum. Remove the scrap paper and record the spectrum. If you are to integrate your spectrum, cover it with scrap paper while you make the adjustments described in "Integrating a Spectrum;" then remove the paper and record the integral on the original spectrum.

When you have finished scanning and integrating your spectrum, remove the spectrum and record the control settings and other relevant information on it. Then remove the sample tube as demonstrated by your instructor; follow directions carefully or the tube may break. Clean the sample tube immediately and thoroughly using a Pasteur pipet and an appropriate

Special NMR-tube cleaners are available commercially.

solvent. The protic form of the solvent in which the sample was dissolved is generally used for cleaning. For example, if the solvent was $CDCl_3$, rinse the tube with $CHCl_3$—*not* the much more expensive deuterated solvent. Invert the tube in a suitable rack and let it drain dry. Before being reused, an NMR tube should be dried in an oven to remove all traces of the wash solvent.

Waste Disposal: Dispose of the sample and wash solvent as directed by your instructor or as indicated in an experiment's directions.

Summary

1. Prepare solution; add TMS, if necessary.
2. Transfer solution to NMR tube and cap tube.
3. Wipe tube and insert in sample spinner.
4. Insert spinner in probe; adjust spinning rate.
5. Align chart paper and cover with scrap paper.
6. Set sweep, RF power, and filter response time controls.
7. Scan spectrum and adjust spectrum amplitude control.
8. Zero TMS signal.
9. Set baseline; remove scrap paper.
10. Scan spectrum.
11. Integrate spectrum.
12. Remove and clean sample tube; dispose of solution.

When Things Go Wrong

If the NMR spectrum of a sample run in $CDCl_3$ has a small extraneous peak at δ 7.3, don't worry about it; the peak arises from the small amount of $CHCl_3$ in the solvent. If you are using some other deuterated solvent, check Table G3 to see where the signal of the protic form of that solvent occurs, and disregard any small peaks at that location. (See "NMR Solvents.")

If each signal in your NMR spectrum is flanked by two considerably smaller peaks equidistant from the signal, the extraneous signals are probably spinning sidebands. Increase the sample spinning rate and scan over the same region. If the peaks change position but don't disappear, try to identify the cause and take corrective action. (See "Spinning Rate.")

If the peaks in your NMR spectrum are distorted or unusually broad, the sample may be spinning too fast (forming a vortex), too slow (causing field inhomogeneity), or not at all. Check the spinning rate and adjust it, if necessary; you might also need to increase the sample size to prevent vortexing problems or decrease it to reduce inhomogeneity. (See "Spinning Rate.") If the peaks are still too broad, check to see if the NMR tube is straight and uniform; if it isn't, transfer the sample to a different NMR tube. (See "Sample Preparation.") If the sample might contain ferromagnetic impurities, filter it as you transfer it to the other NMR tube. (See "Sample Preparation.") If that doesn't help, the spectrum amplitude control may be set too high or the magnetic field may be inhomogeneous; ask your instructor for help. (See "Signal Amplitude" and "Field Homogeneity.")

If some of the peaks in your spectrum extend to the top of the chart paper and flatten out there, your sample solution may be too concentrated. Dilute it by half and try again. (See "Sample Preparation.") If the sample concentration is appropriate, the signal amplitude control may be set too high. See your instructor about having it readjusted. (See "Signal Amplitude.")

If the chemical shifts of all your peaks are off by the same amount, the reference peak wasn't positioned correctly. Use the sweep zero control to reposition the reference peak to zero for TMS, or to the appropriate value for a different reference compound. (See "Sweep.") If there is no reference peak, add TMS and then adjust the sweep zero control. (See "Sample Preparation" and "Sweep.")

If you are running the NMR spectrum of a carboxylic acid, phenol, or enolic compound and can't find the signal for the OH proton, change the sweep range to include the region above 10 ppm. (See "Sweep.")

If the baseline of your NMR spectrum is not straight and horizontal, adjust the phasing control until it is. (See "Phasing.")

Interpretation of ^{1}H NMR Spectra

A proton NMR spectrum provides numerical data in the form of chemical shifts, signal areas, signal multiplicities, and coupling constants. Working out the structure of a molecule from these numbers is a fascinating mental exercise comparable to the work of a cryptographer who reconstructs meaningful messages from coded symbols.

The *chemical shift* (δ) is the distance, measured in hertz or parts per million, from the center of a signal to some reference signal, usually that of TMS. The TMS signal occurs farther upfield (to the right) than nearly all other proton signals, so the chemical shift of a signal is usually measured as its distance downfield (to the left) from that of TMS, as shown in Figure G39. Note that a signal may have more than one peak (four peaks in this example).

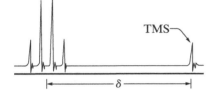

Figure G39 Chemical shift of a proton NMR signal

The *signal area,* which is the sum of the areas under all of the peaks in a signal, is proportional to the number of protons giving rise to the signal. Signal areas are determined by using an electronic integrator that traces a line across each proton signal after it is recorded. On a manually integrated spectrum, the area of a signal is proportional to the vertical rise of the integrator pen as it crosses the signal, that is, to the height of the "steps" drawn by the integrator pen, as shown in Figure G38. Integrated signal areas can be converted to proton numbers using the following relationship:

number of protons responsible for signal $=$

$$\text{total number of protons} \times \frac{\text{area under signal}}{\text{area under all signals}}$$

For example, suppose that a compound with the molecular formula $C_{10}H_{14}$ has four signals with relative areas of 42, 7, 14, and 35. The sum of the areas is 98, so the number of protons responsible for the first signal is

$$14 \times \frac{42}{98} = 6$$

By similar calculations, it can be shown that 1, 2, and 5 protons, respectively, are responsible for the other three signals. If the molecular formula of a compound is not known, relative proton numbers can be obtained by reducing the signal areas to the lowest ratio of integers.

The signal generated by a given set of protons may be split into several peaks as a result of *coupling* interactions with nearby proton sets (refer to your lecture textbook or see your instructor for an explanation of coupling). The *multiplicity* of a signal is simply the number of separate peaks it contains; its *coupling constant* is the distance between two adjacent peaks in

Stop and Think: What is the most likely structure for this compound if it contains a benzene ring and one alkyl side chain?

the signal, measured in hertz (Hz). Figure G40 shows the signals of two sets of protons that are interacting with each other; the protons of set *a* have split the signal of the protons of set *b* into four peaks (a quartet), and the *b* protons have split the signal of the *a* protons into three peaks (a triplet). The coupling constant, which is equal for the two signals, is represented by J_{ab}. In the simplest case, the number of protons responsible for splitting the signal of a neighboring set of protons can be determined by subtracting 1 from the number of peaks in that signal. Thus, the three peaks in the *a* signal are produced by two neighboring *b* protons, and the four peaks in the *b* signal by three neighboring *a* protons. An interacting triplet–quartet grouping of this kind is good evidence for an ethyl (CH_3CH_2—) group.

Ideal triplets and quartets should be symmetrical, having relative peak area ratios of 1:2:1 and 1:3:3:1, respectively. As shown in Figure G40, however, the signals in an actual spectrum are often somewhat distorted, giving paired peaks of unequal height. Note that the two signals in the figure aren't perfectly symmetrical but appear to "lean" toward each other, with the peaks on the side that face the other signal being higher than predicted. This and the fact that their coupling constants are equal provide additional evidence that the protons responsible for the two signals are, in fact, coupling with each other and not with some other proton sets in the molecule.

The following general procedure should help you derive structural information from a proton NMR spectrum.

1. Measure the integrated area of each signal and use it to determine the number of protons responsible for the signal. Each set of equivalent protons (protons in the same molecular environment) gives rise to a signal, and the relative signal areas can tell you how many protons are in each set. For example, 3,3-dimethyl-2-butanone has nine hydrogen atoms on the three equivalent methyl groups to the left of the carbonyl group and three on the other methyl group, so its ^1H NMR spectrum has two signals with an area ratio of 3:1.

2. Determine the chemical shift of each signal on the delta scale by measuring the distance, in parts per million, from the center of the signal to the TMS reference peak. The chemical shift of a signal may indicate what kinds of protons are responsible for the signal, and it may suggest their relative locations in the molecule. For example, alkyl hydrogen atoms that are remote from electron-withdrawing substituents should have a chemical shift of approximately 0.9 ppm if they are primary, 1.3 ppm if they are secondary, and 1.5 ppm if they are tertiary. Electron-withdrawing groups that contain oxygen, nitrogen, or halogens tend to move ^1H NMR signals downfield, thereby increasing their chemical shifts. Benzene rings give rise to large downfield shifts, making it quite easy to recognize aromatic compounds from their ^1H NMR spectra. The correlation chart in Figure G41 (and also on the back endpaper) summarizes chemical-shift data for a number of proton types. Chemical-shift values for compounds from the common families of organic compounds are given in Table G4.

3. Determine the multiplicity of each signal by counting the number of distinguishable peaks in the signal. (Very small peaks may be obscured by baseline noise.) If the signal of a proton set is reasonably symmetrical and contains evenly spaced peaks, it may be possible to determine how many nearby protons are coupled with the protons in that set by

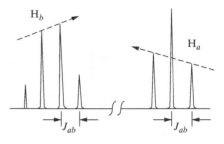

Figure G40 Signals of nearest neighbor protons

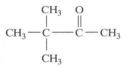

3,3-dimethyl-2-butanone

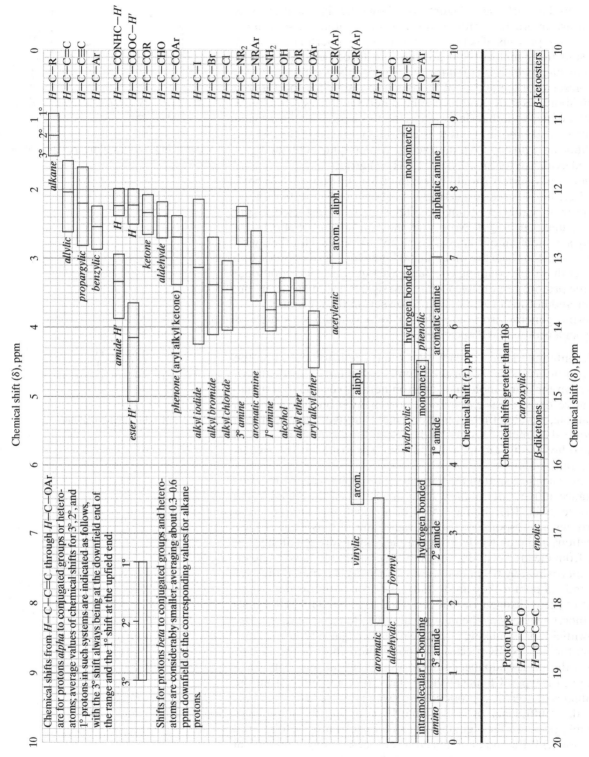

Figure G41 Correlation chart relating ¹H NMR chemical shifts to proton environments

Table G4 Approximate ^{1}H NMR chemical-shift ranges for different types of protons

Family	Proton type	Chemical shift range (δ, ppm)
alcohol	H—O—R	1–5.5
	H—C—OH	3.4–4
phenol	H—O—Ar	4–12
	H—Ar	6–8.5
aldehyde	H—C=O	9–10
	H—C—CHO	2.2–2.7
ketone	H—C—COR	2–2.5
carboxylic acid	H—O—C=O	10.5–12
	H—C—COOH	2–2.6
ester	H—C—COOR	2–2.5
	H—C—OC=O	3.5–5
amine	H—N—R (aliphatic)	1–3
	*H—N—R (aromatic)	3–5
	H—C—N	2.2–4
amide	*H—N—C=O	5–9.5
	H—C—CO—N	2–2.4
	H—C—NC=O	3–4
halide	H—C—Br	2.5–4
	H—C—Cl	3–4
aromatic hydrocarbon	H—Ar	6–8.5
	H—C—Ar	2.2–3

Note: Signals of proton types marked with an asterisk are often very broad.

subtracting 1 from the multiplicity of the signal. Irregular signals and signals that have been split by several dissimilar proton sets must be analyzed by more advanced methods.

4. Measure the coupling constant of each signal that contains more than one peak and try to determine from the resulting values and the way each signal "leans" what other signals might be coupled with it.

All of this information can be used to build up the structure of a molecule piece by piece. For example, consider the ^{1}H NMR spectrum in Figure G42 of a ketone that has the molecular formula $C_7H_{14}O$. The spectrum has only two signals, *a* and *b*, which have a relative area ratio of 6:1. Because the compound contains 14 protons, $\frac{6}{7}$ of them, or 12, must be responsible for signal *a*, and $\frac{1}{7}$ of them, or 2, for signal *b*. Signal *a* has only two peaks, indicating that the *a* protons have only one neighboring proton. The seven peaks in signal *b* (visible under a magnifying glass) indicate that the *b* protons have six neighbors, and the higher chemical shift of their signal suggests that they are closer to the electron-withdrawing carbonyl group than are the *a* protons. The only alkyl group in which a single proton has six equivalent protons for neighbors is the isopropyl group, $(CH_3)_2CH—$. Two such groups provide the required total of 12 *a* and 2 *b* protons, and attaching them both to a carbonyl group gives the complete structure of the ketone, which is 2,4-dimethyl-3-pentanone. Note that the structure in the margin accounts for all of the features of the ^{1}H NMR spectrum: the 6:1 area ratio for the *a* and *b* protons; the higher chemical shift of the signal for the *b* protons resulting from their proximity to the carbonyl group; the splitting

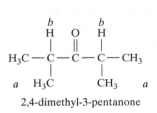

2,4-dimethyl-3-pentanone

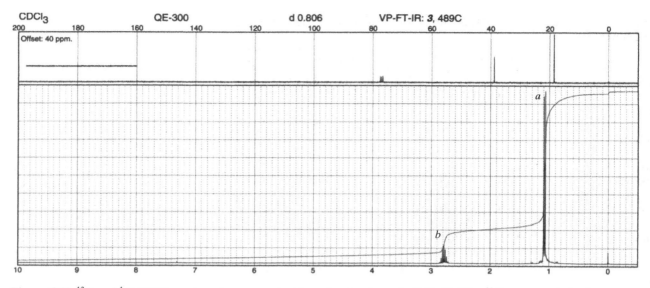

Figure G42 ^{13}C and ^1H NMR spectra of compound with molecular formula $C_7H_{14}O$. (The ^{13}C spectrum is in the narrow strip at the top.)

of the *a* signal into two peaks by each neighboring *b* proton; the splitting of the *b* signal into seven peaks by each group of six neighboring *a* protons; and the identical coupling constants of the two signals.

For further information about the interpretation of ^1H NMR spectra and information on advanced topics such as second-order effects, two-dimensional NMR, and computer simulation of NMR spectra, refer to your lecture textbook or to appropriate sources in Category F of the Bibliography, if included.

b. ^{13}C NMR Spectrometry

Except where noted here, most of the principles and experimental methods described previously for ^1H NMR spectrometry also apply to ^{13}C NMR spectrometry. Because carbon-13 nuclei are much less abundant than hydrogen nuclei, signals from the ^{13}C nuclei in a typical sample are about 6000 times weaker than those from its ^1H nuclei. A CW–NMR spectrometer can hardly distinguish such weak signals from electronic baseline noise, so carbon-13 NMR spectra are ordinarily recorded using Fourier-transform NMR instruments. Because such instruments are complex and vary widely in design and operation, no attempt will be made here to describe their operating procedures.

A typical ^{13}C NMR spectrum is usually simpler and easier to interpret than the ^1H NMR spectrum of the same compound. Carbon–carbon splitting is unimportant, because carbon-13 nuclei cannot couple with nonmagnetic carbon-12 nuclei and because there is only a slight chance that two carbon-13 atoms will be next to each other in the same molecule. Hydrogen nuclei couple strongly with carbon-13 nuclei, however—not only with the nuclei of the carbon atoms that they are bonded to but with those of more distant carbons as well. Such coupling results in very complex spectra, so it is usually prevented by various *decoupling* techniques. For *broadband proton decoupling*,

Anasazi Instruments converts 60 MHz and 90 MHz CW–NMR spectrometers to FT–NMR instruments that are capable of recording NMR spectra from carbon-13 and other nuclei.

the sample is subjected to continuous broad-spectrum RF radiation that covers the resonance frequencies of its protons, causing all of the protons to flip over (change spin states) so rapidly that their coupling effects on the adjacent carbon atoms average out to zero. In a broadband-decoupled ^{13}C NMR spectrum, each ^{13}C signal is a single peak rather than a multiplet. For an example, see the broadband-decoupled ^{13}C NMR spectrum in Figure G42, which is displayed in a narrow strip above the ^{1}H NMR spectrum. (The three closely spaced peaks near 78 ppm arise from the solvent, chloroform-d.)

Another decoupling technique, *off-resonance decoupling,* yields *proton-coupled* spectra, in which only those hydrogens that are attached directly to a carbon atom split the signal of that carbon atom. Thus, the three protons of a methyl group will split the signal of the methyl carbon into a quartet, but they will not split the signal of any other carbon in the molecule. Proton-coupled spectra are less common and harder to interpret than broadband-decoupled spectra, so we won't consider them further.

The area of a ^{13}C signal, unlike that of an ^{1}H signal, is not directly proportional to the number of atoms responsible for the signal, so ^{13}C NMR spectra are not integrated. Consequently, three of the four parameters that can be obtained from ^{1}H NMR spectra are not present in a broadband-decoupled ^{13}C NMR spectra. Because there is no integration, there are no signal areas, and because all of the signals are singlets, there are no multiplicities or coupling constants to interpret. That leaves only the chemical shifts—which, as it happens, are extraordinarily useful.

The ^{13}C NMR spectrum of a compound gives us direct information about the compound's carbon "backbone;" information that often is not available from its ^{1}H NMR spectrum. A broadband-decoupled ^{13}C NMR spectrum of a compound contains one sharp peak for each kind of carbon atom in its molecules. Because many compounds have few, if any, magnetically equivalent carbon atoms, most of the peaks in a typical ^{13}C NMR spectrum are one-carbon peaks, each arising from a different carbon atom. Thus, the absence of a linear relationship between signal area and the number of carbon atoms is not a serious handicap.

Carbon-13 chemical shifts cover a much broader range than proton chemical shifts—about 250 ppm compared to 15 ppm or so for protons (see Table G5). As a result, the peaks on a ^{13}C NMR spectrum are usually well separated. The chemical shift of a carbon-13 atom is very sensitive to changes in its hybridization and molecular environment. Carbon atoms that are sp^2 hybridized have much higher chemical shifts (δ 100—160) than sp^3 carbons (δ 0—60), and the chemical shifts of sp carbons are somewhere in between (δ 60—105). As in ^{1}H NMR spectrometry, electron-withdrawing groups cause downfield chemical shifts at nearby carbon atoms, but they can cause upfield shifts at more distant carbon atoms. For example, a chlorine atom increases the chemical shift of an α-carbon atom by about 30 ppm and of a β-carbon atom by about 10 ppm, but it *decreases* the chemical shift of a γ-carbon atom by about 5 ppm.

$$\begin{array}{cccc} \gamma & \beta & \alpha & \\ C & C & C & Cl \\ -5 & +10 & +30 & \end{array}$$

Other electron-withdrawing groups have similar effects. Electron-donating groups have the opposite effect, decreasing the chemical shifts of α and β carbon atoms and increasing the chemical shifts of γ carbon atoms.

J. Chem. Educ. **1987,** *64,* 915 *describes a method for estimating ^{13}C chemical shifts.*

Table G5 ^{13}C NMR chemical-shift ranges for different types of carbon atoms

Type of carbon atom	Chemical-shift range (δ, ppm)
1° alkyl, **R**CH$_3$	0–40
2° alkyl, **R**$_2$CH$_2$	10–50
3° alkyl, **R**$_3$CH	15–50
alkene, **C**=**C**	100–160
alkyne, **C**≡**C**	60–90
aryl, 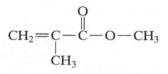**C**—	100–170
alkyl halide, **C**—X (X=Cl, Br)	5–75
alcohol or ether, **C**—O	40–90
amine, **C**—N	10–70
aldehyde or ketone, **C**=O	180–220
carboxylic acid or ester, O=**C**—O	160–185
amide, O=**C**—N	150–180

Table G5 shows chemical-shift ranges for some kinds of ^{13}C atoms. Such tables can be used to assign the peaks in a ^{13}C NMR spectrum to specific carbon atoms. For example, the ^{13}C NMR spectrum of methyl methacrylate has five peaks with chemical shifts of 18, 52, 125, 137, and 167 ppm.

$$CH_2{=}C{-}\overset{\overset{\displaystyle O}{\parallel}}{C}{-}O{-}CH_3$$
$$\underset{CH_3}{|}$$

methyl methacrylate

From Table G5, we find the following information for carbon atoms like those in methyl methacrylate:

ester carbonyl carbon: 160–185 ppm

alkene carbon: 100–160 ppm

carbon single-bonded to oxygen (C—O): 40–90 ppm

primary alkyl carbon: 0–40 ppm

Note that the C—O chemical-shift range from the table is for alcohols and ethers, but a carbon atom on the alcohol portion of an ester is in a similar environment. From this information, it is easy to match the peak at 167 ppm with the carbonyl carbon, the peaks at 125 ppm and 137 ppm with the alkene carbons, the peak at 52 ppm with the OCH$_3$ methyl group, and the peak at 18 ppm with the remaining methyl group. Because the alkene carbon *beta* to the two oxygen atoms would be expected to have a higher chemical shift than the alkene carbon *gamma* to them, we can assign chemical-shift values to the carbon atoms as shown in the margin. Such assignments can often be confirmed by a technique called *distortionless enhanced polarization transfer (DEPT)*, which can pinpoint the carbon atom that is responsible for a particular signal.

$$\underset{125}{CH_2}{=}\underset{137}{C}{-}\underset{167}{C}{-}O{-}\underset{52}{CH_3}$$

Ultraviolet–Visible Spectrometry

Principles and Applications

Ultraviolet–visible (UV–VIS) spectrometers, which detect the absorption of radiation in the visible (~400–800 nm) and near ultraviolet (~200–400 nm) regions of the electromagnetic spectrum, are useful for both qualitative and quantitative analysis of certain organic compounds, particularly those that have conjugated double bonds or aromatic rings. Radiation in these regions may induce molecules to undergo transitions from an electronic ground state to one or more excited states. The energy required for an electronic transition is much greater than that needed to induce a vibrational or nuclear magnetic transition, so the wavelength of the radiation used is much shorter: 200–800 nm compared to about 2.5–50 μm for IR spectrometry and several meters for NMR. Most transitions involving electrons in single bonds and isolated double bonds require wavelengths shorter than 200 nm, but conventional UV–VIS spectrometers aren't designed to scan this region, because oxygen from the air absorbs UV radiation below 200 nm. Therefore, the electronic transitions that give rise to UV–VIS spectral bands usually involve nonbonded electrons or the pi electrons in aromatic and conjugated aliphatic systems. An example of such a transition is illustrated in Figure G43, in which a pi electron in the ground-state electron configuration of 1,3-butadiene jumps from its bonding molecular orbital to an unoccupied antibonding molecular orbital.

1 nanometer (nm) = 10^{-9} m. The older unit "millimicrons" (mμ) is sometimes used for nm.

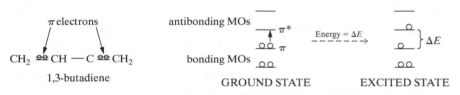

Figure G43 Electronic energy transition in 1,3-butadiene

A UV–VIS spectrum is often quite featureless compared to an IR or NMR spectrum, and it may consist of only one or two broad *absorption bands*. The broad-band structure is caused by rotational and vibrational transitions that accompany each electronic transition; each different combination of rotational and vibrational transitions has a different energy, so collectively they span a broad range of wavelengths. The height of an absorption band above the baseline of a UV–VIS spectrum is measured in units of *absorbance, A*. The position of an absorption band is given by its wavelength of maximum absorbance, λ_{max}, which is measured from the top of the band. For example, the absorption band illustrated in Figure G44 has an absorbance of 0.80 and a λ_{max} of 350 nm. Absorbance is related to *transmittance (T)*, the fraction of incident radiation transmitted through a sample, by the following equation:

$$A = \log(1/T) = -\log T \qquad (1)$$

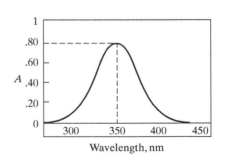

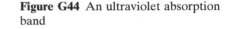

Figure G44 An ultraviolet absorption band

From *Operational Organic Chemistry: A Problem Solving Approach to the Laboratory*, Fourth Edition, John W. Lehman. Copyright © 2009 by Pearson Education. Published by Prentice Hall. All rights reserved.

Thus, the transmittance of a UV–VIS band is equal to 10^{-A}. For a band with $A = 0.80$, $T = 10^{-0.80} = 0.16$, meaning that about 16% of the light entering the sample passes through unchanged; the remaining 84% is absorbed by the sample.

a. UV–VIS Spectra

Sample Preparation

Routine UV–VIS spectra are nearly always obtained in solution. The solvent must be transparent (or nearly so) in the regions to be scanned. Water, 95% ethanol, methanol, dioxane, acetonitrile, and cyclohexane are suitable down to about 210–220 nm; other solvents can be used at higher wavelengths. The preferred solvent is 95% ethanol, in part because it doesn't require additional purification; most other solvents must be purified or purchased as spectral-grade solvents. The solvent must not, of course, react with the solute. For example, alcohols shouldn't be used as solvents for aldehydes.

If possible, the solution to be analyzed should produce a maximum absorbance of about 1 when the solute's strongest absorption band is scanned. Using Beer's law (see Equation **2**) we can show that the molar concentration of such a solution, if analyzed in a 1-cm sample cell, should be less than or equal to $1/\varepsilon_{max}$, where we define ε_{max} as the maximum molar absorptivity of the solute over the wavelength range to be scanned. For example, if the solute's strongest band has a molar absorptivity of 10,000 at its λ_{max} value, the solution concentration should be about $1 \times 10^{-4} M$. To make up such dilute solutions accurately, it may be necessary to prepare a stock solution that is too concentrated by several powers of 10, and then measure an aliquot of this solution and dilute it. For example, to prepare a $1.0 \times 10^{-4} M$ solution of cinnamic acid (mol wt = 148), you could measure 0.15 g (1.0 mmol) of the solid into a 100-mL volumetric flask and fill it to the mark with solvent; then transfer a 1-mL aliquot of this 0.010 M solution into another 100-mL volumetric flask and fill it to the mark with solvent. For qualitative work, when knowing the exact concentration of the solution isn't necessary, you can omit the dilution step and use a 10-μL syringe to measure a specified or calculated amount of a liquid sample into about 25 mL of the solvent. If the molar absorptivity of the solute is not known, it may be necessary to find the optimum concentration by trial and error, starting with a more concentrated solution and diluting it as needed to bring all of the absorption bands on scale.

Sample Cells

The most commonly used *spectrophotometer cell* is a transparent rectangular container with a square cross-section, having a path length of 1.00 cm and a capacity of about 3 mL. Two sides of a typical cell are nontransparent (usually frosted) and the other two are transparent. Silica or quartz cells are used for the UV region; optical glass or plastic cells are suitable in the visible region. Cells must be scrupulously cleaned; they should never be touched on their transparent sides—even a fingerprint can yield a spectrum.

Recording a Spectrum

The construction of UV–VIS spectrometers varies widely. Both single- and double-beam instruments are available, with and without recording capability. For a double-beam recording instrument, two identical spectrophotometer cells are filled about two-thirds full with (1) a solution of the compound being analyzed (the sample) and (2) the solvent used to prepare the solution. For a single-beam instrument, the same cell is used for both the sample and the pure solvent. A spectrophotometer cell filled with the sample or solvent is held by its nontransparent sides and inserted into the appropriate cell holder inside the instrument's sample compartment, oriented so that the light beam will pass through its transparent faces.

Before a spectrum is recorded, the user selects the wavelength region to be scanned and may also select a radiation source appropriate for that region. A tungsten lamp can be used between 300 and 800 nm and a hydrogen lamp between 190 and 350 nm. The absorbance range of some instruments can be preset; a typical range is from zero to one or two absorbance units. Modern computerized instruments allow the operator to apply a baseline correction, so that the instrument automatically subtracts any absorption due to the solvent as the spectrum is scanned. Such instruments have a monitor to display the spectrum and a printer or plotter to record it. Most older instruments record UV–VIS spectra on a roll of chart paper that feeds onto a flat recorder bed as the spectrum is scanned.

Once a spectrum has been recorded, the data it contains can be presented as a tabulation of λ_{max} values giving either the absorbance, molar absorptivity (ε), or log ε at each wavelength specified. For example, the UV spectrum of cinnamic acid is reported in one reference book as "λ^{al} 210 (4.24), 215 (4.28), 221 (4.18), 268 (4.31)." The numbers in parentheses are log ε values for peaks having the λ_{max} values (in nanometers) given, and "al" indicates that the spectrum was run in ethyl alcohol.

DIRECTIONS FOR OPERATING A RECORDING UV–VIS SPECTROMETER

Equipment and Supplies

UV–VIS spectrometer
sample
solvent(s)
sample cell(s)
lens paper

Do not attempt to operate the instrument without prior instruction and proper supervision. Do not make any adjustments to the controls, other than the ones specified, except with your instructor's permission. UV–VIS spectrometers vary widely in construction and operation, so the following is intended only as a general guide and may not be applicable to the instrument you will be using. Specific operating instructions should be learned from in-class demonstrations or the operator's manual.

Prepare a solution of the sample in an appropriate solvent as described in "Sample Preparation." Unless otherwise instructed, clean a sample cell (or two, for a double-beam instrument) by wiping its surfaces with a lens paper moistened with spectral-grade methanol or another appropriate solvent, and then let the solvent evaporate. This should leave the cell surfaces free of contaminants that may have accumulated since the cell was last used. Be sure that the instrument, recorder or printer, and source lamps are on and have had sufficient time to warm up. If necessary, select the appropriate radiation source for the desired wavelength range and set the absorbance range to 0–1 or another appropriate value. Set the starting and ending wavelengths. If the instrument scans from high to low wavelength, the starting wavelength will be the highest wavelength of the range to be scanned. If there is no provision for setting the ending wavelength, you will have to end the scan manually. Some instruments require manual adjustment of zero and 100% transmittance values (or infinite and zero absorbance values) before a spectrum or baseline is run; if so, make the adjustments as directed by your instructor. If the instrument provides for a baseline correction, fill the cell with the solvent, cap it, and place it in the sample compartment with a transparent side facing the light source. Then close the compartment door and record the baseline (if necessary) as directed by your instructor.

For a single-beam instrument, remove the solvent from the sample cell, rinse it with a small amount of the solution to be analyzed, fill it with that solution, cap it, and place it in the cell holder in the sample compartment. For a double-beam instrument, place one capped cell, filled with the sample, in the sample-cell holder; place another cell, filled with the solvent, in the reference-cell holder. Close the sample compartment door. If the instrument uses chart paper, position it so that the scan starts on an ordinate (vertical) line, label this line with the starting wavelength, lower the pen to the paper, and begin to scan the spectrum. For a computerized instrument, start the scan as directed by your instructor. If any absorption band goes off-scale so that its top is "chopped off," change the absorbance range or dilute the sample. If both ultraviolet and visible regions are to be scanned, change the radiation source, if necessary (many instruments do this automatically), and scan the spectrum in the other region. If the scan doesn't stop automatically when the end of the wavelength range has been reached, stop it manually. If the instrument has a chart recorder, raise the pen from the chart and tear off the chart paper; then write down the wavelength and absorbance ranges along its x- and y-axes and record the wavelength interval between chart units. If the instrument has a printer or plotter, initiate printing or plotting of the spectrum. Measure and write down the λ_{max} and absorbance values of all significant bands.

Rinse the sample cell several times with an appropriate solvent. If necessary, clean it further using a liquid detergent or a special cleaning solution. Never use a *dry* lens paper, an abrasive cleanser, or any scrubbing implement (such as a pipe cleaner with a wire core) that might scratch the cell. Drain both cells of excess solvent and dry them as directed by your instructor.

Waste Disposal: Dispose of the solution and used solvent as directed by your instructor or as indicated in an experiment's directions.

Summary

1. Clean sample cell(s).
2. Select source, if necessary.
3. Set absorbance and wavelength ranges.
4. Record baseline, if necessary.

5. Scan spectrum of sample.

6. Record spectral parameters.

7. Dispose of used solvent and solution; clean sample cell(s).

b. Colorimetry

Inexpensive nonrecording single-beam UV–VIS spectrometers, often called *colorimeters,* are frequently used for routine quantitative analysis of compounds in solution. The Spectronic 20 illustrated in Figure G45 is a widely used colorimeter, and most other colorimeters are operated similarly. The solution to be analyzed is prepared as described for a recording spectrometer and is then placed in a *cuvette* that is inserted into the sample compartment. The wavelength control is set to a wavelength at which the sample absorbs strongly and, after some preliminary adjustments, the absorbance (or percent transmittance) of the solution is read from the scale.

A cuvette looks like a small test tube— but it should never be used as one!

The concentration of a solution can be determined from its absorbance value using either Beer's law (Equation **2**) or a calibration curve of absorbance versus molar concentration.

Beer's law

$$c = \frac{A}{\varepsilon \cdot b}$$ (2)

c = molar concentration

A = absorbance

b = cell path length, in cm

ε = molar absorptivity, in L mol^{-1} cm^{-1}

Equation **2** can be used to determine concentrations only when solutions of the solute obey Beer's law over the appropriate concentration range and when the absorptivity of the solute is known.

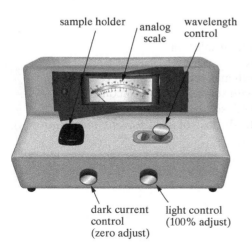

Figure G45 Spectronic 20 spectrophotometer

DIRECTIONS FOR OPERATING A COLORIMETER

Equipment and Supplies

colorimeter
solution to be analyzed
solvent
cuvette(s)

Do not attempt to operate the instrument without prior instruction and proper supervision. These directions are for operation of the Bausch & Lomb Spectronic 20 or a similar instrument and may not be applicable to all such instruments.

Obtain or prepare the solution to be analyzed. Make sure that the instrument has been switched on and that adequate time has been allowed for warmup. Set the wavelength to the desired value. Rotate the zero adjust control until the digital readout or the pointer of an analog dial indicates 0% transmittance. To read an analog scale, position your eyes so that the pointer is directly over its reflection in the mirror; this prevents parallax errors. Insert a clean cuvette containing the pure solvent (the one used to prepare the solution being analyzed) into the sample holder, making sure that the alignment mark on the cuvette is opposite the mark on the cell holder. Adjust the 100% control until the transmittance reading is 100%. Rinse the cuvette with a little of the solution to be analyzed, and then fill it with that solution. Replace it in the sample holder, being careful to position it in exactly the same alignment as before. If you are using an instrument with an analog dial, read the percent transmittance as accurately as possible; otherwise, you can read the absorbance directly. Note that it is more accurate to read %T from a dial and convert it to absorbance than to read the absorbance directly from the nonlinear absorbance scale.

Different cuvettes are sometimes used for the solvent and sample, but errors will result if the cuvettes aren't well matched; for precise work, it is best to use the same cuvette for all measurements.

If another solution containing the same solvent and solute is to be analyzed, empty the cuvette and rinse it with that solution before you make the next measurement. After the last measurement, rinse the cuvette with pure solvent, clean it, and let it air-dry. Convert the percent transmittance values to absorbance values, if necessary, using the equation $A = \log(100/\%\,T)$.

Waste Disposal: Dispose of the used solvent and solution(s) as directed by your instructor or as indicated in an experiment's directions.

Summary

1. Prepare or obtain solution.
2. Clean cuvette.
3. Set wavelength and zero adjustment control.
4. Fill cuvette with solvent; set 100% control.
5. Fill cuvette with solution; record %T.
6. Clean cuvette; dispose of used solvent and solution(s).

Mass Spectrometry

The other kinds of spectrometry described in this instrumental analysis section use some kind of electromagnetic radiation—radio frequency, infrared, ultraviolet, or visible—to gently probe the molecules of a sample and induce them to reveal their secrets. No molecules are damaged; once the spectrum is recorded, they return to their former states. By contrast, mass spectrometry uses a brute-force approach to determine molecular structures. Molecules that enter a mass spectrometer are pummeled by high-energy electrons and shattered into fragments, which are pushed and pulled along a curved path until they smash into an ion collector at journey's end. The fragments cannot be put back together to form the original molecule, so mass spectrometry is a destructive method of analysis.

Mass spectrometry isn't really a spectroscopic method in the usual sense, in that no electromagnetic radiation is absorbed. But a mass spectrum does resemble a conventional spectrum in that it consists of a series of peaks of different amplitude plotted along a numerical scale. Although mass spectra are not easily interpreted, and mass spectrometers are costly and complex instruments, mass spectrometry has become an increasingly valuable analytical tool for scientists and technologists in a variety of fields.

Principles and Applications

When a compound is bombarded with a beam of high-energy electrons in a mass spectrometer, each of its molecules (M) can lose an electron and form a *molecular ion*, $M^{\cdot+}$.

$$M \longrightarrow M^{\cdot+} + e^-$$

Because a molecular ion contains both an unpaired electron and a positive charge, it is called a *radical cation*. If the energy of the electron beam is high enough, many of the molecular ions will have enough excess vibrational and electronic energy to break apart into fragments. Each pair of fragments consists of another positive ion (A^+), called a *daughter ion*, and a neutral molecule (X).

$$M^{\cdot+} \longrightarrow A^+ + X$$

The unpaired electron from the molecular ion may end up on either A^+ or X, depending on the kind of fragmentation. Each daughter ion may in turn break down, losing a neutral fragment to form yet another daughter ion, and so on.

$$A^+ \longrightarrow B^+ + Y$$

For example, the fragmentation of an ammonia molecule takes place as shown, forming ions (cations and radical cations) with approximate masses of 17, 16, 15, and 14 atomic mass units.

ammonia   molecular ion   daughter ions

From *Operational Organic Chemistry: A Problem Solving Approach to the Laboratory*, Fourth Edition, John W. Lehman. Copyright © 2009 by Pearson Education. Published by Prentice Hall. All rights reserved.

The positive ions formed during these transformations are accelerated into an evacuated chamber in which they are separated according to their mass-to-charge ratios (m/e), usually by means of strong electric and magnetic fields (see Figure G46). As a beam of ions with a given m/e value impinges on an *ion collector*, it gives rise to an electrical current that is amplified and displayed on a monitor as a peak whose amplitude is proportional to the number of ions striking the detector. A *mass spectrum* is a record, usually printed out as a table of data or a computer-generated bar graph, of the relative abundances of all the ions arranged in order of their m/e values. Because most daughter ions have a charge of +1, the m/e value associated with a peak is nearly always equal to the mass of the ion that gave rise to that peak—or, in rare cases, to one-half of its mass. A large molecule may be fragmented into several hundred different ions with different m/e values and relative abundances, so mass spectrometers are provided with microprocessors that record, store, and process the data.

Mass spectrometry is an extremely valuable tool for structural analysis; it can be used to identify or characterize a host of organic (and inorganic) compounds, including biologically active substances with very complex molecular structures. The mass spectrum of a compound usually gives the mass of its molecular ion, which is essentially equal to its molecular weight. It also provides the masses of smaller pieces of its molecules, which can often be identified with the help of published tables of molecular fragments. A high-resolution mass spectrum provides data that can be used to determine a compound's molecular formula. Such information often makes it possible to piece together the compound's molecular structure, or at least to learn more about its structural features.

Different compounds yield distinctively different patterns of ion fragments, so an unknown compound can sometimes be identified by a comparison of its mass spectrum with mass spectral data from the scientific literature. Peak intensities on mass spectra are very sensitive to instrumental parameters, such as the energy of the electron beam. Therefore, there may be significant differences in the mass spectra recorded on different instruments, or even by different operators using the same instrument. Nevertheless, it is often possible to make a tentative identification from a literature comparison and then to confirm it by recording the mass spectra of the unknown and the most likely known compounds under identical operating conditions. This process can be facilitated by using a computer to compare the spectrum of the unknown with the mass spectra in a memory bank, which may contain tens of thousands of such spectra.

Instrumentation

Mass spectrometers come in a wide variety of sizes and configurations, ranging from high-resolution mass spectrometers that may take up most of an instrument room to compact "tabletop" mass spectrometers that can be used as detectors for gas and liquid chromatographs. Although research-grade mass spectrometers are very expensive, tabletop mass spectrometers are within the equipment budgets of some undergraduate chemistry programs.

In a conventional *single-focusing* mass spectrometer (diagrammed in Figure G46), the sample is introduced into a sample inlet system that is

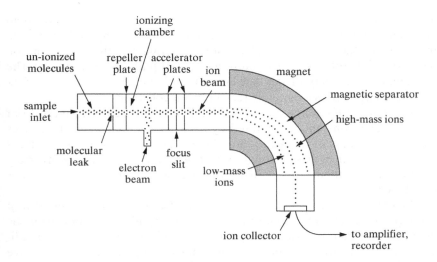

Figure G46 Schematic diagram of a single-focusing mass spectrometer

heated to keep some or all of its molecules in the vapor state. These molecules find their way into the *ionizing chamber* through an aperture called a *molecular leak,* which may be a tiny hole in a piece of gold foil. The ionizing chamber is kept at a pressure of about 10^{-6} torr to minimize collisions between particles and interference from ionized air. Molecules that wander into the path of the *electron beam* are ionized to molecular ions, some of which undergo fragmentation to yield daughter ions. These ions are pushed toward a focus slit by a positively charged *repeller plate,* accelerated to a high velocity by electrically charged *accelerator plates,* and directed into a *magnetic separator.* In the magnetic separator, a powerful magnetic field deflects each kind of ion into a curved path whose radius depends on the ion's mass-to-charge ratio. Lighter (lower m/e) ions are deflected more than heavier (higher m/e) ions. At a given magnetic-field strength, only ions of a given mass (or m/e value) can pass through the slit that leads to the *ion collector.* As the field strength is increased, ions of progressively higher mass reach the ion collector and are detected. When a beam of ions strikes the ion collector, an electrical signal is generated with an intensity proportional to the number of ions in the beam—that is, to their abundance. The signals are amplified and displayed by a monitor screen or recorder to produce a mass spectrum.

In a single-focusing mass spectrometer, variations in the kinetic energies of ions that have the same mass cause their ion beam to broaden as it passes through the magnetic separator, reducing the instrument's resolving power. In a high-resolution *double-focusing* mass spectrometer, the ions are initially directed along a curved path by an electrostatic field, which allows only particles of the same kinetic energy to pass through a slit leading to the magnetic separator. Double-focusing instruments can often resolve such ions as CH_2N^+ and N_2^+, whose mass numbers (28.0187 and 28.0061) differ by less than 0.05%.

Other kinds of mass spectrometers separate ions by very different methods. In a *quadrupole* mass spectrometer, the ions are introduced between

In mass spectrometry, two adjacent peaks of equal amplitude are said to be resolved *when the height of the valley between them is no more than 10% of their height.*

four parallel metal rods that create a rapidly oscillating magnetic field between them. Ions whose mass-to-charge ratio is compatible with the frequency of the field will oscillate along a straight path toward the ion collector, while other ions will follow a different path and be removed. The frequency or intensity of the oscillating field is varied so that ions of all mass-to-charge ratios eventually reach the ion collector.

In a *time-of-flight* mass spectrometer, ion beams are produced by brief pulses of electrons and accelerated by an electrical field pulse that gives all ions, regardless of mass, the same kinetic energy. Ions of a given mass (or m/e value) then pass through a *drift tube* at a speed that is inversely proportional to their mass, so lighter ions reach the ion collector sooner than heavier ions.

In a *Fourier-transform* mass spectrometer (sometimes called an *ion trap* mass spectrometer), ions are forced into a circular path by a strong magnetic field and subjected to a radio-frequency pulse. If the frequency of the radiation is equal to the frequency at which ions of a given m/e value move around their circular path (their *cyclotron frequency*), the ions will be accelerated and spiral outward. At the end of the RF pulse, they will be moving around a larger circle in a coherent packet. This packet of revolving ions generates an *image current* that decays with time after the pulse ends, producing a signal that is similar to the free induction decay signal generated by an FT–NMR spectrometer. The frequency of the RF pulse is varied to match the cyclotron frequencies of all ions in a sample, causing each kind of ion to produce its own image current. The resulting image currents are then detected and converted to a conventional mass spectrum by Fourier-transform analysis. Some Fourier-transform mass spectrometers are capable of resolving ions whose masses differ by only 0.001% or so.

Gas Chromatography/Mass Spectrometry

Rapid-scan mass spectrometers—including some quadrupole, Fourier-transform, and time-of-flight instruments—can be interfaced with gas chromatographs and used to analyze the components of a mixture as they emerge from the GC column. This combination of instruments, not surprisingly, is called a *gas chromatograph/mass spectrometer (GC/MS)*. The output of a GC capillary column [OP-37] can often be introduced directly into the ionization chamber of a mass spectrometer. With a packed column, however, most of the carrier gas must be removed to maintain a sufficiently low pressure in the evacuated ionizing chamber. The mass spectra of the components can be displayed by a screen or recorder in "real time," as each component exits the gas chromatogram, or they can be stored to be printed out later.

Instruments in which mass spectrometers are interfaced with high-performance liquid chromatographs (LC/MS) and even with other mass spectrometers (MS/MS) are also available.

Gas chromatograph/mass spectrometers are particularly useful for identifying the components of natural products, biological systems, and ecosystems. For example, flavor and odor components of essential oils, physiologically active components of plants, and chemical pollutants in the environment can be characterized by GC/MS. Forensic chemists can use GC/MS to identify drug metabolites in the body fluids of a suspect, and physicians can diagnose certain illnesses on the basis of a GC/MS analysis of a patient's breath.

Experimental Considerations

Samples prepared for mass spectrometry should be very pure, because traces of impurities can make interpretation of a mass spectrum difficult. Sample sizes range from less than a microgram to several milligrams, and no special sample preparation is required. Liquids are inserted directly into the sample inlet with a syringe, micropipet, or break-off device, and solids can be introduced by means of a melting-point capillary. The samples vaporize in the sample inlet system, after which their molecules flow through a molecular leak into the evacuated ionization chamber.

A typical single-focus mass spectrometer is prepared for operation by turning on the magnet current and adjusting controls that set the potential of the repeller plates, the accelerating voltage, the ionizing current (the number of electrons in the electron beam), and the energy of the electron beam. Increasing the repeller potential reduces the time that the ions spend in the ionization chamber, and increasing the accelerating voltage increases the speed that the ions attain by the time they enter the mass separator. Increasing the ionizing current increases the number of ions that are formed, and increasing the energy of the electron beam increases the amount of fragmentation. Because the settings of these controls determine the appearance of a mass spectrum, it is important to set them within ranges that are appropriate for a given analysis. The user also selects the range of masses to be scanned and the scan time. The mass spectrum is then scanned and recorded as a chart or computer printout.

Other types of instruments may operate quite differently, so no operating procedures will be given here. These must be learned by special instruction and by studying the manufacturer's operating manual. Computer programs that simulate the operation of specific mass spectrometers may also be available for your use.

Interpretation of Mass Spectra

Each peak recorded on a mass spectrum is characterized by the mass-to-charge ratio of the ion that gave rise to it and the ion-beam intensity (also called *relative abundance*). This information can be displayed by a variety of output devices, including oscilloscopes, strip-chart recorders, and computer printers. The height of an ion's peak is proportional to its ion-beam intensity. The most intense peak in a mass spectrum, called the *base peak,* is assigned a relative intensity of 100, and the intensities of all other peaks are reported as percentages of the base-peak intensity. The molecular-ion peak may be the base peak, but often it is not.

Molecular Weight and Molecular Formula

For most organic compounds, the molecular weight of the compound is virtually equal to the mass of its strongest molecular-ion peak. This molecular-ion peak is usually the last strong peak on the spectrum, because no daughter ion should have a higher mass than the original molecular ion. However, the molecular-ion peak is usually followed by at least two low-intensity peaks corresponding to isotopic variations of the molecular ion, because most of the elements in organic compounds have at least one isotope of higher mass number than the common form.

Just over one carbon atom in a hundred (1.08%) is a carbon-13 atom; the rest are carbon-12 atoms. Benzene, for example, contains six carbon atoms, so the chance that any one of the six will be carbon-13 is 6 × 1.08%, or 6.48%. Thus, the molecular-ion peak of benzene (C_6H_6, mol wt = 78) should be followed by a peak for a "heavy" form of benzene ($C_5^{13}CH_6$, mol wt = 79) with an intensity that is 6.48% of the parent peak intensity. Actually, the $m/e = 79$ peak, called the *M + 1 peak*, has a slightly higher intensity than this, because benzene also contains minute quantities of benzene-d_1 (C_6H_5D), which also has an approximate molecular weight of 79. Likewise, oxygen-18 occurs naturally to the extent of about 0.20 atoms for every 100 atoms of oxygen-16, so formaldehyde shows an *M + 2 peak* (corresponding to $CH_2^{18}O$) with an intensity that is 0.20% of the molecular-ion peak's intensity.

Intensities of the M + 1 and M + 2 peaks (relative to the molecular-ion peak's intensity) for a compound $C_wH_xN_yO_z$ can be calculated using Equations **1** and **2**:

$$\%(M + 1) = 1.08w + 0.015x + 0.37y + 0.037z \qquad \textbf{(1)}$$

$$\%(M + 2) = 0.006w(w - 1) + 0.0002wx + 0.004wy + 0.20z \qquad \textbf{(2)}$$

For example, quinine (as the hydrate) has the molecular formula $C_{20}H_{30}N_2O_3$. Using Equations **1** and **2** gives the intensity of its M + 1 and M + 2 peaks as 22.9% and 3.16%, respectively, of the M peak intensity.

$$\%(M + 1) = 1.08(20) + 0.015(30) + 0.37(2) + 0.037(3) = 22.9$$

$$\%(M + 2) = 0.006(20)(19) + 0.0002(20)(30)$$

$$+ 0.004(20)(2) + 0.20(3) = 3.16$$

No nonidentical sets of atoms are likely to yield M + 1 and M + 2 peaks of exactly the same relative intensity. Therefore, if the intensities of these peaks in the mass spectrum of an unknown compound can be measured to two or more decimal places, its molecular formula (or several possible formulas) can be determined using published formula mass tables, such as the one in *Spectrometric Identification of Organic Compounds* [Bibliography, F20]. Following is a general procedure for determining molecular formulas.

1. Locate the molecular-ion peak and determine its mass.
2. Measure the intensities of the M, M + 1, and M + 2 peaks, and express the latter two as a percentage of the intensity of the M peak.
3. Find the formula (or formulas) listed under its M value that give M + 1 and M + 2 intensities close to the experimental values and that make sense from a chemical standpoint.

Some formulas can be eliminated immediately because they don't correspond to stable molecules or because compounds with those formulas would be impossible to obtain from a given reaction or source. Others can be eliminated because they don't have the expected *index of hydrogen deficiency (IHD)*, where the IHD of a compound is equal to the number of rings plus the number of pi bonds (or their aromatic equivalent) in a molecule of the compound. For compounds with the general formula $C_wH_xN_yO_z$, the IHD can be calculated using Equation **3**.

$$\text{IHD} = \tfrac{1}{2}(2w - x + y + 2) \qquad (3)$$

For example, the calculated IHD of Compound **1** is 7, which is consistent with its molecular structure—one ring and six pi bonds.

$$\text{IHD} = \tfrac{1}{2}(18 - 7 + 1 + 2) = 7$$

A useful generalization that applies to most organic compounds is the *nitrogen rule,* which states that a stable compound whose molecular weight is an even number can have only zero or an even number of nitrogen atoms, whereas one whose molecular weight is an odd number can have only an odd number of nitrogen atoms.

Fragmentation Patterns

The use of fragmentation patterns to determine molecular structures is a broad subject covered in detail elsewhere (refer to Category F of the Bibliography), so only a few generalizations will be given here. A molecular ion or daughter ion often breaks down by eliminating small neutral molecules or free radicals such as CO, H_2O, HCN, C_2H_2, $H\cdot$, or $\cdot CH_3$, yielding ions with masses equal to $M - X$, where M represents the mass of the molecular ion or a daughter ion undergoing fragmentation, and X is the mass of the neutral species. Table G6 gives the masses and postulated structural formulas of some neutral species that are often lost by fragmentation.

Table G6 Formulas of some neutral species lost from molecular ions

Mass of neutral species	Mass of resulting ion	Possible formulas
1	$M - 1$	$H\cdot$
15	$M - 15$	$\cdot CH_3$
16	$M - 16$	$\cdot NH_2$
17	$M - 17$	$\cdot OH$, NH_3
18	$M - 18$	H_2O
26	$M - 26$	C_2H_2, $\cdot CN$
27	$M - 27$	$\cdot C_2H_3$, HCN
28	$M - 28$	CO, C_2H_4
29	$M - 29$	$\cdot CHO$, $\cdot C_2H_5$
30	$M - 30$	H_2CO, NO
31	$M - 31$	$CH_3O\cdot$, $\cdot CH_2OH$
35, 37	$M - 35, M - 37$	$Cl\cdot$
36	$M - 36$	HCl
42	$M - 42$	CH_2CO
43	$M - 43$	$CH_3CO\cdot$, $\cdot C_3H_7$
44	$M - 44$	CO_2, $\cdot CONH_2$
45	$M - 45$	$\cdot CO_2H$, $C_2H_5O\cdot$
46	$M - 46$	$\cdot NO_2$
49	$M - 49$	$\cdot CH_2Cl$
57	$M - 57$	$CH_3COCH_2\cdot$
59	$M - 59$	$\cdot CO_2CH_3$
77	$M - 77$	$C_6H_5\cdot$
79, 81	$M - 79, M - 81$	$Br\cdot$

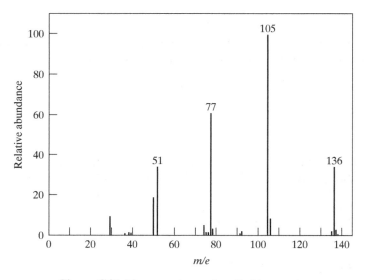

Figure G47 Mass spectrum of methyl benzoate

To see how such data can be used to interpret mass spectra, consider the mass spectrum of methyl benzoate in Figure G47. The m/e value of the molecular-ion peak in this spectrum is 136, that of the base peak is 105, and there are other strong peaks at $m/e = 77$ and 51. The molecular ion is believed to be a radical cation with the structure shown in the margin. Because the mass numbers of the base peak and molecular-ion peak differ by 31 mass units, a neutral species with a mass number of 31 must have been lost from the molecular ion to produce the base-peak ion. Table G6 shows two neutral fragments, $CH_3O \cdot$ and $\cdot CH_2OH$, with that mass number. Because the molecular ion has a methoxyl group, it must have lost $CH_3O \cdot$ to form the base-peak ion, which must therefore be a benzoyl cation. The difference between the mass number of the benzoyl ion and that of the next major peak is $105 - 77 = 28$. Two neutral species with mass numbers of 28 are CO and C_2H_4; loss of CO from the benzoyl cation should yield a phenyl cation with the expected mass number of 77. Formation of the next major species ($m/e = 51$) requires a loss of 26 mass units from the phenyl ion. From Table G6, two species with that mass are $\cdot CN$ and C_2H_2 (acetylene), of which only the latter is a possibility. Loss of acetylene from the phenyl ion yields an ion with the formula $C_4H_3^+$; this species is often encountered in the mass spectra of aromatic compounds. A number of smaller peaks in the methyl benzoate spectrum may provide additional structural information, but usually it isn't possible (or necessary) to characterize all of the peaks in a mass spectrum.

In the previous example, the interpretation was simplified because each major ion was produced from the preceding one along a single reaction path. Often there are fragmentation paths leading directly from the molecular ion to a number of different daughter ions. It is therefore a common practice to compare the mass number of the molecular ion with those of the possible daughter ions before attempting to compare the mass numbers of individual daughter ions.

$$\overset{O^+}{\underset{\parallel}{C_6H_5COCH_3}} \xrightarrow{-CH_3 \cdot} C_6H_5C\equiv O+$$

molecular ion   benzoyl ion
($m/e = 136$)   ($m/e = 105$)

$$C_6H_5C\equiv O+ \xrightarrow{-CO} C_6H_5^+$$

benzoyl ion   phenyl ion
($m/e = 105$)   ($m/e = 77$)

$$C_6H_5^+ \xrightarrow{-C_2H_2} C_4H_3^+$$

phenyl ion   ($m/e = 51$)
($m/e = 77$)

The fragment ions described previously and other common fragment ions are listed in Table G7. Structures have been determined for some (but not all) of these cations. For example, the $C_7H_7^+$ ion with mass number 91, which results from the cleavage of alkylbenzenes, has been formulated as either a benzyl cation or a tropylium ion; in most cases, it appears to have the latter structure. Before you can interpret a mass spectrum proficiently using data like those in Tables G6 and G7, you need to learn about the characteristic fragmentation patterns and mechanisms for different classes of organic compounds. This kind of information and some general rules for interpretation of mass spectra are given in references on mass spectrometry listed in Category F of the Bibliography.

Table G7   Some common fragment ions

m/e	Possible formulas
15	CH_3^+
17	OH^+
18	H_2O^+, NH_4^+
26	$C_2H_2^+$
27	$C_2H_3^+$
28	$CO^+, C_2H_4^+$
29	$CHO^+, C_2H_5^+$
30	$CH_2NH_2^+, NO^+$
31	CH_2OH^+, CH_3O^+
35, 37	Cl^+
39	$C_3H_3^+$
41	$C_3H_5^+$
43	$CH_3CO^+, C_3H_7^+$
44	$CO_2^+, C_3H_8^+$
45	$CH_3OCH_2^+, CO_2H^+$
46	NO_2^+
49	CH_2Cl^+
51	$C_4H_3^+$
57	$C_4H_9^+, C_2H_5CO^+$
59	$COOCH_3^+$
65	$C_5H_5^+$
66	$C_5H_6^+$
71	$C_5H_{11}^+, C_3H_7CO^+$
76	$C_6H_4^+$
77	$C_6H_5^+$
78	$C_6H_6^+$
79, 81	Br^+
91	$C_7H_7^+, C_6H_5N^+$
93	$C_6H_5O^+$
94	$C_6H_6O^+$
105	$C_6H_5CO^+$

Laboratory Equipment

Chemical Glassware

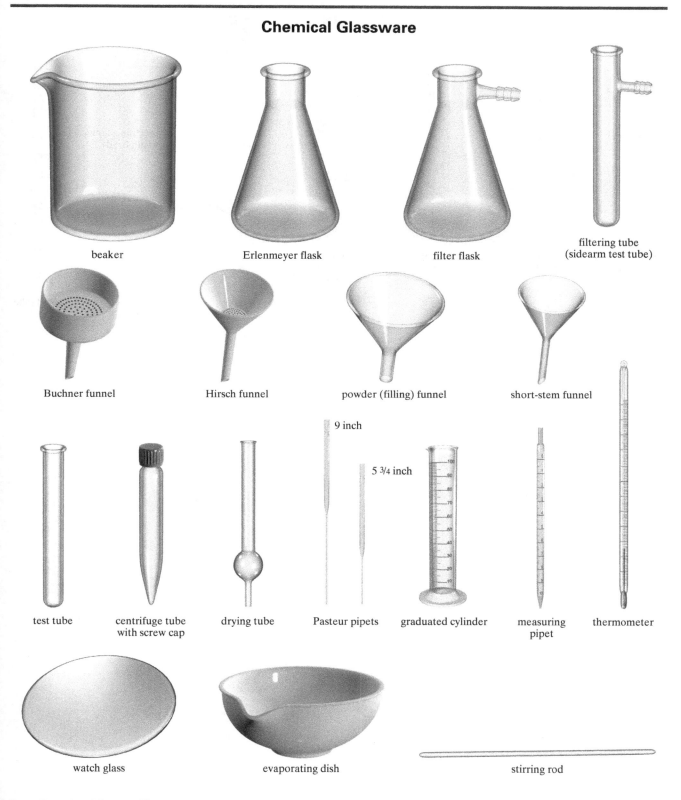

beaker

Erlenmeyer flask

filter flask

filtering tube
(sidearm test tube)

Buchner funnel

Hirsch funnel

powder (filling) funnel

short-stem funnel

9 inch

5 3/4 inch

test tube

centrifuge tube
with screw cap

drying tube

Pasteur pipets

graduated cylinder

measuring
pipet

thermometer

watch glass

evaporating dish

stirring rod

From *Operational Organic Chemistry: A Problem Solving Approach to the Laboratory*, Fourth Edition, John W. Lehman. Copyright © 2009 by Pearson Education. Published by Prentice Hall. All rights reserved.

Lab Kit Components

stopper

round-bottom
flask

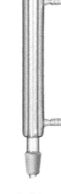

West
condenser

distilling
column

separatory----
addition
funnel

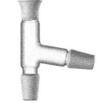

thermometer
adapter

connecting adapter
(still head)

vacuum
adapter

Claisen
adapter

bleed tube

Hardware

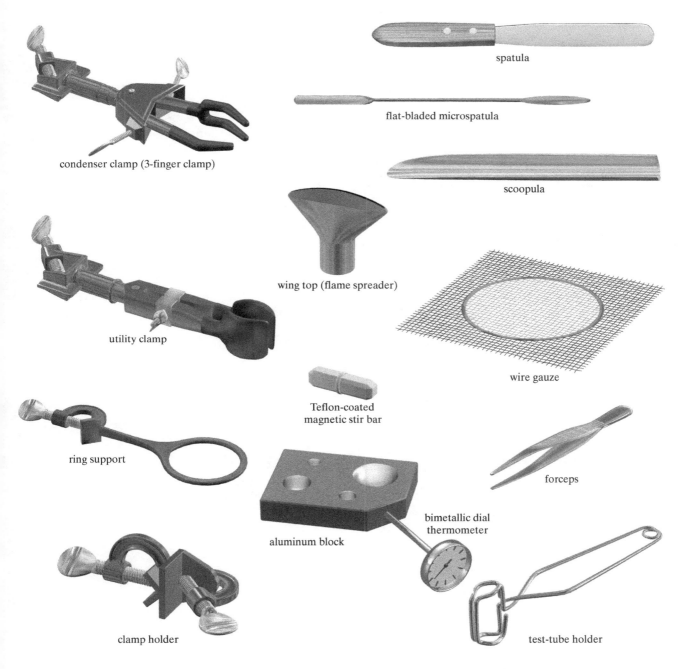

condenser clamp (3-finger clamp)

utility clamp

ring support

clamp holder

spatula

flat-bladed microspatula

scoopula

wing top (flame spreader)

wire gauze

Teflon-coated
magnetic stir bar

forceps

aluminum block

bimetallic dial
thermometer

test-tube holder

Keeping a Laboratory Notebook

Your instructor may require that you maintain a laboratory notebook, write formal laboratory reports, or both. In either case, you should write an experimental plan before you begin most of the experiments in this book. This appendix tells you how to keep a laboratory notebook.

A laboratory notebook is essentially a factual account of work performed in the laboratory. It may also include the writer's interpretation of the results. Your laboratory work may not require the documentation expected of a research chemist, but you should at least be aware of the characteristics of a good laboratory notebook. Although any kind of notebook can be used to record data and information, a notebook suitable for organic chemistry labs should be bound and have quadrilled (square-ruled) pages. If your instructor requires you to turn in a copy of your notes for each experiment, your notebook should also have duplicate pages. The first page or two should be reserved for a table of contents, and the pages should be numbered sequentially so that you can find information quickly. Whenever possible, each entry should be written immediately after the work is performed, and it should be dated and signed by the experimenter (notebooks of research chemists are usually signed by a witness as well). Each section of the notebook should have a clear, descriptive heading, and the writing should be grammatically correct and sufficiently legible to be read and understood by any knowledgeable individual.

Before each experiment, you should write an experimental plan in your lab notebook, summarizing what you expect to do in the laboratory and how you intend to go about it, and providing other relevant information. Your prelab write-up should include items from the following list:

- The experiment number and title
- For a preparation, balanced equations for all significant reactions, including possible side reactions that might reduce the yield
- A table that lists relevant properties (mol wt, mp, solubility, hazardous characteristics, etc.) of the reactants, products, solvents, and any other chemicals involved in the experiment
- A calculation of the theoretical yield of product and any other necessary stoichiometric calculations, when applicable
- A list of the materials (chemicals, supplies, equipment) needed for the experiment
- A checklist, flow diagram, or other kind of outline summarizing the experimental procedure

Some of these items may not apply to certain kinds of experiments, such as kinetic studies or qualitative analysis experiments. At your instructor's request, you may also include the following:

- A clear, concise statement of the scientific problem the experiment is designed to solve
- A brief statement that explains how you will attempt to solve the problem
- When appropriate, a working hypothesis predicting the outcome of the experiment

From *Operational Organic Chemistry: A Problem Solving Approach to the Laboratory*, Fourth Edition, John W. Lehman. Copyright © 2009 by Pearson Education. Published by Prentice Hall. All rights reserved.

During the experiment, you should keep a detailed account of your work, reporting everything of importance that you actually did and saw. Your notes should not simply restate the textbook procedure but should describe in your own words how you carried out the experiment. You should include all relevant data, such as the quantities of materials that you actually used (not the quantities calculated or given in the procedure, unless they are exactly the same) and the results of any analyses you performed. Raw data should be recorded with particular care; if you forget to record data at the time you measure it, or if you record it incorrectly or illegibly, the results of an entire experiment may be invalidated. As you gather evidence pertaining to any scientific problem that the experiment is designed to solve, you can write down one or more tentative hypotheses and describe how you tested them. You should also report any observations that might have a bearing on the problem, such as those that provide clues to the nature of the reaction or the identity of the product.

You may find it helpful to think of your lab notebook as telling a story about your accomplishments (or misadventures) in the laboratory. Although most professional journal articles are written in a dry, impersonal style, this need not be true of a lab notebook. The American Chemical Society's publication *Writing the Laboratory Notebook* [Bibliography, L46] suggests a more personal approach, stating that "the use of the active voice in the first person tells the story and clearly indicates who did the work." (For example, "I recorded the infrared spectrum of benzaldehyde. . . .") Other scientists prefer to write in the passive voice, avoiding the use of personal pronouns. (For example, "The infrared spectrum of benzaldehyde was recorded. . . .") If your instructor has a strong preference either way, you should follow his or her recommendation.

After you have finished an experiment, you should summarize your major results, write down any conclusion(s) you can draw from them, and explain how you arrived at your conclusion. If your notebook pages are to be turned in as your laboratory report, include answers to assigned exercises and any other information requested by your instructor.

Writing a Laboratory Report

You will be expected to submit a report for each experiment, either (1) from your laboratory notebook, (2) on a report form provided, or (3) on blank pages, bound or stapled together. Your instructor should tell you what kind of report he or she prefers. Handwritten reports are usually acceptable if they are written legibly in ink. Your report should include information under some or all of the following headings, as specified by your instructor:

1. *Prelab Assignments:* Your experimental plan, calculations, and any other information requested in the "Before You Begin" section. This may also include a prelab write-up.

2. *Observations:* Any significant observations made during the course of the experiment. You should record all observations that might be of help to you (or another experimenter) if you were to repeat the experiment at a later time. These include quantities of solvents or drying agents used, reaction times, distillation ranges, and a description of any experimental difficulties you encounter. You should also make note of phenomena that might provide clues about the nature of chemical or physical transformations taking place during the experiment, such as color changes, phase separations, tar formation, and gas evolution. If you keep a detailed record of your observations in a laboratory notebook, it may not be necessary to include them in a separate report.

3. *Raw Data:* All numerical data obtained directly from an experiment, before they are graphed, used in calculations, or otherwise processed. This can include quantities of reactants and products, titration volumes, kinetic data, gas chromatograph (GC) retention times, integrated GC peak areas, and spectrometric parameters.

4. *Calculations:* Yield and stoichiometry calculations and any other calculations based on the raw data. If a number of repetitive calculations are required, one or two sample calculations of each type may suffice.

5. A list, graph, tabulation, or verbal description of the significant results of the experiment. For a preparation, this should include a physical description of the product (color, physical state, evidence of purity, etc.), the percent yield, and all significant physical constants, spectral data, and analytical data obtained for the product. For the qualitative analysis of an unknown compound, the results of all tests and derivative preparations should be included, along with spectral data and physical constants. The results of calculations based on the raw data should be reported in this section as well.

6. *Discussion:* In this section, you should interpret your results and discuss possible sources of error. For example, if you obtain an impure or unexpected product, or a low yield of an expected product, you should propose reasons for these outcomes. At the instructor's request, your discussion can include a description of the scientific problem that the experiment was designed to solve, your interpretation of the results as they pertain to the problem, and a discussion of the significance of the results. You may also be asked to include statements of any working hypotheses you formulated and describe how they were tested, reporting

From *Operational Organic Chemistry: A Problem Solving Approach to the Laboratory*, Fourth Edition, John W. Lehman. Copyright © 2009 by Pearson Education. Published by Prentice Hall. All rights reserved.

and interpreting the relevant experimental evidence. When appropriate, this section may include your interpretation of spectra or chromatograms, which should be attached to the report.

7. *Conclusions:* A statement of your final conclusion (or conclusions) relating to the problem and an explanation of how you arrived at your conclusion, showing clearly how it is supported by the experimental evidence.

8. *Exercises:* Your answers to all exercises assigned by your instructor, showing your calculations and describing your reasoning (when applicable).

Each report should also include (on the first page or cover) the name and number of the experiment, your name, and the date the report was submitted to the instructor.

Your instructor should tell you what kind of report he or she prefers. The following example illustrates the kind of report that might be prepared by a conscientious student.

Experiment 60: Preparation of Tetrahedranol

Name: Cynthia Sizer
Date: Nov. 25, 2008

(*Attached*: Experimental plan, IR spectrum, gas chromatograph, and worked exercises)

Prelab Calculations

Tetrahedryl acetate required:

$$\text{mass} = 0.0150 \text{ mol} \times \frac{110 \text{ g}}{1 \text{ mol}} = 1.65 \text{ g}$$

$$\text{volume} = 1.65 \text{ g} \times \frac{0.951 \text{ g}}{1 \text{ mL}} = 1.57 \text{ mL}$$

6.0 *M* sodium hydroxide required:

$$\text{volume} = 0.060 \text{ mol} \times \frac{1 \text{ L}}{6.0 \text{ mol}} \times \frac{1000 \text{ mL}}{1 \text{ L}} = 10 \text{ mL}$$

Observations

The reaction of 1.644 g of the ester (tetrahedryl acetate) with 10 mL of 6.0 *M* NaOH was carried out under reflux for 60 minutes, during which time the organic (top) layer dissolved slowly to give a homogeneous solution and the "fruity" odor of the ester disappeared. The organic layer was no longer visible after 45 minutes of heating. The acidified reaction mixture was extracted with two 10-mL portions of diethyl ether, the ether extracts were washed with two 10-mL portions of saturated aqueous sodium chloride, and the ether solution was dried over 0.70 g of anhydrous magnesium sulfate. The residue was distilled over a 4°C boiling range and the distillate solidified on cooling. After the product was dried for 1 week in a desiccator, its mass was 0.854 g. Approximately 0.10 g of the product was dissolved in 0.50 mL of dichloromethane, and gas chromatograms were recorded for (1) the original solution and (2) the solution spiked with an authentic sample of tetrahedryl acetate. The relative area of the second (72 s) product peak was considerably larger in the second chromatogram than in the first. The gas chromatograms were obtained using a 2-meter, $\frac{1}{8}$ inch i.d., OV-101/Chromosorb W packed column. The infrared spectrum of the product was recorded using a thin film between heated silver chloride plates.

Data

Mass of tetrahedryl acetate: 1.644 g
Mass of dry product: 0.854 g
Distillation boiling range of product: 78–82°C
Capillary-tube boiling point of product: 81°C
Gas chromatography data:

Column temperature: 110°C
Injector temperature: 150°C
Detector temperature: 150°C
Helium flow rate: 25 cm^3/minute

Component	Retention time	Peak area
tetrahedranol	47 s	320 mm^2
tetrahedryl acetate	72 s	12 mm^2

Calculations

Percentage of tetrahedranol in product:

$$\frac{320 \text{ mm}^2}{332 \text{ mm}^2} \times 100\% = 96.4\%$$

Mass of tetrahedranol in product:

$$0.854 \text{ g} \times \frac{96.4\%}{100\%} = 0.823 \text{ g}$$

Theoretical yield of tetrahedranol (TetOAc = tetrahedryl acetate; TetOH = tetrahedranol):

$$1.644 \text{ g TetOAc} \times \frac{1 \text{ mol TetOAc}}{110.1 \text{ g TetOAc}} \times \frac{68.1 \text{ g TetOH}}{1 \text{ mol TetOH}} = 1.017 \text{ g TetOH}$$

Percent yield of tetrahedranol:

$$\frac{0.823 \text{ g}}{1.017 \text{ g}} \times 100\% = 80.9\%$$

Results

Tetrahedranol was obtained in 80.9% yield from the alkaline hydrolysis of tetrahedryl acetate. At room temperature, tetrahedranol was a colorless, almost transparent solid with a mild spirituous odor. It could easily be melted on a steam bath to form a clear, colorless liquid. It had a distillation boiling range of 78–82°C and a capillary-tube boiling point of 81°C. Its infrared spectrum contained significant absorption bands at 3370, 2975, 2885, and 1194 cm^{-1}.

Discussion

Statement of the problem: Can tetrahedranol with a purity of 95% or more be prepared by the alkaline hydrolysis of tetrahedryl acetate?

Working Hypothesis 1: The alkaline hydrolysis of tetrahedryl acetate *will* yield tetrahedranol as one of the products.

I based this hypothesis on (1) our textbook's statement that the alkaline hydrolysis of an ester yields the corresponding hydroxy compound (alcohol or phenol) and the salt of the corresponding carboxylic acid, and (2) the results of Experiment 4, in which I obtained salicylic acid (a phenol) from the alkaline hydrolysis of methyl salicylate. Observations in support of Hypothesis 1 include the following:

1. The slow disappearance of the organic layer during the reaction suggests that the water-insoluble ester was being converted to a water-soluble product. According to Table 60.1 in the lab textbook, tetrahedranol is soluble in water.
2. The disappearance of the "fruity" odor of tetrahedryl acetate also suggests that the ester was reacting.
3. The solidification of the distillate and easy melting of the solid between heated AgCl plates are consistent with the hypothesis, because Table 60.1 indicates that tetrahedranol has a melting point of 27°C.

Hypothesis 1 was tested by obtaining a boiling point and infrared spectrum of the product, with the following results:

1. The observed boiling point of 81°C is consistent with the hypothesis, because tetrahedranol has a reported boiling point of 82°C.
2. The infrared spectrum, suggesting a tertiary alcohol, is consistent with the hypothesis.

Wave number/cm^{-1}	Assignment	Interpretation
3370 (3368.4)	O—H stretch	alcohol or phenol
2975, 2885 (2975.1, 2884.2)	C—H stretch	absence of C—H absorption above 3000 cm^{-1} eliminates a phenol as a possibility
1194 (1193.6)	C—O stretch	consistent with a tertiary alcohol

The wave numbers of these bands are nearly identical to those on a published FTIR spectrum of tetrahedranol (shown in parentheses), and the band shapes and positions in the fingerprint region matched those of the published spectrum. My spectrum did have a weak band at 1739 cm^{-1} that wasn't present on the published spectrum, but this is probably the carbonyl (C=O) band of the tetrahedryl acetate impurity that was detected by gas chromatography.

Working Hypothesis 2: The purity of the product will *not* be 95% or better. I based this hypothesis on (1) the statement in the lecture textbook that some ester hydrolysis reactions, especially those involving esters of bulky alcohols, take more than an hour to reach completion; and (2) the fact that the ester and alcohol boiling points are only 15°C apart, suggesting that (as we learned in Experiment 5) simple distillation won't remove all of the impurity.

Hypothesis 2 was tested by obtaining a gas chromatogram of the product, identifying the peaks, and calculating the percentage of tetrahedranol in the product from the peak areas. Because the small 72 s peak became larger when the sample was spiked with tetrahedryl acetate, it must be the tetrahedryl acetate peak. Because the IR spectrum showed that the major product was tetrahedranol, the much larger peak at 47 s must be the tetrahedranol peak. The calculated mass percentage of tetrahedranol, 96.4%, is *not* consistent with my hypothesis. I'm not disappointed with this result—it was nice to know that the experiment came out better than expected! My assumptions that the reaction wouldn't go to completion in an hour and that the impurity wouldn't be completely removed from the product by simple distillation were both correct, but the reaction was more nearly complete than I had guessed.

The yield of tetrahedranol (0.823 g) was 0.194 g less than the theoretical value. Of this, at least 0.019 g resulted from incomplete reaction of tetrahedryl acetate, based on the 0.031 g (0.854 g−0.823 g) of ester in the distillate. The remaining losses could have arisen from (1) losses during transfers, (2) losses during the extraction and washing operations, and (3) losses during the distillation. During each transfer, I used additional solvent (ether or water) to rinse out the vessel from which the product was transferred, so losses during transfers should not be a major factor. About 0.1 mL of residue remained in the boiling flask used for distillation; this can account for no more than 0.1 g of the loss, because some of the residue must have been tetrahedryl acetate. Most of the remaining losses must have occurred during the extraction and washing operations, due to the partial solubility of tetrahedranol in water. Such losses might have been reduced by saturating the aqueous layer with potassium carbonate to salt out the alcohol or by carrying out several more ether extractions.

Conclusion

I conclude that tetrahedranol with a purity of 95% or more can be prepared by the hydrolysis of tetrahedryl acetate. I base this conclusion primarily on the infrared spectrum of the product, whose resemblance to the published spectrum leaves little doubt that the product is tetrahedranol, and on the gas chromatographic analysis, which indicates a purity of 96.4%. My conclusion that the product is tetrahedranol is supported by the other evidence cited in the discussion. My conclusion that the purity of the product is greater than 95% might possibly be in error, because the GC peak areas were not corrected by applying detector response factors.

Often, the quantities of many reactants are given in units of chemical amount (amount of substance), moles or millimoles. You have to convert such quantities to units of mass or volume before you can begin a synthetic experiment. In any experiment, it is the relationship between these *chemical* quantities that is significant, not the relationship between such *physical* quantities as mass and volume. Because there are no "mole meters" that measure chemical amounts directly, we are forced to use balances and volumetric glassware for that purpose. That shouldn't obscure the fact that the chemical units are fundamental; only by knowing the chemical amounts of reactants involved in a preparation, for example, can you recognize the stoichiometric relationships between them or predict the yield of the expected product.

It is helpful to regard a chemical calculation as a process by which a given quantity is "converted" to the required quantity. This can be accomplished by multiplying the given quantity by a series of ratios used as unit or dimensional *conversion factors*. Unit conversions are carried out by using conversion factors, such as 454 g/lb, that are written as ratios between two quantities whose quotient is unity (for example, 454 g = 1 lb, so 454 g/1 lb = 1). Dimensional conversions are carried out by using conversion factors that are ratios of quantities in different *dimensions,* such as mass, volume, and chemical amount. For example, the density of a substance can be regarded as a conversion factor linking the two dimensions of mass and volume, so it is used to convert the mass of a given quantity of the substance to units of volume, and vice versa. A conversion factor can be inverted when necessary. For example, the molar mass of butyl acetate, written as 116 g/1 mol, will convert moles of butyl acetate to grams; the inverse ratio, 1 mol/116 g, will convert grams of butyl acetate to moles. All calculations should be checked by making sure that the units involved cancel to yield the correct units in the answer. This doesn't ensure that your answer is correct, but if the units do *not* cancel, the answer is almost certainly wrong.

The following examples illustrate some fundamental types of calculations that you can expect to encounter in an organic chemistry lab course.

Chemical Amount and Mass. The chemical amount (in moles or millimoles) of a substance is converted to its mass by multiplying by its molar mass. Remember that the molar mass of a substance is obtained by simply appending the units g/mol to its molecular weight, which is a dimensionless quantity. For example, the mass of 15.0 mmol of butyl acetate (mol wt = 116) is 1.74 g.

$$15.0 \text{ mmol} \times \frac{1 \text{ mol}}{1000 \text{ mmol}} \times \frac{116 \text{ g}}{1 \text{ mol}} = 1.74 \text{ g}$$

Note that the chemical amount in millimoles must be converted to moles before the conversion factor is applied; otherwise, the units will not cancel. Mass can be converted to chemical amount by inverting the conversion factor before multiplying.

From *Operational Organic Chemistry: A Problem Solving Approach to the Laboratory*, Fourth Edition, John W. Lehman. Copyright © 2009 by Pearson Education. Published by Prentice Hall. All rights reserved.

Chemical Amount and Volume. The chemical amount (in moles or millimoles) of a pure liquid is converted to volume by multiplying by the liquid substance's molar mass and by the inverse of its density. For example, the volume of 25.0 mmol of acetic acid (mol wt = 60.1; d = 1.049 g/mL) is 1.43 mL.

$$25.0 \text{ mmol} \times \frac{1 \text{ mol}}{1000 \text{ mmol}} \times \frac{60.1 \text{ g}}{1 \text{ mol}} \times \frac{1 \text{ mL}}{1.049 \text{ g}} = 1.43 \text{ mL}$$

The volume of a solution needed to provide a specified chemical amount of solute is calculated by multiplying the number of moles required by the inverse of the solution's molar concentration. For example, the volume of 6.0 M HCl (which contains 6.0 mol of HCl per liter of solution) needed to provide 18 mmol of HCl is 3.0 mL.

$$18 \text{ mmol} \times \frac{1 \text{ mol}}{1000 \text{ mmol}} \times \frac{1 \text{ L}}{6.0 \text{ mol}} \times \frac{1000 \text{ mL}}{1 \text{ L}} = 3.0 \text{ mL}$$

Note that concentrations expressed in mol/L and mmol/mL have the same numerical value. Thus, a 6.0 M solution also has a concentration of 6.0 mmol/mL; using these units simplifies the previous calculation considerably:

$$18 \text{ mmol} \times \frac{1 \text{ mL}}{6.0 \text{ mmol}} = 3.0 \text{ mL}$$

Theoretical Yield. The maximum quantity of a product (usually expressed in mass units) that could be attained from a reaction is called the *theoretical yield* of the product. Theoretical yields can be calculated using *stoichiometric factors*—ratios derived from the coefficients (expressed in moles) of the products and reactants in a balanced equation for the reaction. For example, the stoichiometric factors relating the chemical amount of the organic product to the chemical amounts of the two reactants in the following reaction are (1 mol dibenzalacetone)/(1 mol acetone) and (1 mol dibenzalacetone)/(2 mol benzaldehyde).

$$2\text{PhCHO} + \text{CH}_3\overset{\displaystyle O}{\overset{\displaystyle \|}{\text{C}}}\text{CH}_3 \xrightarrow{\text{NaOH}} \text{PhCH}=\text{CHC}\overset{\displaystyle O}{\overset{\displaystyle \|}{\text{C}}}\text{CH}=\text{CHPh} + 2\text{H}_2\text{O}$$

benzaldehyde (B)   acetone (A)   dibenzalacetone (DBA)

Suppose you were trying to prepare dibenzalacetone (mol wt = 234.3) starting with 5.00 g of benzaldehyde (mol wt = 106.1) and 1.50 g of acetone (mol wt = 58.1). (For convenience, we will abbreviate the names as dibenzalacetone = DBA, benzaldehyde = B, and acetone = A.) You can calculate the maximum chemical amount of product that could be formed from each reactant by converting the given quantity to moles, and then applying the appropriate stoichiometric factor:

$$5.00 \text{ g B} \times \frac{1 \text{ mol B}}{106.1 \text{ g B}} \times \frac{1 \text{ mol DBA}}{2 \text{ mol B}} = 0.0236 \text{ mol DBA}$$

$$1.50 \text{ g A} \times \frac{1 \text{ mol A}}{58.1 \text{ g A}} \times \frac{1 \text{ mol DBA}}{1 \text{ mol A}} = 0.0258 \text{ mol DBA}$$

Because there is only enough benzaldehyde to produce 0.0236 mmol of dibenzalacetone, it is impossible to obtain more than that from the specified quantities of reactants. Once that much product has been formed, the reaction mixture will have run out of benzaldehyde, and the *excess* (leftover) acetone will have nothing to react with. Therefore, benzaldehyde is the *limiting reactant* upon which the yield calculations must be based. The theoretical yield of dibenzalacetone, in grams, is then 5.53 g.

$$0.0236 \text{ mol DBA} \times \frac{234.3 \text{ g DBA}}{1 \text{ mol DBA}} = 5.53 \text{ g DBA}$$

Remember that the limiting reactant is always the one that would produce the least amount of product, which is not necessarily the one present in the lowest amount. In this example, benzaldehyde is the limiting reactant even though the mass and chemical amount of benzaldehyde are much greater than the mass and chemical amount of acetone.

Percent Yield.   It is seldom, if ever, possible to attain the theoretical yield of product from an organic preparation. The reaction may not go to completion during the designated reaction period, leaving unreacted starting materials. There may be side reactions that reduce the yield of product, as in the reaction of benzaldehyde with acetone, where some benzalacetone ($PhCH{=}CHCOCH_3$) is formed as a by-product. In addition, there are invariably material losses when the product is separated from the reaction mixture and purified. The *percent yield* of a preparation compares the actual yield to the theoretical yield, as defined here:

$$\text{Percent yield} = \frac{\text{actual yield}}{\text{theoretical yield}} \times 100\%$$

For example, if you prepared 4.09 g of dibenzalacetone from 5.00 g of benzaldehyde and 1.50 g of acetone (theoretical yield = 5.53 g), the percent yield of your synthesis would be

$$\text{Percent yield} = \frac{4.09 \text{ g DBA}}{5.53 \text{ g DBA}} \times 100\% = 74.0\%$$

In many experiments, you will estimate the theoretical yield of a preparation based on the amounts of reactants given in the "Before You Begin" section. This will help you assess your performance by comparing your actual yield with an estimate of the "ideal" yield. But the percent yield that you *report* should be based on the amounts of reactants that you actually used in the synthesis, not on the amounts given (unless they are exactly the same).

Mass Percentage and Percent Recovery.   The mass percentage of a substance present in a particular mixture, such as the percentage of the compound cinnamaldehyde in a sample of cinnamon, is calculated by dividing the mass of the component by the mass of the mixture and multiplying by 100%.

$$\text{Mass percentage} = \frac{\text{mass of component of a mixture}}{\text{mass of mixture}} \times 100\%$$

For example, if 5.00 g of cinnamon contains 0.065 g of cinnamldehyde, the mass percentage of cinnamaldehyde is 1.3%.

$$\text{Mass percentage} = \frac{0.065\text{ g}}{5.00\text{ g}} \times 100\% = 1.3\%$$

The percent recovery of a process that is used to isolate one or more components from a mixture is calculated similarly, but because the process is unlikely to isolate all of a component, it is not the same as the component's actual mass percentage.

$$\text{Percent recovery} = \frac{\text{mass of component recovered}}{\text{mass of mixture}} \times 100\%$$

For example, if you isolate 0.625 g of clove oil by steam distilling 5.00 g of cloves, the percent recovery of clove oil is 12.5%.

$$\text{Percent recovery} = \frac{0.625\text{ g}}{5.00\text{ g}} \times 100\% = 12.5\%$$

Preparation of Solutions. Suppose you need to prepare 75 mL of ~2.0 M sodium carbonate (Na_2CO_3) from solid sodium carbonate. First calculate the chemical amount of sodium carbonate (mol wt = 106.0) contained in 75 mL of 2.0 M sodium carbonate.

$$75\text{ mL} \times \frac{1\text{ L}}{1000\text{ mL}} \times \frac{2.0\text{ mol}}{1\text{ L}} = 0.15\text{ mol}$$

Now calculate the mass of that number of moles.

$$0.15\text{ mol} \times 106\text{ g}/1\text{ mol} = 16\text{ g}$$

You can, of course, combine these calculations.

$$75\text{ mL} \times \frac{1\text{ L}}{1000\text{ mL}} \times \frac{2.0\text{ mol}}{1\text{ L}} \times \frac{106\text{ g}}{1\text{ mol}} = 16\text{ g}$$

The volume of solvent used to disolve the solute should be substantially less than the target volume of the solution.

For most purposes, you could prepare the solution by dissolving 16 g of sodium carbonate in distilled water, transferring it to a 100-mL graduated cylinder, and adding more distilled water to the 75 mL mark. If the concentration must be more accurate, you could use a 100-mL volumetric flask to prepare 100 mL of 2.00 M solution, which will require 21.2 g of sodium carbonate (do that calculation yourself).

Now suppose you need to prepare 9.0 mL of 3.0 M sulfuric acid by diluting concentrated sulfuric acid, which has a concentration of 18 mol/L. You need to know what volume of the concentrated acid must be diluted to yield the desired volume of 3.0 M sulfuric acid. The easiest way to do such a calculation is to use the dilution equation $M_1 \times V_1 = M_2 \times V_2$, where the terms on the left are the molar concentration and volume of the undiluted solution and the terms on the right are the molar concentration and volume of the diluted solution. Because V_1 is unknown,

$$18\ M \times V_1 = 3.0\ M \times 9.0\text{ mL}$$

Solving for V_1 then yields

$$V_1 = \frac{3.0\ M \times 9.0\text{ mL}}{18\ M} = 1.5\text{ mL}$$

So, to prepare the 3.0 *M* sulfuric acid, you could *carefully* pour 1.5 mL of concentrated sulfuric acid into an amount of distilled water that is less than the final volume (5 mL, for example), wait for the solution to cool down (dilution of concentrated acids generates heat), and then transfer it to a 10-mL graduated cylinder and add more distilled water to the 9.0 mL mark. If it is important to control the concentration more accurately, you should calculate the volume of concentrated solution to three significant figures and use volumetric glassware to prepare the diluted solution.

Planning an Experiment

Writing an Experimental Plan

Before starting any project—whether you are making a bookshelf, duck à l'orange, or isopentyl acetate—you must have a plan. An *experimental plan* should summarize what you expect to do in the laboratory and how you intend to go about it. You should state how the work is to be done in short phrases, without excessive detail. You can always refer to the directions section of the experiment and the operation descriptions for the details, but as you become more proficient in the laboratory, you should find yourself relying less on the textbook and more on your experimental plan. A good plan should give you quick access to the essential information you will need while performing the experiment. Quantities of chemicals (including wash solvents, drying agents, etc.), reaction times, physical properties, hazard warnings, and other useful data should be included. You can list the supplies and equipment you will need for each operation (these are specified in most operation descriptions) so that you can have them cleaned and ready when you need them. You may also wish to sketch the apparatus you will be using so that you can assemble it quickly in the laboratory.

An experimental plan should help you organize your time efficiently by listing tasks in the approximate order in which you expect to accomplish them. For example, whenever a reflux period is specified in a procedure, you will have some free time to set up the apparatus for the next step, reorganize your work area, review an operation, start a minilab, take a melting point, record the spectrum of a previous product, or tie up other loose ends. Your plan should be flexible enough that you can alter it or deviate from it during the experiment, if there is good reason to do so. One simple and effective way of organizing your time is to use a laboratory checklist. You should refer to relevant sections of the experiment (especially "Understanding the Experiment" and the directions) as you prepare your checklist, as well as to the appropriate "Operation" descriptions. Leave enough space between the items on your checklist so that you can add new ones, as necessary, during the experiment. As you complete each task in the laboratory, simply check it off the list and go on to the next one.

Creating a Flow Diagram

A flow diagram can help you organize your time by giving you a quick overview of the procedure, showing the purpose of each step. To create such a flow diagram, first list all of the substances that you know to be present in

From *Operational Organic Chemistry: A Problem Solving Approach to the Laboratory*, Fourth Edition, John W. Lehman. Copyright © 2009 by Pearson Education. Published by Prentice Hall. All rights reserved.

the reaction mixture before the reaction starts (reactants, solvents, catalysts), as shown in the following general flow diagram:

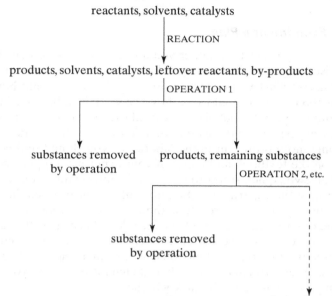

The reaction equation in the "Reactions and Properties" section tells you what substances will form as a result of the reaction. At the end of the reaction period, the reaction mixture will contain these products as well as the reaction solvent (if any), catalyst (if any), leftover reactants, and usually some by-products formed by various side reactions. The flow diagram should show how all of the unwanted substances in the reaction mixture are separated from the desired product. Each separation or purification operation is represented by a branch in the flow diagram, with the substance(s) being removed on one side and the desired product, along with any remaining substances, on the other side. After the last operation, the product stands alone, with all of the impurities eliminated—on paper, at least!

Properties of Organic Compounds

The tables in this appendix are to be used in conjunction with the procedures described in, "Qualitative Organic Analysis." Compounds that melt below ordinary ambient temperature (about 25°C) are listed in order of increasing boiling point (bp); those that (when pure) are generally solid at room temperature are listed in order of increasing melting point (mp). Both melting and boiling points are specified for some borderline cases; if either value is out of sequence, it is shown in italics.

Derivative preparations are described in the "Preparation of Derivatives" section of "Qualitative Organic Analysis" and are referred to by number in the headings of the appropriate columns. Melting points in parentheses are for derivatives that exist in more than one crystalline form or for which significantly different melting points have been reported in the literature. Sometimes the recrystallization solvent will determine the form in which a derivative crystallizes, so a significant deviation from a listed melting point shouldn't be considered conclusive proof that a product is not the expected derivative. If a given compound can form more than one product (for instance, mononitro and dinitro derivatives of an aromatic hydrocarbon), the reaction conditions for the preparation may determine the derivative isolated (a mixture of derivatives may also result). A dash (—) in a derivative column indicates either that the derivative has not been reported in the literature or that it is not suitable for identification (it may be a liquid, for example). See references from Category G in the Bibliography for physical constants and derivative melting points not listed in these tables.

Most compounds are listed by their systematic (IUPAC) names, except when those names would be too lengthy.

Abbreviations Used in Tables

d = decomposes on melting

s = sublimes at or below melting point

m = monosubstituted derivative (such as a mononitrated aromatic hydrocarbon)

di = disubstituted derivative

t = trisubstituted derivative

tet = tetrasubstituted derivative

From *Operational Organic Chemistry: A Problem Solving Approach to the Laboratory*, Fourth Edition, John W. Lehman. Copyright © 2009 by Pearson Education. Published by Prentice Hall. All rights reserved.

Table 1 Alcohols

Compound	bp	mp	3,5-Dinitro-benzoate, D-1	4-Nitro-benzoate, D-1	α-Naphthyl-urethane, D-2	Phenyl-urethane, D-2
methanol	65		108	96	124	47
ethanol	78		93	57	79	52
2-propanol	82		123	110	106	88
2-methyl-2-propanol*	83	*26*	142	—	—	136
2-propen-1-ol	97		49	28	108	70
1-propanol	97		74	35	105	57
2-butanol	99		76	26	97	65
2-methyl-2-butanol	102		116	85	72	42
2-methyl-1-propanol	108		87	69	104	86
3-pentanol	116		101	17	95	48
1-butanol	118		64	36	71	61
2-pentanol	120		62	24	74	—
3-methyl-3-pentanol	123		94 (62)	69	104	43
3-methyl-1-butanol	132		61	21	68	57
4-methyl-2-pentanol	132		65	26	88	143
1-pentanol	138		46	11	68	46
cyclopentanol	141		115	62	118	132
2-ethyl-l-butanol	148		51	—	60	—
1-hexanol	157		58	5	59	42
cyclohexanol*	161	25	113	50	129	82
furfuryl alcohol	172		80	76	130	45
1-heptanol	177		47	10	62	60
2-octanol	179		32	28	63	114
1-octanol	195		61	12	67	74
1-phenylethanol	202		95	43	106	92
benzyl alcohol	205		113	85	134	77
2-phenylethanol	219		108	62	119	78
1-decanol	231		57	30	73	60
3-phenylpropanol	236		45	47	—	92
1-dodecanol*	259	24	60	45 (42)	80	74
1-tetradecanol		39	67	51	82	74
(−)-menthol		44	153	62	119	111
1-hexadecanol		49	66	58	82	73
1-octadecanol		59	77	64	89	79
diphenylmethanol		68	141	132	136	139
cholesterol		148	—	185	176	168
(+)-borneol		208	154	137 (153)	132 (127)	138

*May be solid at or just below room temperature.
Note: All temperatures are in °C. Italics designate melting or boiling points that are out of sequence.

Table 2 Aldehydes

Compound	bp	mp	2,4-Dinitrophenyl-hydrazone, D-3	Semicarbazone, D-4	Oxime, D-5
ethanal	21		168 (157)	162	47
propanal	48		148 (155)	154	40
propenal	52		165	171	—
2-methylpropanal	64		187 (183)	125 (119)	—
butanal	75		123	106	—
3-methylbutanal	92		123	107	48
pentanal	103		106 (98)	—	52
2-butenal	104		190	199	119
2-ethylbutanal	117		95 (30)	99	—
hexanal	130		104	106	51
heptanal	153		106	109	57
2-furaldehyde	162		212 (230)	202	91
2-ethylhexanal	163		114 (120)	254d	—
octanal	171		106	101	60
benzaldehyde	179		239	222	35
4-methylbenzaldehyde	204		234	234 (215)	80
3,7-dimethyl-6-octenal	207		77	84 (91)	—
2-chlorobenzaldehyde	213		213 (209)	229 (146)	76 (101)
4-methoxybenzaldehyde	248		253d	210	133
phenylethanal	*195*	33	121 (110)	153 (156)	99
2-methoxybenzaldehyde		38	254	215	92
4-chlorobenzaldehyde		48	265	230	110 (146)
3-nitrobenzaldehyde		58	290	246	120
4-nitrobenzaldehyde		106	320	221 (211)	133 (182)

Note: All temperatures are in °C. Italics designate melting or boiling points that are out of sequence.

Table 3 Ketones

Compound	bp	mp	2,4-Dinitrophenyl-hydrazone, D-3	Semicarbazone, D-4	Oxime, D-5
acetone	56		126	187	59
2-butanone	80		118	146	—
3-methyl-2-butanone	94		124	113	—
2-pentanone	102		143	112 (106)	58
3-pentanone	102		156	138	69
3,3-dimethyl-2-butanone	106		125	157	75 (79)
4-methyl-2-pentanone	117		95 (81)	132	58
2,4-dimethyl-3-pentanone	124		95 (88)	160	34
2-hexanone	128		110	125	49
4-methyl-3-penten-2-one	130		205	164 (133)	48
cyclopentanone	131		146	210 (203)	56
4-heptanone	144		75	132	—
2-heptanone	151		89	123	—
cyclohexanone	156		162	166	91
2,6-dimethyl-4-heptanone	168		92	122	210
2-octanone	173		58	124	—
cycloheptanone	181		148	163	23
2,5-hexanedione	194		257 (di)	185 (m) 224 (di)	137 (di)

continued

Table 3 Ketones *continued*

Compound	bp	mp	2,4-Dinitrophenyl-hydrazone, D-3	Semicarbazone, D-4	Oxime, D-5
acetophenone	202	*20*	238	198 (203)	60
2-methylacetophenone	214		159	205	61
propiophenone	218	*21*	191	182 (174)	54
3-methylacetophenone	220		207	203	57
2-undecanone	228		63	122	44
4-phenyl-2-butanone	235		127	142	87
3-methoxyacetophenone	240		—	196	—
2-methoxyacetophenone	245		—	183	83 (96)
4-methylacetophenone	*226*	28	258	205	88
4-methoxyacetophenone		38	228	198	87
4-phenyl-3-buten-2-one		42	227 (223)	187	117
benzophenone		48	238	167	144
2-acetonaphthone		54	262d	235	145
3-nitroacetophenone		80	228	257	132
9-fluorenone		83	283	234	195
(−)-camphor		179	177	237	118

Note: All temperatures are in °C. Italics designate melting or boiling points that are out of sequence.

Table 4 Amides

Compound	bp	mp	Carboxylic acid, D-6	N-Xanthylamide, D-7
formamide	195d		—	184
propanamide		81	—	211
ethanamide		82	17	240
heptanamide		96	—	155
nonanamide		99	12	148
hexanamide		100	—	160
hexadecanamide		106	63	142
pentanamide		106	—	167
octadecanamide		109	69	141
butanamide		115	—	187
chloroacetamide		120	61 (53)	209
4-methylpentanamide		121	—	160
succinimide		126	185	247
2-methylpropanamide		129	—	211
benzamide		130	122	223
3-methylbutanamide		136	—	183
o-toluamide		143	104 (108)	200
furamide		143	133	210
phenylacetamide		156	77	195
p-toluamide		159	180	225
4-nitrobenzamide		201	240	233
phthalimide		238	210d	177

Note: All temperatures are in °C.

Table 5 Primary and secondary amines

Compound	bp	mp	Benzamide, D-8	p-Toluene-sulfonamide, D-9	Phenylthio-urea, D-10	Picrate, D-12
t-butylamine	44		134	—	120	198
propylamine	48		84	52	63	135
diethylamine	56		42	60	34	155
sec-butylamine	63		76	55	101	140
2-methylpropylamine	69		57	78	82	150
butylamine	77		42	—	65	151
diisopropylamine	84		—	—	—	140
pyrrolidine	89		—	123	—	112 (164)
3-methylbutylamine	95		—	65	102	138
pentylamine	104		—	—	69	139
piperidine	106		48	96	101	152
dipropylamine	109		—	—	69	75
morpholine	128		75	147	136	146
pyrrole	131		—	—	143	69d
hexylamine	132		40	—	77	126
cyclohexylamine	134		149	—	148	—
diisobutylamine	139		—	—	113	121
N-methylcyclohexylamine	147		86	—	—	170
dibutylamine	159		—	—	86	59
N-ethylbenzylamine	181		—	95	—	118
aniline	184		163	103	154	198 (180)
benzylamine	185		105	116 (185)	156	199 (194)
N-methylaniline	196		63	94	87	145
o-toluidine	200		144	108	136	213
m-toluidine	203		125	114	104 (92)	200
N-ethylaniline	205		60	87	89	138
2-chloroaniline	209		99	105 (193)	156	134
2,6-dimethylaniline	215		168	212	204	180
2-methoxyaniline	225		60	127	136	200
2-ethoxyaniline	229		104	164	137	—
3-chloroaniline	230		120	138 (210)	124 (116)	177
4-ethoxyaniline	250		173	106	136	69
dicyclohexylamine	255d		153 (57)	—	—	173
N-benzylaniline		37	107	149	103	48
p-toluidine		44	158	118	141	182d
diphenylamine		54	180 (109)	141	152	182
4-methoxyaniline		58	154	114	157 (171)	170
4-bromoaniline		66	204	101	148	180
2-nitroaniline		71	110 (98)	142	—	73
4-chloroaniline		72	192	95 (119)	152	178
1,2-diaminobenzene		102	301 (di)	260 (di)	—	208
3-nitroaniline		114	155 (di)	138	160	143
1,4-diaminobenzene		142	300 (di)	266 (di)	—	—
4-nitroaniline		147	199 (di)	191	—	100

Note: All temperatures are in °C. See other references in the Bibliography (Category G) for melting points of benzenesulfonamides and α-naphthylthioureas.

Table 6 Tertiary amines

Compound	bp	mp	Methiodide, D-11	Picrate, D-12
triethylamine	89		280	173
pyridine	115		117	167
2-methylpyridine	129		230	169
3-methylpyridine	143		92	150
4-methylpyridine	143		152	167
tripropylamine	157		207	116
2,4-dimethylpyridine	159		113	183 (169)
N,N-dimethylbenzylamine	183		179	93
N,N-dimethylaniline	193		228d	163
tributylamine	216 (211)		186	105
N,N-diethylaniline	217		102	142
quinoline	237		133 (72)	203
isoquinoline	243	26	159	222
tribenzylamine	—	91	184	190
acridine	—	111	224	208

Note: All temperatures are in °C.

Table 7 Carboxylic acids

Compound	bp	mp	Amide, D-13	p-Toluidide, D-14	Anilide, D-14	p-Nitrobenzyl ester, D-15
formic acid	101		43	53	50	31
acetic acid	118		82	148	114	78
propenoic acid	139		85	141	104	—
propanoic acid	141		81	124	103	31
2-methylpropanoic acid	154		128	107	105	—
butanoic acid	164		115	75	95	35
3-methylbutanoic acid	176		135	107	109	—
pentanoic acid	186		106	74	63	—
2-chloropropanoic acid	186		80	124	92	—
dichloroacetic acid	194		98	153	125	—
2-methylpentanoic acid	196		79	80	95	—
hexanoic acid	205		101	75	95	—
2-bromopropanoic acid	205d	*24*	123	125	99	—
octanoic acid	239		107	70	57	—
nonanoic acid	254		99	84	57	—
decanoic acid		32	108	78	70	—
2,2-dimethylpropanoic acid	*164*	35	178 (154)	—	129 (133)	—
dodecanoic acid		44	110 (99)	87	78	—
3-phenylpropanoic acid		48	105	135	98	36
tetradecanoic acid		54	103	93	84	—
hexadecanoic acid		62	106	98	90	42
chloroacetic acid		63	120	162	137	—
octadecanoic acid		70	109	102	95	—
trans-2-butenoic acid		72	160	132	118	67
phenylacetic acid		77	156	136	118	65
2-methoxybenzoic acid		101	129	—	131	113
oxalic acid (dihydrate)		101	419d (di)	268 (di)	254 (di)	204 (di)
2-methylbenzoic acid		104	142	144	125	91
nonanedioic acid		106	175 (di)	201 (di)	186 (di)	44

continued

Table 7 Carboxylic acids *continued*

Compound	bp	mp	Amide, D-13	p-Toluidide, D-14	Anilide, D-14	p-Nitrobenzyl ester, D-15
3-methylbenzoic acid		112	94	118	126	87
benzoic acid		122	130	158	163	89
maleic acid		130	181 (m) 266 (di)	142 (di)	187 (di)	91
decanedioic acid		133	170 (m) 210 (di)	201 (di)	122 (m) 200 (di)	73 (di)
cinnamic acid		133	147	168	153	117
propanedioic acid		135	50 (m) 170 (di)	86 (m) 253 (di)	132 (m) 230 (di)	86
2-chlorobenzoic acid		140	140	131	118	106
3-nitrobenzoic acid		140	143	162	155	141
diphenylacetic acid		148	167	172	180	—
2-bromobenzoic acid		150	155	—	141	110
hexanedioic acid		152	125 (m) 224 (di)	238	151 (m) 241 (di)	106
4-methylbenzoic acid		180s	160	160 (165)	145	104
4-methoxybenzoic acid		184	167 (163)	186	169	132
butanedioic acid		188	157 (m) 260 (di)	180 (m) 255 (di)	143 (m) 230 (di)	—
3,5-dinitrobenzoic acid		205	183	—	234	157
phthalic acid		210d	220 (di)	201 (di)	253 (di)	155
4-nitrobenzoic acid		240	201	204	211	168
4-chlorobenzoic acid		242	179	—	194	129
terephthalic acid		>300s	—	—	337	263 (di)

Note: All temperatures are in °C. Italics designate melting or boiling points that are out of sequence.

Table 8 Esters

Compound	bp	mp	Carboxylic acid, D-16	Alcohol or phenol, D-16	N-Benzyl-amide, D-17	3,5-Dinitro-benzoate, D-18
ethyl formate	54		8	—	60	93
methyl acetate	57		17	—	61	108
ethyl acetate	77		17	—	61	93
methyl propanoate	80		—	—	43	108
methyl acrylate	80		13	—	237	108
isopropyl acetate	91		17	—	61	123
tert-butyl acetate	98		17	26	61	142
ethyl propanoate	99		—	—	43	93
methyl 2,2-dimethylpropanoate	101		35	—	—	108
propyl acetate	102		17	—	61	74
methyl butanoate	102		—	—	38	108
ethyl 2-methylpropanoate	111		—	—	87	93
sec-butyl acetate	112		17	—	61	76
methyl 3-methylbutanoate	117		—	—	54	108
isobutyl acetate	117		17	—	61	87
ethyl butanoate	122		—	—	38	93
butyl acetate	126		17	—	61	64
methyl pentanoate	128		—	—	43	108
ethyl 3-methylbutanoate	135		—	—	54	93
3-methylbutyl acetate	142		17	—	61	61
ethyl chloroacetate	145		63	—	—	93
pentyl acetate	149		17	—	61	46
ethyl hexanoate	168		—	—	53	93
hexyl acetate	172		17	—	61	58

continued

Table 8 Esters *continued*

Compound	bp	mp	Carboxylic acid, D-16	Alcohol or phenol, D-16	N-Benzyl-amide, D-17	3,5-Dinitro-benzoate, D-18
cyclohexyl acetate	175		17	25	61	113
dimethyl malonate	182		135	—	142	108
diethyl oxalate	185		101*	—	223	93
heptyl acetate	192		17	—	61	47
phenyl acetate	197		17	42	61	146
methyl benzoate	199		122	—	105	108
diethyl malonate	199		135	—	142	93
o-tolyl acetate	208		17	31	61	135
m-tolyl acetate	212		17	12	61	165
ethyl benzoate	213		122	—	105	93
p-tolyl acetate	213		17	36	61	189
methyl o-toluate	215		104	—	—	108
benzyl acetate	217		17	—	61	113
diethyl succinate	218		188	—	206	93
isopropyl benzoate	218		122	—	105	123
methyl phenylacetate	220		77s	—	122	108
diethyl maleate	223		137	—	150	93
ethyl phenylacetate	228		77s	—	122	93
propyl benzoate	230		122	—	105	74
diethyl adipate	245		152	—	189	93
butyl benzoate	250		122	—	105	64
ethyl cinnamate	271		133	—	226	93
dimethyl phthalate	284		210d	—	179	108
(+)-bornyl acetate	*226*	27	17	208	61	154
methyl p-toluate		33	180s	—	133	108
methyl cinnamate		36	133	—	226	108
benzyl cinnamate		39	133	—	226	113
1-naphthyl acetate		49	17	94	61	217
ethyl p-nitrobenzoate		56	240	—	—	93
phenyl benzoate		69	122	42	105	146
2-naphthyl acetate		71	17	123	61	210
p-tolyl benzoate		71	122	36	105	189
methyl m-nitrobenzoate		78	140	—	101	108
methyl p-nitrobenzoate		96	240	—	142	108

Note: All temperatures are in °C. Additional derivatives of the acid and alcohol portions of most esters can be found in Tables 1 and 7. Italics designate melting or boiling points that are out of sequence.
*Dihydrate; the anhydrous acid melts at 190°C.

Table 9 Alkyl halides

Compound	bp	Density, d^{20}, C-10	S-Alkylthiuronium picrate, D-19
bromoethane	38	1.461	188
2-bromopropane	60	1.314	196
1-chloro-2-methylpropane	69	0.879	167 (174)
3-bromopropene	71	1.398	155
1-bromopropane	71	1.354	177
iodoethane	72	1.936	188
1-chlorobutane	78	0.884	177

continued

Table 9 Alkyl halides *continued*

Compound	bp	Density, d^{20}, C-10	S-Alkylthiuronium picrate, D-19
2-iodopropane	89	1.703	196
1-bromo-2-methylpropane	93	1.264	167 (174)
1-chloro-3-methylbutane	100	0.875	173
1-bromobutane	101	1.274	177
1-iodopropane	102	1.749	177
3-iodopropene	102	1.848	155
1-chloropentane	108	0.882	154
1-bromo-3-methylbutane	119	1.207	173 (179)
2-iodobutane	119	1.595	166
1-iodo-2-methylpropane	120	1.606	167 (174)
1-bromopentane	129	1.218	154
1-iodobutane	131	1.617	177
1-chlorohexane	134	0.876	157
1-iodo-3-methylbutane	148	1.503	173
1-iodopentane	155	1.516	154
1-bromohexane	155	1.173	157
1-iodohexane	181	1.439	157
1-bromooctane	201	1.112	134
1-iodooctane	225	1.330	134

Note: All temperatures are in °C; density is in g/mL, at 20°C.

Table 10 Aryl halides

Compound	bp	mp	Density, d^{20}, C-10	Nitro derivative, D-20	Carboxylic acid, D-21
chlorobenzene	132		1.106	52	—
bromobenzene	156		1.495	51 (70)	—
2-chlorotoluene	159		1.083	63	140
3-chlorotoluene	162		1.072	91	158
4-chlorotoluene	162		1.071	38 (m)	242
1,3-dichlorobenzene	173		1.288	103	—
1,2-dichlorobenzene	181		1.306	110	—
2-bromotoluene	182		1.423	82	150
3-bromotoluene	184		1.410	103	155
iodobenzene	188		1.831	171 (m)	—
2,6-dichlorotoluene	199		1.269	50 (m)	139
2,4-dichlorotoluene	200		1.249	104	164
3-iodotoluene	204		1.698	108	187
2-iodotoluene	211		1.698	103 (m)	162
1-chloronaphthalene	259		1.191	180	—
4-bromotoluene	*184*	28	—	—	251
4-iodotoluene		35	—	—	270
1,4-dichlorobenzene		53	—	106, 54 (m)	—
2-chloronaphthalene		56	—	175	—
1,4-dibromobenzene		89	—	84	—

Note: All temperatures are in °C; density is in g/mL, at 20°C. Nitro derivatives signified by (m) are mononitro compounds; all others are dinitro derivatives. Italics designate melting or boiling points that are out of sequence.

Table 11 Aromatic hydrocarbons

Compound	bp	mp	Nitro derivative, D-20	Carboxylic acid, D-21	Picrate, D-12
benzene	80		89 (di)	—	84u
toluene	111		70 (di)	122	88u
ethylbenzene	136		37 (t)	122	96u
p-xylene	138		139 (t)	300s	90u
m-xylene	139		183 (t)	330s	91u
o-xylene	144		118 (di)	210d	88u
isopropylbenzene	152		109 (t)	122	—
propylbenzene	159		—	122	103u
1,3,5-trimethylbenzene	165		86 (di) 235 (t)	350 (t)	97u
t-butylbenzene	169		62 (di)	122	—
4-isopropyltoluene	177		54 (di)	300s	—
1,3-diethylbenzene	181		62 (t)	330s	—
1,2,3,4-tetrahydronaphthalene	206		96 (di)	210d	—
diphenylmethane	262	26	172 (tet)	—	—
1,2-diphenylethane		53	180 (di) 169 (tet)	—	—
naphthalene		80	61 (m)	—	149
triphenylmethane		92	206 (t)	—	—
acenaphthene		96	101 (m)	—	161
fluorene		114	199 (di) 156 (m)	—	87 (77)
anthracene		216	—	—	138u

Note: All temperatures are in °C. Picrates designated "u" are unstable and cannot easily be purified by recrystallization.

Table 12 Phenols

Compound	bp	mp	Aryloxyacetic acid, D-22	Bromo derivative, D-23	α-Naphthyl-urethane, D-24
2-chlorophenol	176		145	49 (m) 76 (di)	120
3-methylphenol	202		—	84 (t)	128
2-methylphenol	*192*	31	152	56 (di)	142
4-methylphenol	*232*	36	135	49 (di) 108 (tet)	146
phenol	*182*	42	99	95 (t)	133
4-chlorophenol		43	156	33 (m) 90 (di)	166
2-nitrophenol		45	158	117 (di)	113
4-ethylphenol		47	97	—	128
5-methyl-2-isopropylphenol		50	149	55 (m)	160
3,4-dimethylphenol		63	163	171 (t)	142
4-bromophenol		64	157	95 (t)	169
2,5-dimethylphenol		75	118	178 (t)	173
1-naphthol		94	194	105 (di)	152
3-nitrophenol		97	156	91 (di)	167
4-t-butylphenol		100	86	50 (m)	110
1,2-dihydroxybenzene		105	—	193 (tet)	175
1,3-dihydroxybenzene		110	195	112 (di)	206
4-nitrophenol		114	187	142 (di)	150
2-naphthol		123	154	84 (m)	157
1,2,3-trihydroxybenzene		133	198	158 (di)	—
1,4-dihydroxybenzene		172	250	186 (di)	—

Note: All temperatures are in °C. Italics designate melting or boiling points that are out of sequence.

The Chemical Literature

The literature of chemistry consists of *primary, secondary,* and *tertiary* sources. Most primary sources in chemistry contain descriptions of original research carried out by professional chemists. They include scientific periodicals (such as the *Journal of Organic Chemistry*), patents, dissertations, technical reports, and government bulletins. Secondary sources contain material from the primary literature that has been systematically organized, condensed, or restated to make it more accessible and understandable to users. Secondary sources include most monographs, textbooks, dictionaries, encyclopedias, reference works, review publications, and abstracting journals that deal with chemistry. Tertiary sources are intended to aid users of the primary and secondary sources or to provide facts about chemists and their work. Tertiary sources include guides to the chemical literature, directories of scientists and scientific organizations, bibliographies, trade catalogs, and publications devoted to the financial and professional aspects of chemistry. Some sources may combine several different functions; for example, *Chemical & Engineering News* prints articles about chemical research as well as financial and professional information, and thus serves as both a secondary and a tertiary source.

Although a few secondary sources critically evaluate primary material and correct errors before printing it, primary sources should be used when it is important to obtain the most accurate and detailed information available on a topic. Errors can always occur when the material reappears in a secondary source, and important information may be left out. Because primary sources aren't organized in any systematic way, it is generally necessary to refer to other sources to determine where the desired information can be found. The Bibliography lists a number of secondary and tertiary sources that can be used to obtain information directly, to gain access to the primary literature, or both. For example, *Beilstein's Handbook of Organic Chemistry* (hereafter referred to as *Beilstein*) gives detailed, reliable information about organic compounds and also provides citations to the literature in which the information was first reported. References to the Bibliography will be given in the form (C7), where the letter indicates a category (such as "Laboratory Safety") and the number indicates a specific work in that category.

Using *Chemical Abstracts* and *Beilstein*

Most of the reference works cited in the Bibliography are limited in scope; they make no attempt to cover the entire field of chemistry or to list all of the known organic compounds. The two major works that do attempt that kind of coverage are *Beilstein* (A3) and *Chemical Abstracts* (J3). *Beilstein* summarizes all of the important information published about specific compounds, but it is many years behind the current literature in most areas. The earlier volumes of *Beilstein* are available only in German, so at least a rudimentary knowledge of that language is necessary to make good use of this resource. *Chemical Abstracts (CA)* prints *abstracts* (brief summaries) of scientific papers, patents, and other printed material related to chemistry shortly after their publication.

From *Operational Organic Chemistry: A Problem Solving Approach to the Laboratory*, Fourth Edition, John W. Lehman. Copyright © 2009 by Pearson Education. Published by Prentice Hall. All rights reserved.

Before using *Chemical Abstracts* for the first time, read the introduction that appears in Issue 1 of each volume (two volumes are published each year), which describes the layout of the abstracts. Each abstract of a scientific paper (or other article) contains an abstract number, the title and author of the paper, a citation that tells where the original paper can be located, and a concise summary of the important information in the paper. The contents of *CA* can be searched by computer (as described in "On-Line Searches") or by consulting the indexes. Although each weekly issue of *CA* has its own indexes, the semiannual and collective indexes are far more useful for literature searches. A Collective Index is published every 5 years; prior to 1957, these indexes came out every 10 years. In 1972, the Subject Index was divided into two parts: the Chemical Substances Index and the General Subject Index. Author, formula, and patent indexes are also published, along with ancillary materials such as the Ring Systems Handbook (A4), Registry Handbook, Index Guide, and Service Source Index, which are updated periodically.

The first thing you must do before searching *Chemical Abstracts* for information about a particular compound or subject is to find the *CA index name* of the compound or the *CA index heading* for the subject. In some cases, it may be possible to derive (or guess) the index name, but that isn't always easy—*CA* follows its own rules of nomenclature, which often differ from IUPAC rules. The Index Guide, which now appears with each Collective Index and at intervals in between, gives cross-references from alternative names of substances to the *CA* index name. Thus, the entry under "aniline" lists the index name benzeneamine, followed by the *CA registry number* [62-53-3]. The Index Guide doesn't list every compound indexed or give every synonym for the compounds it does list, so you may have to try different approaches to find what you are looking for. If you can't locate a specific compound, try looking up a possible parent (unsubstituted) compound under its trivial name; the index name of this parent compound should begin with a root name under which you will find your compound listed in the Chemical Substances Index (or the Subject Index, prior to 1972). For example, suppose that you are searching for the following compound:

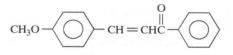

The unsubstituted compound (PhCH=CHCOPh) is known by such names as chalcone and benzalacetophenone. Looking up "chalcone" in a recent Index Guide provides the *CA* index name "2-propen-1-one, 1,3-diphenyl," so you will find the substituted compound listed—under the same root name—as "2-propen-1-one, 3-(4-methoxy)phenyl-1-phenyl." Keep in mind that the index name of a compound may change from time to time. This compound was listed under "chalcone, 4-methoxy" during the eighth Collective Index period (1967–1971) and before. Between the eighth and ninth Collective Index periods, some major changes were made in the *CA* nomenclature rules, which now require rigorously systematic names for most chemical substances.

If you have trouble finding the *CA* index name for a compound using the Index Guide, you might look for it in another source, such as *The Merck Index* (A11) or the *Dictionary of Organic Compounds* (A12). If you can locate the registry number for a compound, you can easily find its index name in the Registry Handbook. If you have a fairly good idea what the index name for a compound might be, you may be able to locate it in the formula indexes.

Once you locate the index name in use during a particular index period, you can locate abstracts listed under that name in the Chemical Substances Index or Subject Index for that period. Abstract citations in indexes from 1967 on are given in the form **80**:12175e, where the first number is the *CA* volume number and the second is the abstract number. In an index from prior to 1967, an abstract citation such as **51**:4321^b refers to the volume and column number (there are two columns on each page) in which the abstract appears; the superscript (either a letter from "a" to "i" or a number from 1 to 9) indicates the location of the abstract in that column.

The letter "e" in this citation is a check letter. If you looked up abstract number 12715 by mistake, you would find that its check letter is "b."

The information you are looking for may appear in the abstract itself, or you may have to read the original article cited in the abstract. Citations for such articles now appear in the form *Tetrahedron Lett.* **1996**, 37(37), 6767–6770 (Eng.), where the abbreviated name of the publication appears first, followed by the date, volume and issue number, page numbers, and language in which the paper is written. (Earlier citations were given with the volume number first, followed by the pages and year.) The full name of the publication will be found in the *Chemical Abstracts Service Source Index* (*CASSI*, A5), which also provides a brief publication history of each source and a list of the libraries that carry it.

To carry out a thorough index search of the print version of *Chemical Abstracts*, it is best to start with the most recent Collective Index (and all semiannual indexes published since then) and work your way back through the previous Collective Indexes, using the index guides or other sources to locate the appropriate index names. If you are looking for information about a specific compound, you may find it easier to search *Beilstein* through the most recent supplemental series that lists the compound, and *Chemical Abstracts* from that time to the present. For further information about the use of *Chemical Abstracts*, refer to one or more of the literature guides in Category K of the Bibliography.

Beilstein's Handbook of Organic Chemistry (*Handbuch der Organischen Chemie*) is by far the most comprehensive source of organized information about organic compounds. *Beilstein* provides information on the structure, characterization, natural occurrence, preparation, purification, energy parameters, physical properties, and chemical properties of organic compounds. It also cites the primary sources from which the information was obtained. *Beilstein*, unlike *Chemical Abstracts*, evaluates its sources critically and corrects errors that appeared in previous series. Beginning with the fifth supplemental series, which covers the period from 1960 to 1979, Beilstein is available in an English-language edition. The basic series (*Hauptwerke*) and four previous supplemental series (*Ergänzungswerke* I–IV, abbreviated E I–IV) are available only in German and cover the literature through 1959.

To obtain all of the information about a particular compound in *Beilstein*, you must search the basic series and all of the available supplemental series. The enormous size of this so-called "handbook"—along with the language barrier—could make that seem a monumental task, but there is really no reason to be intimidated by *Beilstein*. The amount of German you need to know is quite limited and can be learned with the help of the *Beilstein Dictionary* (A2), a slim dictionary written specifically for *Beilstein* users. And *Beilstein* is so well organized that it isn't difficult to find the information you seek. If a compound has been around for some time, you can locate its *Beilstein* entries by the following procedure:

1. Write the molecular formula of the compound with C and H first, followed by other elements in alphabetical order.
2. Locate the formula in volume (*Band*) 29 of the second supplemental series (*General–Formelregister, Zweites Ergänzungswerke*) and look for the name of the compound among those listed under that formula. Although the names are in German, many are similar or identical to the English names. (If you need help, use a German–English dictionary.)
3. Write down the volume number and pages on which information about the compound appears in the basic series (H), and the first and second supplemental series (E I and E II), and look up the appropriate entries in those volumes. (Each volume may include several individually bound subvolumes.)
4. Once you know the index name of the compound and its page number in the basic series, you can locate its entry in the corresponding volume of any later series. Alternatively, you can look it up in the cumulative subject index for that volume. Each compound is also assigned a system number, which can be used to locate its entries in the same way.

For example, the notation for indigo ($C_{16}H_{10}N_2O_2$) in volume 29 of E II reads "Indigo **24**, 417, I 370, II 233." So you will find entries for indigo on page 417 of volume 24 in the basic series and on pages 370 and 233 of volume 24 in the first and second supplemental series, respectively. The page number in the basic series, written as "**H**, 417," is called its *coordinating reference;* to find indigo's entry in volume 24 of a later series, you can locate the pages with **H**, 417 printed at the top and leaf through them until you find the entry for indigo. Knowing the E II index name of a compound may also help you locate it in the current cumulative subject index (*Sachsregister*) for the appropriate volume. The cumulative indexes for some volumes are combined; thus, the listing for indigo is found in the volume 23–25 subject index, and it reads "**24** 417 d, I 370 d, II 233 e, IV 469." The letters refer to the location of an entry on the page; for example, "II 233 e" means that information about indigo will be found under the fifth entry on page 233 of E II. There is no listing for E III, because supplementary series III and IV were issued jointly for volumes 17–27. Entries in the joint series are designated by E IV rather than by E III/IV.

Locating entries for a compound such as adamantane, which doesn't appear in the E II formula indexes, may take a little more time. All *Beilstein* entries are organized according to a detailed system, and learning that system is the best way to get complete access to the information contained in this work. However, you can usually locate such entries by either (1) finding the volume number in which a structurally similar compound appears and searching the cumulative indexes of that volume or (2) locating a *Beilstein* reference from another source. The E II indexes indicate that cyclohexane appears in volume 5, which contains all cyclic compounds lacking functional

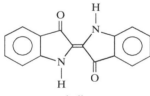

indigo

adamantane

The Beilstein *system is described in the "Notes for Users" (in English) at the beginning of each volume in the recent supplemental series.*

groups, so you will find adamantane listed in the cumulative indexes for that volume. You can also find *Beilstein* references for many compounds in certain reference books (A1, A6, and older editions of A11 and A15, for example). The entry for adamantane in the *Aldrich Catalog* (A1) gives the notation "Beil. **5**, IV, 469," referring to a *Beilstein* entry on page 469 in volume 5 of E IV. If you look up that entry, you will find a back reference (E III 393) and a coordinating reference (**H**, 165) that will help you find information about adamantane in the other series. For more detailed information about searching *Beilstein*, see reference K2 or other sources in Category K of the Bibliography.

On-Line Searches

Both *Chemical Abstracts* and *Beilstein* can be searched electronically using a variety of on-line search services. Limited *Chemical Abstracts* searching capabilities are available through FirstSearch CA Student Edition, with coverage of the most commonly held journals at academic libraries. More sophisticated search options are available using the on-line service STN (Scientific & Technical Information Network) International, which is operated by the Chemical Abstracts Service (CAS) and provides a variety of scientific and technical databases. The fundamental CAS database, called *CAplus*, includes all entries from the printed *Chemical Abstracts* since 1970 (and some back to 1967), plus additional bibliographic information. Other CAS databases available through STN International include *CAOLD*, which includes abstracts from *CA* prior to 1967; the *REGISTRY* File, a list of virtually all currently known chemicals with their *CA* registry numbers; *CJACS*, which gives the complete texts of articles published in selected American Chemical Society journals since 1982; *CASREACT*, a database of recent organic reactions; *CHEMSOURCES*, a database of information on chemical products and their suppliers; and *CHEMLIST*, a listing of regulated and other hazardous substances. STN databases are available by subscription and can be accessed with any computer that is connected to a telecommunications network; they are often accessible through university libraries. A simplified search option called STN*Easy* provides access to a variety of STN databases through the internet and features a graphical interface that doesn't require special training to use. Basic and advanced searches are available on STN*Easy*, and on-line help is provided when needed. For a basic search, the user simply enters a category that determines the databases to be searched, types in the words to be searched, and selects a search strategy. Search strategies include "any of these terms," which retrieves references that contain any or all of the words listed, and "all of these words," which retrieves only those references that contain all of them.

Access to *Beilstein* is available through the BEILSTEIN on-line database (provided by STN International), DIALOG, and other vendors. The database is intended to cover not only the contents of the printed work but also information from Beilstein file cards and primary literature up to the current date. For detailed information about on-line searching of *Beilstein* or *CA*, see reference K3 or K6 in the Bibliography.

Using the Bibliography

A number of books, articles, and other literature sources in organic chemistry are listed in the following Bibliography under 12 general categories:

A. Reference Works
B. Organic Reactions and Syntheses ·
C. Laboratory Safety
D. General Laboratory Techniques
E. Chromatography
F. Spectrometry and Structure Analysis
G. Qualitative Organic Analysis
H. Reaction Mechanisms and Advanced Topics
J. Reports of Chemical Research
K. Guides to the Chemical Literature
L. Sources on Selected Topics
M. Software for Organic Chemistry

Each source is referred to here by the category letter and its number within the category.

Category A: Reference Works

Whereas *Beilstein* attempts to provide all of the important information about the millions of organic compounds mentioned in the chemical literature, the reference books that follow provide selected information about a much smaller number of compounds, usually numbering in the tens of thousands. The *CRC Handbook of Chemistry and Physics* (A15), *Lange's Handbook of Chemistry* (A6), and *Dean's Handbook of Organic Chemistry* (A7) tabulate physical properties and other data for many common organic compounds and contain a large amount of useful information about chemistry. *The Merck Index* (A11) is an excellent source of information on approximately 10,000 organic and inorganic compounds. It describes their uses and hazardous properties, provides detailed physical and structural data, and gives literature references for the isolation and synthesis of many compounds. The *CRC Handbook of Data on Organic Compounds (HODOC)* (A9) contains data and references to published spectra for more than 27,000 organic compounds. The *Aldrich Catalog* (A1) lists the many chemicals manufactured by the Aldrich Chemical Company and gives their physical properties, hazard warnings, procedures for safe disposal, references to published Aldrich spectra, and references to listings in *The Merck Index, Beilstein*, and *Fieser* (B7). The *Dictionary of Organic Compounds (DOC)* (A12) is an important multivolume set—updated by annual supplements—that gives structures, physical constants, hazard descriptions, sources, uses, derivatives, and bibliographic references for more than 145,000 organic compounds. It is also available on CD-ROM. Figure 1 shows the level of information provided by three of these reference works.

Before you use such a reference work to find information about organic compounds, always read the introduction or explanatory material at the beginning of the work or preceding the table you intend to use. The introductory section of a reference work will usually (1) describe the content

No.	Name	Formula	Formula weight	Beilstein reference	Density, g/mL	Refractive index	Melting point, °C	Boiling point, °C	Flash point, °C	Solubility in 100 parts solvent
b44	Benzoic acid	C_6H_5COOH	122.12	9, 92	1.321		122.4	249	121 (CC)	0.29 aq^{25}; 43 alc; 10 bz; 22 chl; 33 eth; 33 acet; 30 CS_2

A. *Lange's Handbook of Chemistry.* (Reprinted with permission from *Lange's Handbook of Chemistry,* 15th ed., by N. A. Lange, edited by J. A. Dean. Copyright McGraw-Hill, Inc., New York, 1999.)

1092. Benzoic Acid. [65-85-0] Benzenecarboxylic acid; phenylformic acid; dracylic acid. $C_7H_6O_2$; mol wt 122.12. C 68.85%, H 4.95%, O 26.20%. Occurs in nature in free and combined forms. Gum benzoin may contain as much as 20%. Most berries contain appreciable amounts (around 0.05%). Excreted mainly as hippuric acid by almost all vertebrates, except fowl. Mfg processes include the air oxidation of toluene, the hydrolysis of benzotrichloride, and the decarboxylation of phthalic anhydride: *Faith, Keyes & Clark's Industrial Chemicals,* F. A. Lowenheim, M. K. Moran, Eds. (Wiley-Interscience, New York, 4th ed., 1975) pp 138-144. Lab prepn from benzyl chloride: A. I. Vogel, *Practical Organic Chemistry* (Longmans, London, 3rd ed, 1959) p 755; from benzaldehyde: Gattermann-Wieland, *Praxis des organischen Chemikers* (de Gruyter, Berlin, 40th ed., 1961) p 193. Prepn of ultra-pure benzoic acid for use as titrimetric and calorimetric standard: Schwab, Wicher, *J. Res. Nat. Bur. Standards* **25**, 747 (1940). *Review:* A. E. Williams in *Kirk-Othmer Encyclopedia of Chemical Technology* vol. 3 (Wiley-Interscience, New York, 3rd ed., 1978) pp 778-792.

Monoclinic tablets, plates, leaflets. d 1.321 (also reported as 1.266). mp 122.4°. Begins to sublime at ~100°. bp$_{760}$ 249.2°; bp$_{400}$ 227°; bp$_{200}$ 205.8°; bp$_{100}$ 186.2°; bp$_{60}$ 172.8°; bp$_{40}$ 162.6°; bp$_{20}$ 146.7°; bp$_{10}$ 132.1°. Volatile with steam. Flash pt 121°C. pK (25°) 4.19. pH of satd soln at 25°: 2.8. Soly in water (g/l) at 0° = 1.7; at 10° = 2.1; at 20° = 2.9; at 25° = 3.4; at 30° = 4.2; at 40° = 6.0; at 50° = 9.5; at 60° = 12.0; at 70° = 17.7; at 80° = 27.5; at 90° = 45.5; at 95° = 68.0. Mixtures of excess benzoic acid and water form two liquid phases beginning at 89.7°. The two liquid phases unite at the critical soln temp of 117.2°. Composition of critical mixture: 32.34% benzoic acid, 67.66% water: see Ward, Cooper, *J. Phys. Chem.* **34**, 1484 (1930). One gram dissolves in 2.3 ml cold alc, 1.5 ml boiling alc, 4.5 ml chloroform, 3 ml ether, 3 ml acetone, 30 ml carbon tetrachloride, 10 ml benzene, 30 ml carbon disulfide, 23 ml oil of turpentine; also sol in volatile and fixed oils, slightly in petr ether. The soly in water is increased by alkaline substances, such as borax or trisodium phosphate, *see also* Sodium Benzoate.

Barium salt dihydrate. Barium benzoate. $C_{14}H_{10}$-$BaO_4.2H_2O$. Nacreous leaflets. *Poisonous!* Soluble in about 20 parts water; slightly sol in alc.

Calcium salt trihydrate. Calcium benzoate. $C_{14}H_{10}$-$CaO_4.3H_2O$. Orthorhombic crystals or powder. d 1.44. Soluble in 25 parts water; very sol in boiling water.

Cerium salt trihydrate. Cerous benzoate. $C_{21}H_{15}$-$CeO_6.3H_2O$. White to reddish-white powder. Sol in hot water or hot alc.

Copper salt dihydrate. Cupric benzoate. $C_{14}H_{10}$-$CuO_4.2H_2O$. Light blue, cryst powder. Slightly soluble in cold water, more in hot water; sol in alc or in dil acids with separation of benzoic acid.

Lead salt dihydrate. Lead benzoate. $C_{14}H_{10}O_4Pb.2H_2O$. Cryst powder. *Poisonous!* Slightly sol in water.

Manganese salt tetrahydrate. Manganese benzoate. C_{14}-$H_{10}MnO_4.4H_2O$. Pale-red powder. Sol in water, alc. Also occurs with $3H_2O$.

Nickel salt trihydrate. Nickel benzoate. $C_{14}H_{10}$-$NiO_4.3H_2O$. Light-green odorless powder. Slightly sol in water; sol in ammonia; dec by acids.

Potassium salt trihydrate. Potassium benzoate. C_7H_5-$KO_2.3H_2O$. Crystalline powder. Sol in water, alc.

Silver salt. Silver benzoate. $C_7H_5AgO_2$. Light-sensitive powder. Sol in 385 parts cold water, more sol in hot water; very slightly sol in alc.

Uranium salt. Uranium benzoate; uranyl benzoate. $C_{14}H_{10}$-O_6U. Yellow powder. Slightly sol in water, alc.

Caution: Mild irritant to skin, eyes, mucous membranes.

USE: Preserving foods, fats, fruit juices, alkaloidal solns, etc; manuf benzoates and benzoyl compds, dyes; as a mordant in calico printing; for curing tobacco. As standard in volumetric and calorimetric analysis. Pharmaceutic aid (antifungal).

THERAP CAT (VET): Has been used with salicylic acid as a topical antifungal.

B. *The Merck Index: An Encyclopedia of Chemicals, Drugs, and Biologicals,* 13th Edition, Maryadele J. O'Neil, Ann Smith, Patricia E. Heckelman, John R. Obenchain Jr., Eds. (Reproduced with permission from *The Merck Index,* 13th Edition. Copyright © 2001 by Merck & Co., Ind., Whitehouse Station, NJ, USA. All rights reserved.)

Figure 1 Entries for benzoic acid from some reference works

Benzoic acid, 9CI   **B-0-00650**
Benzenecarboxylic acid
[65-85-0]

PhCOOH

$C_7H_6O_2$ M 122.1
Widespread in plants esp. in essential oils, mostly in esterified form. Obt. in 17th Century by sublimation of *Styrax* spp. resin. Produced industrially mainly by oxidation of toluene. Preservative in the food industry. Used in manuf. of preservatives, plasticisers, alkyd resin coatings and caprolactam. Antiseptic and expectorant. Used as alkalimetric standard; in photometric detn. of U and Zr (anionic complexes associated with basic dyes). Reference material used in elemental microanalysis. Leaflets or needles (H_2O). V. spar. sol. H_2O. Mp 122°. Bp 249°, Bp_{10} 133°, Subl. *ca.* 100°. Steam-volatile.
▶ Fl. p. 121°, autoignition temp. 570°. Eye, skin and mucous membrane irritant. Hypersensitivity reactions reported. Low systemic toxicity. DG0875000.

Na salt: [532-32-1].
Used as food preservative, anticorrosion agent. Cryst.
▶ DH6650000.

K salt: [582-25-2].
Cryst.

Me ester: [93-58-3]. *Methyl benzoate*
$C_8H_8O_2$ M 136.1   Used in perfumery and flavourings. Liq. d_{15}^{22} 1.09. Fp −12.3°. Bp 199.6°, Bp_{24} 96-98°.
▶ Fl. p. 83°. Skin and eye irritant. LD_{50} (rat, orl) 1350 mg/kg. DH3850000.

Et ester: [93-89-0]. *Ethyl benzoate*
$C_9H_{10}O_2$ M 150.1   Polymerisation catalyst. Used in perfumery and flavourings. Liq. d_4^{25} 1.04. Fp −34°. Bp 212.9°, Bp_{10} 87.2°.
▶ Fl. p. 88°, autoignition temp. 490°. Skin and eye irritant. LD_{50} (rat, orl) 2100 mg/kg. DH0200000.

Vinyl ester: see *Ethenol*, E-0-00320
Propyl ester: [2315-68-6]. *Propyl benzoate*
$C_{10}H_{12}O_2$ M 164.2   Flavour ingredient. d_{15}^{15} 1.03. Bp 230°.

Isopropyl ester: [939-48-0]. *Isopropyl benzoate*
Polymerisation catalyst, flavour ingredient. d_{15}^{15} 1.02. Bp 218-219°.
▶ Fl. p. 89/99°. Skin and eye irritant. LD_{50} (rat, orl) 3730 mg/kg. DH3150000.

Butyl ester: [136-60-7]. *Butyl benzoate*
$C_{11}H_{14}O_2$ M 178.2   Dye carrier; used in perfumery. d_{15}^{15} 1.01. Bp 248-249°.
▶ Fl. p. 107° (oc). Eye and skin irritant. DG4925000.

tert-Butyl ester: [774-65-2]. *tert-Butyl benzoate*
$C_{11}H_{14}O_2$ M 178.2 Bp_2 96°.

Benzyl ester: [120-51-4]. *Benzyl benzoate,* USAN. Ascabin. Benylate. Vanzoate. Many other names

$C_{14}H_{12}O_2$ M 212.2   Contained in Peru balsam. Isol. from other plants e.g. *Jasminum* spp., ylang-ylang oil. Insect repellant component. Acaricide and pediculicide. Used in perfumery as fixative and in food flavouring. Leaflets. d^{18} 1.11. Mp 21° (19.5°). Bp 323-324° (316-317°), $Bp_{0.1}$ 80-82°. Spar. steam-volatile.
▶ Fl. p. 148°, autoignition temp. 480°. Eye, mucous membrane, and possible skin irritant. Hypersensitivity reactions reported. LD_{50} (rat, orl) 500 mg/kg. DG4200000.

Ph ester: see *Phenyl benzoate, P-0-01360*
Fluoride: [455-32-3]. *Benzoyl fluoride*
C_7H_5FO M 124.1   Fuming liq. Bp 159-161°. Hydrolysed by hot H_2O.
▶ Highly irritant, causes burns, violent reaction with DMSO. Fl. p. 72/102°.

Chloride: [98-88-4]. *Benzoyl chloride*
C_7H_5ClO M 140.5   Polymerisation catalyst, benzoylating agent. Can be used for synth. of aliphatic acid chlorides. Used to derivatise steroids and carbohydrates for chromatog. Fuming liq. d_4^4 1.22. Fp −1°. Bp 197°.
▶ Fl. p. 72/102°. Violent reaction with DMSO. Corrosive and irritating to all tissues. Potent lachrymator. DM6600000.

Bromide: [618-32-6]. *Benzoyl bromide*
C_7H_5BrO M 185.0   Fuming liq. d^{15} 1.57. Fp −24°. Bp 218-219°, $Bp_{0.05}$ 48-50°.
Iodide: [618-38-2]. *Benzoyl iodide*
C_7H_5IO M 232.0   Needles. Mp 3°. Bp_{20} 128°.
Amide: see *Benzamide, B-0-00069*
Anilide: see *Benzanilide, B-0-00074*
Azide: *Benzoylazimide*
$C_7H_5N_3O$ M 147.1   Plates. Mp 32°.
▶ Explodes on heating.

Hydrazide: [613-94-5]. *Benzoylhydrazine*
$C_7H_8N_2O$ M 136.1   Used as 0.2*M* aq. soln. for photometric detn. of V (λ_{max} 400 nm, ε 9000); as 0.1*M* aq. soln. for photometric detn. of $IO_4^{\ominus}$. Cryst. (H_2O). Sol. H_2O, acids, EtOH, C_6H_6, Me_2CO. Mp 112.5°.
▶ DH1575000.

Hydroxamate: see *N-Hydroxybenzamide, H-0-01671*
Nitrile: see *Benzonitrile, B-0-00747*
Anhydride: [93-97-0]. *Benzoic anhydride*
$C_{14}H_{10}O_3$ M 226.2   Cross-linking agent for polymers. Acylation and decarboxylating agent, can be used in polymer-linked form. Can be used to prep. derivs. of e.g. glycosphingolipids for hplc. Rhombic prisms. d^{15} 1.99. Mp 42°. Bp 360°.
▶ Mild irritant and allergen.

Aldrich Library of ^{13}C and ^1H FT NMR Spectra, 2, 1063B, 1199A, 1240A, 1240B, 1241A, 1241B, 1244A, 1337C, 1411A (*nmr*)
Aldrich Library of FT-IR Spectra, 1st edn., 2, 186A, 271B, 291B, 291C, 292D, 340A, 340B, 340C, 380D (*ir*)

Aldrich Library of FT-IR Spectra: Vapor Phase, 3, 181D, 1322C, 1357D, 1358A, 1358B, 1358C, 1360A, 1389D, 1390A, 1390B (*ir*)
Org. Synth., Coll. Vol., 1, 1932, 75, 361 (*synth, deriv*)
Jesson, J.P. *et al, Proc. R. Soc. London, A,* 1962, 268, 68 (*Raman*)
Beynon, J.H. *et al, Z. Naturforsch., A,* 1965, 20, 883 (*ms*)
Moeken, H.H. *et al, Anal. Chim. Acta,* 1967, 37, 480 (*detn, U*)
Fieser and Fieser's Reagents for Organic Synthesis, Wiley, 1967, 1, 49, 1004; 1975, 5, 23, 24, 249; 1979, 7, 405 (*use*)
Evans, H.B. *et al, J. Phys. Chem.,* 1968, 72, 2552 (*pmr*)
Escarrilla, A.M. *et al, Anal. Chim. Acta,* 1969, 45, 199 (*use*)
Analyst (London), 1972, 97, 740 (*microanal*)
Bel'tyukova, S.V. *et al, Zh. Anal. Khim.,* 1972, 27, 191 (*detn, Zr*)
Fitzpatrick, F.A. *et al, Anal. Chem.,* 1973, 45, 2310 (*chloride, use*)
Morris, W.W., *J. Assoc. Off. Anal. Chem.,* 1973, 56, 1037 (*ir*)
Dubey, S.C. *et al, Talanta,* 1977, 24, 266 (*detn, U*)
Pilipenko, A.T. *et al, Zh. Anal. Khim.,* 1977, 32, 1369 (*hydrazide, detn, V*)
Fauvet, G. *et al, Acta Cryst. B,* 1978, 34, 1376 (*cryst struct, nitrile*)
White, C.A. *et al, Carbohydr. Res.,* 1979, 76, 1 (*chloride, use*)
Opdyke, D.L.J., *Food Cosmet. Toxicol.,* 1979, 17, 715 (*rev, tox*)
Hassan, M.M.A. *et al, Anal. Profiles Drug Subst.,* 1981, 10, 55 (*rev, benzyl ester*)
Rama Rao, A.V. *et al, Chem. Ind. (London),* 1984, 270 (*synth*)
Ullmann's Encycl. Ind. Chem., 5th Ed, VCH, Weinheim, 1985, A3, 555 (*rev*)
Lewandowski, W., *Can. J. Spectrosc.,* 1987, 32, 41 (*salts, ir*)
Ullman, M.D. *et al, Methods Enzymol.,* 1987, 138, 117 (*use, anhydride*)
Negwer, M., *Organic-Chemical Drugs and their Synonyms,* 6th edn., Akademie-Verlag, Berlin, 1987, 3041.
Cook, I.B., *Aust. J. Chem.,* 1989, 42, 1493 (*cmr*)
Lewis, R.J., *Food Additives Handbook,* Van Nostrand Reinhold International, New York, 1989, BCL750, BCM000, EGR000, MHA500.
Merck Index, 11th edn., 1989, No. 1107, No. 1141 (*nitrile, benzyl ester*)
Kirk-Othmer Encycl. Chem. Technol., 4th edn., Wiley, New York, 1991, 4, 103 (*rev*)
Martindale, The Extra Pharmacopoeia, 30th edn., Pharmaceutical Press, London, 1993, 1124, 1132.
Lewis, R.J., *Sax's Dangerous Properties of Industrial Materials,* 8th edn., Van Nostrand Reinhold, 1992, BBV250, BCL750, BCM000, BCQ250, BDM500, BQK250, EGR000, IOD000, MHA750, PKW760, SFB000.
Bretherick, L., *Handbook of Reactive Chemical Hazards,* 4th edn., Butterworth, London and Boston, 1990, 2511.
Luxon, S.G., *Hazards in the Chemical Laboratory,* 5th edn., Royal Society of Chemistry, Cambridge, 1992, 117.
Chemical Hazards of the Workplace, (eds. Proctor, N.H. *et al*), 3rd edn., VNR, 1991, 107.

C. *Dictionary of Organic Compounds.* (Reprinted with permission from *Dictionary of Organic Compounds,* 6th ed., edited by P. H. Rhodes. Copyright Chapman & Hall, London, 1995.)

Figure 1 (*continued*)

and organization of the material, (2) list symbols and abbreviations, and (3) describe the system of nomenclature used. Different sources often use very different naming systems. For example, *The Merck Index* emphasizes therapeutic uses of compounds, so it lists aspirin under that name; but in *Lange's Handbook* you will find aspirin listed as "acetylsalicylic acid," and in the *CRC Handbook of Chemistry and Physics* it appears as "salicylic acid acetate." In earlier editions of the *CRC Handbook,* compounds were entered under the name of the parent compound; thus, 2,4-dinitrobenzene was listed as "benzene, 2,4-dinitro." More recent editions list the names as they are ordinarily written out. Often, the index of a reference work provides the quickest and most reliable access to a given entry. When using *The Merck Index* or the *Dictionary of Organic Compounds,* you should first consult the name index to locate the entry for a given compound. If you can't find the compound in the name index, you may be able to locate it in a formula index. In most formula indexes, carbon and hydrogen are listed first, followed by the other elements in alphabetical order.

Other useful reference works in organic chemistry include the *Ring Systems Handbook* (A4), which (with its supplements) records all known organic ring systems and provides information allowing users to locate compounds that have a particular ring system; and *CASSI* (A5), which provides bibliographic information for the journals and other sources indexed by *Chemical Abstracts* and lists the libraries holding each source. The *Beilstein Dictionary* (A2) is an invaluable aid to understanding the parts of *Beilstein* (A3) that are available only in German. *The Organic Chemist's Desk Reference* (A13) includes a user's guide to the *Dictionary of Organic Chemistry* as well as a discussion of nomenclature in *Chemical Abstracts,* a list of reference works in organic chemistry, and other useful information. *The Chemist's Ready Reference Handbook* (A14) provides practical information about a variety of theoretical and experimental topics. *Organic Chemistry: An Alphabetical Guide* (A10) discusses and defines many terms used in organic chemistry. *Kirk–Othmer* (A8) is an excellent source of comprehensive, up-to-date articles on a variety of chemical topics. It offers particularly good coverage of industrial chemistry and commercial products, but it also includes entries on natural products, such as coffee, terpenoids, and vitamins.

Category B: Organic Reactions and Syntheses

The works in this category are intended primarily to help chemists and chemistry students design and carry out organic syntheses. Although you may not be required to work out synthetic procedures on your own, an understanding of the strategy and techniques of organic synthesis will help you perform better in your lab and lecture courses and get more out of them. The article by Nicolaou (B17) gives an interesting account of the evolution of organic synthesis, especially as it applies to the synthesis of natural products. *Modern Organic Synthesis* (B35) and *Organic Synthesis: Concepts and Methods* (B9) each provide a general overview of organic synthesis. *Organic Synthesis: The Disconnection Approach* (B30) describes strategies for planning an organic synthesis. At a more advanced level, *The Logic of Chemical Synthesis* (B6) deals with the analysis of complex synthetic problems, and *Principles of Organic Synthesis* (B18) discusses such topics as thermodynamics, kinetics, and stereochemistry as they apply to organic synthesis.

A number of works can help the experimenter select the type of reaction that will best accomplish a given synthetic transformation. *Synthetic Organic Chemistry* (B34) and *Modern Synthetic Reactions* (B12) survey many important synthetic reactions, with references to the earlier literature. More comprehensive coverage of organic transformations, including the more recent synthetic reactions, can be found in *Modern Methods of Organic Synthesis* (B4), *Compendium of Organic Synthetic Methods* (B11), *Comprehensive Organic Transformations* (B13), *Comprehensive Organic Synthesis* (B33), and *Theilheimer's Synthetic Methods of Organic Chemistry* (B32). Reaction files from Theilheimer and other works can be searched online using the *REACCS* database from Molecular Design, Ltd.

General works on organic synthetic reactions range from the *Reaction Guide for Organic Chemistry* (B16), a basic compilation of most reactions covered in the sophomore-level organic chemistry course, to *Organic Reactions* (B19), a multivolume set containing very comprehensive monographs on a large variety of reactions. *Organic Reactions* describes each reaction's mechanism, scope, limitations, and experimental conditions. It also provides some typical experimental procedures and a table that lists examples of each reaction with references to the original sources. *Named Organic Reactions* (B14) describes those synthetic reactions that—like the Hell–Volhard–Zelinskii reaction—are identified by the names of one or more discoverers. *Rodd's Chemistry of Carbon Compounds* (B5) describes the reactions of different classes of organic compounds in considerable depth. Each volume of *Chemistry of Functional Groups* (B22) covers the chemical reactions of a different functional group. *Asymmetric Synthesis* (B25) deals with the synthesis of chiral compounds, and *Stereoselective Synthesis* (B1) with the use of stereoselective reactions in organic synthesis. Many books cover only one type of synthetic reaction, such as the Diels–Alder reaction and related cycloaddition reactions (B3, B8); a search of your library's catalog should reveal similar works about other types of reactions. *Protective Groups in Organic Synthesis* (B10) describes the use of protective groups in syntheses involving multifunctional reactants. *Microwaves in Organic Synthesis* (B15) covers the theory and applications of microwave-assisted synthesis. In addition to the works dedicated to organic reactions, several advanced textbooks, such as March (H11) and Carey–Sundberg (H1), describe the most important synthetic reactions and give literature references to specific synthetic procedures.

Three multivolume sources of information about chemical reagents are *Fiesers' Reagents for Organic Syntheses* (B7), *Encyclopedia of Reagents for Organic Synthesis* (B21), and *Handbook of Reagents for Organic Synthesis* (B23). *Fieser* provides information about the preparation, purification, handling, and hazards of many chemical reagents, as well as examples of their use, with literature citations. Only the individual volumes are indexed, but if you locate the entry for a reagent in a recent volume, it will provide back references to the previous volumes. The *Encyclopedia of Reagents* reviews nearly 3500 reagents, listed alphabetically, and gives a critical assessment of each reagent. The four-volume *Handbook of Reagents* (B23) covers some 500 reagents selected from this encyclopedia. *Borane Reagents* (B24) deals with the applications of boranes in organic synthesis. *Organic Solvents* (B26) gives physical properties and purification methods for many solvents used in organic synthesis.

Although the primary chemical literature is the most important source of experimental procedures, a number of secondary sources (in addition to *Organic Reactions*) provide relatively detailed, reliable procedures. *Organic Syntheses* (B20) is a continuing series that contains an excellent selection of carefully tested synthetic procedures. Other works that provide experimental procedures include *Organicum* (B2), several works by Sandler and Karo (B27, B28, B29), and *Vogel's Textbook of Practical Organic Chemistry* (B31). Vogel is also a good source of information about laboratory techniques. *Houben-Weyl* (D5), which is listed under "General Laboratory Techniques," includes many synthetic procedures (in German) as well.

Category C: Laboratory Safety

Accidents can happen in the organic chemistry lab, so it is important to know how to prevent accidents and what to do in case of an accident. *Working Safely with Chemicals in the Laboratory* (C2) is a short booklet about laboratory safety written for students. *Prudent Practices in the Laboratory* (C7) is an authoritative guide to safe laboratory practices; it also includes procedures for the safe handling and disposal of chemicals. *Hazards in the Chemical Laboratory* (C6) describes the toxic effects of hazardous substances and reviews recent developments in the safe design and operation of chemical laboratories. The *CRC Handbook of Laboratory Safety* (C1) deals with the recognition and control of hazards and compliance with safety regulations, and includes a chapter on responding to laboratory emergencies. The *First Aid Manual for Chemical Accidents* (C3) gives first aid procedures for accidents caused by specific chemicals and classes of chemicals. *The Sigma–Aldrich Library of Regulatory and Safety Data* (C4) and *Sax's Dangerous Properties of Industrial Materials* (C5) provide detailed health and safety data for many common chemicals. *Bretherick's Handbook of Reactive Chemical Hazards* (C8) describes the properties of chemicals that are hazardous by virtue of their instability or their tendency to react with other chemicals. The ninth edition of *The Merck Index* (see A11) contains a section on first aid for poisoning and chemical burns; however, this section is not included in the more recent editions.

Category D: General Laboratory Techniques

Although this textbook covers the techniques you are most likely to use in your organic chemistry lab course, sources from this category and the following two categories may provide more detailed practical and theoretical information about specific lab techniques, information about more advanced techniques, or a different approach to the methods described here. *The Organic Chem Lab Survival Manual* (D11) describes many of the lab techniques used by organic chemistry students and tells you what things *not* to do, such as plugging a heating mantle directly into a wall socket. *Guide for the Perplexed Organic Experimentalist* (D3) deals with the practical aspects of laboratory work for anyone intending to do research in organic chemistry. Weissberger's *Technique of Organic Chemistry* (D7) and *Techniques of Chemistry* (D8) are multivolume sets that cover a wide variety of experimental methods. Information on classical laboratory techniques, such as distillation and recrystallization, can be found in Volume I of reference D7, which is subtitled *Physical Methods of Organic Chemistry*. The first four volumes of *Houben-Weyl* (D5) describe many laboratory methods for organic chemistry, in German. Microscale techniques based on Mayo–Pike and Williamson-type glassware, respectively, are described in *Microscale Techniques for the Organic Laboratory* (D4) and *Macroscale and Microscale Organic Experiments* (D9). The *Encyclopedia of Separation Technology* (D6) and *Encyclopedia of Separation Science* (D10) provide comprehensive, up-to-date descriptions of separation techniques. *Purification of Laboratory Chemicals* (D1) provides methods for the purification of more than 4000 common chemicals. *Natural Products* (D2) describes laboratory techniques and gives specific procedures for the isolation and structure determination of natural products.

Category E: Chromatography

During your organic chemistry lab course, you will probably use a variety of chromatographic methods for the separation and analysis of organic compounds. These methods include thin-layer chromatography (TLC), paper chromatography (PC), gas chromatography (GC), and high-performance liquid chromatography (HPLC). *Chromatography Today* (E6) and *Principles and Practice of Chromatography* (E7) are good general sources of information on the theory and practice of all types of chromatography. *Gas Chromatography* (E1) and *High Performance Liquid Chromatography* (E3) are "open learning" texts designed for self-study. The remaining works provide up-to-date coverage of GC, HPLC, and TLC techniques and applications. *Principles of Instrumental Analysis* (F21), in the next section, has chapters on instrumental chromatographic methods.

Category F: Spectrometry and Structure Analysis

During your organic chemistry lab course, you will probably need to record and interpret various kinds of spectra of organic compounds, such as infrared (IR) spectra, nuclear magnetic resonance (NMR) spectra, ultraviolet–visible (UV–VIS) spectra, and mass spectra (MS). *Principles of Instrumental Analysis* (F21) is a good source of information about the principles and applications of all important kinds of spectrometric methods, as well as other instrumental methods of analysis. An article in the *Journal of Chemical Education* (F9) covers the basics of IR and NMR spectral interpretation. The works by Silverstein (F20), Feinstein (F5), Kemp (F10), Pavia (F14), Whittaker (F24), and Yadav (F25) are good one-volume introductions to the interpretation of spectra of organic compounds. More comprehensive coverage of specific spectrometric methods is provided for infrared spectrometry by references F4 and F22; for nuclear magnetic resonance spectrometry by F1, F2, F6, and F13; for mass spectrometry by F3, F7, F8, F11, F12, and F23; and for ultraviolet–visible spectrometry by F15. The *Sadtler Standard Spectra* (F19) series consists of a large number of IR, NMR, and UV–VIS spectra in ring binders; although they aren't arranged systematically, individual spectra can be located using the index volumes. Spectra in the Aldrich collections (F16–F18) are arranged by functional class and in order of increasing molecular complexity within a functional class, making it possible to observe the effect of various structural features on the spectra.

Category G: Qualitative Organic Analysis

During your organic chemistry lab course, you may be required to identify one or more unknown organic compounds using either "wet-chemistry" methods (involving chemical tests and derivative preparations) or spectrometric methods, or both. *Organic Structure Determination* (G4), *The Systematic Identification of Organic Compounds* (G6), and *Spectral and Chemical Characterization of Organic Compounds* (G2) cover the traditional wet-chemistry methods but include chapters on spectrometric methods as well. *Qualitative Organic Analysis* (G3) emphasizes spectral methods of identification, and *Organic Structure Analysis* (G1) focuses on the use of multiple spectrometric methods to identify a molecule's major structural elements. The *CRC Handbook of Tables for Organic Compound Identification* (G5) lists the properties and derivative melting points for many organic compounds from the most important functional classes.

Category H: Reaction Mechanisms and Advanced Topics

Although reaction mechanisms are more often explored in an organic chemistry lecture course than in the laboratory course, you may be expected to understand and write mechanisms for some of the reactions you perform in the lab. *Electron Flow in Organic Chemistry* (H10) teaches an intuitive approach to organic chemistry by breaking down reaction mechanisms into elementary electron-flow pathways. *A Guidebook to Mechanism in Organic Chemistry* (H12) by Sykes is an excellent survey of reaction mechanisms suitable for advanced students; his *Primer* (H13) is a more basic introduction to mechanisms based on a simplified classification scheme. Other how-to books include *The Art of Writing Reasonable Reaction Mechanisms* (H4), *Writing Reaction Mechanisms in Organic Chemistry* (H7), and *Reaction Mechanisms at a Glance* (H8). *Name Reactions* (H5) provides detailed mechanisms for reactions known familiarly by the names of their discoverers. *Mechanism and Theory in Organic Chemistry* (H6) and *Perspectives on Structure and Mechanism in Organic Chemistry* (H3) are advanced textbooks that present the theoretical aspects of organic chemistry and provide up-to-date information about important reaction mechanisms. *Advanced Organic Chemistry* (H1) and *March's Advanced Organic Chemistry* (H11) provide good coverage of the mechanisms and synthetic applications of a large number of organic reactions, giving numerous references to the primary literature. *Determination of Organic Reaction Mechanisms* (H2) describes experimental techniques for studying reaction mechanisms, and *Organic Reaction Mechanisms* (H9) is an annual survey of recent developments in the field.

Category J: Reports of Chemical Research

Most professional chemists do *chemical research*—experimental or theoretical work designed to discover new facts about the various forms of matter, develop new techniques that can be used to study matter, or provide new insights about the fundamental nature of matter. Papers describing the results of their research are reported in such a large number of professional journals and other publications that it impossible for anyone to investigate them all. For that reason, scientists consult various reports of chemical research to locate the papers that deal with their own research interests.

Chemical Abstracts (J3), previously described in detail, is the most comprehensive single source of information about research in chemistry. The *Science Citation Index* (J7) is an index of literature citations to papers, patents, and books published in the past. For example, if you find an interesting paper by Linus Pauling in a chemistry journal, you can look up the paper in the *Science Citation Index* to find later articles that were based, in part, on Pauling's original paper. In this way, you can sometimes trace the development of an idea or a method from its origin to the present day. A similar index for chemistry, the *Chemistry Citation Index,* is available on CD-ROM. *Chemical Titles* (J4) and *Current Contents* (J5) reproduce the current tables of contents of the most important chemistry journals to inform chemists quickly of recent research in their fields. *Index Chemicus* (J6), a weekly guide to new organic compounds and their chemistry, is available in print and on a searchable database. The other works in this category (J1, J2) provide annual summaries and reviews of research in organic chemistry.

Category K: Guides to the Chemical Literature

If you need specific information to complete a lab report or write a research paper, you have to know where to look for it. *Information Sources in Chemistry* (K1) and *How to Find Chemical Information* (K4) are general guides to the chemical literature that list and describe a large number of information sources. *Library Handbook for Organic Chemists* (K5) is an up-to-date guide to the use of library information resources. *The Beilstein System* (K2) and *The Beilstein Online Database* (K3) tell how to search and use *Beilstein's* print and on-line versions, respectively. *From CA to CAS Online* (K6) serves the same function for *Chemical Abstracts.* The three articles by Somerville (K7) describe the contents and uses of some major works on organic reactions and syntheses. A brief but useful guide to information sources for organic chemistry can be found in Appendix A of *March's Advanced Organic Chemistry* (H11).

Category L: Sources on Selected Topics

This category includes a number of books and articles that can be used as resources for library research papers. Others can simply be read for enjoyment and enlightenment, on topics ranging from coffee and perfumes to the O. J. Simpson trial. Many are about topics related to the experiments or minilabs, such as reference L20 on sweetness L61 on perfumes and L65 on gas hydrates. Some works are listed here because they don't fit into any of the other categories. For example, L16 and L46 are guides for writing scientific papers and laboratory notebooks, L41 gives suggestions about presenting papers and posters, and L22 tells you how to name organic compounds.

Category M: Software for Organic Chemistry

A number of software titles are designed to be used in preparation for or during an organic chemistry laboratory. *Identification of Organic Compounds* (M8) and *MacSQUALOR* (M9) allow the user to identify simulated unknowns for qualitative organic analysis. *Introduction to Spectroscopy* (M4) helps the user analyze and interpret spectral data. *IR Simulator* (M10) and *NMR Simulator* (M11) generate simulated IR and NMR spectra from information entered by the user. *MassSpec* (M5) helps the user identify the structural fragments that correspond to peaks on a mass spectrum. *SynTree* (M7) helps the user work out retrosynthetic pathways leading from a selected target compound back to a readily available starting material. *ChemDraw* (M2) allows the user to generate a variety of chemical structures. *Name It* (M6) provides practice in naming organic compounds and drawing structures from their names. *Beaker* (M1) predicts properties and generates spectra of organic molecules, as well as providing some structure-drawing tools. *Chem3D* (M3) and *Spartan Student Edition* (M12) are used for molecular modeling and computational chemistry applications.

Bibliography

The Bibliography lists a number of useful works in organic chemistry, ranging from enormous multivolume sets such as *Chemical Abstracts* to short papers from the *Journal of Chemical Education*. References to entries listed in the Bibliography are made throughout this book in the form [Bibliography, F20], where the letter refers to a category and the number to a location within that category; for example, F20 is the twentieth book listed under category F, Spectrometry. Citations to journal articles are given in the form *J. Chem. Educ.* **2002,** *79,* 721, where the abbreviated journal name (the *Journal of Chemical Education,* in this example) is followed by the date, volume number, and page number.

A. Reference Works

1. *Aldrich Catalog Handbook of Fine Chemicals.* Milwaukee, WI: Aldrich Chemical Co., 2005–06 (and other years).
2. *Beilstein Dictionary: German–English: For the Users of the Beilstein Handbook of Organic Chemistry.* Ft. Worth, TX: W. B. Saunders, 1992.
3. *Beilstein's Handbook of Organic Chemistry.* New York: Springer-Verlag, 1918 to date.
4. *Chemical Abstracts Ring Systems Handbook.* Washington, DC: American Chemical Society, 1993 with cumulative supplements.
5. *Chemical Abstracts Service Source Index (CASSI).* Washington, DC: American Chemical Society, 1907–2004 with quarterly supplements.
6. Dean, J. A., ed., *Lange's Handbook of Chemistry,* 16th ed. New York: McGraw-Hill, 2004.
7. Gokel, G. W., *Dean's Handbook of Organic Chemistry.* New York: McGraw-Hill, 2004.
8. *Kirk–Othmer Encyclopedia of Chemical Technology,* 5th ed. New York: Wiley, 2004–.
9. Lide, D. R., and Milne, G. W. A., eds., *CRC Handbook of Data on Organic Compounds,* 3rd ed. Boca Raton, FL: CRC Press, 1994.
10. Mundy, B. P., and Ellerd, M. G., *Organic Chemistry: An Alphabetical Guide.* New York: Wiley, 1996.
11. O'Neil, M. J., et al., eds., *The Merck Index: An Encyclopedia of Chemicals, Drugs, and Biologicals,* 14th ed. Whitehouse Station, NJ: Merck & Co., 2006.
12. Rhodes, P. H., ed., *Dictionary of Organic Compounds,* 6th ed. London: Chapman & Hall, 1995.
13. Rhodes, P. H., *The Organic Chemist's Desk Reference: A Companion Volume to the Dictionary of Organic Compounds,* 6th ed. London: Chapman & Hall, 1995.
14. Shugar, G. J., and Dean, J. A., *The Chemist's Ready Reference Handbook.* New York: McGraw-Hill, 1990.
15. Weast, R. C., ed., *CRC Handbook of Chemistry and Physics,* new editions annually. Boca Raton, FL: CRC Press, 2007 (and other years).

B. Organic Reactions and Syntheses

1. Atkinson, R. S., *Stereoselective Synthesis.* New York: Wiley, 1995.
2. Becker, H., et al., *Organicum: Practical Handbook of Organic Chemistry,* trans. by B. J. Hazzard. Reading, MA: Addison-Wesley, 1973.
3. Carruthers, W., *Cycloaddition Reactions in Organic Synthesis.* New York: Pergamon Press, 1990.
4. Carruthers, W., *Modern Methods of Organic Synthesis,* 4th ed. Cambridge, UK: Cambridge University Press, 2004.
5. Coffey, S. (1964–89), and Ansell, M. F. (1973–), eds., *Rodd's Chemistry of Carbon Compounds,* 2nd ed. and supplements, New York: Elsevier, 1964–.
6. Corey, E. J., and Cheng, X.-M., *The Logic of Chemical Synthesis.* New York: Wiley, 1995.
7. Fieser, L. F., et al., *Fiesers' Reagents for Organic Synthesis.* New York: Wiley, 1967–.
8. Fringuelli, F., and Taticchi, A., *The Diels–Alder Reaction: Selected Practical Methods.* New York: Wiley, 2002.
9. Fuhrhop, J.-H., and Li, G., *Organic Synthesis: Concepts and Methods,* 3rd ed. New York: Wiley, 2003.
10. Greene, T. W., and Wuts, P. G. M., *Protective Groups in Organic Synthesis,* 3rd ed. New York: Wiley, 1999.
11. Harrison, I. T., and Harrison, S., *Compendium of Organic Synthetic Methods.* New York: Wiley, 1971–.
12. House, H. O., *Modern Synthetic Reactions,* 2nd ed. Menlo Park, CA: Benjamin, 1972.
13. Larock, R. C., *Comprehensive Organic Transformations: A Guide to Functional Group Preparations,* 2nd ed. New York: Wiley, 1999.
14. Laue, T., and Plagens, A., *Named Organic Reactions.* New York: Wiley, 2000.
15. Loupy, A., *Microwaves in Organic Synthesis.* New York: Wiley, 2003.
16. Millam, M. J., *Reaction Guide for Organic Chemistry.* Lexington, MA: D. C. Heath, 1989.
17. Nicolaou, K. C., et al., "The Art and Science of Organic and Natural Product Synthesis." *J. Chem. Educ.* **1998,** *75,* 1225.
18. Norman, R. O. C., and Coxon, J. M., *Principles of Organic Synthesis,* 3rd ed. Cheltenham, UK: Stanley Thornes, 1993.
19. *Organic Reactions.* New York: Wiley, 1942–.
20. *Organic Syntheses,* 2nd ed, *Collective Volumes.* New York: Wiley, 2004 (and previous years).
21. Paquette, L. A., ed., *Encyclopedia of Reagents for Organic Synthesis.* New York: Wiley, 1995.
22. Patai, S., ed., *Chemistry of Functional Groups.* New York: Wiley, 1964–.
23. Pearson, A. J., *Handbook of Reagents for Organic Synthesis.* New York: Wiley, 1999.
24. Pelter, A., Smith, K., and Brown, H. C., *Borane Reagents.* London: Academic Press, 1988.

From *Operational Organic Chemistry: A Problem Solving Approach to the Laboratory,* Fourth Edition, John W. Lehman. Copyright © 2009 by Pearson Education. Published by Prentice Hall. All rights reserved.

25. Proctor, R. G., *Asymmetric Synthesis*. New York: Oxford University Press, 1996.
26. Riddick, J. A., and Bunger, W. M., *Organic Solvents: Physical Properties and Methods of Purification*, 4th ed. New York: Wiley, 1986.
27. Sandler, S. R., and Karo, W., *Organic Functional Group Preparations*, 2nd ed. Orlando, FL: Academic Press, 1983, 1986, 1989.
28. Sandler, S. R., and Karo, W., *Polymer Syntheses*, 2nd ed. Orlando, FL: Academic Press, 1997.
29. Sandler, S. R., and Karo, W., *Sourcebook of Advanced Organic Laboratory Preparations*. San Diego, CA: Academic Press, 1992.
30. Stuart, W., *Organic Synthesis: The Disconnection Approach*. New York: Wiley, 1982.
31. Tatchell, A. R., et al., *Vogel's Textbook of Practical Organic Chemistry*, 5th ed. New York: Wiley, 1989.
32. Theilheimer, W. (1948–81), and Finch, A. F. (1982–), eds., *Theilheimer's Synthetic Methods of Organic Chemistry*. Basel: Karger, 1946–.
33. Trost, B. M., and Fleming, I., eds., *Comprehensive Organic Synthesis: Selectivity, Strategy & Efficiency in Modern Organic Chemistry*. Elmsford, NY: Pergamon Press, 1991.
34. Wagner, R. B., and Zook, H. D., *Synthetic Organic Chemistry*. New York: Wiley, 1953.
35. Zweifel, G., and Nantz, M., *Modern Organic Synthesis: An Introduction*. New York: Freeman, 2006.

C. Laboratory Safety

1. Furr, A. K., ed., *CRC Handbook of Laboratory Safety*, 5th ed. Boca Raton, FL: CRC Press, 2000.
2. Gorman, C. E., ed., *Working Safely with Chemicals in the Laboratory*, 2nd ed. Schenectady, NY: Genium, 1995.
3. Lefèvre, M. J., *First Aid Manual for Chemical Accidents*, 2nd ed. New York: Van Nostrand Reinhold, 1989.
4. Lenga, R. E., ed., *The Sigma–Aldrich Library of Regulatory and Safety Data*. Milwaukee, WI: Sigma–Aldrich, 1993.
5. Lewis, R. J., Sr., *Sax's Dangerous Properties of Industrial Materials*, 10th ed. New York: Wiley, 2000.
6. Luxon, S. G., ed., *Hazards in the Chemical Laboratory*, 5th ed. Cambridge, UK: Royal Society of Chemistry, 1992.
7. National Research Council, *Prudent Practices in the Laboratory: Handling and Disposal of Chemicals*. Washington, DC: National Academies Press, 1995.
8. Urben, P. G., ed., *Bretherick's Handbook of Reactive Chemical Hazards*, 7th ed. Burlington, MA: Academic Press, 2006.

D. General Laboratory Techniques

1. Armarego, W. L. F., and Chai, C., *Purification of Laboratory Chemicals*, 5th ed. New York: Elsevier, 2003.
2. Ikan, R., *Natural Products: A Laboratory Guide*, 2nd ed. San Diego, CA: Academic Press, 1991.
3. Loewenthal, H. J. E., *Guide for the Perplexed Organic Experimentalist*, 2nd ed. New York: Wiley, 1992.
4. Mayo, D. W., et al., *Microscale Techniques for the Organic Laboratory*, 2nd ed. New York: Wiley, 2000.
5. *Methoden der Organischen Chemie, Houben-Weyl,* 4th ed. Stuttgart: Georg Thieme, 1952–.
6. Ruthven, D., *Encyclopedia of Separation Technology*. New York: Wiley, 1997.
7. Weissberger, A., ed., *Technique of Organic Chemistry*, 3rd ed. New York: Wiley, 1959–.
8. Weissberger, A., ed., *Techniques of Chemistry*. New York: Wiley, 1971–.
9. Williamson, K. L., *Macroscale and Microscale Organic Experiments*, 5th ed. Boston, MA: Houghton Mifflin, 2007.
10. Wilson, I. D., et al., eds., *Encyclopedia of Separation Science*. Orlando, FL: Academic Press, 2000.
11. Zubrick, J. W., *The Organic Chem Lab Survival Manual: A Student's Guide to Techniques*, 6th ed. New York: Wiley, 2004.

E. Chromatography

1. Fowlis, I. A., *Gas Chromatography*, 2nd ed. New York: Wiley, 1995.
2. Grob, R. L., and Barry, E. F., eds., *Modern Practice of Gas Chromatography*, 4th ed. New York: Wiley, 2004.
3. Lindsay, S., *High Performance Liquid Chromatography*, 2nd ed. New York: Wiley, 1992.
4. McNair, H. M., and Miller, J. M., *Basic Gas Chromatography*. New York: Wiley, 1998.
5. Meyer, V. R., *Practical High-Performance Liquid Chromatography*, 3rd ed. Chichester, UK: Wiley, 1999.
6. Poole, C. F., and Poole, S. K., *Chromatography Today*. New York: Elsevier, 1991.
7. Ravindranath, B., *Principles and Practice of Chromatography*. New York: Halsted, 1989.
8. Schomburg, G., *Gas Chromatography: A Practical Course*. New York: VCH, 1990.
9. Sherma, J., and Fried, B., *Thin-Layer Chromatography: Techniques and Applications*, 3rd ed. New York: Marcel Dekker, 1996.
10. Touchstone, J. C., *Practice of Thin Layer Chromatography*, 3rd ed. New York: Wiley, 1992.

F. Spectrometry and Structure Analysis

1. Akitt, J. W., and Mann, B. E., *NMR and Chemistry: An Introduction to Modern NMR Spectroscopy,* 4th ed. Cheltenham, UK: Stanley Thornes, 2000.
2. Bovey, F. A., *Nuclear Magnetic Resonance Spectroscopy*, 2nd ed. San Diego, CA: Academic Press, 1988.
3. Chapman, J. R., *Practical Organic Mass Spectrometry: A Guide for Chemical and Biochemical Analysis*, 2nd ed. New York: Wiley, 1995.
4. Colthup, N. B., Daly, L. H., and Wiberley, S. E., *Introduction to Infrared and Raman Spectroscopy*, 3rd ed. Orlando, FL: Academic Press, 1990.

5. Feinstein, K., *Guide to Spectroscopic Identification of Organic Compounds*. Boca Raton, FL: CRC Press, 1995.

6. Günther, H., *NMR Spectroscopy: Basic Principles, Concepts, and Applications in Chemistry*, 2nd ed. New York: Wiley, 1995.

7. Herbert, C. G., and Johnstone, R. A. W., *Mass Spectrometry Basics*. Boca Raton, FL: CRC Press, 2002.

8. Hoffmann, Edmond de, *Mass Spectrometry: Principles and Applications*. New York: Wiley, 1996.

9. Ingham, A. M., and Henson, R. C., "Interpreting Infrared and Nuclear Magnetic Resonance Spectra of Simple Organic Compounds for the Beginner." *J. Chem. Educ.* **1984**, *61*, 704.

10. Kemp, W., *Organic Spectroscopy*, 3rd ed. New York: W. H. Freeman, 1991.

11. Lee, T. A., *A Beginner's Guide to Mass Spectral Interpretation*. New York: Wiley, 1998.

12. McLafferty, F. W., and Turecek, F., *Interpretation of Mass Spectra*, 4th ed. Mill Valley, CA: University Science Books, 1993.

13. Nelson, J. H., *Nuclear Magnetic Resonance Spectroscopy*. Upper Saddle River, NJ: Prentice Hall, 2003.

14. Pavia, D. L., et al., *Introduction to Spectroscopy: A Guide for Students of Organic Chemistry*, 4th ed. Belmont, CA: Brooks/Cole, 2008.

15. Perkampus, H.-H., *UV–VIS Spectroscopy and its Applications*. New York: Springer-Verlag, 1992.

16. Pouchert, C. J., and Behnke, J., *The Aldrich Library of ^{13}C and ^1H FT–NMR Spectra*. Milwaukee, WI: Aldrich Chemical Co., 1992.

17. Pouchert, C. J., and Campbell, J. R., *The Aldrich Library of NMR Spectra*, 2nd ed. Milwaukee, WI: Aldrich Chemical Co., 1983.

18. Pouchert, C. J., *The Aldrich Library of FT–IR Spectra*, 2nd ed. Milwaukee, WI: Aldrich Chemical Co., 1997.

19. *Sadtler Standard Spectra* (Collections of infrared, ultraviolet, and NMR spectra). Philadelphia, PA: Sadtler Research Laboratories.

20. Silverstein, R. M., et al., *Spectrometric Identification of Organic Compounds*, 7th ed. New York: Wiley, 2003.

21. Skoog, D. A., et al., *Principles of Instrumental Analysis*, 5th ed. Belmont, CA: Brooks/Cole, 1997.

22. Smith, B. C., *Fundamentals of Fourier Transform Infrared Spectroscopy*. Boca Raton, FL: CRC Press, 1996.

23. Smith, R. M., *Understanding Mass Spectra, A Basic Approach*, 2nd ed. Hoboken, NJ: Wiley-Interscience, 2004.

24. Whittaker, D., *Interpreting Organic Spectra*. New York: Springer-Verlag, 2000.

25. Yadav, L. D. S., *Organic Spectroscopy*. Norwell, MA: Kluwer Academic, 2003.

G. Qualitative Organic Analysis

1. Crews, P., et al., *Organic Structure Analysis*. New York: Oxford University Press, 1998.

2. Criddle, W. J., *Spectral and Chemical Characterization of Organic Compounds: A Laboratory Handbook*, 3rd ed. New York: Wiley, 1990.

3. Kemp, W., *Qualitative Organic Analysis: Spectrochemical Techniques*, 2nd ed. New York: McGraw-Hill, 1986.

4. Pasto, D. J., and Johnson, C. R., *Organic Structure Determination*. Englewood Cliffs, NJ: Prentice Hall, 1969.

5. Rappoport, Z., ed., *CRC Handbook of Tables for Organic Compound Identification*, 3rd ed. Cleveland, OH: Chemical Rubber Co., 1967.

6. Shriner, R. L., et al., *The Systematic Identification of Organic Compounds*, 8th ed. New York: Wiley, 2003.

H. Reaction Mechanisms and Advanced Topics

1. Carey, F. A., and Sundberg, R. J., *Advanced Organic Chemistry*, 4th ed. New York: Springer, 2000.

2. Carpenter, B. K., *Determination of Organic Reaction Mechanisms*. New York: Wiley, 1984.

3. Carroll, F. A., *Perspectives on Structure and Mechanism in Organic Chemistry*. Belmont, CA: Brooks/Cole, 1998.

4. Grossman, R. B., *The Art of Writing Reasonable Organic Reaction Mechanisms*, 2nd ed. New York: Springer, 2003.

5. Li, J. J., *Name Reactions: A Collection of Detailed Reaction Mechanisms*. New York: Springer, 2002.

6. Lowry, T. H., and Richardson, K. S., *Mechanism and Theory in Organic Chemistry*, 3rd ed. New York: Harper & Row, 1987.

7. Miller, A., and Solomon, P. H., *Writing Reaction Mechanisms in Organic Chemistry*, 2nd ed. San Diego, CA: Harcourt/Academic Press, 2000.

8. Moloney, M. G., *Reaction Mechanisms at a Glance: A Stepwise Approach to Problem-Solving in Organic Chemistry*. Oxford, UK: Blackwell Science, 2000.

9. *Organic Reaction Mechanisms*. New York: Wiley, 1965–.

10. Scudder, P. H., *Electron Flow in Organic Chemistry*. New York: Wiley, 1992.

11. Smith, M., *March's Advanced Organic Chemistry: Reactions, Mechanisms and Structure*, 6th ed. New York: Wiley, 2006.

12. Sykes, P., *A Guidebook to Mechanism in Organic Chemistry*, 6th ed. Upper Saddle River, NJ: Prentice Hall, 1996.

13. Sykes, P., *A Primer to Mechanism in Organic Chemistry*. Upper Saddle River, NJ: Prentice Hall, 1996.

J. Reports of Chemical Research

1. *Annual Reports in Organic Synthesis*. New York: Academic Press, 1970–.

2. *Annual Reports on the Progress of Chemistry, Section B: Organic Chemistry*. London: Royal Society of Chemistry, 1904–.

3. *Chemical Abstracts*. Columbus, OH: CA Service, American Chemical Society, 1907–.

4. *Chemical Titles*. Columbus, OH: CA Service, American Chemical Society, 1961–.

5. *Current Contents: Physical, Chemical & Earth Sciences.* Philadelphia, PA: ISI Press, 1967–.
6. *Index Chemicus.* Philadelphia, PA: ISI Press, 1960–.
7. *Science Citation Index.* Philadelphia, PA: ISI Press, 1961–.

K. Guides to the Chemical Literature

1. Bottle, R. T., and Rowland, J. F. B., eds., *Information Sources in Chemistry*, 4th ed. New Providence, NJ: Bowker–Saur, 1993.
2. Heller, S. R., ed., *The Beilstein System: Strategies for Effective Searching.* New York: Oxford University Press, 1997.
3. Heller, S. R., ed., *The Beilstein Online Database: Implementation, Content, and Retrieval.* New York: Oxford University Press, 1990.
4. Maizell, R. E., *How to Find Chemical Information: A Guide for Practicing Chemists, Educators, and Students*, 3rd ed. New York: Wiley, 1998.
5. Poss, A. J., *Library Handbook for Organic Chemists.* New York: Chemical Publ., 2000.
6. Schulz, H., and Georgy, U., *From CA to CAS Online: Databases in Chemistry*, 2nd ed. New York: Springer-Verlag, 1994.
7. Somerville, A. N., "Information Sources for Organic Chemistry." *J. Chem. Educ.* **1991**, *68*, 553, 843; **1992**, *69*, 379.

L. Sources on Selected Topics

1. Agosta, W. C., *Bombardier Beetles and Fever Trees: A Close-up Look at Chemical Warfare and Signals in Animals and Plants.* Reading, MA: Addison-Wesley, 1996.
2. Agosta, W. C., "Medicines and Drugs from Plants." *J. Chem. Educ.* **1997**, *74*, 857.
3. Agosta, W. C., *Chemical Communication: The Language of Pheromones.* New York: Scientific American Library, 1992.
4. Anastas, P. T., and Warner, J. C., *Green Chemistry: Theory and Practice.* New York: Oxford University Press, 2000.
5. Atkins, P. W., and Atkins, P., *Atkins' Molecules.* Cambridge, UK: Cambridge University Press, 2003.
6. Bauer, K., et al., *Common Fragrance and Flavor Materials: Preparation, Properties, and Uses*, 2nd ed. Deerfield Beach, FL: VCH, 1990.
7. Belitz, H. D., and Grosch, W., *Food Chemistry*, 2nd ed. New York: Springer-Verlag, 1999.
8. Benfey, O. T., *From Vital Force to Structural Formulas.* Philadelphia, PA: Beckman Center for the History of Chemistry, 1992.
9. Buxton, S. R., and Roberts, S. M., *Guide to Organic Stereochemistry: From Methane to Macromolecules.* Menlo Park, CA: Benjamin/Cummings, 1996.
10. Carraher, C. E., Jr., *Polymer Chemistry*, 5th ed. New York: Marcel Dekker, 2000.
11. Cole, L. A., *The Eleventh Plague: The Politics of Biological and Chemical Warfare.* Darby, PA: Diane Publishing, 2001.
12. Coultate, T. P., *Food: The Chemistry of Its Components*, 4th ed. Cambridge, UK: Royal Society of Chemistry, 2002.
13. Cresswell, S. L., and Haswell, S. J., "Microwave Ovens—Out of the Kitchen." *J. Chem. Educ.* **2001**, *78*, 900.
14. Dehmlow, E. V., and Dehmlow, S. S., *Phase Transfer Catalysis*, 3rd ed. New York: VCH, 1993.
15. Djerassi, C., *From the Lab into the World: A Pill for People, Pets, and Bugs.* Washington, DC: American Chemical Society, 1994.
16. Dodd, J. S., ed., *The ACS Style Guide: A Manual for Authors and Editors*, 3rd ed. Washington, DC: American Chemical Society, 2006.
17. Donnelly, T. H., "The Origins of the Use of Antioxidants in Foods." *J. Chem. Educ.* **1996**, *73*, 159.
18. DuPré, D. B., "Blood or Taco Sauce? The Chemistry behind Criminalists' Testimony in the O. J. Simpson Murder Case." *J. Chem. Educ.* **1996**, *73*, 60.
19. Eliel, E. L., et al., *Basic Organic Stereochemistry.* New York: Wiley, 2001.
20. Ellis, J. W., et al., "Symposium: Sweeteners and Sweetness Theory." *J. Chem. Educ.* **1995**, *72*, 671, 676, 680.
21. Fossey, J., et al., *Free Radicals in Organic Chemistry.* New York: Wiley, 1995.
22. Fox, R. B., and Powell, W. H., *Nomenclature of Organic Compounds: Principles and Practice*, 2nd ed. Washington, DC: American Chemical Society, 2000.
23. Foye, W. O., et al., *Principles of Medicinal Chemistry*, 4th ed. Baltimore, MD: Lippincott Williams & Wilkins, 1995.
24. French, L. G., "The Sassafras Tree and Designer Drugs: from Herbal Tea to Ecstasy." *J. Chem. Educ.* **1995**, *72*, 479.
25. Gerber, S. M., ed., *Chemistry and Crime: from Sherlock Holmes to Today's Courtroom.* New York: Oxford University Press, 1983.
26. Gerber, S. M., and Saferstein, R., eds., *More Chemistry and Crime: From Marsh Arsenic Test to DNA Profile.* New York: Oxford University Press, 1997.
27. Giffin, G. A., et al., "Modern Sport and Chemistry: What a Chemically Aware Sports Fanatic Should Know." *J. Chem. Educ.* **2002**, *79*, 813.
28. Gilchrist, T. L., *Heterocyclic Chemistry*, 3rd ed. New York: Wiley, 1997.
29. Goldsmith, R. H., "A Tale of Two Sweeteners." *J. Chem. Educ.* **1987**, *64*, 954.
30. Goodman, J. M., *Chemical Applications of Molecular Modeling*, 2nd ed. Cambridge, UK: Royal Society of Chemistry, 2007.
31. Gribble, G. W., "Natural Organohalogens: A New Frontier for Medicinal Agents?" *J. Chem. Educ.* **2004**, *81*, 1441.
32. Gribble, G. W., "Natural Organohalogens: Many More than You Think!" *J. Chem. Educ.* **1994**, *71*, 907.
33. Gunstone, F. D., *Fatty Acid and Lipid Chemistry.* New York: Blackie, 1996.
34. Hammond, G. S., and Kuck, V. J., *Fullerenes: Synthesis, Properties, and Chemistry of Large Carbon Clusters.* Washington, DC: American Chemical Society, 1992.

35. Hirsch, A., et al., *Fullerenes: Chemistry and Reactions*. New York: Wiley, 2005.

36. Hocking, M. B., "Vanillin: Synthetic Flavoring from Spent Sulfite Liquor." *J. Chem. Educ.* **1997**, *74*, 1055.

37. Höltje, H.-D. et. al., *Molecular Modeling: Basic Principles and Applications*, 2nd ed. Weinheim, Germany: Wiley–VCH, 2003.

38. Honeybourne, C. L., "Organic Vapor Sensors for Food Quality Assessment," *J. Chem. Educ.* **2000**, *77*, 338.

39. Hosler, D. M., and Mikita, M. A., "Ethnobotany: The Chemist's Source for the Identification of Useful Natural Products." *J. Chem. Educ.* **1987**, *64*, 328.

40. Houghton, P. J., "Old Yet New—Pharmaceuticals from Plants." *J. Chem. Educ.* **2001**, *78*, 175.

41. Huddle, P. A., "How to Present a Paper or Poster." *J. Chem. Educ.* **2000**, *77*, 1091.

42. Hughes, P., "Was Markovnikov's Rule an Inspired Guess?" *J. Chem. Educ.* **2006**, *83*, 1152.

43. Jacques, J., *The Molecule and Its Double*. New York: McGraw-Hill, 1993.

44. James, L. K., ed., *Nobel Laureates in Chemistry, 1901–1992*. Washington, DC: American Chemical Society, 1993.

45. Jandacek, R. J., "The Development of Olestra, a Noncaloric Substitute for Dietary Fat." *J. Chem. Educ.* **1991**, *68*, 476.

46. Kanare, H. M., *Writing the Laboratory Notebook*. Washington, DC: American Chemical Society, 1985.

47. Kauffman, G. B., "Wallace Hume Carothers and Nylon, the First Completely Synthetic Fiber." *J. Chem. Educ.* **1988**, *65*, 803.

48. Kauffman, G. B., and Seymour, R. B., "Elastomers: I. Natural Rubber." *J. Chem. Educ.* **1990**, *67*, 422.

49. Kent, J. A., ed., *Kent and Riegel's Handbook of Industrial Chemistry and Biotechnology*, 11th ed. New York: Springer, 2006.

50. Kikuchi, S., "A History of the Structural Theory of Benzene—the Aromatic Sextet Rule." *J. Chem. Educ.* **1997**, *74*, 194.

51. Kimbrough, D. R., "Hot and Spicy vs. Cool and Minty as an Example of Organic Structure-Activity Relationships." *J. Chem. Educ.* **1997**, *74*, 861.

52. Kimbrough, D. R., "The Photochemistry of Sunscreens." *J. Chem. Educ.* **1997**, *74*, 51.

53. King, F. D., ed., *Medicinal Chemistry: Principles and Practice*, 2nd ed. Cambridge, UK: Royal Society of Chemistry, 2003.

54. Kopecky, J., *Organic Photochemistry: A Visual Approach*. New York: Wiley, 1992.

55. Laing, M., "Beware—Fertilizer Can EXPLODE!" *J. Chem. Educ.* **1993**, *70*, 393.

56. Lancaster, M., *Green Chemistry: An Introductory Text*. Cambridge, UK: Royal Society of Chemistry, 2002.

57. Leung, A. Y., and Foster, S., *Encyclopedia of Common Natural Ingredients Used in Foods, Drugs, and Cosmetics*, 2nd ed. New York: Wiley, 2003.

58. Manahan, S. E., *Green Chemistry and the Ten Commandments of Sustainability*, 2nd ed. Columbia, MO: ChemChar Research, 2005.

59. Mann, J., et al., *Natural Products: Their Chemistry and Biological Significance*. New York: Wiley, 1994.

60. Milgrom, L. R., *The Colours of Life: An Introduction to the Chemistry of Porphyrins and Related Compounds*. New York: Oxford University Press, 1997.

61. Morris, E. T., *Fragrance: The Story of Perfume from Cleopatra to Chanel*. Mineola, NY: Dover Publications, 2002.

62. Nicholson, J. W., and Anstice, H. M., "The Chemistry of Modern Dental Filling Materials." *J. Chem. Educ.* **1999**, *76*, 1497.

63. Ohloff, G., *Scent and Fragrances: The Fascination of Odors and Their Chemical Perspectives*. New York: Springer-Verlag, 1994.

64. Parsons, A., *An Introduction to Free-Radical Chemistry*. Malden, MA: Blackwell, 2000.

65. Pellenbarg, R. E., and Max, M. D., "Gas Hydrates: From Laboratory Curiosity to Potential Global Powerhouse." *J. Chem. Educ.* **2001**, *78*, 896.

66. Perrine, D. M., *The Chemistry of Mind-Altering Drugs: History, Pharmacology, and Cultural Context*. New York: Oxford University Press, 1996.

67. Petracco, M., "Our Everyday Cup of Coffee: The Chemistry behind Its Magic." *J. Chem. Educ.* **2005**, *82*, 1161.

68. Pinto, G., "Chemistry of Moth Repellents." *J. Chem. Educ.* **2005**, *82*, 1267.

69. Robinson, M. J. T., *Organic Stereochemistry*. New York: Oxford University Press, 2000.

70. Schmid, G., *Nanoparticles: From Theory to Application*. New York: Wiley, 2004.

71. Selinger, B., *Chemistry in the Marketplace*, 5th ed. Orlando, FL: Academic Press, 1998.

72. Seymour, R. B., and Kauffman, G. B., "The Ubiquity and Longevity of Fibers." *J. Chem. Educ.* **1993**, *70*, 449.

73. Silverman, R. B., *The Organic Chemistry of Drug Design and Drug Action*, 2nd ed. San Diego, CA: Academic Press, 2004.

74. Sotheeswaran, S., "Herbal Medicine: The Scientific Evidence." *J. Chem. Educ.* **1992**, *69*, 444.

75. Spessard, G. O., and Miessler, G. L., *Organometallic Chemistry*. Upper Saddle River, NJ: Prentice Hall, 1997.

76. Starks, C. M., et al., *Phase Transfer Catalysis: Fundamentals, Applications, and Industrial Perspectives*. New York: Chapman & Hall, 1994.

77. Stick, R. V., *Carbohydrates: The Sweet Molecules of Life*. San Diego, CA: Academic Press, 2001.

78. Stocker, J. H., *Chemistry and Science Fiction*. New York: Oxford University Press, 1998.

79. Sundberg, R. J., *Indoles*. San Diego, CA: Academic Press, 1996.

80. Tannenbaum, G., "Chocolate: A Marvelous Natural Product of Chemistry." *J. Chem. Educ.* **2004**, *81*, 1131.

81. Turro, N., *Modern Molecular Photochemistry of Organic Molecules*. Sausalito, CA: University Science Books, 2006.

82. Vartanian, P. F., "The Chemistry of Modern Petroleum Product Additives." *J. Chem. Educ.* **1991**, *68*, 1015.

83. Waddell, T. G., and Rybolt, T. R., "The Chemical Adventures of Sherlock Holmes: The Ghost of Gordon Square." *J. Chem. Educ.* **2000**, *77*, 471.

84. Waddell, T. G., et al., "Legendary Chemical Aphrodisiacs." *J. Chem. Educ.* **1980**, *57*, 341.

85. Walters, E. E., et al., eds., *Sweeteners: Discovery, Molecular Design, and Chemoreception*. Washington, DC: American Chemical Society, 1991.

86. Waring, D. R., and Hallas, G., eds., *The Chemistry and Application of Dyes*. New York: Plenum Press, 1990.

87. Weissermel, K., and Arpe, H.-J., *Industrial Organic Chemistry*, 4th ed. New York: Wiley-VCH, 2003.

88. White, M. A., "The Chemistry behind Carbonless Copy Paper." *J. Chem. Educ.* **1999**, *75*, 1061.

89. Wigfield, D. C., *Environmental Aspects of Organic Chemistry*. Winnipeg, Canada: Wuerz, 1997.

90. Yee, G. T., "Through the Looking Glass and What Alice Ate There." *J. Chem. Educ.* **2002**, *79*, 569.

91. Zanger, M., et al., "The Aromatic Substitution Game." *J. Chem. Educ.* **1993**, *70*, 985.

92. Zielinski, T. J., and Swift, M. L., eds., *Using Computers in Chemistry and Chemical Education*. New York: Oxford University Press, 1997.

93. Zimpleman, J. M., "Dioxin, Not Doomsday." *J. Chem. Educ.* **1999**, *76*, 1662.

M. Software for Organic Chemistry

1. Brockwell, J. C., et al., *Beaker: An Expert System for the Organic Chemistry Student* (Windows or Macintosh). Belmont, CA: Thomson-Wadsworth, 1995.

2. *ChemDraw* (Windows or Macintosh). CambridgeSoft.com.

3. *Chem3D* (Windows or Macintosh). CambridgeSoft.com.

4. Clough, F. W., *Introduction to Spectroscopy: IR, NMR, CMR, and Mass Spec* (Windows). Campton, NH: Trinity Software.

5. Figueras, J., *MassSpec: A Graphics-Based Mass Spectrum Analyzer* (Windows or Macintosh). Campton, NH: Trinity Software.

6. Figueras, J., *Name It* (Windows or Macintosh). Campton, NH: Trinity Software.

7. Figueras, J., *SynTree: A Program for Exploring Organic Synthesis* (Windows or Macintosh). Campton, NH: Trinity Software.

8. Pavia, D. L., and Clough, F. W., *Identification of Organic Compounds* (Windows). Campton, NH: Trinity Software.

9. Pavia, D. L., and Clough, F. W., *MacSQUALOR* (Macintosh). Campton, NH: Trinity Software.

10. Schatz, P. F., *IR Simulator* (Windows or Macintosh). Wentworth, NH: Falcon Software.

11. Schatz, P. F., *NMR Simulator* (Windows or Macintosh). Wentworth, NH: Falcon Software.

12. *Spartan Student Edition for Macintosh* and *Spartan Student Edition for Windows*. Irvine, CA: Wavefunctions, Inc.